*The Directory of*

# Westminster & Whitehall

## 2004/5

ISBN 1-901581-71-3  ISSN 1360-1199

*Carlton Publishing and Printing Limited*
Wenta Business Centre, Colne Way
Watford, Hertfordshire, WD24 4ND
*Telephone* (01923) 800801
*Facsimile* (01923) 800802
*E-mails* carltongroup@compuserve.com
info@carlton-group.co.uk
*Web* http://www.carlton-group.co.uk

*Published by* Carlton Publishing and Printing Limited
The contents of this book are believed correct at the time of printing. Nevertheless, the publisher can accept no responsibility for errors or omissions or changes in the details given.

*Illustrations by* Jeanette Sutton Designs.
*Typeset and Produced by* Carlton Publishing and Printing Limited and Printed in England.

# Contents

# Westminster Section

# Whitehall Section

**MSF Section**

AMICUS MSF Centre
33-37 Moreland Street
London
EC1V 8HA

Tel: 020 7505 3000

Fax: 020 7505 3020

minicom: 020 7505 0023

E-mail: info@msf.org.uk

Web: www.msf.org.uk

Contact:
*Richard O'Brien*
**Head of Campaigns
and Media**

*Roger Lyons*
**General Secretary**

The Labour Government has played a leading role in Europe ensuring that British people share in all the benefits and opportunities of the single market. Economic reform is creating long-term growth and employment opportunities across Europe; and in the area of "Social Affairs", the Labour government has made significant progress in advancing employment legislation.

MSF welcomes the progress the Labour government has made in signing the "social chapter" and implementing measures such as: the Parental Leave Directive, granting parents at work the right to 3 months unpaid leave at the birth or adoption of a child; and the Part-Time Workers Directive, entitling the same pro-rata terms and conditions of employment as full-time workers.

Much more needs to be done, particularly to ensure that workers are better informed and consulted about possible redundancies, when companies are planning to merge or restructure their operations.

MSF is pleased that the government has simplified the process of achieving equal pay. The improved system could cut waiting times by half. MSF has campaigned for 16 years to achieve these much needed reforms, but more still needs to be done before we truly see a situation of equal pay for equal worth.

The employment relations act was a huge step forward but without statutory protection from bullying at work many employees will be afraid to claim their new rights such as parental leave and time off for family emergencies as well as the right not to work more than 48 hours per week. MSF want to see the introduction of a new law to protect employees from bullying in the work place.

# INTRODUCTION

The Directory of Westminster and Whitehall is a consumer's directory of government, reflecting the same priorities as the companion works: *The Guide to the House of Lords, The Guide to the Governance of Britain in Europe, The Guide to the Executive Agencies, The Guide to Public Bodies – "Quangos", The Directory of London Government, The Directory of Northern Ireland Government, The Directory of Scottish Government, The Directory of Welsh Government, The Directory of English Regional Government, The Directory of Health Bodies and The Guide to Local Authorities.*

The Directory of Westminster and Whitehall is divided into two sections. The Westminster section deals mainly with Parliament, and in particular the House of Commons; while the Whitehall section deals mainly with government departments.

The Westminster section provides information not only on the MPs themselves, but also on their staff and constituency offices. This is particularly important since, over recent years, there has been a considerable increase in the number of people employed by MPs in both their constituency offices and in Parliament itself.

We are most grateful to those MPs who have supplied the information included in this book – CVs, staff names, office addresses, telephone and fax numbers, E-mail and Web addresses, etc.

The Whitehall section of The Directory of Westminster and Whitehall places primary emphasis on civil service subject responsibilities rather than on civil service structure and grades. The letters we receive from MPs and others involved in public life attest to the usefulness of the concept.

We are particularly grateful to Douglas Alexander MP, Minister for the Cabinet Office, to other government ministers, to the civil service and to all who have provided information for the Directory.

Imogen Carlton
*Editor*

# A bank that lets you call the tune.

We listen and act on what our customers tell us. We're part of your community and part of your everyday life.

So, if you've got something to say, let us know. If we can help in any way, we will.

Visit your local branch at 22 Victoria Street, Westminster, SW1H 0NJ.

For a premier banking service please call:

Maggie O'Donnell or Vikki Charker

on **020 7699 1364**.

**HSBC**

The world's local bank

# FOREWORD

I am delighted to have the opportunity to provide the foreword to the Directory of Westminster and Whitehall.

I write this foreword at an important time for my Department and for the Government. In 2004 we enter our seventh year in government and this provides a useful opportunity not only to reflect on what has been achieved but also to look forward to the future and to continuing to work in partnership across Westminster and Whitehall.

The knowledge, skills and experience of many of those listed in this directory has meant that this significant advancements have been made towards providing better and more citizen-focused services and more equal opportunities for all. I hope that new members listed in this Directory will help to build on these achievements.

Of course, there is still much to do. As head of the Cabinet Office, I will be aiming to drive forward the Department's vital work in building the capacity of government and shaping Whitehall to enable and facilitate continued advancement in the reform and delivery of public services. This reform remains an absolute priority and we will continue to work in partnership to deliver this vital goal.

However, this Directory is not only useful for those in politics to communicate with each other; it also provides an important gateway for those who have an interest in how government works, as well as providing valuable access to those who can make a difference.

Douglas Alexander MP
*Former Minister for the Cabinet Office and Chancellor of the Duchy of Lancaster*

# Schizophrenia Association of Great Britain

## Charity No 287587
## Founded 1970

Schizophrenia is a disease which affects the chemistry of the brain. As a consequence of this the patient's behaviour, thought and emotions change, thus altering his personality. This change of personality often occurs very gradually as the illness develops. The patient's personality may eventually become the opposite of what it was when he was well. He may believe it is those around him who have changed and not he himself. Few, if any, of those who care for him medically will have known him when he was well, yet the aim of good treatment must always be the restoration of the patient's true personality.

Everyone with schizophrenia has a personality disorder because their disease changes their personality. At present communication between the medical staff and the family is almost nil in very many cases. Because the personality of someone suffering from schizophrenia changes he may often be given a different and meaningless 'diagnosis' of personality disorder or psychopathic disorder, both depending on the doctor in charge. The use of these diagnoses illustrates a huge lack of understanding of the nature of the schizophrenia disease process.

All those who have the real disease of schizophrenia have a personality disorder and there is absolutely no need to invent a new category. The use of the terms *personality disorder* or *psychopathic disorder* is derogatory and give no disease connotations. They are said by some doctors to be untreatable. These terms should be abolished. Their use hinders the proper understanding of and treatment of schizophrenia.

**SAGB exists to inform the general public as well as patients and their families about the nature of schizophrenia.**

For a free information pack including nutritional advice contact:
SAGB Bryn Hyfryd
The Crescent BANGOR
Gwynedd LL57 2AG
Tel: 01248 354048  Fax: 01248 353659
E-mail: info@sagb.co.uk
Web: http://www.sagb.co.uk

# WESTMINSTER

# THE SPEAKER'S OFFICE

House of Commons, London, SW1A 0AA
Tel: (020) 7219 5300

**Speaker of the House of Commons** . . . . . . . . . . Rt Hon Michael Martin MP
*Speaker's Secretary* . . . . . . . . . . . . . . . . . . . . . . . Mr Roger Daw
*Speaker's Counsel* . . . . . . . . . . . . . . . . . . . . . . . . Mr John Vaux
*Speaker's Chaplain* . . . . . . . . . . . . . . . . . . . . . . Rev Canon Robert Wright

**Chairman of Ways and Means** . . . . . . . . . . . . . Rt Hon Sir Alan Haselhurst MP
*Secretary to the Chairman of Ways and Means* . . . . . Mr John Whatley

**First Deputy Chairman of Ways and Means** . . . . Sylvia Heal MP

**Second Deputy Chairman of Ways and Means** . . Sir Michael Lord MP

## Members of the Chairmen's Panel

| | | |
|---|---|---|
| Irene Adams MP | David Amess MP | Janet Anderson MP |
| Nigel Beard MP | Anne Begg MP | Joe Benton MP |
| Sir John Butterfill MP | Martin Caton MP | David Chidgey MP |
| Derek Conway MP | Frank Cook MP | James Cran MP |
| John Cummings MP | Rt Hon Eric Forth MP | Roger Gale MP |
| Win Griffiths MP | Mike Hancock MP | Jimmy Hood MP |
| Kevin Hughes MP | Alan Hurst MP | Eric Illsley MP |
| John McWilliam MP | Bill O'Brien MP | Eddie O'Hara MP |
| Bill Olner MP | Peter Pike MP | Dame Marion Roe MP |
| Jonathan Sayeed MP | George Stevenson MP | David Taylor MP |
| Rt Hon Ann Widdecombe MP | Sir Nicholas Winterton MP | |

# LEADER OF THE HOUSE OF COMMONS

**Office of the Leader of the House of Commons**
2 Carlton Gardens, London, SW1Y 5AA
Tel: (020) 7210 1025   Fax: (020) 7210 1075

House of Commons, London, SW1A 0AA
Tel: (020) 7219 4040  Fax: (020) 7219 6845

**Lord Privy Seal and**
    **Leader of the House of Commons** . . . . . . . Rt Hon Peter Hain MP
*Principal Private Secretary* . . . . . . . . . . . . . . . . . . . Mr Glynne Jones . . . . . . . . . . . . . . . . . . . . . . Tel: (020) 7210 1025
*Private Secretary (Deputy Head of Office)* . . . . . . . . Mr Stephen Hillcoat . . . . . . . . . . . . . . . . . Tel: (020) 7210 1025
*Private Secretary (Parliamentary Affairs)* . . . . . . . . Mr Mike Winter . . . . . . . . . . . . . . . . . . . . Tel: (020) 7210 1025
*Private Secretary (Policy and Legislation)* . . . . . . . . Mr James Newman . . . . . . . . . . . . . . . . . . Tel: (020) 7210 1025
*Special Advisers* . . . . . . . . . . . . . . . . . . . . . . . . . . Mr Greg Power . . . . . . . . . . . . . . . . . . . . . Tel: (020) 7210 1084
    Mr Philip Taylor . . . . . . . . . . . . . . . . . . . . . Tel: (020) 7210 1084

**Deputy Leader of the House of Commons** . . . . Phil Woolas MP
*Private Secretary* . . . . . . . . . . . . . . . . . . . . . . . . . Mrs Frances Slee . . . . . . . . . . . . . . . . . . . Tel: (020) 7210 1022

**Diary Secretary** . . . . . . . . . . . . . . . . . . . . . . . . . Mr Kevin Tyson . . . . . . . . . . . . . . . . . . . . Tel: (020) 7210 1021

# HOUSE OF COMMONS ADMINISTRATION

House of Commons, London, SW1A 0AA
Tel: (020) 7219 3000 *(Main Switchboard)*

**House of Commons Commission**

Chairman . . . . . . . . . . . . . . . . . . . . . . . . . . . . . . . . . . . Rt Hon Michael Martin MP *(Speaker)*
Members . . . . . . . . . . . . . . . . . . . . . . . . . . . . . . . . . . . Rt Hon Peter Hain MP *(Leader of the House)*
Sir Stuart Bell MP
Sir Patrick Cormack MP
Oliver Heald MP
Sir Archy Kirkwood MP
Commission Secretary . . . . . . . . . . . . . . . . . . . . . . . . Mr Robert Rogers

**Board of Management**

Chief Executive of the House of Commons . . . . . . . . . . . . . . Mr Roger Sands
Serjeant at Arms . . . . . . . . . . . . . . . . . . . . . . . . . . . . . . . . . . Sir Michael Cummins
Clerk of Committees . . . . . . . . . . . . . . . . . . . . . . . . . . . . . . . Mr George Cubie CB
Director of Catering Services . . . . . . . . . . . . . . . . . . . . . . . . Mrs Sue Harrison
Director of Finance and Administration . . . . . . . . . . . . . . . . Mr Andrew Walker
Editor, Official Report . . . . . . . . . . . . . . . . . . . . . . . . . . . . . Mr Bill Garland
Librarian . . . . . . . . . . . . . . . . . . . . . . . . . . . . . . . . . . . . . . . . Miss Priscilla Baines
*Secretary, Board of Management* . . . . . . . . . . . . . . . . . . . . . Dr Richard Ware

# HOUSE OF COMMONS: CONTACT INFORMATION

House of Commons, London, SW1A 0AA
Tel: (020) 7219 3000 *(Main Switchboard, both Houses)*

Information Office . . . . . . . . . . . . . . . . . . . . . . . . . . . . . . Tel: (020) 7219 4272
Fax: (020) 7219 5839
E-mail: hcinfo@parliament.uk

House of Commons Commission . . . . . . . . . . . . . . . . . . Tel: (020) 7219 3299
E-mail: hofccommission@parliament.uk
Office of the Clerk . . . . . . . . . . . . . . . . . . . . . . . . . . . . . Tel: (020) 7219 1707
E-mail: officeoftheclerk@parliament.uk
Committee Office . . . . . . . . . . . . . . . . . . . . . . . . . . . . . . Tel: (020) 7219 4300
Finance and Administration Department . . . . . . . . . . . . . Tel: (020) 7219 5306/6347
Library . . . . . . . . . . . . . . . . . . . . . . . . . . . . . . . . . . . . . . Tel: (020) 7219 4272
Official Report (Hansard) . . . . . . . . . . . . . . . . . . . . . . . . Tel: (020) 7219 4786
Refreshment Department . . . . . . . . . . . . . . . . . . . . . . . . Tel: (020) 7219 3686
Serjeant-at-Arms Department . . . . . . . . . . . . . . . . . . . . . Tel: (020) 7219 5555
Parliamentary Archives . . . . . . . . . . . . . . . . . . . . . . . . . Tel: (020) 7219 3074
Fax: (020) 7219 2570
E-mail: hlro@parliament.uk
Parliamentary Bookshop . . . . . . . . . . . . . . . . . . . . . . . . Tel: (020) 7219 3074
Fax: (020) 7219 2570
E-mail: bookshop@parliament.uk
Parliamentary Education Unit . . . . . . . . . . . . . . . . . . . . . Tel: (020) 7219 4750
Fax: (020) 7219 0818
E-mail: edunit@parliament.uk

# PARLIAMENTARY COUNSEL

36 Whitehall, London, SW1A 2AY
Tel: (020) 7210 6611  Fax: (020) 7210 6632
E-mail: linda.howes@cabinet-office.x.gsi.gov.uk
Web: http://www.parliamentary-counsel.gov.uk

First Parliamentary Counsel . . . . . . . . . . . . . . . . . . . . . . . . . . . . . . . . . . . . . . . Mr Geoffrey Bowman CB

# PARLIAMENTARY COMMISSIONER FOR STANDARDS

House of Commons, London, SW1A 0AA
Tel: (020) 7219 0320  Fax: (020) 7219 0490
E-mail: mawerp@parliament.uk
Web: http://www.parliament.uk

**Parliamentary Commissioner for Standards** . . . . . . Sir Philip Mawer

# PARLIAMENTARY OFFICE OF SCIENCE AND TECHNOLOGY

7 Millbank, London, SW1P 3JA
Tel: (020) 7219 2840  Fax: (020) 7219 2849
E-mail: post@parliament.co.uk
Web: http://www.parliament.uk/post

**Director** . . . . . . . . . . . . . . . . . . . . . . . . . . . . . . . Professor David Cope

# ELECTORAL COMMISSION

Trevelyan House, Great Peter Street, London, SW1P 2HW
Tel: (020) 7271 0500  Fax: (020) 7271 0505
E-mail: info@electoralcommission.org.uk
Web: http://www.electoralcommission.org.uk

**Chairman** . . . . . . . . . . . . . . . . . . . . . . . . . . . . . . Mr Sam Younger

**Commissioners** . . . . . . . . . . . . . . . . . . . . . . . . . . . . Ms Pamela Gordon             Mr Glyn Mathias
                                                        Sir Neil McIntosh              Mr Karamjit Singh CBE
                                                        Professor Graham Zellick

**Deputy Commissioners** . . . . . . . . . . . . . . . . . . . . . . Professor Michael Clarke        Mr Robin Gray
                                                        Ms Joan Jones CBE              Ms Ann M Kelly
                                                        Professor Colin Mellors

**Chief Executive** . . . . . . . . . . . . . . . . . . . . . . . . . . Mr Roger Creedon

**Director, The Boundary Committee** . . . . . . . . . . . . Mr Archie Gall

**Director, Policy** . . . . . . . . . . . . . . . . . . . . . . . . . . Ms Nicole Smith

# PRIME MINISTER'S OFFICE

10 Downing Street, London, SW1A 2AA
Tel: (020) 7930 4433
Web: http://www.pmo.gov.uk

**Prime Minister and First Lord of the Treasury** . . . . . . Rt Hon Tony Blair MP

**Parliamentary Private Secretary** . . . . . . . . . . . . . . . . . David Hanson MP

**Chief of Staff** . . . . . . . . . . . . . . . . . . . . . . . . . . . . . . Mr Jonathan Powell

**Principal Private Secretary and Head of
    Policy Directorate** . . . . . . . . . . . . . . . . . . . . . . . . Mr Ivan Rogers

**Director of Communications and Strategy** . . . . . . . . . Mr David Hill

**Director of Government and Political Relations** . . . . . Baroness Morgan of Huyton

**Director of Political Operations** . . . . . . . . . . . . . . . . . Mr Pat McFadden

**Adviser on Education, Public Services and
    Constitutional Reform** . . . . . . . . . . . . . . . . . . . . . . Mr Andrew Adonis

**Adviser on EU Affairs and Head of the European
    Secretariat** . . . . . . . . . . . . . . . . . . . . . . . . . . . . . . . Sir Stephen Wall

**Adviser on Foreign Policy and Head of the
    Overseas and Defence Secretariat** . . . . . . . . . . . . . Sir Nigel Sheinwald

**Head of Policy and Director, Strategy Unit** . . . . . . . . *Vacant*

**Policy Directorate** . . . . . . . . . . . . . . . . . . . . . . . . . . . Dr Arnab Banerji
                                                                                                Mr Patrick Diamond
                                                                                                Mr Matthew Elson
                                                                                                Mr Julian Le Grand
                                                                                                Ms Sarah Hunter
                                                                                                Mr Martin Hurst
                                                                                                Mr Alasdair McGowan
                                                                                                Mr John McTernan
                                                                                                Mr Geoffrey Norris
                                                                                                Mr Alasdair McGowan
                                                                                                Mr Carey Oppenheim
                                                                                                Mr Nicholas Rowley
                                                                                                Mr Justin Russell
                                                                                                Mr Simon Stevens
                                                                                                Ms Clare Sumner
                                                                                                Mr Simon Morys
                                                                                                Mr Matthew Taylor

**Foreign Policy Advisers** . . . . . . . . . . . . . . . . . . . . . . . Mr Roger Liddle
                                                                                                Ms Liz Lloyd
                                                                                                Mr David Quarrey
                                                                                                Mr Matthew Rycroft

**Director of Events and Visits** . . . . . . . . . . . . . . . . . . . Ms Jo Gibbons

# PRIME MINISTER'S OFFICE

**Secretary for Appointments** . . . . . . . . . . . . . . . . . . . . Mr William Chapman

**Executive Secretary** . . . . . . . . . . . . . . . . . . . . . . . . . Mr Jay Jayasundara

**Delivery Unit**

Prime Minister's Chief Adviser on Delivery . . . . . . . . . Professor Michael Barber    Tel: (020) 7270 5860
Deputy Directors

     Analytical Research . . . . . . . . . . . . . . . . . . . . . . . . Mr William Jordan      Tel: (020) 7270 5830
     Problem Solving and Capacity Building. . . . . . . . . . Mr Peter Thomas      Tel: (020) 7270 5884
Analytical Research (Team Leader) . . . . . . . . . . . . . . . Mr Tony O'Connor      Tel: (020) 7270 5853
Chief Problem Solver. . . . . . . . . . . . . . . . . . . . . . . . Mr Adrian Masters      Tel: (020) 7270 5845

**Implementation Group** . . . . . . . . . . . . . . . . . . . . . . . Ms Kate Garvey
                                                 Ms Sarah Hunter
                                                 Ms Liz Lloyd

**Strategy Unit**

Director, Strategy Unit. . . . . . . . . . . . . . . . . . . . . . . . Mr Geoff Mulgan      Tel: (020) 7276 1702
Deputy Directors . . . . . . . . . . . . . . . . . . . . . . . . . . . Ms Catriona Lang      Tel: (020) 7276 1967
                                                 Ms Patricia Greer      Tel: (020) 7276 1431
                                                 Mr Jamie Rentoul      Tel: (020) 7276 1468
Director of Policy Studies. . . . . . . . . . . . . . . . . . . . . Ms Sue Duncan      Tel: (020) 7276 1327
Chief Economist . . . . . . . . . . . . . . . . . . . . . . . . . . . Mr Stephen Aldridge      Tel: (020) 7276 1470

**Head of Office of Public Services Reform** . . . . . . . . . Ms Wendy Thomson

**Personal Assistant to Prime Minister (Diary)** . . . . . . . Ms Katie Kay

**Parliamentary Clerk** . . . . . . . . . . . . . . . . . . . . . . . . Mr Nicholas Howard

**Prime Minister's Official Spokesman** . . . . . . . . . . . . . Mr Tom Kelly

**Chief Press Officer** . . . . . . . . . . . . . . . . . . . . . . . . . Ms Anne Shevas

**Press Officers.** . . . . . . . . . . . . . . . . . . . . . . . . . . . . Ms Hilary Coffman
                                                 Mr Ian Gleeson
                                                 Ms Rachel Grant
                                                 Mr Martin Sheehan
                                                 Mr Simon Watts
                                                 Mr Ben Wilson

**Direct Communications Unit** . . . . . . . . . . . . . . . . . . . Ms Jan Taylor

**Research and Information Unit** . . . . . . . . . . . . . . . . . Ms Joanna Nadin
                                                 Ms Catherine Rimmer

**Strategic Communications Unit** . . . . . . . . . . . . . . . . . Mr Godric Smith
                                                 Mr David Bradshaw

# THE CABINET

| | |
|---|---|
| **Prime Minister, First Lord of the Treasury and Minister for the Civil Service** | Rt Hon Tony Blair MP |
| **Deputy Prime Minister and First Secretary of State** | Rt Hon John Prescott MP |
| **Chancellor of the Exchequer** | Rt Hon Gordon Brown MP |
| **Chancellor of the Duchy of Lancaster** | Rt Hon Alan Milburn MP |
| **Leader of the House of Commons, Lord Privy Seal and Secretary of State for Wales** | Rt Hon Peter Hain MP |
| **Secretary of State for Constitutional Affairs and Lord Chancellor** | Rt Hon Lord Falconer of Thoroton QC |
| **Secretary of State for Foreign and Commonwealth Affairs** | Rt Hon Jack Straw MP |
| **Secretary of State for the Home Department** | Rt Hon David Blunkett MP |
| **Secretary of State for Environment, Food and Rural Affairs** | Rt Hon Margaret Beckett MP |
| **Secretary of State for International Development** | Rt Hon Hilary Benn MP |
| **Secretary of State for Work and Pensions** | Rt Hon Alan Johnson MP |
| **Secretary of State for Transport and Secretary of State for Scotland** | Rt Hon Alistair Darling MP |
| **Secretary of State for Health** | Rt Hon John Reid MP |
| **Secretary of State for Northern Ireland** | Rt Hon Paul Murphy MP |
| **Secretary of State for Defence** | Rt Hon Geoff Hoon MP |
| **Chief Secretary, HM Treasury** | Rt Hon Paul Boateng MP |
| **Leader of the House of Lords and Lord President of the Council** | Rt Hon Baroness Amos |
| **Secretary of State for Trade and Industry and Minister for Women** | Rt Hon Patricia Hewitt MP |
| **Secretary of State for Education and Skills** | Rt Hon Charles Clarke MP |
| **Secretary of State for Culture, Media and Sport** | Rt Hon Tessa Jowell MP |
| **Parliamentary Secretary, HM Treasury and Chief Whip** | Rt Hon Hilary Armstrong MP |
| **Minister without Portfolio** | Rt Hon Ian McCartney MP *(also Chairman of the Labour Party)* |

# MINISTERS BY GOVERNMENT DEPARTMENT

*Note: In this section – and throughout the Directory – Parliamentary Secretary is used as the shortened term for Parliamentary Under Secretary of State.*

## PRIME MINISTER
*10 Downing Street, London, SW1A 2AA* . . . . . . . . . . . . . . . . . . . . Tel: (020) 7270 3000
                                                                                                                            Web: http://www.number-10.gov.uk

**Prime Minister, First Lord of the Treasury
   and Minister for the Civil Service** . . . . . . . . . . . . . . . . . Rt Hon Tony Blair MP


## CABINET OFFICE
*70 Whitehall, London, SW1A 2AS*. . . . . . . . . . . . . . . . . . . . . . . Tel: (020) 7276 3000
                                                                                                                            Web: http://www.cabinet-office.gov.uk

**Chancellor of the Duchy of Lancaster** . . . . . . . . . . . . . . . . Rt Hon Alan Milburn MP

**Minister for the Cabinet Office** . . . . . . . . . . . . . . . . . . . . . . Ruth Kelly MP

**Minister without Portfolio**. . . . . . . . . . . . . . . . . . . . . . . . . . . Rt Hon Ian McCartney MP *(also Chairman of the
                                                                                                                                    Labour Party)*


## DEPARTMENT FOR CONSTITUTIONAL AFFAIRS
*Selbourne House, 54-60 Victoria Street, London, SW1E 6QW*. . . . . . Tel: (020) 7210 8532
                                                                                                                            Web: http://www.lcd.gov.uk
**Secretary of State and Lord Chancellor** . . . . . . . . . . . . . . . Rt Hon Lord Falconer of Thoroton QC
**Parliamentary Secretaries** . . . . . . . . . . . . . . . . . . . . . . . . . . Baroness Ashton of Upholland
                                                                                                                            David Lammy MP
                                                                                                                            Christopher Leslie MP
                                                                                                                            Anne McGuire MP *(Scotland)*
                                                                                                                            Don Touhig MP *(Wales)*
**Advocate General for Scotland** . . . . . . . . . . . . . . . . . . . . . . Dr Lynda Clark QC MP


## DEPARTMENT FOR CULTURE, MEDIA AND SPORT
*2-4 Cockspur Street, London, SW1Y 5DH* . . . . . . . . . . . . . . . . . . . Tel: (020) 7211 6000
                                                                                                                            Web: http://www.culture.gov.uk
**Secretary of State** . . . . . . . . . . . . . . . . . . . . . . . . . . . . . . . . . Rt Hon Tessa Jowell MP
**Ministers of State**. . . . . . . . . . . . . . . . . . . . . . . . . . . . . . . . . . Rt Hon Richard Caborn MP *(Sport and Tourism)*
                                                                                                                            Rt Hon Estelle Morris MP *(The Arts)*
**Parliamentary Secretary**. . . . . . . . . . . . . . . . . . . . . . . . . . . . . Rt Hon Lord McIntosh of Haringey *(Media and Heritage)*

## MINISTRY OF DEFENCE
*Old War Office Building, Whitehall, London, SW1A 2HB* . . . . . . . . Tel: (020) 7218 9000
                                                                                                                            E-mail: public@ministers.mod.uk
                                                                                                                            Web: http://www.mod.uk
**Secretary of State** . . . . . . . . . . . . . . . . . . . . . . . . . . . . . . . . . Rt Hon Geoff Hoon MP
**Minister of State**. . . . . . . . . . . . . . . . . . . . . . . . . . . . . . . . . . . Rt Hon Adam Ingram MP *(The Armed Forces)*
**Parliamentary Secretaries** . . . . . . . . . . . . . . . . . . . . . . . . . . Lord Bach of Lutterworth *(Defence Procurement)*
                                                                                                                            Ivor Caplin MP *(Veterans)*


## OFFICE OF DEPUTY PRIME MINISTER
*26 Whitehall, London, SW1A 2WH*. . . . . . . . . . . . . . . . . . . . . . . Tel: (020) 7944 4400
                                                                                                                            Web: http://www.odpm.gov.uk
**Deputy Prime Minister and First Secretary of State for
   Local Government and the Regions**. . . . . . . . . . . . . . . . . . Rt Hon John Prescott MP
**Ministers of State**. . . . . . . . . . . . . . . . . . . . . . . . . . . . . . . . . . Rt Hon Keith Hill MP *(Housing and Planning)*
                                                                                                                            Rt Hon Nick Raynsford MP *(Local and Regional Government)*
                                                                                                                            Rt Hon Lord Rooker *(Regeneration and
                                                                                                                                    Regional Development)*
**Parliamentary Secretaries** . . . . . . . . . . . . . . . . . . . . . . . . . . Yvette Cooper MP
                                                                                                                            Philip Hope MP

# MINISTERS BY GOVERNMENT DEPARTMENT

## DEPARTMENT FOR EDUCATION AND SKILLS
*Sanctuary Buildings, Great Smith Street, London, SW1P 3BT* . . . . . Tel: (020) 7925 5000
E-mail: dfes.ministers@dfes.gsi.gov.uk
Web: http://www. dfes.gov.uk

**Secretary of State** . . . . . . . . . . . . . . . . . . . . . . . . . . . . . . . . Rt Hon Charles Clarke MP

**Ministers of State** . . . . . . . . . . . . . . . . . . . . . . . . . . . . . . . . Rt Hon Margaret Hodge MBE MP *(Children)*
Dr Kim Howells MP *(Lifelong Learning,*
*Further and Higher Education)*
David Miliband MP *(School Standards)*

**Parliamentary Secretaries** . . . . . . . . . . . . . . . . . . . . . . . . . Lord Filkins *(Sure Start, Early Years and*
*Child Care; also at DWP)*
Ivan Lewis MP *(Skills and Vocational Education)*
Stephen Twigg MP *(Schools)*


## DEPARTMENT OF ENVIRONMENT, FOOD AND RURAL AFFAIRS
*Nobel House, 17 Smith Square, London, SW1P 3JR.* . . . . . . . . . . . . Tel: (020) 7238 6000
Web: http://www.defra.gov.uk

**Secretary of State** . . . . . . . . . . . . . . . . . . . . . . . . . . . . . . . . Rt Hon Margaret Beckett MP

**Ministers of State** . . . . . . . . . . . . . . . . . . . . . . . . . . . . . . . . Rt Hon Alun Michael MP *(Rural Affairs)*
Elliot Morley MP *(Environment and Agri-Environment)*

**Parliamentary Secretaries** . . . . . . . . . . . . . . . . . . . . . . . . . Ben Bradshaw MP *(Nature Conservation and Fisheries)*
Lord Whitty *(Food, Farming and Sustainable Energy)*


## FOREIGN AND COMMONWEALTH OFFICE
*King Charles Street, London, SW1A 2AH* . . . . . . . . . . . . . . . . . . . Tel: (020) 7270 1500
Web: http://www.fco.gov.uk

**Secretary of State** . . . . . . . . . . . . . . . . . . . . . . . . . . . . . . . . Rt Hon Jack Straw MP

**Ministers of State** . . . . . . . . . . . . . . . . . . . . . . . . . . . . . . . . Dr Denis MacShane MP *(Europe)*
Douglas Alexander MP *(Trade, also at DTI)*
Rt Hon Baroness Symons of Vernham Dean
*(Middle East; also Deputy Leader, House of Lords)*

**Parliamentary Secretaries** . . . . . . . . . . . . . . . . . . . . . . . . . Chris Mullin MP
Bill Rammell MP


## DEPARTMENT OF HEALTH
*Richmond House, 79 Whitehall, London, SW1A 2NS* . . . . . . . . . . . Tel: (020) 7210 3000
Web: http://www.doh.gov.uk

**Secretary of State** . . . . . . . . . . . . . . . . . . . . . . . . . . . . . . . . Rt Hon John Reid MP

**Ministers of State** . . . . . . . . . . . . . . . . . . . . . . . . . . . . . . . . Rt Hon John Hutton MP
Rosie Winterton MP

**Parliamentary Secretaries** . . . . . . . . . . . . . . . . . . . . . . . . . Melanie Johnson MP
Dr Stephen Ladyman MP
Lord Warner

## HOME OFFICE
*50 Queen Anne's Gate, London, SW1H 9AT.* . . . . . . . . . . . . . . . . Tel: (020) 7273 4000
E-mail: public.enquiries@homeoffice.gsi.gov.uk
Web: http://www.homeoffice.gov.uk

**Secretary of State** . . . . . . . . . . . . . . . . . . . . . . . . . . . . . . . . Rt Hon David Blunkett MP

**Ministers of State** . . . . . . . . . . . . . . . . . . . . . . . . . . . . . . . . Hazel Blears MP *(Crime Reduction,*
*Policing and Community Safety)*
Desmond Browne MP *(Citizenship and Immigration and*
*Counter-Terrorism)*
Rt Hon Baroness Scotland of Asthal QC
*(Criminal Justice System and Law Reform)*

**Parliamentary Secretaries** . . . . . . . . . . . . . . . . . . . . . . . . . Caroline Flint MP *(Race Equality, Community*
*Policy and Civil Renewal)*
Paul Goggins MP *(Correctional Services)*
Fiona Mactaggart MP *(European and International Issues;*
*Anti-Drugs Co-ordination)*

# MINISTERS BY GOVERNMENT DEPARTMENT

### DEPARTMENT FOR INTERNATIONAL DEVELOPMENT
*1 Palace Street, London, SW1E 5HE* . . . . . . . . . . . . . . . . . . . . . . Tel: (020) 7023 0000
Web: http://www.dfid.gov.uk
**Secretary of State** . . . . . . . . . . . . . . . . . . . . . . . . . . . . . . . Rt Hon Hilary Benn MP
**Parliamentary Secretary** . . . . . . . . . . . . . . . . . . . . . . . . . . . Gareth R Thomas MP

### OFFICE OF LEADER OF THE HOUSE OF COMMONS
*2 Carlton House Gardens, London, SW1Y 5AA* . . . . . . . . . . . . . . . . Tel: (020) 7210 1025
Web: http://www.commonsleader.gov.uk
**Lord Privy Seal and Leader of the House of Commons** . . . . Rt Hon Peter Hain MP *(also Secretary of State for Wales)*
**Deputy Leader of the House of Commons** . . . . . . . . . . . . . Phil Woolas MP

### LAW OFFICERS' DEPARTMENT
*Attorney General's Chambers, 9 Buckingham Gate, London, SW1E 6JP* Tel: (020) 7271 2400
**Attorney General** . . . . . . . . . . . . . . . . . . . . . . . . . . . . . . . . Rt Hon Lord Goldsmith QC
**Solicitor General** . . . . . . . . . . . . . . . . . . . . . . . . . . . . . . . . Rt Hon Harriet Harman QC MP

### NORTHERN IRELAND OFFICE
*11 Millbank, London SW1P 4PN* . . . . . . . . . . . . . . . . . . . . . . . Tel: (020) 7210 3000
*Stormont Castle, Belfast, BT4 3SG* . . . . . . . . . . . . . . . . . . . . . . Tel: (028) 9052 0700
Web: http://www.nio.gov.uk
**Secretary of State** . . . . . . . . . . . . . . . . . . . . . . . . . . . . . . . Rt Hon Paul Murphy MP
**Minister of State** . . . . . . . . . . . . . . . . . . . . . . . . . . . . . . . . Rt Hon John Spellar MP
**Parliamentary Secretaries** . . . . . . . . . . . . . . . . . . . . . . . . . Barry Gardiner MP
Ian Pearson MP
Angela Smith MP

### PRIVY COUNCIL OFFICE
*2 Carlton House Gardens, London, SW1Y 5AA* . . . . . . . . . . . . . . . Tel: (020) 7210 3000
Web: http://www.privy-council.org.uk
**Lord President of the Council and**
**Leader of the House of Lords** . . . . . . . . . . . . . . . . . . . . . Rt Hon Baroness Amos

### SCOTLAND OFFICE *(Part of Constitutional Affairs Department)*
*Dover House, Whitehall, London, SW1A 2AU* . . . . . . . . . . . . . . . . Tel: (020) 7270 6754
*1 Melville Crescent, Edinburgh, EH3 7HW* . . . . . . . . . . . . . . . . . Tel: (0131) 244 9010
Web: http://www.scottishsecretary.gov.uk
**Secretary of State** . . . . . . . . . . . . . . . . . . . . . . . . . . . . . . . Rt Hon Alistair Darling MP
*(also Secretary of State for Transport)*
**Parliamentary Secretary** . . . . . . . . . . . . . . . . . . . . . . . . . . . Anne McGuire MP

### DEPARTMENT OF TRADE AND INDUSTRY
*1 Victoria Street, London, SW1H 0ET* . . . . . . . . . . . . . . . . . . . . Tel: (020) 7215 5000
Web: http://www.dti.gov.uk
**Secretary of State** . . . . . . . . . . . . . . . . . . . . . . . . . . . . . . . Rt Hon Patricia Hewitt MP *(also Minister for Women)*
**Ministers of State** . . . . . . . . . . . . . . . . . . . . . . . . . . . . . . . Mike O'Brien MP *(E-Commerce and Competitiveness)*
Rt Hon Jacqui Smith MP *(Industry and the*
*Regions; also Deputy Minister for Women)*
Douglas Alexander MP *(Trade; also at FCO)*
**Parliamentary Secretaries** . . . . . . . . . . . . . . . . . . . . . . . . . Nigel Griffiths MP *(Small Business)*
Lord Sainsbury of Turville *(Science and Innovation)*
Gerry Sutcliffe MP *(Employment Relations,*
*Competition and Consumers)*

# MINISTERS BY GOVERNMENT DEPARTMENT

## DEPARTMENT OF TRANSPORT

*Great Minster House, 76 Marsham Street, London, SW1P 4DR* . . . . . Tel: (020) 7944 8300
Web: http://www.dft.gov.uk

**Secretary of State** . . . . . . . . . . . . . . . . . . . . . . . . . . . . . . . Rt Hon Alistair Darling MP
*(also Secretary of State for Scotland)*
**Minister of State** . . . . . . . . . . . . . . . . . . . . . . . . . . . . . . . Tony McNulty MP
**Parliamentary Secretaries** . . . . . . . . . . . . . . . . . . . . . . . . Charlotte Atkins MP
David Jamieson MP

## H M TREASURY

*1 Horseguards Road, London, SW1A 2HQ* . . . . . . . . . . . . . . . . . . Tel: (020) 7270 5000
E-mail: ministers@hm-treasury.gov.uk
Web: http://www.hm-treasury.gov.uk

**Chancellor of the Exchequer** . . . . . . . . . . . . . . . . . . . . . . . Rt Hon Gordon Brown MP
**Chief Secretary** . . . . . . . . . . . . . . . . . . . . . . . . . . . . . . . . . Rt Hon Paul Boateng MP
**Paymaster General** . . . . . . . . . . . . . . . . . . . . . . . . . . . . . . Rt Hon Dawn Primarolo MP
**Financial Secretary** . . . . . . . . . . . . . . . . . . . . . . . . . . . . . Stephen Timms MP
**Economic Secretary** . . . . . . . . . . . . . . . . . . . . . . . . . . . . . John Healey MP
**Parliamentary Secretary** *(Government Chief Whip)* . . . . . . . . . Rt Hon Hilary Armstrong MP

## WALES OFFICE *(part of Constitutional Affairs Department)*

*Gwydyr House, Whitehall, London, SW1A 2ER* . . . . . . . . . . . . . . Tel: (020) 7270 3000
*National Assembly for Wales, Cardiff Bay, Cardiff, CF99 1NA* . . . . Tel: (029) 2082 5111
E-mail: wales.office@wales.gsi.gov.uk
Web: http://www.ossw.pwales.gov.uk

**Secretary of State** . . . . . . . . . . . . . . . . . . . . . . . . . . . . . . . Rt Hon Peter Hain MP *(also Lord Privy Seal*
*and Leader of the House of Commons)*
**Parliamentary Secretary** . . . . . . . . . . . . . . . . . . . . . . . . . . Don Touhig MP

## DEPARTMENT FOR WORK AND PENSIONS

*Richmond House, 79 Whitehall, London, SW1A 2NS* . . . . . . . . . . . Tel: (020) 7238 0800
E-mail: ministers@dwp.gsi.gov.uk
Web: http://www.dwp.gov.uk

**Secretary of State** . . . . . . . . . . . . . . . . . . . . . . . . . . . . . . . Rt Hon Alan Johnson MP
**Ministers of State** . . . . . . . . . . . . . . . . . . . . . . . . . . . . . . . Rt Hon Jane Kennedy MP *(Minister for Work)*
Malcolm Wicks MP *(Pensions)*
**Parliamentary Secretaries** . . . . . . . . . . . . . . . . . . . . . . . . Maria Eagle MP *(Disabled People)*
Rt Hon Baroness Hollis of Heigham
Chris Pond MP

*Notes:* (i) *Lord Commissioners of the Treasury and relevant members of HM Household are listed under Government Whips below.*

(ii) *The Second Church Estates Commissioner, representing the Church Commissioners, answers questions on their behalf form the Government frontbench, but it is not formally a member of the Government. The current holder of the post is Sir Stuart Bell* MP

# GOVERNMENT WHIPS (COMMONS)

9 Downing Street, London, SW1A 2AG
Tel: (020) 7276 2020

**Parliamentary Secretary to the Treasury and Government Chief Whip** . . . Rt Hon Hilary Armstrong MP
*Special Advisers* . . . . . . . . . . . . . . . . . . . . . . . . . . . . . . . . . . . . . . Ms Fiona Gordon
Ms Sue Jackson

**Treasurer of Her Majesty's Household and Deputy Chief Whip** . . . . . . . . Bob Ainsworth MP

**Comptroller of Her Majesty's Household** . . . . . . . . . . . . . . . . . . . . . . . Rt Hon Tommy McAvoy MP

**Vice-Chamberlain of Her Majesty's Household** . . . . . . . . . . . . . . . . . . . Jim Fitzpatrick MP

**Lords Commissioners of the Treasury** . . . . . . . . . . . . . . . . . . . . . . . . . Nick Ainger MP
John Heppell MP
Jim Murphy MP
Joan Ryan MP
Derek Twigg MP

**Assistant Whips** . . . . . . . . . . . . . . . . . . . . . . . . . . . . . . . . . . . . . . . Paul Clark MP
Vernon Coaker MP
Fraser Kemp MP
Gillian Merron MP
Margaret Moran MP
Bridget Prentice MP
Tom Watson MP

# GOVERNMENT WHIPS (LORDS)

House of Lords, Westminster, London, SW1A 0PW
Tel: (020) 7219 3131

**Captain of the Gentlemen-at-Arms and Chief Whip** . . . . . . . . . . . . . . . . . . . Rt Hon Lord Grocott
*Private Secretary* . . . . . . . . . . . . . . . . . . . . . . . . . . . . . . . . . . . . . . . . . Mr Andrew Makower
*Special Adviser* . . . . . . . . . . . . . . . . . . . . . . . . . . . . . . . . . . . . . . . . . . Ms Margaret Ounsley

**Captain of the Yeomen of the Guard and Deputy Chief Whip** . . . . . . . . . . Lord Davies of Oldham

**Lords and Baronesses in Waiting** . . . . . . . . . . . . . . . . . . . . . . . . . . . . . Baroness Andrews OBE
Lord Bassam of Brighton
Baroness Crawley
Lord Evans of Temple Guiting CBE
Baroness Farrington of Ribbleton
Lord Triesman

# MINISTERS' PARLIAMENTARY PRIVATE SECRETARIES

| DEPARTMENT/OFFICE | MINISTER | PPS |
|---|---|---|
| **Prime Minister** | Rt Hon Tony Blair MP | David Hanson MP |
| **Deputy Prime Minister** | | |
| Deputy Prime Minister and First Secretary of State | Rt Hon John Prescott MP | Dave Watts MP |
| Ministers of State | Rt Hon Keith Hill MP | Terry Rooney MP |
| | Rt Hon Nick Raynsford MP | Linda Gilroy MP |
| **Cabinet Office** | | |
| Chancellor of the Duchy of Lancaster | Rt Hon Alan Milburn MP | |
| Minister for the Cabinet Office | Ruth Kelly MP | James Purnell MP |
| Minister without Portfolio | Rt Hon Ian McCartney MP | Neil Turner MP |
| **Constitutional Affairs** | | |
| Secretary of State and Lord Chancellor | Rt Hon Lord Falconer of Thoroton QC | Laura Moffatt MP |
| | *Ministerial Team* | Geraint Davies MP |
| **Culture, Media and Sport** | | |
| Secretary of State | Rt Hon Tessa Jowell MP | Gordon Marsden MP |
| Ministers of State | Rt Hon Richard Caborn MP | Ben Chapman MP |
| | Rt Hon Estelle Morris | Dr Howard Stoate MP |
| **Defence** | | |
| Secretary of State | Rt Hon Geoff Hoon MP | Liz Blackman MP |
| Minister of State | Rt Hon Adam Ingram MP | Alan Campbell MP |
| | *Ministerial Team* | Syd Rapson BEM MP |
| **Education and Skills** | | |
| Secretary of State | Rt Hon Charles Clarke MP | Stephen McCabe MP |
| Ministers of State | Rt Hon Margaret Hodge MBE MP | Meg Munn MP |
| | Dr Kim Howells MP | David Borrow MP |
| | David Miliband MP | Ian Cawsey MP |
| | *Ministerial Team* | Michael John Foster MP |
| **Environment, Food and Rural Affairs** | | |
| Secretary of State | Rt Hon Margaret Beckett MP | Mark Hendrick MP |
| Ministers of State | Rt Hon Alun Michael MP | Peter Bradley MP |
| | Elliot Morley MP | Tony Cunningham MP |
| | *Ministerial Team* | Dr Nick Palmer MP |
| **Foreign and Commonwealth Office** | | |
| Secretary of State | Rt Hon Jack Straw MP | Colin Pickthall MP |
| Ministers of State | Douglas Alexander MP | Lawrie Quinn MP |
| | Dr Denis MacShane MP | Dr Phyllis Starkey MP |
| | Rt Hon Baroness Symons of Vernham Dean | Mark Todd MP |
| | *Ministerial Team* | Roger Casale MP |
| **Health** | | |
| Secretary of State | Rt Hon John Reid MP | Mike Hall MP |
| Ministers of State | Rt Hon John Hutton MP | Claire Ward MP |
| | Rosie Winterton MP | Jim Knight MP |

# MINISTERS' PARLIAMENTARY PRIVATE SECRETARIES

### Home Office
| | | |
|---|---|---|
| Secretary of State | Rt Hon David Blunkett MP | Andrew Burnham MP |
| Ministers of State | Hazel Blears MP | Dari Taylor MP |
| | Desmond Browne MP | Kali Mountford MP |
| | Rt Hon Baroness Scotland of Asthal QC | Shona McIsaac MP |

### International Development
| | | |
|---|---|---|
| Secretary of State | Rt Hon Hilary Benn MP | Dr Ashok Kumar MP |
| | | Tom Levitt MP |

### Law Officers
| | | |
|---|---|---|
| Attorney General | Rt Hon Lord Goldsmith QC | Michael Jabez Foster MP |
| Solicitor General | Rt Hon Harriet Harman MP | Michael Jabez Foster MP |

### Leader of the House of Commons
| | | |
|---|---|---|
| Lord Privy Seal, Leader of the House of Commons and Secretary of State for Wales | Rt Hon Peter Hain MP | Martin Linton MP |
| | | Chris Ruane MP |

### Northern Ireland Office
| | | |
|---|---|---|
| Secretary of State | Rt Hon Paul Murphy MP | Gareth Thomas MP |
| Minister of State | Rt Hon John Spellar MP | Tom Harris MP |

### Privy Council Office
| | | |
|---|---|---|
| Lord President of the Council and Leader of the House of Lords | Rt Hon Baroness Amos | Russell Brown MP |

### Trade and Industry
| | | |
|---|---|---|
| Secretary of State | Rt Hon Patricia Hewitt MP | Oona King MP |
| Ministers of State | Douglas Alexander MP | Laurie Quinn MP |
| | Mike O'Brien MP | Eric Joyce MP |
| | Rt Hon Jacqui Smith MP | Andrew Love MP |
| | *Ministerial Team* | Jackie Lawrence MP |
| | | Andrew Miller MP |

### Transport
| | | |
|---|---|---|
| Secretary of State for Transport and Secretary of State for Scotland | Rt Hon Alistair Darling MP | Ann Coffey MP |
| | | David Stewart MP |
| Minister of State | Tony McNulty MP | *Vacant* |

### Treasury
| | | |
|---|---|---|
| Chancellor of the Exchequer | Rt Hon Gordon Brown MP | Ann Keen MP |
| Chief Secretary | Rt Hon Paul Boateng MP | Helen Southworth MP |
| Paymaster General | Rt Hon Dawn Primarolo MP | *Vacant* |
| Financial Secretary | Stephen Timms MP | Ian Stewart MP |

### Department for Work and Pensions
| | | |
|---|---|---|
| Secretary of State | Alan Johnson MP | Bob Laxton MP |
| Ministers of State | Rt Hon Jane Kennedy MP | Huw Irranca-Davies MP |
| | Malcolm Wicks MP | David Cairns MP |

# LEADER OF THE OPPOSITION'S OFFICE

House of Commons, London, SW1A 0AA
Tel: (020) 7219 4410
E-mail: howardm@conservatives.uk  Web: http://www.conservatives.com

**Leader of the Opposition** . . . . . . . . . . . . . . . . . . . . . . Rt Hon Michael Howard QC MP
Parliamentary Private Secretaries . . . . . . . . . . . . . . . . . . Graham Brady MP
Alistair Burt MP
**Deputy Leader of the Opposition** . . . . . . . . . . . . . . . Rt Hon Michael Ancram QC MP
*Parliamentary Private Secretary* . . . . . . . . . . . . . . . . . Andrew Selous MP

# OPPOSITION FRONT BENCH

*Notes: (i) Members of the Shadow Cabinet are denoted by\**
*(ii) Principal Spokesman in the Commons are listed first in each subject area*
*(iii) Spokesmen in the Lords may carer more than are subject.*

**HOUSE OF COMMONS**

**Leader of the Opposition** . . . . . . . . . . . . . . . . . Rt Hon Michael Howard QC MP*

**Economic Affairs** . . . . . . . . . . . . . . . . . . . . . . Rt Hon Oliver Letwin MP* *(Shadow Chancellor of the Exchequer)*
Rt Hon John Redwood MP *(Shadow Secretary for Deregulation)*
Rt Hon James Arbuthnot MP *(Shadow Secretary Trade)*
David Willetts MP* *(Shadow Secretary for Work and Pensions;*
*also Welfare Reform)*
George Osborne MP *(Shadow Chief Secretary to the Treasury)*
Stephen O'Brien MP *(Shadow Secretary for Industry)*
Henry Bellingham MP
Michael Fabricant MP
Mark Francois MP
Howard Flight MP *(Special Envoy to the City of London)*
Paul Goodman MP *(Disabled People)*
Andrew Mitchell MP
Mark Prisk MP
Laurence Robertson MP
Richard Spring MP
Andrew Tyrie MP
Nigel Waterson MP

**Education** . . . . . . . . . . . . . . . . . . . . . . . . . . . Tim Collins CBE MP* *(Shadow Secretary for Education)*
Chris Grayling MP
Charles Hendry MP *(Young People)*
Mark Hoban MP
Mark Simmonds MP
Angela Watkinson MP

**Environment and Transport** . . . . . . . . . . . . . . . Tim Yeo MP* *(Shadow Secretary for*
*Environment and Transport)*
Richard Ottaway MP *(Shadow Secretary for Environment)*
James Paice OBE MP *(Shadow Secretary for Agriculture,*
*Fisheries and Food)*
Christopher Chope OBE MP
James Gray MP
Rt Hon Greg Knight MP
Anne McIntosh MP
Owen Paterson MP

# OPPOSITION FRONT BENCH

**Family** . . . . . . . . . . . . . . . . . . . . . . . . . . . . . . . . . . . . . Rt Hon Theresa May MP *(Shadow Secretary for the Family)*

Eleanor Laing MP *(Women)*

Tim Loughton MP *(Children)*

**Home, Constitutional and Legal Affairs** . . . . . . . . . . Rt Hon David Davis MP\* *(Shadow Home Secretary and Secretary for Constitutional and Legal Affairs)*

Alan Duncan MP *(Constitutional Affairs)*

Dominic Grieve MP *(Shadow Attorney General)*

Julie Kirkbride MP *(Shadow Secretary for Culture, Media and Sport)*

Tim Boswell MP

Jonathan Djanogly MP

Cheryl Gillan MP

Boris Johnson MP *(Arts)*

Jacqui Lait MP

Oliver Heald MP *(Shadow Secretary for Constitutional Affairs)*

John Whittingdale MP *(Shadow Secretary for Culture, Media and Sport)*

Dr Julian Lewis MP *(Cabinet Office)*

Humfrey Malins CBE MP

Patrick Mercer OBE MP *(Home and Security)*

Andrew Mitchell MP

Malcolm Moss MP

Hugh Robertson MP *(Sport)*

**International Affairs** . . . . . . . . . . . . . . . . . . . . . . . . . Rt Hon Michael Ancram QC MP\* *(Shadow Foreign Secretary; also Deputy Leader)*

Hon Nicholas Soames MP\* *(Shadow Secretary for Defence)*

Alan Duncan MP *(Shadow Secretary for International Development)*

Rt Hon James Arbuthnot MP *(Shadow Secretary for Trade)*

Graham Brady MP

Julian Brazier MP

Gerald Howarth MP

Dr Julian Lewis MP

Mark Simmonds MP

Keith Simpson MP

Gary Streeter MP

**House of Commons** . . . . . . . . . . . . . . . . . . . . . . . . . Oliver Heald MP *(Shadow Leader of the House)*

**Local and Devolved Government Affairs** . . . . . . . . . . Caroline Spelman MP\* *(Shadow Secretary of State)*

Eric Pickles MP *(Local Government)*

Hon Bernard Jenkin MP *(The Regions)*

David Lidington MP *(Shadow Secretary for Northern Ireland)*

Peter Duncan MP *(Shadow Secretary for Scotland)*

Bill Wiggin MP *(Shadow Secretary for Wales)*

Mark Field MP *(London)*

Philip Hammond MP

John Hayes MP

Desmond Swayne TD MP

Robert Syms MP

# OPPOSITION FRONT BENCH

**Health** . . . . . . . . . . . . . . . . . . . . . . . . . . . . . . . . . . . . . Andrew Lansley CBE MP* *(Shadow Secretary for Health)*

John Barron MP

Simon Burns MP

Dr Andrew Murrison MP

**Whips (House of Commons)** . . . . . . . . . . . . . . . . . . . . . Rt Hon David Maclean MP* *(Chief Whip)*

Patrick McLoughlin MP *(Deputy Chief Whip)*

Peter Luff MP *(Assistant Chief Whip)*

Peter Atkinson MP

Gregory Barker MP

Geoffrey Clifton-Brown MP

Mark Francois MP

John Randall MP

Hugh Robertson MP

David Ruffley MP

Hugo Swire MP

Angela Watkinson MP

David Wilshire MP

OPPOSITION FRONT BENCH

## HOUSE OF LORDS

**Leader** . . . . . . . . . . . . . . . . . . . . . . . . . . . . . . . . . . . . Rt Hon Lord Strathclyde*

**Deputy Leader** . . . . . . . . . . . . . . . . . . . . . . . . . . . . Rt Hon Baroness Blatch CBE

**Economic Affairs** . . . . . . . . . . . . . . . . . . . . . . . . . . Earl Attlee
Rt Hon Lord Higgins KBE
Lord Hodgson CBE
Baroness Miller of Hendon
Baroness Noakes DBE
Lord Skelmersdale
Baroness Wilcox

**Education** . . . . . . . . . . . . . . . . . . . . . . . . . . . . . . . . Rt Hon Baroness Blatch

**Environment and Transport** . . . . . . . . . . . . . . . . . . Viscount Astor
Baroness Byford DBE
Lord Dixon-Smith
Lord Luke
Duke of Montrose
Lord Rotherwick

**Family** . . . . . . . . . . . . . . . . . . . . . . . . . . . . . . . . . . Earl Howe

**Health** . . . . . . . . . . . . . . . . . . . . . . . . . . . . . . . . . . Earl Howe
Lord McColl of Dulwich
Lord Skelmersdale

**Home, Constitutional and Legal Affairs** . . . . . . . . . . Rt Hon Lord Kingsland QC *(Shadow Lord Chancellor)*
Baroness Anelay DBE
Viscount Bridgeman
Baroness Buscombe
Lord Hodgson CBE
Lord Luke
Lord Moynihan *(Sport)*

**International Affairs** . . . . . . . . . . . . . . . . . . . . . . . . Lord Luke
Rt Hon Lord Howell of Guildford
Lord Astor of Hever *(Defence)*
Baroness Rawlings

**Local Government and Devolved Affairs** . . . . . . . . . . Viscount Bridgeman
Lord Glentoran CBE DL
Baroness Hanham CBE
Lord Hanningfield
Lord Luke
Duke of Montrose
Rt Hon Lord Roberts of Conwy

# OPPOSITION FRONT BENCH

**Whips (House of Lords)** . . . . . . . . . . . . . . . . . . . . . . Rt Hon Lord Cope of Berkeley (Chief Whip)
Baroness Seccombe DBE
Lord Astor of Hever
Earl Attlee
Viscount Bridgeman
Baroness Hanham
Lord Hanningfield
Lord Luke
Duke of Montrose
Lord Rotherwick
Lord Skelmersdale
Baroness Wilcox

## CONSERVATIVE PARTY ORGANISATION

**Co-chairmen**. . . . . . . . . . . . . . . . . . . . . . . . . . . . . Dr Liam Fox MP*
Lord Saatchi*

**Deputy Chairman** . . . . . . . . . . . . . . . . . . . . . . . . Charles Hendry MP

**Head of Policy Co-ordination** . . . . . . . . . . . . . . . . . David Cameron MP

# LIBERAL DEMOCRAT SPOKESMEN

## HOUSE OF COMMONS

House of Commons, London, SW1A 0AA
Leaders Office: Tel: (020) 7219 6690
Whips Office: Tel: (020) 7219 5654

*Notes: (i) The principal spokesman is listed first for each area of responsibility. Members of the Liberal Democrat Shadow Cabinet are denoted by\*.*

*(ii) Some spokesmen may cover more than one subject.*

**Leader** . . . . . . . . . . . . . . . . . . . . . . . . . . . . . . . . . Rt Hon Charles Kennedy MP\*

**Deputy Leader** . . . . . . . . . . . . . . . . . . . . . . . . . . . Rt Hon Sir Menzies Campbell CBE QC MP\*

**Cabinet Office** . . . . . . . . . . . . . . . . . . . . . . . . . . . Richard Allan MP *(also Information Technology)*

**Constitutional Affairs** . . . . . . . . . . . . . . . . . . . . . David Heath CBE MP

**Culture, Media and Sport** . . . . . . . . . . . . . . . . . . Don Foster MP
Bob Russell MP *(Sport)*
Adrian Sanders MP

**Defence** . . . . . . . . . . . . . . . . . . . . . . . . . . . . . . . . . Paul Keetch MP\*
Colin Breed MP

**Disability Issues** . . . . . . . . . . . . . . . . . . . . . . . . . . Paul Holmes MP

**Education and Skills** . . . . . . . . . . . . . . . . . . . . . . . Phil Willis MP\*
Dr John Pugh MP
David Rendel MP *(Higher Education)*

**Energy** . . . . . . . . . . . . . . . . . . . . . . . . . . . . . . . . . . Andrew Stunell MP

**Environment** . . . . . . . . . . . . . . . . . . . . . . . . . . . . . Norman Baker MP\* *(Environment)*
Sue Doughty MP

**Foreign and Commonwealth Affairs** . . . . . . . . . . Rt Hon Sir Menzies Campbell CBE QC MP\*
Michael Moore MP\*

**Health** . . . . . . . . . . . . . . . . . . . . . . . . . . . . . . . . . . Paul Burstow MP\*
Patsy Calton MP
Sarah Teather MP

**Home Affairs** . . . . . . . . . . . . . . . . . . . . . . . . . . . . Mark Oaten MP\*
Annette Brooke MP
John Burnett MP
David Heath CBE MP

**House of Commons** . . . . . . . . . . . . . . . . . . . . . . . Paul Tyler MP\*

**Housing, Local Government and the Regions**
*(Office of the Deputy Prime Minister)* . . . . . . . . . . Edward Davey MP\*
Matthew Green MP *(Young People)*
Richard Younger-Ross MP

# LIBERAL DEMOCRAT SPOKESMEN

**International Development**............................Tom Brake MP*
John Barrett MP

**Legal and Constitutional Affairs**.......................John Burnett MP

**London** ............................................Simon Hughes MP*

**Northern Ireland** ..................................Lembit Öpik MP*
Alistair Carmichael MP

**Rural Affairs and Food** .............................Andrew George MP*
Roger Williams MP

**Scotland** .........................................John Thurso MP*
Alan Reid MP

**Science** ..........................................David Heath MP

**Trade and Industry** ................................Malcolm Bruce MP
Brian Cotter MP *(Small Businesses)*

**Transport** ........................................John Thurso MP*
Paul Marsden MP

**Treasury** .........................................Dr Vincent Cable MP* *(Shadow Chancellor)*
David Laws MP* *(Shadow Chief Secretary)*
Norman Lamb MP

**Wales**...........................................Lembit Öpik MP*
Roger Williams MP

**Women's Issues and Older People**.....................Sandra Gidley MP*

**Work and Pensions** ................................Steven Webb MP
Paul Holmes MP

**Young People**.....................................Mathew Green MP

**Whips, (House of Commons)** ........................Andrew Stunell MP* *(Chief Whip)*
Sir Robert Smith MP *(Deputy Chief Whip)*
Tom Brake MP
Annette Brooke MP
Alan Reid MP
Bob Russell MP

**Chairman, Parliamentary Liberal Democrat Party** .......Matthew Taylor MP*

*Note: Sir Archy Kirkwood also attends the Liberal Democrat Shadow Cabinet in an individual capacity.*

## LIBERAL DEMOCRAT SPOKESMEN

### HOUSE OF LORDS

*Note: Members of the Liberal Democrat Shadow Cabinet are denoted by\*.*

**Leader** . . . . . . . . . . . . . . . . . . . . . . . . . . . . . . . . . . . . . . Rt Hon Baroness Williams of Crosby*

**Deputy Leader** . . . . . . . . . . . . . . . . . . . . . . . . . . . . . . . Lord McNally

**Culture, Media and Sport** . . . . . . . . . . . . . . . . . . . . . . Viscount Falkland
Lord Addington *(Sport)*
Lord McNally *(Broadcasting)*

**Defence** . . . . . . . . . . . . . . . . . . . . . . . . . . . . . . . . . . . . Lord Redesdale

**Education and and Skills** . . . . . . . . . . . . . . . . . . . . . . . Baroness Sharp of Guildford

**Environment, Food and Rural Affairs** . . . . . . . . . . . . . . Baroness Miller of Chilthorne Domer
Lord Livsey of Talgarth *(Agriculture)*

**Foreign and Commonwealth Affairs** . . . . . . . . . . . . . . . Lord Wallace of Saltaire
Lord Watson of Richmond
Lord Avebury *(Africa)*
Rt Hon Lord Maclennan of Rogart *(Europe)*

**Health** . . . . . . . . . . . . . . . . . . . . . . . . . . . . . . . . . . . . Lord Clement-Jones

**Home Office** . . . . . . . . . . . . . . . . . . . . . . . . . . . . . . . . Lord McNally
Lord Thomas of Gresford
Baroness Walmsley

**International Development** . . . . . . . . . . . . . . . . . . . . . . Baroness Northover

**Legal and Constitutional Affairs** . . . . . . . . . . . . . . . . . Lord Goodhart

**Local Government and the Regions**
*(Office of Deputy Prime Minister)* . . . . . . . . . . . . . . . . . Baroness Hamwee
Baroness Maddock

**Northern Ireland** . . . . . . . . . . . . . . . . . . . . . . . . . . . . . Lord Smith of Clifton
Lord Shutt of Greetland
Baroness Harris of Richmond

**Scotland** . . . . . . . . . . . . . . . . . . . . . . . . . . . . . . . . . . . *Vacant*

**Trade and Industry** . . . . . . . . . . . . . . . . . . . . . . . . . . . Lord Razzall
Lord Sharman
Lord Ezra *(Energy)*

**Transport** . . . . . . . . . . . . . . . . . . . . . . . . . . . . . . . . . . Lord Bradshaw
Baroness Scott of Needham Market

**Treasury** . . . . . . . . . . . . . . . . . . . . . . . . . . . . . . . . . . . Lord Newby
Lord Oakeshott of Seagrove Bay *(Pensions)*
Lord Taverne

**Wales** . . . . . . . . . . . . . . . . . . . . . . . . . . . . . . . . . . . . . Lord Thomas of Gresford
Lord Carlile of Berriew

**Women's Issues and Older People** . . . . . . . . . . . . . . . . Baroness Thomas of Walliswood

**Work and Social Security** . . . . . . . . . . . . . . . . . . . . . . Earl Russell
Lord Addington *(Disability Issues)*
Baroness Barker *(Social Services)*

**Whips (House of Lords)** . . . . . . . . . . . . . . . . . . . . . . . . Lord Roper* *(Chief Whip)*
Lord Shutt of Greetland *(Deputy Chief Whip)*
Lord Addington
Baroness Harris of Richmond
Earl of Mar and Kellie

*Note: Lord Dholakia (Party President) and Lord Razzall (Chairman of the Party's Campaign and Communications Committee)
are also members of the Liberal Democrat Shadow Cabinet.*

# PARTY HEADQUARTERS AND REGIONAL OFFICES

## CONSERVATIVE PARTY
### Headquarters
*25 Victoria Street, London, SW1H 0DL*

    **Co-Chairmen**........................ Dr Liam Fox MP

    Lord Saatchi ................. Tel: (020) 7222 9000

    E-mail: correspondence@conservatives.com

    Web: http://www.conservatives.com

### Scotland
*83 Princes Street, Edinburgh, EH2 2ER*

    **Honorary Secretary**.................... Mr William Macreath ........... Tel: (0131) 247 6890

    E-mail: central.office@scottishtories.org.uk

    Web: http://www.scottishtories.org.uk

### Wales
*4 Penlline Road, Whitchurch, Cardiff, CF14 2XS*

    **Director**............................... Mr Leigh Jeffes ............. Tel: (029) 2061 6031

    E-mail: info@welshconservatives.com

    Web: http://www.welshconservatives.com

## DEMOCRATIC UNIONIST PARTY
### Headquarters
*91 Dundela Avenue, Belfast, BT4 3BU*

    **General Secretary** ..................... Mr Nigel Dodds ............... Tel: (028) 9047 1155

    E-mail: info@dup.org.uk   Web: http://www.dup.org.uk

## LABOUR PARTY
### Headquarters
*16 Old Queen Street, London, SW1H 9HP*

    **General Secretary** ..................... Mr Matt Carter.............. Tel: (08705) 900200

    E-mail: info@new.labour.org.uk   Web: http://www.labour.org.uk

### East Midlands
*Harold Wilson House, 23 Barratt Lane, Attenborough, Nottingham, NG9 6AD*

    **Regional Director** .................... Mr Roy Kennedy ............. Tel: (0115) 943 1777

    E-mail: eastmidlands@new.labour.org.uk

    Web: http://www.eastmidslabour.org.uk

### Eastern
*97 Fore Street, Ipswich, Suffolk, IP4 1JZ*

    **Regional Director** .................... Mr Alan Olive ............... Tel: (01473) 228700

    E-mail: eastern@new.labour.org.uk

    Web: http://www.laboureast.labour.co.uk

### Greater London
*16 Old Queen Street, London, SW1H 9HP*

    **Regional Director** .................... Mrs Hilary Perrin.............. Tel: (020) 7490 4904

    E-mail: london@new.labour.org.uk   Web: http://www.london-labour.org.uk

### North
*4th Floor, Eldon House, Regent Centre, Gosforth, Newcastle-upon-Tyne, NE3 3PW*

    **Deputy General Secretary**............... Mr Chris Lennie............. Tel: (0191) 296 1800

    **Regional Director** .................... Ms Emma Thorne

    E-mail: north@new.labour.org.uk   Web: http://www.labour-north.org.uk

# PARTY HEADQUARTERS AND REGIONAL OFFICES

*Labour Party (Continued)*

### North West
*Suite 12, St James Court, Wilderspool Causeway, Warrington, WA4 6PS*

**Regional Director** . . . . . . . . . . . . . . . . . . . . . Mr Kevin Lee . . . . . . . . . . . . . . . Tel: (01925) 574913
E-mail: northwest@new.labour.org.uk
Web: http://www.northwest-labour.org.uk

### South East
*St Giles House, 10 Church Street, Reading, RG1 2SD*

**Regional Director** . . . . . . . . . . . . . . . . . . . . . Mr Mike Creighton . . . . . . . . . . . . . Tel: (0118) 959 5326
E-mail: southeast@new.labour.org.uk Web: http://www.labour-southeast.org.uk

### South West
*1 Newfoundland Street, Bristol, BS2 9AP*

**Regional Director** . . . . . . . . . . . . . . . . . . . . . Ms Sheila Murphy . . . . . . . . . . . . . Tel: (0117) 942 1900
E-mail: southwest@new.labour.org.uk
Web: http://www.laboursouthwest.labour.co.uk

### West Midlands
*Terry Duffy House, Thomas Street, off George Street, West Bromwich, B70 6NT*

**Regional Director** . . . . . . . . . . . . . . . . . . . . . Mr Ian Reilly . . . . . . . . . . . . . . . . Tel: (0121) 553 6601
E-mail: westmidlands@new.labour.org.uk

### Yorkshire and the Humber
*20-22 Cheapside, Wakefield, WF1 2TF*

**Regional Director** . . . . . . . . . . . . . . . . . . . . . Ms Nan Sloane . . . . . . . . . . . . . . . Tel: (01924) 291221
E-mail: yorkshire@new.labour.org.uk

### Scotland
*John Smith House, First Floor, 146-165 West Regent Street, Glasgow, G2 4RE*

**General Secretary** . . . . . . . . . . . . . . . . . . . . . Mrs Lesley Quinn . . . . . . . . . . . . . Tel: (0141) 572 6900
E-mail: scotland@new.labour.org.uk Web: http://www.scottishlabour.org.uk

### Wales
*Transport House, 1 Cathedral Road, Cardiff, CF11 9HA*

**General Secretary** . . . . . . . . . . . . . . . . . . . . . Ms Jessica Morden . . . . . . . . . . . . . Tel: (029) 2087 7700
E-mail: wales@new.labour.org.uk Web: http://www.welshlabour.org.uk

## LIBERAL DEMOCRATS

### Headquarters
*4 Cowley Street, London, SW1P 3NB*

**Chief Executive** . . . . . . . . . . . . . . . . . . . . . Mr Chris Rennard . . . . . . . . . . . . . Tel: (020) 7222 7999
E-mail: libdems@cix.co.uk Web: http://www.libdems.org.uk

### Devon and Cornwall
*35 Shire Close, Paignton, Devon, TQ4 7SW*

**Regional Secretary** . . . . . . . . . . . . . . . . . . . . . Mr Dave Browne . . . . . . . . . . . . . Tel: (01803) 842246
E-mail: thedavebrowne@aol.com

### East Midlands
*351 Worksop Road, Mastin Moor, Chesterfield, S43 3DH*

**Regional Administrator** . . . . . . . . . . . . . . . . . Ms Julie Hirst . . . . . . . . . . . . . . . Tel: (0115) 846 0661
E-mail: ld_eastmidland@yahoo.co.uk

### East of England
*269 Cavendish Street, Ipswich, Suffolk, IP3 8BQ*

**Regional Secretary** . . . . . . . . . . . . . . . . . . . . Mr Robin Whitmore . . . . . . . . . . . Tel: (01473) 424892
E-mail: robin.whitmoroe1@ntlworld.com Web: http://www.east.libdems.org

## PARTY HEADQUARTERS AND REGIONAL OFFICES

*Liberal Democrats (Continued)*

**London**
*4 Cowley Street, London, SW1P 3NB*
> **Regional Administrator** . . . . . . . . . . . . . . . . . Ms Flick Rea . . . . . . . . . . . . . . . . . Tel: (020) 7222 0134
> E-mail: londonlibdems@cix.co.uk
> Web: http://www.london.libdems.org

**North West**
*87a Castle Street, Edgeley, Stockport, Lancashire, SK3 9AR*
> **Regional Administrator** . . . . . . . . . . . . . . . . . Ms Jen Yockney . . . . . . . . . . . . . . Tel: (0161) 477 0939
> E-mail: libdemnorthwest@cix.co.uk

**Northern**
*38A Clayport Street, Alnwick, Northumberland, NE66 1LE*
> **Regional Secretary** . . . . . . . . . . . . . . . . . . . . Ms Eileen Blakey . . . . . . . . . . . . . . Tel: (01665) 605887
> E-mail: northernreglibdem@cix.co.uk
> Web: http://www.northern-libdems.org.uk

**South Central**
*77 Oakwood Drive, Bletchley, Milton Keynes, MK2 2JG*
> **Regional Organiser** . . . . . . . . . . . . . . . . . . . Ms Vanessa McPake . . . . . . . . . . . Tel: (01908) 373418
> E-mail: chilternlibdem@cix.co.uk

**South East**
*Hadleigh, Newnham Lane, Steyning, Sussex, BN44 3LR*
> **Regional Secretary** . . . . . . . . . . . . . . . . . . . . Ms Sue Stokes . . . . . . . . . . . . . . . Tel: (01903) 879983
> E-mail: seregion@cix.co.uk

**West Midlands**
*10 Avenue Road, Wolverhampton, WV3 9JR*
> **Regional Secretary** . . . . . . . . . . . . . . . . . . . . Mr Bryan Lewis . . . . . . . . . . . . . . Tel: (01902) 423372
> E-mail: bryanlewis@choicecom.freeserve.co.uk
> Web: http://www.wmlibdems.org

**Western Counties**
*29 Nunney Road, Frome, Somerset, BA11 4CA*
> **Regional Secretary** . . . . . . . . . . . . . . . . . . . . Ms Claire Hudson . . . . . . . . . . . . . Tel: (01373) 302656
> E-mail: claire@primex.co.uk

**Yorkshire and the Humber**
*75 Station Parade, Harrowgate, HG1 1ST*
> **Chairman** . . . . . . . . . . . . . . . . . . . . . . . . . . . Mr Ian Cuthbertson . . . . . . . . . . . Tel: (01423) 528888
> Web: http://www.yhld.pwp.blueyonder.co.uk

# PLAID CYMRU
**Headquarters**
*18 Park Grove, Cardiff, CF10 3BN*
> **Chief Executive** . . . . . . . . . . . . . . . . . . . . . . Mr Dafydd Trystan . . . . . . . . . . . . Tel: (029) 2064 6000
> E-mail: post@plaidcymru.org  Web: http://www.plaidcymru.org

# SCOTTISH NATIONAL PARTY
**Headquarters**
*107 McDonald Road, Edinburgh, EH7 4NW*
> National Secretary . . . . . . . . . . . . . . . . . . . . . . Mr Stewart Hosie . . . . . . . . . . . . . Tel: (0131) 525 8900
> E-mail: snp.hq@snp.org  Web: http://www.snp.org

# PARTY HEADQUARTERS AND REGIONAL OFFICES

## SINN FEIN
**Headquarters**

*51-53 Falls Road, Belfast, B12 4PD*

General Secretary . . . . . . . . . . . . . . . . . . . . . . . Mr Robbie Smith . . . . . . . . . . . . . . Tel: (028) 9022 3000

E-mail: sfadmin@eircom.net  Web: http://www.sinnfein.ie

## SOCIAL DEMOCRATIC AND LABOUR PARTY
**Headquarters**

*121 Ormeau Road, Belfast, BT7 1SH*

General Secretary . . . . . . . . . . . . . . . . . . . . . . Mrs Gerry Cosgrove . . . . . . . . . . . . . Tel: (028) 9024 7700

E-mail: sdlp@indigo.ie  Web: http://www.sdlp.ie

## ULSTER UNIONIST PARTY
**Headquarters**

*Cunningham House, 429 Hollywood Road, Belfast, BT4 2LN*

Chief Executive . . . . . . . . . . . . . . . . . . . . . . . . Mr Lyle Rea . . . . . . . . . . . . . . . . . . Tel: (028) 9076 5500

E-mail: uup@uup.org  Web: http://www.uup.org

# HOUSE OF COMMONS COMMITTEES

*Note: (i) In addition to members of House of Commons Select Committees, Commons members of Joint Committees with House of Lords are listed here. For details of House of Lords members of Joint Committees see The Guide to the House of Lords, published annually by Carlton Publishing and Printing Ltd.* •

*(ii) Information contained in this section was correct at the time of going to press. Changes in membership take place from time to time and updated information can be obtained from the House of Commons Information Office, House of Commons, London, SW1A 2TT Tel: (020) 7219 4272.*

*(iii) Telephone enquiry numbers are given for individual committees, where available. Otherwise, enquiries should be directed to the Committee Office Tel: (020) 7219 4300 or to the House of Commons Information Office as shown above.*

## ACCOMMODATION AND WORKS COMMITTEE

*Chairman:* Derek Conway

*Members:*

| | | |
|---|---|---|
| Bob Ainsworth | Tony Banks | Harold Best |
| Stephen Hepburn | Patrick McLoughlin | Albert Owen |
| Anne Picking | Sir Robert Smith | |

*Clerk:* Mr Tim Jarvis

*Tel:* (020) 7219 2420
*Fax:* (020) 7219 2622
*E-mail:* jarvistm@parliament.uk
    accworkcom@parliament.uk

## ADMINISTRATION COMMITTEE

*Chairman:* Dame Marion Roe

*Members:*

| | | |
|---|---|---|
| Nick Ainger | Patsy Calton | Caroline Flint |
| Martin Linton | Peter Luff | Iain Luke |
| John MacDougall | Julie Morgan | |

*Clerk:* Mr Tim Jarvis

*Tel:* (020) 7219 2420
*Fax:* (020) 7219 2622
*E-mail:* jarvistm@parliament.uk

# HOUSE OF COMMONS COMMITTEES

## BROADCASTING COMMITTEE

*Chairman:* David Lepper

*Members:*

| | | |
|---|---|---|
| Gregory Barker | Helen Clark | Roger Gale |
| David Hamilton | Iain Luke | John Lyons |
| Khalid Mahmood | Alan Reid | Jim Sheridan |

*Clerk*: Mr Gordon Clarke

*Tel*: (020) 7219 3275
*Fax*: (020) 7219 2622
*E-mail:* clarkeg@parliament.uk

*Note: This Committee monitors and makes recommendations on the broadcasting of House of Commons proceedings.*

## CATERING COMMITTEE

*Chairman:* Dennis Turner

*Members:*

| | | |
|---|---|---|
| Janet Anderson | Peter Atkinson | Ronnie Campbell |
| Tony Cunningham | Janet Dean | Lindsay Hoyle |
| Julie Kirkbride | Peter Wishart | |

*Clerk*: Mr Gordon Clarke

*Tel*: (020) 7219 3275
*Fax*: (020) 7219 2622
*E-mail:* clarkeg@parliament.uk

## CONSOLIDATION ETC BILLS JOINT COMMITTEE

*The House of Commons members are:*

*House of Commons Members:*

| | | |
|---|---|---|
| Russell Brown | John Burnett | David Cairns |
| Martin Caton | Colin Challen | Sir Patrick Cormack |
| Jim Dobbin | Paul Farrelly | Barry Gardiner |
| John MacDougall | Nicholas Soames | Anthony Steen |

*Clerk*: Ms Nerys Welfoot

*Tel*: (020) 7219 3256

*Note: This is a joint Committee with the House of Lords.*

# HOUSE OF COMMONS COMMITTEES

## CONSTITUTIONAL AFFAIRS COMMITTEE

*Chairman:* Rt Hon Alan Beith

*Members:*

| | | |
|---|---|---|
| Peter Bottomley | James Clappison | Ross Cranston |
| Ann Cryer | Jim Cunningham | Hilton Dawson |
| Andrew Rosindell | Clive Soley | Keith Vaz |
| Dr Alan Whitehead | | |

*Clerk*: Mr Roger Phillips

*Tel:* (020) 7219 8195
*Fax:* (020) 7219 0843
*E-mail:* conaffcom@parliament.uk

## COURT OF REFEREES

*Ex Officio:*

Rt Hon Sir Alan Haselhurst *(Chairman of Ways and Means)*
Sylvia Heal *(First Deputy Chairman of Ways and Means)*
Sir Michael Lord *(Second Deputy Chairman of Ways and Means)*

*Members:*

| | | |
|---|---|---|
| Peter Atkinson | Sir John Butterfill | Sir Archy Kirkwood |
| Linda Perham | Bridget Prentice | Ernie Ross |
| Dennis Turner | | |

*Clerk*: Mr Frank Cranmer          *Tel*: (020) 7219 3257

*Note: This Committee hears matters relating to Private Bills, in particular who should be allocated to petition. In addition to the above, the Counsel to the Speaker (Mr John Vaux) is an ex officio member.*

## CULTURE, MEDIA AND SPORT COMMITTEE

*Chairman:* Rt Hon Sir Gerald Kaufman

*Members:*

| | | |
|---|---|---|
| Chris Bryant | Frank Doran | Michael Fabricant |
| Adrian Flook | Nick Hawkins | Alan Keen |
| Rosemary McKenna | Debra Shipley | John Thurso |
| Derek Wyatt | | |

*Clerk*: Mr Fergus Reid

*Tel*: (020) 7219 5739
*Fax*: (020) 7219 2031
*E-mail:* cmscom@parliament.uk

# HOUSE OF COMMONS COMMITTEES

## DEFENCE COMMITTEE

*Chairman:* Rt Hon Bruce George

*Members:*

| | | |
|---|---|---|
| Crispin Blunt | James Cran | David Crausby |
| Mike Gapes | Mike Hancock | Dai Havard |
| Kevan Jones | Frank Roy | Rachel Squire |
| Peter Viggers | | |

*Clerk*: Mr Mark Hutton

*Tel*: (020) 7219 5745
*Fax*: (020) 7219 6952
*E-mail:* defcom@parliament.uk

## OFFICE OF THE DEPUTY PRIME MINISTER: HOUSING, PLANNING, LOCAL GOVERNMENT AND THE REGIONS COMMITTEE

*Chairman:* Andrew Bennett

*Members:*

| | | |
|---|---|---|
| Sir Paul Beresford | Clive Betts | Graham Brady |
| David Clelland | John Cummings | Eleanor Laing |
| Chris Mole | Bill O'Brien | Christine Russell |
| Adrian Sanders | | |

*Clerk*: Miss Kate Emms

*Tel*: (020) 7219 5462
*Fax*: (020) 7219 6101
*E-mail:* odpmcom@parliament.uk

## OFFICE OF THE DEPUTY PRIME MINISTER COMMITTEE: URBAN AFFAIRS SUB-COMMITTEE

*Chairman:* Clive Betts

*Members:*

| | | |
|---|---|---|
| Andrew Bennett | Sir Paul Beresford | Alistair Burt |
| David Clelland | John Cummings | Eleanor Laing |
| Chris Mole | Bill O'Brien | Christine Russell |
| Gary Streeter | | |

*Clerks*: Miss Kate Emms
      Miss Libby Preston

*Tel*: (020) 7219 5462
*E-mail:* odpmcom@parliament.uk

# HOUSE OF COMMONS COMMITTEES

## ECCLESIASTICAL COMMITTEE

*House of Commons Members:*

| | | |
|---|---|---|
| Nigel Beard | Sir Stuart Bell | Peter Bottomley |
| Sir Sydney Chapman | Sir Patrick Cormack | David Drew |
| Gwyneth Dunwoody | Rt Hon Frank Field | Rt Hon Derek Foster |
| Rt Hon John Gummer | Simon Hughes | Gordon Marsden |
| Peter Pike | David Taylor | Steven Webb |

*Clerk:* Miss Jenny McCullough          *Tel:* (020) 7219 3130

*Note: This is a Joint Committee with the House of Lords*

## EDUCATION AND SKILLS COMMITTEE

*Chairman:* Barry Sheerman

*Members:*

| | | |
|---|---|---|
| David Chaytor | Valerie Davey | Jeff Ennis |
| Nick Gibb | Paul Holmes | Robert Jackson |
| Helen Jones | Kerry Pollard | Jonathan Shaw |
| Andrew Turner | | |

*Clerk*: Mr David Lloyd          *Tel*: (020) 7219 5774
*Fax*: (020) 7219 0848
*E-mail:* edskillscom@parliament.uk

## ENVIRONMENT, FOOD AND RURAL AFFAIRS COMMITTEE

*Chairman:* Rt Hon Michael Jack

*Members:*

| | | |
|---|---|---|
| Candy Atherton | Colin Breed | David Burnside |
| David Drew | Patrick Hall | Mark Lazarowicz |
| David Lepper | Ian Liddell-Graingeer | Austin Mitchell |
| Diana Organ | Joan Ruddock | Rt Hon Gillian Shephard |
| Alan Simpson | David Taylor | Paddy Tipping |
| Bill Wiggin | | |

*Clerk:* Mr Gavin Devine          *Tel*: (020) 7219 3262
*Fax*: (020) 7219 2094
*E-mail:* efracom@parliament.uk

# HOUSE OF COMMONS COMMITTEES

## ENVIRONMENTAL AUDIT COMMITTEE

*Chairman:* Peter Ainsworth

*Members:*

| | | |
|---|---|---|
| Gregory Barker | Harold Best | Colin Challen |
| David Chaytor | Helen Clark | Sue Doughty |
| Paul Flynn | Mark Francois | John Horam |
| John McWilliam | Elliot Morley | Malcolm Savidge |
| Simon Thomas | Joan Walley | David Wright |

*Clerk:* Mr Mike Hennessy

*Tel*: (020) 7219 5776
*Fax*: (020) 7219 1224
*E-mail:* eacom@parliament.uk

## EUROPEAN SCRUTINY COMMITTEE

*Chairman:* Jimmy Hood

*Members:*

| | | |
|---|---|---|
| Richard Bacon | Bill Cash | Michael Connarty |
| Wayne David | Jim Dobbin | Nick Harvey |
| Rt Hon David Heathcoat-Amory | Sandra Osborne | Anne Picking |
| Angus Robertson | John Robertson | Anthony Steen |
| Bill Tynan | | |

*Clerk:* Mr Dorian Gerhold

*Tel*: (020) 7219 3296
*Fax*: (020) 7219 2509
*E-mail:* escom@parliament.uk

## FINANCE AND SERVICES COMMITTEE

*Chairman:* Sir Stuart Bell

*Members:*

| | | |
|---|---|---|
| Irene Adams | Bob Ainsworth | Derek Conway |
| Robert Key | David Lepper | Rt Hon Tommy McAvoy |
| Patrick McLoughlin | Dame Marion Roe | Andrew Stunell |
| Dennis Turner | | |

*Clerk:* Mr Robert Rogers

*Tel*: (020) 7219 3270
*Fax*: (020) 7219 2622
*E-mail:* rogersr@parliament.uk

# HOUSE OF COMMONS COMMITTEES

## FOREIGN AFFAIRS COMMITTEE

*Chairman:* Rt Hon Donald Anderson

*Members:*

| | | |
|---|---|---|
| David Chidgey | Fabian Hamilton | Eric Illsley |
| Rt Hon Andrew MacKay | Andrew Mackinlay | John Maples |
| Bill Olner | Greg Pope | Rt Hon Sir John Stanley |
| Gisela Stuart | | |

*Clerk:* Mr Steve Priestley

*Tel*: (020) 7219 6105
*Fax*: (020) 7219 5365
*E-mail:* foraffcom@parliament.uk

## HEALTH COMMITTEE

*Chairman:* David Hinchliffe

*Members:*

| | | |
|---|---|---|
| David Amess | John Austin | Rt Hon Keith Bradley |
| Simon Burns | Paul Burstow | Jim Dowd |
| Jon Owen Jones | Siobhain McDonagh | Dr Doug Naysmith |
| Dr Richard Taylor | | |

*Clerk:* Dr John Benger

*Tel*: (020) 7219 5466
*Fax*: (020) 7219 5171
*E-mail:* healthcom@parliament.uk

## HOME AFFAIRS COMMITTEE

*Chairman:* Rt Hon John Denham

*Members:*

| | | |
|---|---|---|
| Janet Anderson | David Cameron | James Clappison |
| Claire Curtis-Thomas | Janet Dean | Gwyn Prosser |
| Bob Russell | Marsha Singh | John Taylor |
| David Winnick | | |

*Clerk:* Dr Robin James

*Tel*: (020) 7219 3282
*Fax*: (020) 7219 2744
*E-mail:* homeoffcom@parliament.uk

# HOUSE OF COMMONS COMMITTEES

## HOUSE OF LORDS REFORM JOINT COMMITTEE

*Chairman:* Rt Hon Dr Jack Cunningham

*House of Commons Members:*

| | | |
|---|---|---|
| Janet Anderson | Rt Hon James Arbuthnot | Chris Bryant |
| Rt Hon Kenneth Clarke | Rt Hon William Hague | Stephen McCabe |
| Rt Hon Joyce Quin | Terry Rooney | Clive Soley |
| Paul Stinchcombe | Paul Tyler | |

*Clerk:* Dr Malcolm Jack          *Tel:* (020) 7219 2743

*Note: This is a Joint Committee with the House of Lords*

## HUMAN RIGHTS JOINT COMMITTEE

*Chairman:* Rt Hon Jean Corston

*House of Commons Members:*

| | | |
|---|---|---|
| David Chidgey | Kevin McNamara | Richard Shepherd |
| Paul Stinchcombe | Shaun Woodward | |

*Clerk:* Mr Paul Evans          *Tel:* (020) 7219 3318

*Note: This Committee is a Joint Committee with the House of Lords.*

## INFORMATION COMMITTEE

*Chairman:* Robert Key

*Members:*

| | | |
|---|---|---|
| Richard Allan | Neil Gerrard | Peter Luff |
| Ann McKechin | John Mann | Margaret Moran |
| Gwyn Prosser | James Sheridan | |

*Clerk:* Mr Gordon Clarke

*Tel:* (020) 7219 3275
*Fax:* (020) 7219 2622
*E-mail:* clarkeg@parliament.uk
infocom@parliament.uk

# HOUSE OF COMMONS COMMITTEES

## INTELLIGENCE AND SECURITY COMMITTEE

*Chairman:* Rt Hon Ann Taylor

*Members:*

| | | |
|---|---|---|
| Rt Hon James Arbuthnot | Rt Hon Kevin Barron | Rt Hon Alan Beith |
| Rt Hon Alan Howarth | Rt Hon Michael Mates | Rt Hon Joyce Quin |
| Rt Hon Gavin Strang | | |

*Clerk:* Mr Alistair Corbett　　　　　*Tel*: (020) 7270 1234 *(Cabinet Office)*

*Note: In addition to the above, Rt Hon Lord Archer of Sandwell is a member of this committee.*

## INTERNATIONAL DEVELOPMENT COMMITTEE

*Chairman:* Tony Baldry

*Members:*

| | | |
|---|---|---|
| John Barrett | Rt Hon John Battle | Hugh Bayley |
| Ann Clwyd | Tony Colman | Quentin Davies |
| Priara Khabra | Chris McCafferty | Andrew Robathan |
| Tony Worthington | | |

*Clerk:* Mr Alistair Doherty　　　　　*Tel*: (020) 7219 1221
　　　　　　　　　　　　　　　　　　　*Fax*: (020) 7219 2891
　　　　　　　　　　　　　　　　　　　*E-mail*: indcom@parliament.uk

## LIAISON COMMITTEE

*Chairman:* Rt Hon Alan Williams

*Members:*

| | | |
|---|---|---|
| Irene Adams | Peter Ainsworth | Richard Allan |
| Rt Hon Donald Anderson | Tony Baldry | Rt Hon Alan Beith |
| Sir Stuart Bell | Andrew Bennett | Derek Conway |
| Rt Hon Jean Corston | Rt Hon John Denham | Gwyneth Dunwoody |
| Rt Hon Bruce George | Dr Ian Gibson | David Hinchliffe |
| Jimmy Hood | Rt Hon Michael Jack | Martyn Jones |
| Rt Hon Sir Gerald Kaufman | Robert Key | Sir Archy Kirkwood |
| Edward Leigh | David Lepper | Rt Hon John McFall |
| John McWilliam | Rt Hon Michael Mates | Martin O'Neill |
| Peter Pike | Dame Marion Roe | Barry Sheerman |
| David Treddinick | Dennis Turner | Sir Nicholas Winterton |
| Dr Tony Wright | Rt Hon Sir George Young | |

*Clerk:* Mr George Cubie　　　　　*Tel*: (020) 7219 3313
　　　　　　　　　　　　　　　　　*Fax*: (020) 7219 6952
　　　　　　　　　　　　　　　　　*E-mail*: liaisoncommittee@parliament.uk

*Note: This Committee includes all the Chairmen of Select Committees.*

# HOUSE OF COMMONS COMMITTEES

## MODERNISATION OF THE HOUSE OF COMMONS COMMITTEE

*Chairman:* Rt Hon Peter Hain *(Leader of the House)*

*Members:*

| | | |
|---|---|---|
| Ann Coffey | Barbara Follett | Oliver Heald |
| David Kidney | Martin Linton | Patrick McLoughlin |
| Anne Picking | Peter Pike | Joan Ruddock |
| Martin Salter | Richard Shepherd | Andrew Stunell |
| Paul Tyler | Sir Nicholas Winterton | |

*Clerk:* Mr George Cubie

*Tel*: (020) 7219 3259
*Fax*: (020) 7219 2269
*E-mail:* modcom@parliament.uk
                infocom@parliament.uk

## NORTHERN IRELAND AFFAIRS COMMITTEE

*Chairman:* Rt Hon Michael Mates

*Members:*

| | | |
|---|---|---|
| Adrian Bailey | Roy Beggs | Gregory Campbell |
| Tony Clarke | Stephen Hepburn | Iain Luke |
| Eddie McGrady | Stephen Pound | Rev Martin Smyth |
| Hugo Swire | Mark Tami | Bill Tynan |

*Clerk:* Dr John Patterson

*Tel*: (020) 7219 2171
*Fax*: (020) 7219 0300
*E-mail:* northircom@parliament.uk

## PRIVATE BILLS: UNOPPOSED BILLS PANEL

*Ex Officio:*
Rt Hon Sir Alan Haselhurst *(Chairman of Ways and Means)*
Sylvia Heal *(First Deputy Chairman of Ways and Means)*
Sir Michael Lord *(Second Deputy Chairman of Ways and Means)*

*Members:*

| | | |
|---|---|---|
| John Austin | Adrian Bailey | Nigel Beard |
| Peter Bottomley | Sir John Butterfill | Colin Challen |
| Parmjit Dhanda | Paul Farrelly | Brian Jenkins |
| Helen Jones | Siobhain McDonagh | John Mann |
| Sir Robert Smith | Sir Peter Tapsell | Jon Trickett |
| Robert Walter | Ann Winterton | |

*Clerk:* Mr John Whatley

*Tel*: (020) 7219 3771

# HOUSE OF COMMONS COMMITTEES

## PROCEDURE COMMITTEE

*Chairman:* Sir Nicholas Winterton

*Members:*

| | | |
|---|---|---|
| Peter Atkinson | John Burnett | David Hamilton |
| Eric Illsley | Huw Irranca-Davies | Eric Joyce |
| Iain Luke | Rosemary McKenna | Tony McWalter |
| Sir Robert Smith | Desmond Swayne | David Wright |

*Clerk:* Mr Simon Patrick

*Tel*: (020) 7219 3318
*Fax*: (020) 7219 2269
*E-mail:* proccom@parliament.uk

## PUBLIC ACCOUNTS COMMITTEE

*Chairman:* Edward Leigh

*Members:*

| | | |
|---|---|---|
| Richard Allan | Richard Bacon | Angela Browning |
| Jon Cruddas | Rt Hon David Curry | Ian Davidson |
| Rt Hon Frank Field | Brian Jenkins | Nigel Jones |
| Ruth Kelly | James Sheridan | Siôn Simon |
| Gerry Steinberg | Jon Trickett | Rt Hon Alan Williams |

*Clerk:* Mr Nick Wright

*Tel*: (020) 7219 5708
*Fax*: (020) 7219 2782
*E-mail:* pubaccom@parliament.uk

**National Audit Office**
157-197 Buckingham Palace Road, London, SW1W 9SP
Tel: (020) 7798 7000  Fax: (020) 7828 7070
Web: http://www.nao.gov.uk
**Comptroller and Auditor General** – Sir John Bourn KCB
**Deputy Comptroller and Auditor General** – Mr Tim Burr

*Note: The National Audit Office (NAO) is independent from Government and answers to Parliament through the Public Accounts Committee. The Comptroller and Auditor General is an Officer of the House of Commons. The NAO provides information and advice concerning all aspects of the financial operations of government departments and of various publicly-funded bodies. It examines and certifies their accounts; and it reports on their efficiency and effectiveness in using public funds.*

# HOUSE OF COMMONS COMMITTEES

## PUBLIC ADMINISTRATION COMMITTEE

*Chairman:* Dr Tony Wright

*Members:*

| | | |
|---|---|---|
| Kevin Brennan | Annette Brooke | Anne Campbell |
| Sir Sydney Chapman | David Heyes | Kelvin Hopkins |
| Ian Liddell-Grainger | Gordon Prentice | Michael Trend |
| Brian White | | |

*Clerk:* Mr Phillip Aylett

*Tel:* (020) 7219 5466
*E-mail:* pubadmincom@parliament.uk

## REGULATORY REFORM COMMITTEE

*Chairman:* Peter Pike

*Members:*

| | | |
|---|---|---|
| Russell Brown | Brian Cotter | Jeffrey Donaldson |
| Dai Havard | Andy King | Mark Lazarowicz |
| Andrew Love | John MacDougall | Chris Mole |
| Denis Murphy | Dr Doug Naysmith | Archie Norman |
| Andrew Rosindell | Anthony Steen | Brian White |

*Clerk:* Mr Martyn Atkins

*Tel:* (020) 7219 2833
*Fax:* (020) 7219 2509
*E-mail:* regrefcom@parliament.uk

## SCIENCE AND TECHNOLOGY COMMITTEE

*Chairman:* Dr Ian Gibson

*Members:*

| | | |
|---|---|---|
| Paul Farrelly | Dr Evan Harris | Kate Hoey |
| Dr Brian Iddon | Robert Key | Tony McWalter |
| Dr Andrew Murrison | Geraldine Smith | Dr Robert Spink |
| Dr Desmond Turner | | |

*Clerk:* Mr Chris Shaw

*Tel:* (020) 7219 2794
*Fax:* (020) 7219 0896
*E-mail:* scitechcom@parliament.uk

# HOUSE OF COMMONS COMMITTEES

## SCOTTISH AFFAIRS COMMITTEE

*Chairman:* Irene Adams

*Members:*

| | | |
|---|---|---|
| Alistair Carmichael | Peter Duncan | David Hamilton |
| Ian Liddell-Grainger | John Lyons | John MacDougall |
| Ann McKechin | John Robertson | Mohammed Sarwar |
| Michael Weir | | |

*Clerk:* Mr Mike Clark

*Tel*: (020) 7219 6125
*Fax*: (020) 7219 2519
*E-mail:* scotaffcom@parliament.uk

## COMMITTEE OF SELECTION

*Chairman:* John McWilliam

*Members:*

| | | |
|---|---|---|
| Bob Ainsworth | Jim Fitzpatrick | John Heppell |
| Peter Luff | Lawrie Quinn | Joan Ryan |
| Andrew Stunell | Rt Hon Sir George Young | |

*Clerk:* Miss Sián Jones

*Note: This Committee appoints members to Standing Committees and proposes members for most Select Committees.*

## SPEAKER'S COMMITTEE ON THE ELECTORAL COMMISSION

*Chairman:* Rt Hon Michael Martin *(Speaker)*

*House of Commons Members:*

| | | |
|---|---|---|
| Rt Hon Alan Beith | Angela Browning | Lady Hermon |
| Rt Hon Sir Gerald Kaufman | Humfrey Malins | Rt Hon Nick Raynsford |
| Peter Viggers | | |

*Clerk:* Dr Christopher Ward

Tel: (020) 7219 3000

# HOUSE OF COMMONS COMMITTEES

## STANDARDS AND PRIVILEGES COMMITTEE

*Chairman:* Rt Hon Sir George Young

*Members:*

| | | |
|---|---|---|
| Angela Browning | Ross Cranston | Andrew Dismore |
| Rt Hon Derek Foster | David Heath | Rt Hon Andrew Mackay |
| Kevin McNamara | Stephen Pound | |
| Simon Thomas | | |

*Clerk:* Dr Christopher Ward

*Tel*: (020) 7219 3259
*Fax*: (020) 7219 2269
*E-mail:* wardc@parliament.uk

*Note: This Committee considers matters relating to privileges and to the conduct of MPs. It oversees the work of the Parliamentary Commissioner for Standards (whose responsibilities include the Register of Members' Interests).*

## STANDING ORDERS COMMITTEE

*Ex officio:*
Rt Hon Sir Alan Haselhurst *(Chairman of Ways and Means)*
Sylvia Heal *(First Deputy Chairman of Ways and Means)*
Sir Michael Lord *(Second Deputy Chairman of Ways and Means)*

*Members:*

| | | |
|---|---|---|
| Sir Patrick Cormack | Brian Jenkins | Helen Jones |
| Ann McKechin | Bill O'Brien | Ernie Ross |
| Sir Robert Smith | Sir Nicholas Winterton | |

*Clerk:* Mr John Whatley

## STATUTORY INSTRUMENTS JOINT COMMITTEE

*Chairman:* David Tredinnick

*House of Commons Members:*

| | | |
|---|---|---|
| Andrew Bennett | Jeffrey Donaldson | Rt Hon Eric Forth |
| Kevin Hughes | Chris Mole | Brian White |

*Clerk:* Mr Martyn Atkins

*Tel*: (020) 7219 2830
*Fax*: (020) 7219 2441
*E-mail:* jcsi@parliament.uk

*Note: This is a Joint Committee with the House of Lords, but Commons members sit separately to consider Statutory Instruments which would have financial effect.*

# HOUSE OF COMMONS COMMITTEES

## TAX LAW REWRITE BILLS JOINT COMMITTEE

*House of Commons Members:*

Rt Hon Kenneth Clarke

David Laws

Anthony D Wright

Parmjit Dhanda

Chris Pond

Rt Hon Michael Jack

Rt Hon Dawn Primarolo

*Clerks:* Mr Richard Cook        *Tel:* (020) 7219 3258

*Note: This is a Joint Committee with the House of Lords.*

## TRADE AND INDUSTRY COMMITTEE

*Chairman:* Martin O'Neill

*Members:*

Roger Berry

Johnathan Djanogly

Andrew Lansley

Sir Robert Smith

Richard Burden

Nigel Evans

Judy Mallaber

Michael Clapham

Lindsay Hoyle

Linda Perham

*Clerk:* Mrs Elizabeth Flood

*Tel:* (020) 7219 5779
*Fax:* (020) 7219 2731
*E-mail:* tradeindcom@parliament.uk

## TRANSPORT COMMITTEE

*Chairman:* Gwyneth Dunwoody

Jeffrey Donaldson

Louise Ellman

Paul Marsden

Graham Stringer

*Members:*

Brian Donohoe

Ian Lucas

John Randall

Clive Efford

Anne McIntosh

George Stevenson

*Clerk:* Ms Eve Samson

*Tel:* (020) 7219 6263
*Fax:* (020) 7219 0909
*E-mail:* transcom@parliament.uk

# HOUSE OF COMMONS COMMITTEES

## TREASURY COMMITTEE

*Chairman:* Rt Hon John McFall

*Members:*

| | | |
|---|---|---|
| Nigel Beard | Jim Cousins | Angela Eagle |
| Michael Fallon | Rt Hon David Heathcoat-Amory | Norman Lamb |
| John Mann | George Mudie | James Plaskitt |
| Robert Walter | | |

*Clerk:* Mr Crispin Poyser

*Tel:* (020) 7219 5769
*Fax:* (020) 7219 2782
*E-mail:* treascom@parliament.uk

## WELSH AFFAIRS COMMITTEE

*Chairman:* Martyn Jones

*Members:*

| | | |
|---|---|---|
| Martin Caton | Huw Edwards | Nigel Evans |
| Dr Hywel Francis | Julie Morgan | Albert Owen |
| Mark Prisk | Betty Williams | Hywel Williams |
| Roger Williams | | |

*Clerk:* Mr James Davies

*Tel:* (020) 7219 3264
*Fax:* (020) 7219 0300
*E-mail:* welshcom@parliament.uk

## WORK AND PENSIONS

*Chairman:* Sir Archy Kirkwood

*Members:*

| | | |
|---|---|---|
| Vera Baird | Anne Begg | Karen Buck |
| Andrew Dismore | Paul Goodman | David Hamilton |
| Joan Humble | Robert Marris | Andrew Selous |
| Nigel Waterson | | |

*Clerk:* Mr Phillip Moon

*Tel:* (020) 7219 5833
*Fax:* (020) 7219 0580
E-mail: workpencom@parliament.uk

## WORKS OF ART ADVISORY COMMITTEE

*Chairman:* Tony Banks

*Members:*

| | | |
|---|---|---|
| Peter Ainsworth | John Burnett | Frank Cook |
| Mark Fisher | Robert Jackson | Hugo Swire |
| Michael Trend | Shaun Woodward | Derek Wyatt |

*Clerk:* Mr Tim Jarvis

## M P s   I N   A L P H A B E T I C A L   O R D E R

### A

Abbott, Diane
Adams, Gerry
Adams, Irene
Ainger, Nick
Ainsworth, Bob
Ainsworth, Peter
Alexander, Douglas
Allan, Richard
Allen, Graham
Amess, David
Ancram, Rt Hon Michael
Anderson, Rt Hon Donald
Anderson, Janet
Arbuthnot, Rt Hon James
Armstrong, Rt Hon Hilary
Atherton, Candy
Atkins, Charlotte
Atkinson, David
Atkinson, Peter
Austin, John

### B

Bacon, Richard
Bailey, Adrian
Baird, Vera
Baker, Norman
Baldry, Tony
Banks, Tony
Barker, Gregory
Barnes, Harry
Baron, John
Barrett, John
Barron, Rt Hon Kevin
Battle, Rt Hon John
Bayley, Hugh
Beard, Nigel
Beckett, Rt Hon Margaret
Begg, Anne
Beggs, Roy
Beith, Rt Hon Alan
Bell, Sir Stuart
Bellingham, Henry
Benn, Rt Hon Hilary
Bennett, Andrew
Benton, Joe
Bercow, John
Beresford, Sir Paul
Berry, Dr Roger
Best, Harold
Betts, Clive
Blackman, Liz
Blair, Rt Hon Tony
Blears, Hazel
Blizzard, Bob
Blunkett, Rt Hon David
Blunt, Crispin
Boateng, Rt Hon Paul
Borrow, David

Boswell, Tim
Bottomley, Peter
Bottomley, Rt Hon Virginia
Bradley, Rt Hon Keith
Bradley, Peter
Bradshaw, Ben
Brady, Graham
Brake, Tom
Brazier, Julian
Breed, Colin
Brennan, Kevin
Brooke, Annette
Brown, Rt Hon Gordon
Brown, Rt Hon Nick
Brown, Russell
Browne, Desmond
Browning, Angela
Bruce, Malcolm
Bryant, Chris
Buck, Karen
Burden, Richard
Burgon, Colin
Burnett, John
Burnham, Andrew
Burns, Simon
Burnside, David
Burstow, Paul
Burt, Alistair
Butterfill, Sir John
Byers, Rt Hon Stephen
Byrne, Liam

### C

Cable, Dr Vincent
Caborn, Rt Hon Richard
Cairns, David
Calton, Patsy
Cameron, David
Campbell, Alan
Campbell, Anne
Campbell, Gregory
Campbell, Rt Hon Sir Menzies
Campbell, Ronnie
Caplin, Ivor
Carmichael, Alistair
Casale, Roger
Cash, Bill
Caton, Martin
Cawsey, Ian
Challen, Colin
Chapman, Ben
Chapman, Sir Sydney
Chaytor, David
Chidgey, David
Chope, Christopher
Clapham, Michael
Clappison, James
Clark, Helen
Clark, Dr Lynda

Clark, Paul
Clarke, Rt Hon Charles
Clarke, Rt Hon Kenneth
Clarke, Rt Hon Tom
Clarke, Tony
Clelland, David
Clifton-Brown, Geoffrey
Clwyd, Ann
Coaker, Vernon
Coffey, Ann
Cohen, Harry
Coleman, Iain
Collins, Tim
Colman, Tony
Connarty, Michael
Conway, Derek
Cook, Frank
Cook, Rt Hon Robin
Cooper, Yvette
Corbyn, Jeremy
Cormack, Sir Patrick
Corston, Rt Hon Jean
Cotter, Brian
Cousins, Jim
Cox, Tom
Cran, James
Cranston, Ross
Crausby, David
Cruddas, Jon
Cryer, Ann
Cryer, John
Cummings, John
Cunningham, Rt Hon Dr Jack
Cunningham, Jim
Cunningham, Tony
Curry, Rt Hon David
Curtis-Thomas, Claire

### D

Dalyell, Tam
Darling, Rt Hon Alistair
Davey, Edward
Davey, Valerie
David, Wayne
Davidson, Ian
Davies, Rt Hon Denzil
Davies, Geraint
Davies, Quentin
Davis, Rt Hon David
Dawson, Hilton
Dean, Janet
Denham, Rt Hon John
Dhanda, Parmjit
Dismore, Andrew
Djanogly, Jonathan
Dobbin, Jim
Dobson, Rt Hon Frank
Dodds, Nigel
Doherty, Pat

## MPs IN ALPHABETICAL ORDER

Donaldson, Jeffrey
Donohoe, Brian
Doran, Frank
Dorrell, Rt Hon Stephen
Doughty, Sue
Dowd, Jim
Drew, David
Drown, Julia
Duncan, Alan
Duncan, Peter
Duncan Smith, Rt Hon Iain
Dunwoody, Gwyneth

### E

Eagle, Angela
Eagle, Maria
Edwards, Huw
Efford, Clive
Ellman, Louise
Ennis, Jeff
Etherington, Bill
Evans, Nigel
Ewing, Annabelle

### F

Fabricant, Michael
Fallon, Michael
Farrelly, Paul
Field, Rt Hon Frank
Field, Mark
Fisher, Mark
Fitzpatrick, Jim
Fitzsimons, Lorna
Flight, Howard
Flint, Caroline
Flook, Adrian
Flynn, Paul
Follett, Barbara
Forth, Rt Hon Eric
Foster, Rt Hon Derek
Foster, Don
Foster, Michael Jabez
Foster, Michael John
Foulkes, Rt Hon George
Fox, Dr Liam
Francis, Dr Hywel
Francois, Mark

### G

Gale, Roger
Galloway, George
Gapes, Mike
Gardiner, Barry
Garnier, Edward
George, Andrew
George, Rt Hon Bruce
Gerrard, Neil
Gibb, Nick
Gibson, Dr Ian

Gidley, Sandra
Gildernew, Michelle
Gillan, Cheryl
Gill, Pamjit Singh
Gilroy, Linda
Godsiff, Roger
Goggins, Paul
Goodman, Paul
Gray, James
Grayling, Chris
Green, Damian
Green, Matthew
Greenway, John
Grieve, Dominic
Griffiths, Jane
Griffiths, Nigel
Griffiths, Win
Grogan, John
Gummer, Rt Hon John

### H

Hague, Rt Hon William
Hain, Rt Hon Peter
Hall, Mike
Hall, Patrick
Hamilton, David
Hamilton, Fabian
Hammond, Philip
Hancock, Mike
Hanson, David
Harman, Rt Hon Harriet
Harris, Dr Evan
Harris, Tom
Harvey, Nick
Haselhurst, Rt Hon Sir Alan
Havard, Dai
Hawkins, Nick
Hayes, John
Heal, Sylvia
Heald, Oliver
Healey, John
Heath, David
Heathcoat-Amory, Rt Hon David
Henderson, Doug
Henderson, Ivan
Hendrick, Mark
Hendry, Charles
Hepburn, Stephen
Heppell, John
Hermon, Lady [Sylvia]
Hesford, Stephen
Hewitt, Rt Hon Patricia
Heyes, David
Hill, Rt Hon Keith
Hinchliffe, David
Hoban, Mark
Hodge, Rt Hon Margaret
Hoey, Kate
Hogg, Rt Hon Douglas

Holmes, Paul
Hood, Jimmy
Hoon, Rt Hon Geoff
Hope, Philip
Hopkins, Kelvin
Horam, John
Howard, Rt Hon Michael
Howarth, Rt Hon Alan
Howarth, George
Howarth, Gerald
Howells, Dr Kim
Hoyle, Lindsay
Hughes, Rt Hon Beverley
Hughes, Kevin
Hughes, Simon
Humble, Joan
Hume, John
Hunter, Andrew
Hurst, Alan
Hutton, Rt Hon John

### I

Iddon, Dr Brian
Illsley, Eric
Ingram, Rt Hon Adam
Irranca-Davies, Huw

### J

Jack, Rt Hon Michael
Jackson, Glenda
Jackson, Helen
Jackson, Robert
Jamieson, David
Jenkin, Hon Bernard
Jenkins, Brian
Johnson, Rt Hon Alan
Johnson, Boris
Johnson, Melanie
Jones, Helen
Jones, Jon Owen
Jones, Kevan
Jones, Dr Lynne
Jones, Martyn
Jones, Nigel
Jowell, Rt Hon Tessa
Joyce, Eric

### K

Kaufman, Rt Hon Sir Gerald
Keeble, Sally
Keen, Alan
Keen, Ann
Keetch, Paul
Kelly, Ruth
Kemp, Fraser
Kennedy, Rt Hon Charles
Kennedy, Rt Hon Jane
Key, Robert
Khabra, Piara Singh
Kidney, David

## MPs IN ALPHABETICAL ORDER

Kilfoyle, Peter
King, Andy
King, Oona
Kirkbride, Julie
Kirkwood, Sir Archy
Knight, Rt Hon Greg
Knight, Jim
Kumar, Dr Ashok

### L

Ladyman, Dr Stephen
Laing, Eleanor
Lait, Jacqui
Lamb, Norman
Lammy, David
Lansley, Andrew
Lawrence, Jackie
Laws, David
Laxton, Bob
Lazarowicz, Mark
Leigh, Edward
Lepper, David
Leslie, Christopher
Letwin, Rt Hon Oliver
Levitt, Tom
Lewis, Ivan
Lewis, Dr Julian
Lewis, Terry
Liddell, Rt Hon Helen
Liddell-Grainger, Ian
Lidington, David
Lilley, Rt Hon Peter
Linton, Martin
Lloyd, Tony
Llwyd, Elfyn
Lord, Sir Michael
Loughton, Tim
Love, Andrew
Lucas, Ian
Luff, Peter
Luke, Iain
Lyons, John

### M

McAvoy, Rt Hon Tommy
McCabe, Stephen
McCafferty, Christine
McCartney, Rt Hon Ian
McDonagh, Siobhain
MacDonald, Calum
McDonnell, John
MacDougall, John
McFall, Rt Hon John
McGrady, Eddie
McGuiness, Martin
McGuire, Anne
McIntosh, Anne
McIssaac, Shona

MacKay, Rt Hon Andrew
McKechin, Ann
McKenna, Rosemary
Mackinlay, Andrew
Maclean, Rt Hon David
McLoughlin, Patrick
McNamara, Kevin
McNulty, Tony
MacShane, Dr Denis
Mactaggart, Fiona
McWalter, Tony
McWilliam, John
Mahmood, Khalid
Mahon, Alice
Malins, Humfrey
Mallaber, Judy
Mallon, Seamus
Mann, John
Maples, John
Marris, Robert
Marsden, Gordon
Marsden, Paul
Marshall, David
Marshall-Andrews, Robert
Martin, Rt Hon Michael
Martlew, Eric
Mates, Rt Hon Michael
Maude, Rt Hon Francis
Mawhinney, Rt Hon Sir Brian
May, Rt Hon Theresa
Meacher, Rt Hon Michael
Meale, Alan
Mercer, Patrick
Merron, Gillian
Michael, Rt Hon Alun
Milburn, Rt Hon Alan
Miliband, David
Miller, Andrew
Mitchell, Andrew
Mitchell, Austin
Moffatt, Laura
Mole, Chris
Moonie, Dr Lewis
Moore, Michael
Moran, Margaret
Morgan, Julie
Morley, Elliott
Morris, Rt Hon Estelle
Moss, Malcolm
Mountford, Kali
Mudie, George
Mullin, Chris
Munn, Meg
Murphy, Denis
Murphy, Jim
Murphy, Rt Hon Paul
Murrison, Dr Andrew

### N

Naysmith, Dr Doug
Norman, Archie
Norris, Dan

### O

O'Brien, Bill
O'Brien, Mike
O'Brien, Stephen
O'Hara, Eddie
O'Neill, Martin
Oaten, Mark
Olner, Bill
Öpik, Lembit
Organ, Diana
Osborne, George
Osborne, Sandra
Ottaway, Richard
Owen, Albert

### P

Page, Richard
Paice, James
Paisley, Rev Ian
Palmer, Dr Nick
Paterson, Owen
Pearson, Ian
Perham, Linda
Picking, Anne
Pickles, Eric
Pickthall, Colin
Pike, Peter
Plaskitt, James
Pollard, Kerry
Pond, Chris
Pope, Greg
Portillo, Rt Hon Michael
Pound, Stephen
Prentice, Bridget
Prentice, Gordon
Prescott, Rt Hon John
Price, Adam
Primarolo, Rt Hon Dawn
Prisk, Mark
Prosser, Gwyn
Pugh, Dr John
Purchase, Ken
Purnell, James

### Q

Quin, Rt Hon Joyce
Quinn, Lawrie

### R

Rammell, Bill
Randall, John
Rapson, Syd
Raynsford, Rt Hon Nick

## MPs IN ALPHABETICAL ORDER

Redwood, Rt Hon John
Reed, Andrew
Reid, Alan
Reid, Rt Hon John
Rendel, David
Robathan, Andrew
Robertson, Angus
Robertson, Hugh
Robertson, John
Robertson, Laurence
Robinson, Geoffrey
Robinson, Iris
Robinson, Peter
Roche, Barbara
Roe, Dame Marion
Rooney, Terry
Rosindell, Andrew
Ross, Ernie
Roy, Frank
Ruane, Chris
Ruddock, Joan
Ruffley, David
Russell, Bob
Russell, Christine
Ryan, Joan

### S
Salmond, Alex
Salter, Martin
Sanders, Adrian
Sarwar, Mohammad
Savidge, Malcolm
Sawford, Phil
Sayeed, Jonathan
Sedgemore, Brian
Selous, Andrew
Shaw, Jonathan
Sheerman, Barry
Shephard, Rt Hon Gillian
Shepherd, Richard
Sheridan, James
Shipley, Debra
Short, Rt Hon Clare
Simmonds, Mark
Simon, Siôn
Simpson, Alan
Simpson, Keith
Singh, Marsha
Skinner, Dennis
Smith, Rt Hon Andrew
Smith, Angela
Smith, Rt Hon Chris
Smith, Geraldine
Smith, Rt Hon Jacqui
Smith, John
Smith, Llew
Smith, Sir Robert
Smyth, Rev Martin

Soames, Hon Nicholas
Soley, Clive
Southworth, Helen
Spellar, Rt Hon John
Spelman, Caroline
Spicer, Sir Michael
Spink, Dr Robert
Spring, Richard
Squire, Rachel
Stanley, Rt Hon Sir John
Starkey, Dr Phyllis
Steen, Anthony
Steinberg, Gerry
Stevenson, George
Stewart, David
Stewart, Ian
Stinchcombe, Paul
Stoate, Dr Howard
Strang, Rt Hon Gavin
Straw, Rt Hon Jack
Streeter, Gary
Stringer, Graham
Stuart, Gisela
Stunell, Andrew
Sutcliffe, Gerry
Swayne, Desmond
Swire, Hugo
Syms, Robert

### T
Tami, Mark
Tapsell, Sir Peter
Taylor, Rt Hon Ann
Taylor, Dari
Taylor, David
Taylor, Ian
Taylor, John
Taylor, Matthew
Taylor, Dr Richard
Taylor, Sir Teddy
Teather, Sarah
Thomas, Gareth
Thomas, Gareth R
Thomas, Simon
Thurso, John
Timms, Stephen
Tipping, Paddy
Todd, Mark
Tonge, Dr Jenny
Touhig, Don
Tredinnick, David
Trend, Michael
Trickett, Jon
Trimble, Rt Hon David
Truswell, Paul
Turner, Andrew
Turner, Dennis
Turner, Dr Desmond
Turner, Neil

Twigg, Derek
Twigg, Stephen
Tyler, Paul
Tynan, Bill
Tyrie, Andrew

### V
Vaz, Keith
Viggers, Peter
Vis, Dr Rudi

### W
Walley, Joan
Walter, Robert
Ward, Claire
Wareing, Robert
Waterson, Nigel
Watkinson, Angela
Watson, Tom
Watts, Dave
Webb, Steven
Weir, Michael
White, Brian
Whitehead, Dr Alan
Whittingdale, John
Wicks, Malcolm
Widdecombe, Rt Hon Ann
Wiggin, Bill
Wilkinson, John
Willetts, David
Williams, Rt Hon Alan
Williams, Betty
Williams, Hywel
Williams, Roger
Willis, Phil
Wills, Michael
Wilshire, David
Wilson, Rt Hon Brian
Winnick, David
Winterton, Ann
Winterton, Sir Nicholas
Winterton, Rosie
Wishart, Peter
Wood, Mike
Woodward, Shaun
Woolas, Phil
Worthington, Tony
Wray, Jimmy
Wright, Anthony D
Wright, David
Wright, Iain
Wright, Dr Tony
Wyatt, Derek

### Y
Yeo, Tim
Young, Rt Hon Sir George
Younger-Ross, Richard

## MPs BY CONSTITUENCY

*Note: The following abbreviations are used:*

Con . . . . Conservative
Ind. . . . . Independent
Lib Dem. .Liberal Democrat
SDLP. . . Social Democratic and Labour Party
SNP. . . . Scottish National Party

DU. . . . . . . . Democratic Unionist
Lab . . . . . . . Labour
PC. . . . . . . . Plaid Cymru
SF . . . . . . . . Sinn Fein
UU. . . . . . . . Ulster Unionist

### A

Aberavon ...............................Dr Hywel Francis (Lab)
Aberdeen Central ..........................Frank Doran (Lab)
Aberdeen North ......................Malcolm Savidge (Lab)
Aberdeen South..............................Anne Begg (Lab)
Aberdeenshire West and Kincardine .Sir Robert Smith (Lib Dem)
Airdrie and Shotts......................Rt Hon Helen Liddell (Lab)
Aldershot...............................Gerald Howarth (Con)
Aldridge-Brownhills ..................Richard Shepherd (Con)
Altrincham and Sale West...................Graham Brady (Con)
Alyn and Deeside..........................Mark Tami (Lab)
Amber Valley........................Judy Mallaber (Lab)
Angus.............................Michael Weir (SNP)
Antrim East .............................Roy Beggs (UU)
Antrim North ......................Rev Ian Paisley (DU)
Antrim South ......................David Burnside (UU)
Argyll and Bute .........................Alan Reid (Lib Dem)
Arundel and South Downs ...........Howard Flight (Con)
Ashfield ..........................Rt Hon Geoff Hoon (Lab)
Ashford..............................Damian Green (Con)
Ashton-under-Lyne ......................David Heyes (Lab)
Aylesbury.............................David Lidington (Con)
Ayr ..............................Sandra Osborne (Lab)

### B

Banbury .............................Tony Baldry (Con)
Banff and Buchan......................Alex Salmond (SNP)
Barking..........................Rt Hon Margaret Hodge (Lab)
Barnsley Central .........................Eric Illsley (Lab)
Barnsley East and Mexborough ...........Jeff Ennis (Lab)
Barnsley West and Penistone ..........Michael Clapham (Lab)
Barrow and Furness......................Rt Hon John Hutton (Lab)
Basildon .............................Angela Smith (Lab)
Basingstoke.........................Andrew Hunter (Ind)
Bassetlaw .............................John Mann (Lab)
Bath..............................Don Foster (Lib Dem)
Batley and Spen ..........................Mike Wood (Lab)
Battersea .............................Martin Linton (Lab)
Beaconsfield..........................Dominic Grieve (Con)
Beckenham ..........................Jacqui Lait (Con)
Bedford..............................Patrick Hall (Lab)
Bedfordshire North East ...............Alistair Burt (Con)
Bedfordshire South West ...............Andrew Selous (Con)
Belfast East ..........................Peter Robinson (DU)
Belfast North  ..........................Nigel Dodds (DU)
Belfast South....................Rev Martin Smyth (Ulster Unionist)
Belfast West .............................Gerry Adams (SF)
Berwick-upon-Tweed ..............Rt Hon Alan Beith (Lib Dem)
Bethnal Green and Bow......................Oona King (Lab)
Beverley and Holderness ...............James Cran (Con)
Bexhill and Battle ....................Gregory Barker (Con)

Bexleyheath and Crayford.................Nigel Beard (Lab)
Billericay .............................John Baron (Con)
Birkenhead.....................Rt Hon Frank Field (Lab)
Birmingham Edgbaston ...............Gisela Stuart (Lab)
Birmingham Erdington.................Siôn Simon (Lab)
Birmingham Hall Green.............Stephen McCabe (Lab)
Birmingham Hodge Hill.................Liam Byrne (Lab)
Birmingham Ladywood..........Rt Hon Clare Short (Lab)
Birmingham Northfield.............Richard Burden (Lab)
Birmingham Perry Barr .............Khalid Mahmood (Lab)
Birmingham Selly Oak.................Dr Lynne Jones (Lab)
Birmingham Sparkbrook and Small Heath......Roger Godsiff (Lab)
Birmingham Yardley.............Rt Hon Estelle Morris (Lab)
Bishop Auckland .................Rt Hon Derek Foster (Lab)
Blaby............................Andrew Robathan (Con)
Blackburn .................Rt Hon Jack Straw (Lab)
Blackpool North and Fleetwood.............Joan Humble (Lab)
Blackpool South ....................Gordon Marsden (Lab)
Blaenau Gwent.........................Llew Smith (Lab)
Blaydon ..........................John McWilliam (Lab)
Blyth Valley ......................Ronnie Campbell (Lab)
Bognor Regis and Littlehampton.............Nick Gibb (Con)
Bolsover ..........................Dennis Skinner (Lab)
Bolton North East ....................David Crausby (Lab)
Bolton South East ....................Dr Brian Iddon (Lab)
Bolton West ..........................Ruth Kelly (Lab)
Bootle..............................Joe Benton (Lab)
Boston and Skegness .............Mark Simmonds (Con)
Bosworth ..........................David Tredinnick (Con)
Bournemouth East ...................David Atkinson (Con)
Bournemouth West................Sir John Butterfill (Con)
Bracknell.....................Rt Hon Andrew MacKay (Con)
Bradford North ......................Terry Rooney (Lab)
Bradford South ....................Gerry Sutcliffe (Lab)
Bradford West ......................Marsha Singh (Lab)
Braintree ..............................Alan Hurst (Lab)
Brecon and Radnorshire .....Roger Williams (Lib Dem)
Brent East......................Sarah Teather (Lib Dem)
Brent North ......................Barry Gardiner (Lab)
Brent South ...............Rt Hon Paul Boateng (Lab)
Brentford and Isleworth ...................Ann Keen (Lab)
Brentwood and Ongar...................Eric Pickles (Con)
Bridgend .............................Win Griffiths (Lab)
Bridgwater ..................Ian Liddell-Grainger (Con)
Brigg and Goole......................Ian Cawsey (Lab)
Brighton Kemptown ...............Dr Desmond Turner (Lab)
Brighton Pavilion .....................David Lepper (Lab)
Bristol East ...................Rt Hon Jean Corston (Lab)
Bristol North West ...................Dr Doug Naysmith (Lab)
Bristol South ...............Rt Hon Dawn Primarolo (Lab)
Bristol West .......................Valerie Davey (Lab)

# MPs BY CONSTITUENCY

| | |
|---|---|
| Bromley and Chislehurst | Rt Hon Eric Forth (Con) |
| Bromsgrove | Julie Kirkbride (Con) |
| Broxbourne | Dame Marion Roe (Con) |
| Broxtowe | Dr Nick Palmer (Lab) |
| Buckingham | John Bercow (Con) |
| Burnley | Peter Pike (Lab) |
| Burton | Janet Dean (Lab) |
| Bury North | David Chaytor (Lab) |
| Bury South | Ivan Lewis (Lab) |
| Bury St Edmunds | David Ruffley (Con) |

## C

| | |
|---|---|
| Caernarfon | Hywel Williams (PC) |
| Caerphilly | Wayne David (Lab) |
| Caithness, Sutherland and Easter Ross | John Thurso (Lib Dem) |
| Calder Valley | Christine McCafferty (Lab) |
| Camberwell and Peckham | Rt Hon Harriet Harman (Lab) |
| Cambridge | Anne Campbell (Lab) |
| Cambridgeshire North East | Malcolm Moss (Con) |
| Cambridgeshire North West | Rt Hon Sir Brian Mawhinney (Con) |
| Cambridgeshire South | Andrew Lansley (Con) |
| Cambridgeshire South East | James Paice (Con) |
| Cannock Chase | Dr Tony Wright (Lab) |
| Canterbury | Julian Brazier (Con) |
| Cardiff Central | Jon Owen Jones (Lab) |
| Cardiff North | Julie Morgan (Lab) |
| Cardiff South and Penarth | Rt Hon Alun Michael (Lab) |
| Cardiff West | Kevin Brennan (Lab) |
| Carlisle | Eric Martlew (Lab) |
| Carmarthen East and Dinefwr | Adam Price (PC) |
| Carmarthen West and South Pembrokeshire | Nick Ainger (Lab) |
| Carrick, Cumnock and Doon Valley | Rt Hon George Foulkes (Lab) |
| Carshalton and Wallington | Tom Brake (Lib Dem) |
| Castle Point | Dr Robert Spink (Con) |
| Ceredigion | Simon Thomas (PC) |
| Charnwood | Rt Hon Stephen Dorrell (Con) |
| Chatham and Aylesford | Jonathan Shaw (Lab) |
| Cheadle | Patsy Calton (Lib Dem) |
| Chelmsford West | Simon Burns (Con) |
| Cheltenham | Nigel Jones (Lib Dem) |
| Chesham and Amersham | Cheryl Gillan (Con) |
| Chester, City of | Christine Russell (Lab) |
| Chesterfield | Paul Holmes (Lib Dem) |
| Chichester | Andrew Tyrie (Con) |
| Chingford and Woodford Green | Rt Hon Iain Duncan Smith (Con) |
| Chipping Barnet | Sir Sydney Chapman (Con) |
| Chorley | Lindsay Hoyle (Lab) |
| Christchurch | Christopher Chope (Con) |
| Cities of London and Westminster | Mark Field (Con) |
| Cleethorpes | Shona McIsaac (Lab) |
| Clwyd South | Martyn Jones (Lab) |
| Clwyd West | Gareth Thomas (Lab) |
| Clydebank and Milngavie | Tony Worthington (Lab) |
| Clydesdale | Jimmy Hood (Lab) |
| Coatbridge and Chryston | Rt Hon Tom Clarke (Lab) |
| Colchester | Bob Russell (Lib Dem) |
| Colne Valley | Kali Mountford (Lab) |
| Congleton | Ann Winterton (Con) |
| Conwy | Betty Williams (Lab) |

| | |
|---|---|
| Copeland | Rt Hon Dr Jack Cunningham (Lab) |
| Corby | Philip Hope (Lab) |
| Cornwall North | Paul Tyler (Lib Dem) |
| Cornwall South East | Colin Breed (Lib Dem) |
| Cotswold | Geoffrey Clifton-Brown (Con) |
| Coventry North East | Bob Ainsworth (Lab) |
| Coventry North West | Geoffrey Robinson (Lab) |
| Coventry South | Jim Cunningham (Lab) |
| Crawley | Laura Moffatt (Lab) |
| Crewe and Nantwich | Gwyneth Dunwoody (Lab) |
| Crosby | Claire Curtis-Thomas (Lab) |
| Croydon Central | Geraint Davies (Lab) |
| Croydon North | Malcolm Wicks (Lab) |
| Croydon South | Richard Ottaway (Con) |
| Cumbernauld and Kilsyth | Rosemary McKenna (Lab) |
| Cunninghame North | Rt Hon Brian Wilson (Lab) |
| Cunninghame South | Brian Donohoe (Lab) |
| Cynon Valley | Ann Clwyd (Lab) |

## D

| | |
|---|---|
| Dagenham | Jon Cruddas (Lab) |
| Darlington | Rt Hon Alan Milburn (Lab) |
| Dartford | Dr Howard Stoate (Lab) |
| Daventry | Tim Boswell (Con) |
| Delyn | David Hanson (Lab) |
| Denton and Reddish | Andrew Bennett (Lab) |
| Derby North | Bob Laxton (Lab) |
| Derby South | Rt Hon Margaret Beckett (Lab) |
| Derbyshire North East | Harry Barnes (Lab) |
| Derbyshire South | Mark Todd (Lab) |
| Derbyshire West | Patrick McLoughlin (Con) |
| Devizes | Rt Hon Michael Ancram (Con) |
| Devon East | Hugo Swire (Con) |
| Devon North | Nick Harvey (Lib Dem) |
| Devon South West | Gary Streeter (Con) |
| Devon West and Torridge | John Burnett (Lib Dem) |
| Dewsbury | Rt Hon Ann Taylor (Lab) |
| Don Valley | Caroline Flint (Lab) |
| Doncaster Central | Rosie Winterton (Lab) |
| Doncaster North | Kevin Hughes (Lab) |
| Dorset North | Robert Walter (Con) |
| Dorset South | Jim Knight (Lab) |
| Dorset West | Rt Hon Oliver Letwin (Con) |
| Dover | Gwyn Prosser (Lab) |
| Down North | Lady [Sylvia] Hermon (UU) |
| Down South | Eddie McGrady (SDLP) |
| Dudley North | Ross Cranston (Lab) |
| Dudley South | Ian Pearson (Lab) |
| Dulwich and West Norwood | Rt Hon Tessa Jowell (Lab) |
| Dumbarton | Rt Hon John McFall (Lab) |
| Dumfries | Russell Brown (Lab) |
| Dundee East | Iain Luke (Lab) |
| Dundee West | Ernie Ross (Lab) |
| Dunfermline East | Rt Hon Gordon Brown (Lab) |
| Dunfermline West | Rachel Squire (Lab) |
| Durham, City of | Gerry Steinberg (Lab) |
| Durham North | Kevan Jones (Lab) |
| Durham North West | Rt Hon Hilary Armstrong (Lab) |

## MPs BY CONSTITUENCY

### E

Ealing Acton and Shepherds Bush ....................Clive Soley (Lab)
Ealing North ...............................................Stephen Pound (Lab)
Ealing Southall .......................................Piara Singh Khabra (Lab)
Easington...................................................John Cummings (Lab)
East Ham .......................................................Stephen Timms (Lab)
East Kilbride ................................Rt Hon Adam Ingram (Lab)
East Lothian.....................................................Anne Picking (Lab)
Eastbourne...............................................Nigel Waterson (Con)
Eastleigh..............................................David Chidgey (Lib Dem)
Eastwood..........................................................Jim Murphy (Lab)
Eccles.................................................................Ian Stewart (Lab)
Eddisbury..........................................Stephen O'Brien (Con)
Edinburgh Central........................Rt Hon Alistair Darling (Lab)
Edinburgh East and Musselburgh .......Rt Hon Gavin Strang (Lab)
Edinburgh North and Leith.........................Mark Lazarowicz (Lab)
Edinburgh Pentlands.............................Dr Lynda Clark (Lab)
Edinburgh South .......................................Nigel Griffiths (Lab)
Edinburgh West ................................John Barrett (Lib Dem)
Edmonton.......................................................Andrew Love (Lab)
Ellesmere Port and Neston ........................Andrew Miller (Lab)
Elmet ..............................................................Colin Burgon (Lab)
Eltham..............................................................Clive Efford (Lab)
Enfield North .......................................................Joan Ryan (Lab)
Enfield Southgate....................................Stephen Twigg (Lab)
Epping Forest............................................Eleanor Laing (Con)
Epsom and Ewell .......................................Chris Grayling (Con)
Erewash ...........................................................Liz Blackman (Lab)
Erith and Thamesmead.................................John Austin (Lab)
Esher and Walton .............................................Ian Taylor (Con)
Essex North ...................................Hon Bernard Jenkin (Con)
Exeter ..........................................................Ben Bradshaw (Lab)

### F

Falkirk East..............................................Michael Connarty (Lab)
Falkirk West .......................................................Eric Joyce (Lab)
Falmouth and Camborne...........................Candy Atherton (Lab)
Fareham.............................................................Mark Hoban (Con)
Faversham and Mid Kent .........................Hugh Robertson (Con)
Feltham and Heston ......................................Alan Keen (Lab)
Fermanagh and South Tyrone.................Michelle Gildernew (SF)
Fife Central .........................................John MacDougall (Lab)
Fife North East .............Rt Hon Sir Menzies Campbell (Lib Dem)
Finchley and Golders Green ...........................Dr Rudi Vis (Lab)
Folkestone and Hythe...................Rt Hon Michael Howard (Con)
Forest of Dean .............................................Diana Organ (Lab)
Foyle.................................................................John Hume (SDLP)
Fylde.....................................................Rt Hon Michael Jack (Con)

### G

Gainsborough ................................................Edward Leigh (Con)
Galloway and Upper Nithsdale .......................Peter Duncan (Con)
Gateshead East and Washington West...Rt Hon Joyce Quin (Lab)
Gedling ........................................................Vernon Coaker (Lab)
Gillingham.........................................................Paul Clark (Lab)
Glasgow Anniesland....................................John Robertson (Lab)
Glasgow Baillieston ..........................................Jimmy Wray (Lab)
Glasgow Cathcart................................................Tom Harris (Lab)
Glasgow Govan ..................................Mohammad Sarwar (Lab)
Glasgow Kelvin.............................................George Galloway (Ind)

Glasgow Maryhill.........................................Ann McKechin (Lab)
Glasgow Pollok .............................................Ian Davidson (Lab)
Glasgow Rutherglen .......................Rt Hon Tommy McAvoy (Lab)
Glasgow Shettleston.................................David Marshall (Lab)
Glasgow Springburn ..........Rt Hon Michael Martin (Speaker)
Gloucester..................................................Parmjit Dhanda (Lab)
Gordon.......................................................Malcolm Bruce (Lib Dem)
Gosport..........................................................Peter Viggers (Con)
Gower..............................................................Martin Caton (Lab)
Grantham and Stamford .............................Quentin Davies (Con)
Gravesham .....................................................Chris Pond (Lab)
Great Grimsby.............................................Austin Mitchell (Lab)
Great Yarmouth ......................................Anthony D Wright (Lab)
Greenock and Inverclyde..............................David Cairns (Lab)
Greenwich and Woolwich................Rt Hon Nick Raynsford (Lab)
Guildford ..................................................Sue Doughty (Lib Dem)

### H

Hackney North and Stoke Newington..............Diane Abbott (Lab)
Hackney South and Shoreditch..................Brian Sedgemore (Lab)
Halesowen and Rowley Regis ..........................Sylvia Heal (Lab)
Halifax...............................................................Alice Mahon (Lab)
Haltemprice and Howden....................Rt Hon David Davis (Con)
Halton................................................................Derek Twigg (Lab)
Hamilton North and Bellshill..................Rt Hon John Reid (Lab)
Hamilton South .................................................Bill Tynan (Lab)
Hammersmith and Fulham ............................Iain Coleman (Lab)
Hampshire East .................................Rt Hon Michael Mates (Con)
Hampshire North East .................Rt Hon James Arbuthnot (Con)
Hampshire North West ...............Rt Hon Sir George Young (Con)
Hampstead and Highgate ..........................Glenda Jackson (Lab)
Harborough .................................................Edward Garnier (Con)
Harlow..............................................................Bill Rammell (Lab)
Harrogate and Knaresborough .....................Phil Willis (Lib Dem)
Harrow East ...................................................Tony McNulty (Lab)
Harrow West ...............................................Gareth R Thomas (Lab)
Hartlepool .......................................................Iain Wright (Lab)
Harwich ........................................................Ivan Henderson (Lab)
Hastings and Rye .......................Michael Jabez Foster (Lab)
Havant..............................................................David Willetts (Con)
Hayes and Harlington............................John McDonnell (Lab)
Hazel Grove.......................................Andrew Stunell (Lib Dem)
Hemel Hempstead.....................................Tony McWalter (Lab)
Hemsworth......................................................Jon Trickett (Lab)
Hendon ......................................................Andrew Dismore (Lab)
Henley..............................................................Boris Johnson (Con)
Hereford ...................................................Paul Keetch (Lib Dem)
Hertford and Stortford....................................Mark Prisk (Con)
Hertfordshire North East...............................Oliver Heald (Con)
Hertfordshire South West..............................Richard Page (Con)
Hertsmere ................................................James Clappison (Con)
Hexham .........................................................Peter Atkinson (Con)
Heywood and Middleton..................................Jim Dobbin (Lab)
High Peak...........................................................Tom Levitt (Lab)
Hitchin and Harpenden ...................Rt Hon Peter Lilley (Con)
Holborn and St Pancras ...................Rt Hon Frank Dobson (Lab)
Hornchurch ......................................................John Cryer (Lab)
Hornsey and Wood Green............................Barbara Roche (Lab)
Horsham .........................................Rt Hon Francis Maude (Con)
Houghton and Washington East......................Fraser Kemp (Lab)

## MPs BY CONSTITUENCY

| | |
|---|---|
| Hove | Ivor Caplin (Lab) |
| Huddersfield | Barry Sheerman (Lab) |
| Hull East | Rt Hon John Prescott (Lab) |
| Hull North | Kevin McNamara (Lab) |
| Hull West and Hessle | Rt Hon Alan Johnson (Lab) |
| Huntingdon | Jonathan Djanogly (Con) |
| Hyndburn | Greg Pope (Lab) |

*I*

| | |
|---|---|
| Ilford North | Linda Perham (Lab) |
| Ilford South | Mike Gapes (Lab) |
| Inverness East, Nairn and Lochaber | David Stewart (Lab) |
| Ipswich | Chris Mole (Lab) |
| Isle of Wight | Andrew Turner (Con) |
| Islington North | Jeremy Corbyn (Lab) |
| Islington South and Finsbury | Rt Hon Chris Smith (Lab) |
| Islwyn | Don Touhig (Lab) |

*J*

| | |
|---|---|
| Jarrow | Stephen Hepburn (Lab) |

*K*

| | |
|---|---|
| Keighley | Ann Cryer (Lab) |
| Kensington and Chelsea | Rt Hon Michael Portillo (Con) |
| Kettering | Phil Sawford (Lab) |
| Kilmarnock and Loudoun | Desmond Browne (Lab) |
| Kingston and Surbiton | Edward Davey (Lib Dem) |
| Kingswood | Dr Roger Berry (Lab) |
| Kirkcaldy | Dr Lewis Moonie (Lab) |
| Knowsley North and Sefton East | George Howarth (Lab) |
| Knowsley South | Eddie O'Hara (Lab) |

*L*

| | |
|---|---|
| Lagan Valley | Jeffrey Donaldson (DU) |
| Lancashire West | Colin Pickthall (Lab) |
| Lancaster and Wyre | Hilton Dawson (Lab) |
| Leeds Central | Rt Hon Hilary Benn (Lab) |
| Leeds East | George Mudie (Lab) |
| Leeds North East | Fabian Hamilton (Lab) |
| Leeds North West | Harold Best (Lab) |
| Leeds West | Rt Hon John Battle (Lab) |
| Leicester East | Keith Vaz (Lab) |
| Leicester South | Parmjit Singh Gill (Lib Dem) |
| Leicester West | Rt Hon Patricia Hewitt (Lab) |
| Leicestershire North West | David Taylor (Lab) |
| Leigh | Andrew Burnham (Lab) |
| Leominster | Bill Wiggin (Con) |
| Lewes | Norman Baker (Lib Dem) |
| Lewisham Deptford | Joan Ruddock (Lab) |
| Lewisham East | Bridget Prentice (Lab) |
| Lewisham West | Jim Dowd (Lab) |
| Leyton and Wanstead | Harry Cohen (Lab) |
| Lichfield | Michael Fabricant (Con) |
| Lincoln | Gillian Merron (Lab) |
| Linlithgow | Tam Dalyell (Lab) |
| Liverpool Garston | Maria Eagle (Lab) |
| Liverpool Riverside | Louise Ellman (Lab) |
| Liverpool Walton | Peter Kilfoyle (Lab) |
| Liverpool Wavertree | Rt Hon Jane Kennedy (Lab) |
| Liverpool West Derby | Robert Wareing (Lab) |
| Livingston | Rt Hon Robin Cook (Lab) |

| | |
|---|---|
| Llanelli | Rt Hon Denzil Davies (Lab) |
| Londonderry East | Gregory Campbell (DU) |
| Loughborough | Andrew Reed (Lab) |
| Louth and Horncastle | Sir Peter Tapsell (Con) |
| Ludlow | Matthew Green (Lib Dem) |
| Luton North | Kelvin Hopkins (Lab) |
| Luton South | Margaret Moran (Lab) |

*M*

| | |
|---|---|
| Macclesfield | Sir Nicholas Winterton (Con) |
| Maidenhead | Rt Hon Theresa May (Con) |
| Maidstone and the Weald | Rt Hon Ann Widdecombe (Con) |
| Makerfield | Rt Hon Ian McCartney (Lab) |
| Maldon and Chelmsford East | John Whittingdale (Con) |
| Manchester Blackley | Graham Stringer (Lab) |
| Manchester Central | Tony Lloyd (Lab) |
| Manchester Gorton | Rt Hon Sir Gerald Kaufman (Lab) |
| Manchester Withington | Rt Hon Keith Bradley (Lab) |
| Mansfield | Alan Meale (Lab) |
| Medway | Robert Marshall-Andrews (Lab) |
| Meirionnydd Nant Conwy | Elfyn Llwyd (PC) |
| Meriden | Caroline Spelman (Con) |
| Merthyr Tydfil and Rhymney | Dai Havard (Lab) |
| Mid Bedfordshire | Jonathan Sayeed (Con) |
| Mid Dorset and Poole North | Annette Brooke (Lib Dem) |
| Mid Norfolk | Keith Simpson (Con) |
| Mid Sussex | Hon Nicholas Soames (Con) |
| Mid Ulster | Martin McGuiness (SF) |
| Mid Worcestershire | Peter Luff (Con) |
| Middlesbrough | Sir Stuart Bell (Lab) |
| Middlesbrough South and East Cleveland | Dr Ashok Kumar (Lab) |
| Midlothian | David Hamilton (Lab) |
| Milton Keynes North East | Brian White (Lab) |
| Milton Keynes South West | Dr Phyllis Starkey (Lab) |
| Mitcham and Morden | Siobhain McDonagh (Lab) |
| Mole Valley | Sir Paul Beresford (Con) |
| Monmouth | Huw Edwards (Lab) |
| Montgomeryshire | Lembit Öpik (Lib Dem) |
| Moray | Angus Robertson (SNP) |
| Morecambe and Lunesdale | Geraldine Smith (Lab) |
| Morley and Rothwell | Colin Challen (Lab) |
| Motherwell and Wishaw | Frank Roy (Lab) |

*N*

| | |
|---|---|
| Neath | Rt Hon Peter Hain (Lab) |
| New Forest East | Dr Julian Lewis (Con) |
| New Forest West | Desmond Swayne (Con) |
| Newark | Patrick Mercer (Con) |
| Newbury | David Rendel (Lib Dem) |
| Newcastle-under-Lyme | Paul Farrelly (Lab) |
| Newcastle-upon-Tyne Central | Jim Cousins (Lab) |
| Newcastle-upon-Tyne East and Wallsend | Rt Hon Nick Brown (Lab) |
| Newcastle-upon-Tyne North | Doug Henderson (Lab) |
| Newport East | Rt Hon Alan Howarth (Lab) |
| Newport West | Paul Flynn (Lab) |
| Newry and Armagh | Seamus Mallon (SDLP) |
| Norfolk North | Norman Lamb (Lib Dem) |
| Norfolk North West | Henry Bellingham (Con) |
| Norfolk South | Richard Bacon (Con) |
| Norfolk South West | Rt Hon Gillian Shephard (Con) |

## MPs BY CONSTITUENCY

| | |
|---|---|
| Normanton | Bill O'Brien (Lab) |
| Northampton North | Sally Keeble (Lab) |
| Northampton South | Tony Clarke (Lab) |
| Northavon | Steven Webb (Lib Dem) |
| Norwich North | Dr Ian Gibson (Lab) |
| Norwich South | Rt Hon Charles Clarke (Lab) |
| Nottingham East | John Heppell (Lab) |
| Nottingham North | Graham Allen (Lab) |
| Nottingham South | Alan Simpson (Lab) |
| Nuneaton | Bill Olner (Lab) |

### O

| | |
|---|---|
| Ochil | Martin O'Neill (Lab) |
| Ogmore | Huw Irranca-Davies (Lab) |
| Old Bexley and Sidcup | Derek Conway (Con) |
| Oldham East and Saddleworth | Phil Woolas (Lab) |
| Oldham West and Royton | Rt Hon Michael Meacher (Lab) |
| Orkney and Shetland | Alistair Carmichael (Lib Dem) |
| Orpington | John Horam (Con) |
| Oxford East | Rt Hon Andrew Smith (Lab) |
| Oxford West and Abingdon | Dr Evan Harris (Lib Dem) |

### P

| | |
|---|---|
| Paisley North | Irene Adams (Lab) |
| Paisley South | Douglas Alexander (Lab) |
| Pendle | Gordon Prentice (Lab) |
| Penrith and the Border | Rt Hon David Maclean (Con) |
| Perth | Annabelle Ewing (SNP) |
| Peterborough | Helen Clark (Lab) |
| Plymouth Devonport | David Jamieson (Lab) |
| Plymouth Sutton | Linda Gilroy (Lab) |
| Pontefract and Castleford | Yvette Cooper (Lab) |
| Pontypridd | Dr Kim Howells (Lab) |
| Poole | Robert Syms (Con) |
| Poplar and Canning Town | Jim Fitzpatrick (Lab) |
| Portsmouth North | Syd Rapson (Lab) |
| Portsmouth South | Mike Hancock (Lib Dem) |
| Preseli Pembrokeshire | Jackie Lawrence (Lab) |
| Preston | Mark Hendrick (Lab) |
| Pudsey | Paul Truswell (Lab) |
| Putney | Tony Colman (Lab) |

### R

| | |
|---|---|
| Rayleigh | Mark Francois (Con) |
| Reading East | Jane Griffiths (Lab) |
| Reading West | Martin Salter (Lab) |
| Redcar | Vera Baird (Lab) |
| Redditch | Rt Hon Jacqui Smith (Lab) |
| Regent's Park and Kensington North | Karen Buck (Lab) |
| Reigate | Crispin Blunt (Con) |
| Renfrewshire West | James Sheridan (Lab) |
| Rhondda | Chris Bryant (Lab) |
| Ribble South | David Borrow (Lab) |
| Ribble Valley | Nigel Evans (Con) |
| Richmond Park | Dr Jenny Tonge (Lib Dem) |
| Richmond (Yorkshire) | Rt Hon William Hague (Con) |
| Rochdale | Lorna Fitzsimons (Lab) |
| Rochford and Southend East | Sir Teddy Taylor (Con) |
| Romford | Andrew Rosindell (Con) |
| Romsey | Sandra Gidley (Lib Dem) |
| Ross, Skye and Inverness West | Rt Hon Charles Kennedy (Lib Dem) |

| | |
|---|---|
| Rossendale and Darwen | Janet Anderson (Lab) |
| Rother Valley | Rt Hon Kevin Barron (Lab) |
| Rotherham | Dr Denis MacShane (Lab) |
| Roxburgh and Berwickshire | Sir Archy Kirkwood (Lib Dem) |
| Rugby and Kenilworth | Andy King (Lab) |
| Ruislip-Northwood | John Wilkinson (Con) |
| Runnymede and Weybridge | Philip Hammond (Con) |
| Rushcliffe | Rt Hon Kenneth Clarke (Con) |
| Rutland and Melton | Alan Duncan (Con) |
| Ryedale | John Greenway (Con) |

### S

| | |
|---|---|
| Saffron Walden | Rt Hon Sir Alan Haselhurst (Con) |
| St Albans | Kerry Pollard (Lab) |
| St Helens North | Dave Watts (Lab) |
| St Helens South | Shaun Woodward (Lab) |
| St Ives | Andrew George (Lib Dem) |
| Salford | Hazel Blears (Lab) |
| Salisbury | Robert Key (Con) |
| Scarborough and Whitby | Lawrie Quinn (Lab) |
| Scunthorpe | Elliott Morley (Lab) |
| Sedgefield | Rt Hon Tony Blair (Lab) |
| Selby | John Grogan (Lab) |
| Sevenoaks | Michael Fallon (Con) |
| Sheffield Attercliffe | Clive Betts (Lab) |
| Sheffield Brightside | Rt Hon David Blunkett (Lab) |
| Sheffield Central | Rt Hon Richard Caborn (Lab) |
| Sheffield Hallam | Richard Allan (Lib Dem) |
| Sheffield Heeley | Meg Munn (Lab) |
| Sheffield Hillsborough | Helen Jackson (Lab) |
| Sherwood | Paddy Tipping (Lab) |
| Shipley | Christopher Leslie (Lab) |
| Shrewsbury and Atcham | Paul Marsden (Lib Dem) |
| Shropshire North | Owen Paterson (Con) |
| Sittingbourne and Sheppey | Derek Wyatt (Lab) |
| Skipton and Ripon | Rt Hon David Curry (Con) |
| Sleaford and North Hykeham | Rt Hon Douglas Hogg (Con) |
| Slough | Fiona Mactaggart (Lab) |
| Solihull | John Taylor (Con) |
| Somerton and Frome | David Heath (Lib Dem) |
| South Holland and The Deepings | John Hayes (Con) |
| South Shields | David Miliband (Lab) |
| Southampton Itchen | Rt Hon John Denham (Lab) |
| Southampton Test | Dr Alan Whitehead (Lab) |
| Southend West | David Amess (Con) |
| Southport | Dr John Pugh (Lib Dem) |
| Southwark North and Bermondsey | Simon Hughes (Lib Dem) |
| Spelthorne | David Wilshire (Con) |
| Stafford | David Kidney (Lab) |
| Staffordshire Moorlands | Charlotte Atkins (Lab) |
| Staffordshire South | Sir Patrick Cormack (Con) |
| Stalybridge and Hyde | James Purnell (Lab) |
| Stevenage | Barbara Follett (Lab) |
| Stirling | Anne McGuire (Lab) |
| Stockport | Ann Coffey (Lab) |
| Stockton North | Frank Cook (Lab) |
| Stockton South | Dari Taylor (Lab) |
| Stoke-on-Trent Central | Mark Fisher (Lab) |
| Stoke-on-Trent North | Joan Walley (Lab) |
| Stoke-on-Trent South | George Stevenson (Lab) |

## MPs BY CONSTITUENCY

| | |
|---|---|
| Stone | Bill Cash (Con) |
| Stourbridge | Debra Shipley (Lab) |
| Strangford | Iris Robinson (DU) |
| Stratford-on-Avon | John Maples (Con) |
| Strathkelvin and Bearsden | John Lyons (Lab) |
| Streatham | Rt Hon Keith Hill (Lab) |
| Stretford and Urmston | Rt Hon Beverley Hughes (Lab) |
| Stroud | David Drew (Lab) |
| Suffolk Central and Ipswich North | Sir Michael Lord (Con) |
| Suffolk Coastal | Rt Hon John Gummer (Con) |
| Suffolk South | Tim Yeo (Con) |
| Suffolk West | Richard Spring (Con) |
| Sunderland North | Bill Etherington (Lab) |
| Sunderland South | Chris Mullin (Lab) |
| Surrey East | Peter Ainsworth (Con) |
| Surrey Heath | Nick Hawkins (Con) |
| Surrey South West | Rt Hon Virginia Bottomley (Con) |
| Sutton and Cheam | Paul Burstow (Lib Dem) |
| Sutton Coldfield | Andrew Mitchell (Con) |
| Swansea East | Rt Hon Donald Anderson (Lab) |
| Swansea West | Rt Hon Alan Williams (Lab) |
| Swindon North | Michael Wills (Lab) |
| Swindon South | Julia Drown (Lab) |

### T

| | |
|---|---|
| Tamworth | Brian Jenkins (Lab) |
| Tatton | George Osborne (Con) |
| Taunton | Adrian Flook (Con) |
| Tayside North | Peter Wishart (SNP) |
| Teignbridge | Richard Younger-Ross (Lib Dem) |
| Telford | David Wright (Lab) |
| Tewkesbury | Laurence Robertson (Con) |
| Thanet North | Roger Gale (Con) |
| Thanet South | Dr Stephen Ladyman (Lab) |
| Thurrock | Andrew Mackinlay (Lab) |
| Tiverton and Honiton | Angela Browning (Con) |
| Tonbridge and Malling | Rt Hon Sir John Stanley (Con) |
| Tooting | Tom Cox (Lab) |
| Torbay | Adrian Sanders (Lib Dem) |
| Torfaen | Rt Hon Paul Murphy (Lab) |
| Totnes | Anthony Steen (Con) |
| Tottenham | David Lammy (Lab) |
| Truro and St Austell | Matthew Taylor (Lib Dem) |
| Tunbridge Wells | Archie Norman (Con) |
| Tweeddale, Ettrick and Lauderdale | Michael Moore (Lib Dem) |
| Twickenham | Dr Vincent Cable (Lib Dem) |
| Tyne Bridge | David Clelland (Lab) |
| Tynemouth | Alan Campbell (Lab) |
| Tyneside North | Rt Hon Stephen Byers (Lab) |

### U

| | |
|---|---|
| Upminster | Angela Watkinson (Con) |
| Upper Bann | Rt Hon David Trimble (UU) |
| Uxbridge | John Randall (Con) |

### V

| | |
|---|---|
| Vale of Clwyd | Chris Ruane (Lab) |
| Vale of Glamorgan | John Smith (Lab) |
| Vale of York | Anne McIntosh (Con) |
| Vauxhall | Kate Hoey (Lab) |

### W

| | |
|---|---|
| Wakefield | David Hinchliffe (Lab) |
| Wallasey | Angela Eagle (Lab) |
| Walsall North | David Winnick (Lab) |
| Walsall South | Rt Hon Bruce George (Lab) |
| Walthamstow | Neil Gerrard (Lab) |
| Wansbeck | Denis Murphy (Lab) |
| Wansdyke | Dan Norris (Lab) |
| Wantage | Robert Jackson (Con) |
| Warley | Rt Hon John Spellar (Lab) |
| Warrington North | Helen Jones (Lab) |
| Warrington South | Helen Southworth (Lab) |
| Warwick and Leamington | James Plaskitt (Lab) |
| Warwickshire North | Mike O'Brien (Lab) |
| Watford | Claire Ward (Lab) |
| Waveney | Bob Blizzard (Lab) |
| Wealden | Charles Hendry (Con) |
| Weaver Vale | Mike Hall (Lab) |
| Wellingborough | Paul Stinchcombe (Lab) |
| Wells | Rt Hon David Heathcoat-Amory (Con) |
| Welwyn Hatfield | Melanie Johnson (Lab) |
| Wentworth | John Healey (Lab) |
| West Bromwich East | Tom Watson (Lab) |
| West Bromwich West | Adrian Bailey (Lab) |
| West Ham | Tony Banks (Lab) |
| West Tyrone | Pat Doherty (SF) |
| Westbury | Dr Andrew Murrison (Con) |
| Western Isles | Calum MacDonald (Lab) |
| Westmorland and Lonsdale | Tim Collins (Con) |
| Weston-super-Mare | Brian Cotter (Lib Dem) |
| Wigan | Neil Turner (Lab) |
| Wiltshire North | James Gray (Con) |
| Wimbledon | Roger Casale (Lab) |
| Winchester | Mark Oaten (Lib Dem) |
| Windsor | Michael Trend (Con) |
| Wirral South | Ben Chapman (Lab) |
| Wirral West | Stephen Hesford (Lab) |
| Witney | David Cameron (Con) |
| Woking | Humfrey Malins (Con) |
| Wokingham | Rt Hon John Redwood (Con) |
| Wolverhampton North East | Ken Purchase (Lab) |
| Wolverhampton South East | Dennis Turner (Lab) |
| Wolverhampton South West | Robert Marris (Lab) |
| Woodspring | Dr Liam Fox (Con) |
| Worcester | Michael John Foster (Lab) |
| Worcestershire West | Sir Michael Spicer (Con) |
| Workington | Tony Cunningham (Lab) |
| Worsley | Terry Lewis (Lab) |
| Worthing East and Shoreham | Tim Loughton (Con) |
| Worthing West | Peter Bottomley (Con) |
| Wrekin, The | Peter Bradley (Lab) |
| Wrexham | Ian Lucas (Lab) |
| Wycombe | Paul Goodman (Con) |
| Wyre Forest | Dr Richard Taylor (Ind) |
| Wythenshawe and Sale East | Paul Goggins (Lab) |

### Y

| | |
|---|---|
| Yeovil | David Laws (Lib Dem) |
| Ynys Môn | Albert Owen (Lab) |
| York, City of | Hugh Bayley (Lab) |
| Yorkshire East | Rt Hon Greg Knight (Con) |

# MPs BY POLITICAL PARTY

## Conservative

### A

Ainsworth, Peter ...................................................Surrey East
Amess, David ...............................................Southend West
Ancram, Rt Hon Michael.................................Devizes
Arbuthnot, Rt Hon James .......................Hampshire North East
Atkinson, David.............................................Bournemouth East
Atkinson, Peter ..................................................Hexham

### B

Bacon, Richard.................................................Norfolk South
Baldry, Tony ...................................................Banbury
Barker, Gregory ...................................Bexhill and Battle
Baron, John..........................................................Billericay
Bellingham, Henry ...........................Norfolk North West
Bercow, John ..................................................Buckingham
Beresford, Sir Paul...........................................Mole Valley
Blunt, Crispin ...................................................Reigate
Boswell, Tim ...................................................Daventry
Bottomley, Peter ...................................Worthing West
Bottomley, Rt Hon Virginia ...........................Surrey South West
Brady, Graham .....................Altrincham and Sale West
Brazier, Julian ..........................................Canterbury
Browning, Angela.........................Tiverton and Honiton
Burns, Simon ...........................................Chelmsford West
Burt, Alistair.................................Bedfordshire North East
Butterfill, Sir John ...........................Bournemouth West

### C

Cameron, David ................................................Witney
Cash, Bill ...........................................................Stone
Chapman, Sir Sydney ...........................Chipping Barnet
Chope, Christopher.......................................Christchurch
Clappison, James.............................................Hertsmere
Clarke, Rt Hon Kenneth ................................Rushcliffe
Clifton-Brown Geoffrey .................................Cotswold
Collins, Tim ...................Westmorland and Lonsdale
Conway, Derek......................Old Bexley and Sidcup
Cormack, Sir Patrick ...........................Staffordshire South
Cran, James ...........................Beverley and Holderness
Curry, Rt Hon David .....................Skipton and Ripon

### D

Davies, Quentin ...........................Grantham and Stamford
Davis, Rt Hon David .........................Haltemprice and Howden
Djanogly, Jonathan ........................................Huntingdon
Dorrell, Rt Hon Stephen..............................Charnwood
Duncan, Alan ...........................Rutland and Melton
Duncan, Peter.........................Galloway and Upper Nithsdale
Duncan Smith, Rt Hon Iain ........Chingford and Woodford Green

### E

Evans, Nigel.................................................Ribble Valley

### F

Fabricant, Michael ..........................................Lichfield
Fallon, Michael...............................................Sevenoaks
Field, Mark...........................Cities of London and Westminster
Flight, Howard.............................Arundel and South Downs
Flook, Adrian ..................................................Taunton
Forth, Rt Hon Eric..........................Bromley and Chislehurst
Fox, Dr Liam ...............................................Woodspring
Francois, Mark ...............................................Rayleigh

### G

Gale, Roger ...........................................Thanet North
Garnier, Edward ...........................................Harborough
Gibb, Nick ...................Bognor Regis and Littlehampton
Gillan, Cheryl ...........................Chesham and Amersham
Goodman, Paul ...........................................Wycombe
Gray, James ........................................Wiltshire North
Grayling, Chris ...........................Epsom and Ewell
Green, Damian...............................................Ashford
Greenway, John.............................................Ryedale
Grieve, Dominic...........................................Beaconsfield
Gummer, Rt Hon John ...........................Suffolk Coastal

### H

Hague, Rt Hon William ...........................Richmond (Yorkshire)
Hammond, Philip...........................Runnymede and Weybridge
Haselhurst, Rt Hon Sir Alan ...........................Saffron Walden
Hawkins, Nick...........................................Surrey Heath
Hayes, John ...........................South Holland and The Deepings
Heald, Oliver ...........................Hertfordshire North East
Heathcoat-Amory, Rt Hon David...........................Wells
Hendry, Charles ...........................................Wealden
Hoban, Mark ...................................................Fareham
Hogg, Rt Hon Douglas ...................Sleaford and North Hykeham
Horam, John ...............................................Orpington
Howard, Rt Hon Michael..........................Folkestone and Hythe
Howarth, Gerald ...........................................Aldershot

### J

Jack, Rt Hon Michael.........................................Fylde
Jackson, Robert..............................................Wantage
Jenkin, Hon Bernard.................................Essex North
Johnson, Boris ................................................Henley

### K

Key, Robert ...................................................Salisbury
Kirkbride, Julie ...........................................Bromsgrove
Knight, Rt Hon Greg .............................Yorkshire East

### L

Laing, Eleanor.....................................Epping Forest
Lait, Jacqui.................................................Beckenham
Lansley, Andrew ...........................Cambridgeshire South
Leigh, Edward ........................................Gainsborough
Letwin, Rt Hon Oliver ................................Dorset West
Lewis, Dr Julian ...........................New Forest East

## MPs BY POLITICAL PARTY

*Conservative (Continued)*

| | |
|---|---|
| Liddell-Grainger, Ian | Bridgwater |
| Lidington, David | Aylesbury |
| Lilley, Rt Hon Peter | Hitchin and Harpenden |
| Lord, Sir Michael | Suffolk Central and Ipswich North |
| Loughton, Tim | Worthing East and Shoreham |
| Luff, Peter | Mid Worcestershire |

### M

| | |
|---|---|
| McIntosh, Anne | Vale of York |
| MacKay, Rt Hon Andrew | Bracknell |
| Maclean, Rt Hon David | Penrith and the Border |
| McLoughlin, Patrick | Derbyshire West |
| Malins, Humfrey | Woking |
| Maples, John | Stratford-on-Avon |
| Mates, Rt Hon Michael | Hampshire East |
| Maude, Rt Hon Francis | Horsham |
| Mawhinney, Rt Hon Sir Brian | Cambridgeshire North West |
| May, Rt Hon Theresa | Maidenhead |
| Mercer, Patrick | Newark |
| Mitchell, Andrew | Sutton Coldfield |
| Moss, Malcolm | Cambridgeshire North East |
| Murrison, Dr Andrew | Westbury |

### N

| | |
|---|---|
| Norman, Archie | Tunbridge Wells |

### O

| | |
|---|---|
| O'Brien, Stephen | Eddisbury |
| Osborne, George | Tatton |
| Ottaway, Richard | Croydon South |

### P

| | |
|---|---|
| Page, Richard | Hertfordshire South West |
| Paice, James | Cambridgeshire South East |
| Paterson, Owen | Shropshire North |
| Pickles, Eric | Brentwood and Ongar |
| Portillo, Rt Hon Michael | Kensington and Chelsea |
| Prisk, Mark | Hertford and Stortford |

### R

| | |
|---|---|
| Randall, John | Uxbridge |
| Redwood, Rt Hon John | Wokingham |
| Robathan, Andrew | Blaby |
| Robertson, Hugh | Faversham and Mid Kent |
| Robertson, Laurence | Tewkesbury |
| Roe, Dame Marion | Broxbourne |
| Rosindell, Andrew | Romford |
| Ruffley, David | Bury St Edmunds |

### S

| | |
|---|---|
| Sayeed, Jonathan | Mid Bedfordshire |
| Selous, Andrew | Bedfordshire South West |
| Shephard, Rt Hon Gillian | Norfolk South West |
| Shepherd, Richard | Aldridge-Brownhills |
| Simmonds, Mark | Boston and Skegness |

| | |
|---|---|
| Simpson, Keith | Mid Norfolk |
| Soames, Hon Nicholas | Mid Sussex |
| Spelman, Caroline | Meriden |
| Spicer, Sir Michael | Worcestershire West |
| Spink, Dr Robert | Castle Point |
| Spring, Richard | Suffolk West |
| Stanley, Rt Hon Sir John | Tonbridge and Malling |
| Steen, Anthony | Totnes |
| Streeter, Gary | Devon South West |
| Swayne, Desmond | New Forest West |
| Swire, Hugo | Devon East |
| Syms, Robert | Poole |

### T

| | |
|---|---|
| Tapsell, Sir Peter | Louth and Horncastle |
| Taylor, Ian | Esher and Walton |
| Taylor, John | Solihull |
| Taylor, Sir Teddy | Rochford and Southend East |
| Tredinnick, David | Bosworth |
| Trend, Michael | Windsor |
| Turner, Andrew | Isle of Wight |
| Tyrie, Andrew | Chichester |

### V

| | |
|---|---|
| Viggers, Peter | Gosport |

### W

| | |
|---|---|
| Walter, Robert | Dorset North |
| Waterson, Nigel | Eastbourne |
| Watkinson, Angela | Upminster |
| Whittingdale, John | Maldon and Chelmsford East |
| Widdecombe, Rt Hon Ann | Maidstone and the Weald |
| Wiggin, Bill | Leominster |
| Wilkinson, John | Ruislip-Northwood |
| Willetts, David | Havant |
| Wilshire, David | Spelthorne |
| Winterton, Ann | Congleton |
| Winterton, Sir Nicholas | Macclesfield |

### Y

| | |
|---|---|
| Yeo, Tim | Suffolk South |
| Young, Rt Hon Sir George | Hampshire North West |

## *Democratic Unionist*

| | |
|---|---|
| Campbell, Gregory | Londonderry East |
| Dodds, Nigel | Belfast North |
| Donaldson Jeffrey | Lagan Valley |
| Paisley, Rev Ian | Antrim North |
| Robinson, Iris | Strangford |
| Robinson, Peter | Belfast East |

# MPs BY POLITICAL PARTY

## *Labour*

### A

Abbott, Diane....................Hackney North and Stoke Newington
Adams, Irene ..................................................................Paisley North
Ainger, Nick ..........Carmarthen West and South Pembrokeshire
Ainsworth, Bob...................................Coventry North East
Alexander, Douglas.................................................Paisley South
Allen, Graham ......................................................Nottingham North
Anderson, Rt Hon Donald ...................................Swansea East
Anderson, Janet ......................................Rossendale and Darwen
Armstrong, Rt Hon Hilary.......................Durham North West
Atherton, Candy .............................Falmouth and Camborne
Atkins, Charlotte ...................................Staffordshire Moorlands
Austin, John ....................................Erith and Thamesmead

### B

Bailey, Adrian ...........................................West Bromwich West
Baird, Vera ..........................................................................Redcar
Banks, Tony .....................................................................West Ham
Barnes, Harry ...........................................Derbyshire North East
Barron, Rt Hon Kevin .............................................Rother Valley
Battle, Rt Hon John ........................................Leeds West
Bayley, Hugh ..........................................................City of York
Beard, Nigel ....................................Bexleyheath and Crayford
Beckett, Rt Hon Margaret...........................Derby South
Begg, Anne ....................................................Aberdeen South
Bell, Sir Stuart ..............................................Middlesbrough
Benn, Rt Hon Hilary....................................Leeds Central
Bennett, Andrew...................................Denton and Reddish
Benton, Joe ............................................................Bootle
Berry, Dr Roger........................................................Kingswood
Best, Harold..........................................Leeds North West
Betts, Clive .........................................Sheffield Attercliffe
Blackman, Liz.......................................................Erewash
Blair, Rt Hon Tony ........................................Sedgefield
Blears, Hazel ..........................................................Salford
Blizzard, Bob ..................................................Waveney
Blunkett, Rt Hon David..............................Sheffield Brightside
Boateng, Rt Hon Paul...............................Brent South
Borrow, David........................................................Ribble South
Bradley, Rt Hon Keith .......................Manchester Withington
Bradley, Peter ............................................The Wrekin
Bradshaw, Ben ..................................................Exeter
Brennan, Kevin ............................................Cardiff West
Brown, Rt Hon Gordon.............................Dunfermline East
Brown, Rt Hon Nick ...Newcastle-upon-Tyne East and Wallsend
Brown, Russell ..............................................Dumfries
Browne, Desmond ..............................Kilmarnock and Loudoun
Bryant, Chris.......................................................Rhondda
Buck, Karen ...............Regent's Park and Kensington North
Burden, Richard ..................................Birmingham Northfield
Burgon, Colin..........................................................Elmet
Burnham, Andrew ..................................................Leigh
Byers, Rt Hon Stephen .......................................Tyneside North

Byrne, Liam ...............................Birmingham Hodge Hill

### C

Caborn, Rt Hon Richard.................................Sheffield Central
Cairns, David ....................................Greenock and Inverclyde
Campbell, Alan .................................................Tynemouth
Campbell, Anne .................................................Cambridge
Campbell, Ronnie .............................................Blyth Valley
Caplin, Ivor...........................................................Hove
Casale, Roger...................................................Wimbledon
Caton, Martin ........................................................Gower
Cawsey, Ian.......................................Brigg and Goole
Challen, Colin ..................................Morley and Rothwell
Chapman, Ben ..............................................Wirral South
Chaytor, David.....................................................Bury North
Clapham, Michael ................Barnsley West and Penistone
Clark, Helen..............................................Peterborough
Clark, Dr Lynda..............................Edinburgh Pentlands
Clark, Paul ...............................................Gillingham
Clarke, Rt Hon Charles................................Norwich South
Clarke, Rt Hon Tom..........................Coatbridge and Chryston
Clarke, Tony ...................................Northampton South
Clelland, David.............................................Tyne Bridge
Clwyd, Ann .....................................................Cynon Valley
Coaker, Vernon........................................................Gedling
Coffey, Ann ...................................................Stockport
Cohen, Harry ...............................Leyton and Wanstead
Coleman, Iain................................Hammersmith and Fulham
Colman, Tony ..........................................................Putney
Connarty, Michael ....................................Falkirk East
Cook, Frank........................................Stockton North
Cook, Rt Hon Robin ..............................Livingston
Cooper, Yvette ...................Pontefract and Castleford
Corbyn, Jeremy.................................Islington North
Corston, Rt Hon Jean......................................Bristol East
Cousins, Jim.....................Newcastle-upon-Tyne Central
Cox, Tom .....................................................Tooting
Cranston, Ross........................................Dudley North
Crausby, David ...................................Bolton North East
Cruddas, Jon.....................................................Dagenham
Cryer, Ann .......................................................Keighley
Cryer, John.....................................................Hornchurch
Cummings, John ...............................................Easington
Cunningham, Rt Hon Dr Jack ................................Copeland
Cunningham, Jim ..................................Coventry South
Cunningham, Tony ........................................Workington
Curtis-Thomas, Claire ..........................................Crosby

### D

Dalyell, Tam .....................................................Linlithgow
Darling, Rt Hon Alistair .............................Edinburgh Central
Davey, Valerie.................................................Bristol West
David, Wayne .................................................Caerphilly
Davidson, Ian.........................................Glasgow Pollok
Davies, Rt Hon Denzil..............................................Llanelli
Davies, Geraint...........................................Croydon Central

# MPs BY POLITICAL PARTY

*Labour (Continued)*

Dawson, Hilton.....................................Lancaster and Wyre
Dean, Janet.....................................Burton
Denham, Rt Hon John.....................................Southampton Itchen
Dhanda, Parmjit.....................................Gloucester
Dismore, Andrew.....................................Hendon
Dobbin, Jim.....................................Heywood and Middleton
Dobson, Rt Hon Frank.....................................Holborn and St Pancras
Donohoe, Brian.....................................Cunninghame South
Doran, Frank.....................................Aberdeen Central
Dowd, Jim.....................................Lewisham West
Drew, David.....................................Stroud
Drown, Julia.....................................Swindon South
Dunwoody, Gwyneth.....................................Crewe and Nantwich

## E

Eagle, Angela.....................................Wallasey
Eagle, Maria.....................................Liverpool Garston
Edwards, Huw.....................................Monmouth
Efford, Clive.....................................Eltham
Ellman, Louise.....................................Liverpool Riverside
Ennis, Jeff.....................................Barnsley East and Mexborough
Etherington, Bill.....................................Sunderland North

## F

Farrelly, Paul.....................................Newcastle-under-Lyme
Field, Rt Hon Frank.....................................Birkenhead
Fisher, Mark.....................................Stoke-on-Trent Central
Fitzpatrick, Jim.....................................Poplar and Canning Town
Fitzsimons, Lorna.....................................Rochdale
Flint, Caroline.....................................Don Valley
Flynn, Paul.....................................Newport West
Follett, Barbara.....................................Stevenage
Foster, Rt Hon Derek.....................................Bishop Auckland
Foster, Michael Jabez.....................................Hastings and Rye
Foster, Michael John.....................................Worcester
Foulkes, Rt Hon George......Carrick, Cumnock and Doon Valley
Francis, Dr Hywel.....................................Aberavon

## G

Gapes, Mike.....................................Ilford South
Gardiner, Barry.....................................Brent North
George, Rt Hon Bruce.....................................Walsall South
Gerrard, Neil.....................................Walthamstow
Gibson, Dr Ian.....................................Norwich North
Gilroy, Linda.....................................Plymouth Sutton
Godsiff, Roger............Birmingham Sparkbrook and Small Heath
Goggins, Paul.....................................Wythenshawe and Sale East
Griffiths, Jane.....................................Reading East
Griffiths, Nigel.....................................Edinburgh South
Griffiths, Win.....................................Bridgend
Grogan, John.....................................Selby

## H

Hain, Rt Hon Peter.....................................Neath
Hall, Mike.....................................Weaver Vale
Hall, Patrick.....................................Bedford
Hamilton, David.....................................Midlothian
Hamilton, Fabian.....................................Leeds North East
Hanson, David.....................................Delyn
Harman, Rt Hon Harriet.....................................Camberwell and Peckham
Harris, Tom.....................................Glasgow Cathcart
Havard, Dai.....................................Merthyr Tydfil and Rhymney
Heal, Sylvia.....................................Halesowen and Rowley Regis
Healey, John.....................................Wentworth
Henderson, Doug.....................................Newcastle-upon-Tyne North
Henderson, Ivan.....................................Harwich
Hendrick, Mark.....................................Preston
Hepburn, Stephen.....................................Jarrow
Heppell, John.....................................Nottingham East
Hesford, Stephen.....................................Wirral West
Hewitt, Rt Hon Patricia.....................................Leicester West
Heyes, David.....................................Ashton-under-Lyne
Hill, Rt Hon Keith.....................................Streatham
Hinchliffe, David.....................................Wakefield
Hodge, Rt Hon Margaret.....................................Barking
Hoey, Kate.....................................Vauxhall
Hood, Jimmy.....................................Clydesdale
Hoon, Rt Hon Geoff.....................................Ashfield
Hope, Philip.....................................Corby
Hopkins, Kelvin.....................................Luton North
Howarth, Rt Hon Alan.....................................Newport East
Howarth, George.....................................Knowsley North and Sefton East
Howells, Dr Kim.....................................Pontypridd
Hoyle, Lindsay.....................................Chorley
Hughes, Rt Hon Beverley.....................................Stretford and Urmston
Hughes, Kevin.....................................Doncaster North
Humble, Joan.....................................Blackpool North and Fleetwood
Hurst, Alan.....................................Braintree
Hutton, Rt Hon John.....................................Barrow and Furness

## I

Iddon Dr Brian.....................................Bolton South East
Illsley Eric.....................................Barnsley Central
Ingram, Rt Hon Adam.....................................East Kilbride
Irranca-Davies, Huw.....................................Ogmore

## J

Jackson, Glenda.....................................Hampstead and Highgate
Jackson, Helen.....................................Sheffield Hillsborough
Jamieson, David.....................................Plymouth Devonport
Jenkins, Brian.....................................Tamworth
Johnson, Rt Hon Alan.....................................Hull West and Hessle
Johnson, Melanie.....................................Welwyn Hatfield
Jones, Helen.....................................Warrington North
Jones, Jon Owen.....................................Cardiff Central
Jones, Kevan.....................................Durham North
Jones, Dr Lynne.....................................Birmingham Selly Oak
Jones, Martyn.....................................Clwyd South
Jowell, Rt Hon Tessa.....................................Dulwich and West Norwood
Joyce, Eric.....................................Falkirk West

# MPs BY POLITICAL PARTY

*Labour (Continued)*

## K

Kaufman, Rt Hon Sir Gerald.......................Manchester Gorton
Keeble, Sally ........................................Northampton North
Keen, Alan.............................................Feltham and Heston
Keen, Ann...............................Brentford and Isleworth
Kelly, Ruth ...................................................Bolton West
Kemp, Fraser ...................Houghton and Washington East
Kennedy, Rt Hon Jane..................Liverpool Wavertree
Khabra, Piara Singh............................Ealing Southall
Kidney, David...............................................Stafford
Kilfoyle, Peter.................................Liverpool Walton
King, Andy ...............................Rugby and Kenilworth
King, Oona ...........................Bethnal Green and Bow
Knight, Jim .................................................Dorset South
Kumar, Dr Ashok........Middlesbrough South and East Cleveland

## L

Ladyman, Dr Stephen...............................Thanet South
Lammy, David ............................................Tottenham
Lawrence, Jackie.........................Preseli Pembrokeshire
Laxton, Bob ...............................................Derby North
Lazarowicz, Mark ...................Edinburgh North and Leith
Lepper, David.........................................Brighton Pavilion
Leslie, Christopher...........................................Shipley
Levitt, Tom .................................................High Peak
Lewis, Ivan .................................................Bury South
Lewis, Terry .................................................Worsley
Liddell, Rt Hon Helen ......................Airdrie and Shotts
Linton, Martin .............................................Battersea
Lloyd, Tony ...........................Manchester Central
Love, Andrew.............................................Edmonton
Lucas, Ian .................................................Wrexham
Luke, Iain .................................................Dundee East
Lyons, John .........................Strathkelvin and Bearsden

## M

McAvoy, Rt Hon Tommy ..................Glasgow Rutherglen
McCabe, Stephen ..................Birmingham Hall Green
McCafferty, Christine ...........................Calder Valley
McCartney, Rt Hon Ian...................................Makerfield
McDonagh, Siobhain ...............Mitcham and Morden
MacDonald, Calum.........................................Western Isles
McDonnell, John ...................Hayes and Harlington
MacDougall, John.........................................Fife Central
McFall, Rt Hon John...................................Dumbarton
McGuire, Anne.............................................Stirling
McIsaac, Shona.............................................Cleethorpes
McKechin, Ann ...............................Glasgow Maryhill
McKenna, Rosemary ...........Cumbernauld and Kilsyth
Mackinlay, Andrew.........................................Thurrock
McNamara, Kevin ...........................................Hull North
McNulty, Tony.........................................Harrow East
MacShane, Dr Denis.........................................Rotherham

Mactaggart, Fiona...............................................Slough
McWalter, Tony ...........................Hemel Hempstead
McWilliam, John...............................................Blaydon
Mahmood, Khalid.................Birmingham Perry Barr
Mahon, Alice...............................................Halifax
Mallaber, Judy .........................................Amber Valley
Mann, John...............................................Bassetlaw
Marris, Robert...................Wolverhampton South West
Marsden, Gordon.........................................Blackpool South
Marshall, David.........................Glasgow Shettleston
Marshall-Andrews, Robert ...............................Medway
Martlew, Eric...............................................Carlisle
Meacher, Rt Hon Michael ..................Oldham West and Royton
Meale, Alan .............................................Mansfield
Merron, Gillian .............................................Lincoln
Michael, Rt Hon Alun...................Cardiff South and Penarth
Milburn, Rt Hon Alan .........................................Darlington
Miliband, David.........................................South Shields
Miller, Andrew...................Ellesmere Port and Neston
Mitchell, Austin ...........................Great Grimsby
Moffatt, Laura...............................................Crawley
Mole, Chris...............................................Ipswich
Moonie, Dr Lewis...............................................Kirkcaldy
Moran, Margaret...........................................Luton South
Morgan, Julie .........................................Cardiff North
Morley, Elliott ...........................................Scunthorpe
Morris, Rt Hon Estelle ...............Birmingham Yardley
Mountford, Kali ...........................................Colne Valley
Mudie, George ...........................................Leeds East
Mullin, Chris...................................Sunderland South
Munn, Meg.........................................Sheffield Heeley
Murphy, Denis ...............................................Wansbeck
Murphy, Jim...............................................Eastwood
Murphy, Rt Hon Paul...............................................Torfaen

## N

Naysmith, Dr Doug ...........................Bristol North West
Norris, Dan ...............................................Wansdyke

## O

O'Brien, Bill...............................................Normanton
O'Brien, Mike...................Warwickshire North
O'Hara, Eddie...............................................Knowsley South
O'Neill, Martin ...............................................Ochil
Olner, Bill...............................................Nuneaton
Organ, Diana...................................Forest of Dean
Osborne, Sandra.............................................Ayr
Owen, Albert...............................................Ynys Môn

## P

Palmer, Dr Nick...............................................Broxtowe
Pearson, Ian...............................................Dudley South
Perham, Linda...............................................Ilford North

## MPs BY POLITICAL PARTY

*Labour (Continued)*

Picking, Anne ......................................................East Lothian
Pickthall, Colin................................................Lancashire West
Pike, Peter...................................................................Burnley
Plaskitt, James .............................Warwick and Leamington
Pollard, Kerry ...........................................................St Albans
Pond, Chris.............................................................Gravesham
Pope, Greg .............................................................Hyndburn
Pound, Stephen ..................................................Ealing North
Prentice, Bridget ..........................................Lewisham East
Prentice, Gordon .........................................................Pendle
Prescott, Rt Hon John ........................................... Hull East
Primarolo, Rt Hon Dawn ............................Bristol South
Prosser, Gwyn..............................................................Dover
Purchase, Ken ....................Wolverhampton North East
Purnell, James .................................Stalybridge and Hyde

## Q

Quin, Rt Hon Joyce.........Gateshead East and Washington West
Quinn, Lawrie ...........................Scarborough and Whitby

## R

Rammell, Bill.............................................................Harlow
Rapson, Syd ...........................................Portsmouth North
Raynsford, Rt Hon Nick ....................Greenwich and Woolwich
Reed, Andrew.................................................Loughborough
Reid, Rt Hon John .......................Hamilton North and Bellshill
Robertson, John ..........................Glasgow Anniesland
Robinson, Geoffrey ...............................Coventry North West
Roche, Barbara .........................Hornsey and Wood Green
Rooney, Terry.......................................Bradford North
Ross, Ernie ........................................................Dundee West
Roy, Frank ......................................Motherwell and Wishaw
Ruane, Chris ..............................................Vale of Clwyd
Ruddock, Joan.....................................Lewisham Deptford
Russell, Christine ...............................City of Chester
Ryan, Joan ......................................................Enfield North

## S

Salter, Martin .......................................Reading West
Sarwar, Mohammad..................................Glasgow Govan
Savidge, Malcolm ..................................Aberdeen North
Sawford, Phil ..........................................................Kettering
Sedgemore, Brian ..............Hackney South and Shoreditch
Shaw, Jonathan ...................Chatham and Aylesford
Sheerman, Barry .............................................Huddersfield
Sheridan, James ...............................Renfrewshire West
Shipley, Debra .....................................................Stourbridge
Short, Rt Hon Clare ................Birmingham Ladywood
Simon, Siôn ...............................Birmingham Erdington
Simpson, Alan .....................................Nottingham South
Singh, Marsha ..........................................Bradford West
Skinner, Dennis ......................................................Bolsover
Smith, Rt Hon Andrew ..................................Oxford East

Smith, Angela.........................................................Basildon
Smith, Rt Hon Chris.....................Islington South and Finsbury
Smith, Geraldine.................Morecambe and Lunesdale
Smith, Rt Hon Jacqui ....................................Redditch
Smith, John..............................................Vale of Glamorgan
Smith, Llew ...............................................Blaenau Gwent
Soley, Clive.....................Ealing Acton and Shepherds Bush
Southworth, Helen ...............................Warrington South
Spellar, Rt Hon John ...........................................Warley
Squire, Rachel.....................................Dunfermline West
Starkey, Dr Phyllis ..........................Milton Keynes South West
Steinberg, Gerry...................................City of Durham
Stevenson, George ....................................Stoke-on-Trent South
Stewart, David ..................Inverness East, Nairn and Lochaber
Stewart, Ian............................................................Eccles
Stinchcombe, Paul ..................................Wellingborough
Stoate, Dr Howard.............................................Dartford
Strang, Rt Hon Gavin ............Edinburgh East and Musselburgh
Straw, Rt Hon Jack ......................................Blackburn
Stringer, Graham.................................Manchester Blackley
Stuart, Gisela............................Birmingham Edgbaston
Sutcliffe, Gerry.......................................Bradford South

## T

Tami, Mark.....................................................Alyn and Deeside
Taylor, Rt Hon Ann .................................................Dewsbury
Taylor, Dari .....................................................Stockton South
Taylor, David ....................Leicestershire North West
Thomas, Gareth .......................................Clwyd West
Thomas, Gareth R ..........................................Harrow West
Timms, Stephen..............................................East Ham
Tipping, Paddy...................................................Sherwood
Todd, Mark ......................................Derbyshire South
Touhig, Don...........................................................Islwyn
Trickett, Jon .......................................................Hemsworth
Truswell, Paul.......................................................Pudsey
Turner, Dennis ...............................Wolverhampton South East
Turner, Dr Desmond ...................Brighton Kemptown
Turner, Neil ..............................................................Wigan
Twigg, Derek ...........................................................Halton
Twigg, Stephen....................................Enfield Southgate
Tynan, Bill ...............................................Hamilton South

## V

Vaz, Keith ...................................................Leicester East
Vis, Dr Rudi ................................Finchley and Golders Green

## W

Walley, Joan ...........................................Stoke-on-Trent North
Ward, Claire ...........................................................Watford
Wareing, Robert .................................Liverpool West Derby
Watson, Tom ..................................West Bromwich East
Watts, Dave ..................................................St Helens North
White, Brian............................Milton Keynes North East
Whitehead, Dr Alan.................................Southampton Test

## MPs BY POLITICAL PARTY

*Labour (Continued)*

Wicks, Malcolm ...................................................Croydon North
Williams, Rt Hon Alan.........................................Swansea West
Williams, Betty.........................................................Conwy
Wills, Michael ...................................................Swindon North
Wilson, Rt Hon Brian.....................................Cunninghame North
Winnick, David ....................................................Walsall North
Winterton, Rosie...............................................Doncaster Central
Wood, Mike.....................................................Batley and Spen
Woodward, Shaun ...............................................St Helens South
Woolas, Phil ....................................Oldham East and Saddleworth
Worthington, Tony .......................Clydebank and Milngavie
Wray, Jimmy.................................................Glasgow Baillieston
Wright, Anthony D ...........................................Great Yarmouth
Wright, David ............................................................Telford
Wright, Iain .........................................................Hartlepool
Wright, Dr Tony....................................................Cannock Chase
Wyatt, Derek .................................Sittingbourne and Sheppey

## *Liberal Democrat*

### *A*

Allan, Richard.................................................Sheffield Hallam

### *B*

Baker, Norman ...........................................................Lewes
Barrett, John.................................................Edinburgh West
Beith, Rt Hon Alan.....................................Berwick-upon-Tweed
Brake, Tom ...................................Carshalton and Wallington
Breed, Colin ...........................................Cornwall South East
Brooke, Annette.....................Mid Dorset and Poole North
Bruce, Malcolm ......................................................Gordon
Burnett, John .......................................Devon West and Torridge
Burstow, Paul ...................................Sutton and Cheam

### *C*

Cable, Dr Vincent .....................................Twickenham
Calton, Patsy ...........................................................Cheadle
Campbell, Rt Hon Sir Menzies ............................Fife North East
Carmichael, Alistair......................................Orkney and Shetland
Chidgey, David.....................................................Eastleigh
Cotter, Brian ...........................................Weston-super-Mare

### *D*

Davey, Edward........................................Kingston and Surbiton
Doughty, Sue...........................................................Guildford

### *F*

Foster, Don ..................................................................Bath

### *G*

George, Andrew ........................................................St Ives
Gidley, Sandra .........................................................Romsey
Gill, Parmjit Singh.............................................Leicester South
Green, Matthew ......................................................Ludlow

### *H*

Hancock, Mike ...........................................Portsmouth South
Harris, Dr Evan............................Oxford West and Abingdon
Harvey, Nick ....................................................Devon North
Heath, David ..........................................Somerton and Frome
Holmes, Paul ....................................................Chesterfield
Hughes, Simon .....................Southwark North and Bermondsey

### *J*

Jones, Nigel .......................................................Cheltenham

### *K*

Keetch, Paul...........................................................Hereford
Kennedy, Rt Hon Charles...........Ross, Skye and Inverness West
Kirkwood, Sir Archy........................Roxburgh and Berwickshire

### *L*

Lamb, Norman .................................................Norfolk North
Laws, David .............................................................Yeovil

### *M*

Marsden, Paul............................Shrewsbury and Atcham
Moore, Michael.....................Tweeddale, Ettrick and Lauderdale

### *O*

Oaten, Mark ....................................................Winchester
Öpik, Lembit....................................................Montgomeryshire

### *P*

Pugh, Dr John ....................................................Southport

### *R*

Reid, Alan............................................Argyll and Bute
Rendel, David .......................................................Newbury
Russell, Bob ......................................................Colchester

### *S*

Sanders, Adrian.........................................................Torbay
Smith, Sir Robert...............Aberdeenshire West and Kincardine
Stunell, Andrew ................................................Hazel Grove

### *T*

Taylor, Matthew ...........................Truro and St Austell
Teather, Sarah ..................................................Brent East
Thurso, John ..................Caithness, Sutherland and Easter Ross
Tonge, Dr Jenny ..........................................Richmond Park
Tyler, Paul .....................................................Cornwall North

### *W*

Webb, Steven.......................................................Northavon
Williams, Roger.............................Brecon and Radnorshire
Willis, Phil .................................Harrogate and Knaresborough

### *Y*

Younger-Ross, Richard .....................................Teignbridge

# MPs BY POLITICAL PARTY

## Plaid Cymru

Llwyd, Elfyn..............................Meirionnydd Nant Conwy
Price, Adam....................Carmarthen East and Dinefwr
Thomas, Simon......................................Ceredigion
Williams, Hywel ...................................Caernarfon

## Scottish National Party

Ewing, Annabelle ......................................Perth
Robertson, Angus.......................................Moray
Salmond, Alex..............................Banff and Buchan
Weir, Michael .........................................Angus
Wishart, Peter...............................Tayside North

## Sinn Fein

Adams, Gerry .....................................Belfast West
Doherty, Pat .....................................West Tyrone
Gildernew, Michelle......................Fermanagh and South Tyrone
McGuiness, Martin ..................................Mid Ulster

## Social Democratic and Labour Party

Hume, John .............................................Foyle
Mallon, Seamus.........................Newry and Armagh
McGrady, Eddie .................................Down South

## Ulster Unionist

Beggs, Roy ........................................Antrim East
Burnside, David .................................Antrim South
Hermon, Lady [Sylvia]...........................Down North
Smyth, Rev Martin...............................Belfast South
Trimble, Rt Hon David ..........................Upper Bann

## Independent

Galloway, George................................Glasgow Kelvin
Hunter, Andrew..................................Basingstoke
Taylor, Dr Richard.............................Wyre Forest

## Speaker

Martin, Rt Hon Michael ...............Glasgow Springburn

## MPs BY POLITICAL PARTY

*Co-operative Party*

*Notes: (i) All Co-operative Party MPs are also Labour MPs.*
*(ii) The address of the Co-operative Party is:*
*77 Weston Street, London, SE1 3SD*
*Tel: (020) 7357 0230  Fax: (020) 7407 4476*
*Web: http://www.party.coop*

| | |
|---|---|
| Bailey, Adrian | West Bromwich West |
| Davidson, Ian | Glasgow Pollok |
| Dobbin, Jim | Heywood and Middleton |
| Drew, David | Stroud |
| Ellman, Louise | Liverpool Riverside |
| Foulkes, Rt Hon George | Carrick, Cumnock and Doon Valley |
| Gapes, Mike | Ilford South |
| Gilroy, Linda | Plymouth Sutton |
| Hendrick, Mark | Preston |
| Hope, Philip | Corby |
| Jones, Jon Owen | Cardiff Central |
| Keen, Alan | Feltham and Heston |
| Lazarowicz, Mark | Edinburgh North and Leith |
| Lepper, David | Brighton Pavilion |
| Love, Andrew | Edmonton |
| McAvoy Rt Hon Tommy | Glasgow Rutherglen |
| McFall, Rt Hon John | Dumbarton |
| McWalter, Tony | Hemel Hempstead |
| Michael, Rt Hon Alun | Cardiff South and Penarth |
| Moonie, Dr Lewis | Kirkcaldy |
| Munn, Meg | Sheffield Heeley |
| Naysmith, Dr Doug | Bristol North West |
| Purchase, Ken | Wolverhampton North East |
| Reed, Andrew | Loughborough |
| Sheerman, Barry | Huddersfield |
| Smith, Angela | Basildon |
| Taylor, David | Leicestershire North West |
| Thomas, Gareth R | Harrow West |
| Touhig, Don | Islwyn |
| Turner, Dennis | Wolverhampton South East |

# MEMBERS OF THE HOUSE OF COMMONS

*Notes: (i) The main House of Commons switchboard telephone number is (020) 7219 3000. The House of Commons' postal address is: House of Commons, London, SW1A 0AA.*

*(ii) Where individual contact details are known, these are listed below.*

*(iii) Parliamentary Secretary is used as the shortened term for Parliamentary Under Secretary of State. PPS is used as the shortened term for Parliamentary Private Secretary.*

## A

**Abbott, Diane** . . . . . Hackney North and Stoke Newington
**Labour** . . . . . . . . . . . Majority 13,651 over Con
*Born* . . . . . . . . . . . . . . 27th September 1953 in Paddington, London
*Educated* . . . . . . . . . . . Harrow County Girls' Grammar School;
Newnham College, Cambridge
*Elected* . . . . . . . . . . . . 1987 MP for Hackney North and
Stoke Newington
*Commons Office* . . . . . . E-mail: abbottd@parliament.uk
*Parliamentary Interests* . Economic Matters; Caribbean;
Third World Debt; Foreign Affairs
*Recreational Interests* . . Theatre; Film; Cricket; Football; Reading

**Adams, Gerry** . . . . . Belfast West
**Sinn Fein** . . . . . . . . . Majority 19,342 over SDLP
*Born* . . . . . . . . . . . . . . 6th October 1948 in West Belfast
*Educated* . . . . . . . . . . . Saint Mary's Grammar School, Belfast
*Elected* . . . . . . . . . . . . 1983 - 92 MP for Belfast West
*(did not take seat at Westminster)*
1997 MP for Belfast West
*(has not taken seat at Westminster)*
*Offices Held* . . . . . . . . 1983 - President, Sinn Fein
1998 - Member, Northern Ireland Assembly
*Constituency Office* . . . . Sinn Fein, 53 Bothar na bhFal,
Belfast, BT12 4PD
Tel: (028) 9022 3000 Fax: (028) 9022 0045
Constituency Manager – Mr Ciaran Quinn
Westminster Representative –
Mrs Dodie McGuinness
*Leisure Interests* . . . . . . Writing; Reading; Walking; Music

**Adams, Irene** . . . . . Paisley North
**Labour** . . . . . . . . . . . Majority 9,321 over SNP
*Born* . . . . . . . . . . . . . . 27th December 1947 in Paisley
*Educated* . . . . . . . . . . . Stanley Green High School, Paisley
*Elected* . . . . . . . . . . . . 1990 MP for Paisley North (By-election)
*Offices Held* . . . . . . . . 2001 - Chairman, Scottish Affairs Select
Committee, House of Commons
*Leisure Interests* . . . . . . Reading; Walking

**Ainger, Nick** . . . . . . Carmarthen West and South Pembrokeshire
**Labour** . . . . . . . . . . . Majority 4,538 over Con
*Born* . . . . . . . . . . . . . . 24th October 1949 in Sheffield, Yorkshire
*Educated* . . . . . . . . . . . Netherthorpe Grammar School, Derbyshire
*Elected* . . . . . . . . . . . . 1992 MP for Pembroke, then (1997)
for Carmarthen West and Pembrokeshire South
*Offices Held* . . . . . . . . 1997 - 01 PPS to successive secretaries of
State for Wales
2001 - Government Whip (Lord
Commissioner, HM Treasury)
*Commons Office* . . . . . . Tel: (020) 7219 4004 Fax: (020) 7219 2690
E-mail: aingern@parliament.uk
Web: http://www.nickainger.labour.co.uk
Research Assistant – Ms Michelle Kane
Tel: (020) 7219 2241
E-mail: kanem@parliament.uk
*Constituency Office* . . . . Ferry Lane Works, Ferry Lane, Pembroke
Dock, Pembrokeshire, SA71 4RE
Tel: (01646) 684404 Fax: (01646) 682954
Assistant – Mrs Sally Ainger
Constituency Assistant – Mrs Cilla Stubbs
*Parliamentary Interests* . Health; Environment; Transport
*Leisure Interests* . . . . . . Walking; Theatre; Films; Books

**Ainsworth, Bob** . . . Coventry North East
**Labour** . . . . . . . . . . . Majority 15,751 over Con
*Born* . . . . . . . . . . . . . . 19th June 1952 in Coventry
*Educated* . . . . . . . . . . . Foxford Comprehensive School
*Elected* . . . . . . . . . . . . 1992 MP for Coventry North East
*Offices Held* . . . . . . . . 1995 - 97 Opposition Whip
1997 - 01 Government Whip
(Lord Commissioner, H M Treasury)
2001 (Jan-June) Parliamentary Secretary,
Department for Environment, Transport
and Regions
2001 - 03 Parliamentary Secretary,
Home Office
2003 - Deputy Government Chief Whip
(Treasurer, HM Household)
*Commons Office* . . . . . . Tel: (020) 7219 4047 Fax: (020) 7219 2889
E-mail: ainsworthr@parliament.uk
Web: http://www.epolitix.com/bob-ainsworth
Caseworker – Mr Neil Smith
*Constituency Office* . . . . Suite 3/4, 3rd Floor, Coventry Point,
Market Way, Coventry, CV1 1EA
Tel: (024) 7622 6707 Fax: (024) 7655 3576
Personal Assistant – Ms Carole Wise
Secretary - Mrs Jackie Bruce

**Ainsworth, Peter** . . Surrey East
**Conservative** . . . . . . . Majority 13,203 over Lib Dem
*Born* . . . . . . . . . . . . . . 16th November 1956 in Rowlands Castle,
Hampshire
*Educated* . . . . . . . . . . . Bradfield College, Berkshire;
Lincoln College, Oxford
*Elected* . . . . . . . . . . . . 1992 MP for Surrey East
*Offices Held* . . . . . . . . 1996 - 97 Assistant Government Whip
1997 - 98 Opposition Deputy Chief Whip
1998 - 2001 Shadow Secretary of State for
Culture, Media and Sport
2001 - 02 Shadow Secretary of State for
Environment, Food, and Rural Affairs
2003 - Chairman, Environmental Audit
Committee, House of Commons
*Commons Office* . . . . . . Tel: (020) 7219 5078 Fax: (020) 7219 2527
E-mail: ainsworthp@parliament.uk
Web: http://www.peterainsworth.com
Parliamentary Assistant –
Miss Chrysoulla Kyprianou
E-mail: kyprianouc@parliament.uk
*Constituency Office* . . . . 2 Hoskins Road, Oxted, Surrey, RH8 9HT
Tel: (01883) 715782 Fax: (01883) 730576
*Leisure Interests* . . . . . . Family; Music; Reading; Gardening

# MEMBERS OF THE HOUSE OF COMMONS

**Alexander, Douglas** Paisley South
**Labour** . . . . . . . . . . . Majority 11,910 over SNP
*Born*. . . . . . . . . . . . . . 26th October 1967 in Glasgow
*Educated* . . . . . . . . . Park Mains High School, Erskine;
Lester B Pearson College, Vancouver;
University of Pennsylvania;
Edinburgh University
*Elected*. . . . . . . . . . . . 1997 MP for Paisley South (By-election)
*Offices Held* . . . . . . . . 2001 - 02 Minister of State, Department
of Trade and Industry
2002 - 04 Minister for the Cabinet Office and
(from 2003) Chancellor of the
Duchy of Lancaster
2004 - Minister of State, Department of
Trade and Industry (also at Foreign and
Commonwealth Office)
*Constituency Office* . . . . 2014 Mile End Mill, Abbey Mill Business
Centre, Seedhill Road, Paisley, PA1 1JS
Tel: (0141) 561 0333 Fax: (0141) 561 0334
E-mail: dalexandermp@talk21.com
Web: http://www.dalexander.labour.co.uk
Constituency Assistant – Ms Joyce Llewellyn
Research and Communications Officer –
Mr Donald Morrison
*Parliamentary Interests* . Employment; Industry; Constitution

**Allan, Richard** . . . . Sheffield Hallam
**Liberal Democrat** . . . Majority 9,347 over Con
*Born*. . . . . . . . . . . . . . 11th February 1966 in Sheffield
*Educated* . . . . . . . . . . Cambridge University; Bristol Polytechnic
*Elected*. . . . . . . . . . . . 1997 MP for Sheffield Hallam
*Offices Held* . . . . . . . . 1997 - 99 Liberal Democrat Spokesman on
Community Development and Urban Affairs
1999 - 2001 Liberal Democrat Spokesman on
Employment, IT and Childcare
2001 - Liberal Democrat Spokesman on
Information Technology (also Shadow
Minister for Cabinet Office)
*Commons Office* . . . . . . Tel: (020) 7219 1104 Fax: (020) 7219 0971
E-mail: allenr@parliament.uk
Research Assistants – Mr John Alker
Ms Ruth Brock
E-mails: [surnameinitial]@parliament.uk
*Constituency Office* . . . . 85 Nethergreen Road, Sheffield, S11 7EH
Tel: (0114) 230 9002 Fax: (0114) 230 9614
E-mail: richardallan@sheffieldhallam.co.uk
Web: http://www.sheffieldhallam.co.uk
Casework Assistant – Mrs Barbara Masters
Constituency Assistant – Cllr Kate Dawson
*Parliamentary Interests* . Information Technology; South America
*Leisure Interests* . . . . . Information Technology

**Allen, Graham** . . . . Nottingham North
**Labour** . . . . . . . . . . . Majority 12,204 over Con
*Born*. . . . . . . . . . . . . . 11th January 1953 in Nottingham
*Educated* . . . . . . . . . . Forest Fields Grammar School;
City of London Polytechnic; Leeds University
*Elected*. . . . . . . . . . . . 1987 MP for Nottingham North
*Offices Held* . . . . . . . . 1991 - 92 Opposition Spokesman on
Social Security
1992 - 94 Opposition Spokesman on
Home Affairs
1994 - 95 Opposition Spokesman on
National Heritage
1995 - 96 Opposition Spokesman on Transport
1996 - 97 Opposition Spokesman on
Environment (Health and Safety)
1997 - 01 Government Whip
(Lord Commissioner, H M Treasury then
Vice-Chamberlain, H M Household)
*Parliamentary Interests* . Economic Policy; The Democratic Agenda
*Leisure Interests* . . . . . . Family; Cooking; Cricket and Sport; Walking;
Oil Painting

**Amess, David** . . . . . Southend West
**Conservative** . . . . . . . Majority 7,941 over Lab
*Born*. . . . . . . . . . . . . . 26th March 1952 in Plaistow, London
*Educated* . . . . . . . . . . St Anthony's Junior and Senior School;
St Bonaventure's Grammar School;
Bournemouth College of Technology
*Elected*. . . . . . . . . . . . 1983 - 97 MP for Basildon
1997 MP for Southend West
*Offices Held* . . . . . . . . 1987 - 88 PPS to Edwina Curry and Lord
Skelmersdale, DHSS
1988 - 97 PPS to Michael Portillo
(including as Secretary of State for
Employment and Defence)
*Commons Office* . . . . . . Tel: (020) 7219 3452 Fax: (020) 7219 2245
E-mail: amessd@parliament.uk
*Parliamentary Interests* . Health
*Leisure Interests* . . . . . . Reading; Writing; Sport; Theatre; Gardening;
Popular Music

**Ancram, Rt Hon Michael** QC Devizes
**Conservative** . . . . . . . Majority 11,896 over Lab
*Born*. . . . . . . . . . . . . . 7th July 1945
*Educated* . . . . . . . . . . Ampleforth College;
Christ Church College, Oxford;
Edinburgh University
*Elected*. . . . . . . . . . . . 1974 (Feb - Oct) MP for Berwickshire and
East Lothian
1979 - 87 MP for Edinburgh South
1992 MP for Devizes
*Offices Held* . . . . . . . . 1983 - 87 Parliamentary Secretary,
Scottish Office
1993 - 94 Parliamentary Secretary,
Northern Ireland Office
1994 - 97 Minister of State,
Northern Ireland Office
1997 - 98 Opposition Spokesman on
Constitutional Affairs, Scotland and Wales
1998 Deputy Chairman, Conservative Party
1998 - 2001 Chairman, Conservative Party
2001 - Shadow Foreign Secretary and
Deputy Leader, Conservative Party
*Commons Office* . . . . . . Tel: (020) 7219 5072 Fax: (020) 7219 2528
E-mail: ancramm@parliament.uk
Web: http://www.michaelancram.com
Private Secretary – Miss Victoria Bridgeman
Constituency Secretary –
Mrs Caroline Donnelly
Tel & Fax: (020) 7627 1383
*Constituency Office* . . . . 116 High Street, Marlborough,
Wiltshire, SN8 1LZ
Tel: (01672) 512675 Fax: (01672) 515682
E-mail: office@devizesconservatives.org.uk
Agent – Mr Ian Ramsay
Assistant Administrator – Mr Ian Philpott
*Parliamentary Interests* . Rural Affairs; Agriculture
*Leisure Interests* . . . . . . Fishing; Guitar; Singing; Skiing

# MEMBERS OF THE HOUSE OF COMMONS

**Anderson, Rt Hon Donald** Swansea East
**Labour** . . . . . . . . . . Majority 16,146 over Plaid Cymru
*Born.* . . . . . . . . . . . . . 17th June 1939 in Swansea
*Educated* . . . . . . . . . . Swansea Grammar School;
University of Swansea;
Inner Temple
*Elected.* . . . . . . . . . . . 1974 MP for Swansea East
*Offices Held* . . . . . . . . 1982 - 83 Chairman, Welsh Affairs Select
Committee, House of Commons
1983 - 92 Opposition Spokesman on Foreign
and Commonwealth Affairs
1992 - 94 Opposition Spokesman on Defence
1994 - 95 Shadow Solicitor General
1997 - Chairman, Foreign Affairs Select
Committee, House of Commons
*Commons Office* . . . . . Tel: (020) 7219 3425/5217
Fax: (020) 7219 4801
Personal Assistant – Ms Grace Trotman
E-mail: trotmang@parliament.uk
Researcher – Miss Kirsty Jackson
E-mail: jacksonk@parliament.uk
Secretary and Personal Assistant –
Mrs Betty Wilson
*Parliamentary Interests* . Foreign Affairs
*Leisure Interests* . . . . . . Walking

**Anderson, Janet** . . . Rossendale and Darwen
**Labour** . . . . . . . . . . . Majority 5,223 over Con
*Born.* . . . . . . . . . . . . . . 6th December 1949 in Newcastle-upon-Tyne
*Educated* . . . . . . . . . . Kingsfield Comprehensive;
Central London Polytechnic;
University of Nantes, France
*Elected.* . . . . . . . . . . . . 1992 MP for Rossendale and Darwen
*Offices Held* . . . . . . . . 1995 - 96 Opposition Whip
1996 - 97 Shadow Minister for Women
1997 - 98 Government Whip (Vice
Chamberlain, H M Household)
1998 - 2001 Parliamentary Secretary,
Department for Culture, Media and Sport
(Minister for Tourism, Film and
Broadcasting)
*Commons Office* . . . . . Tel: (020) 7219 5375  Fax: (020) 7219 2148
E-mail: andersonj@parliament.uk
*Leisure Interests* . . . . . . Reading; Music; Walking

**Arbuthnot, Rt Hon James** Hampshire North East
**Conservative** . . . . . . Majority 13,257 over Lib Dem
*Born.* . . . . . . . . . . . . . . 4th August 1952 in Deal, Kent
*Educated* . . . . . . . . . . Eton College; Trinity College, Cambridge
*Elected.* . . . . . . . . . . . . 1987 - 97 MP for Wanstead and Woodford
1997 MP for Hampshire North East
*Offices Held* . . . . . . . . 1992 - 94 Government Whip
1994 - 95 Parliamentary Secretary,
Department of Social Security
1995 - 97 Minister of State, Ministry of
Defence (Minister for Defence Procurement)
1997 - 01 Opposition Chief Whip
2003 - Shadow Secretary for Trade
*Commons Office* . . . . . Tel: (020) 7219 4649 Fax: (020) 7219 3910
Secretary – Mrs Rosemary Zonneveld
*Constituency Office* . . . . 14a Butts Road, Alton, Hampshire,
GU34 1ND
Tel: (01420) 84122 Fax: (01420) 84925
*Leisure Interests* . . . . . . Family; Computers; Music; Skiing

**Armstrong, Rt Hon Hilary** Durham North West
**Labour** . . . . . . . . . . Majority 16,333 over Con
*Born.* . . . . . . . . . . . . . 30th November 1945 in Sunderland
*Educated* . . . . . . . . . . Monkwearmouth Comprehensive;
West Ham College; Birmingham University
*Elected.* . . . . . . . . . . . 1987 MP for Durham North West
*Offices Held* . . . . . . . . 1988 - 92 Opposition Spokeswoman on
Education
1992 - 94 PPS to John Smith
(Leader of the Opposition)
1994 - 95 Opposition Spokeswoman on
Treasury and Economic Affairs
1995 - 97 Opposition Spokeswoman on
Environment (Local Government)
1997 - 2001 Minister of State, Department
for Environment, Transport and the Regions
2001 - Government Chief Whip and
Parliamentary Secretary, H M Treasury
*Constituency Office* . . . . North House, 17 North Terrace, Crook,
County Durham, DL15 9AZ
Tel: (01388) 767065  Fax: (01388) 767923
E-mail: armstronghj@parliament.uk
Web: http://www.hilaryarmstrong.com
Research Assistant – Mr Neil Fleming
E-mail: flemingn@parliament.uk
Secretary – Ms Carol Storey
E-mail: storeyc@parliament.uk
Caseworker – Mr Kevin Graham
E-mail: grahamk@parliament.uk
*Recreational Interests* . . Reading; Spending time with friends

**Atherton, Candy** . . Falmouth and Camborne
**Labour** . . . . . . . . . . Majority 4,527 over Con
*Born.* . . . . . . . . . . . . . 21st September 1955 in Surrey
*Educated* . . . . . . . . . . Midhurst Grammar School, Sussex;
North London Polytechnic
*Elected.* . . . . . . . . . . . 1997 MP for Falmouth and Camborne
*Offices Held* . . . . . . . . 1989 - 90 Mayor, London Borough of Islington
*Commons Office* . . . . . Tel: (020) 7219 4094 Fax: (020) 7219 0982
E-mail: athertonc@parliament.uk
Web: http://www.candyatherton.labour.co.uk
Parliamentary Assistant – Ms Jude Robinson
Tel: (020) 7219 1207
E-mail: robinsonj@parliament.uk
Research Assistant – Mr Tom Phillips
Tel: (020) 7219 0034
E-mail: phillipst@parliament.uk
*Constituency Office* . . . . 4 Webber Hill, Falmouth, Cornwall, TR11 2BU
Tel: (01326) 314440 Fax: (01326) 314415
Senior Caseworker – Ms Vanessa Lidyard
Caseworker – Mr Tony Bunt
*Leisure Interests* . . . . . . Inland Waterways; Birdwatching; Gardening

# MEMBERS OF THE HOUSE OF COMMONS

**Atkins, Charlotte** . . Staffordshire Moorlands
**Labour** . . . . . . . . . . . Majority 5,838 over Con
*Born.* . . . . . . . . . . . . . 24th September 1950 in Chelmsford
*Educated* . . . . . . . . . . Colchester County High School, Essex;
    London School of Economics
*Elected.* . . . . . . . . . . . 1997 MP for Staffordshire Moorlands
*Offices Held* . . . . . . . . 2001 - 02 PPS to Baroness Symons (Minister
    of State, Foreign and Commonwealth Office
    and Department of Trade and Industry)
    2002 - 04 Assistant Government Whip
    2004 - Parliamentary Secretary,
    Department for Transport
*Commons Office* . . . . . Tel: (020) 7219 3591
    E-mail: atkinsc@parliament.uk
    Press/Information Officer – Mr Gus Brain
    Tel & Fax: (01538) 371188
*Constituency Office* . . . . Former Police House, 15 Ravenscliffe Road,
    Midsgrove, Stoke on Trent, ST7 4ET
    Tel & Fax: (01782) 777661
    Office Manager – Ms Jeanette Walley
    E-mail: walleyj@parliament.uk
*Parliamentary Interests* . Education; Employment; Agriculture;
    Trade and Development
*Leisure Interests* . . . . . Keeping Fit; Swimming; Theatre; Gardening;
    Chess

**Atkinson, David** . . . Bournemouth East
**Conservative** . . . . . . Majority 3,434 over Lib Dem
*Born.* . . . . . . . . . . . . . . 24th March 1940 in Westcliff-on-Sea, Essex
*Educated* . . . . . . . . . . St George's College, Weybridge;
    Southend College of Technology;
    College of Automobile and Aeronautical
    Engineering, Chelsea
*Elected.* . . . . . . . . . . . 1977 MP for Bournemouth East (By-election)
*Office Held* . . . . . . . . Leader, Conservative Delegation to Council
    of Europe and Western European Union
    (Chairman, European Democrat Group)
*Commons Office* . . . . . Tel: (020) 7219 3598  Fax: (020) 7219 3847
    E-mail: atkinsond@parliament.uk
    Personal Assistant – Mr Darren Bryant
    E-mail: bryantd@parliament.uk
    Secretary – Mrs Katerina Allen
    Tel: (020) 7219 3600
*Constituency Office* . . . . Boscombe Conservative Club,
    Haviland Road West, Boscombe,
    Bournemouth, BH1 4JW
    Tel: (01202) 397047
    Secretary – Mrs Sue Anderson
*Parliamentary Interests* . Mental Health; Tourism; Missile Defence;
    Council of Europe
*Leisure Interests* . . . . . . Art; Architecture; Mountaineering

**Atkinson, Peter** . . . Hexham
**Conservative** . . . . . . Majority 2,529 over Lab
*Born.* . . . . . . . . . . . . . 19th January 1943 in Northumberland
*Educated* . . . . . . . . . . Cheltenham College
*Elected.* . . . . . . . . . . . 1992 MP for Hexham
*Offices Held* . . . . . . . . 1996 - 97 PPS to Sir George Young
    (Secretary of State for Transport)
    2001 - Opposition Whip
*Parliamentary Interests* . Agricultural Matters; Countryside
*Leisure Interests* . . . . . Racing; Shooting

**Austin, John** . . . . . . Erith and Thamesmead
**Labour** . . . . . . . . . . . Majority 11,167 over Con
*Born.* . . . . . . . . . . . . . 21st August 1944 in Blaby, Leicestershire
*Educated* . . . . . . . . . . Glyn Grammar School, Epsom;
    Goldsmith's College, London;
    Bristol University
*Elected.* . . . . . . . . . . . 1992 MP for Woolwich, then (since 1997)
    MP for Erith and Thamesmead
*Offices Held* . . . . . . . . 1982 - 87 Leader, Greenwich London
    Borough Council
    1987 - 89 Mayor of Greenwich
*Commons Office* . . . . . Tel: (020) 7219 5195 Fax: (020) 7219 2706
    E-mail: austinj@parliament.uk
    Web: http://www.john-austin-mp.org
    Assistants – Mr Daniel Francis
    Ms Angie Hill
    E-mails: [surnameinitial]@parliament.uk
*Constituency Office* . . . . 301 Plumstead High Street,
    London, SE18 1JX
    Tel: (020) 8311 4444  Fax: (020) 8311 6666
    Assistants/Caseworkers – Mr Chris Jeffrey
    Ms Janice Marnham
    E-mail: [surnameinitial]@parliament.uk
*Parliamentary Interests* . Equalities; Health; Foreign Affairs
    (Middle East, Eastern Europe);
    Environment; Race and Immigration
*Leisure Interests* . . . . . . Cooking; Gardening; Running

# B

**Bacon, Richard** . . . Norfolk South
**Conservative** . . . . . . Majority 6,893 over Lib Dem
*Born.* . . . . . . . . . . . . . 3rd December 1962 in Solihull
*Educated* . . . . . . . . . . King's School, Worcester;
    London School of Economics;
    Goethe Institut, Berlin
*Elected.* . . . . . . . . . . . 2001 MP for Norfolk South
*Commons Office* . . . . . Tel: (020) 7219 8301
    E-mail: baconr@parliament.uk
*Parliamentary Interests* . Public Expenditure; Health; Agriculture;
    Education
*Leisure Interests* . . . . . . Reading; Writing; Music; Cinema; Languages

# M E M B E R S   O F   T H E   H O U S E   O F   C O M M O N S

**Bailey, Adrian** . . . . West Bromwich West
**Labour** . . . . . . . . . . . Majority 11,355 over Con
*Born*. . . . . . . . . . . . . . . 11th December 1945
*Educated* . . . . . . . . . . . Cheltenham Grammar School;
  Exeter University
*Elected*. . . . . . . . . . . . . 2000 MP for West Bromwich West
  (By-election)
*Office Held* . . . . . . . . . 1997 - 2000 Deputy Leader, Sandwell
  Metropolitan Borough Council
*Commons Office* . . . . . . Tel: (020) 7219 2572 Fax: (020) 7219 1202
  Mobile: 07715 103217
  Pager: 07644 065158
  Research/Parliamentary Assistant –
  Ms Sally Benton
  E-mail: bentnons@parliament.uk
*Constituency Office* . . . . Terry Duffy House, Thomas Street,
  West Bromwich, B70 6NT
  Tel: (0121) 569 1926/1934
  Fax: (0121) 569 1936
  Secretary/Caseworkers – Ms Lorraine Ashman
  Mrs Maria Crompton
  E-mail: cromptonm@parliament.uk
*Parliamentary Interests* . Cooperatives; Animal Welfare;
  Law and Order; Finance/Taxation
*Leisure Interests* . . . . . . Swimming; Dog Walking; Football

**Baird, Vera** QC . . . . Redcar
**Labour** . . . . . . . . . . . Majority 13,443 over Con
*Educated* . . . . . . . . . . Chadderton Grammar School, Oldham;
  University of Northumbria;
  Open University; London Guildhall University,
*Elected*. . . . . . . . . . . . 2001 MP for Redcar
*Commons Office* . . . . . . Tel: (020) 7219 8312 Fax: (020) 7219 1790
  E-mail: bairdv@parliament.uk
  Personal Assistant – Mrs Lucie Wibberley
  Tel: (020) 7219 3863 Fax: (020) 7219 0371
  E-mail: wibberleyl@parliament.uk
*Constituency Office* . . . . Unit 12, Redcar Station Business Centre,
  Station Road, Redcar, TS10 1RD
  Tel: (01642) 471777 Ext: 312
  Fax: (01642) 484347
  Agent: Mr Peter Scott
  E-mail: scottjp@parliament.uk
  Office Administrator – Mrs Jennifer Scott
  Senior Caseworker – Mrs Eileen Johnson
*Parliamentary Interests* . Equality for Women; Regeneration;
  Pensions; International Development; Criminal
  Law and Justice Issues; Human Rights
*Leisure Interests* . . . . . . Walking; Running; Tennis; Reading

**Baker, Norman** . . . Lewes
**Liberal Democrat** . . . Majority 9,710 over Con
*Born*. . . . . . . . . . . . . . 26th July 1957 in Aberdeen
*Educated* . . . . . . . . . . Royal Liberty School, Gidea Park;
  Royal Holloway College, London
*Elected*. . . . . . . . . . . . 1997 MP for Lewes
*Offices Held* . . . . . . . . 1991 - 97 Leader, Lewes District Council
  1997 - 99 Liberal Democrat Spokesman on
  Environment and Transport
  1999 - 2003 Liberal Democrat Spokesman
  variously on Broadcasting, Consumer
  Affairs, Home Affairs and Animal Welfare
  2003 - Liberal Democrat Spokesman on the
  Environment and Animal Welfare
*Commons Office* . . . . . . Tel: (020) 7219 5138 Fax: (020) 7219 0445
  E-mail: bakern@parliament.uk
  Tel: (020) 7219 2864
*Parliamentary Interests* . Environment; Transport; Genetic Modification;
  Animal Welfare; Tibet
*Leisure Interests* . . . . . . Music

**Baldry, Tony**. . . . . Banbury
**Conservative** . . . . . . . Majority 5,219 over Lab
*Born*. . . . . . . . . . . . . . 10th July 1950 in Middlesex
*Educated* . . . . . . . . . . Leighton Park School, Reading;
  Sussex University; Lincoln's Inn
*Elected*. . . . . . . . . . . . 1983 MP for Banbury
*Offices Held* . . . . . . . . 1990 Parliamentary Secretary,
  Department of Energy
  1990 - 94 Parliamentary Secretary,
  Department of the Environment
  1994 - 95 Parliamentary Secretary,
  Foreign and Commonwealth Office
  1995 - 97 Minister of State, Ministry of
  Agriculture, Fisheries and Food
  2001 - Chairman, International Development
  Committee, House of Commons
*Commons Office* . . . . . . Tel: (020) 7219 4491 Fax: (020) 7219 5826
  Mobile: 07798 840570
  E-mail: baldryt@parliament.uk
  Web: http://www.epolitix.com/tony-baldry
  Secretary – Ms Jinny McLeod Hatch
  Tel: (020) 7219 4476
  E-mail: hatchj@parliament.uk
  Research Assistant – Mr Richard Blakeway
  Tel: (020) 7219 6465
  E-mail: blakewayr@parliament.uk
*Constituency Office* . . . . 16a North Bar, Banbury,
  Oxfordshire, OX16 0TF
  Tel: (01295) 262341 Fax: (01295) 263140
  Agent – Mr Kevin Thorpe
*Parliamentary Interests* . Trade and Industry; Foreign Affairs;
  Overseas Development
*Leisure Interests* . . . . . . Gardening; Walking

**Banks, Tony** . . . . . . West Ham
**Labour** . . . . . . . . . . . Majority 15,645 over Con
*Born*. . . . . . . . . . . . . . 8th April 1945 in Belfast
*Educated* . . . . . . . . . . Archbishop Tennison's Grammar School,
  Kennington, London; York University;
  London School of Economics
*Elected*. . . . . . . . . . . . 1983 MP for Newham North West, then
  (1997) MP for West Ham
*Offices Held* . . . . . . . . 1985 - 86 Chairman, Greater London Council
  1987 - 88 Opposition Whip
  1990 - 92 Opposition Spokesman on
  Social Security
  1992 - 93 Opposition Spokesman on
  London Transport
  1997 - 99 Parliamentary Secretary,
  Department for Culture, Media and Sport
  (Minister for Sport)
  2001 - Chairman, Works of Art Advisory
  Committee, House of Commons
*Commons Office* . . . . . . Tel: (020) 7219 3522 Fax: (020) 7219 4560
*Leisure Interests* . . . . . . Animal Welfare; Football (Chelsea FC);
  18th Century Political Iconography

# MEMBERS OF THE HOUSE OF COMMONS

**Barker, Gregory** . . Bexhill and Battle
**Conservative** . . . . . . Majority 10,503 over Lib Dem
*Born*. . . . . . . . . . . . . 1966 in Shoreham, Sussex
*Educated* . . . . . . . . . Steyning Grammar School; Lancing College;
Royal Holloway College, London
*Elected*. . . . . . . . . . . 2001 MP for Bexhill and Battle
*Office Held*. . . . . . . . 2003 - Opposition Whip
*Commons Office* . . . . . Tel: (020) 7219 1852 Fax: (020) 7219 1971
E-mail: barkerg@parliament.uk
Web: http://www.GregoryBarker.com
Secretary – Miss Diane Craig
E-mail: craigdi@parliament.uk
Researcher – Mr Michael Fordham
Tel: (020) 7219 8136 Fax; (020) 7219 1742
E-mail: fordhamm@parliament.uk
*Constituency Office* . . . . 6a Amhurst Road, Bexhill-on-Sea,
East Sussex, TN40 1NJ
Tel: (01424) 219117 Fax: (01424) 218367
Agent – Mrs Gillian Wheeler
E-mail: gillian@bbca.demon.co.uk
*Parliamentary Interests* . Environmental Issues
*Leisure Interests* . . . . . . Hunting; Racing; Skiing

**Barnes, Harry** . . . . Derbyshire North East
**Labour** . . . . . . . . . . . Majority 12,258 over Con
*Born*. . . . . . . . . . . . . . 22nd July 1936 in Easington, Co Durham
*Educated* . . . . . . . . . . Ryhope Grammar School;
Ruskin College, Oxford; Hull University
*Elected*. . . . . . . . . . . . 1987 MP for Derbyshire North East
*Commons Office* . . . . . Tel: (020) 7219 4521 Fax: (020) 7219 0667
Mobile: 07761 265794
Pager: 07644 001025
E-mail: harrybarnesmp@parliament.uk
Research Assistant – Mr Gary Kent
Tel: (020) 7219 5013  Fax: (020) 7219 2881
E-mail: kentg@parliament.uk
*Constituency Office* . . . . 16 Gosforth Lane, Dronfield,
Derbyshire, S18 1PN
Tel & Fax: (01246) 412588
Secretary – Mrs Ann Barnes
Secretary – Mrs Jane Holden
E-mail: jcholden@btopenworld.com
*Parliamentary Interests* . Northern Ireland; Electoral Registration;
Disability Rights; Environmental Protection
*Leisure Interests* . . . . . . Philosophy; Football; Family

**Baron, John** . . . . . . Billericay
**Conservative** . . . . . . Majority 5,013 over Lab
*Born*. . . . . . . . . . . . . . 21st June 1959 in Redhill, Surrey
*Educated* . . . . . . . . . . Jesus College, Cambridge;
Royal Military Academy, Sandhurst
*Elected*. . . . . . . . . . . . 2001 MP for Billericay
*Office Held*. . . . . . . . . 2002 - Opposition Spokesman on Health
*Commons Office* . . . . . Tel: (020) 7219 8183 Fax: (020) 7219 1743
E-mail: baronj@parliament.uk
Political Researcher – Mr Philip Whittington
Tel: (020) 7219 2352
E-mail: whittingtonp@parliament.uk
*Constituency Office* . . . . 125 Bramble Tye, Noak Bridge, Laindon,
Essex, SS15 5GR
Tel: (01268) 520765 Fax: (01268) 524009
Constituency Assistants – Mrs Ann Akinin
Mrs Ann Blake
Mrs Jo Turner
*Parliamentary Interests* . Voluntary Sector; Environment;
Small Businesses; Law and Order; Health;
Education; Europe
*Leisure Interests* . . . . . . Cycling; Walking; Reading; History

**Barrett, John**  Edinburgh West
**Liberal Democrat** . . . Majority 7,589 over Lab
*Educated* . . . . . . . . . . Telford College; Napier College
*Elected*. . . . . . . . . . . . 2001 MP for Edinburgh West
*Office Held*. . . . . . . . . 2002 - Liberal Democrat Spokesman on
International Development
*Commons Office* . . . . . Tel: (020) 7219 8224 Fax: (020) 7219 1762
E-mail: barrettj@parliament.uk
Web: http://www.johnbarrettmp.com
Parliamentary Assistant – Mr Kevin Lang
E-mail: langk@parliament.uk
*Constituency Office* . . . . 1A Drum Brae Avenue, Edinburgh,
EH12 8TE
Tel: (0131) 339 0339 Fax: (0131) 476 7101
Constituency Organiser – Mr Andrew Jolly
Constituency Assistant – Mr Ewan Irvine
Tel: (0131) 339 0353
*Parliamentary Interests* . Overseas Aid; Environment and Energy
Production; Transport; Air and Rail Safety;
Pensions
*Leisure Interests* . . . . . . Film; Theatre; Travel; Music

**Barron, Rt Hon Kevin**  Rother Valley
**Labour** . . . . . . . . . . . Majority 14,882 over Con
*Born*. . . . . . . . . . . . . . 26th October 1946 in Tadcaster, Yorkshire
*Educated* . . . . . . . . . . Maltby Hall Secondary Modern School;
Ruskin College, Oxford
*Elected*. . . . . . . . . . . . 1983 MP for Rother Valley
*Offices Held* . . . . . . . . 1985 - 87 PPS to Neil Kinnock
(Leader of the Opposition)
1988 - 92 Opposition Spokesman on Energy
1993 - 95 Opposition Spokesman on
Employment
1995 - 97 Opposition Spokesman on Health
*Commons Office* . . . . . Tel: (020) 7219 6306 Fax: (020) 7219 5952
E-mail: barronk@parliament.uk
*Constituency Office* . . . . Tel: (01909) 568611 Fax: (01909) 569974
*Parliamentary Interests* . Health; Environment
*Leisure Interests* . . . . . . Family; Fishing; Film; Football

**Battle, Rt Hon John**  Leeds West
**Labour** . . . . . . . . . . . Majority 14,935 over Con
*Born*. . . . . . . . . . . . . . 26th April 1951 in Bradford, Yorkshire
*Educated* . . . . . . . . . . Upholland College; Leeds University
*Elected*. . . . . . . . . . . . 1987 MP for Leeds West
*Offices Held* . . . . . . . . 1992 - 94 Opposition Spokesman on Housing
1994 - 95 Opposition Spokesman on
Science and Technology
1995 - 97 Opposition Spokesman on Energy
1997 - 99 Minister of State, Department of
Trade and Industry
1999 - 2001 Minister of State, Foreign and
Commonwealth Office
*Commons Office* . . . . . Tel: (020) 7219 4201 Fax: (020) 7219 4286
Web: http://www.johnbattle-mp.org.uk
*Constituency Office* . . . . Unit 31, Whingate Business Park,
Leeds, LS12 3AT
Tel: (0113) 231 0258 Fax: (0113) 279 5850
E-mail: john.battle@leedswest.freeserve.co.uk
Parliamentary Assistant - Mr Ben Niblett
Personal Assistant – Ms Christine Towler
*Parliamentary Interests* . Poverty: International Development
*Leisure Interests* . . . . . . Football (Leeds United); Walking; Poetry

# MEMBERS OF THE HOUSE OF COMMONS

**Bayley, Hugh** . . . . . City of York
**Labour** . . . . . . . . . . Majority 13,779 over Con
*Born.* . . . . . . . . . . . . . 9th January 1952 in Oxford
*Educated* . . . . . . . . . Haileybury School;
 Bristol University; York University
*Elected* . . . . . . . . . . . . 1992 MP for City of York
*Offices Held* . . . . . . . . 1997 - 99 PPS to Frank Dobson
 (Secretary of State for Health)
 1998 - 2001 Parliamentary Secretary,
 Department of Social Security
*Commons Office* . . . . . . Tel: (020) 7219 6824 Fax: (020) 7219 0346
*Constituency Office* . . . . 59 Holgate Road, York, YO24 4AA
 Tel: (01904) 623713 Fax: (01904) 623260
 E-mail: dellaganal@parliament.uk
 Assistants – Ms Lesley Della Gana
 Mr Christopher Read
*Parliamentary Interests* . Health; Economics;
 International Development; Defence
*Leisure Interests* . . . . . . Fell Walking; Skiing; Photography

**Beard, Nigel** . . . . . . Bexleyheath and Crayford
**Labour** . . . . . . . . . . . Majority 1,472 over Con
*Born.* . . . . . . . . . . . . . . 10th October 1936 in Leeds
*Educated* . . . . . . . . . . Castleford Grammar School;
 University College, London
*Elected.* . . . . . . . . . . . 1997 MP for Bexleyheath and Crayford
*Commons Office* . . . . . . Tel: (020) 7219 5061 Fax: (020) 7219 2708
 Pager: 07644 001048
 E-mail: beardn@parliament.uk
 Web: http://www.mymp.org.uk/nigelbeard
 Research Assistant – Miss Sophie Walker
*Constituency Office* . . . . 50 Peareswood Road, Slade Green, Erith,
 Kent, DA8 2HP
 Tel: (01322) 332261 Fax: (01322) 332279
 Executive Secretary – Mrs Pat Gray
 Constituency Assistants – Mrs Doreen Ives
 Mr Trevor Perrin
*Parliamentary Interests* . Defence; Foreign Policy; Economic Policy;
 Financial Services; Industry;
 Science and Technology;
*Leisure Interests* . . . . . . Theatre; Walking; Reading; Modern Art

**Beckett, Rt Hon Margaret** Derby South
**Labour** . . . . . . . . . . . Majority 13,855 over Con
*Born.* . . . . . . . . . . . . . . 15th January 1943 in Ashton-under-Lyne,
 Lancashire
*Educated* . . . . . . . . . . Notre Dame High School, Manchester;
 Manchester College of Science and
 Technology; John Dalton Polytechnic
*Elected.* . . . . . . . . . . . 1974 - 79 MP for Lincoln
 1983 MP for Derby South
*Offices Held* . . . . . . . . 1975 - 76 Assistant Government Whip
 1976 - 79 Parliamentary Secretary,
 Department of Education
 1984 - 89 Opposition Spokesman on
 Social Security
 1989 - 92 Shadow Chief Secretary to
 the Treasury
 1992 - 94 Deputy Leader of Labour Party and
 Shadow Leader of the House of Commons
 1994 (May-July) Acting Leader of Labour Party
 1994 - 95 Shadow Health Secretary
 1995 - 97 Shadow President of the
 Board of Trade
 1997 - 98 President of the Board of Trade
 1998 - 2001 President of the Council and
 Leader of the House of Commons
 1998 - 2001 Chairman, Modernisation of the
 House of Commons Select Committee
 2001 - Secretary of State for Environment,
 Food and Rural Affairs
*Commons Office* . . . . . . Tel: (020) 7219 6662 Fax: (020) 7219 4780
 Office Manager – Mr Leo Beckett
 Senior Secretary/PA – Ms Nicola Brown
 Tel: (020) 7219 5135
 Researcher/PA – Ms Elizabeth Dudley
 Tel: (020) 7219 2088
*Constituency Office* . . . . 2A Wentworth House, Vernon Gate, Derby,
 DE1 1UR
 Tel: (01332) 345636 Fax: (01332) 371306
 Agent – Mr James Shires
*Leisure Interests* . . . . . . Cooking; Reading; Caravanning

**Begg, Anne** . . . . . . . Aberdeen South
**Labour** . . . . . . . . . . . Majority 4,388 over Lib Dem
*Born.* . . . . . . . . . . . . . . 6th December 1955 in Forfar
*Educated* . . . . . . . . . . Brechin High School; Aberdeen University
*Born.* . . . . . . . . . . . . . . 1997 MP for Aberdeen South
*Commons Office* . . . . . . Tel: (020) 7219 2140 Fax: (020) 7219 1264
 Mobile: 07711 237743
 Pager: 07644 001084
 E-mail: begga@parliament.uk
 Web: http://www.annebegg.info
*Constituency Office* . . . . 166 Market Street, Aberdeen, AB11 5PP
 Tel: (01224) 252704 Fax: (01224) 252705
 Secretary – Mrs Pamela Fryer
*Parliamentary Interests* . Scotland; Broadcasting; Welfare Reform;
 Energy; Disability
*Leisure Interests* . . . . . . Reading; Cinema; Theatre

# MEMBERS OF THE HOUSE OF COMMONS

**Beggs, Roy** . . . . . . . Antrim East
**Ulster Unionist** . . . . Majority 128 over Democratic Unionist
*Born*. . . . . . . . . . . . . 20th February 1936 in Belfast
*Educated* . . . . . . . . . Ballyclare High School;
    Stranmillis Training College
*Elected*. . . . . . . . . . . 1983 - 85 MP for Antrim East
    1986 MP for Antrim East (By-election)
*Offices Held* . . . . . . . Ulster Unionist Chief Whip and Spokesman on
    Education, Employment and Culture
    1978 - 83 Mayor of Larne
    1982 - 86, 1998 - Member, Northern Ireland
    Assembly
*Commons Office* . . . . . Tel: (020) 7219 6305  Fax: (020) 7219 2347
    Mobile: 07711 842550
    Research Assistant – Miss Claire Kirk
    Tel: (020) 7219 0505 Fax: (020) 7219 0575
    E-mail: kirkc@parliament.uk
    Assistant – Miss Margaret McKee
    Tel: (020) 7219 5679 Fax: (020) 7219 2347
*Constituency Office* . . . . 41 Station Road, Larne, Co Antrim, BT40 3AA
    Tel: (028) 2827 3258 Fax: (028) 2827 3007
    E-mail: office@roybeggsmp.com
    Personal Assistant – Dr Ken Bishop
    Secretary – Mr Andrew Wilson
    Secretarial Assistant – Mrs Sandra Beggs
*Parliamentary Interests* . Education; Employment; Culture; Agriculture
*Leisure Interests* . . . . . . Fishing

**Beith, Rt Hon Alan**  Berwick-upon-Tweed
**Liberal Democrat** . . . Majority 8,458 over Con
*Born*. . . . . . . . . . . . . . 20th April 1943 in Cheshire
*Educated* . . . . . . . . . . King's School, Macclesfield;
    Balliol College, Oxford;
    Nuffield College, Oxford
*Elected*. . . . . . . . . . . . 1973 MP for Berwick-upon-Tweed
    (By-election)
*Offices Held* . . . . . . . . 1976 - 85 Liberal Chief Whip
    1985 - 88 Deputy Leader, Liberal Party
    1985 - 87 Liberal, then Alliance
    Spokesman on Foreign Affairs
    1987 Alliance Spokesman on Foreign Affairs
    1987 - 94 Liberal Democrat Spokesman on
    Treasury
    1994 - 97 Liberal Democrat Spokesman on
    Home Affairs
    1993 - 2003 Deputy Leader,
    Liberal Democrats
    2003 - Chairman, Constitutional Affairs
    Committee, House of Commons
*Commons Office* . . . . . Tel: (020) 7219 3540 Fax: (020) 7219 5890
    Web: http://www.alanbeith.org.uk
    Head of Office – Miss Gill Cheeseman
    E-mail: cheesemang@parliament.uk
*Constituency Office* . . . . 54 Bondgate Within, Alnwick,
    Northumberland, NE66 1JD
    Tel: (01665) 602901 Fax: (01665) 605702
    E-mail: berwicklibdems@cix.compulink.co.uk
    Constituency Secretary – Miss Lisa Brown
    Parliamentary Assistant – Mrs Fiona Hall
    Tel: (01665) 574383
*Parliamentary Interests* . Home Affairs; Constitution; Heritage; Culture
*Leisure Interests* . . . . . . Boating; Walking; Reading; Music

**Bell, Sir Stuart** . . . . Middlesbrough
**Labour** . . . . . . . . . . . Majority 16,330 over Con
*Born*. . . . . . . . . . . . . 16th May 1938 in Co Durham
*Educated* . . . . . . . . . . Hookergate Grammar School, Durham;
    Pitman's College; Council for Legal Education
*Elected*. . . . . . . . . . . . 1983 MP for Middlesbrough
*Offices Held* . . . . . . . . 1984 - 87 Opposition Spokesman on
    Northern Ireland
    1992 - 97 Opposition Spokesman on
    Trade and Industry
    1997 - Second Church Estates Commissioner
    2000 - Chairman, Finance and Services
    Committee, House of Commons
*Commons Office* . . . . . Tel: (020) 7219 3577 Fax: (020) 7219 4873
    Web: http://www.stuartbellmp.org
    Private Secretary – Mr Gary Killick
    E-mail: killickg@parliament.uk
*Constituency Office* . . . . Tel: (01642) 851252 Fax: (01642) 850170
    E-mail: contact@stuartbellmp.org
    Secretary – Mrs Margaret Bell
*Parliamentary Interests* . Church of England; Europe; Economy
*Leisure Interests* . . . . . . Writing Short Stories and Novels

**Bellingham, Henry** Norfolk North West
**Conservative** . . . . . . . Majority 3,485 over Lab
*Born*. . . . . . . . . . . . . . 29th March 1955 in Cheltenham
*Educated* . . . . . . . . . . Eton College;
    Magdalene College, Cambridge
*Elected*. . . . . . . . . . . . 1983 - 97, 2001 MP for Norfolk North West
    (as Defence and Foreign Secretary)
*Offices Held* . . . . . . . . 1991 - 97 PPS to Malcolm Rifkind
    2002 - 03 Opposition Spokesman on Trade
    and Industry
    2003 - Opposition Spokesman on Economic
    Affairs
*Commons Office* . . . . . Tel: (020) 7219 8484
*Parliamentary Interests* . Defence; Foreign Affairs; Northern Ireland;
    Environment; Rural Affairs
*Leisure Interests* . . . . . . Cricket; Country Pursuits

**Benn, Rt Hon Hilary**  Leeds Central
**Labour** . . . . . . . . . . . Majority 14,381 over Con
*Born*. . . . . . . . . . . . . . 26th November 1953
*Educated* . . . . . . . . . . Holland Park Comprehensive School;
    University of Sussex
*Elected*. . . . . . . . . . . . 1999 MP for Leeds Central (By-election)
*Offices Held* . . . . . . . . 1986 - 90 Deputy Leader, London Borough
    of Ealing Council
    2001 - 02 Parliamentary Secretary,
    Department for International Development
    2002 - 03 Parliamentary Secretary,
    Home Office (Minister for Prisons)
    2003 Minister of State, Department for
    International Development
    2003 - Secretary of State for International
    Development
*Commons Office* . . . . . Tel: (020) 7219 5770 Fax: (020) 7219 2639
    Pager: 07644 001765
    E-mail: bennh@parliament.uk
    Web: http://www.epolitix.com/webminster/
    hilary-benn
    Parliamentary Assistant - Ms Sally Clark
    Tel: (020) 7219 6714
    E-mail: clarks@parliament.uk
*Constituency Office* . . . . 2 Blenheim Terrace, Leeds, LS2 9JG
    Tel: (0113) 244 1097 Fax: (0113) 234 1176
    Office Manager – Mrs Judy Box
    Constituency Assistant – Ms Liz Trainor
*Parliamentary Interests* . Home Affairs; Education; Urban
    Regeneration; International Development
*Leisure Interests* . . . . . . Watching Sport; Gardening

# MEMBERS OF THE HOUSE OF COMMONS

**Bennett, Andrew** . . Denton and Reddish
**Labour** . . . . . . . . . . . Majority 20,311 over Con
*Born*. . . . . . . . . . . . . . 9th March 1939 in Manchester
*Educated* . . . . . . . . . . Hulme Grammar School, Manchester;
Birmingham University
*Elected*. . . . . . . . . . . . 1974 MP for Stockport North, then (1983)
MP for Denton and Reddish
*Offices Held* . . . . . . . . 1983 - 88 Opposition Spokesman on
Education
1995 - 97 Chairman, Environment Committee,
House of Commons
1997 - 2001 Joint Chairman, Environment,
Transport and Regions Select Committee
(also Chairman, Environment
Sub-Committee)
2001 - Chairman Office of the Deputy Prime
Minister, Housing, Planning,
Local Government and the Regions
Select Committee
*Commons Office* . . . . . . Tel: (020) 7219 4155
Pager: 07644 001106
E-mail: bennett.andrew@pop3.poptel.org.uk
*Constituency Office* . . . . Denton Town Hall, Market Street,
Denton, M34 2AP
Tel: (0161) 320 1504 Fax: (0161) 320 1503
Secretary – Ms Sheila Bailey
Researcher – Mr Andrew Gwynne
Tel: (0161) 342 2988
*Parliamentary Interests* . Environment
*Leisure Interests* . . . . . . Walking

**Benton, Joe**. . . . . . . Bootle
**Labour** . . . . . . . . . . . Majority 19,043 over Lib Dem
*Born*. . . . . . . . . . . . . . 28th September 1933 in Bootle, Merseyside
*Educated* . . . . . . . . . . St Monica's Secondary School;
Bootle Technical College
*Elected*. . . . . . . . . . . . 1990 MP for Bootle (By-election)
*Offices Held* . . . . . . . . 1985 - 90 Leader, Sefton Metropolitan
Borough Council
1994 - 97 Opposition Whip
*Commons Office* . . . . . . Tel: (020) 7219 6973
*Constituency Office* . . . . 23a Oxford Road, Bootle, Liverpool, L20 9HJ
Tel: (0151) 933 8432 Fax (0151) 933 4746
E-mail: joebenton.bootle@lineone.net
Personal Assistant – Ms Ann McCartney
E-mail: mccartneya@parliament.uk
Agent – Mr Peter Dowd
*Parliamentary Interests* . Education; Housing; Local Government;
Ireland
*Leisure Interests* . . . . . . Classical Music; Reading; Spanish; Squash;
Swimming; Walking

**Bercow, John** . . . . . Buckingham
**Conservative** . . . . . . Majority 13,325 over Lab
*Born*. . . . . . . . . . . . . . 19th January 1963 in Edgware, Middlesex
*Educated* . . . . . . . . . . Finchley Manor Hill School; Essex University
*Elected*. . . . . . . . . . . . 1997 MP for Buckingham
*Offices Held* . . . . . . . . 1999 - 2000 Opposition Spokesman on
Education and Employment
2000 - 01 Opposition Spokesman on Home
Affairs
2001 - 02 Shadow Chief Secretary to
the Treasury
2002 Opposition Spokesman on Work and
Pensions
2003 - 04 Shadow Secretary for International
Development
*Commons Office* . . . . . Tel: (020) 7219 6346 Fax: (020) 7219 0981
Pager: 07626 801475
E-mail: bercowj@parliament.uk
Secretary – Mrs Rosie Daniels
E-mail: danielsrj@parliament.uk
*Constituency Office* . . . . 34 Buckingham Road, Winslow,
Buckinghamshire, MK13 3DY
Tel: (01296) 714240 Fax: (01296) 714273
Web:
http://www.buckinghamconservative.co.uk
Agent – Mrs Evelyn Joy
E-mail: bccaagent@onetel.com
*Parliamentary Interests* . Trade and Industry; Education;
European Affairs
*Leisure Interests* . . . . . . Music; Reading; Squash; Swimming; Tennis

**Beresford, Sir Paul** Mole Valley
**Conservative** . . . . . . Majority 10,153 over Lib Dem
*Born*. . . . . . . . . . . . . . 6th April 1946 in New Zealand
*Educated* . . . . . . . . . . Waimea College, New Zealand;
Otago University, New Zealand;
Eastman Dental Hospital, London
*Elected*. . . . . . . . . . . . 1992 - 97 MP for Croydon Central
1997 MP for Mole Valley
*Offices Held* . . . . . . . . Formerly Leader, London Borough of
Wandsworth Council
1994 - 97 Parliamentary Secretary,
Department of Environment
*Commons Office* . . . . . Tel: (020) 7219 5018 Fax: (020) 7219 2349
Secretary – Mrs Maureen Duke
Diary Secretary – Lady Beresford
*Constituency Office* . . . . 86 South Street, Dorking, Surrey, RH4 2EZ
Tel: (01306) 883312
Agent – Mr Maurice Cook
Secretary – Mrs Janet Phillips
*Parliamentary Interests* . Local Government
*Leisure Interests* . . . . . . Rugby; DIY

**Berry, Dr Roger** . . Kingswood
**Labour** . . . . . . . . . . . Majority 13,962 over Con
*Born*. . . . . . . . . . . . . . 4th July 1948 in Huddersfield
*Educated* . . . . . . . . . . Huddersfield New College;
Bristol University; Sussex University
*Elected*. . . . . . . . . . . . 1992 MP for Kingswood
*Commons Contact*. . . . . Mobile: 07748 965655
Pager: 07644 001111
E-mail: berryr@parliament.uk
*Constituency Office* . . . . PO Box 130, Fishponds, Bristol, BS16 5FB
Tel: (0117) 956 1837 Fax: (0117) 970 1363
Parliamentary Assistants – Ms Chris Cooper
Ms Julie Snelling
*Parliamentary Interests* . Disability Rights; Economic Policy;
Trade and Industry
*Leisure Interests* . . . . . . Travel; Cooking; Reading; Gardening

# MEMBERS OF THE HOUSE OF COMMONS

**Best, Harold** . . . . . . Leeds North West
**Labour** . . . . . . . . . . . Majority 5,236 over Con
*Born* . . . . . . . . . . . . . . 18th December 1937 in Leeds
*Educated* . . . . . . . . . . Meanwood Secondary School, Leeds
*Elected* . . . . . . . . . . . . 1997 MP for Leeds North West
*Commons Office* . . . . . . Tel: (020) 7219 6979 Fax: (020) 7219 2806
    Pager: 07644 001778
    E-mail: besth@parliament.uk
    Web: http://www.haroldbest.co.uk
*Constituency Office* . . . . 7 Iveson Approach, Ireland Wood,
    Leeds, LS16 6LJ
    Tel: (0113) 261 0002 Fax: (0113) 261 0199
    Researchers/Caseworkers –
      Mr Terry Price
      Ms Catherine Simes
    PA and Office Manager – Mrs Josephine Best
    E-mail: [surnameinitial]@parliament.uk
*Parliamentary Interests* . Home Affairs; Health; Employment;
    Housing; Environment
*Leisure Interests* . . . . . . Cricket; Rugby League

**Betts, Clive** . . . . . . . Sheffield Attercliffe
**Labour** . . . . . . . . . . . Majority 18,844 over Con
*Born* . . . . . . . . . . . . . . 13th January 1950 in Sheffield, Yorkshire
*Educated* . . . . . . . . . . King Edward VII School, Sheffield;
    Pembroke College, Cambridge
*Elected* . . . . . . . . . . . . 1992 MP for Sheffield Attercliffe
*Offices Held* . . . . . . . . 1987 - 92 Leader, Sheffield City Council
    1996 - 97 Opposition Whip
    1997 - 98 Assistant Government Whip
    1998 - 2001 Government Whip (Lord
      Commissioner, H M Treasury)
    2001 - Chairman, Urban Affairs
      Sub-Committee (ODPM Committee),
      House of Commons
*Commons Office* . . . . . . Tel: (020) 7219 5114 Fax: (020) 7219 2289
    E-mail: bettsc@parliament.uk
    Web: http://www.clivebetts.labour.co.uk
    Parliamentary Assistant –
      Ms Alison McGovern
    E-mail: mcgoverna@parliament.uk
*Constituency Office* . . . . 2nd Floor, Barkers Pool House,
    Burgess Street, Sheffield, S1 2HF
    Tel: (0114) 273 4444 Fax: (0114) 273 9666
    Constituency Assistant – Mr Steven Vincent
    Assistant – Mrs Liz Callister
*Parliamentary Interests* . Economic Policy; Housing; Local Government
*Leisure Interests* . . . . . . Cricket; Football; Squash; Hill Walking;
    Real Ale

**Blackman, Liz** . . . . Erewash
**Labour** . . . . . . . . . . . Majority 6,932 over Con
*Born* . . . . . . . . . . . . . . 26th September 1949
*Educated* . . . . . . . . . . Carlisle County High School;
    Prince Henry's Grammar School;
    Clifton College, Nottingham
*Elected* . . . . . . . . . . . . 1997 MP for Erewash
*Offices Held* . . . . . . . . 1995 - 97 Deputy Leader,
      Broxtowe Borough Council
    2000 - PPS to Geoff Hoon (Secretary of
      State for Defence)
*Commons Office* . . . . . . Tel: (020) 7219 2397 Fax: (020) 7219 4837
    Mobile: 07719 954212
    Pager: 07644 001785
    Parliamentary Assistant – Dr Glynis Forster
    E-mail: forsterg@parliament.uk
*Constituency Office* . . . . 23 Barratt Road, Attenborough,
    Nottingham, NG9 6AD
    Tel: (0115) 922 4380 Fax: (0115) 943 1860
    Constituency Secretary –
      Ms Marietta Farnsworth
    E-mail: farnsworthm@parliament.uk
*Parliamentary Interests* . Education; Economic Regeneration; Health
*Leisure Interests* . . . . . . Family; Reading; Gardening

**Blair, Rt Hon Tony** Sedgefield
**Labour** . . . . . . . . . . . Majority 17,713 over Con
*Born* . . . . . . . . . . . . . . 6th May 1953 in Edinburgh
*Educated* . . . . . . . . . . Durham Cathedral School;
    Fettes College, Edinburgh;
    St John's College, Oxford
*Elected* . . . . . . . . . . . . 1983 MP for Sedgefield
*Offices Held* . . . . . . . . 1984 - 87 Opposition Spokesman on
      Treasury and Economic Affairs
    1987 - 88 Opposition Spokesman on
      Trade and Industry
    1988 - 89 Shadow Energy Secretary
    1989 - 92 Shadow Employment Secretary
    1992 - 94 Shadow Home Secretary
    1994 - 97 Leader of the Opposition
    1997 - Prime Minister First Lord of the
      Treasury and Minister for the Civil Service
*Constituency Office* . . . . Myrobella House, Trimdon Colliery,
    County Durham, TS29 6DU
    Tel: (01429) 882202 Fax: (01429) 880950
    Agent – Mr John Burton
*Leisure Interests* . . . . . . Family; Football (Newcastle United FC);
    Music

*(Note: for Prime Minister's Office, see pp9-10 above)*

# MEMBERS OF THE HOUSE OF COMMONS

**Blears, Hazel** . . . . . Salford
**Labour** . . . . . . . . . . . Majority 11,012 over Con
*Born*. . . . . . . . . . . . . . 14th May 1956 in Salford
*Educated* . . . . . . . . . . Wardley Grammar School; Trent Polytechnic
*Elected* . . . . . . . . . . . . 1997 MP for Salford
*Offices Held* . . . . . . . . 2001 - 03 Parliamentary Secretary,
  Department of Health
  2003 - Minister of State, Home Office
*Commons Office* . . . . . Tel: (020) 7219 6595 Fax: (020) 7219 0949
  E-mail: blearsh@parliament.uk
  Web: http://www.hazelblears.labour.co.uk
*Constituency Office* . . . . 51 The Crescent, Salford, M5 4WX
  Tel: (0161) 925 0705 Fax: (0161) 743 9173
  Parliamentary Organiser –
  Mrs Margaret Broderick
  Parliamentary Assistant – Miss Eve Sandler
  Administrative Officer – Ms Charlotte Mogg
*Parliamentary Interests* . Home Affairs; Health; The Arts
*Leisure Interests* . . . . . . Dance; Motorcycling

**Blizzard, Bob** . . . . . Waveney
**Labour** . . . . . . . . . . . Majority 8,553 over Con
*Born*. . . . . . . . . . . . . . 31st May 1950
*Educated* . . . . . . . . . . Culford School, Bury St Edmunds;
  Birmingham University
*Elected*. . . . . . . . . . . . 1997 MP for Waveney
*Offices Held* . . . . . . . . 1991 - 97 Leader, Waveney District Council
*Commons Office* . . . . . Tel: (020) 7219 3880 Fax: (020) 7219 3980
  E-mail: blizzardb@parliament.uk
  Web: http://www.bobblizzardmp.co.uk
  Parliamentary Researcher and Press Officer –
  Mrs Eleanor Dusic
  E-mail: dusice@parliament.uk
*Constituency Office* . . . . 27 Milton Road East, Lowestoft,
  Suffolk, NR32 1NT
  Tel: (01502) 514913 Fax: (01502) 580694
  Senior Caseworker – Ms Lynn Derges
  Assistant Caseworker – Mrs Jo Bellham
*Parliamentary Interests* . Transport; Education; Health; Rural Affairs;
  Employment; Energy
*Leisure Interests* . . . . . . Walking; Skiing; Jazz; Rugby; Cricket

**Blunkett, Rt Hon David** Sheffield Brightside
**Labour** . . . . . . . . . . . Majority 17,049 over Con
*Born*. . . . . . . . . . . . . . 6th June 1947 in Sheffield, Yorkshire
*Educated* . . . . . . . . . . Sheffield School for the Blind;
  Royal Normal College for the Blind;
  Shrewsbury Technical College;
  Sheffield Richmond College of Further
  Education; Sheffield University;
  Huddersfield College of Education
*Elected*. . . . . . . . . . . . 1987 MP for Sheffield Brightside
*Offices Held* . . . . . . . . 1980 - 87 Leader, Sheffield City Council
  1988 - 92 Opposition Spokesman on
  Environment
  1992 - 94 Shadow Health Secretary
  1994 - 95 Shadow Education Secretary
  1995 - 97 Shadow Education and Employment
  Secretary
  1997 - 2001 Secretary of State for Education
  and Employment
  2001 - Home Secretary
*Commons Office* . . . . . Tel: (020) 7219 4043 Fax: (020) 7219 5903
*Constituency Office* . . . . 4th Floor, Palatine Chambers,
  Pinstone Street, Sheffield, S1 2HN
  Tel: (0114) 273 5987 Fax: (0114) 278 0384
  Constituency Assistants –
  Mrs Julie Roche
  Ms Tracey Barker
*Leisure Interests* . . . . . . Music; Poetry; Sailing; Walking

**Blunt, Crispin** . . . . . Reigate
**Conservative** . . . . . . . Majority 8,025 over Lab
*Born*. . . . . . . . . . . . . . 15th July 1960
*Educated* . . . . . . . . . . Wellington College;
  Royal Military Academy, Sandhurst;
  Durham University;
  Cranfield School of Management
*Elected*. . . . . . . . . . . . 1997 MP for Reigate
*Offices Held* . . . . . . . . 2001 - 02 Opposition Spokesman on
  Northern Ireland
  2002 - 03 Opposition Spokesman on Trade
  and Industry
*Commons Office* . . . . . Tel: (020) 7219 2254 Fax: (020) 7219 3373
  E-mail: crispinbluntmp@parliament.uk
  Web: http://www.crispinbluntmp.com
  Secretary – Ms Penelope Tay
  E-mail: tayp@parliament.uk
  Research Assistant – Mr David McFarlane
  E-mail: mcfarlaned@parliament.uk
*Constituency Office* . . . . 86a South Street, Dorking, Surrey, RH4 2EW
  Tel: (01306) 888228 Fax: (01306) 889228
  E-mail: reigate and banstead@btconnect.com
*Parliamentary Interests* . Defence; Environment; Foreign Affairs
*Leisure Interests* . . . . . . Bridge; Cricket

**Boateng, Rt Hon Paul** Brent South
**Labour** . . . . . . . . . . . Majority 17,380 over Con
*Born*. . . . . . . . . . . . . . 14th June 1951 in Hackney, London
*Educated* . . . . . . . . . . Ghana International School; Accra Academy;
  Apsley Grammar School;
  Bristol University; College of Law
*Elected*. . . . . . . . . . . . 1987 MP for Brent South
*Offices Held* . . . . . . . . 1989 - 92 Opposition Spokesman on Treasury
  and Economic Affairs
  1992 - 97 Opposition Spokesman,
  Lord Chancellor's Department
  1997 - 98 Parliamentary Secretary,
  Department of Health
  1998 - 2001 Minister of State, Home Office
  2001 - 02 Financial Secretary,
  H M Treasury
  2002 - Chief Secretary, H M Treasury
*Commons Office* . . . . . Tel: (020) 7219 6816 Fax: (020) 7219 4970
  E-mail: boatengp@parliament.uk
  E-mail: champmanra@parliament.uk
  Special Assistant – Mr Richard Chapman
  Tel: (020) 7219 0335
  E-mail: aityounes@parliament.uk
  Caseworker – Mrs Leana Ait-Younes

# MEMBERS OF THE HOUSE OF COMMONS

**Borrow, David** .... Ribble South
**Labour** . . . . . . . . . . . Majority 3,792 over Con
*Born.* . . . . . . . . . . . . . . 2nd August 1952 in Huddersfield
*Educated* . . . . . . . . . . Mirfield Grammar School, Yorkshire;
Coventry University
*Elected.* . . . . . . . . . . . 1997 MP for Ribble South
*Offices Held* . . . . . . . . 1992 - 94, 1995 - 97
Leader, Preston Borough Council
2003 - PPS to Dr Kim Howells (Minister of
State, Department of Transport then (from
2004) Department for Education and Skills)
*Commons Office* . . . . . . Tel & Fax: (020) 7219 4126
E mail: borrowd@parliament.uk
*Constituency Office* . . . . Crescent House, 2-6 Sandy Lane,
Leyland, Lancashire, PR25 2EB
Tel: (01772) 454727 Fax: (01772) 422982
Researcher – Mr Richard Newman-Thompson
Personal Assistant – Ms Tracy Grant
Administrator/Caseworker –
Mr Andy Bennison
*Parliamentary Interests* . Aerospace; Electoral Reform;
Local Government; Finance; Agriculture;
Rural Affairs; HIV and AIDS
*Leisure Interests* . . . . . . Football (Huddersfield Town FC); Theatre;
Working Out

**Boswell, Tim** . . . . . . Daventry
**Conservative** . . . . . . . Majority 9,649 over Lab
*Born.* . . . . . . . . . . . . . . 2nd December 1942 in Essex
*Educated* . . . . . . . . . . Marlborough College; New College, Oxford
*Elected.* . . . . . . . . . . . 1987 MP for Daventry
*Offices Held* . . . . . . . . 1990 - 92 Assistant Government Whip
1992 Government Whip (Lord
Commissioner, H M Treasury)
1992 - 95 Parliamentary Secretary,
Department of Education
1995 - 97 Parliamentary Secretary, Ministry of
Agriculture, Fisheries and Food
1997 Opposition Spokesman on
Treasury Affairs
1997 - 99 Opposition Spokesman on
Trade and Industry
1999 - 2002 Opposition Spokesman
on Education, Employment, Pensions and
Disability Issues
2002 - 03 Opposition Spokesman on
Education
2003 - Opposition Spokesman on Home,
Constitutional and Legal Affairs
*Commons Office* . . . . . . Tel: (020) 7219 3520 Fax: (020) 7219 4919
Personal Secretary – Mrs Mary Hodges
Tel: (020) 8767 6931
*Constituency Office* . . . . 2/3 Church Walk, Daventry,
Northamptonshire, NN11 4BL
Tel: (01327) 703192 Fax: (01327) 310263
Agent – Mrs Sally Smith

**Bottomley, Peter** . . Worthing West
**Conservative** . . . . . . Majority 9,037 over Lib Dem
*Born.* . . . . . . . . . . . . . . 30th July 1944 in Shropshire
*Educated* . . . . . . . . . . Gordon Junior High School, Washington DC;
Westminster School;
Trinity College, Cambridge
*Elected.* . . . . . . . . . . . 1975 - 83 MP for Woolwich West
(By-election), then (1983 - 97) for Eltham
1997 MP for Worthing West
*Offices Held* . . . . . . . . 1984 - 86 Parliamentary Secretary,
Department of Employment
1986 - 89 Parliamentary Secretary,
Department of Transport
1989 - 90 Parliamentary Secretary, Northern
Ireland Office
*Commons Office* . . . . . . Tel: (020) 7219 5060 Fax: (020) 7219 1212
E-mail: bottomleyp@parliament.uk
Parliamentary Assistant –
Mrs Libby Dewdney-Herbert
E-mail: herbertl@parliament.uk
*Constituency Office* . . . . Tel: (01903) 235168 Fax: (01903) 219755
*Parliamentary Interests* . Media; Family Policy; Northern Ireland
*Leisure Interests* . . . . . . Playing Games

**Bottomley, Rt Hon Virginia** Surrey South West
**Conservative** . . . . . . . Majority 861 over Lib Dem
*Born.* . . . . . . . . . . . . . . 12th March 1948
*Educated* . . . . . . . . . . Putney High School; Essex University;
London School of Economics
*Elected.* . . . . . . . . . . . 1984 MP for Surrey South West (By-election)
*Offices Held* . . . . . . . . 1987 - 88 PPS to Sir Geoffrey Howe
(Foreign Secretary)
1988 - 89 Parliamentary Secretary,
Department of the Environment
1989 - 92 Minister of State, Department of
Health
1992 - 95 Secretary of State for Health
1995 - 97 Secretary of State for National
Heritage
*Commons Office* . . . . . . Tel: (020) 7219 6499  Fax: (020) 7219 6279
E-mail: bottomleyv@parliament.uk
Personal Assistant - Miss Joanne Gardner
E-mail: gardnerj@parliament.uk
*Constituency Office* . . . . 2 Royal Parade, Tilford Road, Hindhead,
Surrey, GU26 6TD
Tel: (01428) 604520 Fax: (01428) 607498
E-mail: agent@swsca.co.uk
*Leisure Interests* . . . . . . Grandchildren

# MEMBERS OF THE HOUSE OF COMMONS

**Bradley, Rt Hon Keith**  Manchester Withington
**Labour** . . . . . . . . . . . Majority 11,524 over Lib Dem
*Born*. . . . . . . . . . . . . . 17th May 1950 in Birmingham
*Educated* . . . . . . . . . . Bishops Vesey's Grammar School;
Aston University; Manchester Polytechnic;
York University
*Elected*. . . . . . . . . . . . 1987 MP for Manchester Withington
*Offices Held* . . . . . . . . 1991 - 96 Opposition Spokesman on
Social Security
1996 - 97 Opposition Spokesman on Transport
1997 - 98 Parliamentary Secretary,
Department of Social Security
1998 - 01 Deputy Government Chief Whip
(Treasurer, H M Household)
2001 - 02 Minister of State, Home Office
(Minister for Prisons)
*Commons Office* . . . . . Tel: (020) 7219 5124 Fax: (020) 7219 5901
E-mail: keithbradleymp@parliament.uk
Web: http://www.keithbradley.org.uk
*Constituency Office* . . . . 226 Burton Road, West Didsbury,
Manchester, M20 2LW
Tel: (0161) 446 2047 Fax: (0161) 445 5543
Personal Assistant/Caseworker –
Miss Diane McAddey
Political Assistants – Ms Anna Ross
Mr Ian McGarry
*Parliamentary Interests* . Housing; Social Security; Local Government;
Transport; Education
*Leisure Interests* . . . . . . Food and Drink; Theatre; Cinema

**Bradley, Peter** . . . . The Wrekin
**Labour** . . . . . . . . . . . Majority 3,587 over Con
*Born*. . . . . . . . . . . . . . 12th April 1953 in Birmingham
*Educated* . . . . . . . . . . Abingdon School; Sussex University;
Occidental College, Los Angeles
*Elected*. . . . . . . . . . . . 1997 MP for The Wrekin
*Office Held* . . . . . . . . . 2001 - PPS to Alun Michael
(Minister of State, Department of
Environment, Food and Rural Affairs)
*Commons Office* . . . . . . Tel: (020) 7219 4051
Web: http://www.peterbradley.org.uk
Secretary – Ms Mary Jo Bishop
E-mail: bishopmj@parliament.uk
Researcher – Ms Caroline McGinn
Tel: (020) 7219 4081
E-mail: mcginnc@parliament.uk
*Constituency Office* . . . . 19 Tan Bank, Wellington, Telford, TF1 1MJ
Tel: (01952) 240010 Fax: (01952) 240455
Assistant – Ms Angela McClements
IT Co-ordinator/Office Administrator –
Ms Emma Byrne
*Parliamentary Interests* . Economy; Health; Education; Transport;
Rural Affairs
*Leisure Interests* . . . . . . Cricket; Football (Aston Villa FC); Reading;
Walking

**Bradshaw, Ben** . . . . Exeter
**Labour** . . . . . . . . . . . Majority 11,759 over Con
*Born*. . . . . . . . . . . . . . 30th August 1960 in London
*Educated* . . . . . . . . . . Thorpe St. Andrew's School, Norwich;
Sussex University
*Elected*. . . . . . . . . . . . 1997 MP for Exeter
*Office Held* . . . . . . . . . 2001 - 02 Parliamentary Secretary,
Foreign and Commonwealth Office
2002 - 03 Parliamentary Secretary,
Privy Council Office
2003 - Parliamentary Secretary,
Department of Environment, Food and
Rural Affairs
*Commons Office* . . . . . Tel: (020) 7219 6597 Fax: (020) 7219 0950
Pager: 07623 147126
E-mail: bradshawb@parliament.uk
Web: http://www.benbradshaw.co.uk
Political Assistant – Mr Lenny Shallcross
E-mail: shallcrossl@parliament.uk
*Constituency Office* . . . . 26b Clifton Hill, Exeter, EX1 2DJ
Tel: (01392) 424464 Fax: (01392) 425630
Constituency Secretary – Mrs Brenda Lopez
*Parliamentary Interests* . Foreign Affairs (particularly Europe);
Electoral Reform; Modernisation of Parliament
*Leisure Interests* . . . . . . Walking; Tennis; Cycling

**Brady, Graham** . . . Altrincham and Sale West
**Conservative** . . . . . . . Majority 2,941 over Lab
*Born*. . . . . . . . . . . . . . 20th May 1967 in Salford
*Educated* . . . . . . . . . . Altrincham Grammar School;
Durham University
*Elected*. . . . . . . . . . . . 1997 MP for Altrincham and Sale West
*Offices Held* . . . . . . . . 2000 Opposition Whip
2000 - 01 Opposition Spokesman on
Employment
2001 - 03 Opposition Spokesman on
Education
2003 - 04 PPS to Michael Howard (Leader of
the Opposition)
2004 - Opposition Spokesman on
International Affairs
*Commons Office* . . . . . Tel: (020) 7219 1260 Fax: (020) 7219 1649
E-mail: bradyg@parliament.uk
Web: http://www.grahambradymp.co.uk
Secretary – Mrs Sybil Crowther
E-mail: crowthers@parliament.uk
*Constituency Office* . . . . Thatcher House, Delaheys Farm, Green Lane,
Timperly, Altrincham, WA15 8QW
Tel: (0161) 904 8828 Fax: (0161) 904 8868
*Parliamentary Interests* . Health; Education; Grammar Schools;
Trade and Industry; European Policy
*Leisure Interests* . . . . . . Family; Gardening

# M E M B E R S   O F   T H E   H O U S E   O F   C O M M O N S

**Brake, Tom** . . . . . . . Carshalton and Wallington
**Liberal Democrat** . . . Majority 4,547 over Con
*Born.* . . . . . . . . . . . . . . 6th May 1962 in Melton Mowbray
*Educated* . . . . . . . . . . Lycee International, Paris;
                Imperial College, London
*Elected.* . . . . . . . . . . . 1997 MP for Carshalton and Wallington
*Offices Held* . . . . . . . . 1997 - 2001 Liberal Democrat Whip and
                Spokesman on Environment
                2001 - 03 Liberal Democrat Whip and
                Spokesman on Transport and London
                2003 - Liberal Democrat Whip and
                Spokesman on International Development
*Commons Office* . . . . . Tel: (020) 7219 0924 Fax: (020) 7219 6491
                Mobile: 07958 536377
                E-mail: braket@parliament.uk
                Web: http://www.tombrake.co.uk
                Researcher – Ms Hong Ling Dyer
                E-mail: dyerh@parliament.uk
*Constituency Office* . . . . Kennedy House, 5 Nightingale Road,
                Carshalton, SM5 2DN
                Tel: (020) 8255 8155 Fax: (020) 8395 4453
                E-mail: cwlibs@cix.co.uk
                Office Manager – Ms Cate Ison
                Business Co-ordinator – Mr Colin Hall
                Senior Caseworker – Mr Roger Thistle
*Parliamentary Interests* . Environment; Transport; Foreign Affairs
*Leisure Interests* . . . . . . Sport; Cinema; Foreign Travel

**Brazier, Julian** . . . . Canterbury
**Conservative** . . . . . . Majority 2,069 over Lab
*Born.* . . . . . . . . . . . . . . 24th July 1953 in Dartford, Kent
*Educated* . . . . . . . . . . Wellington College;
                Brasenose College, Oxford;
                London Business School
*Elected.* . . . . . . . . . . . 1987 MP for Canterbury
*Offices Held* . . . . . . . . 1992 - 95 PPS to Gillian Shephard
                (Secretary of State for Environment,
                then Agriculture and Education)
                2001 - 02 Opposition Whip
                2002 - 03 Opposition Spokesman on Work
                and Pensions
                2003 - Opposition Spokesman on Foreign
                Affairs (International Development and
                Overseas Trade)
*Commons Office* . . . . . Tel: (020) 7219 5178 Fax: (020) 7219 0643
                Web: http://www.julianbrazier.co.uk
                Secretary - Mrs Hilary Dannatt
                Research Assistants – Miss Emma Hayward
                              Mr Andrew Williams
*Parliamentary Interests* . Defence; Family; Constitutional Issues;
                Economics; Immigration
*Leisure Interests* . . . . . . Science; Philosophy; Running

**Breed, Colin** . . . . . . Cornwall South East
**Liberal Democrat** . . . Majority 5,375 over Con
*Born.* . . . . . . . . . . . . . . 4th May 1947 in London
*Educated* . . . . . . . . . . Torquay Grammar School
*Elected.* . . . . . . . . . . . 1997 MP for Cornwall South East
*Offices Held* . . . . . . . . 1997 - 99 Liberal Democrat Spokesman on
                Competition and Consumer Affairs
                1999 - 2001 Liberal Democrat Spokesman on
                Agriculture, Rural Affairs and Fisheries
                2002 - Liberal Democrat Spokesman on
                Defence
*Commons Office* . . . . . Tel: (020) 7219 2588 Fax: (020) 7219 5905
                E-mail: colinbreedmp@aol.com
                Web: http://www.colinbreed.org.uk
                Assistant Research Officer –
                Miss Aimee Parnell
                E-mail: parnella@parliament.uk
*Constituency Office* . . . . Barras Street, Liskeard, Cornwall, PL14 6AD
                Secretary – Mrs Pauline Quickfall
                Tel: (01579) 342150 Fax: (01579) 347019
                Office Manager – Mr Frank Atkins
                Tel: (01579) 344577
*Parliamentary Interests* . Small Businesses; Foreign Affairs;
                Agriculture; Rural Affairs
*Leisure Interests* . . . . . . Watching Sport; Golf

**Brennan, Kevin** . . . Cardiff West
**Labour** . . . . . . . . . . . Majority 11,321 over Con
*Educated* . . . . . . . . . . St Alban's RC School, Pontypool;
                Pembroke College, Oxford;
                University College of Wales, Cardiff;
                University of Glamorgan
*Elected.* . . . . . . . . . . . 2001 MP for Cardiff West
*Commons Office* . . . . . Tel: (020) 7219 8156 Fax: (020) 7219 1753
                Mobile: 07796 335146
                E-mail: brennank@parliament.uk
                Web: http://www.kevinbrennan.freeuk.com
*Constituency Office* . . . . 4th Floor, Transport House, 1 Cathedral Road,
                Cardiff, CF1 9SD
                Tel: (029) 2022 3207/3370
                Fax: (029) 2023 0422
                Secretary – Mrs Elaine Simmons
                E-mail: simmonse@parliament.uk
                Researcher – Mr David Thomas
*Parliamentary Interests* . Public Administration; Welsh Affairs;
                Constitutional Affairs; International Issues;
                Economic Policy
*Leisure Interests* . . . . . . Rugby; Music

# MEMBERS OF THE HOUSE OF COMMONS

**Brooke, Annette** . . Mid Dorset and Poole North
**Liberal Democrat** . . . Majority 384 over Con
*Born*. . . . . . . . . . . . . . 7th June 1947
*Educated* . . . . . . . . . . Romford Technical School;
London School of Economics;
Hughes Hall, Cambridge
*Elected*. . . . . . . . . . . . 2001 MP for Mid Dorset and Poole North
*Offices Held* . . . . . . . . 1997 - 98 Mayor, Poole Borough Council
2001 - Liberal Democrat Whip and
Spokesman on Home Affairs
*Commons Office* . . . . . . Tel: (020) 7219 8473
E-mail: brookea@parliament.uk
Researcher – Ms Peta Cubberley
Tel: (020) 7219 8193 Fax: (020) 7219 1898
*Constituency Office* . . . . 14 York Road, Broadstone, Dorset, BH18 8ET
Tel: (01202) 693555 Fax: (01202) 658420
Office Manager– Mrs J Mackay
*Parliamentary Interests* . Young People; Education; Prisons;
Health and Social Issues; Youth Justice
*Leisure Interests* . . . . . . Health and Fitness; Reading; Shopping

**Brown, Rt Hon Gordon**  Dunfermline East
**Labour** . . . . . . . . . . . Majority 15,063 over SNP
*Born*. . . . . . . . . . . . . . 20th February 1951 in Glasgow
*Educated* . . . . . . . . . . Kirkcaldy High School; Edinburgh University
*Elected*. . . . . . . . . . . . 1983 MP for Dunfermline East
*Offices Held* . . . . . . . . 1985 - 87 Opposition Spokesman on Trade
and Industry
1987 - 89 Shadow Chief Secretary to the
Treasury
1989 - 92 Shadow Trade and Industry
Secretary
1992 - 97 Shadow Chancellor of the
Exchequer
1997 - Chancellor of the Exchequer
*Contacts*. . . . . . . . . . . Private Office, HM Treasury
Tel: (020) 7270 4330
*Constituency Office* . . . . Unit 1B, Cowdenbeath Business Centre,
318-324 High Street, Cowdenbeath,
Fife, KY4 9QJ
Tel: (01383) 611702 Fax: (01383) 611703
Office Manager – Ms Rhona White
E-mail: whiterh@parliament.uk
*Parliamentary Interests* . Economy
*Leisure Interests* . . . . . . Golf; Tennis; Watching all Sports

**Brown, Rt Hon Nick**   Newcastle-upon-Tyne East and Wallsend
**Labour** . . . . . . . . . . . Majority 14,223 over Lib Dem
*Born*. . . . . . . . . . . . . . 13th June 1950 in Hawkhurst, Kent
*Educated* . . . . . . . . . . Swattenden Secondary Modern School;
Tunbridge Wells Technical High School;
Manchester University
*Elected*. . . . . . . . . . . . 1983 MP for Newcastle East,  then (1997)
Newcastle-upon-Tyne East and Wallsend
*Offices Held* . . . . . . . . 1985 - 87 Opposition Spokesman on
Legal Affairs
1987 - 92 Opposition Spokesman on Treasury
and Economic Affairs
1992 - 94 Shadow Deputy Leader of the
House and Campaign Co-ordinator
1994 - 95 Opposition Spokesman on Health
1996 - 97 Opposition Deputy Chief Whip
1997 - 98 Government Chief Whip
1998 - 2001 Minister of Agriculture,
Fisheries and Food
2001 - 03 Minister of State, Department for
Work and Pensions (Minister for Work)
*Commons Office* . . . . . . Tel: (020) 7219 6814
*Constituency Office* . . . . 1 Mosley Street, Newcastle-upon-Tyne,
NE1 1YE
Tel: (0191) 261 1408 Fax: (0191) 261 1409
Assistant – Mr Chris Wilkie
E-mail: wilkiec@parliament.uk
*Leisure Interests* . . . . . . Opera

**Brown, Russell** . . . . Dumfries
**Labour** . . . . . . . . . . . Majority 8,834 over Con
*Born*. . . . . . . . . . . . . . 17th September 1951 in Annan
*Educated* . . . . . . . . . . Annan Academy
*Elected*. . . . . . . . . . . . 1997 MP for Dumfries
*Office Held* . . . . . . . . . 2002 - PPS to Lord Williams of Mostyn,
then (from 2003) Baroness Amos
(successive Leaders of the House of Lords)
*Commons Office* . . . . . . Tel: (020) 7219 4429 Fax: (020) 7219 0922
Mobile: 07798 703162
Pager: 07626 134284
E-mail: russell@brownmp.new.labour.org.uk
Web: http://www.russellbrown.labour.co.uk
*Constituency Office* . . . . 5 Friars Vennel, Dumfries, DG1 2RQ
Tel: (01387) 247902 Fax: (01387) 247903
Personal Assistant/Researcher –
Mr Brian Roy
Secretary – Mrs Janice Richardson
*Parliamentary Interests* . Employment Legislation; Health and Safety
*Leisure Interests* . . . . . . Sport (especially Football)

# MEMBERS OF THE HOUSE OF COMMONS

**Browne, Desmond**. Kilmarnock and Loudoun
**Labour** . . . . . . . . . . . Majority 10,334 over SNP
*Born*. . . . . . . . . . . . . . 22nd March 1952 in Ayrshire
*Educated* . . . . . . . . . . St Michael's Academy, Kilwinning;
Glasgow University
*Elected*. . . . . . . . . . . . 1997 MP for Kilmarnock and Loudoun
*Offices Held* . . . . . . . . 1998 - 99 PPS to Donald Dewar
(Secretary of State for Scotland)
2000 PPS to Adam Ingram
(Minister of State, Northern Ireland Office)
2001 - 03 Parliamentary Secretary,
Northern Ireland Office
2003 - 04 Minister of State, Department for
Work and Pensions (Minister for Work)
2004 - Minister of State, Home Office
(Minister for Citizenship, Immigration and
Counter Terrorism)
*Commons Office* . . . . . Tel: (020) 7219 2918 Fax:(020) 7219 2423
Mobile: 07980 577221
Pager: 07644 001259
E-mail: browned@parliament.uk
*Constituency Office* . . . . 32 Grange Street, Kilmarnock,
Ayrshire, KA1 2DD
Tel: (01563) 520267 Fax: (01563) 539439
Assistant – Ms Maureen Murphy
Research Assistant – Mr Jim O'Neill
Caseworker – Mr Bruce Fitzpatrick
*Parliamentary Interests* . Northern Ireland; International Development;
Pensions; Social Security
*Leisure Interests* . . . . . . Football; Tennis; Swimming; Reading;
Family and Friends

**Browning, Angela** . Tiverton and Honiton
**Conservative** . . . . . . . Majority 6,284 over Lib Dem
*Born*. . . . . . . . . . . . . . 4th December 1946 in Reading, Berkshire
*Educated* . . . . . . . . . . Westwood Grammar School;
Reading College of Technology;
Bournemouth College of Technology
*Elected*. . . . . . . . . . . . 1992 MP for Tiverton, then (1997)
Tiverton and Honiton
*Offices Held* . . . . . . . . 1994 - 97 Parliamentary Secretary, Ministry
of Agriculture, Fisheries and Food
1997 - 98 Opposition Spokesman on
Education and People with Disabilities
1999 - 2000 Shadow Trade and Industry
Secretary
2000 - 01 Shadow Leader of the House of
Commons
*Commons Office* . . . . . Tel: (020) 7219 5067 Fax: (020) 7219 2557
E-mail: browningaf@parliament.uk
PA - Mr David Browning
E-mail: browningd@parliament.uk
Caseworker – Ms Fay Stockwell

**Bruce, Malcolm** . . . Gordon
**Liberal Democrat** . . . Majority 7,879 over Con
*Born*. . . . . . . . . . . . . . 17th November 1944 in Birkenhead,
Merseyside
*Educated* . . . . . . . . . . Wrekin College, Shropshire;
St Andrews University;
Strathclyde University;
Middlesex University
*Elected*. . . . . . . . . . . . 1983 MP for Gordon
*Offices Held* . . . . . . . . 1983 - 85 Liberal Spokesman on Scotland
1986 - 87 Liberal Spokesman on Energy
1987 Alliance Spokesman on Employment
1987 - 88, 1992 - 94 Liberal Democrat
Spokesman on Trade and Industry
1988 - 90 Liberal Democrat Spokesman on
Environment and Natural Resources
1990 - 92 Liberal Democrat Spokesman on
Scottish Affairs
1992 - 94 Liberal Democrat Spokesman on
Trade and Industry
1994 - 99 Liberal Democrat Spokesman on
Treasury Matters
1999 - 2001 Chairman, Liberal Democrat
Parliamentary Party
2001 - 02 Liberal Democrat Spokesman on
Environment, Food and Rural Affairs
2003 - Liberal Democrat Spokesman on
Trade and Industry
*Commons Office* . . . . . Tel: (020) 7219 6233 Fax:(020) 7219 2334
E-mail: brucem@parliament.uk
*Constituency Office* . . . . 71 High Street, Inverurie, Aberdeenshire,
AB51 3QJ
Tel: (01467) 623413 Fax: (01467) 624994
Web: http://www.malcolmbruce.libdems.org.uk
*Leisure Interests* . . . . . . Theatre; Music; Golf; Walking

**Bryant, Chris** . . . . . Rhondda
**Labour** . . . . . . . . . . . Majority 16,047 over Plaid Cymru
*Educated* . . . . . . . . . . Cheltenham College;
Mansfield College, Oxford;
Ripon College, Cuddesdon
*Elected*. . . . . . . . . . . . 2001 MP for Rhondda
*Commons Office* . . . . . Tel: (020) 7219 8315 Fax: (020) 7219 1792
Pager: 07626 409577
E-mail: bryantc@parliament.uk
Web: http://www.chrisbryantmp.co.uk
Researcher – Ms Anna Yearley
*Constituency Office* . . . . 5 Cemetery Road, Porth, Rhondda, CF39 0LG
Tel: (01443) 687697 Fax: (01443) 686405
Constituency Adviser – Mr Kevin Morgan
*Parliamentary Interests* . Europe; Broadcasting; Media; Welsh Affairs
*Leisure Interests* . . . . . . Modern Art; Swimming; Theatre

**Buck, Karen** . . . . . . Regent's Park and Kensington North
**Labour** . . . . . . . . . . . Majority 10,266 over Con
*Born*. . . . . . . . . . . . . . 30th August 1958 in Castle Derg,
Northern Ireland
*Educated* . . . . . . . . . . Chelmsford High School;
London School of Economics
*Elected*. . . . . . . . . . . . 1997 MP for Regent's Park and
Kensington North
*Constituency Office* . . . . Tel: (020) 8968 7999 Fax: (020) 8960 0150
E-mail: k.buck@rpkn-labour.co.uk
*Parliamentary Interests* . Housing; London; Social Services

# MEMBERS OF THE HOUSE OF COMMONS

**Burden, Richard** . . Birmingham Northfield
**Labour** . . . . . . . . . . Majority 7,798 over Con
*Born.* . . . . . . . . . . . . 1st September 1954 in Liverpool
*Educated* . . . . . . . . . . Wallasey Technical Grammar School;
Bramhall Comprehensive School;
St John's College of Further Education,
Manchester;  Warwick University;
York University
*Elected.* . . . . . . . . . . . 1992 MP for Birmingham Northfield
*Commons Office* . . . . . . Tel: (020) 7219 5002/2318
Fax: (020) 7219 2170
E-mail: burdenr@parliament.uk
Web: http://www.richardburden.com
Researcher – Ms Victoria Barr
E-mail: barrv@parliament.uk
*Constituency Office* . . . . Tel: (0121) 475 9295 Fax: (0121) 476 2400
Personal Assistant/Caseworker –
Ms Kuldip Bhatti
Caseworker – Mrs Fiona Saxon
*Parliamentary Interests* . Health; Motor Industry; Electoral Reform;
Regeneration; Middle East
*Leisure Interests* . . . . . . Cinema; Food; Motor Racing

**Burgon, Colin** . . . . . Elmet
**Labour** . . . . . . . . . . . Majority 4,171 over Con
*Born.* . . . . . . . . . . . . . 22nd April 1948 in Leeds
*Educated* . . . . . . . . . . St Michael's College, Leeds;
Carnegie College, Leeds;
Huddersfield Polytechnic
*Elected.* . . . . . . . . . . . 1997 MP for Elmet
*Constituency Office* . . . . 22A Main Street, Garforth, Leeds, LS25 1AA
Tel: (0113) 287 5198 Fax: (0113) 287 5958
*Parliamentary Interests* . Education; Green Belt; Planning;
Sporting Issues
*Leisure Interests* . . . . . . History (Particularly the American Civil War);
Leeds United; Walking

**Burnett, John** . . . . . Devon West and Torridge
**Liberal Democrat** . . . Majority 1,194 over Con
*Born.* . . . . . . . . . . . . . 19th September 1945 in Shropshire
*Educated* . . . . . . . . . . Ampleforth College;
Royal Marines Commando Training Centre;
Britannia Royal Naval College, Dartmouth;
College of Law, London
*Elected.* . . . . . . . . . . . 1997 MP for Devon West and Torridge
*Offices Held* . . . . . . . . 1997 - 2001 Liberal Democrat Spokesman on
Legal Affairs
2001 - Liberal Democrat Spokesman on
Home Affairs (also, from 2002, Legal
Affairs)
*Constituency Office* . . . . 13 St James's Street, Okehampton, Devon,
EX20 1DJ
Tel: (01837) 55881 Fax: (01837) 55694
*Parliamentary Interests* . Legal Affairs; Economy; Defence; Agriculture
*Leisure Interests* . . . . . . Walking; Swimming; Tennis; Travel

**Burnham, Andrew** . Leigh
**Labour** . . . . . . . . . . . Majority 16,462 over Con
*Born.* . . . . . . . . . . . . . 7th January 1970 in Liverpool
*Educated* . . . . . . . . . . Fitzwilliam College, Cambridge
*Elected.* . . . . . . . . . . . 2001 MP for Leigh
*Office Held.* . . . . . . . . PPS to David Blunkett (Home Secretary)
*Commons Office* . . . . . Tel: (020) 7219 8250 Fax: (020) 7219 4381
E-mail: burnhama@parliament.uk
*Constituency Office* . . . 10 Market Street, Leigh,
Lancashire, WN7 1DS
Tel: (01942) 682353 Fax: (01942) 682354
Assistant – Mrs Linda Graham
E-mail: grahamlm@parliament.uk
Researcher – Mr Tom Sherratt
*Parliamentary Interests* . Health; Media; Sport; Crime
*Leisure Interests* . . . . . . Cricket; Football; Rugby League

**Burns, Simon** . . . . . Chelmsford West
**Conservative** . . . . . . . Majority 6,261 over Labour
*Born.* . . . . . . . . . . . . . 6th September 1952 in Nottingham
*Educated* . . . . . . . . . . Christ the King School, Accra, Ghana;
Stamford School, Lincolnshire;
Worcester College, Oxford
*Elected.* . . . . . . . . . . . 1987 MP for Chelmsford, then (1997)
Chelmsford West
*Offices Held* . . . . . . . . 1994 - 95 Assistant Government Whip
1995 - 96 Government Whip (Lord
Commissioner, H M Treasury)
1996 - 97 Parliamentary Secretary,
Department of Health
1997 - 98 Opposition Spokesman on
Social Security
1998 - 99 Opposition Spokesman on
Environment
2001 - Opposition Spokesman on Health
*Commons Office* . . . . . Tel: (020) 7219 4052 Fax: (020) 7219 1035
*Constituency Office* . . . . 88 Rectory Lane, Chelmsford,
Essex, CM1 1RF
Tel: (01245) 352872
Agent – Mrs Carole Patient
*Parliamentary Interests* . Health; Social Security
*Leisure Interests* . . . . . . American Politics; Secondhand Books;
Reading

**Burnside, David** . . . Antrim South
**Ulster Unionist** . . . . . Majority 1,011 over Democratic Unionist
*Born.* . . . . . . . . . . . . . 1951
*Educated* . . . . . . . . . . Queen's University, Belfast
*Elected.* . . . . . . . . . . . 2001 MP for Antrim South
*Office Held.* . . . . . . . . 2003 - Member, Northern Ireland Assembly
*Commons Office* . . . . . Tel: (020) 7219 8493
Staff – Miss Margaret McKee
Tel: (020) 7219 5679 Fax: (020) 7219 2347
E-mail: mckeem@parliament.uk
*Parliamentary Interests* . Tourism; Countryside Issues; Culture, Media
and Sport; Defence; Environment, Food and
Rural Affairs
*Leisure Interests* . . . . . . Fishing; Motorcycling; Shooting

# MEMBERS OF THE HOUSE OF COMMONS

**Burstow, Paul** . . . . . Sutton and Cheam
**Liberal Democrat** . . . Majority 4,304 over Con
*Born*. . . . . . . . . . . . . . 13th May 1962 in Carshalton
*Educated* . . . . . . . . . . Glastonbury High School for Boys, Carshalton;
South Bank Polytechnic
*Elected*. . . . . . . . . . . . 1997 MP for Sutton and Cheam
*Offices Held* . . . . . . . . 1994 - 97 Deputy Leader,
London Borough of Sutton Council
1997 - 99 Liberal Democrat Spokesman on
Local Government, Social Services and
Community Care
1999 - 01 Liberal Democrat Spokesman on
Social Security (Pensions)
2001 - 03 Liberal Democrat Spokesman on
Health and Older People's Issues
2003 - Liberal Democrat Spokesman on
Health
*Commons Office* . . . . . Tel: (020) 7219 1196 Fax: (020) 7219 0974
*Constituency Office* . . . . Epsom House, 312-314 High Street, Sutton,
Surrey, SM1 1PR
Tel: (020) 8288 6555 Fax: (020) 8288 6550
Web: http://www.paulburstow.libdems.org.uk
Head of Office – Ms Ruth Dombey
E-mail: dombeyr@parliament.uk
*Parliamentary Interests* . Older People; MS; ME; Disability Issues;
Low and Nil Emission Vehicle Technology
*Leisure Interests* . . . . . . Cooking; Gym; Reading; Walking

**Burt, Alistair**. . . . . . Bedfordshire North East
**Conservative** . . . . . . . Majority 8,577 over Lab
*Educated* . . . . . . . . . . . Bury Grammar School;
St John's College, Oxford
*Elected*. . . . . . . . . . . . 1983 - 97 MP for Bury North
2001 MP for Bedfordshire North East
*Offices Held* . . . . . . . . 1992 - 95 Parliamentary Secretary,
Department for Social Security
1995 - 97 Minister of State
(for the Disabled), Department of
Social Security
2001 - 02 Opposition Spokesman on
Education and Skills
2002 - PPS to Iain Duncan Smith, then
(from 2003) Michael Howard
(successive Leaders of the Opposition)
*Commons Office* . . . . . Tel: (020) 7219 8132 Fax: (020) 7219 1740
Pager 07644 008777
E-mail: burta@parliament.uk
Web: http://www.alistair-burt.co.uk
Personal Assistant – Mrs Eve Burt
Secretary – Miss Lara Durbin
E-mail: durbinl@parliament.uk
*Constituency Office* . . . . Biggleswade Conservative Club,
St Andrew's Street, Biggleswade,
Bedfordshire, SG18 8YB
Tel: (01767) 313385 Fax: (01767) 316697
E-mail: nebca@biggles64.fsnet.co.uk
Organising Secretary – Mrs Liz Hobbs
*Parliamentary Interests* . Health; Welfare; Engineering; Rural Issues;
International Issues; Higher Education
*Leisure Interests* . . . . . . Church; Family; Football; Running

**Butterfill, Sir John** Bournemouth West
**Conservative** . . . . . . Majority 4,718 over Lab
*Born*. . . . . . . . . . . . . . 14th February 1941 in Surrey
*Educated* . . . . . . . . . . Caterham School;
College of Estate Management, London
*Elected*. . . . . . . . . . . . 1983 MP for Bournemouth West
*Office Held*. . . . . . . . . 1988 - 90 PPS to Cecil Parkinson (Secretary
of State for Energy then Secretary of State
for Transport)
*Commons Office* . . . . . Tel: (020) 7219 6375 Fax: (020) 7219 3899
E-mail: butterfillj@parliament.uk
*Constituency Office* . . . . 135 Hankinson Road, Bournemouth,
Dorset, BH9 1HR
Tel: (01202) 776607 Fax: (01202) 521481
Agent – Mrs Wendy Keene
*Parliamentary Interests* . Pensions; Financial Services;
Trade and Industry
*Leisure Interests* . . . . . . Bridge; Music; Tennis; Skiing

**Byers, Rt Hon Stephen** Tyneside North
**Labour** . . . . . . . . . . . Majority 20,668 over Con
*Born*. . . . . . . . . . . . . . 13th April 1953 in Wolverhampton
*Educated* . . . . . . . . . . Chester City Grammar School;
Chester College of Further Education;
Liverpool Polytechnic
*Elected*. . . . . . . . . . . . 1992 MP for Wallsend, then (1997)
Tyneside North
*Offices Held* . . . . . . . . 1994 - 95 Opposition Whip
1995 - 97 Opposition Spokesman on
Education and Employment
1997 - 98 Minister of State, Department for
Education and Employment
1998 - 99 Chief Secretary, H M Treasury
1999 - 2001 Secretary of State for
Trade and Industry
2001 - 02 Secretary of State for Transport,
Local Government and the Regions
*Commons Office* . . . . . Tel: (020) 7219 4085 Fax: (020) 7219 5041
*Constituency Office* . . . . 7 Palmersville, Great Lime Road, Forest Hall,
Newcastle-upon-Tyne, NE12 9HN
Tel: (0191) 268 9111 Fax: (0191) 268 9777
Personal Assistant – Mr Terry Hammond

**Byrne, Liam**. . . . . . Birminham Hodge Hill
**Labour** . . . . . . . . . . . Majority 460 over Lib Dem
*Born*. . . . . . . . . . . . . . 13th April 1953 in Wolverhampton
*Elected*. . . . . . . . . . . . 2004 (By-election)

# MEMBERS OF THE HOUSE OF COMMONS

## C

**Cable, Dr Vincent** . Twickenham
**Liberal Democrat** . . . Majority 7,655 over Con
*Born* . . . . . . . . . . . . . . 9th May 1943 in York
*Educated* . . . . . . . . . . . Nunthorpe Grammar School;
Cambridge University; Glasgow University
*Elected* . . . . . . . . . . . . . 1997 MP for Twickenham
*Offices Held* . . . . . . . . 1997 - 99 Liberal Democrat Spokesman on
Treasury Matters
1999 - 2003 Liberal Democrat Spokesman on
Trade and Industry
2003 - Liberal Democrat Shadow
Chancellor of the Exchequer
*Commons Office* . . . . . . Tel: (020) 7219 4572 Fax: (020) 7219 1191
E-mail: vincentcablemp@parliament.uk
Web: http://www.vincentcable.com
Researcher/Head of Office –
Mr Chris Saunders
Tel: (020) 7219 1106
E-mail: saundersc@parliament.uk
*Constituency Office* . . . . 7 Kestrel House, 111 Heath Road,
Twickenham, Middlesex, TW1 4AF
Tel: (020) 8892 0215 Fax: (020) 8892 0218
E-mail: vincentcable@cix.co.uk
Secretary – Mrs Joan Bennett
Caseworker – Ms Sandra Fayle
*Parliamentary Interests* . Economic Policy; Crime; Health
*Leisure Interests* . . . . . . Ballroom and Latin Dancing; Classical Music

**Caborn, Rt Hon Richard** Sheffield Central
**Labour** . . . . . . . . . . . . Majority 16,906 over Lib Dem
*Born* . . . . . . . . . . . . . . 6th October 1943 in Sheffield, Yorkshire
*Educated* . . . . . . . . . . . Hurlfield Comprehensive School, Sheffield;
Granville College of Further Education;
Sheffield Polytechnic
*Elected* . . . . . . . . . . . . . 1983 MP for Sheffield Central
*Offices Held* . . . . . . . . 1987 - 90 Opposition Spokesman on
Trade and Industry
1992 - 95 Chairman, Trade and Industry
Select Committee, House of Commons
1995 - 97 Shadow Minister for National
Competitiveness and Regulation
1997 - 99 Minister of State, Department of
Environment, Transport and the Regions
1999 - 2001 Minister of State, Department of
Trade and Industry
2001 - Minister of State, Department for
Culture, Media and Sport (Minister
for Sport and Tourism)
*Commons Office* . . . . . . Tel: (020) 7219 6259 Fax: (020) 7219 4866
*Constituency Office* . . . . 2nd Floor, Barkers Pool House,
Burgess Street, Sheffield, S1 2HF
Tel: (0114) 273 7947 Fax: (0114) 275 3944
Secretaries – Ms Donna Parker
Mr Jason Read

**Cairns, David** . . . . . Greenock and Inverclyde
**Labour** . . . . . . . . . . . Majority 9,890 over Lib Dem
*Born* . . . . . . . . . . . . . . 7th August 1966
*Educated* . . . . . . . . . . Notre Dame High School;
Gregorian University, Rome;
Franciscan Study Centre, Canterbury
*Elected* . . . . . . . . . . . . 2001 MP for Greenock and Inverclyde
*Office Held* . . . . . . . . . 2003 - PPS to Malcolm Wicks
(Minister of State, Department for
Work and Pensions)
*Commons Office* . . . . . Tel: (020) 7219 8242 Fax: (020) 7219 1772
E-mail: cairnsd@parliament.uk
Web: http://www.davidcairns.com
Parliamentary Researcher –
Mr Leighton Veale
E-mail: vealel@parliament.uk
*Constituency Office* . . . . 20 Union Street, Greenock, PA16 8JL
Tel: (01475) 791820 Fax: (01475) 791821
Caseworker – Ms Christina Boyd
PA – Ms Ann Dinning
*Parliamentary Interests* . Defence; Israel; Employment
*Leisure Interests* . . . . . . Travel

**Calton, Patsy** . . . . . . Cheadle
**Liberal Democrat** . . . Majority 33 over Con
*Born* . . . . . . . . . . . . . . 19th September 1948
*Educated* . . . . . . . . . . Wymondham College, Norfolk; UMIST
*Elected* . . . . . . . . . . . . 2001 MP for Cheadle
*Office Held* . . . . . . . . . 2002 - Liberal Democrat Spokesman on
Health
*Commons Office* . . . . . Tel: (020) 7219 8471 Fax: (020) 7219 1958
E-mail: caltonp@parliament.uk
Web: http://www.patsycalton.org.uk
Researcher – Mr Clive Calton
*Constituency Office* . . . . Hillson House, 3 Gillbent Road,
Cheadle Hulme, Cheshire, SK8 7LE
Tel: (0161) 486 1359 Fax: (0161) 486 9005
Personal Assistant – Ms Elaine Maltby
*Parliamentary Interests* . Health; Education; Transport; Governance;
Disability
*Leisure Interests* . . . . . . Gardening; Marathon Running

**Cameron, David** . . . Witney
**Conservative** . . . . . . . Majority 7,973 over Lab
*Educated* . . . . . . . . . . Eton College; Brasenose College, Oxford
*Elected* . . . . . . . . . . . . 2001 MP for Witney
*Office Held* . . . . . . . . . 2003 - 04 Opposition Spokesman on
Local Government and Devolved Affairs
2004 - Head of policy Co-ordination,
Conservative Party and Member of the
Shadow Cabinet)
*Commons Office* . . . . . Tel: (020) 7219 3475 Fax: (020) 7219 1945
E-mail: camerond@parliament.uk
Assistant – Mrs Caroline Balcon
E-mail: balconc@parliament.uk
Research Assistant – Mr Patrick Clark
E-mail: clarkpj@parliament.uk
*Constituency Office* . . . . 10 Bridge Street, Witney, Oxon, OX28 1HY
Tel: (01993) 702302 Fax: (01993) 776639
E-mail: office@witneytory.co.uk
*Parliamentary Interests* . Home Affairs; Treasury; Rural Issues
*Leisure Interests* . . . . . . Cooking; Tennis; Country Sports

# MEMBERS OF THE HOUSE OF COMMONS

**Campbell, Alan** . . . Tynemouth
**Labour** . . . . . . . . . . Majority 8,678 over Con
*Born* . . . . . . . . . . . . . 8th July 1957
*Educated* . . . . . . . . . Blackfyne Secondary School, Consett;
Lancaster University; Leeds University;
Northumbria University
*Elected* . . . . . . . . . . . 1997 MP for Tynemouth
*Offices Held* . . . . . . . . 2003 - PPS to Adam Ingram
(Minister of State, Ministry of Defence)
*Commons Office* . . . . . Tel: (020) 7219 6619 Fax: (020) 7219 3006
E-mail: campbellal@parliament.uk
Web: http://www.alancampbell.co.uk
*Constituency Office* . . . . 99 Howard Street, North Shields, NE30 1NA
Tel: (0191) 257 1927 Fax: (0191) 257 6537
E-mail: phillipss@parliament.uk
Assistant – Miss Sarah Phillips
Secretary – Mrs Liz Livesley
*Parliamentary Interests* . Civil Defence; Education; Shipbuilding;
Offshore Industries

**Campbell, Anne** . . . Cambridge
**Labour** . . . . . . . . . . Majority 8,579 over Lib Dem
*Born* . . . . . . . . . . . . . 6th April 1940 in Dewsbury, Yorkshire
*Educated* . . . . . . . . . Penistone Grammar School;
Newnham College, Cambridge
*Elected* . . . . . . . . . . . 1992 MP for Cambridge
*Offices Held* . . . . . . . . 1992 - 97 Chairman, Science and Technology
Select Committee, House of Commons
1999 - 2003 PPS to Patricia Hewitt
(as Minister of State, then Secretary of
State for Trade and Industry)
*Commons Office* . . . . . Tel: (020) 7219 5089 Fax: (020) 7219 2264
E-mail: campbella@parliament.uk
Web: http://www.annecampbell.org.uk
Research Assistant – Miss Louisa Thomson
Tel: (020) 7219 5900
E-mail: thomsonlm@parliament.uk
*Constituency Office* . . . . Alex Wood Hall, Norfolk Street,
Cambridge, CB1 2LD
Tel: (01223) 506500 Fax: (01223) 311315
Office Manager – Miss Gosia McBride
E-mail: mcbrideg@parliament.uk
Agent – Miss Alex Mayer
Tel: (01223) 500515
*Parliamentary Interests* . Science; Education; Environment
*Leisure Interests* . . . . . . Gardening; Reading; Skiing; Tennis; Walking

**Campbell, Gregory** Londonderry East
**Democratic Unionist**. Majority 1,901 over Ulster Unionist
*Born* . . . . . . . . . . . . . 15th February 1953 in Londonderry
*Educated* . . . . . . . . . . Londonderry Technical College
*Elected* . . . . . . . . . . . 2001 MP for Londonderry East
*Offices Held* . . . . . . . . 1998 - Member, Northern Ireland Assembly
(Minister for Regional Development
2000 - 01)
*Commons Office* . . . . . Tel: (020) 7219 8495
*Constituency Offices* . . . 25 Bushmills Road, Coleraine,
Co Londonderry, BT52 2BP
Tel: (028) 7032 7327 Fax: (028) 7032 7328
E-mail: colerainehq@dup.org.uk
Senior Researcher – Mr Mark Fielding
Secretaries – Ms Margaret Semple
Mrs Hazel Wilkinson
*Parliamentary Interests* . Transport; Local Government and Regions
*Leisure Interests* . . . . . . Soccer; Music; Reading

**Campbell, Rt Hon Sir Menzies** CBE QC  Fife North East
**Liberal Democrat** . . . Majority 9,736 over Con
*Born* . . . . . . . . . . . . . 22nd May 1941 in Glasgow
*Educated* . . . . . . . . . Hillhead High School, Glasgow;
Glasgow University; Stanford University, USA
*Elected* . . . . . . . . . . . 1987 MP for Fife North East
*Offices Held* . . . . . . . . 1991 - Liberal Democrat Spokesman on
Foreign Affairs (also Defence and
Europe 1997 - 2001)
2003 - Deputy Leader, Liberal Democrats
*Commons Office* . . . . . Tel: (020) 7219 4446 Fax: (020) 7219 0559
Researcher – Mr Spencer Grady
E-mail: gradys@parliament.uk
*Constituency Office* . . . . 16 Millgate, Cupar, Fife, KY15 5HP
Tel: (01334) 656361 Fax: (01334) 654045
*Parliamentary Interests* . Foreign Affairs; Defence; Sport; Legal Affairs
*Leisure Interests* . . . . . . Sports; Theatre; Music

**Campbell, Ronnie** . Blyth Valley
**Labour** . . . . . . . . . . Majority 12,188 over Lib Dem
*Born* . . . . . . . . . . . . . 14th August 1943 in Blyth, Northumberland
*Educated* . . . . . . . . . Ridley High School, Blyth
*Elected* . . . . . . . . . . . 1987 MP for Blyth Valley
*Commons Office* . . . . . Tel: (020) 7219 4216 Fax: (020) 7219 4358
*Constituency Office* . . . . 42 Renwick Road, Blyth,
Northumberland, NE24 2LQ
Tel & Fax: (01670) 363050
E-mail: ronniecampbellmp@btconnect.com
Secretary/Research Assistant –
Mrs Jeanette Kerrison
*Parliamentary Interests* . Health; Transport
*Leisure Interests* . . . . . . Furniture Restoration; Antiques;
Stamp Collecting

**Caplin, Ivor** . . . . . . Hove
**Labour** . . . . . . . . . . Majority 3,171 over Con
*Born* . . . . . . . . . . . . . 8th November 1958 in Brighton
*Educated* . . . . . . . . . King Edwards School, Witley, Surrey
*Elected* . . . . . . . . . . . 1997 MP for Hove
*Offices Held* . . . . . . . . 1995 - 97 Leader, Hove Borough Council
1997 - 98 Deputy Leader, Brighton and
Hove Council
1998 - 2001 PPS to Margaret Beckett
(Leader of the House of Commons)
2001 - Assistant Government Whip
2003 - Parliamentary Secretary, Ministry of
Defence (Minister for Veterans)
*Commons Office* . . . . . Tel: (020) 7219 2146 Fax: (020) 7219 0259
E-mail: caplini@parliament.uk
Web: http://www.ivorcaplinmp.com
Parliamentary Assistant – Mr David Ward
E-mail: wardda@parliament.uk
*Constituency Office* . . . . Parliamentary Office, Town Hall,
Norton Road, Hove, BN3 4AH
Tel: (01273) 292933 Fax: (01273) 291054
Office Manager – Ms Sue John
Constituency Caseworker –
Mr James Sachon
*Parliamentary Interests* . Finance; Animal Welfare; Culture; Sport
*Leisure Interests* . . . . . . Football; Cricket; Music; Eating Out

# MEMBERS OF THE HOUSE OF COMMONS

**Carmichael, Alistair**   Orkney and Shetland
**Liberal Democrat** . . .   Majority 3,475 over Lab
*Born*. . . . . . . . . . . . . . .   15th July 1965 in Islay, Argyll
*Educated* . . . . . . . . . .   Islay High School, Argyll;
         Aberdeen University
*Elected*. . . . . . . . . . . .   2001 MP for Orkney and Shetland
*Office Held*. . . . . . . . .   2001 - Liberal Democrat Spokesman on
         Northern Ireland (also Scotland to 2004)
*Commons Office* . . . . . .   Tel: (020) 7219 8307 Fax: (020) 7219 1787
         E-mail: carmichaela@parliament.uk
         Web: http://www.alistaircarmichael-org.uk
         Secretary – Ms Diane Davidson
         Tel: (020) 7219 8181
         E-mail: davidsond@parliament.uk
         Researcher – Mr Peter Taylor
         E-mail: taylorpc@parliament.uk
*Constituency Offices* . . .   31 Broad Street, Kirkwall, Orkney,
         KW15 1DH
         Tel: (01856) 876541 Fax: (01856) 876162
         Caseworker – Mrs Jenny Devlin
         Constituency Assistant (Shetland) –
         Mrs Elinor Nicolson
         Tel: (01595) 690044 Fax: (01595) 690055
*Parliamentary Interests*.   Energy; Agriculture; Fishing
*Leisure Interests* . . . . . .   Music; Theatre; Cooking


**Casale, Roger** . . . . .   Wimbledon
**Labour** . . . . . . . . . . . .   Majority 3,744 over Con
*Born*. . . . . . . . . . . . . . .   22nd May 1960 in Wimbledon
*Educated* . . . . . . . . . .   Brasenose College, Oxford;
         Johns Hopkins, Bologna
*Elected*. . . . . . . . . . . .   1997 MP for Wimbledon
*Office Held*. . . . . . . . .   2002 - PPS to Foreign and
         Commonwealth Office Ministers
*Commons Office* . . . . . .   Tel: (020) 7219 4565 Fax: (020) 7219 0789
         E-mail: casaler@parliament.uk
         Web: http://www.rogercasale.labour.co.uk
         Parliamentary Assistant –
         Ms Ciarra Brannigan
         E-mail: branniganc@parliament.uk
*Constituency Office* . . . .   Nelson Hospital, Kingston Road,
         Wimbledon, London, SW20 8DB
         Tel: (020) 8540 1012 Fax: (020) 8540 1018
*Parliamentary Interests*.   Foreign Affairs; Treasury
*Leisure Interests* . . . . . .   Tennis; Family and Friends


**Cash, Bill** . . . . . . . .   Stone
**Conservative** . . . . . . .   Majority 6,036 over Lab
*Born*. . . . . . . . . . . . . . .   10th May 1940 in London
*Educated* . . . . . . . . . .   Stoneyhurst College; Lincoln College, Oxford
*Elected*. . . . . . . . . . . .   1984 MP for Stafford (By-election),
         then (1997) for Stone
*Office Held*. . . . . . . . .   2001 - 03 Shadow Attorney-General
*Constituency Office* . . . .   50 High Street, Stone, Staffordshire,
         ST15 8AU
         Tel & Fax: (01785) 811000
*Parliamentary Interests*.   Africa; Europe; Industry; Third World Debt
*Leisure Interests* . . . . . .   Jazz; Cricket; History


**Caton, Martin** . . . . .   Gower
**Labour** . . . . . . . . . . .   Majority 7,395 over Con
*Born*. . . . . . . . . . . . . . .   15th June 1951 in Bishops Stortford
*Educated* . . . . . . . . . .   Newport Grammar School, Essex;
         School of Agriculture, Norfolk;
         Aberystwyth College of Further Education
*Elected*. . . . . . . . . . . .   1997 MP for Gower
*Commons Office* . . . . .   Tel: (020) 7219 5111
         Personal Assistant – Ms Bethan Caton
         E-mail: catonb@parliament.uk
*Constituency Office* . . . .   26 Pontardulais Road, Gorseinon,
         Swansea, SA4 4FE
         Tel: (01792) 892100 Fax: (01792) 892375
         Secretary – Ms Lorraine Davies
         E-mail: daviesl@parliament.uk
         Secretarial Assistant – Ms Nicola Pallett
*Parliamentary Interests*.   Community Development; Environment
*Leisure Interests* . . . . . .   Reading; Walking


**Cawsey, Ian** . . . . . . .   Brigg and Goole
**Labour** . . . . . . . . . . .   Majority 3,961 over Con
*Born*. . . . . . . . . . . . . .   14th April 1960 in Grimsby
*Educated* . . . . . . . . . .   Wintringham School, Grimsby
*Elected*. . . . . . . . . . . .   1997 MP for Brigg and Goole
*Offices Held* . . . . . . . .   1995 - 97 Leader, North Lincolnshire Council
         2001 - 02 PPS to Lord Williams of Mostyn
         (Leader of the House of Lords)
         2002 - PPS to David Miliband (Minister of
         State, Department of Education and Skills)
*Commons Office* . . . . .   Tel: (020) 7219 5237 Fax: (020) 7219 3047
         Mobile: 07774 216870
         Pager: 07644 001347
         E-mail: cawseyi@parliament.uk
*Constituency Offices* . . .   7 Market Place, Brigg, North Lincolnshire,
         DN20 8HA
         Tel: (01652) 621327 Fax: (01652) 657132
         PA/Secretary – Mrs Maggie Taylor
         PA/Research Assistant – Mr Bernard Tong
         Tel: (01652) 651146
         The Courtyard, Boothferry Road, Goole,
         DN14 6AE
         Tel: (01405) 767744 Fax: (01405) 767733
         PA/Secretary – Mrs Rita Patterson
*Parliamentary Interests*.   Animal Welfare; Home Affairs;
         Local Government
*Leisure Interests* . . . . . .   Music; Sport


**Challen, Colin** . . . . .   Morley and Rothwell
**Labour** . . . . . . . . . . .   Majority 12,090 over Con
*Born*. . . . . . . . . . . . . .   12th June 1953 in Scarborough
*Educated* . . . . . . . . . .   Norton Secondary School;
         Malton Grammar School;
         Open University; Hull University
*Elected*. . . . . . . . . . . .   2001 MP for Morley and Rothwell
*Commons Office* . . . . . .   Tel: (020) 7219 8260
*Constituency Office* . . . .   2 Commercial Street, Morley, Leeds,
         LS27 8HY
         Tel & Fax: (0113) 238 1312
*Leisure Interests* . . . . . .   Art; Music; Rambling; Writing

# MEMBERS OF THE HOUSE OF COMMONS

**Chapman, Ben** . . . . Wirral South
**Labour** . . . . . . . . . . . Majority 5,049 over Con
*Born.* . . . . . . . . . . . . . . 8th July 1940 in Kirkby Stephen, Cumbria
*Educated* . . . . . . . . . . Appleby Grammar School
*Elected* . . . . . . . . . . . . 1997 MP for Wirral South (By-election)
*Offices Held* . . . . . . . . 1997 - PPS to Richard Caborn (successively
　　　　　　　　　　　Minister of State at Department of
　　　　　　　　　　　Environment, Transport and the Regions;
　　　　　　　　　　　Department of Trade and Industry and
　　　　　　　　　　　Department for Culture, Media and Sport)
*Commons Office* . . . . . . Tel: (020) 7219 1143 Fax: (020) 7219 1179
　　　　　　　　　　　E-mail: chapmanb@parliament.uk
　　　　　　　　　　　Web: http://www.ben-chapman.org
　　　　　　　　　　　Parliamentary Assistant – Mr Tim Rowbottom
　　　　　　　　　　　E-mail: rowbottomt@parliament.uk
　　　　　　　　　　　Research Assistant – Mr David Tinline
　　　　　　　　　　　Tel: (020) 7219 6917
　　　　　　　　　　　E-mail: tinlined@parliament.uk
*Constituency Office* . . . . 52 Bebington Road, New Ferry,
　　　　　　　　　　　Wirral, CH62 5BM
　　　　　　　　　　　Tel: (0151) 643 8797 Fax: (0151) 643 8546
　　　　　　　　　　　Parliamentary Assistant –
　　　　　　　　　　　　Mr Rob Buckingham
　　　　　　　　　　　Caseworker – Mr Chris Lawler
*Parliamentary Interests* . Economic Development; Foreign Affairs;
　　　　　　　　　　　Regional Development; Trade and Industry;
　　　　　　　　　　　China; Vietnam
*Leisure Interests* . . . . . . Opera; Theatre; Music; Reading; Walking;
　　　　　　　　　　　Sculpture; Football (Tranmere Rovers FC)

**Chapman, Sir Sydney** Chipping Barnet
**Conservative** . . . . . . . Majority 2,701 over Lab
*Born.* . . . . . . . . . . . . . . 17th October 1935 in Macclesfield
*Educated* . . . . . . . . . . Rugby School; Manchester University
*Elected.* . . . . . . . . . . . . 1970 - 74 MP for Birmingham Handsworth
　　　　　　　　　　　1979 MP for Chipping Barnet
*Offices Held* . . . . . . . . 1988 - 90 Assistant Government Whip
　　　　　　　　　　　1990 - 95 Government Whip
　　　　　　　　　　　　(Lord Commissioner H M Treasury, then
　　　　　　　　　　　　Vice-Chamberlain, H M Household)
　　　　　　　　　　　1997 - 2001 Chairman, Accommodation and
　　　　　　　　　　　　Works Committee, House of Commons
*Constituency Office* . . . . 163 High Street, Barnet, Hertfordshire,
　　　　　　　　　　　EN5 5SU
　　　　　　　　　　　Tel: (020) 8449 7345 Fax: (020) 8449 7346
　　　　　　　　　　　E-mail: chapmansb@parliament.uk
　　　　　　　　　　　Agent – Mr Stephen Payne
*Parliamentary Interests* . Environment; Construction;
　　　　　　　　　　　Architectural Heritage
*Leisure Interests* . . . . . . Tree Spotting

**Chaytor, David** . . . . Bury North
**Labour** . . . . . . . . . . . Majority 6,532 over Con
*Born.* . . . . . . . . . . . . . . 3rd August 1949 in Bury
*Educated* . . . . . . . . . . Bury Grammar School; University of London;
　　　　　　　　　　　Leeds University
*Elected* . . . . . . . . . . . . 1997 MP for Bury North
*Commons Office* . . . . . . Tel: (020) 7219 6625 Fax: (020) 7219 0952
　　　　　　　　　　　E-mail: chaytord@parliament.uk
　　　　　　　　　　　Office Manager – Ms Sheena Whittingham
　　　　　　　　　　　E-mail: whittinghams@parliament.uk
*Constituency Office* . . . . 14a Market Street, Bury, Lancashire, BL9 0AJ
　　　　　　　　　　　Tel: (0161) 764 2023 Fax: (0161) 763 3410
　　　　　　　　　　　E-mail: turnerj@parliament.uk
　　　　　　　　　　　Office Manager – Mrs Janet Turner
*Parliamentary Interests* . Environment; Education; International
　　　　　　　　　　　Development; Trade and Industry;
　　　　　　　　　　　Foreign Affairs
*Leisure Interests* . . . . . . Walking; Cycling; Restoring Old Buildings;
　　　　　　　　　　　Forestry; Film; Opera

**Chidgey, David** . . . . Eastleigh
**Liberal Democrat** . . . Majority 3,058 over Con
*Born.* . . . . . . . . . . . . . . 1942
*Educated* . . . . . . . . . . Portsmouth Polytechnic;
　　　　　　　　　　　Portsmouth Naval College
*Elected.* . . . . . . . . . . . . 1994 MP for Eastleigh (By-election)
*Offices Held* . . . . . . . . 1995 - 97 Liberal Democrat Spokesman on
　　　　　　　　　　　Transport
　　　　　　　　　　　1997 - 99 Liberal Democrat Spokesman on
　　　　　　　　　　　Trade and Industry
*Commons Office* . . . . . . Tel: (020) 7219 4298 Fax: (020) 7219 2810
　　　　　　　　　　　E-mail: chidgeyd@parliament.uk
　　　　　　　　　　　Office Manager – Miss Kate Heywood
　　　　　　　　　　　E-mail: heywoodk@parliament.uk
*Constituency Office* . . . . 109A Leigh Road, Eastleigh,
　　　　　　　　　　　Hampshire, SO50 9DR
　　　　　　　　　　　Tel: (023) 8062 0007 Fax: (023) 8061 8245
　　　　　　　　　　　Manager – Mrs Scilla Davies-Dear
*Parliamentary Interests* . Built Environment; Commerce, Foreign
　　　　　　　　　　　Affairs; Defence; Industry; International
　　　　　　　　　　　Development; Transport
*Leisure Interests* . . . . . . Cricket; Golf; Tennis

**Chope, Christopher** OBE Christchurch
**Conservative** . . . . . . . Majority 13,544 over Lib Dem
*Born.* . . . . . . . . . . . . . . 1947
*Educated* . . . . . . . . . . Marlborough College; St Andrews University;
　　　　　　　　　　　Inns of Court Law School
*Elected.* . . . . . . . . . . . . 1983 - 92 MP for Southampton Itchen
　　　　　　　　　　　1997 MP for Christchurch
*Offices Held* . . . . . . . . 1979 - 83 Leader, London Borough of
　　　　　　　　　　　Wandsworth Council
　　　　　　　　　　　1986 - 90 Parliamentary Secretary,
　　　　　　　　　　　Department of Environment
　　　　　　　　　　　1990 - 92 Minister for Roads and Traffic,
　　　　　　　　　　　Department of Transport
　　　　　　　　　　　1997 - 98 Opposition Spokesman on
　　　　　　　　　　　Environment, Transport and the Regions
　　　　　　　　　　　1998 - 99 Opposition Spokesman on Trade
　　　　　　　　　　　and Industry
　　　　　　　　　　　2001 - 02 Opposition Spokesman on
　　　　　　　　　　　Treasury Matters
　　　　　　　　　　　2002 - Opposition Spokesman on
　　　　　　　　　　　Transport and Environment
*Commons Office* . . . . . . Tel: (020) 7219 5808
*Constituency Office* . . . . Tel: (01425) 674120 Fax: (01425) 674558
　　　　　　　　　　　Personal Assistant – Mrs C Chope
*Parliamentary Interests* . Trade and Industry; Shipping;
　　　　　　　　　　　Local Government; Law and Order

# MEMBERS OF THE HOUSE OF COMMONS

**Clapham, Michael** . Barnsley West and Penistone
**Labour** . . . . . . . . . . . Majority 12,352 over Con
*Born.* . . . . . . . . . . . . . 15th May 1943 in Barnsley, Yorkshire
*Educated* . . . . . . . . . . Barnsley Technical College;
Leeds Polytechnic; Leeds University;
Bradford University
*Elected* . . . . . . . . . . . . 1992 MP for Barnsley West and Penistone
*Commons Office* . . . . . Tel: (020) 7219 2907 Fax: (020) 7219 5015
E-mail: claphamm@parliament.uk
Executive Secretary/Personal Assistant –
Mrs Yvonne Clapham
Tel: (020) 7219 0477
E-mail: claphamy@parliament.uk
*Constituency Office* . . . . 18b Regent Street, Barnsley,
South Yorkshire, S70 2HG
Tel: (01226) 731244 Fax: (01226) 731259
Secretary – Mrs Molly Sheerian
*Parliamentary Interests* . Coal Industry; Education; Energy;
Health; Health and Safety at Work;
Industry; Social Security;
*Leisure Interests* . . . . . . Family; Gardening; Reading; Walking

**Clappison, James** . . Hertsmere
**Conservative** . . . . . . . Majority 4,902 over Lab
*Born.* . . . . . . . . . . . . . 14th September 1956 in Beverley, Yorkshire
*Educated* . . . . . . . . . . St Peter's School, York;
Queen's College, Oxford;
Central London Polytechnic
*Elected* . . . . . . . . . . . . 1992 MP for Hertsmere
*Offices Held* . . . . . . . . 1995 - 97 Parliamentary Secretary,
Department of Environment
1997 - 99 Opposition Spokesman on
Home Affairs
1999 - 2000 Opposition Spokesman on
Employment and Education
2000 - 01, 2002 Opposition Spokesman
on Treasury Matters
2001 - 02 Opposition Spokesman on Work
*Commons Office* . . . . . Tel: (020) 7219 4152 Fax: (020) 7219 0514
E-mail: clappisonj@parliament.uk
*Constituency Office* . . . . 104 High Street, London Colney,
Hertfordshire, AL2 1QL
Tel: (01727) 828221 Fax: (01727) 824044
Constituency Agent – Mr Mark Swan
E-mail: mark@tory-herts.org
*Parliamentary Interests* . Personal Freedom. Free Enterprise Economy;
International Affairs; Law and Order;
Agriculture; Education
*Leisure Interests* . . . . . . Reading; Bridge; Family

**Clark, Helen** . . . . . Peterborough
**Labour** . . . . . . . . . . . Majority 2,854 over Con
*Born.* . . . . . . . . . . . . . 23rd December 1954 in Derby
*Educated* . . . . . . . . . . Spondon Park Grammar School, Derby;
Bristol University
*Elected.* . . . . . . . . . . . 1997 MP for Peterborough
*(first elected as Helen Brinton)*
*Commons Office* . . . . . Tel: (020) 7219 4469 Fax: (020) 7219 0951
Political Assistant – Mrs Isobel Moses
Tel: (020) 7219 6881
Political Adviser – Dr Maggie Voysey Paun
Tel: (020) 7219 6062
E-mail: paunm@parliament.uk
*Constituency Office* . . . . Peterborough Business Centre,
Thurston House, 80 Lincoln Road,
Peterborough, PE1 2SN
Tel: (01733) 703000 Fax: (01733) 704000
*Parliamentary Interests* . Environment; Home Affairs; Health
*Leisure Interests* . . . . . . Reading; Modern Films

**Clark, Dr Lynda** QC Edinburgh Pentlands
**Labour** . . . . . . . . . . . Majority 1,742 over Con
*Born.* . . . . . . . . . . . . . 26th February 1949 in Dundee
*Educated* . . . . . . . . . . Lawside Academy, Dundee;
St Andrews University; Edinburgh University
*Elected.* . . . . . . . . . . . 1997 MP for Edinburgh Pentlands
*Office Held.* . . . . . . . . 1999 - Advocate General for Scotland
*Commons Office* . . . . . Tel: (020) 7219 2198 Fax: (020) 7219 2423
*Parliamentary Interests* . Constitutional Reform; Health; Older People
*Leisure Interests* . . . . . . Reading; Arts

**Clark, Paul** . . . . . . . Gillingham
**Labour** . . . . . . . . . . . Majority 2,272 over Con
*Born.* . . . . . . . . . . . . . 29th April 1957 in Gillingham
*Educated* . . . . . . . . . . Gillingham Grammar School; Keele University
University of Derby
*Elected.* . . . . . . . . . . . 1997 MP for Gillingham
*Office Held.* . . . . . . . . 2003 - Assistant Government Whip
*Commons Office* . . . . . Tel: (020) 7219 5207 Fax: (020) 7219 2545
E-mail: clarkp@parliament.uk
Web: http://www.paulclark.labour.co.uk
PA/Researcher – Ms Amanda Fitzgerald
E-mail: fitzgeralda@parliament.uk
*Constituency Office* . . . . 62a Watling Street, Gillingham,
Kent, ME7 2YN
Tel: (01634) 574261 Fax: (01634) 574276
Case Worker – Mr Rob Russel-Pavier
E-mail: russelpavierr@parliament.uk
Administrator/Diary Secretary –
Mrs Julie Clark
E-mail: clarkjh@parliament.uk
Researcher Assistant –
Ms Jennie Scott
Tel (01634) 281180
E-mail: scottj@parliament.uk
*Parliamentary Interests* . Transport; Strategic Planning; Environment;
Regional Economy; Japan and Far East
*Leisure Interests* . . . . . . Family; Reading Political Biographies;
Genealogy

# MEMBERS OF THE HOUSE OF COMMONS

**Clarke, Rt Hon Charles**  Norwich South
**Labour** . . . . . . . . . . Majority 8,816 over Con
*Born*. . . . . . . . . . . . . 21st September 1950 in London
*Educated* . . . . . . . . . Highgate School, London;
     King's College, Cambridge
*Elected*. . . . . . . . . . . 1997 MP for Norwich South
*Offices Held* . . . . . . . 1998 - 99 Parliamentary Secretary,
     Department for Education and Employment
     1999 - 2001 Minister of State, Home Office
     2001 - 02 Minister without Portfolio and
     Chairman of the Labour Party
     2002 - Secretary of State for Education
     and Skills
*Commons Office* . . . . . Tel: (020) 7219 1194/6496
     Fax: (020) 7219 0526
     Special Adviser – Ms Lisa Tremble
     E-mail: tremblel@parliament.uk
     Research Assistant – Miss Chloe Smith
     E-mail: smithce@parliament.uk
*Constituency Office* . . . . 59 Bethel Street, Norwich, Norfolk, NR2 1NL
     Tel: (01603) 219902 Fax: (01603) 663502
     Web: http://www.norwich-labour-mps.org.uk
     Senior Caseworker – Ms Sally Maclaine

**Clarke, Rt Hon Kenneth,** QC Rushcliffe
**Conservative** . . . . . . Majority 7,357 over Lab
*Born*. . . . . . . . . . . . . . 2nd July 1940 in Nottingham
*Educated* . . . . . . . . . . Nottingham High School;
     Gonville and Caius College, Cambridge
*Elected*. . . . . . . . . . . . 1970 MP for Rushcliffe
*Offices Held* . . . . . . . . 1972 - 74 Assistant Government Whip
     1974 - Government Whip (Lord
     Commissioner, H M Treasury)
     1974 - 76 Opposition Spokesman on Social
     Services
     1976 - 79 Opposition Spokesman on Industry
     1979 - 82 Parliamentary Secretary,
     Department of Transport
     1982 - 85 Minister of State, Department of
     Health and Social Security
     1985 - 87 Paymaster General and
     Minister for Employment
     1987 - 88 Chancellor of the Duchy of
     Lancaster and Minister for
     Trade and Industry
     1988 - 90 Secretary of State for Health
     1990 - 92 Secretary of State for
     Education and Science
     1992 - 93 Home Secretary
     1993 - 97 Chancellor of the Exchequer
*Commons Office* . . . . . Tel: (020) 7219 5189 Fax: (020) 7219 4841
     E-mail: clarkek@parliament.uk
     Private Secretary – Ms Debbie Sugg
     E-mail: suggd@parliament.uk
*Constituency Office* . . . . Rushcliffe House, 17/19 Rectory Road,
     West Bridgford, Nottingham, NG2 6BE
     Tel: (0115) 981 7224 Fax: (0115) 981 7273
     Agent – Mr Ian Cooper

**Clarke, Rt Hon Tom** CBE Coatbridge and Chryston
**Labour** . . . . . . . . . . Majority 15,314 over SNP
*Born*. . . . . . . . . . . . . 10th January 1941 in Coatbridge
*Educated* . . . . . . . . . Columba High School, Coatbridge;
     Scottish College of Commerce
*Elected*. . . . . . . . . . . 1982 MP for Coatbridge and Airdrie
     (By-election), then (1983) Monklands West
     and (1997) Coatbridge and Chryston
*Offices Held* . . . . . . . 1975 - 82 Provost of Monklands
     1978 - 80 President, Convention of Scottish
     Local Authorities
     1986 - 87 Opposition Spokesman on
     Scottish Affairs
     1987 - 90 Opposition Spokesman on Health
     and Social Services
     1992 - 93 Shadow Scottish Secretary
     1993 - 94 Opposition Spokesman on
     Development and Co-operation
     1994 - 97 Opposition Spokesman on Disabled
     1997 - 98 Minister of State, Department for
     Culture, Media and Sport
*Commons Office* . . . . . Tel: (020) 7219 5007 Fax: (020) 7219 0760
     E-mail: clarket@parliament.uk
     Parliamentary Assistant – Mr Sam Harty
*Constituency Office* . . . . Municipal Buildings, Kildonan Street,
     Coatbridge, Lanarkshire, ML5 3LF
     Tel: (01236) 600800 Fax: (01236) 600808
     Secretary – Ms Lindsay McNeill
     Assistant Secretary – Mrs Dianne Willis
*Parliamentary Interests* . Disability Issues; Film Industry;
     International Development;
     International Economy
*Leisure Interests* . . . . . Football; Golf; Reading; Walking

**Clarke, Tony** . . . . . . Northampton South
**Labour** . . . . . . . . . . Majority 885 over Con
*Born*. . . . . . . . . . . . . 6th September 1963 in Northampton
*Educated* . . . . . . . . . Lings Upper School, Northampton
*Elected*. . . . . . . . . . . 1997 MP for Northampton South
*Commons Office* . . . . . Tel: (020) 7219 4465 Fax: (020) 7219 2808
     E-mail: clarkea@parliament.uk
     Web: http://www.tonyclarke.labour.co.uk
     Political Assistant – Mr Leo O'Connor
     Tel: (020) 7219 2886
     E-mail: oconnorl@parliament.uk
*Constituency Office* . . . . 41 York Road, Northampton, NN1 5QJ
     Tel: (01604) 250044 Fax: (01604) 250055
     Office Manager – Mr Ron Johnson
     E-mail: johnsonr@parliament.uk
     Personal Assistant – Mrs Jayne Croke
     E-mail: crokej@parliament.uk
*Parliamentary Interests* . Environment; Local Government; Leisure;
     Northern Ireland
*Leisure Interests* . . . . . Football (Northampton Town FC);
     Sport; Travel

# MEMBERS OF THE HOUSE OF COMMONS

**Clelland, David** . . . . Tyne Bridge
**Labour** . . . . . . . . . . . Majority 14,889 over Con
*Born*. . . . . . . . . . . . . . 27th June 1943 in Gateshead, Tyneside
*Educated* . . . . . . . . . . Gateshead Technical College;
                    Hebburn Technical College
*Elected*. . . . . . . . . . . . 1985 MP for Tyne Bridge (By-election)
*Offices Held* . . . . . . . . 1983 - 85 Leader, Gateshead Metropolitan
                    Borough Council
                    1995 - 97 Opposition Whip
                    1997 - 2000 Assistant Government Whip
                    2000 - 01 Government Whip (Lord
                    Commissioner, H M Treasury)
*Commons Office* . . . . . Tel: (020) 7219 3669
                    Pager: 07644 001404
                    E-mail: davidclellandmp@aol.com
                    Web: http://www.david-clelland.org.uk
*Constituency Office*. . . . 19 Ravensworth Road, Dunston, Gateshead,
                    NE11 9AB
                    Tel: (0191) 420 0200 Fax: (0191) 420 0201
                    Secretary/PA– Mrs Brenda Graham
                    Tel: (0191) 420 0300 Fax: (0191) 420 0301
*Parliamentary Interests* . Engineering and Manufacturing Industry;
                    Defence; Civil Service; Environment;
                    Transport; Devolution; House of Lords Reform
*Leisure Interests* . . . . . . Reading; Music. Driving

**Clifton-Brown, Geoffrey** Cotswold
**Conservative** . . . . . . . Majority 11,983 over Lib Dem
*Born*. . . . . . . . . . . . . . 23rd March 1953 in Cambridge
*Educated* . . . . . . . . . . Eton College;
                    Royal Agricultural College, Cirencester
*Elected*. . . . . . . . . . . . 1992 MP for Cirencester and Tewksbury,
                    then (1997) Cotswold
*Offices Held* . . . . . . . . 1999 - 2001, 2004 - Opposition Whip
                    2001 - 02 Opposition Spokesman on
                    Housing and Planning
                    2002 - 04 Opposition Spokesman on Local
                    Government and the Regions
*Commons Office* . . . . . Tel: (020) 7219 5147  Fax: (020) 7219 2550
                    E-mail: cliftonbrowng@parliament.uk
                    Web: http://www.gcbmp.demon.co.uk
*Constituency Office*. . . . 7 Rodney Road, Cheltenham, GL50 1HX
                    Tel: (01242) 514551 Fax: (01242) 514949
                    E-mail: hayward@cotswold.tory.org.uk
                    Agent – Mr Hayward Burt
                    Secretary – Mrs Jo Ball
*Parliamentary Interests* . Agriculture; Economy; Europe
*Leisure Interests* . . . . . . Country Pursuits

**Clwyd, Ann** . . . . . . . Cynon Valley
**Labour** . . . . . . . . . . . Majority 12,998 over Plaid Cymru
*Born*. . . . . . . . . . . . . . 21st March 1937 in Denbigh
*Educated* . . . . . . . . . . Holywell Grammar School;
                    Queen's School, Chester;
                    University College of Wales, Bangor
*Elected*. . . . . . . . . . . . 1984 MP for Cynon Valley (By-election)
*Offices Held* . . . . . . . . 1987 - 88 Opposition Spokeswoman on
                    Education and Women's Rights
                    1989 - 92 Shadow Secretary of State for
                    Overseas Development and Co-operation
                    1992 Shadow Welsh Secretary
                    1992 - 93 Shadow National Heritage Secretary
                    1993 - 94 Opposition Spokeswomen on
                    Employment
                    1994 - 95 Opposition Spokeswomen on
                    Foreign Affairs
                    2003 - Prime Minister's Special Envoy on
                    Human Rights in Iraq
*Commons Office* . . . . . Tel: (020) 7219 6609 Fax: (020) 7219 5943
                    E-mail: clwyda@parliament.uk
                    Researcher – Miss Sarah Montgomery
                    Tel: (020) 7219 3437
                    E-mail: montgomerys@parliament.uk
*Constituency Office*. . . . Flat 6, Dean Court, Aberdare, Mid Glamorgan,
                    CF44 7BN
                    Tel: (01685) 871394 Fax: (01685) 883006
                    PA/Secretary – Ms Jean Fitzgerald
                    E-mail: fitzgeraldj@parliament.uk
*Parliamentary Interests* . Human Rights;  International Development

**Coaker, Vernon** . . . Gedling
**Labour** . . . . . . . . . . . Majority 5,598 over Con
*Born*. . . . . . . . . . . . . . 17th June 1953 in London
*Educated* . . . . . . . . . . Drayton Manor Grammar School;
                    Warwick University
*Elected*. . . . . . . . . . . . 1997 MP for Gedling
*Offices Held* . . . . . . . . 2002 PPS to Estelle Morris (Secretary of
                    State for Education and Skills)
                    2002 - 03 PPS to Tessa Jowell (Secretary of
                    State for Culture, Media and Sport)
                    2003 - Assistant Government Whip
*Commons Office* . . . . . Tel: (020) 7219 6627
                    Pager: 07644 071884
                    E-mail: coakerv@parliament.uk
                    Web: http://www.vernon-coaker-mp.co.uk
*Constituency Office*. . . . 2A Parkyn Road, Daybrook,
                    Nottingham, NG5 6BG
                    Tel: (0115) 920 4224 Fax: (0115) 920 4500
                    Secretary – Mrs Janet Peet
                    Parliamentary Assistant – Dr Colette Roberts
*Parliamentary Interests* . Crime; Education; Foreign Affairs (especially
                    Eastern Europe); International Development;
                    Welfare Reform; Youth
*Leisure Interests* . . . . . . Walking; Media;
                    Sport (Tottenham Hotspur FC)

# MEMBERS OF THE HOUSE OF COMMONS

**Coffey, Ann** . . . . . . Stockport
**Labour** . . . . . . . . . . Majority 11,569 over Con
*Born* . . . . . . . . . . . . 31st August 1946 in Inverness
*Educated* . . . . . . . . . . South Bank Polytechnic, London;
Manchester University;
Walsall College of Education
*Elected* . . . . . . . . . . . 1992 MP for Stockport
*Offices Held* . . . . . . . . 1995 - 96 Opposition Whip
1996 - 97 Opposition Spokesman on Health
1997 - 98 PPS to Tony Blair (Prime Minister)
1999 - PPS to Alistair Darling
(as Secretary of State for Work and
Pensions, then as Secretary of
State for Transport)
*Commons Office* . . . . . Tel: (020) 7219 4546 Fax: (020) 7219 0770
*Constituency Office* . . . 207A Bramhall Lane, Stockport, SK2 6JA
Tel: (0161) 483 2600 Fax: (0161) 483 1070
Constituency Assistant – Ms Bridget Dunbar
E-mail: dunbarb@parliament.uk
Parliamentary Assistant – Mr Keith Fenwick
Tel: (0161) 483 0405 Fax: (0161) 483 1070
E-mail: fenwickk@parliament.uk

**Cohen, Harry** . . . . . Leyton and Wanstead
**Labour** . . . . . . . . . . . 12,904 over Con
*Born* . . . . . . . . . . . . . 10th December 1949 in Hackney, London
*Educated* . . . . . . . . . . George Gascoigne Secondary School;
Birkbeck College, London
*Elected* . . . . . . . . . . . 1983 MP for Leyton, then (1997)
Leyton and Wanstead
*Commons Office* . . . . . Tel: (020) 7219 6376 /2813
Fax: (020) 7219 0438
E-mail: cohenh@parliament.uk
Web: http://www.harrycohen.labour.co.uk
Caseworker – Mr Elijah Mariam
E-mail: mariame@parliament.uk
Researcher/Parliamentary Assistant –
Miss Zoe Williams
E-mail: williamsz@parliament.uk

**Coleman, Iain** . . . . . Hammersmith and Fulham
**Labour** . . . . . . . . . . . Majority 2,015 over Con
*Born* . . . . . . . . . . . . . 18th January 1958 in Hammersmith
*Educated* . . . . . . . . . . Tonbridge School, Kent
*Elected* . . . . . . . . . . . 1997 MP for Hammersmith and Fulham
*Offices Held* . . . . . . . . Formerly Leader and Mayor, Hammersmith
and Fulham London Borough Council
*Constituency Office* . . . . 28 Greyhound Road, London, W6 8NX
Tel: (020) 7381 5074 Fax: (020) 7386 5415
E-mail: sheenanj@parliament.uk
Assistants – Ms Emma Meredith
Ms Jane Sheenan
*Parliamentary Interests* . Housing; Employment; Asylum/Immigration;
Local Government
*Leisure Interests* . . . . . Football; Opera; Cooking

**Collins, Tim** CBE . . . Westmorland and Lonsdale
**Conservative** . . . . . . Majority 3,147 over Lib Dem
*Born* . . . . . . . . . . . . . 7th May 1964
*Educated* . . . . . . . . . . Chigwell School; London School of Economics;
King's College, London
*Elected* . . . . . . . . . . . 1997 MP for Westmorland and Lonsdale
*Offices Held* . . . . . . . . 1998 - 99 Opposition Whip
1999 - 2001 Senior Vice-Chairman,
Conservative Party
2001 - 02 Shadow Minister for the
Cabinet Office
2002 - 03 Shadow Secretary of State for
Transport
2003 - Shadow Secretary for Education
*Constituency Office* . . . . 112 Highgate, Kendal, Cumbria, LA9 4HE
Tel: (01539) 721010 Fax: (01539) 733039
E-mail: listening@timcollins.co.uk
Agent – Mr Peter Williamson
Executive Assistant – Mr Mark Graham
Secretary – Mrs Barbara Lewis
*Parliamentary Interests* . Constitution; Defence; Economy;
Employment; Europe; Transport
*Leisure Interests* . . . . . Theatre; Cinema; Reading

**Colman, Tony** . . . . . Putney
**Labour** . . . . . . . . . . . Majority 2,771 over Con
*Born* . . . . . . . . . . . . . 24th July 1943 in Upper Sheringham, Norfolk
*Educated* . . . . . . . . . . Paston Grammar School, North Walsham,
Norfolk; Magdalene College, Cambridge
*Elected* . . . . . . . . . . . 1997 MP for Putney
*Offices Held* . . . . . . . . 1991 - 97 Leader, London Borough
of Merton Council
*Commons Office* . . . . . Tel: (020) 7219 2843 Fax: (020) 7219 1137
Parliamentary Assistant – Mr William Flower
E-mail: flowerw@parliament.uk
Caseworker – Mr Denis Meehan
Researcher – Ms Ruth Smith
E-mail: smithrm@parliament.uk

**Connarty, Michael** . Falkirk East
**Labour** . . . . . . . . . . . Majority 10,712 over SNP
*Born* . . . . . . . . . . . . . 3rd September 1947 in Coatbridge
*Educated* . . . . . . . . . . St Patrick's High School, Coatbridge;
Langside College; Stirling University;
Glasgow University;
Jordanhill College of Education
*Elected* . . . . . . . . . . . 1992 MP for Falkirk East
*Offices Held* . . . . . . . . 1980 - 90 Leader, Stirling District Council
*Commons Office* . . . . . Tel: (020) 7219 5071 Fax: (020) 7219 2541
Mobile: 07973 311705
E-mail: connartym@parliament.uk
Web: http://www.mconnartymp.org.uk
Researcher – Miss Helen Neal
Tel: (020) 7219 2487 Fax: (020) 7219 2461
E-mail: nealh@parliament.uk
*Constituency Office* . . . . Room 8, 5 Kerse Road, Grangemouth,
Stirlingshire, FK3 8HQ
Tel: (01324) 474832 Fax: (01324) 666811
E-mail: michael1@mconnartymp.org.uk
Secretaries – Mrs Jacqueline Traynor
Ms Jackie West
*Parliamentary Interests* . Chemical Industries; Offshore Oil and Gas
Industry; Science and Technology; Energy;
Middle East
*Leisure Interests* . . . . . Family; Jazz; Opera; Hill Walking

# MEMBERS OF THE HOUSE OF COMMONS

**Conway, Derek** TD. Old Bexley and Sidcup
**Conservative** . . . . . . Majority 3,345 over Lab
*Born.* . . . . . . . . . . . . . 15th February 1953 in Newcastle-upon-Tyne
*Educated* . . . . . . . . . . Beacon Hill Boys School;
Gateshead Technical College;
Newcastle-upon-Tyne Polytechnic
*Elected.* . . . . . . . . . . . 1983 - 97 MP for Shrewsbury and Atcham
2001 MP for Old Bexley and Sidcup
*Offices Held* . . . . . . . . 1993 - 97 Assistant Government Whip
1994 - 97 Government Whip
(Lord Commissioner, H M Treasury; then
Vice-Chamberlain of H M Household)
2001 - Chairman, Accommodation and
Works Committee, House of Commons
*Commons Office* . . . . . . E-mail: conwayd@parliament.uk
*Constituency Office* . . . . 19 Station Road, Sidcup, Kent, DA5 7EB
Tel: (020) 8308 0398 Fax: (0200 8300 9270
*Parliamentary Interests* . Defence; Charities; Animal Welfare;
International Affairs
*Leisure Interests* . . . . . . History

**Cook, Frank** . . . . . . Stockton North
**Labour** . . . . . . . . . . . Majority 14,647 over Con
*Born.* . . . . . . . . . . . . . 3rd November 1935 in Hartlepool
*Educated* . . . . . . . . . . Corby School, Sunderland;
De La Salle College, Manchester;
Leeds Institute of Education
*Elected.* . . . . . . . . . . . 1983 MP for Stockton North
*Commons Office* . . . . . . Tel: (020) 7219 4527 Fax: (020) 7219 4303
Mobile: 07956 882444
E-mail: cookf@parliament.uk
Web: http://www.frankcook.co.uk
*Constituency Office* . . . . Queensway Building, Billingham Health
Centre, Billingham, Cleveland, TS23 2LA
Tel: (01642) 643288 Fax: (01642) 803271
Administrator - Mr William Stonehouse
Caseworker – Mr Andrew McMann
Researcher – Mr George O'Neill
Tel: (01642) 803272
*Parliamentary Interests* . Waste Disposal; Alternative Energy;
Gun Control; Shooters' Rights
*Leisure Interests* . . . . . . Photography; Walking; Teesside Football

**Cook, Rt Hon Robin** Livingston
**Labour** . . . . . . . . . . . Majority 10,616 over SNP
*Born.* . . . . . . . . . . . . . 28th February 1946 in Bellshill
*Educated* . . . . . . . . . . Aberdeen Grammar School;
Royal High School, Edinburgh;
Edinburgh University
*Elected.* . . . . . . . . . . . 1974 MP for Edinburgh Central,
then (1983) Livingston
*Offices Held* . . . . . . . . 1980 - 83 Opposition Spokesman on
Treasury and Economic Affairs
1983 - 84 Opposition Spokesman on
European Affairs
1984 - 86 Labour Party Campaigns
Co-ordinator
1986 - 87 Opposition Spokesman on
Trade and Industry
1987 - 92 Shadow Health Secretary
1992 - 94 Shadow Trade and Industry
Secretary
1994 - 97 Shadow Foreign Secretary
1997 - 2001 Foreign Secretary
2001 - 03 President of the Council and
Leader of the House of Commons
2001 - 03 Chairman, Modernisation of House
of Commons Committee
*Constituency Office* . . . . 4 Newyearfield Farm, Hawk Brae, Ladywell,
Livingston, EH54 5EP
Tel: (01506) 497961 Fax: (01506) 497962
Web: http://www.robincook.org.uk
Personal Assistant – Mr John Duncan
E-mail: john.duncan@scottish.parliament.uk
*Parliamentary Interests* . Foreign Affairs; Housing
*Leisure Interests* . . . . . . Horse Racing

**Cooper, Yvette** . . . . Pontefract and Castleford
**Labour** . . . . . . . . . . . Majority 16,378 over Con
*Born.* . . . . . . . . . . . . . 20th March 1969 in Inverness
*Educated* . . . . . . . . . . Eggars Comprehensive, Alton, Hampshire;
Balliol College, Oxford; Harvard University;
London School of Economics
*Elected.* . . . . . . . . . . . 1997 MP for Pontefract and Castleford
*Offices Held* . . . . . . . . 1999 - 2002 Parliamentary Secretary,
Department of Health
2002 - 03 Parliamentary Secretary,
Lord Chancellor's Department
2003 - Parliamentary Secretary,
Office of the Deputy Prime Minister
*Commons Office* . . . . . . Tel: (020) 7219 5080 Fax: (020) 7219 0912
E-mail: coopery@parliament.uk
*Constituency Office* . . . . 2 Wesley Street, Castleford,
West Yorkshire, WF10 1AE
Tel & Fax: (01977) 553388
E-mail: coopery@parliament.uk
Constituency Manager – Ms Reini Schuhle
*Parliamentary Interests* . Employment; Energy (Coal Industry); EMU;
Economy
*Leisure Interests* . . . . . . Swimming; Painting; Watching Disney Videos

# MEMBERS OF THE HOUSE OF COMMONS

**Corbyn, Jeremy** . . . Islington North
**Labour** . . . . . . . . . . . Majority 12,958 over Lib Dem
*Born*. . . . . . . . . . . . . . 26th May 1949 in Chippenham, Wiltshire
*Educated* . . . . . . . . . . Adams Grammar School, Shropshire
*Elected*. . . . . . . . . . . . 1983 MP for Islington North
*Commons Office* . . . . . Tel: (020) 7219 3545 Fax: (020) 7219 2328
*Constituency Office*. . . . 213a Blackstock Road, London, N5 2LL
Tel: (020) 7226 5775 Fax: (020) 7226 3775
Caseworkers – Ms Ruth Clarke
Mr Dave Horan
*Parliamentary Interests* . Human Rights; Miscarriages of Justice;
Environment; Ireland; Disarmament;
Transport; International Development
*Leisure Interests* . . . . . . Cycling; Gardening; Woodcraft

**Cormack, Sir Patrick** Staffordshire South
**Conservative** . . . . . . . Majority 6,881 over Lab
*Born*. . . . . . . . . . . . . . 18th May 1939 in Lincolnshire
*Educated* . . . . . . . . . . Havelock School, Grimsby; Hull University
*Elected*. . . . . . . . . . . . 1970 MP for Cannock, then (1974)
Staffordshire South West and (from 1983)
Staffordshire South
*Offices Held* . . . . . . . . 1987 - 2001 Chairman, Works of Art Advisory
Committee, House of Commons
1997 - 2000 Deputy Shadow Leader of the
House of Commons
1999 - 2000 Opposition Spokesman on
Constitutional Affairs
*Commons Office* . . . . . . Tel: (020) 7219 5019 Fax: (020) 7219 6805
Secretary – Miss Mary McDonald
PA/Research Assistant – Mr Richard Willmett
*Constituency Office* . . . . The Firs, Station Road, Codsall,
Wolverhampton, WV8 1BX
Tel: (01902) 844985 Fax: (01902) 844949
E-mail: ssca@talk21.com
Secretary – Mrs June Sharman
*Parliamentary Interests* . Foreign Affairs; Heritage; Education
*Leisure Interests* . . . . . . Visiting Old Churches

**Corston, Rt Hon Jean** Bristol East
**Labour** . . . . . . . . . . . Majority 13,392 over Con
*Born*. . . . . . . . . . . . . . 5th May 1942 in Hull
*Educated* . . . . . . . . . . Yeovil Girls' High School; Open University;
London School of Economics
*Elected*. . . . . . . . . . . . 1992 MP for Bristol East
*Offices Held* . . . . . . . . 1997 - 2000 PPS to David Blunkett
(Secretary of State for Education and
Employment)
2001 - Chair, Parliamentary Labour Party
2001 - Chairman, Joint Commons/Lords
Committee on Human Rights
*Commons Office* . . . . . . Tel: (020) 7219 4575 Fax: (020) 7219 4878
Pager: 07644 006454
E-mail: corstonj@parliament.uk
Web: http://www.epolitix.com/jean-corston
Research Assistant – Ms Hilary Evans
Tel: (020) 7219 1568
E-mail: evansh@parliament.uk
*Constituency Office* . . . . PO Box 1105, Bristol, BS99 2DP
Tel: (0117) 939 9901 Fax: (0117) 939 9902
Secretary/Personal Assistant –
Ms Lois Hourigan-Golding
Administration Assistant –
Ms Doreen Lindegaard
*Parliamentary Interests* . Women's Rights; Legal Reform; Children

**Cotter, Brian** . . . . . Weston-super-Mare
**Liberal Democrat** . . . Majority 338 over Con
*Born*. . . . . . . . . . . . . . 24th August 1938 in Ealing
*Educated* . . . . . . . . . . Downside School; North London Polytechnic
*Elected*. . . . . . . . . . . . 1997 MP for Weston-super-Mare
*Office Held* . . . . . . . . . 1997 - Liberal Democrat Spokesman on
Trade and Industry
*Commons Office* . . . . . . Tel: (020) 7219 4357 Fax: (020) 7219 2277
E-mail: cotterb@parliament.uk
Web: http://www.revinell.demon.co.uk
Research Assistant – Miss Sarah Taft
E-mail: tafts@parliament.uk
*Constituency Office* . . . . 8a Alexandra Parade, Weston-super-Mare,
Somerset, BS23 1QT
Tel: (01934) 419200 Fax: (01934) 419300
E-mail: brian@briancotter.org
Head of Office – Ms Lorraine Bedford
*Parliamentary Interests* . Autism; Business; China; Rwanda; Disability;
Tourism
*Leisure Interests* . . . . . . Cinema; Music; Reading; Travel

**Cousins, Jim** . . . . . . Newcastle-upon-Tyne Central
**Labour** . . . . . . . . . . . Majority 11,605 over Lib Dem
*Born*. . . . . . . . . . . . . . 23rd February 1944 in Hammersmith, London
*Educated* . . . . . . . . . . New College, Oxford;
London School of Economics
*Elected*. . . . . . . . . . . . 1987 MP for Newcastle-upon-Tyne Central
*Offices Held* . . . . . . . . 1981 - 86 Deputy Leader, Tyne and Wear
County Council
1992 - 94 Opposition Spokesman on Trade
and Industry
1994 - 95 Opposition Spokesman on Foreign
and Commonwealth Affairs
*Commons Office* . . . . . . Tel: (020) 7219 4204 Fax: (020) 7219 6290
Pager: 07644 002700
E-mail: jcousins@globalnet.co.uk
Parliamentary Assistant – Mr Gareth Myton
Tel: (020) 7219 2268
E-mail: mytong@parliament.uk
*Constituency Office* . . . . 21 Portland Terrace,
Newcastle-upon-Tyne, NE2 1QQ
Tel: (0191) 281 9888 Fax: (0191) 281 3383
Assistant – Mr Jo Mapplebeck
Secretary – Miss Carol MacNeill
*Parliamentary Interests* . Economic Affairs; Financial Services;
Green Issues; Defence
*Leisure Interests* . . . . . . Composting

**Cox, Tom** . . . . . . . . . Tooting
**Labour** . . . . . . . . . . . Majority 10,400 over Con
*Born*. . . . . . . . . . . . . . 9th December 1930 in South Wales
*Educated* . . . . . . . . . . London School of Economics
*Elected*. . . . . . . . . . . . 1970 MP for Wandsworth Central, then
(1974) Tooting
*Offices Held* . . . . . . . . 1974 - 77 Assistant Government Whip
1977 - 79 Government Whip
*Constituency Office* . . . . 611 Garratt Lane, Earlsfield, London,
SW18 4SU
Tel: (020) 8946 2641 Fax: (020) 8944 7433
Assistant – Mrs Jane Bigham

# MEMBERS OF THE HOUSE OF COMMONS

**Cran, James** . . . . . . Beverley and Holderness
**Conservative** . . . . . . Majority 781 over Lab
*Born*. . . . . . . . . . . . . 28th January 1944 in Aberdeenshire
*Educated* . . . . . . . . . . Ruthrieston School, Aberdeen;
     Aberdeen University
*Elected*. . . . . . . . . . . . 1987 - MP for Beverley, then (1997)
     Beverley and Holderness
     1995 - 96 PPS to Sir Patrick Mayhew
     (Secretary of State for Northern Ireland)
*Offices Held* . . . . . . . . 1997 - 2001 Opposition Whip
*Commons Office* . . . . . . Tel: (020) 7219 4445 Fax: (020) 7219 2271
     E-mail: cranp@parliament.uk
*Constituency Office* . . . . 9 Cross Street, Beverley, HU17 9AX
     Tel: (01482) 881316 Fax: (01482) 861667
     E-mail: tory@bevhold.fsnet.co.uk
     Office Administrator – Mrs Elaine Aird
*Parliamentary Interests* . Northern Ireland; Europe; Pensions;
     Industrial and Economic Affairs
*Leisure Interests* . . . . . . Travelling; Military History; Reading


**Cranston, Ross** QC . Dudley North
**Labour** . . . . . . . . . . . . Majority 6,800 over Con
*Born*. . . . . . . . . . . . . . 23rd July 1948
*Educated* . . . . . . . . . . Harvard University, USA; Oxford University;
     University of Queensland
*Elected*. . . . . . . . . . . . 1997 MP for Dudley North
*Office Held* . . . . . . . . . 1998 - 01 Solicitor General
*Commons Office* . . . . . . Tel: (020) 7219 5758 Fax: (020) 7219 2726
     Secretary – Ms Jane Enright
*Constituency Office* . . . . Holloway Chambers, 28 Priory Street, Dudley,
     West Midlands, DY1 1EZ
     Tel: (01384) 233100 Fax: (01384) 233099
     Constituency Assistant – Mr Phil Harris
*Parliamentary Interests* . Treasury; Home Office; Legal Affairs


**Crausby, David**. . . . Bolton North East
**Labour** . . . . . . . . . . . . Majority 8,422 over Con
*Born*. . . . . . . . . . . . . . 17th June 1946 in Bury, Lancashire
*Educated* . . . . . . . . . . Derby Grammar School;
     Bury Technical College
*Elected*. . . . . . . . . . . . 1997 MP for Bolton North East
*Commons Office* . . . . . Tel: (020) 7219 4092 Fax: (020) 7219 3713
     Personal Assistant/Secretary –
     Mrs Enid Crausby
     Researcher – Ms Bilkos Ishmail
*Constituency Office* . . . . 570 Blackburn Road, Astley Bridge,
     Bolton, BL1 7AL
     Tel: (01204) 303340  Fax: (01204) 304401
     Constituency Secretaries/PAs –
     Ms Lisa McGuire
     Mrs Enid Ramsden
*Parliamentary Interests* . Defence; Industrial Relations; Pensions
*Leisure Interests* . . . . . . Football; Walking


**Cruddas, Jon**. . . . . . Dagenham
**Labour** . . . . . . . . . . . . Majority 8,693 over Con
*Born*. . . . . . . . . . . . . . 7th April 1962 in Helston, Cornwall
*Educated* . . . . . . . . . . Oaklands RC Comprehensive, Portsmouth;
     Warwick University
*Elected*. . . . . . . . . . . . 2001 MP for Dagenham
*Commons Office* . . . . . . Tel: (020) 7219 8161
     E-mail: cruddasj@parliament.uk
*Parliamentary Interests* . Labour Market; Employment Law;
     Economic Regeneration
*Leisure Interests* . . . . . . Angling; Golf


**Cryer, Ann**. . . . . . . . Keighley
**Labour** . . . . . . . . . . . . Majority 4,005 over Con
*Born*. . . . . . . . . . . . . . 14th December 1939 in St Annes-on-Sea,
     Lancashire
*Educated* . . . . . . . . . . Spring Bank Secondary Modern School
*Elected*. . . . . . . . . . . . 1997 MP for Keighley
*Commons Office* . . . . . Tel: (020) 7219 6649
     Mobile: 07711 000483
     Pager: 07644 006634
*Constituency Office* . . . Bob Cryer House, 35 Devonshire Street,
     Keighley, West Yorkshire, BD21 2BH
     Tel: (01535) 210083 Fax: (01535) 210085
     Personal Assistant – Mr Mark Taylor
     Caseworker – Mr James Pressley
     Diary Secretary – Mrs Cath Rowen
*Parliamentary Interests* . Peace; Railways; Arts; Home Affairs;
     Women's Rights
*Leisure Interests* . . . . . . Cinema; Gardening; Grandchildren; Theatre


**Cryer, John**. . . . . . . Hornchurch
**Labour** . . . . . . . . . . . Majority 1,482 over Con
*Born*. . . . . . . . . . . . . . 11th April 1964 in Darwen, Lancashire
*Educated* . . . . . . . . . . Oakbank Grammar School, Keighley;
     Hatfield Polytechnic
*Elected*. . . . . . . . . . . . 1997 MP for Hornchurch
*Commons Office* . . . . . Tel: (020) 7219 1134 Fax: (020) 7219 1183
     E-mail: cryerj@parliament.uk
     Parliamentary Assistant/Press Officer –
     Dr Laura Bruni
     E-mail: brunil@parliament.uk
*Constituency Office* . . . . 11 Park Lane, Hornchurch, Essex, RM11 1BB
     Tel: (01708) 742674 Fax: (01708) 753576
     Senior Caseworker – Mr Steve King
     Caseworker – Ms Vanessa Woollacott
*Parliamentary Interests* . Education; Economy; Europe; Health;
     Pensions
*Leisure Interests* . . . . . . Old Cars; Reading; Sports


**Cummings, John** . . Easington
**Labour** . . . . . . . . . . . Majority 21,949 over Con
*Born*. . . . . . . . . . . . . . 6th July 1943 in County Durham
*Educated* . . . . . . . . . . Easington and Durham Technical College
*Elected*. . . . . . . . . . . . 1987 - MP for Easington
*Offices Held* . . . . . . . . 1975 - 76 Chairman and (1979 - 87) Leader,
     Easington District Council
     1994 - 97 Opposition Whip
*Commons Office* . . . . . Tel: (020) 7219 5122
*Constituency Office* . . . . Seaton Holme, Hall Walks, Easington Village,
     Peterlee, County Durham, SR8 3BS
     Tel: (0191) 527 3773  Tel: (0191) 527 9640
     E-mail: adcockr@parliament.uk
     Executive Secretary/PA – Mr Robert Adcock
     Agent – Mr Grahame Morris
*Parliamentary Interests* . Energy; Environment; Coal Industry
*Leisure Interests* . . . . . . Jack Russell Terriers; Walking; Travel

# MEMBERS OF THE HOUSE OF COMMONS

**Cunningham, Rt Hon Dr Jack**  Copeland
**Labour** . . . . . . . . . . . . Majority 4,964 over Con
*Born.* . . . . . . . . . . . . . 4th August 1939 in Newcastle-upon-Tyne
*Educated* . . . . . . . . . . Jarrow Grammar School;
Bede College, Durham University
*Elected.* . . . . . . . . . . . 1970 MP for Whitehaven, then (1983)
Copeland
*Offices Held* . . . . . . . . 1974 - 76 PPS to James Callaghan
(Prime Minister)
1976 - 79 Parliamentary Secretary,
Department of Energy
1979 - 83 Opposition Spokesman on Industry
1983 - 89 Shadow Secretary of State for
Environment
1989 - 92 Shadow Leader of the House
1992 - 94 Shadow Foreign Secretary
1994 - 95 Shadow Trade and Industry
Secretary
1995 - 97 Shadow National Heritage Secretary
1997 - 98 Minister of Agriculture, Fisheries
and Food
1998 - 99 Minister for the Cabinet Office and
Chancellor of the Duchy of Lancaster
2002 - Chairman, Joint Committee on
House of Lords Reform
*Commons Office* . . . . . . Tel: (020) 7219 5222
*Constituency Office* . . . . Ingwell Hall, Westlake Science Park, Moor
Row, Cumbria, CA24 3JZ
Tel & Fax: (01946) 62024
E-mail: contact@copelandclp.fsnet.co.uk
Personal Assistant – Ms Wendy Skillicorn
Research Assistant – Ms Judith Andersen
*Leisure Interests* . . . . . . Fishing; Walking; Music

**Cunningham, Jim**. . Coventry South
**Labour** . . . . . . . . . . . . Majority 8,279 over Con
*Born.* . . . . . . . . . . . . . 4th February 1941 in Coatbridge
*Educated* . . . . . . . . . . St Columba's High, Coatbridge;
Tillicoultry Trade Union College, Scotland
*Elected.* . . . . . . . . . . . 1992 MP for Coventry South East,
then (1997) Coventry South
*Office Held.* . . . . . . . . 1988 - 92 Leader, Coventry City Council
*Commons Office* . . . . . . Tel & Fax: (020) 7219 6362
Parliamentary Assistant – Ms Sarah Bains
*Constituency Office* . . . . 9-11, Palmer House, Palmer Lane,
Coventry, CV1 1HL
Tel & Fax: (024) 7655 3159
Secretary – Ms Patricia Brooks
Researcher – Mr George Duggins
*Parliamentary Interests*. The Economy; Europe
*Leisure Interests* . . . . . . Reading; Walking

**Cunningham, Tony** Workington
**Labour** . . . . . . . . . . . . Majority 10,850 over Con
*Born.* . . . . . . . . . . . . . 16th September 1952 in Workington
*Educated* . . . . . . . . . . Workington Grammar School;
Liverpool University
*Elected.* . . . . . . . . . . . 2001 MP for Workington
*Offices Held* . . . . . . . . 1992 - 94 Leader, Alderdale Borough Council
PPS to Elliot Morley (Minister of State,
Department of the Environment, Food and
Rural Affairs)
*Commons Office* . . . . . . Tel: (020) 7219 8344  Fax: (020) 7219 1947
E-mail: cunninghamt@parliament.uk
Assistant – Mr Jonathan Todd
E-mail: toddj@parliament.uk
*Constituency Office* . . . . The Town Hall, Oxford Street, Workington,
Cumbria, CA14 2RS
Tel: (01900) 65815  Fax: (01900) 68348
E-mail: smithjmt@parliament.uk
Secretary – Mrs Jeanette Smith
Researcher – Miss Moira Saunders
*Parliamentary Interests*. Third World; Education; Tourism; Sport
*Leisure Interests* . . . . . . Reading; Running; Sport

**Curry, Rt Hon David**  Skipton and Ripon
**Conservative** . . . . . . . Majority 12,930 over Lib Dem
*Born.* . . . . . . . . . . . . . 13th June 1944 in Burton-on-Trent
*Educated* . . . . . . . . . . Ripon Grammar School;
Corpus Christi College, Oxford;
Harvard University
*Elected.* . . . . . . . . . . . 1987 MP for Skipton and Ripon
*Offices Held* . . . . . . . . 1989 - 92 Parliamentary Secretary,
Ministry of Agriculture, Fisheries and Food
1992 - 93 Minister of State,
Ministry of Agriculture, Fisheries and Food
1993 - 97 Minister of State,
Department of the Environment
1997 Shadow Minister of Agriculture,
Fisheries and Food
2000 - 01 Chairman, Agriculture Select
Committee, House of Commons
2001 - 03 Chairman, Environment, Food and
Rural Affairs Committee,
House of Commons
2003 - 04 Opposition Spokesman on
Local and Devolved Government
*Commons Office* . . . . . . Tel: (020) 7219 6202
Web: http://www.davidcurry.co.uk
Personal Assistant – Miss Jane Rapson
Assistant – Miss Zoe Ashworth
Tel: (020) 7219 1689
E-mail: ashworthz@parliament.uk
*Constituency Office* . . . . Churchill House, 19 Otley Street, Skipton,
North Yorkshire, BD23 1DY
Tel: (01756) 792092 Fax: (01756) 798742
Agent – Mr Ken Houghton
*Parliamentary Interests*. Agriculture; Housing; Urban Regeneration;
Pension Annuities Reform
*Leisure Interests* . . . . . . Gardening; Sailing;

# MEMBERS OF THE HOUSE OF COMMONS

**Curtis-Thomas, Claire**  Crosby
**Labour** . . . . . . . . . . . Majority 8,353 over Con
*Born.* . . . . . . . . . . . . . 30th April 1958 in Neath, South Wales
*Educated* . . . . . . . . . . Mynyddbach Comprehensive School, Swansea;
University College of Wales, Cardiff;
Aston University; Staffordshire University
*Elected.* . . . . . . . . . . . 1997 MP for Crosby
*Commons Office* . . . . . Tel: (020) 7219 4193 Fax: (020) 7219 1540
E-mail: cutisthomasc@parliament.uk
Researcher/Parliamentary Assistant –
Mr Michael Jakub
E-mail: jakubm@parliament.uk
*Constituency Office* . . . . The Minster, 16 Beach Lawn, Waterloo,
Liverpool, L22 8QA
Tel: (0151) 928 7250 Fax: (0151) 928 9325
Office Manager – Mr Michael Jakub
Correspondence Secretary –
Mr Robin Coveney
Communications Manager – Mr James York
*Parliamentary Interests* . Science; Technology; Education;
Human Rights; Economy; Trade and Industry
*Leisure Interests* . . . . . . Engineering; Gardening; Building and Design;
Fashion

# D

**Dalyell, Tam** . . . . . . Linlithgow
**Labour** . . . . . . . . . . . Majority 9,129 over SNP
*Born.* . . . . . . . . . . . . . . 9th August 1932 in Edinburgh
*Educated* . . . . . . . . . . Edinburgh Academy; Eton College;
King's College, Cambridge;
Moray House Teacher Training College,
Edinburgh
*Elected.* . . . . . . . . . . . 1962 - 83 MP for West Lothian,
then (1983) Linlithgow
*Offices Held* . . . . . . . . 1975 - 79 Member of the European Parliament
1980 - 82 Opposition Spokesman on Science
2001 - "Father" of the House of Commons
*Commons Office* . . . . . Tel: (020) 7219 4343
*Constituency Office* . . . . The Binns, Linlithgow, EH49 7NA
Tel: (01506) 834255
*Parliamentary Interests* . Libya; Iraq; Kosovo; Science Policy
*Leisure Interests* . . . . . . Scottish History

**Darling, Rt Hon Alistair**  Edinburgh Central
**Labour** . . . . . . . . . . . Majority 8,142 over Lib Dem
*Born.* . . . . . . . . . . . . . 28th November 1953 in London
*Educated* . . . . . . . . . . Loretto School; Aberdeen University
*Elected.* . . . . . . . . . . . 1987 MP for Edinburgh Central
*Offices Held* . . . . . . . . 1988 - 92 Opposition Spokesman on
Home Affairs
1992 - 96 Opposition Spokesman on the City
and Financial Services
1996 - 97 Shadow Chief Secretary
to the Treasury
1997 - 98 Chief Secretary to the Treasury
1998 - 01 Secretary of State for Social
Security
2001 - 02 Secretary of State for
Work and Pensions
2002 - Secretary of State for Transport; also
(from 2003) Secretary of State for Scotland
*Constituency Office* . . . . 15a Stafford Street, Edinburgh, EH3 7BU
Tel: (0131) 476 2552 Fax: (0131) 476 3574
Personal Assistant – Mrs Isobel Forrester
Research Assistant – Ms Edna Milne
Tel: (0131) 225 2060

**Davey, Edward.** . . . Kingston and Surbiton
**Liberal Democrat** . . . Majority 15,676 over Con
*Born.* . . . . . . . . . . . . . 25th December 1965 in Nottinghamshire
*Educated* . . . . . . . . . . Nottingham High School;
Jesus College, Oxford;
Birkbeck College, London
*Elected.* . . . . . . . . . . . 1997 MP for Kingston and Surbiton
*Offices Held* . . . . . . . . 1997 - 2002 Liberal Democrat Spokesman on
Economic Affairs
2002 - Liberal Democrat Spokesman on
Housing, Local Government and Regions
(Office of Deputy Prime Minister)
*Commons Office* . . . . . Tel: (020) 7219 1125/3512
Fax: (020) 7219 0250
E-mail: daveye@parliament.uk
Web: http://www.edwarddavey.co.uk
Head of Office – Ms Belinda Eyre-Brook
Parliamentary Assistant –
Miss Suzanna Jones
*Constituency Office* . . . . 21 Berrylands Road, Surbiton, KT5 8QX
Tel: (020) 8288 0161 Fax: (020) 8288 1090
Head of Office – Mrs Belinda Eyre-Brook
E-mail: belinda@edwarddavey.co.uk
Casework Manager – Ms Fran Coyne
Tel: (020) 8288 0297
E-mail: fran@edwarddavey.co.uk
Caseworker – Mr Max Camplin
Tel: (020) 8288 0296
E-mail: max@fedwarddavey.co.uk
*Parliamentary Interests* . Local Government; Housing; Environment;
Democracy
*Leisure Interests* . . . . . . Walking

**Davey, Valerie** . . . . Bristol West
**Labour** . . . . . . . . . . . Majority 4,426 over Lib Dem
*Born.* . . . . . . . . . . . . . 16th April 1940 in Sutton, Surrey
*Educated* . . . . . . . . . . Birmingham University;
University of London Institute of Education
*Elected.* . . . . . . . . . . . 1997 MP for Bristol West
*Commons Office* . . . . . Tel: (020) 7219 3576 Fax: (020) 7219 3658
Pager: 07644 006457
E-mail: valerie.davey@labourbriswest.org.uk
Web: http://www.valeriedavey.labour.co.uk
Research Assistant/Secretary –
Mr Simon Alcock
*Constituency Office* . . . . PO Box 1947, Bristol, BS99 2UG
Tel: (0117) 907 7464 Fax: (0117) 907 7465
Parliamentary Assistant – Miss Rachel Wright
Caseworker – Miss Rachel Pykett
*Parliamentary Interests* . Education; Human Rights
*Leisure Interests* . . . . . . Gardens; Walking; Marmalade making

# MEMBERS OF THE HOUSE OF COMMONS

**David, Wayne** . . . . . Caerphilly
**Labour** . . . . . . . . . . Majority 14,425 over Plaid Cymru
*Born.* . . . . . . . . . . . 1st July 1957 in Bridgend
*Educated* . . . . . . . . . Cynffig Comprehensive School;
University College of Wales, Cardiff;
University College of Wales, Swansea
*Elected* . . . . . . . . . . . 2001 MP for Caerphilly
*Offices Held* . . . . . . . 1989 - 99 MEP for South Wales Central, then
(1994 - 99) South Wales
1995 - 98 Leader, European Parliamentary
Labour Party
*Commons Office* . . . . . Tel: (020) 7219 8152  Fax: (020) 7219 1751
Mobile: 07813 300456
E-mail: davidw@parliament.uk
Assistant – Mr Christopher Bradley
Tel: (020) 7219 5867
E-mail: bradleyc@parliament.uk
*Constituency Office* . . . . Suite 5, St Fagans House, St Fagans Road,
Caerphilly, CF38 1FZ
Tel: (029) 2088 1061  Fax: (029) 2088 1954
Office Manager – Mrs Marlene Rickards
*Parliamentary Interests* . Foreign Affairs; Europe; Devolution;
Economic Policy; Youth Policy
*Leisure Interests* . . . . . . Music

**Davidson, Ian** . . . . . Glasgow Pollok
**Labour** . . . . . . . . . . Majority 11,268 over SNP
*Born.* . . . . . . . . . . . . 8th September 1950 in Jedburgh
*Educated* . . . . . . . . . Jedburgh Grammar School;
Galashiels Academy; Edinburgh University;
Jordanhill College
*Elected.* . . . . . . . . . . 1992 MP for Glasgow Govan, then (1997)
Glasgow Pollok
*Commons Office* . . . . . . Fax: (020) 7219 2238
E-mail: iandavidsonmp@parliament.uk
*Constituency Office* . . . . 25 Kilmuir Road, Glasgow, G46 8BH
Tel: (0141) 621 2216 Fax: (0141) 621 2154
*Parliamentary Interests* . Devolution; Defence; Third World
*Leisure Interests* . . . . . . Running; Rugby; Swimming

**Davies, Rt Hon Denzil** Llanelli
**Labour** . . . . . . . . . . Majority 6,403 over Plaid Cymru
*Born.* . . . . . . . . . . . . 9th October 1938 in Conwyl Elfed
*Educated* . . . . . . . . . Queen Elizabeth Grammar School,
Carmarthen; Pembroke College, Oxford
*Elected.* . . . . . . . . . . 1970 MP for Llanelli
*Offices Held* . . . . . . . 1975 - 79 Minister of State, H M Treasury
1979 - 81 Opposition Spokesman on Treasury
and Economic Affairs
1981 - 82 Opposition Spokesman on Foreign
and European Affairs
1982 - 83 Opposition Spokesman on Defence
1983 Shadow Welsh Secretary
1983 - 88 Shadow Defence Secretary
*Constituency Office* . . . . Vauxhall Buildings, Vauxhall, Llanelli,
Carmarthenshire, SA15 3BD
Tel: (01554) 756374
Personal Assistant – Mr Jeff Hopkins
Web: http://www.rthondenzildavies.net

**Davies, Geraint** . . . Croydon Central
**Labour** . . . . . . . . . . Majority 3,984 over Con
*Born.* . . . . . . . . . . . . 3rd May 1960 in Dorking
*Educated* . . . . . . . . . Llanishen Comprehensive, Cardiff;
Jesus College, Oxford
*Elected.* . . . . . . . . . . 1997 MP for Croydon Central
*Offices Held* . . . . . . . 1996 - 97 Leader, London
Borough of Croydon Council
2003 - PPS to Ministers at Department for
Constitutional Affairs
*Commons Office* . . . . . Tel: (020) 7219 4599 Fax: (020) 7219 5962
E-mail: geraintdaviesmp@parliament.uk
Political Researcher – Miss Ruth Hydon
E-mail: hydonr@parliament.uk
Caseworker/Legal Adviser –
Miss Sarah Branson
E-mail: bransons@parliament.uk
*Constituency Office* . . . . PO Box 679, Croydon, CR9 1UQ
Tel: (020) 8680 5833 Fax: (020) 8686 2246
Casework Assistant – Miss Julia Toft
Caseworker/Communications Manager –
Mr John-Paul Wares
*Parliamentary Interests* . Treasury; Trade and Industry; Transport;
Environment; Children's Issues
*Leisure Interests* . . . . . . Family; Travel

**Davies, Quentin** . . . Grantham and Stamford
**Conservative** . . . . . . . Majority 4,518 over Lab
*Born.* . . . . . . . . . . . . 29th May 1944 in Oxford
*Educated* . . . . . . . . . Gonville and Caius College, Cambridge;
Harvard University, USA
*Elected.* . . . . . . . . . . 1987 MP for Stamford and Spalding,
then (1997) Grantham and Stamford
*Offices Held* . . . . . . . 1998 - 99 Opposition Spokesman on
Social Security
1999 - 2000 Opposition Spokesman on
Treasury Matters
2000 - 01 Opposition Spokesman
on Defence
2001 - 03 Shadow Secretary of State for
Northern Ireland
*Commons Office* . . . . . Tel: (020) 7219 5200/5518
Fax: (020) 7219 2963
Private Secretary –
Mrs Jane Gordon-Cummings
Parliamentary Assistant – Mrs Chantal Davies
*Constituency Office* . . . . Conservative Office, North Street, Bourne,
Lincolnshire, PE10 9AJ
Tel: (01778) 421498 Fax: (01778) 394843
Secretary – Mrs Janice Thurston

# MEMBERS OF THE HOUSE OF COMMONS

**Davis, Rt Hon David**   Haltemprice and Howden
**Conservative** . . . . . . Majority 7,514 over Lib Dem
*Born*. . . . . . . . . . . . . 23rd December 1948 in York
*Educated* . . . . . . . . . . Warwick University; London Business School;
    Harvard University, USA
*Elected*. . . . . . . . . . . . 1987 MP for Boothferry, then (1997)
    Haltemprice and Howden
*Offices Held* . . . . . . . . 1990 - 93 Assistant Government Whip
    1993 - 94 Parliamentary Secretary, Office of
    Public Service and Science
    1994 - 97 Minister of State, Foreign and
    Commonwealth Office
    1997 - 2001 Chairman, Public Accounts
    Committee, House of Commons
    2001 - 02 Chairman, Conservative Party
    2002 - 03 Shadow Secretary for
    Office of Deputy Prime Minister
    2003 - Shadow Home Secretary
*Commons Office* . . . . . Tel: (020) 7219 4710 Fax: (020) 7219 5860
    PA – Ms Juliet Donnelly
    E-mail: donnellyj@parliament.uk
    Chief of Staff – Miss Tracey Crouch
    Tel: (020) 7219 2685
    E-mail: croucht@parliament.uk
    Research Assistant – Mr Marc Williams
    Tel: (020) 7219 5873
    E-mail: williamsma@parliament.uk
*Constituency Office* . . . . Tel: (01430) 430365 Fax: (01430) 430253
    Secretary – Mrs Doreen Davies

**Dawson, Hilton**. . . . Lancaster and Wyre
**Labour** . . . . . . . . . . . Majority 481 over Con
*Born*. . . . . . . . . . . . . . 30th September 1953 in Northumberland
*Educated* . . . . . . . . . . Ashington Grammar School;
    Warwick University; Lancaster University
*Elected*. . . . . . . . . . . . 1997 MP for Lancaster and Wyre
*Commons Office* . . . . . Tel & Fax: (020) 7219 4207
    E-mail: dawsonh@parliament.uk
*Constituency Office* . . . . 15a Moor Lane, Lancaster, LA1 1QD
    Tel & Fax: (01524) 380057
    Secretary/PA – Ms Elayne Mallon
    Caseworker – Mrs Sue Dawson
*Parliamentary Interests* . Childrens Right; Child Care; Sudan
*Leisure Interests* . . . . . . Family; Escaping into the Fresh Air

**Dean, Janet**. . . . . . . Burton
**Labour** . . . . . . . . . . . Majority 4,849 over Con
*Born*. . . . . . . . . . . . . . 28th January 1949 in Crewe
*Educated* . . . . . . . . . . Winsford Verdin County Grammar School
*Elected*. . . . . . . . . . . . 1997 MP for Burton
*Commons Office* . . . . . Tel: (020) 7219 6320 Fax: (020) 7219 3010
    Pager: 07644 007856
    E-mail: mcgirrc@parliament.uk
    Research Assistant – Ms Carol McGirr
*Constituency Office* . . . . Suite 13, First Floor,
    Cross Street Business Centre,
    Cross Street, Burton-upon-Trent, DE14 1EF
    Tel: (01283) 509166 Fax: (01283) 569964
    E-mail: coxhilll@parliament.uk
    Secretary – Mrs Linda Coxhill
    Administrative Assistants/Secretaries –
    Mrs Sandra Belcher
    Mrs Jane Reeves
*Parliamentary Interests* . Local Government; Health; Rural Affairs;
    Home Affairs; Education
*Leisure Interests* . . . . . . Reading; Dressmaking

**Denham, Rt Hon John**   Southampton Itchen
**Labour** . . . . . . . . . . . Majority 11,223 over Con
*Born*. . . . . . . . . . . . . . 15th July 1953 in Seaton, Devon
*Educated* . . . . . . . . . . Woodroffe Comprehensive School,
    Lyme Regis; Southampton University
*Elected*. . . . . . . . . . . . 1992 MP for Southampton Itchen
*Offices Held* . . . . . . . . 1995 - 97 Opposition Spokesman on
    Social Security
    1997 - 98 Parliamentary Secretary,
    Department of Social Security
    1998 Minister of State, Department of
    Social Security
    1998 - 2001 Minister of State, Department
    of Health
    2001 - 03 Minister of State, Home Office
    2003 - Chairman, Home Affairs Select
    Committee, House of Commons
*Constituency Office* . . . . 20-22 Southampton Street,
    Southampton, SO15 2ED
    Tel: (023) 8033 9807 Fax: (023) 8033 9907
    E-mail: denhamj@parliament.uk
    Secretary/Office Manager –
    Mrs Caroline Kimber
    Assistants – Mr Tony Fry
    Mrs Cheryl Storrar
    E-mail: frya@parliament.uk

**Dhanda, Parmjit** . . Gloucester
**Labour** . . . . . . . . . . . Majority 3,880 over Con
*Born*. . . . . . . . . . . . . . 17th September 1971 in London
*Educated* . . . . . . . . . . Mellow Lane Comprehensive School;
    Nottingham University
*Elected*. . . . . . . . . . . . 2001 MP for Gloucester
*Commons Office* . . . . . Tel: (020) 7219 8240
    E-mail: dhandap@parliament.uk
    Web: http://www.parmjitdhanda.co.uk
    Researcher – Mr Stuart Hudson
    E-mail: hudsons@parliament.uk
*Constituency Office* . . . . 1 Pullman Court, Great Western Road,
    Gloucester, GL1 3ND
    Tel: (01452) 311870 Fax: (01452) 311874
    E-mail: purchased@parliament.uk
    Personal Assistant – Mr David Purchase
    Caseworker – Miss Patricia Delaney
*Parliamentary Interests* . Local Government; European Union;
    Employment Rights and Protection (Trade
    Unions); Science and Technology
*Leisure Interests* . . . . . . Chess; Cricket; Football; Rugby; Writing

**Dismore, Andrew**. . Hendon
**Labour** . . . . . . . . . . . Majority 7,417 over Con
*Born*. . . . . . . . . . . . . . 2nd September 1954 in Bridlington
*Educated* . . . . . . . . . . Bridlington Grammar School;
    Warwick University;
    London School of Economics
*Elected*. . . . . . . . . . . . 1997 MP for Hendon
*Commons Office* . . . . . Tel: (020) 7219 4026 Fax: (020) 7219 1279
    E-mail: andrewdismoremp@parliament.uk
    Parliamentary Assistant –
    Miss Leticia Thomson
    E-mail: thomsonl@parliament.uk
    Commons Assistant – Ms Marianna Polanska
    Tel: (020) 7219 4408
    E-mail: polanskam@parliament.uk
*Constituency Office* . . . . St George's Lodge, 79 The Burroughs,
    Hendon, London, NW4 4AX
    Tel: (020) 8202 2122 Fax: (020) 8202 2124
*Parliamentary Interests* . Health; Civil Justice; Middle East; Cyprus;
    Social Security
*Leisure Interests* . . . . . . Gardening

## MEMBERS OF THE HOUSE OF COMMONS

**Djanogly, Jonathan**  Huntingdon
**Conservative** . . . . . . Majority 12,792 over Lib Dem
*Born*. . . . . . . . . . . . . . 1965
*Elected*. . . . . . . . . . . . 2001 MP for Huntingdon
*Office Held*. . . . . . . . . 2003 - Opposition Spokesman on Home,
                 Constitutional and Legal Affairs
*Commons Office* . . . . . Tel: (020) 7219 2367
                 E-mail: djanoglyj@parliament.uk
                 Web: http://www.jonathandjanogly.com
                 Parliamentary Assistant – Mrs Olivia Kybett
                 E-mail: kybetto@parliament.uk
*Constituency Office*. . . . 8 Stukeley Road, Huntingdon,
                 Cambridgeshire, PE29 6XG
                 Tel: (01480) 453062
                 Constituency Agent – Sir Peter Brown
                 Constituency Assistant – Miss Nichola Elliott
*Parliamentary Interests* . Trade and Industry; Environment; Transport;
                 Rural Issues
*Leisure Interests* . . . . . Sports; Arts; Theatre; Reading; Countryside

**Dobbin, Jim** . . . . . . Heywood and Middleton
**Labour** . . . . . . . . . . . Majority 11,670 over Con
*Born*. . . . . . . . . . . . . . 26th May 1941 in Kincardine, Fife
*Educated* . . . . . . . . . . St Andrew's High School, Kirkcaldy
                 St Columba's RC High School, Cowdenbeath;
                 Napier College, Edinburgh
*Elected*. . . . . . . . . . . . 1997 MP for Heywood and Middleton
*Office Held*. . . . . . . . . 1996 - 97 Leader, Rochdale Metropolitan
                 Borough Council
*Commons Office* . . . . . Tel: (020) 7219 4530 Fax: (020) 7219 2696
*Constituency Office* . . . . 45 York Street, Heywood, Lancashire,
                 OL10 4NN
                 Tel: (01706) 361135 Fax: (01706) 361137
                 Administrator – Mr Colin Lambert
*Parliamentary Interests* . Europe; Health; Local Government;
                 Northern Ireland
*Leisure Interests* . . . . . Football

**Dobson, Rt Hon Frank**  Holborn and St Pancras
**Labour** . . . . . . . . . . . Majority 11,175 over Lib Dem
*Born*. . . . . . . . . . . . . . 15th March 1940 in York
*Educated* . . . . . . . . . . Archbishop Holgate Grammar School, York;
                 London School of Economics
*Elected*. . . . . . . . . . . . 1979 MP for Holborn and
                 St Pancras South, then (1983)
                 Holborn and St Pancras
*Offices Held* . . . . . . . . 1973 - 75 Leader, Camden London Borough
                 Council
                 1981 - 83 Opposition Spokesman on
                 Education
                 1985 - 87 Opposition Spokesman on Health
                 1987 - 89 Shadow Leader of the House and
                 Labour Party Campaigns Co-ordinator
                 1989 - 92 Shadow Energy Secretary
                 1992 - 93 Shadow Employment Secretary
                 1993 - 94 Shadow Transport Secretary
                 1994 - 97 Shadow Environment Secretary
                 1997 - 99 Secretary of State for Health
*Commons Office* . . . . . Tel: (020) 7219 5040 Fax: (020) 7219 6956
                 Secretary – Ms Barbara Collins
                 Tel: (020) 7219 4452
                 E-mail: collinsb@parliament.uk
                 Researcher – Ms Vikki Mills
                 Tel: (020) 7219 5840
                 E-mail: millsv@parliament.uk
*Constituency Office* . . . . 8 Camden Road, London, NW1 9DP
                 Tel: (020) 7267 1676
*Parliamentary Interests* . Transport; Health; Energy; Problems of
                 Central London; Redistribution of Wealth;
                 Reform of Government
*Leisure Interests* . . . . . . Walking; Theatre; Watching Cricket and
                 Football

**Dodds, Nigel** OBE . . Belfast North
**Democratic Unionist**. Majority 6,387 over Sinn Fein
*Born*. . . . . . . . . . . . . . 20th August 1958 in Londonderry
*Educated* . . . . . . . . . . Portora Royal School, Enniskillen;
                 St John's College, Cambridge
*Elected*. . . . . . . . . . . . 2001 MP for Belfast North
*Offices Held* . . . . . . . . 1988 - 89, 1991 - 92 Lord Mayor of Belfast
                 1998 - Member, Northern Ireland Assembly
                 (Minister for Social Development 2000 - 01)
*Commons Office* . . . . . Tel: (020) 7219 8495 Fax: (020) 7219 1972
                 E-mail: doddsn@parliament.uk
*Constituency Staff* . . . . 210 Shore Road, Belfast, BT15 3QB
                 Tel: (028) 9077 4774 Fax: (028) 9077 7685
                 E-mail: ndodds@dup-belfast.co.uk
                 Secretary – Mrs Yvonne Sloan
*Parliamentary Interests* . Constitution; Europe; Social Issues
*Leisure Interests* . . . . . . History; Reading

**Doherty, Pat** . . . . . Tyrone West
**Sinn Fein** . . . . . . . . . Majority 5,040 over Ulster Unionist
*Born*. . . . . . . . . . . . . . 18th July 1945 in Glasgow
*Educated* . . . . . . . . . . St Joseph's College, Lockwinnock, Scotland
*Elected*. . . . . . . . . . . . 2001 MP for Tyrone West
                 *(has not taken seat at Westminster)*
*Office Held*. . . . . . . . . 1998 - Member, Northern Ireland Assembly
*Constituency Office* . . . . 1 Melvin Road, Strabane, Co Tyrone
                 Tel: (028) 7188 6464 Fax: (028) 7188 6466
                 E-mail: patdoherty@ireland.com
                 PA/Administrator – Mrs Michelle McDermott
                 Administrative Assistant –
                 Mr Colman McCrossan
*Leisure Interests* . . . . . Reading; Stone Wall Building; Hill Walking;
                 Map Reading

**Donaldson, Jeffrey**  Lagan Valley
**Democratic Unionist**. Majority 18,342 over Alliance
                 *(elected as Ulster Unionist)*
*Born*. . . . . . . . . . . . . . 7th December 1962 in Kilkeel
*Educated* . . . . . . . . . . Kilkeel High School; Castlereagh College
*Elected*. . . . . . . . . . . . 1997 MP for Lagan Valley
*Offices Held* . . . . . . . . 2002 - 04 Ulster Unionist Spokesman on
                 Defence, Trade and Industry, Work and
                 Pensions
                 2003 - Member, Northern Ireland Assembly
                 2004 - Democratic Unionist Spokesman on
                 Defence and Education
*Commons Office* . . . . . Tel: (020) 7219 3407 Fax: (020) 7219 0696
                 E-mail: donaldsonjm@parliament.uk
                 Web: http://www.jeffreydonaldson.org
*Constituency Office* . . . . The Old Town Hall, 29 Castle Street, Lisburn,
                 County Antrim, BT27 4DH
                 Tel: (028) 9266 8001 Fax: (028) 9267 1845
                 E-mail: jeffreydonaldsonmp@laganvalley.net
                 Assistant – Mr David Nichol
                 Secretaries – Mrs Gillian Carson
                               Miss Barbara Wilson

# MEMBERS OF THE HOUSE OF COMMONS

**Donohoe, Brian** . . . Cunninghame South
**Labour** . . . . . . . . . . . Majority 11,230 over SNP
*Born* . . . . . . . . . . . . . . 10th September 1948 in Kilmarnock
*Educated* . . . . . . . . . . Irvine Royal Academy;
Kilmarnock Technical College
*Elected* . . . . . . . . . . . . 1992 MP for Cunninghame South
*Commons Office* . . . . . Tel: (020) 7219 6230 Fax: (020) 7219 5388
Mobile: 07774 646600
Pager: 07644 066100
E-mail: donohoeb@parliament.uk
Web: http://www.briandonohoemp.co.uk
Research Assistant – Miss Nicola Roulston
*Constituency Office* . . . . 17 Townhead, Irvine, Ayrshire, KA12 0BL
Tel: (01294) 276844 Fax: (01294) 313463
Secretary – Ms Ruth Brown
Secretarial Assistant – Miss Samantha Mair
*Parliamentary Interests* . Transport; Environment
*Leisure Interests* . . . . . . Gardening

**Doran, Frank** . . . . . Aberdeen Central
**Labour** . . . . . . . . . . . Majority 6,646 over SNP
*Born* . . . . . . . . . . . . . . 13th April 1949 in Edinburgh
*Educated* . . . . . . . . . . Dundee University
*Elected* . . . . . . . . . . . . 1987 - 92 MP for Aberdeen South
1997 MP for Aberdeen Central
*Office Held* . . . . . . . . . 1988 - 92 Opposition Spokesman on Energy
*Commons Office* . . . . . Tel: (020) 7219 3481 Fax: (020) 7219 0682
E-mail: doranf@parliament.uk
*Constituency Office* . . . . 166 Market Street, Aberdeen, AB11 5PP
Tel: (01224) 252715 Fax: (01224) 252716
Researcher – Ms Irene Dillon
Secretary/PA – Miss Anne McNamee
*Parliamentary Interests* . Employment; Energy; Fisheries

**Dorrell, Rt Hon Stephen** Charnwood
**Conservative** . . . . . . Majority 7,739 over Lab
*Born* . . . . . . . . . . . . . . 25th March 1952 in Worcester
*Educated* . . . . . . . . . . Uppingham School; Brasenose College, Oxford
*Elected* . . . . . . . . . . . . 1979 MP for Loughborough,
then (1997) Charnwood
*Offices Held* . . . . . . . . 1987 - 88 Assistant Government Whip
1988 - 90 Government Whip (Lord
Commissioner, H M Treasury)
1990 - 92 Parliamentary Secretary,
Department of Health
1992 - 94 Financial Secretary to the Treasury
1994 - 95 Secretary of State for
National Heritage
1995 - 97 Secretary of State for Health
1997 - 98 Shadow Education and
Employment Secretary
*Commons Office* . . . . . Tel: (020) 7219 4472 Fax: (020) 7219 5838
E-mail: info@stephendorrell.org.uk
Web: http://www.stephendorrell.org.uk
Secretary – Mrs Christine Crickett
E-mail: crickettc@parliament.uk
Political Secretary – Mr Lewis Robinson
E-mail: robinsonle@parliament.uk
*Constituency Office* . . . . 768 Melton Road, Thurmaston,
Leicester, LE4 8BD
Tel: (0116) 260 8609 Fax: (0116) 260 8700
E-mail: cca@charnwood.tory.org.uk
*Parliamentary Interests* . Economics; Social Policy

**Doughty, Sue** . . . . . Guildford
**Liberal Democrat** . . . Majority 538 over Con
*Born* . . . . . . . . . . . . . . 13th April 1948
*Educated* . . . . . . . . . . Northumberland College
*Elected* . . . . . . . . . . . . 2001 MP for Guildford
*Offices Held* . . . . . . . . 2001 - Liberal Democrat Spokesman
on Environment
*Commons Office* . . . . . Tel: (020) 7219 8482 Fax: (020) 7219 1964
E-mail: doughtys@parliament.uk
Web: http://www.suedoughty.org
Researcher – Mr Tim Nichols
Tel: (020) 7219 3739
E-mail: nicholst@parliament.uk
*Constituency Office* . . . . The Hall, 53a Woking Road, Guildford,
Surrey, GU1 1QD
Tel: (01483) 306000 Fax: (01483) 306031
Casework Manager – Mrs Ruth Reed
Secretary – Mrs Fiona Jones
*Parliamentary Interests* . Environment and Waste Management;
Care of the Elderly; International
Development; Education; National Health
Service
*Leisure Interests* . . . . . . Gardening; Music; Travel; Walking

**Dowd, Jim** . . . . . . . . Lewisham West
**Labour** . . . . . . . . . . . Majority 11,920 over Con
*Born* . . . . . . . . . . . . . . 5th March 1951 in Bad Eilsen, Germany
*Educated* . . . . . . . . . . Sedgehill Comprehensive School, London;
London Nautical School
*Elected* . . . . . . . . . . . . 1992 MP for Lewisham West
*Offices Held* . . . . . . . . Formerly Deputy Leader and Mayor,
Lewisham London Borough Council
1993 - 95 Opposition Whip
1995 - 97 Opposition Spokesman on Northern
Ireland
1997 - 2001 Government Whip (Lord
Commissioner, H M Treasury)
*Commons Office* . . . . . Tel: (020) 7219 4617 Fax: (020) 7219 2686
E-mail: jimdowd.newlabour@care4free.net
Web:
http://www.epolitix.com/webminster/jim-dowd
*Constituency Office* . . . . 43 Sunderland Road, Forest Hill,
London, SE23 2PS
Tel & Fax: (020) 8291 5607
Secretary – Ms Fleur Costa
Office Manager – Mr David Thomas
Senior Researcher – Paul Upex
*Parliamentary Interests* . Health; Education; Transport; Economy;
Industry; Animal Welfare
*Leisure Interests* . . . . . . Music; Theatre; Reading

# MEMBERS OF THE HOUSE OF COMMONS

**Drew, David** . . . . . Stroud
**Labour** . . . . . . . . . . Majority 5,039 over Con
*Born.* . . . . . . . . . . . . . 13th April 1952 in South Gloucestershire
*Educated* . . . . . . . . . Kingsfield School, Gloucestershire;
Nottingham University;
Birmingham University;
University of the West of England
*Elected.* . . . . . . . . . . . 1997 MP for Stroud
*Commons Office* . . . . . Tel: (020) 7219 6479 Fax: (020) 7219 0910
Pager: 07644 006469
E-mail: drewd@parliament.uk
Web: http://www.daviddrew.ik.org
Researcher – Mr Carlos Ordonez
*Constituency Office* . . . . 5a Lansdown, Stroud,
Gloucestershire, GL5 1BB
Tel: (01453) 764355 Fax: (01453) 753756
E-mail: daviddrew@mpstroud.freeserve.co.uk
*Parliamentary Interests* . Agriculture; Rural Affairs; Anti-Poverty;
Health; Housing
*Leisure Interests* . . . . . . Reading; Watching Football; Rugby

**Drown, Julia** . . . . . . Swindon South
**Labour** . . . . . . . . . . Majority 7,341 over Con
*Born.* . . . . . . . . . . . . . 23rd August 1962 in London
*Educated* . . . . . . . . . Hampstead Comprehensive, London;
University College, Oxford
*Elected.* . . . . . . . . . . . 1997 MP for Swindon South
*Commons Office* . . . . . Tel: (020) 7219 2392 Fax: (020) 7219 0266
Pager: 07644 006470
E-mail: juliadrownmp@parliament.uk
Web: http://www.epolitix.com/com/julia-drown
Research Assistant – Mr John Slinger
E-mail: slingerj@parliament.uk
*Constituency Office* . . . . 13 Bath Road, Swindon; Wiltshire, SN1 4AS
Tel: (01793) 615444 Fax: (01793) 644752
Organiser – Mr Frank Jeffrey
Administrative Assistant – Mrs Julie Wright
*Parliamentary Interests* . Health; International Development; Social
Services; Human Rights; Gender Issues
*Leisure Interests* . . . . . . Family

**Duncan, Alan** . . . . Rutland and Melton
**Conservative** . . . . . . Majority 8,612 over Lab
*Born.* . . . . . . . . . . . . . 31st March 1957 in Rickmansworth,
Hertfordshire
*Educated* . . . . . . . . . Merchant Taylors' School, Northwood;
St John's College, Oxford;
Harvard University, USA
*Elected.* . . . . . . . . . . . 1992 MP for Rutland and Melton
*Offices Held* . . . . . . . . 1997 - 98 PPS to William Hague
(Leader of the Opposition) and Vice-
Chairman, Conservative Party
1998 - 99 Opposition Spokesman on Health
1999 - 2001 Opposition Spokesman on
Trade and Industry
2001 - 03 Opposition Spokesman on
Foreign and Commonwealth Affairs
2003 - 04 Opposition Spokesman on
Constitutional Affairs
2004 - Shadow Secretary for
International Development
*Commons Office* . . . . . Tel: (020) 7219 5204 Fax: (020) 7219 2529
E-mail: duncana@parliament.uk
Web: http://www.alanduncan.org.uk
Political Assistant – Mr Andrew Smith
E-mail: smithap@parliament.uk
*Constituency Office* . . . . Tel: (01664) 566444
Fax: (01664) 566555
Secretary – Mrs Anne Brutnell
Agent – Mr Allan Dean
Caseworker – Mrs Lesley Baldam
*Parliamentary Interests* . Foreign Affairs; Rural Issues;
Constitutional Affairs
*Leisure Interests* . . . . . . Country Sports; Travel

**Duncan, Peter** . . . . Galloway and Upper Nithsdale
**Conservative** . . . . . . Majority 74 over SNP
*Educated* . . . . . . . . . Ardrossan Academy;
University of Birmingham
*Elected.* . . . . . . . . . . . 2001 MP for Galloway and Upper Nithsdale
*Offices Held* . . . . . . . . 2002 - Shadow secretary for Scotland
*Commons Office* . . . . . Tel: (020) 7219 8235 Fax: (020) 7219 1768
Pager: 07644 013173
E-mail: duncanp@parliament.uk
Web: http://www.peterduncan.org.uk
Research Assistant – Miss Erica Ambrosioni
E-mail: ambrosionie@parliament.uk
*Constituency Office* . . . . 110 Drumlanrig Street, Thornhill, Dumfries,
DG3 5LU
Tel: (01848) 331725 Fax: (01848) 331680
Senior Researcher – Mrs Gill Dykes
Tel: (01848) 331818
E-mail: dykesg@parliament.uk
Researcher – Mr John Dougan
Tel: (01776) 706479 Fax: (01776) 705035
E-mail: douganj@parliament.uk
*Parliamentary Interests* . Energy; Rural Affairs
*Leisure Interests* . . . . . . Scottish Rugby; English County Cricket

# MEMBERS OF THE HOUSE OF COMMONS

**Duncan Smith, Rt Hon Iain** Chingford and Woodford Green
**Conservative** . . . . . . . Majority 5,487 over Lab
*Born*. . . . . . . . . . . . . . 9th April 1952 in Edinburgh
*Educated* . . . . . . . . . . HMS Conway; University di Perugia, Italy; Royal Military Academy, Sandhurst; Dunchurch College of Management
*Elected*. . . . . . . . . . . . 1992 MP for Chingford, then (1997) Chingford and Woodford Green
*Offices Held* . . . . . . . . 1997 - 99 Shadow Social Security Secretary
1999 - 2001 Shadow Defence Secretary
2001 - 03 Leader of the Opposition
*Commons Office* . . . . . . Fax: (020) 7219 4867
Secretary – Miss Annabelle Eyre
Tel: (020) 7219 2664 Fax: (020) 7219 4867
*Constituency Office* . . . . 20a Station Road, Chingford, London, E4 7BE
Tel: (020) 8524 4344
Constituency Assistant – Mr Rikki Radford
*Parliamentary Interests* . Defence; Europe; Economy; Foreign Affairs; Family

**Dunwoody, Gwyneth** Crewe and Nantwich
**Labour** . . . . . . . . . . . Majority 9,906 over Con
*Born*. . . . . . . . . . . . . . 12th December 1930 in Fulham, London
*Educated* . . . . . . . . . . Fulham County Secondary School
*Elected*. . . . . . . . . . . . 1966 - 70 MP for Exeter
1974 MP for Crewe, then (1983) Crewe and Nantwich
*Offices Held* . . . . . . . . 1967 - 70 Parliamentary Secretary, Board of Trade
1979 - 80 Opposition Spokesman on Foreign and Commonwealth Affairs
1981 - 85 Opposition Spokesman on Health
1984 - 85 Shadow Transport Secretary
1997 - 2001 Joint Chairman, Transport, Environment and the Regions Select Committee (and Chairman Transport Sub-Committee) House of Commons
2002 - Chairman, Transport Select Committee, House of Commons
*Commons Office* . . . . . . Tel: (020) 7219 3490 Fax: (020) 7219 6046
Researcher – Mr Alex Phillips
Tel: (020) 7219 0683
*Constituency Office* . . . . 154 Nantwich Road, Crewe, CW2 6BG
Tel: (01270) 589132 Fax: (01270) 589135
Secretary – Mrs Margaret Holland
*Parliamentary Interests* . Transport; Arts; Foreign Affairs; Health
*Leisure Interests* . . . . . . Music

# E

**Eagle, Angela** . . . . Wallasey
**Labour** . . . . . . . . . . . Majority 12,276 over Con
*Born*. . . . . . . . . . . . . . 17th February 1961 in Bridlington, Yorkshire
*Educated* . . . . . . . . . . Formby High School; St John's College, Oxford
*Elected*. . . . . . . . . . . . 1992 MP for Wallasey
*Offices Held* . . . . . . . . 1996 - 97 Opposition Whip
1997 - 98 Parliamentary Secretary, Department of Environment, Transport and the Regions
1998 - 2001 Parliamentary Secretary, Department of Social Security
2001 - 02 Parliamentary Secretary, Home Office
*Commons Office* . . . . . . Tel: (020) 7219 4074 Fax: (020) 7219 2654
E-mail: eaglea@parliament.uk
*Constituency Office* . . . . Sherlock :House, 6 Manor Road, Liscard, Wirral, L45 4JB
Tel: (0151) 637 1979 Fax: (0151) 691 2612
Assistants – Mrs Ann McArdle
Mrs Liz Watkins

**Eagle, Maria** . . . . . . Liverpool Garston
**Labour** . . . . . . . . . . . Majority 12,494 over Lib Dem
*Born*. . . . . . . . . . . . . . 17th February 1961 in Bridlington, Yorkshire
*Educated* . . . . . . . . . . Pembroke College, Oxford; Lancaster Gate College of Law
*Elected*. . . . . . . . . . . . 1997 MP for Liverpool Garston
*Office Held* . . . . . . . . . 2001 - Parliamentary Secretary, Department for Work and Pensions
*Commons Office* . . . . . . Tel: (020) 7219 4019
E-mail: eaglem@parliament.uk
*Constituency Office* . . . . Unit House, Speke Boulevard, Liverpool, L24 9HZ
Tel: (0151) 448 1167 Fax: (0151) 448 0976
Constituency Assistant – Mr Oliver Martins
*Parliamentary Interests* . Equal Opportunities; Employment Policy; Welfare to Work; Housing
*Leisure Interests* . . . . . . Chess; Cricket; Cinema; Fitness

**Edwards, Huw** . . . . Monmouth
**Labour** . . . . . . . . . . . Majority 384 over Con
*Born*. . . . . . . . . . . . . . 12th April 1953 in Carlshalton, Surrey
*Educated* . . . . . . . . . . Eastfield High School, Mitcham; Manchester Polytechnic; York University
*Elected*. . . . . . . . . . . . 1991 - 92 MP for Monmouth (By-election)
1997 MP for Monmouth
*Commons Office* . . . . . . Tel: (020) 7219 3489 Fax: (020) 7219 3949
E-mail: edwardsh@parliament.uk
Researcher – Ms Mandy Platt
E-mail: plattm@parliament.uk
*Constituency Office* . . . . 7 Agincourt Street, Monmouth, NP25 3DZ
Tel: (01600) 713537 Fax: (01600) 712847
Web: http://www.huwedwardsmonmouth.co.uk
Office Manager – Mrs Diane Banner
E-mail: bannerd@parliament.uk
Constituency Assistant –
Mr Robert Jervis-Gibbons
Tel: (01600) 713127
E-mail: jervis-gibbonsr@parliament.uk
*Parliamentary Interests* . Welsh Affairs; Low Pay; Health; Housing; Education
*Leisure Interests* . . . . . . Cricket; Football; Male Voice Choir; Rugby

# MEMBERS OF THE HOUSE OF COMMONS

**Efford, Clive** . . . . . . Eltham
**Labour** . . . . . . . . . . . Majority 6,996 over Con
*Born.* . . . . . . . . . . . . . 10th July 1958 in London
*Educated* . . . . . . . . . . Walworth Comprehensive School, London;
                   Southwark Further Education College
*Elected.* . . . . . . . . . . . 1997 MP for Eltham
*Commons Office* . . . . . Tel: (020) 7219 4057 Fax: (020) 7219 2820
*Constituency Office* . . . . 132 Westmount Road, Eltham,
                   London, SE9 1UT
                   Tel: (020) 8850 5744 Fax: (020) 8294 2166
                   Press/Researcher – Mr William Haddock
*Parliamentary Interests* . Transport; Housing; Health
*Leisure Interests* . . . . . . Football; Reading; Cinema

**Ellman, Louise** . . . . Liverpool Riverside
**Labour** . . . . . . . . . . . Majority 13,950 over Lib Dem
*Born.* . . . . . . . . . . . . . 14th November 1945 in Manchester
*Educated* . . . . . . . . . . Manchester High School for Girls;
                   Hull University; York University
*Elected.* . . . . . . . . . . . 1997 MP for Liverpool Riverside
*Office Held.* . . . . . . . . 1981 - 97 Leader, Lancashire County Council
*Commons Office* . . . . . Tel: (020) 7219 5120 Fax: (020) 7219 2592
                   Mobile: 07966 360066
                   Pager: 07644 006364
                   E-mail: ellmanl@parliament.uk
                   Parliamentary Researchers/Assistants –
                     Mr Zeev Portner
                     Mrs Diane Wall
*Constituency Office* . . . . First Floor, Threlfall Buildings,
                   Trueman Street, Liverpool, L3 2EX
                   Tel: (0151) 236 2969 Fax: (0151) 236 4301
                   Constituency Workers – Mr Rob Carney
                              Ms Julie Lloyd
*Parliamentary Interests* . Regional Devolution; Regeneration;
                   Public Services; Arts; Europe;
                   Local Government; Middle East
*Leisure Interests* . . . . . . Theatre; Reading

**Ennis, Jeff** . . . . . . . Barnsley East and Mexborough
**Labour** . . . . . . . . . . . Majority 16,789 over Lib Dem
*Born.* . . . . . . . . . . . . . 13th November 1952 in Barnsley
*Educated* . . . . . . . . . . Hemsworth Grammar School;
                   Redland College; Bristol University
*Elected.* . . . . . . . . . . . 1997 MP for Barnsley East and Mexborough
*Office Held.* . . . . . . . . 1995 - 96 Leader, Barnsley Metropolitan
                   Borough Council
*Commons Office* . . . . . Tel: (020) 7219 5008 Fax: (020) 7219 2728
                   Mobile: 07950 324338
                   Pager: 07644 006915
                   E-mail: ennisj@parliament.uk
                   Researcher – Mr Neil Ennis
                   E-mail: ennisn@parliament.uk
*Constituency Office* . . . . Brierley Hall, Church Street, Brierley,
                   Barnsley, South Yorkshire, S72 9HP
                   Tel & Fax: (01226) 775080
                   Secretary – Mrs Carole Salter
                   E-mail: salterc@parliament.uk
*Parliamentary Interests* . Local Government; Education; Environment;
                   Fire Service
*Leisure Interests* . . . . . . Walking; Family Activities

**Etherington, Bill** . . Sunderland North
**Labour** . . . . . . . . . . . Majority 13,354 over Con
*Born.* . . . . . . . . . . . . . 17th July 1941 in Sunderland
*Educated* . . . . . . . . . . Monkwearmouth Grammar School;
                   Durham University
*Elected.* . . . . . . . . . . . 1992 MP for Sunderland North
*Commons Office* . . . . . Tel: (020) 7219 4603  Fax: (020) 7219 1186
*Constituency Office* . . . . 7 Bridge House, Bridge Street, Sunderland,
                   SR1 1TE
                   Tel: (0191) 564 2489 Fax; (0191) 564 2486
                   Research Assistant – Ms Jacqueline Apperley
                   Personal Secretary – Mr Gary Hopper

**Evans, Nigel** . . . . . . Ribble Valley
**Conservative** . . . . . . Majority 11,238 over Lib Dem
*Born.* . . . . . . . . . . . . . 10th November 1957 in Swansea
*Educated* . . . . . . . . . . Dynevor School, Swansea;
                   University College of Wales, Swansea
*Elected.* . . . . . . . . . . . 1992 MP for Ribble Valley
*Offices Held* . . . . . . . . 1997 - 2004 Opposition Spokesman on Wales
                   1999 - 2001 Vice-Chairman of
                     Conservative Party (Wales)
*Commons Office* . . . . . Tel: (020) 7219 6939/4165
                   E-mail: nigel@nigelmp.com
                   Web: http://www.nigelmp.com
                   Senior Researcher – Mr Simon Irton-Fell
                   E-mail: fells@parliament.uk
                   Researcher – Mr Robert Rams
                   E-mail: ramsr@parliament.uk
*Constituency Office* . . . . 9 Railway View, Clitheroe,
                   Lancashire, BB7 2HA
                   Tel: (01200) 425939 Fax: (01200) 422904
                   Secretary – Ms Christine Scott
                   Agent – Mr Keith Brunskill
*Parliamentary Interests* . Education; Small Businesses; US Politics;
                   Defence; Europe; Telecommunications;
                   Rural Affairs; Constitutional Affairs
                   (especially Wales)
*Leisure Interests* . . . . . . Travel; Theatre; IT; Spectator Sports; Cinema

**Ewing, Annabelle** . . Perth
**SNP** . . . . . . . . . . . . . Majority 48 over Con
*Born.* . . . . . . . . . . . . . 20th August 1960 in Glasgow
*Educated* . . . . . . . . . . Craigholm School; Glasgow University;
                   Johns Hopkins, Bolegna Center;
                   Europa Institut, Amsterdam University
*Elected.* . . . . . . . . . . . 2001 MP for Perth
*Office Held.* . . . . . . . . SNP Spokesman on Home Affairs,
                   Work and Pensions
*Commons Office* . . . . . Tel: (020) 7219 8309 Fax: (020) 7219 1788
                   E-mail: ewinga@parliament.uk
*Constituency Office* . . . . 55 Commissioner Street, Crieff, PH7 3AY
                   Tel: (01764) 656611 Fax: (01764) 656622
                   E-mail: annabelle.ewingmp@btopenworld.com
                   Parliamentary Assistant – Mrs Dawn Chapman
*Parliamentary Interests* . Work and Pensions; Home Affairs;
                   Legal Affairs
*Leisure Interests* . . . . . . Walking; Swimming; Reading; Politics

# MEMBERS OF THE HOUSE OF COMMONS

## F

### Fabricant, Michael Lichfield
**Conservative** . . . . . . . Majority 4,426 over Lab
*Born* . . . . . . . . . . . . . 12th June 1950 in Brighton, Sussex
*Educated* . . . . . . . . . . Brighton and Hove Grammar School;
Loughborough University; Sussex University;
London University;
University of Southern California, USA;
Oxford University
*Elected* . . . . . . . . . . . . 1992 - MP for Mid Staffordshire,
then (1997) Lichfield
*Offices Held* . . . . . . . . 2001 - 03 Chairman, Information
Committee, House of Commons
2003 - Opposition Spokesman on
Trade and Industry
*Commons Office* . . . . . Tel: (020) 7219 5022
Web: http://www.michael.fabricant.mp.co uk
Parliamentary Assistant – Ms Joanne Godwin
*Constituency Office* . . . . Charter House, Sandford Street, Lichfield,
Staffordshire, WS13 8QA
Tel: (01543) 417868
Constituency Assistant – Mrs Jean Simpson
*Parliamentary Interests* . DTI; Culture; Media; Foreign Affairs
*Leisure Interests* . . . . . . Walking; Listening to the Archers; Eating Out

### Fallon, Michael . . . . Sevenoaks
**Conservative** . . . . . . . Majority 10,154 over Lab
*Born* . . . . . . . . . . . . . 14th May 1952
*Educated* . . . . . . . . . . Epsom College; St Andrews University
*Elected* . . . . . . . . . . . . 1983 - 89 MP for Darlington
1997 MP for Sevenoaks
*Offices Held* . . . . . . . . 1988 - 90 Government Whip
1990 - 92 Parliamentary Secretary,
Department for Education
1997 - 98 Opposition Spokesman on
Department of Trade and Industry
1998 - 99 Opposition Spokesman on
Treasury Matters
*Commons Office* . . . . . Tel: (020) 7219 6482 Fax: (020) 7219 6791
E-mail: fallonm@parliament.uk
Private Secretary – Mrs Helen McIvor
E-mail: mcivorh@parliament.uk
*Parliamentary Interests* . Education

### Farrelly, Paul . . . . . Newcastle-under-Lyme
**Labour** . . . . . . . . . . . Majority 9,986 over Con
*Born* . . . . . . . . . . . . . 2md March 1962
*Educated* . . . . . . . . . . St Edmund Hall, Oxford
*Elected* . . . . . . . . . . . . 2001 MP for Newcastle-under-Lyme
*Commons Office* . . . . . Tel: (020) 7219 8391 Fax: (020) 7219 1986
E-mail: farrellyp@parliament.uk
Researcher – Ms Tracey Loftis
E-mail: loftist@parliament.uk
*Constituency Office* . . . . Waterloo Buildings, Dunkirk,
Newcastle-under-Lyme,
Staffordshire, ST5 2SW
Tel: (01782) 715033 Fax: (01782) 613174
Constituency Caseworker –
Ms Caroline Hopwood
*Parliamentary Interests* . Jobs and Regeneration; Trade and Industry;
Education; Health
*Leisure Interests* . . . . . . Rugby; Football; Writing

### Field, Rt Hon Frank Birkenhead
**Labour** . . . . . . . . . . . Majority 15,591 over Con
*Born* . . . . . . . . . . . . . 16th July 1942 in London
*Educated* . . . . . . . . . . St Clement Danes Grammar School;
Hull University
*Elected* . . . . . . . . . . . . 1979 MP for Birkenhead
*Offices Held* . . . . . . . . 1979 - 81 Opposition Spokesman on
Education
1991 - 97 Chairman, Social Security Select
Committee, House of Commons
1997 - 98 Minister of State, Department of
Social Security (Minister for Welfare
Reform)
*Commons Office* . . . . . Tel: (020) 7219 5193 Fax: (020) 7219 0601
E-mail: fieldf@parliament.uk
Web: http://www.frankfieldmp.com
Secretary – Ms Jill Hendey
E-mail: hendeyj@parliament.uk
Political Researcher – Mr Adam Gray
Tel: (020) 7219 6636
E-mail: graya@parliament.uk

### Field, Mark . . . . . . Cities of London and Westminster
**Conservative** . . . . . . . Majority 4,499 over Lab
*Born* . . . . . . . . . . . . . 6th October 1964
*Educated* . . . . . . . . . . Reading School; St Edmund Hall, Oxford;
College of Law, Chester
*Elected* . . . . . . . . . . . . 2001 MP for Cities of London and
Westminster
*Offices Held* . . . . . . . . 2003 - 04 Opposition Whip
2004 - Opposition Spokesman on
London Issues
*Constituency Office* . . . . Tel: (020) 7730 8181
Agent – Mr Donald Stewart MBE
*Parliamentary Interests* . Small Business; Treasury;
Culture, Media and Sport
*Leisure Interests* . . . . . . Football; Cricket; Motor Racing;
Popular/Rock Music

### Fisher, Mark . . . . . . Stoke-on-Trent Central
**Labour** . . . . . . . . . . . Majority 11,845 over Con
*Born* . . . . . . . . . . . . . 29th October 1944 in Woking, Surrey
*Educated* . . . . . . . . . . Eton College; Trinity College, Cambridge
*Elected* . . . . . . . . . . . . 1983 MP for Stoke-on-Trent Central
*Offices Held* . . . . . . . . 1985 - 87 Opposition Whip
1987 - 92 Opposition Spokesman on
Arts and Media
1992 - 93 Opposition Spokesman on
Citizen's Charter and Women
1993 - 97 Opposition Spokesman on
National Heritage
1997 - 98 Parliamentary Secretary,
Department of Culture, Media and Sport
(Minister for the Arts)
*Commons Office* . . . . . Tel: (020) 7219 6118 Fax: (020) 7219 4894
E-mail: fisherm@parliament.uk
*Constituency Office* . . . . Winton House, Stoke Road, Stoke-on-Trent,
Staffordshire, ST4 7QU
Tel: (01782) 848468 Fax: (01782) 845658
Constituency Secretary – Ms Jan Allerton
*Parliamentary Interests* . Freedom of Information;
Reform of the House of Lords

## MEMBERS OF THE HOUSE OF COMMONS

**Fitzpatrick, Jim** . . . Poplar and Canning Town
**Labour** . . . . . . . . . . . Majority 14,104 over Con
*Born.* . . . . . . . . . . . . . 4th April 1952 in Glasgow
*Educated* . . . . . . . . . . Holyrood Senior Secondary School, Glasgow
*Elected.* . . . . . . . . . . . 1997 MP for Poplar and Canning Town
*Offices Held* . . . . . . . . 1999 - 2001 PPS to Alan Milburn
(Secretary of State for Health)
2001 - 02 Assistant Government Whip
2002 - Government Whip
(Lord Commissioner H M Treasury, then
from 2003, Vice-Chamberlain
HM Household)
*Commons Office* . . . . . . Tel: (020) 7219 5085/6215
Fax: (020) 7219 2776
E-mail: fitzpatrickj@parliament.uk
Web: http://www.jimfitzpatrickmp.co.uk
Parliamentary Assistant – Ms Debbie Fenn
E-mail: fennd@parliament.uk
Research Assistant – Mr Henry Ingham
E-mail: inghamh@parliament.uk
*Constituency Office* . . . . Tel: (020) 7536 0562
Constituency Secretary – Ms Louise Leak
*Parliamentary Interests* . Regeneration; Poverty Issues; Local
Government; Animal Welfare; Anti-Racism
*Leisure Interests* . . . . . . Football (West Ham United FC); Golf;
Reading; TV; Films

**Fitzsimons, Lorna** . Rochdale
**Labour** . . . . . . . . . . . Majority 5,655 over Lib Dem
*Born.* . . . . . . . . . . . . . 6th August 1967 in Rochdale
*Educated* . . . . . . . . . . Wardle High School;
Rochdale College of Art and Design;
Loughborough College of Art and Design
*Elected.* . . . . . . . . . . . 1997 MP for Rochdale
*Office Held* . . . . . . . . . 2001 - 03 PPS to Robin Cook (Leader of the
House of Commons)
*Commons Office* . . . . . . Tel: (020) 7219 3433
E-mail: fitzsimonsl@parliament.uk
*Constituency Office* . . . . 81 Durham Street, Rochdale, Lancashire,
OL11 1LR
Tel: (01706) 7644911 Fax: (01706) 759826
Organisers/Caseworkers –
Ms Angela Robinson
Mr Derek Snowden
*Parliamentary Interests* . Education; Families; Health; Crime
*Leisure Interests* . . . . . . Music; Walking; Art; Cooking

**Flight, Howard** . . . . Arundel and South Downs
**Conservative** . . . . . . . Majority 13,704 over Lib Dem
*Born.* . . . . . . . . . . . . . 16th June 1948
*Educated* . . . . . . . . . . Brentwood School, Essex;
Magdalene College, Cambridge;
University of Michigan Business School, USA
*Elected.* . . . . . . . . . . . 1997 MP for Arundel and South Downs
*Office Held* . . . . . . . . . 1999 - 2004 Opposition Spokesman on
Treasury Matters (Shadow Chief Secretary
from 2002)
2004 - Opposition Spokesman on the
City of London
*Commons Office* . . . . . . Tel: (020) 7219 3461 Fax: (020) 7219 2455
Pager: 07626 802713
E-mail: flighth@parliament.uk
Secretaries – Mrs Helyn Dudley
Mrs Caroline MacNaughton
Tel: (020) 7219 5203/6949
E-mail: macnaughtonc@parliament.uk
*Constituency Office* . . . . The Old Town Hall, 38 High Street, Steyning,
West Sussex, BN44 3YE
Tel: (01903) 816880 Fax: (01903) 816348
E-mail: asdca@btinternet.com
Agent and Researcher – Mr Russell Tanguay
*Parliamentary Interests* . Treasury; Pensions; Social Security;
Environment; Agriculture
*Leisure Interests* . . . . . . Skiing; Gardening; Collecting Antiques

**Flint, Caroline** . . . . Don Valley
**Labour** . . . . . . . . . . . Majority 9,520 over Con
*Born.* . . . . . . . . . . . . . 20th September 1961 in London
*Educated* . . . . . . . . . . Twickenham Girls' School;
Richmond Tertiary College;
University of East Anglia
*Elected.* . . . . . . . . . . . 1997 MP for Don Valley
*Offices Held* . . . . . . . . 2002 - 03 PPS to John Reid (Minister without
Portfolio and Labour Party Chairman)
2003 - Parliamentary Secretary, Home Office
*Commons Office* . . . . . . Tel: (020) 7219 4407 Fax: (020) 7219 1277
E-mail: flintc@parliament.uk
Web: http://www.carolineflint.co.uk
Parliamentary Researcher – Ms Katy Lewis
E-mail: lewisk@parliament.uk
*Constituency Office* . . . . Room 15, 115 St Sepulchre Gate West,
Doncaster, DN1 3AH
Tel: (01302) 366778 Fax: (01302) 328833
Chief of Staff – Mr Phil Cole
Caseworker – Ms Hilary McNamee
*Parliamentary Interests* . Childcare; Education; Law and Order;
Employment/Welfare to Work; Foreign Affairs;
House of Commons Modernisation
*Leisure Interests* . . . . . . Cinema; Tennis; Family

# MEMBERS OF THE HOUSE OF COMMONS

**Flook, Adrian** . . . . . Taunton
**Conservative** . . . . . . . Majority 235 over Lib Dem
*Educated* . . . . . . . . . . King Edward's School, Bath, Somerset;
Oxford University
*Elected* . . . . . . . . . . . 2001 MP for Taunton
*Commons Office* . . . . . Tel: (020) 7219 8464 Fax: (020) 7219 1954
Pager: 07644 002520
E-mail: flooka@parliament.uk
*Constituency Office* . . . 20a Staplegrove Road, Taunton, Somerset,
TA1 1DQ
Tel & Fax: (01823) 282788
Web: http://www.tauntontories.org.uk
Personal Assistant – Mrs Janet Wagstaff
E-mail: wagstaffj@parliament.uk
Agent – Mr Rodney Pilgrim
Tel: (01823) 286106 Fax: (01823) 324453
*Parliamentary Interests* . The Countryside
*Leisure Interests* . . . . . . Watching Rugby

**Flynn, Paul** . . . . . . . Newport West
**Labour** . . . . . . . . . . . Majority 9,304 over Con
*Born* . . . . . . . . . . . . . . 9th February 1935 in Cardiff
*Educated* . . . . . . . . . . St Illtyd's College;
University College of Wales, Cardiff
*Elected* . . . . . . . . . . . 1987 MP for Newport West
*Office Held* . . . . . . . . . 1988 - 90 Opposition Spokesman on Social
Security
*Commons Office* . . . . . Tel: (020) 7219 3478 Fax: (020) 7219 2433
Mobile: 07887 925699
Pager: 07644 007555
E-mail: paulflynnmp@talk21.com
Web: http://www.paulflynnmp.co.uk
Researcher – Ms Jenny Martin
*Constituency Office* . . . Tel & Fax: (01633) 262348
Constituency Assistant – Ms Fern Coster
Fax: (01633) 760532
*Parliamentary Interests* . Pensions; Legalisation of Cannabis;
Animal Welfare; Wales

**Follett, Barbara** . . . Stevenage
**Labour** . . . . . . . . . . . Majority 8,566 over Con
*Born* . . . . . . . . . . . . . . 25th December 1942 in Kingston, Jamaica
*Educated* . . . . . . . . . . Ellerslie Girl's High School, Cape Town;
London School of Economics
*Elected* . . . . . . . . . . . 1997 MP for Stevenage
*Commons Office* . . . . . Tel: (020) 7219 2649 Fax: (020) 7219 1158
Pager: 07644 005126
E-mail: barbara@barbara-follett.org.uk
Web: http://www.barbara-follett.org.uk
Parliamentary Assistant – Ms Cassie Kenny
E-mail: cassie@barbara-follett.org.uk
Research Assistant – Mr Ben Peacock
E-mail: ben@barbara-follett.org.uk
*Constituency Office* . . . 4 Popple Way, Stevenage,
Hertfordshire, SG1 3TG
Tel: (01438) 222800 Fax: (01438) 222292
Constituency Caseworker –
Ms Vickie Warwick
Assistant Caseworker – Ms Debbie Wilson
*Parliamentary Interests* . Trade and Industry; Equalities;
International Development;
Cultural Industries; Foreign Affairs
*Leisure Interests* . . . . . . Scrabble; Photography; Films; Reading

**Forth, Rt Hon Eric** Bromley and Chislehurst
**Conservative** . . . . . . . Majority 9,037 over Lab
*Born* . . . . . . . . . . . . . . 9th September 1944 in Glasgow
*Educated* . . . . . . . . . . Jordanhill College School, Glasgow;
Glasgow University
*Elected* . . . . . . . . . . . 1983 - 97 MP for Mid Worcestershire
1997 MP for Bromley and Chislehurst
*Offices Held* . . . . . . . . 1988 - 90 Parliamentary Secretary,
Department of Trade and Industry
1990 - 92 Parliamentary Secretary,
Department of Employment
1992 - 94 Parliamentary Secretary,
Department for Education
1994 - 97 Minister of State, Department for
Education and Employment
2001 - 03 Shadow Leader of the House of
Commons
*Commons Office* . . . . . Tel: (020) 7219 0366/6344
Office Manager – Miss Susan Butler
Senior Caseworker – Mr Kevin Donnelly
Senior Secretary – Mrs Carroll Goff
*Constituency Office* . . . 5 White Horse Hill, Chislehurst,
Kent, BR7 6DG
Tel: (020) 8295 2639
Agent – Mr Andrew Lee
Secretary – Mrs Faith Fletcher
*Parliamentary Interests* . European Union Matters; UK/USA Relations;
Canada; Australia; New Zealand
*Leisure Interests* . . . . . . Cinema; Political Biography

**Foster, Rt Hon Derek** DL Bishop Auckland
**Labour** . . . . . . . . . . . Majority 13,926 over Con
*Born* . . . . . . . . . . . . . . 25th June 1937 in Sunderland
*Educated* . . . . . . . . . . Bede Grammar School, Sunderland;
St Catherine's College, Oxford
*Elected* . . . . . . . . . . . 1979 MP for Bishop Auckland
*Offices Held* . . . . . . . . 1981 - 82 Opposition Whip
1982 - 83 Opposition Spokesman on
Social Security
1983 - 85 PPS to Neil Kinnock (Leader of
the Opposition)
1985 - 95 Opposition Chief Whip
1995 - 97 Shadow Chancellor of the Duchy
of Lancaster
1997 Minister of State, Cabinet Office
1997 - 2001 Chairman, Employment Sub-
Committee (Education and Employment
Select Committee), House of Commons
*Commons Office* . . . . . Tel: (020) 7219 3582 Fax: (020) 7219 2711
Mobile: 07957 361386
Pager: 07626 409615
E-mail: fosterderek@parliament.uk
Secretary/PA – Mrs Anne Foster
*Constituency Office* . . . Norland House, Hackworth Industrial Park,
Shildon, Co. Durham, DL4 1HE
Tel & Fax: (01388) 777175
Personal Assistant – Mr Bill Neilson
Researchers/PAs – Mrs Paula James
Mrs Gwen Thompson
Tel & Fax: (0191) 417 1580
*Parliamentary Interests* . Education; Employment; Training;
Economics/Finance; Manufacturing Industry
*Leisure Interests* . . . . . . Brass Bands; Choirs; Cricket; Football

# MEMBERS OF THE HOUSE OF COMMONS

**Foster, Don**...... Bath
**Liberal Democrat** ... Majority 9,894 over Con
*Born*............. 31st March 1947 in Preston, Lancashire
*Educated* ......... Lancaster Royal Grammar School;
Keele University; Bath University
*Elected*............ 1992 MP for Bath
*Offices Held* ........ 1992 - 99 Liberal Democrat Spokesman on
Education and Employment
1999 - 2002 Liberal Democrat Spokesman on
Environment, Transport and the Regions
and Social Justice
2002 - 03 Liberal Democrat Spokesman on
Transport
2003 - Liberal Democrat Spokesman on
Culture, Media and Sport
*Commons Office* ...... Tel: (020) 7219 5001/4805
Fax: (020) 7219 2695
E-mail: fosterd@parliament.uk
Web: http://www.donfoster.co.uk
Research Assistant – Mr Daniel Wilson
E-mail: wilsondj@parliament.uk
*Constituency Office* .... 31 James Street West, Bath, BA1 2BT
Tel: (01225) 338973 Fax: (01225) 463630
Personal Assistant – Mrs Diane Bodle
Researcher – Mr Matthew Williams
*Parliamentary Interests* . Local Government; Education; Transport
*Leisure Interests* ...... Music; Films; Sport

**Foster, Michael Jabez** Hastings and Rye
**Labour** ............ Majority 4,308 over Con
*Born*.............. 26th February 1946 in Hastings
*Educated* .......... Hastings Grammar School;
Leicester University
*Elected*............ 1997 MP for Hastings and Rye
*Office Held*......... 1999 - PPS to Law Officers
*Commons Office* ...... Tel: (020) 7219 1600
Mobile: 07973 955454
Pager: 07644 003488
E-mail: mp@1066.net
Web: http://www.michaelfoster.labour.co.uk
*Constituency Office* .... Ellen Draper Centre, 84 Bohemia Road,
St Leonards-on-Sea, East Sussex, TN37 6RN
Tel: (01424) 460070 Fax: (01424) 460072
Secretary – Mrs Emily Westley
Administrator/Diary Manager –
Mrs Rosemary Foster
Tel: (01424) 464604
Researcher – Ms Andrea Samuelson
Tel: (01424) 464602
*Parliamentary Interests*. Pensioners; Poverty; Animal Welfare
*Leisure Interests* ...... Tennis; Table Tennis; Walking

**Foster, Michael John** Worcester
**Labour** ............ Majority 7,425 over Con
*Born*.............. 14th March 1963
*Educated* .......... Great Wyrley High School, Cannock;
Wolverhampton University
*Elected*............ 1997 MP for Worcester
*Office Held*......... 2004 - PPS to Department of
Education and Skills Ministers
*Commons Office* ...... Tel & Fax: (020) 7219 6379
E-mail: fosterm@parliament.uk
Web: http://www.michaelfoster.co.uk
Parliamentary Assistant – Ms Margaret Payne
E-mail: paynem@parliament.uk
*Constituency Office* .... Arboretum Lodge, 24 Sansome Walk,
Worcester, WR1 1LX
Tel & Fax: (01905) 26504
E-mail: watsonme@parliament.uk
Constituency Assistant – Ms Maggie Watson
*Parliamentary Interests* . Further Education; Hunting with Dogs
*Leisure Interests* ...... Sports

**Foulkes, Rt Hon George** Carrick, Cumnock and Doon Valley
**Labour** ............ Majority 14,856 over Con
*Born*.............. 21st January 1942 in Oswestry, Shropshire
*Educated* .......... Keith Grammar School, Banffshire;
Haberdashers' Aske's School;
Edinburgh University
*Elected*............ 1979 MP for South Ayrshire, then (1983)
Carrick, Cumnock and Doon Valley
*Offices Held* ........ 1984 - 92 Opposition Spokesman on Foreign
and Commonwealth Affairs
1992 - 93 Opposition Spokesman on Defence
1994 - 97 Opposition Spokesman on
Overseas Development
1997 - 2001 Parliamentary Secretary,
Department for International Development
2001 - 02 Minister of State, Scotland Office
*Commons Office* ...... Tel: (020) 7219 3474  Fax: (020) 7219 2407
Mobile: 07860 376272
Pager – 07644 003007
E-mail: gfoulkesmp@aol.com
Web: http://www.georgefoulkesmp.co.uk
Researcher – Mr Luke Pollard
Tel: (020) 7219 6509 Fax: (020) 7219 5109
E-mail: pollardl@parliament.uk
*Constituency Office* .... Skerrington House, Glaisnock Road,
Cumnock, KA18 3BU
Tel: (01290) 425859 Fax: (01290) 424973
Office Manager – Mr Douglas Campbell
Constituency Assistant – Ms Audrey Richard
*Parliamentary Interests* . International Development; Foreign Affairs;
Defence; Scotland
*Leisure Interests* ...... Football (Heart of Midlothian FC)

## MEMBERS OF THE HOUSE OF COMMONS

**Fox, Dr Liam** . . . . . Woodspring
**Conservative** . . . . . . . Majority 8,798 over Lab
*Born*. . . . . . . . . . . . . . 22nd September 1961 in Scotland
*Educated* . . . . . . . . . . St Brides High School, East Kilbride;
Glasgow University
*Elected*. . . . . . . . . . . . 1992 MP for Woodspring
*Offices Held* . . . . . . . . 1994 - 95 Assistant Government Whip
1995 - 96 Government Whip (Lord
Commissioner H M Treasury)
1996 - 97 Parliamentary Secretary, Foreign
and Commonwealth Office
1997 - 98 Opposition Spokesman on Scotland
1998 - 99 Opposition Spokesman on
Constitutional Affairs
1999 - 2004 Shadow Secretary of State for
Health
2004 - Co-Chairman, Conservative Party
*Commons Office* . . . . . Tel: (020) 7219 4198 Fax: (020) 7219 3968
Personal Assistant – Mrs Ione Douglas
E-mail: douglasi@parliament.uk
Head of Office – Mr Bill Clare
Tel: (020) 7219 4549 Fax: (020) 7219 2617
E-mail: clareb@parliament.uk
*Constituency Office* . . . . 71 High Street, Nailsea, Somerset, BS48 1AW
Tel: (01275) 790090 Fax: (01275) 790091
Secretary – Mrs Diane Newman

**Francis, Dr Hywel**  Aberavon
**Labour** . . . . . . . . . . . Majority 16,108 over Plaid Cymru
*Born*. . . . . . . . . . . . . . 6th June 1946
*Educated* . . . . . . . . . . Whitchurch Grammar School;
University of Wales, Swansea
*Elected*. . . . . . . . . . . . 2001 MP for Aberavon
*Commons Office* . . . . . Tel: (020) 7219 8121 Fax: (020) 7219 1734
Mobile: 07977 924649
Pager: 07626 409510
E-mail: francish@parliament.uk
Parliamentary Assistant – Mrs Mair Francis
*Constituency Office* . . . . Eagle House, 2 Talbot Road, Port Talbot,
SA13 1DH
Tel: (01639) 897660 Fax (01639) 891725
Press and Community Liaison Officer –
Mr John Slater
Caseworker – Mr Leslie Rees
Secretary – Mrs Lisa Donovan
*Parliamentary Interests* . Steel; Disability; Home Affairs; Welsh Affairs;
Lifelong Learning
*Leisure Interests* . . . . . . Walking; Cycling; Photography; Travel

**Francois, Mark**. . . . Rayleigh
**Conservative** . . . . . . . Majority 8,290 over Lab
*Born*. . . . . . . . . . . . . . 1965
*Educated* . . . . . . . . . . Bristol University; London University
*Elected*. . . . . . . . . . . . 2001 MP for Rayleigh
*Offices Held* . . . . . . . . 2002 - 04 Opposition Whip
2004 - Opposition Spokesman on
Economic Affairs
*Commons Office* . . . . . Tel: (020) 7219 8287 Fax: (020) 7219 1858
*Constituency Office* . . . . 25 Bellingham Lane, Rayleigh,
Essex, SS6 7ED
Tel: (01268) 742044 Fax: (01268) 741833
*Leisure Interests* . . . . . . Travel; Reading; History

# G

**Gale, Roger**. . . . . . . Thanet North
**Conservative** . . . . . . . Majority 6,650 over Lab
*Born*. . . . . . . . . . . . . . 20th August 1943 in Dorset
*Educated* . . . . . . . . . . Hardye's School, Dorchester;
Guildhall School of Music and Drama
*Elected*. . . . . . . . . . . . 1983 MP for Thanet North
*Office Held*. . . . . . . . . 2001 - 03 Vice-Chairman, Conservative Party
*Commons Office* . . . . . Tel: (020) 7219 4087 Fax: (020) 7219 6828
Pager: 07626 802961
E-mail: galerj@parliament.uk
Web: http://www.rogergale.co.uk
*Constituency Office* . . . . 215a Canterbury Road, Birchington,
Kent, CT7 9AH
Tel: (01843) 848588 Fax: (01843) 844856
Parliamentary Office Director –
Mrs Suzy Gale
E-mail: suzy@suzygale.fsworld.co.uk
Parliamentary Office Manager –
Ms Debi Hennessy
Parliamentary Personal Assistant –
Mrs Kay Mileham
*Parliamentary Interests* . Animal Welfare; Media; Broadcasting;
Tourism; Education
*Leisure Interests* . . . . . . Swimming; Sailing

**Galloway, George** . Glasgow Kelvin
**Independent**. . . . . . . . Majority 7,260 over Lib Dem
*Born*. . . . . . . . . . . . . . 16th August 1954 in Dundee
*Educated* . . . . . . . . . . Harris Academy, Dundee
*Elected*. . . . . . . . . . . . 1987 Glasgow Hillhead, then (1997)
Glasgow Kelvin (*elected as Labour*)
*Commons Office* . . . . . Tel: (020) 7219 6940 Fax: (020) 7219 2879
E-mail: gallowayg@parliament.uk
Parliamentary Assistant –
Ms Geraldine Clerck
E-mail: clerckg@parliament.uk
Special Assistant – Ms Iara Sami
Parliamentary Researcher –
Ms Yasmin Ataullah
Tel: (020) 7219 2874
E-mail: ataullahy@parliament.uk
*Parliamentary Interests* . Scotland; Foreign Affairs
*Leisure Interests* . . . . . . Films; Sport; Music

**Gapes, Mike** . . . . . . Ilford South
**Labour** . . . . . . . . . . . Majority 13,997 over Con
*Born*. . . . . . . . . . . . . . 4th September 1952 in Wanstead, Essex
*Educated* . . . . . . . . . . Buckhurst Hill High School, Essex;
Fitzwilliam College, Cambridge;
Middlesex Polytechnic
*Elected*. . . . . . . . . . . . 1992 MP for Ilford South
*Offices Held* . . . . . . . . 1997 - 99 PPS to Rt Hon Paul Murphy
(Minister of State, Northern Ireland Office)
2001 - 02 PPS to Rt Hon Lord Rooker
(Minister of State, Home Office)
*Commons Office* . . . . . Tel: (020) 7219 6485 Fax: (020) 7219 0978
E-mail: gapesm@parliament.uk
*Parliamentary Interests* . Foreign Affairs; Europe; Defence;
Economic Policy; Education
*Leisure Interests* . . . . . . Football (West Ham United FC)

# MEMBERS OF THE HOUSE OF COMMONS

**Gardiner, Barry**... Brent North
**Labour** . . . . . . . . . . . Majority 10,205 over Con
*Born.* . . . . . . . . . . . . . 10th March 1957 in Glasgow
*Educated* . . . . . . . . . . Glasgow High School; Haileybury College;
St Andrews University;
Corpus Christi College, Cambridge;
Harvard University, USA
*Elected* . . . . . . . . . . . . 1997 MP for Brent North
*Offices Held* . . . . . . . . Formerly Mayor of Cambridge
2004 - Parliamentary Secretary, Northern
Ireland Office
*Commons Office* . . . . . Tel: (020) 7219 4046 Fax: (020) 7219 2495
E-mail: gardinerb@parliament.uk
Web: http://www.barrygardiner.com
Office Manager and Caseworker –
Ms Kirsty Horne
E-mail: hornek@parliament.uk
Parliamentary Researcher – Mr Joseph Perry
Tel: (020) 7219 2327
E-mail: perryj@parliament.uk
*Parliamentary Interests* . Foreign Affairs; Trade and Industry; Treasury;
Leasehold Reform; Financial Services; Sport;
India
*Leisure Interests* . . . . . . Singing; Music Making/Listening;
Birdwatching; Hill Walking

**Garnier, Edward** QC Market Harborough
**Conservative** . . . . . . . Majority 5,252 over Lib Dem
*Born.* . . . . . . . . . . . . . 26th October 1952 in Germany
*Educated* . . . . . . . . . . Wellington College; Jesus College, Oxford;
College of Law, London
*Elected* . . . . . . . . . . . . 1992 MP for Harborough
*Offices Held* . . . . . . . . 1995 - 97 PPS to Ministers, Foreign and
Commonwealth Office
1995 - 97 PPS to Attorney General and
Solicitor General
1996 - 97 PPS to Chancellor of the Duchy
of Lancaster
1997 - 99 Opposition Spokesman,
Lord Chancellor's Department
1999 - 2001 Shadow Attorney General
*Commons Office* . . . . . Tel: (020) 7219 4034
E-mail: garniere@parliament.co.uk
Web: http://www.edwardgarnier.co.uk
Secretary – Mrs Shirley Tovell
E-mail: tovells@parliament.uk
*Constituency Office* . . . . 24 Nelson Street, Market Harborough,
Leicestershire, LE16 9AY
Tel: (01858) 464146 Fax: (01858) 410013
E-mail: hca@tory.org
Agent – Mrs Margaret Richards
*Parliamentary Interests* . Foreign Policy; Defence; Agriculture; Law
*Leisure Interests* . . . . . . Cricket; Music; Shooting

**George, Andrew**... St Ives
**Liberal Democrat** . . . Majority 10,053 over Con
*Born.* . . . . . . . . . . . . . 2nd December 1958 in Mullion, Cornwall
*Educated* . . . . . . . . . . Helston Grammar School; Sussex University;
University College, Oxford
*Elected* . . . . . . . . . . . . 1997 MP for St Ives (Cornwall)
*Offices Held* . . . . . . . . 1997 - 99 Liberal Democrat Spokesman on
Fisheries
1999 - 2001 Liberal Democrat Spokesman on
Disabilities
2001 - 02 PPS to Charles Kennedy
(Leader, Liberal Democrats)
2002 - Liberal Democrat Spokesman on
Food and Rural Affairs
*Commons Office* . . . . . Tel: (020) 7219 4588 Fax: (020) 7219 5572
Web: http://www.andrewgeorge.org.uk
Researcher – Mr Jonathan Eddy
E-mail: eddyj@parliament.uk
*Constituency Office* . . . . 1st Floor, Knight's Yard, Belgravia Street,
Penzance, Cornwall, TR18 2EL
Tel: (01736) 360020 Fax: (01736) 332866
Personal Assistant – Mrs Ursula Cooper
Caseworker – Mrs Emma Williams
*Parliamentary Interests* . Anti-Racism; Asylum/Immigration;
Cornish Issues; Economic Development;
Devolution; Education; Environment;
Farming; Fishing; Housing; Minority Rights;
Third World Development; Poverty;
Sea Safety
*Leisure Interests* . . . . . . Cricket; Cycling; Rugby; Football;
Gardening; Painting; Singing;
Swimming; Walking; Writing

**George, Rt Hon Bruce** Walsall South
**Labour** . . . . . . . . . . . Majority 9,931 over Con
*Born.* . . . . . . . . . . . . . 1st June 1942 in Mountain Ash, South Wales
*Educated* . . . . . . . . . . Mountain Ash Grammar School;
University College of Wales, Swansea;
Warwick University
*Elected* . . . . . . . . . . . . 1974 (Feb) MP for Walsall South
*Office Held* . . . . . . . . . 1997 - Chairman, Defence Select Committee,
House of Commons
*Commons Office* . . . . . Tel: (020) 7219 6610/4049
Fax: (020) 7219 3823
E-mail: georgeb@parliament.uk
Research Assistants – Mr Gareth Sutton
Ms Natalie Whatford
Tel: (020) 7219 4049
E-mails: [surnameinitial]@parliament.uk
*Constituency Office* . . . . 34 Bridge Street, Walsall, West Midlands,
WS1 1HQ
Tel: (01922) 724960 Fax: (01922) 724960
Constituency Caseworker – Mrs Rose Burley
Fax: (01922) 621844
*Parliamentary Interests* . Defence; Private Security; Housing
*Leisure Interests* . . . . . . Reading

# MEMBERS OF THE HOUSE OF COMMONS

**Gerrard, Neil** . . . . . Walthamstow
**Labour** . . . . . . . . . . . Majority 15,181 over Con
*Born*. . . . . . . . . . . . . . 3rd July 1942 in Farnworth, Lancashire
*Educated* . . . . . . . . . . Manchester Grammar School;
Wadham College, Oxford;
Chelsea College, London;
South Bank Polytechnic, London
*Elected*. . . . . . . . . . . . 1992 MP for Walthamstow
*Office Held*. . . . . . . . . 1986 - 90 Leader, Waltham Forest London
Borough Council
*Commons Office* . . . . . . Tel: (020) 7219 6368 Fax: (020) 7219 4899
E-mail: gerrardn@parliament.uk
Web: http://www.neilgerrard.co.uk
Assistants – Ms Melanie Gower
Ms Anne Humbles
Ms Gila Tabrizi
Tel: (020) 7219 0595/4899
*Constituency Office* . . . . 23 Orford Road, Walthamstow,
London, E17 9NL
*Parliamentary Interests* . Health (HIV/AIDS);
Home Affairs (Immigration/Asylum);
Foreign Affairs (Middle East/Sri Lanka)

**Gibb, Nick** . . . . . . . . Bognor Regis and Littlehampton
**Conservative** . . . . . . . Majority 5,643 over Lab
*Born*. . . . . . . . . . . . . . 3rd September 1960 in Amersham, Bucks
*Educated* . . . . . . . . . . Maidstone Grammar School;
Roundhay School, Leeds;
Thornes House School, Wakefield;
Durham University
*Elected*. . . . . . . . . . . . 1997 MP for Bognor Regis and Littlehampton
*Offices Held* . . . . . . . . 1998 - 99 Opposition Spokesman on Treasury
Issues
1999 - 2000 Opposition Spokesman on
Trade and Industry
2001 - 04 Opposition Shadow Spokesman on
Transport, Local Government and
the Regions
*Commons Office* . . . . . . Tel: (020) 7219 6374 Fax: (020) 7219 1395
Private Secretary – Miss Diana Dickson
E-mail: dicksond@parliament.uk
*Constituency Office* . . . . 110 London Road, Bognor Regis,
West Sussex, PO21 1BD
Tel: (01243) 826410 Fax: (01243) 842076
Agent – Mrs Hilary Flynn
*Parliamentary Interests* . Treasury; Social Security; Taxation; Education

**Gibson, Dr Ian** . . . . Norwich North
**Labour** . . . . . . . . . . . Majority 5,863 over Con
*Born*. . . . . . . . . . . . . . 26th September 1938 in Dumfries
*Educated* . . . . . . . . . . Dumfries Academy; Edinburgh University
*Elected*. . . . . . . . . . . . 1997 MP for Norwich North
*Office Held*. . . . . . . . . 2001 - Chairman, Science and Technology
Select Committee, House of Commons
*Commons Office* . . . . . . Tel: (020) 7219 1100 Fax: (020) 7219 2799
Mobile: 07714 344550
Pager: 07644 005749
E-mail: gibsoni@parliament.uk
Researcher – Ms Munizha Ahmad
Tel: (020) 7219 4038
E-mail: ahmadm@parliament.uk
Parliamentary Assistant – Ms Sarah Revell
Tel: (020) 7219 3367
E-mail: revells@parliament.uk
*Constituency Office* . . . . 59 Bethel Street, Norwich, Norfolk, NR2 1NL
Tel: (01603) 661144 Fax: (01603) 663502
Web: http://www.norwich-labour-mps.org.uk
Senior Caseworker – Mrs Sonia Wood
*Parliamentary Interests* . Health; Science; Technology
*Leisure Interests* . . . . . . Football

**Gidley, Sandra** . . . . Romsey
**Liberal Democrat** . . . Majority 2,370 over Con
*Born*. . . . . . . . . . . . . . 6th March 1957 in Rossett
*Educated* . . . . . . . . . . Eggars Grammar School, Alton;
Afcent International School, Brunssum,
Netherlands;
Windsor Girls School, Hamm, Germany;
Bath University
*Elected*. . . . . . . . . . . . 2000 MP for Romsey (By-election)
*Offices Held* . . . . . . . . 2001 - Liberal Democrat Spokesman on
Women's Issues and (from 2003)
Older People
*Commons Office* . . . . . . Tel: (020)7219 5986 Fax: (020) 7219 2324
Pager: 07699 704756
E-mail: gidleys@parliament.uk
Web: http://www.sandragidley.org
Researcher – Ms Liza Coffin
E-mail: coffinl@parliament.uk
*Constituency Office* . . . . 3a Victoria Place, Love Lane, Romsey,
Hampshire, SO51 8BE
Tel: (01794) 511900 Fax: (01794) 512538
Personal Assistant – Ms Sally Lamb
Caseworker – Cllr Liz Barron
Caseworker/Researcher – Mr Tony Barron
Secretary – Mrs Marion Barron
*Parliamentary Interests* . Education; Health; Equality Issues
*Leisure Interests* . . . . . . Badminton; Photography; Theatre

# MEMBERS OF THE HOUSE OF COMMONS

**Gildernew, Michelle** Fermanagh and South Tyrone
**Sinn Fein** . . . . . . . . . Majority 53 over Ulster Unionist
*Born.* . . . . . . . . . . . . 28th March 1970 in Brantry, Dungannon
*Educated* . . . . . . . . . . St Catherine's College, Armagh;
   University of Ulster, Coleraine
*Elected.* . . . . . . . . . . . 2001 MP for Fermanagh and South Tyrone
   *(has not taken seat at Westminster)*
*Office Held* . . . . . . . . . 1998 - Member, Northern Ireland Assembly
*Commons Office* . . . . . . Tel: (020) 7219 8162 Fax: (020) 7219 6107
*Constituency Office* . . . . 82 Main Street, Lisnaskea, Co Fermanagh, BT92 0JD
   Tel: (028) 6772 3986 Fax: (028) 6772 3643
   E-mail: gildernewm@parliament.uk
   Secretary – Ms Dora Jonsdottir
   E-mail: jonsdottird@parliament.uk
   Assistant – Mr Barry Monteith
   Tel: (028) 8772 2776  Fax: (028) 8772 7128
   E-mail: southtyronesinnfein@fsmail.net
*Leisure Interests* . . . . . . Gaelic Football; Cinema; Reading;
   Scuba Diving; Socialising; Travel


**Gill, Parmjit Singh** Leicester South
**Liberal Democrat** . . . Majority 1,654 over Lab
*Elected.* . . . . . . . . . . . 2004 (by-election)


**Gillan, Cheryl** . . . . . Chesham and Amersham
**Conservative** . . . . . . . Majority 11,882 over Lib Dem
*Born.* . . . . . . . . . . . . . 21st April 1952 in Llandaff
*Educated* . . . . . . . . . . Cheltenham Ladies College; College of Law
*Elected.* . . . . . . . . . . . 1992 MP for Chesham and Amersham
*Offices Held* . . . . . . . . 1995 - 97 Parliamentary Secretary,
   Department for Education and Employment
   1997 - 98 Opposition Spokesman on
   Trade and Industry
   1998 - 2001 Opposition Spokesman on
   Foreign Affairs and International
   Development
   2001 - 03 Opposition Whip
   2003 - Opposition Spokesman on Home
   Affairs
*Commons Office* . . . . . Tel: (020) 7219 4061 Fax: (020) 7219 2762
   E-mail: gillanc@parliament.uk
   Web: http://www.cherylgillan.co.uk
   Secretary – Ms Elizabeth Ballin
   E-mail: balline@parliament.uk
   Political Assistant – Mr Guy L'Etang
   E-mail: letangg@parliament.uk
   Tel: (020) 7219 3777
*Constituency Office* . . . . 7 Hill Avenue, Amersham,
   Buckinghamshire, HP6 5BW
   Tel: (01494) 721577 Fax: (01494) 722107
   Diary Secretary – Mrs Mary Shaw
   E-mail: shawmj@parliament.uk
*Parliamentary Interests* . Foreign Affairs; Defence; Education
*Leisure Interests* . . . . . . Golf; Music; Gardening


**Gilroy, Linda** . . . . . . Plymouth Sutton
**Labour** . . . . . . . . . . . Majority 7,517 over Con
*Born.* . . . . . . . . . . . . . 19th July 1949
*Educated* . . . . . . . . . . Edinburgh University; Strathclyde University;
   Open University
*Elected.* . . . . . . . . . . . 1997 MP for Plymouth Sutton
*Office Held.* . . . . . . . . 2001 - PPS to Nick Raynsford
   (Minister of State, Office of the
   Deputy Prime Minister)
*Commons Office* . . . . . Tel: (020) 7219 4746 Fax: (020) 7219 0987
   E-mail: gilroyl@parliament.uk
*Constituency Office* . . . . Tel: (01752) 226626 Fax: 01752) 221645
   Secretary – Ms Janet Dingle
*Parliamentary Interests* . Utilities; Energy; Environment;
   Local and Regional Economy
*Leisure Interests* . . . . . . Walking; Swimming; Theatre


**Godsiff, Roger** . . . . Birmingham Sparkbrook and Small Heath
**Labour** . . . . . . . . . . . Majority 16,246 over Con
*Born.* . . . . . . . . . . . . . 28th June 1946 in Lewisham, London
*Educated* . . . . . . . . . . Catford Comprehensive School
*Elected.* . . . . . . . . . . . 1992 MP for Birmingham Small Heath,
   then (1997) Birmingham Sparkbrook and
   Small Heath
*Commons Office* . . . . . Tel: (020) 7219 5191 Fax: (020) 7219 2221
   E-mail: godsiffr@parliament.uk
   Researcher – Mr Ian Hughes
   E-mail: hughesi@parliament.uk
*Constituency Office* . . . . 15D Lloyd Street, Small Heath,
   Birmingham, B10 0LH
   Tel & Fax: (0121) 772 2383
   Personal Assistant – Mr Gulbahar Khan
   Secretary – Mrs Margaret Novell
   Tel & Fax: (0121) 603 2299
*Parliamentary Interests* . Foreign Affairs; Immigration;
   Sport and Leisure
*Leisure Interests* . . . . . . Sport; Reading; Music; Television


**Goggins, Paul** . . . . Wythenshawe and Sale East
**Labour** . . . . . . . . . . . Majority 12,608 over Con
*Born.* . . . . . . . . . . . . . 16th June 1953 in Manchester
*Educated* . . . . . . . . . . St Bede's School, Manchester;
   Birmingham Polytechnic;
   Manchester Polytechnic
*Elected.* . . . . . . . . . . . 1997 MP for Wythenshawe and Sale East
*Offices Held* . . . . . . . . 2000 - 03 PPS to David Blunkett (as
   Secretary of State for Education and
   Employment, then as Home Secretary)
   2003 - Parliamentary Secretary, Home Office
   (Minister for Prisons and Probation)
*Constituency Office* . . . . 2/10 Alderman Downward House, Civic
   Centre, Wythenshawe, Manchester, M22 5RF
   Tel: (0161) 499 7900 Fax: (0161) 499 7911
   E-mail: gogginsp@parliament.uk
   Assistant – Mr Paul Duffy
   Secretary – Mrs Louise Leyland
   Caseworker – Ms Joanne Taylor
*Parliamentary Interests* . Poverty at Home and Overseas; Transport;
   Health; Education
*Leisure Interests* . . . . . . Football (Manchester City FC); Cricket
   (Lancashire CCC); Walking; Music

# MEMBERS OF THE HOUSE OF COMMONS

**Goodman, Paul** ... Wycombe
**Conservative** ....... Majority 3,168 over Lab
*Born*. .............. 17th November 1959
*Educated* .......... Cranleigh School;
  York University
*Elected*. ........... 2001 MP for Wycombe
*Offices Held* ........ 2001 - 02 PPS to David Davies (Conservative
  Party Chairman)
  2003 - 04 Opposition Spokesman on
  Work and Pensions
  2004 - Opposition Spokesman on
  Economic Affairs and Disability Issues
*Commons Office* ...... Tel: (020) 7219 3547 Fax: (020) 7219 4614
  Mobile: 07866 363823
  E-mail: goodmanp@parliament.uk
  Private Secretary – Miss Jane Dickins
  E-mail: dickinsj@parliament.uk
*Constituency Office* .... 150A West Wycombe Road, High Wycombe,
  Buckinghamshire, HP12 3AE
  Tel: (01494) 521777 Fax: (01494) 510042
  E-mail: agent@wycombe.tory.org.uk
  Agent – Mrs Susan Hynard
  Secretary – Mrs Sandy Ashby
*Parliamentary Interests* . Social Exclusion; Works and Pensions;
  Kashmir; Ethnic Minorities

**Gray, James** ...... Wiltshire North
**Conservative** ....... Majority 3,878 over Lib Dem
*Born*. .............. 7th November 1954
*Educated* .......... The High School of Glasgow;
  Glasgow University; Christ Church, Oxford
*Elected*. ........... 1997 MP for Wiltshire North
*Offices Held* ........ 2000 - 01 Opposition Whip
  2001 - 02 Opposition Spokesman on
  Defence
  2002 - Opposition Spokesman on
  Environment, Food and Rural Affairs
  (Environment and Transport from 2004)
*Commons Office* ...... Tel: (020) 7219 6237 Fax: (020) 7219 1163
  Mobile: 07831 552529
  Pager: 07626 802049
  E-mail: jamesgraymp@parliament.uk
  Web: http://www.jamesgray.com
  Secretary – Mrs Catriona Sutherland-Hawes
  E-mail: sutherlandhawesc@parliament.uk
*Constituency Office* .... 44/45 Market Place, Chippenham,
  Wiltshire, SN15 3HG
  Tel: (01249) 652851 Fax: (01249) 448582
  Secretary – Mrs Jennifer Hancock
*Parliamentary Interests* . Defence; Agriculture; Environment; Transport;
  Regional Affairs; Countryside
*Leisure Interests* ...... Countryside; Riding Horses; British Heritage;
  Local History; Army

**Grayling, Chris** .... Epsom and Ewell
**Conservative** ....... Majority 10,080 over Lab
*Educated* .......... Royal Grammar School, High Wycombe;
  Sidney Sussex College, Cambridge
*Elected*. ........... 2001 MP for Epsom and Ewell
*Offices Held* ........ 2002 Opposition Whip
  2002 - 03 Opposition Spokesman on Health
  2003 - 04 Opposition Spokesman on
  Public Services, Health and Education
  2004 - Opposition Spokesman on Education
*Commons Office* ...... Tel: (020) 7219 8226 Fax: (020) 7219 1763
  E-mail: graylingc@parliament.uk
  Web: http://www.chrisgrayling.net
  Researcher – Mrs Beth Mitchell
  Tel: (020) 7219 8194
  E-mail: mitchellb@parliament.uk
  Political Secretary – Mrs Sue Grayling
  Tel: (01372) 270144 Fax: (01372) 270154
  E-mail: graylings@parliament.uk
*Constituency Office* .... 212 Barnett Wood Lane, Ashtead,
  Surrey, KT21 2DB
  Tel: (01372) 271036 Fax: (01372) 270906
  E-mail: eeca@tory.org
  Constituency Secretary –
  Mrs Verna Martin-Verdinos
*Parliamentary Interests* . Transport; Education; Health
*Leisure Interests* ...... Antiques; Cricket; Golf

**Green, Damian** .... Ashford
**Conservative** ....... Majority 7,359 over Lab
*Born*. .............. 17th January 1956
*Educated* .......... Reading School; Balliol College, Oxford
*Elected*. ........... 1997 MP for Ashford
*Offices Held* ........ 1998 - 99 Opposition Spokesman on
  Education and Employment
  1999 - 2001 Opposition Spokesman on
  Environment, Transport and the Regions
  2001 - 03 Opposition Spokesman on
  Education and Skills
  2003 - 04 Opposition Spokesman on Transport
*Commons Office* ...... Tel: (020) 7219 3911 Fax: (020) 7219 0904
  E-mail: greend@parliament.uk
  Web: http://www.damiangreen.org
  Assistant – Miss Susan Ward
  E-mail: wards@parliament.uk
  Researcher – Mrs Emma Gray
  Tel: (020) 7219 4463
  E-mail: grayej@parliament.uk
*Constituency Office* .... Hardy House, The Street,
  Bethersden, Ashford, Kent, TN26 3AG
  Tel: (01233) 820454 Fax: (01233) 820111
  E-mail: ashfordconservatives@
  hardyhouse.freeserve.co.uk
  Secretary – Mrs Shirley Faulkner
*Parliamentary Interests* . Education; Employment; Media; Arts;
  Economy; Environment
*Leisure Interests* ...... Football; Cricket; Opera; Cinema

# MEMBERS OF THE HOUSE OF COMMONS

**Green, Matthew** . . . Ludlow
**Liberal Democrat** . . . Majority 1,630 over Con
*Born.* . . . . . . . . . . . . . . 12th April 1970
*Educated* . . . . . . . . . . Priory School, Shrewsbury;
Birmingham University
*Elected* . . . . . . . . . . . . 2001 MP for Ludlow
*Offices Held* . . . . . . . . 2002 - Liberal Democrat Spokesman on
Housing, Local Government and Regions
(Office of the Deputy Prime Minister's
Office), and on Younger People
*Commons Office* . . . . . . Tel: (020) 7219 8253 Fax: (020) 7219 1778
E-mail: greenm@parliament.uk
Web: http://www.matthewgreen.org.uk
Researcher – Miss Amy France
E-mail: francea@parliament.uk
*Constituency Office* . . . . 33-34 High Street, Bridgnorth,
Shropshire, WV16 4DB
Tel: (01746) 766465 Fax: (01746) 765710
Personal Assistant –
Mrs Caroline Montgomery
Caseworker – Mr Nigel Martin
*Parliamentary Interests* . Agriculture; Alternative Energy; Planning;
Finance; Housing; Local Government
*Leisure Interests* . . . . . . Cricket; Rugby; History; Hill Walking

**Greenway, John** . . . Ryedale
**Conservative** . . . . . . . Majority 4,875 over Lib Dem
*Born.* . . . . . . . . . . . . . . 15th February 1946 in Cheshire
*Educated* . . . . . . . . . . Sir John Deane's Grammar School, Northwich;
Hendon Police College;
London College of Law
*Elected.* . . . . . . . . . . . 1987 MP for Ryedale
*Offices Held* . . . . . . . . 1997 - 2000 Opposition Spokesman on
Home Affairs
2000 - 03 Opposition Spokesman on
Culture, Media and Sport
*Commons Office* . . . . . . Tel: (020) 7219 5483 Fax: (020) 7219 6059
Pager: 07626 801620
E-mail: greenway@parliament.uk
Research Assistant – Miss Sarah Fitch
E-mail: fitchs@parliament.uk
*Constituency Office* . . . . 109 Town Street, Old Malton,
North Yorkshire, YO17 7HD
Tel: (01653) 692023 Fax: (01653) 696108
Secretary – Mrs Hazel Dales
*Parliamentary Interests* . Insurance; Financial Services; Agriculture;
Broadcasting; Media; Law and Order
*Leisure Interests* . . . . . . Football; Racing; Opera; Wine

**Grieve, Dominic** . . Beaconsfield
**Conservative** . . . . . . . Majority 13,065 over Lab
*Born.* . . . . . . . . . . . . . . 24th May 1956 in London
*Educated* . . . . . . . . . . Westminster School;
Magdalen College, Oxford
*Elected.* . . . . . . . . . . . 1997 MP for Beaconsfield
*Offices Held* . . . . . . . . 1999 - 2001 Opposition Spokesman on
Constitutional Affairs (Scotland)
2001 - 03 Opposition Spokesman on
Home Affairs
2003 - Shadow Attorney General
*Commons Office* . . . . . . Tel: (020) 7219 6220 Fax: (020) 7219 4803
Mobile: 07802 215278
Pager: 07626 802581
E-mail: grieved@parliament.uk
Secretary – Mrs Janet Grigg
E-mail: griggj@parliament.uk
Research Assistant – Miss Pippa Stirling
Tel: (020) 7219 1084
E-mail: stirlingp@parliament.uk
*Constituency Office* . . . . 12 Aylesbury End, Beaconsfield,
Buckinghamshire, HP9 1LW
Tel: (01494) 673745 Fax: (01494) 670428
E-mail: bcca@beacon.tory.org.uk
Agent – Mr Philip Dumville
Secretary – Mrs Elizabeth Jarvis
*Parliamentary Interests* . Environment; Defence; Legal Affairs;
Constitution; Northern Ireland
*Leisure Interests* . . . . . . Mountaineering; Skiing; Fell Walking;
Architecture; Art

**Griffiths, Jane** . . . . . Reading East
**Labour** . . . . . . . . . . . Majority 5,588 over Con
*Born.* . . . . . . . . . . . . . . 17th April 1954 in London
*Educated* . . . . . . . . . . Cedars School, Leighton Buzzard;
Durham University
*Elected.* . . . . . . . . . . . 1997 MP for Reading East
*Commons Office* . . . . . . Tel: (020) 7219 4122 Fax: (020) 7219 0719
E-mail: griffithsj@parliament.uk
Web: http://www.janestheone.com
Parliamentary Assistant – Mr Andrew Tattersall
E-mail: tattersalla@parliament.uk
*Constituency Office* . . . . St Giles House, 10 Church Street,
Reading, RG1 2SD
Tel: (0118) 957 3756 Fax: (0118) 958 0949
Caseworker – Ms Andrea Collins
*Parliamentary Interests* . Transport; Environment; Foreign Affairs
*Leisure Interests* . . . . . . Urban Living; Rats

# MEMBERS OF THE HOUSE OF COMMONS

**Griffiths, Nigel** . . . . Edinburgh South
**Labour** . . . . . . . . . . . Majority 5,449 over Lib Dem
*Born*. . . . . . . . . . . . . . 20th May 1955
*Educated* . . . . . . . . . . Hawick Comprehensive School;
Edinburgh University;
Moray House College of Education
*Elected*. . . . . . . . . . . . 1987 MP for Edinburgh South
*Offices Held* . . . . . . . . 1987 - 89 Opposition Whip
1989 - 97 Opposition Spokesman on
Consumer Affairs
1997 - 98, 2001 - Parliamentary Secretary,
Department of Trade and Industry
*Commons Office* . . . . . . Tel: (020) 7219 3424
E-mail: ngriffiths@parliament.uk
*Constituency Office* . . . . 31 Minto Street. Edinburgh, EH9 2BT
Tel: (0131) 662 4520
E-mail: enquiries@nigelgriffiths.co.uk
Personal Assistant – Mrs Elizabeth Lyon
Researcher – Mr Willie Sullivan
*Parliamentary Interests* . Education; Housing; Disability; Scotland;
Arts; Health and Social Service;
Economic Policy
*Leisure Interests* . . . . . . Squash; Travel; Live Entertainment;
Badminton; Hill Walking/Rock Climbing;
Architecture; Reading; Scuba Diving


**Griffiths, Win** . . . . . Bridgend
**Labour** . . . . . . . . . . . Majority 10,045 over Con
*Born*. . . . . . . . . . . . . . 11th February 1943 in South Africa
*Educated* . . . . . . . . . . Brecon Boys' Grammar School;
University College of Wales, Cardiff
*Elected*. . . . . . . . . . . . 1987 MP for Bridgend
*Offices Held* . . . . . . . . 1990 - 92 Opposition Spokesman on
Environmental Protection
1992 - 94 Opposition Spokesman on
Education
1994 - 97 Opposition Spokesman on Wales
1997 - 98 Parliamentary Secretary, Welsh
Office
*Commons Office* . . . . . . Tel: (020) 7219 4461 Fax: (020) 7219 6052
Mobile: 07976 353422
Pager: 07644 008908
E-mail: griffithsw@parliament.uk
Web: http://www.wingriffithsmp.co.uk
Researcher – Ms Emily Bird
Tel: (020) 7219 6538
E-mail: birde@parliament.uk
*Constituency Office* . . . . 47 Nolton Street, Bridgend, CF31 3AA
Tel: (01656) 645432 Fax: (01656) 767551
Secretary – Mrs Cleone Westwood
E-mail: westwoodc@parliament.uk
*Parliamentary Interests* . Animal Welfare; Children's Issues; Education;
European Union; Disability Issues;
Foreign Affairs; Health; Social Services;
Human Rights; Green Issues;
Overseas Development
*Leisure Interests* . . . . . . House Plants; Music; Keeping Fit; Running

**Grogan, John** . . . . . Selby
**Labour** . . . . . . . . . . . Majority 2,138 over Con
*Born*. . . . . . . . . . . . . . 24th February 1961 in Halifax
*Educated* . . . . . . . . . . St Michael's College, Leeds;
St John's College, Oxford
*Elected*. . . . . . . . . . . . 1997 MP for Selby
*Commons Office* . . . . . Tel (020) 7219 4403 Fax: (020) 7219 2676
Web: http://www.johngrogan.co.uk
Senior Research Assistant– Mr John Gray
E-mail: grayjr@parliament.uk
*Constituency Office* . . . . 58 Gowthorpe, Selby, Yorkshire, YO8 4ET
Tel: (01757) 291152 Fax: (01757) 291153
E-mail: selby@johngroganmp.u–net.com
Caseworker and Researcher –
Mr Matthew Pinner
Casework Assistant – Mr Carl Tate
Diary Secretary – Mrs Margaret Waterhouse
Tel: (01937) 531830 Fax: (01937) 531829
*Parliamentary Interests* . Northern Ireland; Licensing Law Reform;
Broadcasting; Europe; Higher Education
*Leisure Interests* . . . . . . Running; Football; Cricket; Reading


**Gummer, Rt Hon John**  Suffolk Coastal
**Conservative** . . . . . . . Majority 4,326 over Lab
*Born*. . . . . . . . . . . . . . 26th November 1939 in Stockport, Cheshire
*Educated* . . . . . . . . . . King's School, Rochester;
Selwyn College, Cambridge
*Elected*. . . . . . . . . . . . 1970 - 74 MP for Lewisham West
1979 MP for Eye, then (1983) Suffolk Coastal
*Offices Held* . . . . . . . . 1981 - 83 Assistant Government Whip
1983 Parliamentary Secretary, Department of
Employment
1983 - 84 Minister of State, Department of
Employment
1984 - 85 Paymaster General and Chairman of
the Conservative Party
1985 - 88 Minister of State, Ministry of
Agriculture, Fisheries and Food
1988 - 89 Minister of State, Department of the
Environment
1989 - 93 Minister of Agriculture, Fisheries
and Food
1993 - 97 Secretary of State for the
Environment
*Commons Office* . . . . . . Tel: (020) 7219 4591 Fax: (020) 7219 5906
E-mail: gummerj@parliament.uk
Personal Assistant – Mr Peter Vines
Secretary – Mrs Pat Fea
*Constituency Office* . . . . The National Hall, Sun Lane, Woodbridge,
Suffolk, IP12 1EG
Tel: (01394) 380001 Fax: (01394) 382570
E-mail:
suffolkcoastalconservatives@btinternet.com
Agent – Mr Terence Eastman
Secretary – Mrs Jenny Petherbridge
*Parliamentary Interests* . Environment; Agriculture; Europe

# MEMBERS OF THE HOUSE OF COMMONS

## H

**Hague, Rt Hon William**  Richmond (Yorkshire)
*Conservative* . . . . . . . Majority 16,319 over Lab
*Born*. . . . . . . . . . . . . . 26th March 1961
*Educated* . . . . . . . . . . Wath-on-Dearne Comprehensive School;
Magdalen College, Oxford;
Institute European d'Administration des
Affaires, France
*Elected*. . . . . . . . . . . . 1989 MP for Richmond,
Yorkshire (by-election)
*Offices Held* . . . . . . . . 1993 - 94 Parliamentary Secretary,
Department of Social Security
1994 - 95 Minister of State, Department of
Social Security
1995 - 97 Secretary of State for Wales
1997 - 2001 Leader of the Opposition
*Commons Office* . . . . . Secretary – Miss Susie Black
E-mail: blacks@parliament.uk
Researcher – Miss Elana Cheah
E-mail: cheahe@parliament.uk
*Constituency Office* . . . . 67 High Street, Northallerton,
North Yorkshire, DL7 8EG
Tel: (01609) 779093 Fax: (01609) 772060
*Leisure Interests* . . . . . . Judo: Skiing; Walking

**Hain, Rt Hon Peter**  Neath
*Labour* . . . . . . . . . . . . Majority 14,816 over Plaid Cymru
*Born*. . . . . . . . . . . . . . 16th February 1950 in Kenya
*Educated* . . . . . . . . . . Queen Mary College, London;
Sussex University
*Elected*. . . . . . . . . . . . 1991 MP for Neath (By-election)
*Offices Held* . . . . . . . . 1995 - 96 Opposition Whip
1996 - 97 Opposition Spokesman on
Employment
1997 - 99 Parliamentary Secretary,
Welsh Office
1999 - 2001 Minister of State,
Foreign and Commonwealth Office
2001 Minister of State, Department of Trade
and Industry (Minister for Energy)
2001 - 02 Minister of State, Foreign and
Commonwealth Office (Minister for Europe)
2002 - Secretary of State for Wales and
(from 2003) Lord Privy Seal and Leader of
the House of Commons
*Commons Office* . . . . . . Tel: (020) 7219 3925 Fax: (020) 7219 3816
Mobile: 07866 572598
Pager: 07659 550326
E-mail: hainp@parliament.uk
Web: http://www.peterhain.org
Secretary – Mrs Jill Hays
E-mail: haysj@parliament.uk
Special Adviser – Mr Philip Taylor
Tel: (020) 7219 4044
*Constituency Office* . . . . 39 Windsor Road, Neath, SA11 1NB
Tel: (01639) 630152 Fax: (01639) 641196
E-mail: pghhd@hotmail.com
Agent – Mr Howard Davies
Secretary – Ms Dilys Richards
Researcher – Ms Victoria Jones
*Leisure Interests* . . . . . . Motor Racing; Soccer; Rugby; Cricket;
Rock and Folk Music; Walking

**Hall, Mike** . . . . . . . Weaver Vale
*Labour* . . . . . . . . . . . Majority 9,637 over Con
*Born*. . . . . . . . . . . . . . 20th September 1952 in Ashton-under-Lyne
*Educated* . . . . . . . . . . St Damian's Secondary School;
Ashton-under-Lyne College of
Further Education;
Stretford Technical College;
Padgate College of Higher Education;
North Cheshire College; Bangor University
*Elected*. . . . . . . . . . . . 1992 MP for Warrington South, then (1997)
Weaver Vale
*Offices Held* . . . . . . . . 1985 - 92 Leader, Warrington Borough
Council
1997 - 98 PPS to Ann Taylor
(Leader of the House of Commons)
1998 - 2001 Assistant Government Whip
2001 - PPS to Alan Milburn, then John Reid
(successive Secretaries of State for
Health)
*Commons Office* . . . . . Tel: (020) 7219 4001
*Constituency Office* . . . . Office 17, Castle Park, Frodsham,
Cheshire, WA6 6UJ
Tel: (01928) 735000 Fax: (01928) 735250
E-mail: mikehall@weavervale.org.uk
Personal Assistant – Mrs Christine Lloyd
Secretary – Mrs Miriam Fryar
*Parliamentary Interests* . Health; Education; Home Affairs
*Leisure Interests* . . . . . . Tennis; Reading; Cooking

**Hall, Patrick** . . . . . Bedford
*Labour* . . . . . . . . . . . Majority 6,157 over Con
*Born*. . . . . . . . . . . . . . 20th October 1951 in Birmingham
*Educated* . . . . . . . . . . Bedford Modern School;
Birmingham University; Oxford Polytechnic
*Elected*. . . . . . . . . . . . 1997 MP for Bedford
*Commons Office* . . . . . Tel: (020) 7219 3605 Fax: (020) 7219 3987
Mobile: 07966 388850
Pager: 07644 005237
E-mail: hallp@parliament.uk
*Constituency Office* . . . . Broadway House, 4-6 The Broadway,
Bedford, MK40 2TE
Tel: (01234) 262699 Fax: (01234) 272981
Office Manager – Mrs Giulia Colclough
Senior Caseworker – Mrs Rosemary Roome
*Parliamentary Interests* . Environment; Health
*Leisure Interests* . . . . . . Gardening; Squash

**Hamilton, David** . . Midlothian
*Labour* . . . . . . . . . . . Majority 9,014 over SNP
*Born*. . . . . . . . . . . . . . 24th October 1950 in Dalkeith, Midlothian
*Educated* . . . . . . . . . . Dalkeith High School
*Elected*. . . . . . . . . . . . 2001 MP for Midlothian
*Commons Office* . . . . . Tel: (020) 7219 8257 Fax: (020) 7219 3606
E-mail: davidhamiltonmp@parliament.uk
Web: http://www.davidhamilton.labour.co.uk
*Constituency Office* . . . . 95 High Street, Dalkeith, Midlothian,
EH22 1AX
Tel: (0131) 654 1585 Fax: (0131) 654 1586
Parliamentary Assistant – Mrs Jean Hamilton
E-mail: hamiltonjt@parliament.uk
Administration Assistant –
Ms Maureen Curran
*Parliamentary Interests* . Europe; Biotechnology; Energy; Northern
Ireland; Gibraltar; Cyprus
*Leisure Interests* . . . . . . Films; Current Affairs; Grandchildren

# MEMBERS OF THE HOUSE OF COMMONS

**Hamilton, Fabian**. Leeds North East
**Labour** . . . . . . . . . . . Majority 7,089 over Con
*Born*. . . . . . . . . . . . . . 12th April 1955 in London
*Educated* . . . . . . . . . . Brentwood School; York University
*Elected*. . . . . . . . . . . . 1997 MP for Leeds North East
*Commons Office* . . . . . . Tel: (020) 7219 3493 Fax: (020) 7219 4945
    Mobile: 07773 429304
    Pager: 07644 006638
*Constituency Office* . . . . 6 Queenshill Approach, Leeds, LS17 6AY
    Tel: (0113) 237 0022 Fax: (0113) 237 0404
    E-mail: fabian@leedsne.co.uk
    Parliamentary Assistant – Cllr Gerald Harper
    Office Manager/Diary Secretary –
      Mr Ian Carnegie
    Personal Assistant – Miss Laura Davies
*Parliamentary Interests*. Middle East; Transport; Environmental Issues;
    Anti-Racism; Education; Small Businesses
    International Development
*Leisure Interests* . . . . . . Cycling; Films; Music; Reading

**Hammond, Philip** . Runnymede and Weybridge
**Conservative** . . . . . . . Majority 8,360 over Lab
*Born*. . . . . . . . . . . . . . 4th December 1955 in Epping, Essex
*Educated* . . . . . . . . . . Shenfield School, Brentwood, Essex;
    University College, Oxford
*Elected*. . . . . . . . . . . . 1997 MP for Runnymede and Weybridge
*Offices Held* . . . . . . . . 1998 - 2001 Opposition Spokesman on Health
    2001 - 02 Opposition Spokesman on
      Trade and Industry
    2002 - Opposition Spokesman on Local and
      Devolved Government
*Commons Office* . . . . . . Tel: (020) 7219 4055 Fax: (020) 7219 5851
    E-mail: hammondp@parliament.uk
    Secretary – Miss Beverley Davis
    E-mail: davisb@parliament.uk
*Parliamentary Interests*. Health; Social Services; Transport
*Leisure Interests* . . . . . . Family; Walking; Highlands

**Hancock, Mike** CBE Portsmouth South
**Liberal Democrat** . . . Majority 6,094 over Con
*Born*. . . . . . . . . . . . . . 9th April 1946 in Portsmouth
*Educated* . . . . . . . . . . Portsmouth Schools
*Elected*. . . . . . . . . . . . 1984 - 87 MP (SDP) for Portsmouth South
      (By-election)
    1997 MP (Lib Dem) for Portsmouth South
*Offices Held* . . . . . . . . 1993 - 97 Leader, Hampshire County Council
    1997 - 99 Liberal Democrat Spokesman on
      Defence
    1999 - 2001 Liberal Democrat Spokesman on
      Planning
*Commons Office* . . . . . . Tel: (020) 7219 1102 Fax: (020) 7219 2496
    Web: http://www.mikehancock.co.uk
    Research Assistant – Mr Alan Lloyd
    E-mail: lloyda@parliament.uk
*Constituency Office* . . . . 1a Albert Road, Southsea, Portsmouth,
    Hampshire, PO5 2SE
    Tel: (023) 9286 1055 Fax: (023) 9283 0530
    E-mail: portsmthldp@cix.co.uk
    Personal Assistant – Ms Mandy Collis
    Constituency Researcher –
      Mr Michael Andrewes
*Parliamentary Interests*. Defence; Animal Rights; Foreign Affairs
*Leisure Interests* . . . . . . Local Events

**Hanson, David** . . . . Delyn
**Labour** . . . . . . . . . . . Majority 8,605 over Con
*Born*. . . . . . . . . . . . . . 5th July 1957 in Liverpool
*Educated* . . . . . . . . . . Verdin Comprehensive School, Winsford;
    Hull University
*Elected*. . . . . . . . . . . . 1992 MP for Delyn
*Offices Held* . . . . . . . . 1989 - 91 Leader, Vale Royal Borough
      Council
    1998 -99 Assistant Government Whip
    1999 - 2001 Parliamentary Secretary,
      Wales Office
    2001 - PPS to the Prime Minister (Tony Blair)
*Commons Office* . . . . . . Tel: (020) 7219 5064 Fax: (020) 7219 2671
    E-mail: hansond@parliament.uk
    Web: http://www.delynmp.org
    Researcher – Mr Christopher Watt
    E-mail: wattc@parliament.uk
*Constituency Office* . . . . 64 Chester Street, Flint, CH6 5DH
    Tel: (01352) 763159 Fax: (01352) 730140
    Secretary – Ms Carol Williams
*Parliamentary Interests*. Treasury; Heritage/Culture; Foreign Affairs
*Leisure Interests* . . . . . . Football; Cinema

**Harman, Rt Hon Harriet** QC Camberwell and Peckham
**Labour** . . . . . . . . . . . Majority 14,123 over Lib Dem
*Born*. . . . . . . . . . . . . . 30th July 1950 in London
*Educated* . . . . . . . . . . St Paul's Girl's School; York University
*Elected*. . . . . . . . . . . . 1982 MP for Peckham (By-election), then
      (1997) Camberwell and Peckham
*Offices Held* . . . . . . . . 1983 - 87 Opposition Spokeswoman on Social
      Security
    1992 - 94 Shadow Chief Secretary to the
      Treasury
    1994 - 95 Shadow Employment Secretary
    1995 - 96 Shadow Health Secretary
    1996 - 97 Shadow Social Security Secretary
    1997 - 98 Secretary of State for Social
      Security and Minister for Women
    2001 - Solicitor General
*Commons Office* . . . . . . Tel: (020) 7219 4218 Fax: (020) 7219 4877
    E-mail: harmanh@parliament.uk

# MEMBERS OF THE HOUSE OF COMMONS

**Harris, Dr Evan** . . . Oxford West and Abingdon
**Liberal Democrat** . . . Majority 9,185 over Con
*Born.* . . . . . . . . . . . . . 21st October 1965 in Sheffield
*Educated* . . . . . . . . . . Bluecoat School, Liverpool;
Harvard High School, Los Angeles;
Wadham College, Oxford;
Oxford University Medical School
*Elected.* . . . . . . . . . . . 1997 MP for Oxford West and Abingdon
*Offices Held* . . . . . . . . 1997 - 99 Liberal Democrat Spokesman
on NHS
1999 - 2001 Liberal Democrat Spokesman on
Higher Education, Science and Women's
Issues
2001 - 03 Liberal Democrat Spokesman on
Health
*Commons Office* . . . . . Tel: (020) 7219 5128 Fax: (020) 7219 2346
Pager: 07699 730635
E-mail: harrise@parliament.uk
Head of Office – Ms Laure Thomas
E-mail: thomasl@parliament.uk
*Constituency Office* . . . . 27 Park End Street, Oxford, OX1 1HU
Tel: (01865) 245584 Fax: (01865) 245589
Secretary/PA – Mrs Sandra Lloyd
Diary Officer – Miss Hilary Fraser
*Parliamentary Interests* . Science; Health; Asylum; Ethics;
Gay and Lesbian Rights
*Leisure Interests* . . . . . Sport; Bridge; TV

**Harris, Tom** . . . . . . Glasgow Cathcart
**Labour** . . . . . . . . . . Majority 10,816 over SNP
*Born.* . . . . . . . . . . . . . 20th February 1964 in Irvine, Ayrshire
*Educated* . . . . . . . . . . Garnock Academy, Kilbirnie, Ayrshire;
Napier College, Edinburgh
*Elected.* . . . . . . . . . . . 2001 MP for Glasgow Cathcart
*Office Held* . . . . . . . . . 2003 - PPS to John Spellar (Minister of State,
Northern Ireland Office)
*Commons Office* . . . . . Tel: (020) 7219 8237 Fax: (020) 7219 1769
E-mail: tomharrismp@parliament.uk
Web: http://www.tomharrismp.com
*Constituency Office* . . . . The Couper Institute, 86 Clarkston Road,
Glasgow, G44 3DA
Tel: (0141) 637 6447 Fax: (0141) 637 9625
E-mail: campbelld@parliament.uk
Researcher – Mr Donald Campbell
*Parliamentary Interests* . Welfare Reform; Northern Ireland;
Drug Laws; Europe; Middle East
*Leisure Interests* . . . . . Badminton; Cinema; Astronomy; Hill Walking

**Harvey, Nick** . . . . . Devon North
**Liberal Democrat** . . . Majority 2,984 over Con
*Born.* . . . . . . . . . . . . . 3rd August 1961 in Chandlers Ford, Hampshire
*Educated* . . . . . . . . . . Queen's College, Taunton;
Middlesex University
*Elected.* . . . . . . . . . . . 1992 MP for Devon North
*Offices Held* . . . . . . . . 1992 - 94 Liberal Democrat Spokesman on
Transport
1994 - 97 Liberal Democrat Spokesman on
Trade and Industry
1994 - 99 Chairman of Campaigns and
Communications, Liberal Democrats
1997 - 99 Liberal Democrat Spokesman on
Constitution (English Regions)
1999 - 2001 Liberal Democrat Spokesman on
Health
2001 - 03 Liberal Democrat Spokesman on
Culture, Media and Sport
*Commons Office* . . . . . Tel: (020) 7219 6232/2621
Fax: (020) 7219 2683
E-mail: harveyn@parliament.uk
Web: http://www.nickharveymp.com
Researchers – Miss Caroline Hames
Miss Olivia Malloy
E-mail: [surnameinitial]@parliament.uk
*Constituency Office* . . . . 23 Castle Street, Barnstaple,
North Devon, EX31 1BA
Tel: (01271) 328631 Fax: (01271) 345664
Office Manager – Ms Yvonne Keer
Caseworker – Mrs Lindi Braund
E-mail: [surnameinitial]@parliament.uk

**Haselhurst, Rt Hon Sir Alan** Saffron Walden
**Conservative** . . . . . . Majority 12,004 over Lib Dem
*Born.* . . . . . . . . . . . . . 23rd June 1937 in Yorkshire
*Educated* . . . . . . . . . . King Edward VI School, Birmingham;
Cheltenham College; Oriel College, Oxford
*Elected.* . . . . . . . . . . . 1970 - 74 MP for Middleton and Prestwich
1977 MP for Saffron Walden (By-election)
*Offices Held* . . . . . . . . 1997 - Chairman of Ways and Means and
Deputy Speaker, House of Commons
*Commons Office* . . . . . Tel: (020) 7219 5214 Fax: (020) 7219 5600
E-mail: haselhursta@parliament.uk
Web: http://www.siralanhaselhurst.net
Research Assistant – Miss Eleanor O'Riordan
Tel: (020) 7219 3340
*Constituency Office* . . . . The Old Armoury, Museum Street,
Saffron Walden, Essex, CB10 1JN
Tel: (01799) 506349 Fax: (01799) 506047
*Leisure Interests* . . . . . Watching Cricket

**Havard, Dai** . . . . . Merthyr Tydfil and Rhymney
**Labour** . . . . . . . . . . Majority 14,923 over Plaid Cymru
*Born.* . . . . . . . . . . . . . 7th February 1950
*Educated* . . . . . . . . . . Quakers Yard Grammar School, Edwardsville
Afon Taf Comprehensive School;
St Peter's College, Birmingham;
Warwick University
*Elected.* . . . . . . . . . . . 2001 MP for Merthyr Tydfil and Rhymney
*Leisure Interests* . . . . . Hill Walking; Horse Riding; Bird Watching

# MEMBERS OF THE HOUSE OF COMMONS

**Hawkins, Nick** .... Surrey Heath
**Conservative** ....... Majority 10,819 over Lib Dem
*Born*.............. 27th March 1957 in St Albans, Hertfordshire
*Educated* .......... Bedford Modern School;
Lincoln College, Oxford;
Inns of Court School of Law, Middle Temple
*Elected*............ 1992 - 97 MP for Blackpool South
1997 MP for Surrey Heath
*Offices Held* ........ 1996 - 97 PPS to Rt Hon Virginia Bottomley
(Secretary of State for National Heritage)
1999 - 2004 Opposition Spokesman on Home
Affairs and Legal Affairs
*Commons Office* ..... Tel: (020) 7219 6329 Fax: (020) 7219 2693
Web: http://www.nickhawkinsmp.org
Personal Assistant – Miss Barbara Campbell
*Parliamentary Interests* . Financial Services and Insurance;
Home Affairs and Legal Matters.; Sport;
Tourism; Education; Small Business;
Trade and Industry; Transport; Defence
*Leisure Interests* ...... Sport (especially Cricket, Swimming, Rugby
Union); Theatre; Music

**Hayes, John**........ South Holland and The Deepings
**Conservative** ....... Majority 11,099 over Lab
*Born*.............. 23rd June 1958
*Educated* .......... Colfe's Grammar School, London;
Nottingham University
*Elected*............ 1997 MP for South Holland and The Deepings
*Offices Held* ........ 1999 - 2000 Vice-Chairman, Conservative Party
2000 - 01 Opposition Spokesman on
Education
2001 - 02 Opposition Whip
2002 - 03 Opposition Spokesman on
Agriculture, Fisheries and Food
2003 - Opposition Spokesman on Local and
Devolved Government
*Commons Office* ..... Tel: (020) 7219 1389 Fax; (020) 7219 2273
Mobile: 07976 983202
Pager: 07626 801288
Research Assistant – Mr Andrew Unterhalter
E-mail: unterhaltera@parliament.uk
*Constituency Office*.... 20 Station Street, Spalding,
Lincolnshire, PE11 1EB
Tel & Fax: (01775) 713905
Research/Administrative Adviser –
Mrs Susan Hayes
Personal Assistant –
Miss Kate Charleston-Stokes
Tel: (01775) 711534
E-mail: charlestonstokesk@parliament.uk
Research Assistant – Mr Craig Jackson
Tel: (01406) 351393 Fax: (01406) 351605
*Parliamentary Interests* . Agriculture and Fisheries; Disability Issues;
Education; Local Government; Housing;
Commerce and Industry; Political Philosophy
*Leisure Interests* ...... Antiques; The Arts; Food; Wine; Sport;
Gardening

**Heal, Sylvia**...... Halesowen and Rowley Regis
**Labour** ........... Majority 7,359 over Con
*Born*.............. 20th July 1942
*Educated* .......... Coleg Harlech;
University College of Wales, Swansea
*Elected*............ 1990 - 92 MP for Mid-Staffordshire
(By-election)
1997 MP for Halesowen and Rowley Regis
*Offices Held* ........ 1991-92 Opposition Spokesman on Health and
Women's Issues
1997 - 2000 PPS to Lord Robertson and
Geoff Hoon (successive Secretaries of
State for Defence)
2000 - First Deputy Chairman of Ways and
Means and Deputy Speaker,
House of Commons
*Commons Office* ..... Tel: (020) 7219 2317 Fax: (020) 7219 0956
Parliamentary Assistant – Ms Anne Bates
E-mail: batesa@parliament.uk
Caseworker – Ms Natasha Burgess
Tel: (020) 7219 0780
E-mail: burgessn@parliament.uk
*Constituency Office*.... Municipal Building, Barrs Road,
Cradley Heath, West Midlands, B64 7JX
Tel: (0121) 569 4646 Fax: (0121) 569 4647
Constituency Assistant – Mr Dan Watson
*Parliamentary Interests* . Health; Education; Employment; Training;
Equal Opportunities
*Leisure Interests* ...... Gardening; Meals with Friends;
Listening to Male Voice Choirs

**Heald, Oliver** ..... Hertfordshire North East
**Conservative** ....... Majority 3,444 over Lab
*Born*.............. 15th December 1954
*Educated* .......... Reading School;
Pembroke College, Cambridge
*Elected*............ 1992 - MP for Hertfordshire North,
then (1997) Hertfordshire North East
*Offices Held* ........ 1995 - 97 Parliamentary Secretary,
Department of Social Security
1997 - 2000 Opposition Whip
2000 - 01 Opposition Spokesman on
Home Affairs
2001 - 02 Opposition Spokesman on Health
2002 - 03 Opposition Spokesman on
Work and Pensions
2003 - 04 Shadow Leader of the House of
Commons
2004 - Shadow Secretary for
Constitutional Affairs
*Commons Office* ..... Tel: (020) 7219 6354
E-mail: healdo@parliament.uk
Web: http://www.oliverhealdmp.com
Secretary – Mrs Christiane Moore
E-mail: moorece@parliament.uk
*Constituency Office*.... Tel & Fax: (01763) 247640
Private Secretary – Mrs Christine Heald
*Parliamentary Interests* . Employment; Pensions; Environment;
Law and Order
*Leisure Interests* ...... Sport; Horse Riding

# MEMBERS OF THE HOUSE OF COMMONS

**Healey, John** . . . . . . Wentworth
**Labour** . . . . . . . . . . . Majority 16,449 over Con
*Born* . . . . . . . . . . . . . . 13th February 1960 in Wakefield
*Educated* . . . . . . . . . . Lady Lumley's, Pickering;
St Peter's School, York;
Christ's College, Cambridge
*Elected* . . . . . . . . . . . . 1997 MP for Wentworth
*Offices Held* . . . . . . . . 1992 - 2001 PPS to Gordon Brown
(as Opposition Spokesman and
Chancellor of the Exchequer)
2001 - 02 Parliamentary Secretary,
Department for Education and Skills
2002 - Economic Secretary, HM Treasury
*Commons Office* . . . . . . Tel: (020) 7219 5170 Fax: (020) 7219 2451
E-mail: healeyj@parliament.uk
Web: http://www.johnhealeymp.co.uk
*Constituency Office* . . . . 79 High Street, Wath-upon-Dearne,
Rotherham, S63 7QB
Tel: (01709) 875943 Fax: (01709) 874207
Private Secretary – Mrs Irene Hartley
Research Assistant – Mr Chris Wellings
Tel: (01709) 512463
Caseworker – Mrs Anne Smith
Tel: (01709) 512465
*Parliamentary Interests* . Employment; Disability; Economic
Regeneration; Local Government Finance;
Opencast Mining

**Heath, David** CBE . . Somerton and Frome
**Liberal Democrat** . . . Majority 668 over Con
*Born* . . . . . . . . . . . . . . 16th March 1954 at Westbury-sub-Mendip
*Educated* . . . . . . . . . . Millfield School; St John's College, Oxford
City University, London
*Elected* . . . . . . . . . . . . 1997 MP for Somerton and Frome
*Offices Held* . . . . . . . . 1985 - 89 Leader, Somerset County Council
1997 - 99 Liberal Democrat Spokesman on
Europe
1999 - 2001 Liberal Democrat Spokesman
Agriculture, Rural Affairs and Fisheries
2001 - 02 Liberal Democrat Spokesman on
Work and Pensions
2002 - Liberal Democrat Spokesman on Home
Affairs and Science; also (from 2003) on
Constitutional Affairs
*Commons Office* . . . . . . Tel: (020) 7219 6245 Fax: (020) 7219 5939
E-mail: davidheath@davidheath.co.uk
Web: http://www.davidheath.co.uk
Researcher – Mr Matthew Sheldon
Tel: (020) 7219 8413
E-mail: sheldonm@parliament.uk
*Constituency Office* . . . . 14 Catherine Hill, Frome, Somerset, BA11 1BZ
Tel: (01373) 473618 Fax: (01373) 455152
Caseworker – Mrs Gail Coleshill
Secretary – Mrs Rosemary Davies
Head of Office/Press Officer –
Ms Claire Hudson
Tel: (01373) 300065
*Parliamentary Interests* . Local Government; Education; Rural Affairs;
Foreign Affairs
*Leisure Interests* . . . . . . Rugby; Cricket; Breeding Rare Pigs

**Heathcoat-Amory, Rt Hon David** Wells
**Conservative** . . . . . . . Majority 2,796 over Lib Dem
*Born* . . . . . . . . . . . . . . 21st March 1949 in London
*Educated* . . . . . . . . . . . Eton College; Christ Church College, Oxford
*Elected* . . . . . . . . . . . . 1983 MP for Wells
*Offices Held* . . . . . . . . 1988 - 89 Assistant Government Whip
1989 Government Whip (Lord Commissioner,
H M Treasury)
1989 - 90 Parliamentary Secretary,
Department of the Environment
1990 - 92 Parliamentary Secretary,
Department of Energy
1992 - 93 Government Deputy Chief Whip
(Treasurer, HM Household)
1993 - 94 Minister of State, Foreign and
Commonwealth Office
1994 - 96 Paymaster General, H M Treasury
1997 - 2000 Shadow Chief Secretary to the
Treasury
2000 - 01 Shadow Trade and Industry
Secretary
*Commons Office* . . . . . . Tel: (020) 7219 6370 Fax: (020) 7219 6270
E-mail: heathcoat-amoryd@parliament.uk
*Constituency Office* . . . . 7 Priory Road, Wells, Somerset, BA5 1SR
Tel: (01749) 673146 Fax: (01749) 679783
E-mail: wca@wells.tory.org.uk
Agent – Mr Mark Merchant

**Henderson, Doug** . Newcastle-upon-Tyne North
**Labour** . . . . . . . . . . . Majority 14,450 over Con
*Born* . . . . . . . . . . . . . . 9th June 1949 in Edinburgh
*Educated* . . . . . . . . . . Waid Academy, Fife; Central College,
Glasgow; Strathclyde University
*Elected* . . . . . . . . . . . . 1987 MP for Newcastle-upon-Tyne North
*Offices Held* . . . . . . . . 1988 - 92 Opposition Spokesman on Trade
and Industry
1992 - 94 Opposition Spokesman on
Environment
1994 - 95 Opposition Spokesman on
Citizen's Charter and Deputy Shadow
Leader of the House
1995 - 97 Opposition Spokesman on Home
Affairs
1997 - 98 Minister of State, Foreign Office
(Minister for Europe)
1998 - 99 Minister of State, Ministry of
Defence (Minister for Armed Forces)
*Commons Contact* . . . . . E-mail: douglas@hendersond.fsbusiness.co.uk
*Constituency Office* . . . . Tel: (0191) 286 2024
Secretary – Mrs Linda Temperley
*Parliamentary Interests* . Economy
*Leisure Interests* . . . . . . Swimming; Football; Hill Walking; Running

# MEMBERS OF THE HOUSE OF COMMONS

**Henderson, Ivan** .. Harwich
**Labour** . . . . . . . . . . . Majority 2,596 over Con
*Born* . . . . . . . . . . . . . . . 7th June 1958 in Harwich
*Educated* . . . . . . . . . . Sir Anthony Deane Comprehensive School
*Elected* . . . . . . . . . . . . 1997 MP for Harwich
*Office Held* . . . . . . . . . 2003 - PPS to Andrew Smith
 (Secretary of State for Work and Pensions)
*Commons Office* . . . . . Tel: (020) 7219 3434  Fax: (020) 7219 1244
 Mobile: 07889 367822
 Pager: 07644 005239
 E-mail: hendersoni@parliament.uk
 Parliamentary Assistant – Mr Jordan Newell
 E-mail: newellja@parliament.uk
*Constituency Office* . . . . 21 Kingsway, Dovercourt, Harwich,
 Essex, CO12 3AB
 Tel: (01255) 552859 Fax: (01255) 556771
 Personal Assistant – Mrs Valerie Atkinson
 Press Officer – Mr Garry Calver
 Tel: (01255) 551940
 Caseworker/Researcher – Mr Peter Brand
 Tel: (01255) 242238
*Parliamentary Interests* . Health; Transport; Employment
*Leisure Interests* . . . . . . Football; Golf; Sailing

**Hendrick, Mark** . . . Preston
**Labour** . . . . . . . . . . . Majority 12,268 over Con
*Born* . . . . . . . . . . . . . . . 6th December 1959 in Jarrow
*Educated* . . . . . . . . . . Salford Grammar School;
 Liverpool Polytechnic; Manchester University
*Elected* . . . . . . . . . . . . 2000 MP for Preston (By-election)
*Office Held* . . . . . . . . . 2003 - PPS to Margaret Beckett
 (Secretary of State for Environment,
 Food and Rural Affairs)
*Commons Office* . . . . . Tel: (020) 7219 4791 Fax: (020) 7219 5220
 E-mail: hendrickm@parliament.uk
 Research Assistant – Mr Richard Daniels
 E-mail: danielsra@parliament.uk
*Constituency Office* . . . . 6 Sedgwick Street, Preston, PR1 1TP
 Tel: (01772) 883575 Fax: (01772) 887188
 E-mail: hendrick@prestonlabour.fsnet.co.uk
 Parliamentary Assistant –
 Mrs Justine Westwell
 Community Liaison Officer –
 Mrs Sazida Desai
*Parliamentary Interests* . Foreign Affairs; Defence; The Economy
*Leisure Interests* . . . . . . Football

**Hendry, Charles** . . . Wealden
**Conservative** . . . . . . Majority 13,772 over Lib Dem
*Born* . . . . . . . . . . . . . . . 1959
*Educated* . . . . . . . . . . Rugby School; Edinburgh University
*Elected* . . . . . . . . . . . . 1992 - 97 MP for High Peak
 2001 MP for Wealden
*Offices Held* . . . . . . . . 1995 - 97 Vice-Chairman, Conservative Party
 2001 - 03 Opposition Whip and Spokesman
 on Education and Skills
 2003 - Opposition Spokesman on Young
 People's Issues and Deputy Chairman,
 Conservative Party
*Commons Office* . . . . . Tel: (020) 7219 8238  Fax: (020) 7219 1977
 E-mail: hendryc@parliament.uk
 Parliamentary Assistant – Mrs Sylvia Hewgill
 E-mail: hewgills@parliament.uk
 Web: http://www.charleshendry.com
 Senior Researcher – Mr Jon Newman
 E-mail: newmanj@parliament.uk
*Constituency Office* . . . . The Granary, Bates Green Farm,
 Arlington, East Sussex, BN26 6SH
 Tel: (01323) 489289 Fax: (01323) 484847
 Agent – Mr P Sabine
*Parliamentary Interests* . Youth Issues; Housing; Rural Affairs

**Hepburn, Stephen** . Jarrow
**Labour** . . . . . . . . . . . Majority 17,595 over Lib Dem
*Born* . . . . . . . . . . . . . . . 6th December 1959 in Jarrow
*Educated* . . . . . . . . . . Springfield Comprehensive;
 Newcastle University
*Elected* . . . . . . . . . . . . 1997 MP for Jarrow
*Office Held* . . . . . . . . . 1991 - 97 Deputy Leader, South Tyneside
 Council
*Constituency Office* . . . . Tedco Business Centre, Viking Industrial
 Estate, Blaydon Street, Jarrow, NE32 3DT
 Tel: (0191) 420 0648 Fax: (0191) 489 7531
 E-mail: hepburn4jarrow@btinternet.com
 Office Manager – Mrs Linda Waggott
 Tel: (0191) 536 3957
 Research Assistants – Mr Anthony Farrell
 Mr Richard Waggott
 Tel: (0191) 428 3396
*Leisure Interests* . . . . . . Football; Cricket; Rugby

# MEMBERS OF THE HOUSE OF COMMONS

**Heppell, John** . . . . . Nottingham East
**Labour** . . . . . . . . . . . Majority 10,320 over Con
*Born*. . . . . . . . . . . . . . 3rd November 1948 in Newcastle-upon-Tyne
*Educated* . . . . . . . . . . Rutherford Grammar School;
Ashington Technical College
*Elected*. . . . . . . . . . . 1992 MP for Nottingham East
*Offices Held* . . . . . . . . 1981 - 93 Deputy Leader, Nottinghamshire
County Council
1998 - 2001 PPS to John Prescott
(Deputy Prime Minister)
2001 - Government Whip
(Lord Commissioner, H M Treasury)
*Constituency Office* . . . . 9 Trinity Square, Nottingham, NG1 4AF
Tel: (0115) 947 4132 Fax: (0115) 947 2029
E-mail: johnheppellmp@yahoo.co.uk
Web: http://www.johnheppell.labour.co.uk
Parliamentary Assistant – Ms Josie Tanvir
Clerical Assistant – Mrs Valerie Ferreday
*Parliamentary Interests* . Transport; Equal Opportunities; Health
*Leisure Interests* . . . . . . Reading; Walking; Swimming; Birdwatching

**Hermon, Lady [Sylvia]** Down North
**Ulster Unionist** . . . . . Majority 7,324 over UK Unionist
*Born*. . . . . . . . . . . . . . 11th August 1955
*Educated* . . . . . . . . . . Dungannon High School for Girls;
University of Wales, Aberystwyth
*Elected*. . . . . . . . . . . 2001 MP for Down North
*Office Held* . . . . . . . . . 2002 - Ulster Unionist Spokesman on Home
Affairs, Culture, Media and Sports, Youth
and Women
*Commons Office* . . . . . . Tel: (020) 7219 8491 Fax: (020) 7219 1969
E-mail: knotts@parliament.uk
Research Assistant – Mr Stephen Knott
*Constituency Office* . . . . 17a Hamilton Road, Bangor, County Down,
BT20 4LF
Tel: (028) 9127 5858 Fax: (028) 9127 5747
E-mail: jamisons@parliament.uk
Office Manager – Ms Stephanie Jamison
Personal Representative –
Mrs Hazel McCalister
*Leisure Interests* . . . . . . Fitness Training; Swimming

**Hesford, Stephen** . . Wirral West
**Labour** . . . . . . . . . . . Majority 4,035 over Con
*Born*. . . . . . . . . . . . . . 27th May 1957 in Lancashire
*Educated* . . . . . . . . . . Urmston Grammar School;
Bradford University;
Central London Polytechnic
*Elected*. . . . . . . . . . . 1997 MP for Wirral West
*Commons Office* . . . . . . Tel: (020) 7219 6227 Fax: (020) 7219 4953
Mobile: 07767 457380
E-mail: hesfords@parliament.uk
*Constituency Office* . . . . 140 Ford Road, Upton, Wirral, CH49 0TQ
Tel: (0151) 522 0531 Fax: (0151) 522 0558
Personal Assistant – Mrs Sue Heald
*Parliamentary Interests* . Health; Home Affairs
*Leisure Interests* . . . . . . Reading; Cricket; Football

**Hewitt, Rt Hon Patricia** Leicester West
**Labour** . . . . . . . . . . . Majority 9,639 over Con
*Born*. . . . . . . . . . . . . . 2nd December 1948 in Canberra, Australia
*Educated* . . . . . . . . . . Canberra Girls' Grammar School;
Newnham College, Cambridge
*Elected*. . . . . . . . . . . 1997 MP for Leicester West
*Offices Held* . . . . . . . . 1998 - 99 Economic Secretary, H M Treasury
1999 - 2001 Minister of State, Department of
Trade and Industry
2001 - Secretary of State for
Trade and Industry and Minister for Women
*Constituency Office* . . . . Janner House, Woodgate, Leicester, LE3 5GH
Tel: (0116) 251 6160 Fax: (0116) 251 0482
E-mail: hewittph@parliament.uk
Web:
http://www.patriciahewittmp.labour.co.uk
Assistant – Ms Sarah Brack
E-mail: bracks@parliament.uk
*Parliamentary Interests* . Economic Policy; Family Policy;
Equal Opportunities; IT
*Leisure Interests* . . . . . . Children; Gardening; Opera; Theatre

**Heyes, David** . . . . . . Ashton-under-Lyne
**Labour** . . . . . . . . . . . Majority 15,518 over Con
*Born*. . . . . . . . . . . . . . 2nd April 1946 in Manchester
*Educated* . . . . . . . . . . Blackley Technical High School, Manchester;
Open University
*Elected*. . . . . . . . . . . 2001 MP for Ashton-under-Lyne
*Commons Office* . . . . . . Tel: (020) 7219 8129 Fax: (020) 7219 1738
E-mail: heyesd@parliament.uk
*Constituency Office* . . . . Suite 4, St Michaels Court,
Ashton-under-Lyne, Lancashire, OL6 6XN
Tel: (0161) 331 9307 Fax: (0161) 330 9420
E-mail: yatesl@parliament.uk
PA/Office Manager – Ms Linda Yates
Caseworker – Miss Sharon Barlow
Agent – Mr Norman Briggs
*Parliamentary Interests* . Public Administration

# MEMBERS OF THE HOUSE OF COMMONS

**Hill, Rt Hon Keith** Streatham
**Labour** . . . . . . . . . . . Majority 14,270 over Lib Dem
*Born*. . . . . . . . . . . . . . 28th July 1943 in Leicester
*Educated* . . . . . . . . . . City of Leicester Boys' Grammar School;
Corpus Christi College, Oxford;
University College of Wales, Aberystwyth
*Elected*. . . . . . . . . . . . 1992 MP for Streatham
*Offices Held* . . . . . . . . 1998 - 99 Assistant Government Whip
1999 - 2001 Parliamentary Secretary,
Department of the Environment, Transport
and the Regions (Minister for London)
2001 - 03 Deputy Government Chief Whip
(Treasurer, H M Household)
2003 - Minister of State, Office of the Deputy
Prime Minister (Minister for Housing
and Planning)
*Commons Office* . . . . . Tel: (020) 7219 0686 Fax: (020) 7219 2565
E-mail: hillk@parliament.uk
Administrative Officer – Mrs Sarah Griggs
Tel: (020) 7219 2781
E-mail: griggss@parliament.uk
Communications Officer – Mr Joe Moll
Tel: (020) 7219 3615
E-mail: mollj@parliament.uk
Caseworker – Ms Lisa Homan
Tel: (020) 7219 2781
E-mail: homanl@parliament.uk
*Parliamentary Interests*. Transport; Environment; International Affairs

**Hinchliffe, David** . . Wakefield
**Labour** . . . . . . . . . . . Majority 7,954 over Con
*Born*. . . . . . . . . . . . . . 14th October 1948 in Wakefield, Yorkshire
*Educated* . . . . . . . . . . Cathedral Secondary School Wakefield;
Wakefield Technical College;
Leeds Polytechnic; Bradford University
*Elected*. . . . . . . . . . . . 1987 MP for Wakefield
*Offices Held* . . . . . . . . 1992 - 97 Opposition Spokesman on Health
1997 - Chairman, Health Select Committee,
House of Commons
*Commons Office* . . . . . Tel: (020) 7219 4447 Fax: (020) 7219 5586
Secretary – Ms Elizabeth Batchelor
Tel: (020) 7219 6176
*Constituency Office* . . . . 6 Rishworth Street, Wakefield, WF1 3BY
Tel: (01924) 290590 Fax: (01924) 290690
Secretaries – Mrs Lynda Gray
Mrs Maggie Heys
Senior Caseworker – Mrs Julia Hinchliffe
*Parliamentary Interests*. Health; Social Services
*Leisure Interests* . . . . . . Rugby League; Inland Waterways; Genealogy

**Hoban, Mark**. . . . . Fareham
**Conservative** . . . . . . Majority 7,009 over Lab
*Educated* . . . . . . . . . . St Leonards RC Comprehensive;
London School of Economics
*Elected*. . . . . . . . . . . . 2001 MP for Fareham
*Office Held*. . . . . . . . . 2002 - 03 Opposition Whip
2003 - 04 Opposition Spokesman on
Public Services, Health and Education
2004 - Opposition Spokesman on Education
*Commons Office* . . . . . Tel: (020) 7219 8191 Fax: (020) 7219 1709
Personal Assistant – Miss Julie Ray
*Constituency Office* . . . . 14 East Street, Fareham, Hampshire,
PO16 0BN
Tel: (01329) 233573 Fax: (01329) 234197
E-mail: help@markhoban.com
Caseworker – Mrs Susan Bayford
*Parliamentary Interests*. Trade and Industry; The Economy; Education
*Leisure Interests* . . . . . . Cooking; Entertaining; Reading; Travel

**Hodge, Rt Hon Margaret** MBE Barking
**Labour** . . . . . . . . . . . Majority 9,534 over Con
*Born*. . . . . . . . . . . . . . 8th September 1944
*Educated* . . . . . . . . . . Bromley High School; Oxford High School;
London School of Economics
*Elected*. . . . . . . . . . . . 1994 MP for Barking (By-election)
*Offices Held* . . . . . . . . 1982 - 92 Leader, London Borough of
Islington Council
1997 - 98 Chairman, Education
Sub-Committee (Education and
Employment Select Committee),
House of Commons
1998 - 2001 Parliamentary Secretary,
Department for Education and Employment
2001 - Minister of State, Department for
Education and Skills
(Minister for Children from 2003)
*Commons Office* . . . . . Tel: (020) 7219 6666 Fax: (020) 7219 3640
Mobile: 07802 321460
Pager: 07641 121667
Research Assistant/Diary and Press
Secretary – Mr Mike Haywood
*Constituency Office* . . . . Tel: (020) 8594 1333 Fax: (020) 8594 1131
Constituency Case Worker –
Ms Jeanne Alexander
*Parliamentary Interests*. Child Care; Education; London
*Leisure Interests* . . . . . . Cooking; Family; Opera; Travel

**Hoey, Kate** . . . . . . . Vauxhall
**Labour** . . . . . . . . . . . Majority 13,018 over Lib Dem
*Born*. . . . . . . . . . . . . . 21st June 1948 in Belfast
*Educated* . . . . . . . . . . Belfast Royal Academy;
Ulster College of Physical Education;
City of London College
*Elected*. . . . . . . . . . . . 1989 MP for Vauxhall (By-election)
*Offices Held* . . . . . . . . 1992 - 93 Opposition Spokeswoman on
Citizen's Charter and Women
1998 - 99 Parliamentary Secretary,
Home Office
1999 - 2001 Parliamentary Secretary,
Department for Culture, Media and Sport
(Minister for Sport)
*Commons Office* . . . . . . Tel: (020) 7219 5989 Fax: (020) 7219 5985
Parliamentary Assistants – Ms Ami Ibitson
Mr Julian Powell
Ms Rebecca Horsley
E-mail: ibitsona@parliament.uk
powellje@parliament.uk
Office Manager – Ms Kathy Duffy
E-mail: duffyk@parliament.uk
*Parliamentary Interests*. Housing; Sport; Young People

# MEMBERS OF THE HOUSE OF COMMONS

**Hogg, Rt Hon Douglas** QC Sleaford and North Hykeham
**Conservative** . . . . . . Majority 8,622 over Lab
*Born* . . . . . . . . . . . . . . 5th February 1945 in London
*Educated* . . . . . . . . . . Eton College; Christ Church College, Oxford;
Lincoln's Inn
*Elected* . . . . . . . . . . . . 1979 MP for Grantham, then (1997)
Sleaford and North Hykeham
*Offices Held* . . . . . . . . 1982 - 86 PPS to Leon Brittan
(Chief Secretary to the Treasury)
1983 - 84 Government Whip
1986 - 89 Parliamentary Secretary,
Home Office
1989 - 90 Minister of State, Department of
Trade and Industry
1990 - 95 Minister of State, Foreign and
Commonwealth Office
1995 - 97 Minister of Agriculture, Fisheries
and Food
*Commons Office* . . . . . Tel: (020) 7219 3444 Fax: (020) 7219 4123
E-mail: hoggd@parliament.uk
Secretary/PA – Mrs Ann Edwards
E-mail: edwardsa@parliament.uk
*Constituency Office* . . . . 6 Market Place, Sleaford, Lincolnshire,
LN5 0PE
Tel: (01529) 419000 Fax: (01529) 419019
E-mail: snhca@compuserve.com
Agent – Ms Rosemary Kaberry-Brown


**Holmes, Paul** . . . . . Chesterfield
**Liberal Democrat** . . . Majority 2,586 over Lab
*Born* . . . . . . . . . . . . . . 16th January 1957 in Sheffield
*Educated* . . . . . . . . . . Firth Park School; York University;
Sheffield University
*Elected* . . . . . . . . . . . . 2001 MP for Chesterfield
*Office Held* . . . . . . . . . 2002 - Liberal Democrat Spokesman on Work
and Pensions and Disability Issues
*Commons Office* . . . . . Tel: (020) 7219 8158 Fax: (020) 7219 1754
E-mail: obrienc@parliament.uk
Web: http://www.paulholmes.org.uk
Researcher – Ms Cath O'Brien
*Constituency Office* . . . . 69 West Bars, Chesterfield, SH0 4TH
Tel: (01246) 234879 Fax: (01246) 206333
Head of Office – Mrs Raelene Holmes
Caseworker – Mr Stuart Bray
*Parliamentary Interests* . Education; Human Rights; Foreign Affairs
*Leisure Interests* . . . . . . History; Reading; Music; Architecture

**Hood, Jimmy** . . . . . Clydesdale
**Labour** . . . . . . . . . . . Majority 7,794 over SNP
*Born* . . . . . . . . . . . . . . 16th May 1948 in Lesmahagow, Clydesdale
*Educated* . . . . . . . . . . Motherwell College;
Nottingham University
*Elected* . . . . . . . . . . . . 1987 MP for Clydesdale
*Office Held* . . . . . . . . . 1992 - 98, 2001 - Chairman,
European Scrutiny Committee,
House of Commons
*Commons Office* . . . . . Tel: (020) 7219 4585 Fax: (020) 7219 5872
Mobile: 07876 772233
E-mail: hoodj@parliament.uk
Web: http://www.jimmyhood.labour.co.uk
*Constituency Office* . . . . Council Offices, South Vennel,
Lanark, ML11 7JT
Tel: (01555) 673177 Fax: (01555) 673188
E-mail: davidsonh@parliament.uk
Secretary/Personal Assistant –
Miss Helen Davidson
*Parliamentary Interests* . Health Service; Home Affairs;
Alcohol Abuse; Industrial Relations
*Leisure Interests* . . . . . . Gardening; Reading; Writing; Walking

**Hoon, Rt Hon Geoff** Ashfield
**Labour** . . . . . . . . . . . Majority 13,268 over Con
*Born* . . . . . . . . . . . . . . 6th December 1953 in Derby
*Educated* . . . . . . . . . . Nottingham High School;
Jesus College, Cambridge
*Elected* . . . . . . . . . . . . 1992 MP for Ashfield
*Offices Held* . . . . . . . . 1984 - 94 Member of European Parliament
1994 - 95 Opposition Whip
1995 - 97 Opposition Spokesman on Trade
and Industry
1997 - 98 Parliamentary Secretary,
Lord Chancellor's Department
1998 - 99 Minister of State,
Lord Chancellor's Department
1999 Minister of State, Foreign and
Commonwealth Office (Minister for Europe)
1999 - Secretary of State for Defence
*Commons Office* . . . . . Tel: (020) 7219 2701 Fax: (020) 7219 2428
Assistant – Ms Mary Jo Bishop
E-mail: bishopmj@parliament.uk
*Constituency Office* . . . . 8 Station Street, Kirkby-in-Ashfield,
Nottinghamshire, NG17 7AR
Tel: (01623) 720399 Fax: (01623) 720398
E-mail: waltersa@parliament.uk
Assistant – Ms Alison Walters


**Hope, Philip** . . . . . . Corby
**Labour** . . . . . . . . . . . Majority 5,700 over Con
*Born* . . . . . . . . . . . . . . 19th April 1955
*Educated* . . . . . . . . . . Wandsworth Comprehensive School;
Exeter University
*Elected* . . . . . . . . . . . . 1997 MP for Corby
*Offices Held* . . . . . . . . 2001 - 03 PPS to John Prescott
(Deputy Prime Minister)
2003 - Parliamentary Secretary, Office of the
Deputy Prime Minister
*Commons Office* . . . . . Tel: (020) 7219 4075 Fax: (020) 7219 2964
Mobile: 07973 768519
Pager: 07644 004830
E-mail: hopep@parliament.uk
Web: http://www.philhope.org
Researcher – Mr Will McDonald
E-mail: mcdonaldw@parliament.uk
*Constituency Office* . . . . Chisholm House, Queen's Square, Corby,
Northamptonshire, NN17 1PD
Tel: (01536) 443325 Fax: (01536) 269462
E-mail: rolfel@parliament.uk
Personal Assistant – Mr Les Rolfe
Secretary – Ms Susan Witowski
*Parliamentary Interests* . Youth; Social Security; International
Development; Voluntary Organisations
*Leisure Interests* . . . . . . Tennis; Juggling; Gardening; Computing

# MEMBERS OF THE HOUSE OF COMMONS

**Hopkins, Kelvin** . . . Luton North
**Labour** . . . . . . . . . . . Majority 9,977 over Con
*Born* . . . . . . . . . . . . . . 22nd August 1941 in Leicester
*Educated* . . . . . . . . . . Queen Elizabeth's Grammar School, Barnet;
    Nottingham University
*Elected* . . . . . . . . . . . . 1997 MP for Luton North
*Commons Office* . . . . . Tel: (020) 7219 6670 Fax: (020) 7219 0957
    E-mail: hopkinsk@parliament.uk
*Constituency Office* . . . . 3 Union Street, Luton, LU1 3AN
    Tel: (01582) 488208 Fax: (01582) 480990
    Secretary/PA – Mrs Patricia Hopkins
    E-mail: hopkinsp@parliament.uk
*Parliamentary Interests* . Transport; Economy
*Leisure Interests* . . . . . . Photography; Sailing; Jazz; Music


**Horam, John** . . . . . . Orpington
**Conservative** . . . . . . . Majority 269 over Lib Dem
*Born* . . . . . . . . . . . . . . 7th March 1939 in Preston, Lancashire
*Educated* . . . . . . . . . . Silcoates School, Wakefield;
    St Catherine's College, Cambridge
*Elected* . . . . . . . . . . . . 1970 - 83 MP for Gateshead West (1970 - 81
    Labour; 1981 - 83 Social Democrat)
    1992 MP for Orpington (Conservative)
*Offices Held* . . . . . . . . 1976 - 79 Parliamentary Secretary,
    Department of Transport
    1979 - 81 Opposition Spokesman on
    Economic Affairs
    1995 Parliamentary Secretary, Office of Public
    Service and Science
    1995 - 97 Parliamentary Secretary,
    Department of Health
    1997 - 2003 Chairman, Environmental Audit
    Committee, House of Commons
*Commons Office* . . . . . . Tel: (020) 7219 6328 Fax: (020) 7219 3806
    E-mail: horamj@parliament.uk
    Secretary – Miss Patricia Bowden
    Tel: (020) 7219 4462
    E-mail: bowdenp@parliament.uk
*Constituency Office* . . . . 6 Sevenoaks Road, Orpington, Kent, BR6 9JJ
    Tel: (01689) 820347 Fax: (01689) 890429
*Parliamentary Interests* . Economic Policy; Environment; Health
*Leisure Interests* . . . . . . Gardening; Opera


**Howard, Rt Hon Michael** QC Folkestone and Hythe
**Conservative** . . . . . . . Majority 5,907 over Lib Dem
*Born* . . . . . . . . . . . . . . 7th July 1941 in Gorseinon, South Wales
*Educated* . . . . . . . . . . Llanelli Grammar School;
    Peterhouse, Cambridge
*Elected* . . . . . . . . . . . . 1983 MP for Folkestone and Hythe
*Offices Held* . . . . . . . . 1985 - 87 Parliamentary Secretary,
    Department of Trade and Industry
    1987 - 90 Minister of State,
    Department of Environment
    1990 - 92 Secretary of State for Employment
    1992 - 93 Secretary of State for Environment
    1993 - 97 Home Secretary
    1997 - 99 Shadow Foreign Secretary
    2001 - 03 Shadow Chancellor of the
    Exchequer
    2003 - Leader of the Opposition
*Commons Office* . . . . . . Tel: (020) 7219 5493
    E-mail: howardm@parliament.uk
    Private Secretary – Mr Jonathan Hellewell
    Diary Secretary – Miss Rebecca Melotte
    Tel: (020) 7219 4410
*Constituency Office* . . . . 4 West Cliff Gardens, Folkestone,
    Kent, CT20 1SP
    Tel: (01303) 253524  Fax: (01303) 251061
    E-mail: consfolkestone@btinternet.com
    Agent – Mr Robert Davidson


**Howarth, Rt Hon Alan** CBE Newport East
**Labour** . . . . . . . . . . . Majority 9,874 over Con
*Born* . . . . . . . . . . . . . . 11th June 1944 in London
*Educated* . . . . . . . . . . Rugby School; King's College, Cambridge
*Elected* . . . . . . . . . . . . 1983 - 97 MP for Stratford-on-Avon
    (1983 - 95 Con; 1995 - 97 Lab)
    1997 MP for Newport East (Lab)
*Offices Held* . . . . . . . . 1987 - 88 Assistant Government Whip
    1988 - 89 Government Whip (Lord
    Commissioner, H M Treasury)
    1989 - 90 Minister for Schools
    1989 - 92 Parliamentary Secretary,
    Department of Education and Science
    1990 - 92 Minister for Higher Education
    and Science
    1997 - 98 Minister for Employment, Equal
    Opportunities and Disabled People
    1998 - 2001 Parliamentary Secretary,
    Department for Culture, Media and Sport
    (Minister for the Arts)
*Commons Office* . . . . . . Tel: (020) 7219 5077 Fax: (020) 7219 0444
    Mobile: 07879 427900
    Pager: 07654 285596
    E-mail: howartha@parliament.uk
    Personal Assistant – Miss Patricia Constant
    Tel: (020) 7219 6421
*Constituency Office* . . . . Ringland Labour Club, Ringland Circle,
    Newport, South Wales, NP19 9PS
    Tel: (01633) 273111/277910
    Fax: (01633) 282793
    Secretary – Cllr Tony Gray
*Parliamentary Interests* . Arts; Economic Policy; Employment;
    Education; Social Security; Charities;
    Voluntary Sector
*Leisure Interests* . . . . . . Arts; Reading; Walking

# MEMBERS OF THE HOUSE OF COMMONS

**Howarth, George** . . Knowsley North and Sefton East
**Labour** . . . . . . . . . . . Majority 26,147 over Con
*Born* . . . . . . . . . . . . . . 29th June 1949 in Whiston, Merseyside
*Educated* . . . . . . . . . . Kirkby College of Further Education;
Liverpool Polytechnic
*Elected* . . . . . . . . . . . . 1986 MP for Knowsley North (By-election),
then (1997) Knowsley North and Sefton East
*Offices Held* . . . . . . . . Formerly Deputy Leader, Knowsley
Metropolitan Borough Council
1990 - 92 Opposition Spokesman on
Housing and Planning
1993 - 94 Opposition Spokesman on
Environment Protection
1994 - 97 Opposition Spokesman on
Home Affairs
1997 - 99 Parliamentary Secretary,
Home Office
1999 - 2001 Parliamentary Secretary,
Northern Ireland Office
*Commons Office* . . . . . . Tel: (020) 7219 6902 Fax: (020) 7219 0495
E-mail: howarthg@parliament.uk
Secretary – Ms Susan Utting
Tel: (020) 7219 4538
*Constituency Office* . . . . 149 Cherryfield Drive, Kirkby, Merseyside,
L32 8SE
Tel & Fax: (0151) 546 9918
Personal Assistant – Mrs Julie Howarth
Caseworker – Mr Michael Murphy
*Parliamentary Interests* . Home Affairs
*Leisure Interests* . . . . . . Family; Reading

**Howarth, Gerald** . . Aldershot
**Conservative** . . . . . . Majority 6,594 over Lib Dem
*Born* . . . . . . . . . . . . . . 12th September 1947 in Guildford
*Educated* . . . . . . . . . . Bloxham School, Banbury;
Southampton University
*Elected* . . . . . . . . . . . . 1983 - 1992 MP for Cannock and Burntwood
1997 MP for Aldershot
*Offices Held* . . . . . . . . 2002 - 03 Opposition Spokesman on Defence
2003 - Opposition Spokesman on International
Affairs
*Commons Office* . . . . . . Tel: (020) 7219 5650 Fax: (020) 7219 1198
*Constituency Office* . . . . Conservative Office, Victoria Road, Aldershot,
Hampshire, GU11 1JX
Tel & Fax: (01252) 323637
Organising Secretary – Mrs Margaret Foyle
*Parliamentary Interests* . Aerospace; Defence; Constitution;
Home Affairs
*Leisure Interests* . . . . . . Photography; Flying

**Howells, Dr Kim** . . Pontypridd
**Labour** . . . . . . . . . . . Majority 17,684 over Plaid Cymru
*Born* . . . . . . . . . . . . . . 27th November 1946 in Merthyr Tydfil
*Educated* . . . . . . . . . . Mountain Ash Grammar School;
Hornsey College of Art;
Cambridge College of Advanced Technology;
Warwick University
*Elected* . . . . . . . . . . . . 1989 MP for Pontypridd (By-election)
*Offices Held* . . . . . . . . 1993 Opposition Spokesman on
Development and Co-operation
1994 Opposition Spokesman on Foreign
Affairs, then on Home Affairs
1995 - 96 Opposition Spokesman on
Trade and Industry
1997 - 98 Parliamentary Secretary,
Department for Education and Employment
1998 - 01 Parliamentary Secretary,
Department of Trade and Industry
2001 - 03 Parliamentary Secretary,
Department for Culture, Media and Sport
2003 - 04 Minister of State, Department of
Transport
2004 - Minister of State, Department for
Education and Skills (Minister for
Higher Education)
*Commons Office* . . . . . . Tel: (020) 7219 5813 Fax: (020) 7219 5526
*Constituency Office* . . . . 16 Tyfica Road, Pontypridd, CF37 2DA
Tel: (01443) 402551 Fax: (01443) 485628
E-mail: raybouldc@parliament.uk
Office Manager – Mrs Christine Raybould
Assistant Office Manager – Mrs E Howells
Tel: (01443) 407822
*Parliamentary Interests* . Culture; Economy; Education; Foreign Affairs
*Leisure Interests* . . . . . . Cinema; Jazz; Mountaineering; Painting

**Hoyle, Lindsay** . . . . Chorley
**Labour** . . . . . . . . . . . Majority 8,444 over Con
*Born* . . . . . . . . . . . . . . 1957 in Chorley
*Educated* . . . . . . . . . . Bolton College of Further Education
*Elected* . . . . . . . . . . . . 1997 MP for Chorley
*Offices Held* . . . . . . . . Formerly Deputy Leader and Mayor,
Chorley Borough Council
*Commons Office* . . . . . . Tel: (020) 7219 3515 Fax: (020) 7219 3831
E-mail: lindsay@lindsayhoyle.co.uk
Research Assistant – Mr Peter Wilson
E-mail: wilsonp@parliament.uk
*Constituency Office* . . . . 35-39 Market Street, Chorley, PR7 2SW
Tel: (01257) 271555 Fax: (01257) 277462
Personal Assistant – Ms Beverley Gore
*Parliamentary Interests* . Defence; Trade and Industry;
Culture, Media and Sport
*Leisure Interests* . . . . . . Rugby League; Cricket; Football

**Hughes, Rt Hon Beverley** Stretford and Urmston
**Labour** . . . . . . . . . . . Majority 13,239 over Con
*Born* . . . . . . . . . . . . . . 30th March 1950
*Educated* . . . . . . . . . . Ellesmere Port Grammar School;
Manchester University; Liverpool University
*Elected* . . . . . . . . . . . . 1997 MP for Stretford and Urmston
*Offices Held* . . . . . . . . 1995 - 97 Leader, Trafford Metropolitan
Council
1999 - 2001 Parliamentary Secretary,
Department for the Environment,
Transport and the Regions
2001 - 02 Parliamentary Secretary, Home
Office
2002 - 04 Minister of State, Home Office
(Minister for Citizenship and Immigration)
*Constituency Office* . . . . Tel: (0161) 749 9120 Fax: (0161) 749 9121
Office Manager – Ms Andrea Jones
E-mail: jonesa@parliament.uk
*Parliamentary Interests* . Home Affairs; Criminal Justice; Education;
Health; Women; Economic Regeneration
*Leisure Interests* . . . . . . Jazz; Walking

# MEMBERS OF THE HOUSE OF COMMONS

**Hughes, Kevin** .... Doncaster North
**Labour** .......... Majority 15,187 over Con
*Born*. ............. 15th December 1952 in Doncaster, Yorkshire
*Educated* .......... Sheffield University
*Elected* ........... 1992 MP for Doncaster North
*Offices Held* ....... 1996 - 97 Opposition Whip
1997 - 2001 Assistant Government Whip
*Commons Office* ..... Tel: (020) 7219 4107 Fax: (020) 7219 2521
E-mail: khughes@mplink.co.uk
Assistant/Researcher – Ms Roberta Hamilton
*Constituency Office* .... Bentley Training Centre, Bentley,
Doncaster, DN5 0AA
Tel: (01302) 873974 Fax: (01302) 876176
Web: http://www.doncasternorth.co.uk
Secretary/Caseworker – Mrs Lynda Hughes
*Parliamentary Interests* . Health; Social Services; Energy

**Hughes, Simon** .... Southwark North and Bermondsey
**Liberal Democrat** ... Majority 9,632 over Lab
*Born*. ............. 17th May 1951 in Cheshire
*Educated* .......... Llandaff Cathedral School;
Christ College, Brecon;
Selwyn College, Cambridge;
Inns of Court School of Law;
College of Europe, Bruges
*Elected*. ........... 1983 MP for Bermondsey (By-election), then
(1983) Southwark and Bermondsey, and
(1997) Southwark North and Bermondsey
*Offices Held* ........ 1983 - 87 Liberal Spokesman on
Environment
1987 - 88 Alliance Spokesman on Health
1988 - 89 Liberal Democrat Spokesman on
Education, Science and Training
1989 Liberal Democrat Deputy Whip
1990 - 94 Liberal Democrat Spokesman on
Environment and Natural Resources
1994 - 95 Liberal Democrat Spokesman on
Community and Urban Affairs and
Young People
1995 - 99 Liberal Democrat Spokesman on
Health
1999 - 2003 Liberal Democrat Spokesman on
Home Affairs
2003 - Liberal Democrat Spokesman for
London
2004 - President, Liberal Democrat Party
*Commons Office* ..... Tel: (020) 7219 6256 Fax: (020) 7219 6567
E-mail: simon@simonhughesmp.org.uk
Web: http://www.simonhughes.org.uk
*Constituency Office* .... Tel: (020) 7403 2860 Fax: (020) 7378 9670
*Parliamentary Interests* . Social Justice; Community Relations; Europe;
The Commonwealth; Human Rights
*Leisure Interests* ...... Music; Reading; Theatre; Countryside;
Family and Friends

**Humble, Joan** .... Blackpool North and Fleetwood
**Labour** .......... Majority 5,721 over Con
*Born*. ............. 3rd March 1951 in Skipton
*Educated* .......... Greenhead Grammar School, Keighley;
Lancaster University
*Elected*. ........... 1997 MP for Blackpool North and Fleetwood
*Commons Office* ..... Tel: (020) 7219 5025 Fax: (020) 7219 2755
Pager: 07644 003986
*Constituency Office* .... 216 Lord Street, Fleetwood, Lancashire,
FY7 6SW
Tel: (01253) 877346 Fax: (01253) 777236
E-mail: sue@humblemp.freeserve.co.uk
Secretary – Ms Sue Rigby
Assistant – Mr Bob Harrison
*Parliamentary Interests* . Social Security; Health; Fishing; Tourism;
Job Creation
*Leisure Interests* ...... Cooking; Gardening; Reading

**Hume, John**. ...... Foyle
**SDLP** ........... Majority 11,560 over Sinn Fein
*Born*. ............. 18th January 1937 in Derry
*Educated* .......... St Columba's College, Derry;
National University of Ireland;
St Patrick's College, Maynooth
*Elected*. ........... 1983 MP for Foyle
*Offices Held* ....... 1979 - 2001 Leader, Social Democratic and
Labour Party
1979 - 2004 Member, European Parliament
1998 - 2000 Member,
Northern Ireland Assembly
*Constituency Office* .... 5 Bayview Terrace, Derry, BT48 7EE
Tel: (028) 7126 5340

**Hunter, Andrew** ... Basingstoke
**Independent**. ...... Majority 880 over Lab
*(elected as Conservative)*
*Born*. ............. 8th January 1943 in Hertfordshire
*Educated* .......... St George's School Harpenden, Hertfordshire;
Durham University;
Jesus College, Cambridge
*Elected*. ........... 1983 MP for Basingstoke
*Commons Office* ..... Tel: (020) 7219 5216 Fax: (020) 7219 0024
E-mail: andrewhuntermp@parliament.uk
Assistant – Mrs Katherine Smith
*Constituency Office* .... 149D Pack Lane, Basingstoke, RG22 5HN
Tel: (01635) 47445 Fax: (01635) 40532
Secretary – Mr Anthony Wood
Tel: (01256) 322207 Fax: (01256) 466236
*Parliamentary Interests* . Northern Ireland; Environment; Home Affairs;
Agriculture
*Leisure Interests* ...... Horse Riding; Watching Cricket and Rugby

**Hurst, Alan** ....... Braintree
**Labour** .......... Majority 358 over Con
*Born*. ............. 2nd September 1945 in Southend
*Educated* .......... Westcliff High School;
University of Liverpool
*Elected*. ........... 1997 MP for Braintree
*Commons Office* ..... Tel: (020) 7219 4068 Fax: (020) 7219 2655
Parliamentary Assistant –
Mr Graham Whitham
Tel: (020) 7219 1636
*Constituency Office* .... The Labour Hall, Collingwood Road,
Witham, Essex, CM8 2EE
Tel: (01376) 520128 Fax: (01376) 517709
Assistants – Ms Eileen Davidson
Mrs Jacqueline Hearn
*Parliamentary Interests* . Agriculture; Rural Affairs; Pensions;
Conservation
*Leisure Interests* ...... Local History; Bird Watching

# MEMBERS OF THE HOUSE OF COMMONS

**Hutton, Rt Hon John**     Barrow and Furness
**Labour** . . . . . . . . . . . Majority 9,889 over Con
*Born*. . . . . . . . . . . . . . 6th May 1955 in London
*Educated* . . . . . . . . . . Westcliff High School;
    Magdalen College, Oxford
*Elected*. . . . . . . . . . . . 1992 MP for Barrow and Furness
*Offices Held* . . . . . . . . 1998 - 99 Parliamentary Secretary,
    Department of Health
    1999 - Minister of State, Department of
    Health
*Commons Office* . . . . . Tel: (020) 7219 6228 Fax: (020) 7219 2418
    E-mail: huttonj@parliament.uk
    Web: http://www.johnhuttonmp.co.uk
*Constituency Office* . . . . 22 Hartington Street, Barrow-in-Furness,
    Cumbria, LA14 5SL
    Tel: (01229) 431204/839668
    Fax: (01229) 432016
    E-mail: mcsorleyt@parliament.uk
    Office Manager – Mr Terry McSorley
    Personal Assistant – Ms Jane Murphy
    Caseworker - Mr Jack Melling
*Parliamentary Interests* . Legal Affairs; Welfare State; Defence;
    Home Affairs
*Leisure Interests* . . . . . Football; Cricket; Films; Music; History

# I

**Iddon, Dr Brian**. . . Bolton South East
**Labour** . . . . . . . . . . . Majority 12,871 over Con
*Born*. . . . . . . . . . . . . . 5th July 1940 in Tarleton, Lancashire
*Educated* . . . . . . . . . . Christ Church Boys School, Southport;
    Southport Technical College;
    University of Hull
*Elected*. . . . . . . . . . . . 1997 MP for Bolton South East
*Commons Office* . . . . . Tel: (020) 7219 4064 Fax: (020) 7219 2653
    E-mail: iddonb@parliament.uk
    Web: http://www.brianiddonmp.org.uk
    Personal Assistant – Miss Kathryn Sutcliffe
    Tel: (020) 7219 2096
    E-mail: sutcliffek@parliament.uk
*Constituency Office* . . . . 60 St George's Road, Bolton, BL1 2DD
    Tel: (01204) 371202 Fax: (01204) 371374
    Personal Assistant – Ms Karen Lawrinson
*Parliamentary Interests* . Education; Health; Science and Technology;
    Social Security
*Leisure Interests* . . . . . Cricket; Gardening; Philately

**Illsley, Eric** . . . . . . Barnsley Central
**Labour** . . . . . . . . . . . Majority 15,130 over Lib Dem
*Born*. . . . . . . . . . . . . . 9th April 1955 in Barnsley, Yorkshire
*Educated* . . . . . . . . . . Barnsley Holgate Grammar School;
    Barnsley College of Technology;
    Leeds University
*Elected*. . . . . . . . . . . . 1987 MP for Barnsley Central
*Offices Held* . . . . . . . . 1991 - 94 Opposition Whip
    1994 Opposition Spokesman on
    Local Government
    1994 - 95 Opposition Spokesman on Health
    1995 - 97 Opposition Spokesman on
    Northern Ireland
*Commons Office* . . . . . Tel: (020) 7219 3501 Fax: (020) 7219 4863
    Mobile: 07831 680968
    Pager: 07644 006910
    E-mail: illsleye@parliament.uk
    Web: http://www.ericillsley.co.uk
*Constituency Office* . . . . 18 Regent Street, Barnsley, S70 2HG
    Tel: (01226) 730692 Fax: (01226) 779429
    Secretaries – Miss Rebecca Simon
    Mrs Pauline Smith
    E-mail: simonr@parliament.uk
    pauline@eric-illsley-mp-new.labour
*Parliamentary Interests* . Social Security; Trade Unions; Foreign Affairs
*Leisure Interests* . . . . . . Gymnasium; Cinema; Golf

**Ingram, Rt Hon Adam**   East Kilbride
**Labour** . . . . . . . . . . . Majority 12,755 over SNP
*Born*. . . . . . . . . . . . . . 1st February 1947 in Glasgow
*Educated* . . . . . . . . . . Cranhill Secondary School, Glasgow;
    Open University
*Elected*. . . . . . . . . . . . 1987 MP for East Kilbride
*Offices Held* . . . . . . . . 1984 - 87 Leader, East Kilbride
    District Council
    1988 - 92 PPS to Neil Kinnock
    (Leader of the Opposition)
    1993 - 95 Opposition Spokesman on
    Social Security
    1995 - 97 Opposition Spokesman on
    Trade and Industry
    1997 - 2001 Minister of State, Northern
    Ireland Office
    2001 - Minister of State, Ministry of Defence
*Commons Office* . . . . . Tel: (020) 7219 4093
    Mobile: 07899 877025
    E-mail: adam_ingram@compuserve.com
*Constituency Office* . . . . Civic Centre, Andrew Street, East Kilbride,
    G74 1AB
    Tel: (01355) 806016 Fax: (01355) 806035
    E-mail: adam_ingram@compuserve.com
    Secretary/Personal Assistant –
    Mrs Maureen Ingram
    Office Assistant – Mrs Isobel Grassom
*Parliamentary Interests* . Energy; Industry; Northern Ireland; Defence
*Leisure Interests* . . . . . Fishing; Reading; Cooking

**Irranca-Davies, Huw** Ogmore
**Labour** . . . . . . . . . . . Majority 5,721 over Plaid Cymru
*Born*. . . . . . . . . . . . . . 22nd January 1963 in Gowerton
*Educated* . . . . . . . . . . Gowerton Comprehensive School;
    Crewe and Alsager College;
    Swansea Institute of Higher Education
*Elected*. . . . . . . . . . . . 2002 MP for Ogmore (By-election)
*Office Held* . . . . . . . . . 2003 - PPS to Jane Kennedy
    (Minister of State, Northern Ireland Office
    then Department of Work and Pensions)
*Commons Office* . . . . . Tel: (020) 7219 4027 Fax: (020) 7219 0134
    Mobile: 07967 556320
    Pager: 07693 275472
    E-mail: irrancadaviesh@parliament.uk
    Research Assistant – Mr Guy Rowland
    E-mail: rowlandg@parliament.uk
*Constituency Office* . . . . 114 Commercial Street, Maesteg, CF34 9DL
    Tel: (01656) 737777 Fax: (01656) 737788
    Personal Assistant/Office Manager –
    Miss Jillian Swinhoe
    Senior Caseworker – Mr Malcolm Reeves
    Caseworker – Ms Catherine Bevan
*Parliamentary Interests* . Domestic and International Poverty;
    Social Inclusion; Equality; Middle East
*Leisure Interests* . . . . . Family; Hill Walking; Sports

# MEMBERS OF THE HOUSE OF COMMONS

## *J*

**Jack, Rt Hon Michael** Fylde
**Conservative** . . . . . . . Majority 9,610 over Lab
*Born*. . . . . . . . . . . . . . 17th September 1946 in Kent
*Educated* . . . . . . . . . . Bradford Grammar School;
    Bradford Technical School;
    Leicester University
*Elected*. . . . . . . . . . . . 1987 MP for Fylde
*Offices Held* . . . . . . . . 1990 - 92 Parliamentary Secretary,
    Department of Social Security
    1992 - 93 Minister of State, Home Office
    1993 - 95 Minister of State, Ministry of
        Agriculture, Fisheries and Food
    1995 - 97 Financial Secretary to the Treasury
    1997 Opposition Spokesman on Health
    1997 - 98 Shadow Minister of Agriculture,
        Fisheries and Food
    2003 - Chairman, Environment, Food and
        Rural Affairs Committee,
        House of Commons
*Commons Office* . . . . . . Tel: (020) 7219 5047
*Leisure Interests* . . . . . . Motor Sport; Dinghy Sailing;
    Growing Vegetables; Boules

**Jackson, Glenda** CBE Hampstead and Highgate
**Labour** . . . . . . . . . . . Majority 7,876 over Con
*Born*. . . . . . . . . . . . . . 9th May 1936 in Birkenhead, Merseyside
*Educated* . . . . . . . . . . West Kirby Grammar School; RADA
*Elected*. . . . . . . . . . . . 1992 MP for Hampstead and Highgate
*Offices Held* . . . . . . . . 1996 - 97 Opposition Spokesman on Transport
    1997 - 99 Parliamentary Secretary,
        Department of Environment,
        Transport and the Regions (Minister for
        Transport in London)
*Commons Office* . . . . . . Tel: (020) 7219 4008 Fax: (020) 7219 2112
    Caseworker – Ms Katharine Sacks-Jones

**Jackson, Helen** . . . . Sheffield Hillsborough
**Labour** . . . . . . . . . . . Majority 14,569 over Lib Dem
*Born*. . . . . . . . . . . . . . 19th May 1939
*Educated* . . . . . . . . . . Berkhamsted School for Girls;
    St Hilda's College, Oxford;
    CF Mott College of Education,
    Prescot, Liverpool
*Elected*. . . . . . . . . . . . 1992 MP for Sheffield Hillsborough
*Office Held*. . . . . . . . 1997 - 2001 PPS to Mo Mowlam, then
    Peter Mandelson and John Reid (successive
    Secretaries of State for Northern Ireland)
*Commons Office* . . . . . . Tel: (020) 7219 6895 Fax: (020) 7219 2442
    E-mail: jacksonh@parliament.uk
    Research Assistant – Ms April Gallwey
    E-mail: gallweya@parliament.uk
*Constituency Office* . . . . Hillsborough Library, Middlewood Road,
    Sheffield, S6 4HD
    Tel: (0114) 232 2439 Fax: (0114) 285 5808
    PA/Secretary – Ms Julie Berrisford
    Secretary – Ms Jane Bullos
*Parliamentary Interests*. Environment; Northern Ireland;
    Parliamentary Reform; Transport
*Leisure Interests* . . . . . . Walking; Reading

**Jackson, Robert** . . . Wantage
**Conservative** . . . . . . Majority 6,039 over Lab
*Born*. . . . . . . . . . . . . . 24th September 1946 in Rhodesia
*Educated* . . . . . . . . . . Falcon College, Rhodesia;
    St Edmund Hall, Oxford;
    All Souls College, Oxford
*Elected*. . . . . . . . . . . . 1983 MP for Wantage
*Offices Held* . . . . . . . . 1979 - 84 Member of European Parliament
    1987 - 90 Parliamentary Secretary of State,
        Department of Education and Science
    1990 - 92 Parliamentary Secretary,
        Department of Employment
    1992 - 93 Parliamentary Secretary, Office of
        Public Service and Science
*Commons Office* . . . . . Tel: (020) 7219 6350 Fax: (020) 7219 2718
    E-mail: jacksonr@parliament.uk
    Private Secretary – Mrs Anne Langley
    E-mail: langleya@parliament.uk
*Constituency Office* . . . . Orchard House, Portway, Wantage,
    Oxfordshire, OX12 9BU
    Tel: (01235) 769090 Fax: (01235) 224833
    E-mail: office@wantage.cca.demon.co.uk
    Web: http://www.wantageconservatives.com
    Agent – Mrs Nicola Matthews

**Jamieson, David** . . . Plymouth Devonport
**Labour** . . . . . . . . . . . Majority 13,033 over Con
*Born*. . . . . . . . . . . . . . 18th May 1947 in Solihull, Warwickshire
*Educated* . . . . . . . . . . Tudor Grange Grammar School, Solihull;
    Solihull Technical College;
    St Peter's College, Birmingham;
    Open University
*Elected*. . . . . . . . . . . . 1992 MP for Plymouth Devonport
*Offices Held* . . . . . . . . 1997 - 98 Assistant Government Whip
    1998 - 2001 Government Whip (Lord
        Commissioner, H M Treasury)
    2001 - Parliamentary Secretary,
        Department for Transport, Local
        Government and the Regions, then
        Department of Transport
*Commons Office* . . . . . . Tel: (020) 7219 0252 Fax: (020) 7219 2388
*Constituency Office* . . . . Tel: (01752) 704077
*Parliamentary Interests*. Education; Children
*Leisure Interests* . . . . . . Gardening; Old Cars; DIY; Walking

# MEMBERS OF THE HOUSE OF COMMONS

**Jenkin, Hon Bernard**  Essex North
**Conservative** . . . . . . Majority 5,476 over Lab
*Born.* . . . . . . . . . . . . . 9th April 1959 in London
*Educated* . . . . . . . . . Highgate School, London;
William Ellis School, London;
Corpus Christi College, Cambridge
*Elected* . . . . . . . . . . . 1992 MP for Colchester North, then (1997)
Essex North
*Offices Held* . . . . . . . 1997 - 98 Opposition Spokesman on
Constitutional Affairs
1998 - 2001 Shadow Minister for Transport
and Spokesman on London
2001 - 03 Shadow Defence Secretary
2003 - Shadow Secretary for the Regions
*Commons Office* . . . . . Tel: (020) 7219 4029 Fax: (020) 7219 5963
Mobile: 07770 224999
E-mail: jenkinb@parliament.uk
Web: http://www.bernardjenkinmp.com
Private Secretary – Mrs Nicola Brogan
E-mail: brogann@parliament.uk
Researcher – Mr Graham Hook
E-mail: hookg@parliament.uk
*Constituency Office* . . . . 107 High Street, Colchester, Essex, CO1 1TH
Tel: (01206) 544114
*Parliamentary Interests* . Defence; Economy; Financial Services;
Foreign Affairs; Small Businesses
*Leisure Interests* . . . . . DIY; Farming; Fishing; Music; Sailing

**Jenkins, Brian** . . . . Tamworth
**Labour** . . . . . . . . . . . Majority 4,598 over Con
*Born.* . . . . . . . . . . . . . 19th September 1942 in South Wales
*Educated* . . . . . . . . . . Kingsbury High School, Tamworth;
Coventry College; Coleg Harlech;
London School of Economics;
Wolverhampton Polytechnic
*Elected.* . . . . . . . . . . . 1996 MP for Staffordshire South East
(By-election), then (1997) Tamworth
*Commons Office* . . . . . Tel: (020) 7219 5256 Fax: (020) 7219 0169
E-mail: jenkinsb@parliament.uk
*Constituency Office* . . . . 31c Market Street, Tarnworth, Staffordshire,
B77 7LR
Tel: (01827) 311957 Fax: (01827) 311958
Caseworker – Mrs Carol Dean
Office Manager – Mrs Linda Brazier
*Parliamentary Interests* . Europe; Home Affairs
*Leisure Interests* . . . . . . Walking; Rugby

**Johnson, Rt Hon Alan**  Hull West and Hessle
**Labour** . . . . . . . . . . . Majority 10,951 over Con
*Born.* . . . . . . . . . . . . . 17th May 1950 in London
*Educated* . . . . . . . . . . Sloane Grammar School, Chelsea
*Elected.* . . . . . . . . . . . 1997 MP for Hull West and Hessle
*Offices Held* . . . . . . . . 1999 - 2001 Parliamentary Secretary,
Department of Trade and Industry
2001 - 03 Minister of State,
Department for Trade and Industry
2003 - 04 Minister of State, Department for
Education and Skills (Minister for Lifelong
Learning, Further and Higher Education)
2004 - Secretary of State for Work and
Pensions
*Commons Office* . . . . . Tel: (020) 7219 6637 Fax: (020) 7219 5856
Mobile: 07714 158645
Pager: 07644 006721
Web: http://www.alanjohnson.org
Secretary – Mrs Jane Davies
E-mail: daviesjd@parliament.uk
Research Assistant – Ms Sally Waters
Tel: (020) 7219 1305
E-mail: waterssa@parliament.uk
*Constituency Office* . . . . Goodwin Centre, Icehouse Road,
Hull, HU3 2HQ
Tel & Fax: (01482) 219211
E-mail: windlet@parliament.uk
Assistant – Ms Tracey Windle
*Parliamentary Interests* . Employment; Industrial Relations;
Post Office; Health
*Leisure Interests* . . . . . Music; Reading; Football; Tennis; Radio 4;
Cooking

**Johnson, Boris** . . . . Henley
**Conservative** . . . . . . Majority 8,458 over Lib Dem
*Born.* . . . . . . . . . . . . . 1964
*Educated* . . . . . . . . . . Eton College; Balliol College, Oxford
*Elected.* . . . . . . . . . . . 2001 MP for Henley
*Offices Held* . . . . . . . . 2003 - 04 Vice-Chairman, Conservative Party
2004 - Opposition Spokesman on the Arts
*Commons Office* . . . . . Tel: (020) 7219 8192 Fax: (020) 7219 1885
E-mail: johnsonb@parliament.uk
*Constituency Office* . . . . 8 Gorwell, Watlington, Oxfordshire, OX9 5QE
Tel: (01491) 612852 Fax: (01491) 612001
E-mail: wloxontory@fsmail.net

**Johnson, Melanie** . . Welwyn Hatfield
**Labour** . . . . . . . . . . . Majority 1,196 over Con
*Born.* . . . . . . . . . . . . . 5th February 1955 in Ipswich
*Educated* . . . . . . . . . . Clifton High School, Bristol;
University College, London;
King's College, Cambridge
*Elected.* . . . . . . . . . . . 1997 MP for Welwyn Hatfield
*Offices Held* . . . . . . . . 1999 - 2001 Economic Secretary,
H M Treasury
2001 - 03 Parliamentary Secretary,
Department of Trade and Industry
2003 - Parliamentary Secretary, Department
of Health
*Constituency Office* . . . . 2 Queensway House, Dog Kennel Lane,
Hatfield, Hertfordshire, AL10 0LW
Tel: (01707) 262920 Fax: (01707) 262834
E-mail: melaniej@netcomuk.co.uk
Web: http://www.melaniejohnson.co.uk
Personal Assistant – Mr Chris Gillen
Secretarial Assistant – Mrs Maureen Cook
Research Assistant – Mr Mike Larkins
*Parliamentary Interests* . Education; Health; Business
*Leisure Interests* . . . . . . Family; Films; Gardening; Food

# MEMBERS OF THE HOUSE OF COMMONS

**Jones, Helen** . . . . . Warrington North
**Labour** . . . . . . . . . . Majority 15,156 over Con
*Born.* . . . . . . . . . . . . 24th December 1954 in Chester
*Educated* . . . . . . . . . Ursuline Convent, Chester;
University College London;
Liverpool University;
Manchester Metropolitan University
*Elected.* . . . . . . . . . . 1997 MP for Warrington North
*Commons Office* . . . . . Tel: (020) 7219 4048 Fax: (020) 7219 2651
E-mail: jonesh@parliament.uk
*Constituency Office* . . . . Gilbert Wakefield House, 67 Bewsey Street,
Warrington, WA2 7JP
Tel: (01925) 232480
Fax: (01925) 232234/232239
E-mail: helen.jonesmp@lineone.net
Constituency Assistant – Mr Mike Vobe
Secretary – Mrs Lynn Irving
*Parliamentary Interests*. Education; Health
*Leisure Interests* . . . . . . Cooking; Gardening; Reading


**Jones, Jon Owen** . . Cardiff Central
**Labour** . . . . . . . . . . Majority 659 over Lib Dem
*Born.* . . . . . . . . . . . . 19th April 1954 in Rhondda
*Educated* . . . . . . . . . Ysgol Gyfun Rhydyfelin;
East Anglia University;
University College of Wales, Cardiff
*Elected.* . . . . . . . . . . 1992 MP for Cardiff Central
*Offices Held* . . . . . . . . 1994 - 97 Opposition Whip
1997 - 98 Government Whip (Lord
Commissioner, H M Treasury)
1998 - 99 Parliamentary Secretary,
Welsh Office
*Commons Office* . . . . . Tel: (020) 7219 4531/6352
Fax: (020) 7219 2698
Mobile: 07860 544101
Pager: (020) 8345 6789 (879078)
Press and Research Officer – Mr Rhodri Jones
E-mail: jonesrh@parliament.uk
*Constituency Office* . . . . 199 Newport Road, Cardiff, CF24 1AJ
Tel: (029) 2063 5811 Fax: (029) 2063 5814
E-mail: jon-owen-jones@cardiff-central-
clp.new.labour.org.uk
Personal Assistants – Mrs Lynn Glaister
Mrs Allison Jones
Researcher – Mr Gerry Moreton
*Parliamentary Interests*. Further and Higher Education; Constitution;
Environmental Protection; Wales
*Leisure Interests* . . . . . . Family


**Jones, Kevan**. . . . . Durham North
**Labour** . . . . . . . . . . Majority 18,683 over Con
*Born.* . . . . . . . . . . . . 25th April 1964
*Educated* . . . . . . . . . Portland Comprehensive School;
Newcastle-upon-Tyne Polytechnic;
University of Southern Maine, USA
*Elected.* . . . . . . . . . . 2001 MP for Durham North
*Commons Office* . . . . . Tel: (020) 7219 8219 Fax: (020) 7219 1759
*Constituency Office* . . . . Co-operative Buildings, 9 Plawsworth Road,
Sacriston, Co Durham, DH7 6HJ
Tel & Fax: (0191) 371 8834
Personal Assistant – Ms Linda Graham
E-mail: grahaml@parliament.uk
*Parliamentary Interests*. Defence; Transport; Regeneration;
Employment; Local and Regional Government
*Leisure Interests* . . . . . . Golf; Reading


**Jones, Dr Lynne** . . Birmingham Selly Oak
**Labour** . . . . . . . . . . Majority 10,339 over Con
*Born.* . . . . . . . . . . . . 26th April 1951 in Birmingham
*Educated* . . . . . . . . . Bartley Green Girls' Grammar School,
Birmingham; Birmingham University;
Birmingham Polytechnic
*Elected.* . . . . . . . . . . 1992 MP for Birmingham Selly Oak
*Commons Office* . . . . . Tel: (020) 7219 4190 Fax: (020) 7219 3870
E-mail: jonesl@parliament.uk
Web: http//www.lynnejones.org.uk
Political Secretary – Ms Ingrid Davidson
E-mail: davidsoni@parliament.uk
*Constituency Office* . . . . The Cotteridge Church, 24 Pershore Road
South, Birmingham, B30 3AS
Tel & Fax: (0121) 486 2808
Senior Caseworker – Mr Matt Francis
Caseworker – Mr Danny Considine
*Parliamentary Interests*. Economy; Science; Mental Health;
Transsexual Rights; Social Security
*Leisure Interests* . . . . . . Cycling

# MEMBERS OF THE HOUSE OF COMMONS

**Jones, Martyn** . . . . . Clwyd South
**Labour** . . . . . . . . . . . Majority 8,898 over Con
*Born* . . . . . . . . . . . . . . 1st March 1947 in Cheshire
*Educated* . . . . . . . . . . Grove Park Grammar School, Wrexham;
Liverpool Polytechnic; Trent Polytechnic
*Elected* . . . . . . . . . . . . 1987 MP for Clwyd South West,
then (1997) Clwyd South
*Offices Held* . . . . . . . . 1988 - 92 Opposition Whip
1994 - 95 Opposition Spokesman on
Agriculture, Food and Rural Affairs
1997 - Chairman, Welsh Affairs Select
Committee, House of Commons
*Commons Office* . . . . . . Tel: (020) 7219 3417 Fax: (020) 7219 6090
Web: http://www.epolitix.com/webminster/
martyn-jones
Researcher – Mr Steve Jones
E-mail: jonesst@parliament.uk
Secretary – Mrs Janet Burgess
Tel: (020) 7219 4007
E-mail: burgessjd@parliament.uk
*Constituency Office* . . . . Foundry Buildings, Gutter Hill, Johnstown,
Wrexham, LL14 1LU
Tel: (01978) 845938 Fax: (01978) 843392
Constituency Assistant – Ms Stella Matthews
*Parliamentary Interests* . Agriculture; Environment; Population;
Development
*Leisure Interests* . . . . . . Sailing; Tennis; Backpacking; Target Shooting

**Jones, Nigel** . . . . . . Cheltenham
**Liberal Democrat** . . . Majority 5,255 over Con
*Born* . . . . . . . . . . . . . . 30th March 1948 in Cheltenham
*Educated* . . . . . . . . . . Prince Henry's Grammar School, Evesham
*Elected* . . . . . . . . . . . . 1992 MP for Cheltenham
*Offices Held* . . . . . . . . 1992 - 94 Liberal Democrat Spokesman on
Housing and Local Government
1994 - 99 Liberal Democrat Spokesman on
Science and Technology
1997 - 2000 Liberal Democrat Spokesman
on Sport
*Commons Office* . . . . . . Tel: (020) 7219 4415 Fax: (020) 7219 2537
Pager: 07699 724694
E-mail: nigeljonesmp@cix.co.uk
Secretary – Mrs Katy Jones
E-mail: katyjones@cix.co.uk
Web: http://www.nigeljones.org.uk
*Constituency Office* . . . . 16 Hewlett Road, Cheltenham,
Gloucestershire, GL52 6AA
Tel: (01242) 224889 Fax: (01242) 256658
*Parliamentary Interests* . Science and Technology; Sport; Third World
*Leisure Interests* . . . . . . Cricket; Football (Cheltenham FC and
Swindon Town FC); Gardening

**Jowell, Rt Hon Tessa** Dulwich and West Norwood
**Labour** . . . . . . . . . . . Majority 12,310 over Con
*Born* . . . . . . . . . . . . . . 17th September 1947 in London
*Educated* . . . . . . . . . . St Margaret's School, Aberdeen;
Aberdeen University; Edinburgh University;
London University
*Elected* . . . . . . . . . . . . 1992 MP for Dulwich, then (1997) Dulwich
and West Norwood
*Offices Held* . . . . . . . . 1994 - 95 Opposition Whip
1995 - 96 Opposition Spokesman on Women
1996 - 97 Opposition Spokesman on Health
1997 - 99 Minister of State, Department of
Health (Minister for Public Health)
1999 - 2001 Minister of State, Department for
Education and Employment
2001 - Secretary of State for Culture, Media
and Sport
*Commons Office* . . . . . Tel: (020) 7219 3409 Fax: (020) 7219 2702
E-mail: jowellt@parliament.uk
Parliamentary Assistant –
Mr Duncan Chapman
Tel: (020) 7219 2517
E-mail: chapmand@parliament.uk
*Constituency Office* . . . . Tel: (020) 8333 1372

**Joyce, Eric** . . . . . . . Falkirk West
**Labour** . . . . . . . . . . . Majority 8,532 over SNP
*Born* . . . . . . . . . . . . . . 13th October 1960 in Perth, Scotland
*Educated* . . . . . . . . . . University of Stirling; University of Bath;
University of Keele
*Elected* . . . . . . . . . . . . 2000 MP for Falkirk West (By-election)
*Office Held* . . . . . . . . . 2003 - PPS to Mike O'Brien (Minister of
State, Foreign and Commonwealth
Office and Department of Trade and
Industry)
*Commons Office* . . . . . Tel: (020) 7219 6210 Fax: (020) 7219 2090
E-mail: ericjoycemp@parliament.uk
Researcher – Ms Joanne Milligan
Tel: (020) 7219 2779
E-mail: milliganj@parliament.uk
*Constituency Office* . . . . Burnfoot Lane, Falkirk, FK1 5BH
Tel: (01324) 638919 Fax: (01324) 679449
E-mail: mcintyrem@parliament.uk
Secretary – Mrs May McIntyre
*Parliamentary Interests* . Foreign Affairs; International Development;
Defence; Economy; Work; Education; Training
*Leisure Interests* . . . . . . Climbing; Judo; Most Sports

# MEMBERS OF THE HOUSE OF COMMONS

## K

**Kaufman, Rt Hon Sir Gerald**  Manchester Gorton
**Labour** . . . . . . . . . . . Majority 11,304 over Lib Dem
*Born* . . . . . . . . . . . . . . 21st June 1930 in Leeds, Yorkshire
*Educated* . . . . . . . . . . Leeds Grammar School;
Queen's College, Oxford
*Elected* . . . . . . . . . . . . 1970 MP for Manchester Ardwick, then
(1983) Manchester Gorton
*Offices Held* . . . . . . . . 1974 - 75 Parliamentary Secretary,
Department of Environment
1975 Parliamentary Secretary,
Department of Industry
1975 - 79 Minister of State,
Department of Industry
1979 - 83 Opposition Environment Spokesman
1983 - 87 Shadow Home Secretary
1987 - 92 Shadow Foreign Secretary
1992 - 97 Chairman, National Heritage
Select Committee, House of Commons
1997 - Chairman, Culture, Media and Sport
Select Committee, House of Commons
*Commons Office* . . . . . . Tel: (020) 7219 5145 Fax: (020) 7219 6825
Secretary – Mrs Nicola Cootes
E-mail: cootesn@parliament.uk
*Constituency Office* . . . . Gorton Sports and Social Club, Ashkirk Street,
Manchester, M18 8LS
Tel & Fax: (0161) 248 0073
Personal Assistant – Mr Brian Sears
Tel & Fax: (0161) 975 0297

**Keeble, Sally** . . . . . Northampton North
**Labour** . . . . . . . . . . . Majority 7,893 over Con
*Born* . . . . . . . . . . . . . . 13th October 1951 in Berlin
*Educated* . . . . . . . . . . Cheltenham Ladies College;
Oxford University;
University of South Africa
*Elected* . . . . . . . . . . . . 1997 MP for Northampton North
*Offices Held* . . . . . . . . 1990 - 93 Leader, London Borough
of Southwark Council
2001 - 02 Parliamentary Secretary,
Department for Transport, Local
Government and the Regions
2002 - 03 Parliamentary Secretary,
Department for International Development
*Commons Office* . . . . . . Tel: (020) 7219 4039 Fax: (020) 7219 2642
E-mail: keebles@parliament.uk
*Constituency Office* . . . . Barratt House, Kingsthorpe Road,
Northampton, NN2 6EZ
Tel: (01604) 716275 Fax: (01604) 716952
Constituency Manager – Mr Martin Chown
E-mail: chownm@parliament.uk
Constituency Assistant – Ms Sherri Sargent
Staff Constituency Assistant –
Ms Catherine  Russell
E-mail: russellca@parliament.uk
*Parliamentary Interests* . Finance; Home Affairs; Education;
Food Safety
*Leisure Interests* . . . . . . Antiques; Walking; Reading

**Keen, Alan** . . . . . . . Feltham and Heston
**Labour** . . . . . . . . . . . Majority 12,657 over Con
*Born* . . . . . . . . . . . . . . 25th November 1937 in Lewisham, London
*Educated* . . . . . . . . . . Sir William Turner's School, Redcar
*Elected* . . . . . . . . . . . . 1992 MP for Feltham and Heston
*Commons Office* . . . . . Tel: (020) 7219 2819 Fax: (020) 7219 0985
Personal Assistant – Mr Tim Green
*Constituency Office* . . . . Manor Place, Feltham, Middlesex, TW14 9BT
Tel: (020) 8890 4489 Fax: (020) 8893 2606
*Parliamentary Interests* . Culture, Media and Sport;
Foreign Affairs; Defence
*Leisure Interests* . . . . . Football; Cricket; Running

**Keen, Ann** . . . . . . . Brentford and Isleworth
**Labour** . . . . . . . . . . . Majority 10,318 over Con
*Born* . . . . . . . . . . . . . . 26th November 1948
*Educated* . . . . . . . . . . Elfed Secondary Modern School, Clwyd;
Surrey University
*Elected* . . . . . . . . . . . . 1997 MP for Brentford and Isleworth
*Offices Held* . . . . . . . . 1997 - 99 PPS to Frank Dobson
(Secretary of State for Health)
2000 - PPS to Gordon Brown
(Chancellor of the Exchequer)
*Commons Office* . . . . . Tel: (020) 7219 5623 Fax: (020) 7219 2233
E-mail: annkeenmp@parliament.uk
Web: http://www.annkeenmp.org.uk
Personal Assistant – Ms Anita Ralli
Caseworker – Mr Simon Baker
*Constituency Office* . . . . 367 Chiswick High Road, London, W4 4AG
Tel: (020) 8995 7289  Fax: (020) 8742 1004
*Parliamentary Interests* . Health; Trade Unions
*Leisure Interests* . . . . . . Football (Brentford FC); Cinema; Classic Cars;
Films

**Keetch, Paul** . . . . . Hereford
**Liberal Democrat** . . . Majority 968 over Con
*Born* . . . . . . . . . . . . . . 21st May 1961 in Hereford
*Educated* . . . . . . . . . . Hereford High School and Sixth Form College
*Elected* . . . . . . . . . . . . 1997 MP for Hereford
*Offices Held* . . . . . . . . 1997 Liberal Democrat Spokesman on Health
1997 - 99 Liberal Democrat Spokesman on
Employment and Training
1999 - Liberal Democrat Spokesman
on Defence
*Commons Office* . . . . . Tel: (020) 7219 2419 Fax: (020) 7210 1184
E-mail: paulkeetch@cix.co.uk
Web: http://www.paulkeetch.libdems.org.uk
*Constituency Office* . . . . 39 Widemarsh Street, Hereford, HR4 9EA
Tel: (01432) 341483  Fax: (01432) 378111
*Parliamentary Interests* . Defence
*Leisure Interests* . . . . . . Entertaining; Swimming; Cycling; History

# MEMBERS OF THE HOUSE OF COMMONS

**Kelly, Ruth** . . . . . . Bolton West
**Labour** . . . . . . . . . . . Majority 6,518 over Con
*Born*. . . . . . . . . . . . . . 9th May 1968 in Northern Ireland
*Educated* . . . . . . . . . . Queen's College, Oxford;
London School of Economics
*Elected*. . . . . . . . . . . . 1997 MP for Bolton West
*Offices Held* . . . . . . . . 1998 - 2001 PPS to Nick Brown
(Minister for Agriculture, Fisheries
and Food)
2001 - 02 Economic Secretary,
HM Treasury
2002 - 04 Financial Secretary, HM Treasury
2004 - Minister for State, Cabinet Office
*Commons Office* . . . . . . Tel: (020) 7219 3496 Fax: (020) 7219 2211
E-mail: kellyr@parliament.uk
Web: http://www.ruthkelly.labour.co.uk
Researcher – Mr George McNamara
E-mail: mcnamarag@parliament.uk
*Constituency Office* . . . . Studio 4, Horwich Business Centre,
86 Lee Lane, Horwich, Bolton, BL6 7AE
Tel: (01204) 693351 Fax: (01204) 693383
Office Manager – Mr Keith Bowes
*Parliamentary Interests* . Economy; Social Security; Family Policy


**Kemp, Fraser** . . . . . Houghton and Washington East
**Labour** . . . . . . . . . . . Majority 19,818 over Con
*Born*. . . . . . . . . . . . . . 1st September 1958 in Washington,
Co Durham
*Educated* . . . . . . . . . . Washington Comprehensive School
*Elected*. . . . . . . . . . . . 1997 MP for Houghton and Washington East
*Offices Held* . . . . . . . . 1997 - 99 Chairman, Administration Select
Committee, House of Commons
1997 - 99 Chairman, Committee of Selection,
House of Commons
2001 - Assistant Government Whip
*Commons Office* . . . . . . Tel: (020) 7219 5181 Fax: (020) 7219 2536
Mobile: 07774 737116
Pager: 07644 005720
*Constituency Office* . . . . 14 Nesham Place, Houghton-le-Spring,
Tyne and Wear, DH5 8AG
Tel: (0191) 584 9266 Fax: (0191) 584 8329
Personal Assistant – Mrs Patricia Elliott
Clerical Assistant – Cllr Denis Whalen
*Parliamentary Interests* . Regional Economy; Gas Safety; Australasia;
Regeneration of Former Mining Areas
*Leisure Interests* . . . . . . People

**Kennedy, Rt Hon Charles**  Ross, Skye and Inverness West
**Liberal Democrat** . . . Majority 12,952 over Lab
*Born*. . . . . . . . . . . . . . 25th November 1959 in Inverness
*Educated* . . . . . . . . . . Lochaber High School, Fort William;
Glasgow University; Indiana University, USA
*Elected*. . . . . . . . . . . . 1983 MP for Ross, Cromarty and Skye
then (1997) for Ross, Skye and
Inverness West
*Offices Held* . . . . . . . . 1983 - 87 SDP Spokesman on Health and
Social Security, Scotland
1986 - 88 SDP Scottish Spokesman
1988 - 89 Liberal Democrat Spokesman on
Trade and Industry
1989 - 92 Liberal Democrat Spokesman on
Health
1990 - 94 Liberal Democrat Party President
1992 - 97 Liberal Democrat Spokesman on
Europe
1997 - 99 Liberal Democrat Spokesman on
Agriculture, Fisheries, Food and
Rural Affairs
1999 - Leader, Liberal Democrats
*Commons Office* . . . . . . Tel: (020) 7219 6226 Fax: (020) 7219 4881
E-mail: charleskennedy@cix.co.uk
Web: http://www.charleskennedy.org
Head of Office – Ms Anna Werrin
Tel: (020) 7219 5090
E-mail: werrina@parliament.uk
Deputy Press Secretary – Mr Olly Kendall
Tel: (020) 7219 5039
Official Spokesperson – Ms Jackie Rowley
Tel: (020) 7219 6695
E-mail: rowleyj@parliament.uk
*Constituency Office* . . . . 1a Montague Row, Inverness, IV3 5DX
Tel: (01463) 714377 Fax: (01463) 714380
Constituency Assistants – Mr Daniel Farthing
Ms Shanea Fraser


**Kennedy, Rt Hon Jane**  Liverpool Wavertree
**Labour** . . . . . . . . . . . Majority 12,319 over Lib Dem
*Born*. . . . . . . . . . . . . . 4th May 1958 in Whitehaven, Cumbria
*Educated* . . . . . . . . . . Haughton Comprehensive School;
Queen Elizabeth Sixth Form College,
Darlington; Liverpool University
*Elected*. . . . . . . . . . . . 1992 MP for Liverpool Broad Green, then
(1997) for Liverpool Wavertree
*Offices Held* . . . . . . . . 1995 - 97 Opposition Whip
1997 - 98 Assistant Government Whip
1998 - 99 Government Whip
(Lord Commissioner, HM Treasury)
1999 - 2001 Parliamentary Secretary, Lord
Chancellor's Department
2001 - 04 Minister of State, Northern Ireland
Office
2004 - Minister of State, Department for
Work and Pensions
*Constituency Office* . . . . Threlfall Building, Trueman Street,
Liverpool, L3 2EX
Tel: (0151) 236 1117 Fax: (0151) 236 0067
E-mail: kennedyj@parliament.uk
Personal Assistant – Ms Jean Stapleton
E-mail: stapletonj@parliament.uk
Parliamentary Assistant – Mr Peter Dowling
Office Assistant – Ms Julie Brumby
*Parliamentary Interests* . Public Services; Home Affairs;
Local Government; Employment;
Economic Development
*Leisure Interests* . . . . . . Dogs; Walking; Riding

# M E M B E R S   O F   T H E   H O U S E   O F   C O M M O N S

**Key, Robert** . . . . . . Salisbury
**Conservative** . . . . . . . Majority 8,703 over Lib Dem
*Born*. . . . . . . . . . . . . 22nd April 1945 in Plymouth, Devon
*Educated* . . . . . . . . . . Salisbury Cathedral School; Sherborne School;
    Clare College, Cambridge
*Elected*. . . . . . . . . . . . 1983 MP for Salisbury
*Offices Held* . . . . . . . . 1990 - 92 Parliamentary Secretary,
    Department of Environment
    1992 - 93 Parliamentary Secretary,
    Department National Heritage
    1993 - 94 Parliamentary Secretary,
    Department of Transport
    1997 - 2001 Opposition Spokesman on
    Defence
    2001 - 02 Opposition Spokesman on
    Trade and Industry
    2002 - 03 Opposition Spokesman for
    International Development
    2004 - Chairman, Information Committee,
    House of Commons
*Constituency Office* . . . . 12 Brown Street, Salisbury, SP1 1HE
    Tel: (01722) 323050 Fax: (01722) 327080
    E-mail: rob@robertkey.com
    Web: http://www.robertkey.com
    Private Secretary – Mrs Sarah Axton
    Local Researcher – Mrs Susie Whalley
*Parliamentary Interests* . Defence; Agriculture; Culture; Tourism
*Leisure Interests* . . . . . Singing; Cooking; Countryside


**Khabra, Piara Singh**   Ealing Southall
**Labour** . . . . . . . . . . . Majority 13,683 over Con
*Born*. . . . . . . . . . . . . 20th November 1924 in Punjab, India
*Educated* . . . . . . . . . . Punjab University
*Elected*. . . . . . . . . . . . 1992 MP for Ealing Southall
*Commons Office* . . . . . Tel: (020) 7219 5010 Fax: (020) 7219 5699
    Mobile: 07754 666544
    Pager: 07626 605772
    Secretary – Ms Beulah Khabra
    Tel: (020) 7219 6429
    Researcher – Mr Jason Miks
    Tel: (020) 7219 5918
    E-mail: miksj@parliament.uk
*Constituency Office* . . . . Ruskin Hall, Church Road, London, W3 8PP
    Tel: (020) 8992 5614 Fax: (020) 8752 1200
    Agent – Mr Yoel Gordon
    Tel: (020) 8357 0389
*Parliamentary Interests* . Health; Foreign Affairs;
    International Development
*Leisure Interests* . . . . . Watching Nature Programmes and
    Documentaries


**Kidney, David** . . . . Stafford
**Labour** . . . . . . . . . . . Majority 5,032 over Con
*Born*. . . . . . . . . . . . . 21st March 1955 in Stoke-on-Trent
*Educated* . . . . . . . . . . Longton High School; Bristol University
*Elected*. . . . . . . . . . . . 1997 MP for Stafford
*Commons Office* . . . . . Tel: (020) 7219 6472 Fax: (020) 7219 0919
    Mobile: 07966 378844
    E-mail: kidneyd@parliament.uk
    Web: http://www.davidkidney.labour.co.uk
    Personal Assistant/Secretary –
    Mrs Mary Hardy
    E-mail: hardym@parliament.uk
*Constituency Office* . . . . Labour Rooms, Meyrick Road, Stafford,
    ST17 4DG
    Tel: (01785) 224444 Fax: (01785) 250357
    Organiser – Mrs Debbie Wakefield
    Assistant Organiser – Ms Shelley Davis
*Parliamentary Interests* . Children; Economy; Environment; Housing
*Leisure Interests* . . . . . Bridge; Chess


**Kilfoyle, Peter** . . . . Liverpool Walton
**Labour** . . . . . . . . . . . Majority 17,996 over Lib Dem
*Born*. . . . . . . . . . . . . 9th June 1946 in Liverpool
*Educated* . . . . . . . . . . St Edward's College, Liverpool;
    Durham University; Christ's College, Liverpool
*Elected*. . . . . . . . . . . . 1991 MP for Liverpool Walton (By-election)
*Offices Held* . . . . . . . . 1992 - 94 Opposition Whip
    1994 - 97 Opposition Spokesman on
    Education
    1997 - 99 Parliamentary Secretary,
    Cabinet Office
    1999 - 2000 Parliamentary Secretary,
    Ministry of Defence
*Commons Office* . . . . . Tel: (020) 7219 2591 Fax: (020) 7219 2356
    E-mail: kilfoylep@parliament.uk
*Constituency Office* . . . . 69-71 County Road, Walton,
    Liverpool, L4 3QD
    Tel & Fax: (0151) 284 4150
    E-mail: info@peterkilfoyle.com
    Secretary – Ms Maureen Byrne
    Parliamentary Assistant – Mr Gary Booth
    E-mail: bothg@parliament.uk
*Parliamentary Interests* . Foreign Affairs; Education; Employment
*Leisure Interests* . . . . . Sport; Reading; Music


**King, Andy** . . . . . . Rugby and Kenilworth
**Labour** . . . . . . . . . . . Majority 2,877 over Con
*Born*. . . . . . . . . . . . . 14th September 1948 in Bellshill
*Educated* . . . . . . . . . . Coatbridge Technical College;
    Missionary Institute, London;
    Hatfield Polytechnic; Stevenage College;
    Nene College
*Elected*. . . . . . . . . . . . 1997 MP for Rugby and Kenilworth
*Commons Office* . . . . . Tel: (020) 7219 1386 Fax: (020) 7219 5855
    E-mail: kinga@parliament.uk
    Web: http://www.andyking.org
    Researcher – Mr Nick Parrott
    E-mail: parrottn@parliament.uk
*Constituency Office* . . . . 12 Regent Place, Rugby, CV21 2PN
    Tel: (01788) 575504 Fax: (01788) 575506
    Personal Assistant – Ms Claire Edwards
    E-mail: edwardsc@parliament.uk
    Research Assistant – Miss Katherine King
    E-mail: kingk@parliament.uk
*Parliamentary Interests* . Health; Social Services; Law and Order
*Leisure Interests* . . . . . Golf; Dominoes; Theatre; Football

# MEMBERS OF THE HOUSE OF COMMONS

**King, Oona** . . . . . . . Bethnal Green and Bow
**Labour** . . . . . . . . . . . Majority 10,057 over Con
*Born.* . . . . . . . . . . . . . . 22nd October 1967 in Sheffield
*Educated* . . . . . . . . . . Haverstock Comprehensive; York University;
    University of California
*Elected.* . . . . . . . . . . . 1997 MP for Bethnal Green and Bow
*Office Held.* . . . . . . . . 2003 - PPS to Patricia Hewitt, Secretary of
    State for Trade and Industry)
*Commons Office* . . . . . Tel: (020) 7219 5020 Fax: (020) 7219 2798
    E-mail: kingot@parliament.uk
    Web: http://www.oonaking.com
    Parliamentary Secretary – Ms Rohema Miah
    E-mail: miahr@parliament.uk
*Constituency Office* . . . . Tel: (020) 7613 2274 Fax: (020) 7613 2014
    Constituency Assistants –
    Mr Kester Dean
    Mr Lesley Rogers
    Ms Frances Simmons
*Parliamentary Interests* . International Development; Immigration;
    Housing; Employment; Europe; Childcare;
    Race Relations; Electoral Reform;
    Equal Opportunities
*Leisure Interests* . . . . . Sport; Languages; Music; Cinema

**Kirkbride, Julie** . . . Bromsgrove
**Conservative** . . . . . . Majority 8,138 over Lab
*Born.* . . . . . . . . . . . . . 5th June 1960 in Halifax
*Educated* . . . . . . . . . . Highlands School. Halifax;
    Girton College, Cambridge
*Elected.* . . . . . . . . . . . 1997 MP for Bromsgrove
*Office Held.* . . . . . . . . 2003 - Shadow Secretary for Culture,
    Media and Sport
*Commons Office* . . . . . Tel: (020) 7219 1101 Fax: (020) 7219 0990
    Mobile: 07710 316862
    Assistant – Ms Danielle Johnston-Jones
    E-mail: johnstonjonesd@parliament.uk
*Constituency Office* . . . . 37 Worcester Road, Bromsgrove, B61 7DN
    Tel: (01527) 872135 Fax: (01527) 575015
    Organising Secretary – Cllr Rita Dent
    Tel: (01527) 835635 Fax: (01527) 575019
*Parliamentary Interests* . Europe; Tax; Social Security; Health
*Leisure Interests* . . . . . . Opera; Walking

**Kirkwood, Sir Archy**  Roxburgh and Berwickshire
**Liberal Democrat** . . . Majority 7,511 over Con
*Born.* . . . . . . . . . . . . . . 22nd April 1946 in Glasgow
*Educated* . . . . . . . . . . Cranhill School; Heriot Watt University
*Elected.* . . . . . . . . . . . 1983 MP for Roxburgh and Berwickshire
*Offices Held* . . . . . . . . 1985 - 87 Liberal Spokesman on Health,
    Social Services and Social Security
    1987 Alliance Spokesman on
    Overseas Development
    1987 - 88 Liberal Scottish Whip
    1989 - 92 Liberal Democrat Deputy Chief
    Whip
    1989 - 94 Liberal Democrat Spokesman on
    Social Security
    1992 - 94 Liberal Democrat Chief Whip
    1994 - 97 Liberal Democrat Spokesman on
    Community Care
    1997 - 2001 Chairman, Social Security Select
    Committee, House of Commons
    2001 - Chairman, Work and Pensions Select
    Committee, House of Commons
*Commons Office* . . . . . Tel: (020) 7219 6253 Fax: (020) 7219 6430
    E-mail: kirkwooda@parliament.uk
    Web: http://www.archykirkwood.co.uk
*Parliamentary Interests* . Freedom of Information; Health;
    Social Security
*Leisure Interests* . . . . . Music; Photography; Horse Riding; Skiing

**Knight, Rt Hon Greg**  Yorkshire East
**Conservative** . . . . . . Majority 4,682 over Lab
*Born.* . . . . . . . . . . . . . 4th April 1949 in Leicester
*Educated* . . . . . . . . . . Alderman Newton's Grammar School;
    Guildford College of Law
*Elected.* . . . . . . . . . . . 1983 - 97 MP for Derby North
    2001 - MP Yorkshire East
*Offices Held* . . . . . . . . 1989 - 90 Assistant Government Whip
    1990 - 93 Government Whip
    (Lord Commissioner, H M Treasury)
    1993 - 96 Deputy Government Chief Whip
    (Treasurer, H M Household)
    1996 - 97 Minister of State for Industry,
    Department of Trade and Industry
    2001 - 03 Shadow Deputy Leader of the
    House of Commons
    2003 - 04 Opposition Spokesman on Culture,
    Media and Sport
    2004 - Opposition Spokesman on
    Environment and Transport
*Commons Office* . . . . . Tel: (020) 7219 8417
    Web: http://www.gregknight.com
    Secretary – Mrs Teresa Sothcott
    Tel: (0845) 090 0203
    E-mail: secretary@gregknight.com
*Parliamentary Interests* . Home Affairs; Trade and Industry;
    Transport Issues
*Leisure Interests* . . . . . The Arts; Classic Cars

# MEMBERS OF THE HOUSE OF COMMONS

**Knight, Jim** . . . . . . . Dorset South
**Labour** . . . . . . . . . . Majority 153 over Con
*Born*. . . . . . . . . . . . . . 6th March 1965 in Bexley, Kent
*Educated* . . . . . . . . . . Eltham College; Cambridge University
*Elected*. . . . . . . . . . . . 2001 MP for Dorset South
*Office Held*. . . . . . . . . 1999 - 2000 Deputy Leader, Mendip
    District Council
*Commons Office* . . . . . Tel: (020) 7219 8466 Fax: (020) 7219 1976
*Constituency Office* . . . . A32 Winfrith Technology Centre,
    Winfrith Newburgh, Dorchester, DT2 8DH
    Tel: (01305) 853408 Fax: (01305) 854643
    Caseworker – Mrs Rachel Rogers
    Secretary – Mrs Lena Huskinson
    E-mail: huskinsonl@parliament.uk
*Parliamentary Interests*. Defence; International Development; Health;
    Culture; Sport
*Leisure Interests* . . . . . Football; Literature; Cooking

**Kumar, Dr Ashok** . Middlesbrough South and East Cleveland
**Labour** . . . . . . . . . . Majority 9,351 over Con
*Born*. . . . . . . . . . . . . . 28th May 1956 in India
*Educated* . . . . . . . . . . Rykneld School for Boys, Derby;
    Aston University
*Elected*. . . . . . . . . . . . 1997 MP for Middlesbrough South and
    East Cleveland
*Office Held*. . . . . . . . . 2003 - PPS to Hilary Benn (Secretary of State
    for International Development)
*Constituency Office* . . . . 6-8 Wilson Street, Guisborough, TS14 6NA
    Tel: (01287) 610878 Fax: (01287) 631894
    E-mail: ashokkumarmp@parliament.uk
    Personal Assistant – Mrs Carole Milward
    Research Assistants – Mr Tom Blenkinsop
    Mr David Walsh
*Parliamentary Interests*. Science; Trade and Industry; Economy;
    Further and Higher Education
*Leisure Interests* . . . . . Cricket; Jazz; Badminton;
    Reading History and Philosophy

# L

**Ladyman, Dr Stephen** Thanet South
**Labour** . . . . . . . . . . Majority 1,792 over Con
*Born*. . . . . . . . . . . . . . 6th November 1952 in Lancashire
*Educated* . . . . . . . . . . Birkenhead Institute; Liverpool Polytechnic;
    Strathclyde University
*Elected*. . . . . . . . . . . . 1997 MP for Thanet South
*Office Held*. . . . . . . . . 2003 - Parliamentary Secretary,
    Department of Health
*Commons Office* . . . . . Tel: (020) 7219 4892 Fax: (020) 7219 1133
    E-mail: ladymans@parliament.uk
*Constituency Office* . . . . 28 Newington Road, Ramsgate,
    Kent, CT12 6EE
    Tel: (01843) 852696 Fax: (01843) 852689
    Office Manager – Mrs Janet Ladyman
    Parliamentary Assistant – Ms Laura Higgs
    Office Administrator – Ms Vicki Holden
*Parliamentary Interests*. Science and Technology; Trade and Industry;
    Medicine/Pharmaceutical Industry; IT;
    Environment; Agriculture; Autism; Defence
*Leisure Interests* . . . . . Soccer; Golf; House Renovation

**Laing, Eleanor** . . . . Epping Forest
**Conservative** . . . . . . Majority 8,426 over Lab
*Born*. . . . . . . . . . . . . . 1st February 1958 in Paisley
*Educated* . . . . . . . . . . St Columba's School, Kilmalcolm,
    Renfrewshire; Edinburgh University
*Elected*. . . . . . . . . . . . 1997 MP for Epping Forest
*Offices Held* . . . . . . . . 1999 - 2000 Opposition Whip
    2000 - 01 Opposition Spokesman on
    Constitutional Affairs
    2001 - 03 Opposition Spokesman on
    Education and Skills
    2003 - Opposition Spokesman on
    Women's Issues
*Commons Office* . . . . . Tel: (020) 7219 2086 Fax: (020) 7219 0980
    E-mail: lainge@parliament.uk
    Private Secretary – Mrs Iona Bensusan
    E-mail: bensusani@parliament.uk
*Constituency Office* . . . . Thatcher House, 4 Meadow Road, Loughton,
    Essex, IG10 4HX
    Tel: (020) 8508) 6608 Fax: (020) 8508 8099
    Assistant – Mrs Beverly Groves
*Parliamentary Interests*. Constitution; Transport; Education; Economy
*Leisure Interests* . . . . . Travel; Theatre; Golf; Agatha Christie Society

**Lait, Jacqui** . . . . . . . Beckenham
**Conservative** . . . . . . Majority 4,959 over Lab
*Born*. . . . . . . . . . . . . . 16th December 1947 in Glasgow
*Educated* . . . . . . . . . . Paisley Grammar School;
    Strathclyde University
*Elected*. . . . . . . . . . . . 1992 - 97 MP for Hastings and Rye
    1997 MP for Beckenham (By-election)
*Offices Held* . . . . . . . . 1996 - 97 Assistant Government Whip
    1999 - 2000 Opposition Whip
    2000 - 01 Opposition Spokesman on Social
    Security
    2001 - 03 Shadow Secretary of State for
    Scotland
    2003 - Opposition Spokesman on Home,
    Constitutional and Legal Affairs
*Commons Office* . . . . . Tel: (020) 7219 1375 Fax: (020) 7219 0141
    E-mail: jacquilaitmp@parliament.uk
    Web: http://www.jacquilaitmp.com
    Office Manager – Mrs Rebekah Gilbert-Dyson
    E-mail: gilbertr@parliament.uk
*Constituency Office* . . . . 31 Beckenham Road, Beckenham, BR3 4PR
    Tel: (020) 8650 1944 Fax: (020) 8658 0099
    E-mail: office@beckenhamconservatives.org
    Caseworker – Mrs Mary Knight
    Tel: (020) 8663 1425 Fax: (020) 8663 1483
*Leisure Interests* . . . . . Walking; Food and Wine; Tapestry

# MEMBERS OF THE HOUSE OF COMMONS

**Lamb, Norman**.... Norfolk North
**Liberal Democrat** ... Majority 483 over Con
*Born*............. 16th September 1957 in Watford
*Educated* .......... Wymondham College, Norfolk;
　　　　　　　　　Leicester University;
　　　　　　　　　City of London Polytechnic
*Elected*............ 2001 MP for Norfolk North
*Offices Held* ........ 2002 - Liberal Democrat Spokesman on
　　　　　　　　　Treasury Matters
　　　　　　　　　2003 - PPS to Charles Kennedy (Leader,
　　　　　　　　　Liberal Democrats)
*Commons Office* ...... Tel: (020) 7219 8480 Fax: (020) 7219 1963
　　　　　　　　　Mobile: 07770 571697
　　　　　　　　　E-mail: normanlamb@hotmail.com
　　　　　　　　　Web: http://www.normanlamb.com
　　　　　　　　　Researcher – Ms Natasha Kirwan
　　　　　　　　　Tel: (020) 7219 4542
　　　　　　　　　E-mail: kirwann@parliament.uk
*Constituency Office* .... 15 Market Place, North Walsham,
　　　　　　　　　Norfolk, NR28 9BP
　　　　　　　　　Tel: (01692) 403752 Fax: (01692) 500818
　　　　　　　　　Personal Assistant – Mrs Barbara McGoun
　　　　　　　　　Case Workers – Mrs Alex Howe
　　　　　　　　　　　　　　Mrs Sian Pearce
*Parliamentary Interests* . Environment; Employment Policy;
　　　　　　　　　Health Service; Constitutional Issues;
　　　　　　　　　International Development; The Economy
*Leisure Interests* ...... Art; Football (Norwich FC)

**Lammy, David**.... Tottenham
**Labour** ........... Majority 16,916 over Con
*Born*.............. 19th July 1972
*Educated* .......... The King's School, Peterborough
*Elected*............ 2000 MP for Tottenham (By-election)
*Offices Held* ........ 2000 Member, London Assembly
　　　　　　　　　2001 - 02 PPS to Estelle Morris
　　　　　　　　　(Secretary of State for Education and Skills)
　　　　　　　　　2002 - 03 Parliamentary Secretary,
　　　　　　　　　Department of Health
　　　　　　　　　2003 - Parliamentary Secretary,
　　　　　　　　　Department for Constitutional Affairs
*Commons Office* ...... Tel: (020) 7219 0767 Fax: (020) 7219 0357
　　　　　　　　　Web: http://www.davidlammy.co.uk
　　　　　　　　　Research Assistant – Mr Aaron Kliner
　　　　　　　　　Caseworkers – Mr Mark Dronfield
　　　　　　　　　　　　　　Ms Jennifer McClafferty
*Parliamentary Interests* . Arts and Culture; Education; Health;
　　　　　　　　　International Development; Recreation
*Leisure Interests* ...... Films; Football (Tottenham Hotspur FC);
　　　　　　　　　Live Music

**Lansley, Andrew** CBE Cambridgeshire South
**Conservative** ...... Majority 8,403 over Lib Dem
*Born*.............. 11th December 1956 in Essex
*Educated* .......... Brentwood School, Essex; Exeter University
*Elected*............ 1997 MP for Cambridgeshire South
*Offices Held* ........ 1998 - 99 Vice-Chairman, Conservative Party
　　　　　　　　　1999 - 2001 Shadow Minister for the
　　　　　　　　　Cabinet Office
　　　　　　　　　2003 - Shadow Secretary for Health
*Commons Office* ..... Tel: (020) 7219 2538 Fax: (020) 7219 6835
　　　　　　　　　E-mail: lansleya@parliament.uk
　　　　　　　　　Web: http://www.andrewlansley.co.uk
　　　　　　　　　Personal Assistant – Miss Olwen Leeland
　　　　　　　　　E-mail: leelando@parliament.uk
*Constituency Office* .... 153 St Neots Road, Hardwick,
　　　　　　　　　Cambridge, CB3 7QJ
　　　　　　　　　Tel & Fax: (01954) 211444
　　　　　　　　　Agent – Mr Stephen Frost
　　　　　　　　　Constituency Secretary – Mrs Mary Flinders
　　　　　　　　　Tel: (01954) 212 7077
　　　　　　　　　Fax: (01954) 212 1625
*Parliamentary Interests* . Health; Industry; Economic Policy;
　　　　　　　　　Local Government; Transport
*Leisure Interests* ...... Biography; Film; History; Travel

**Lawrence, Jackie**.. Preseli Pembrokeshire
**Labour** ........... Majority 2,946 over Con
*Born*.............. 9th August 1948
*Educated* .......... Upperthorpe School and College, Darlington;
　　　　　　　　　Open University
*Elected*............ 1997 MP for Preseli Pembrokeshire
*Office Held* ......... 2003 - PPS to Department of Trade and
　　　　　　　　　Industry Ministers
*Commons Office* ..... Tel: (020) 7219 2757 Fax: (020) 7219 0206
　　　　　　　　　Pager: 07644 007540
　　　　　　　　　E-mail: hcinfo@parliament.uk
　　　　　　　　　Research Assistant – Mr Craig MacDonald
*Constituency Office* .... Suite 9, Milford Marina,
　　　　　　　　　Milford Haven, Pembrokeshire
　　　　　　　　　Tel: (01646) 697969 Fax: (01646) 698830
　　　　　　　　　Caseworkers – Ms Amy Lawrence
　　　　　　　　　　　　　　Ms Beverley Malone
*Parliamentary Interests* . Rural Economy; Environment;
　　　　　　　　　Small Businesses
*Leisure Interests* ...... Walking; Skiing; Photography

**Laws, David**....... Yeovil
**Liberal Democrat** ... Majority 3,928 over Con
*Born*.............. 30th November 1965 in Farnham, Surrey
*Educated* .......... St George's College, Weybridge;
　　　　　　　　　King's College, Cambridge
*Elected*............ 2001 MP for Yeovil
*Offices Held* ........ 2001 - 02 Liberal Democrat Spokesman
　　　　　　　　　on Defence
　　　　　　　　　2002 - Liberal Democrat Spokesman on
　　　　　　　　　Treasury Matters (Shadow Chief Secretary)
*Commons Office* ...... Tel: (020) 7219 8413 Fax: (020) 7219 8188
　　　　　　　　　E-mail: lawsd@parliament.uk
　　　　　　　　　Web: http://www.davidlaws.org.uk
　　　　　　　　　Researcher – Mr Matthew Sheldon
　　　　　　　　　E-mail: sheldonm@parliament.uk
*Constituency Office* .... 94 Middle Street, Yeovil, Somerset, BA20 1LT
　　　　　　　　　Tel: (01935) 423284/425025
　　　　　　　　　Fax: (01935) 433652
　　　　　　　　　E-mail: yeovilld@cix.co.uk
　　　　　　　　　Office Manager – Mrs Sue Weeks
　　　　　　　　　Secretaries – Mrs Sarah Frapple
　　　　　　　　　　　　　　Mrs Claire Margetts
*Parliamentary Interests* . Economic Policy; Education; Pensions
*Leisure Interests* ...... Running; Rugby; Travel

# MEMBERS OF THE HOUSE OF COMMONS

**Laxton, Bob** . . . . . . Derby North
**Labour** . . . . . . . . . . Majority 6,982 over Con
*Born*. . . . . . . . . . . . . 7th October 1944
*Educated* . . . . . . . . . Allestree Woodlands School;
Derby College of Art and Technology
*Elected*. . . . . . . . . . . 1997 MP for Derby North
*Offices Held* . . . . . . . . 1986 - 88, 1994 - 97 Leader, Derby City
Council
2001 - PPS to Alan Johnson (as Minister of
State, Department of Trade and Industry,
then at Department for Education and
Skills and from 2004 Secretary for
Work and Pensions)
*Commons Office* . . . . . Tel: (020) 7219 4096 Fax: (020) 7219 2329
E-mail: laxtonb@parliament.uk
Web: http://www.boblaxton.org.uk
Researcher – Miss Prema Gurunathan
E-mail: gurunathanp@parliament.uk
*Constituency Office* . . . . 1st Floor, Abbots Hill Chambers,
Gower Street, Derby, DE1 1SD
Tel: (01332) 206699 Fax: (01332) 206444
Secretary – Mrs Margot Keats
Office Manager – Mrs Gail Laxton
*Parliamentary Interests* . Trade and Industry; Education
*Leisure Interests* . . . . . . Walking

**Lazarowicz, Mark** . Edinburgh North and Leith
**Labour** . . . . . . . . . . . Majority 8,817 over Lib Dem
*Born*. . . . . . . . . . . . . . 8th August 1953
*Educated* . . . . . . . . . . St Andrews University; Edinburgh University
*Elected*. . . . . . . . . . . . 2001 MP for Edinburgh North and Leith
*Office Held* . . . . . . . . . 1986 - 93 Leader, Edinburgh City Council
*Commons Office* . . . . . Tel: (020) 7219 8199 Fax: (020) 7219 1761
E-mail: mlazarowicz@email.labour.org.uk
Web: http://www.marklazarowicz.labour.co.uk
Researcher – Mr Gary Calder
Tel: (020) 7219 8222
E-mail: calderg@parliament.uk
*Constituency Office* . . . . 86-88 Brunswick Street, Edinburgh,
EH7 5HU
Tel: (0131) 557 0577 Fax: (0131) 557 5759
Office Manager – Ms Karen Doran
Constituency Assistant – Ms Helen Gandy
*Parliamentary Interests* . Environment; Transport;
Constitutional Reform; Finance and Economy;
Consumer Affairs

**Leigh, Edward** . . . . Gainsborough
**Conservative** . . . . . . . Majority 8,071 over Lab
*Born*. . . . . . . . . . . . . . 20th July 1950 in London
*Educated* . . . . . . . . . . Oratory School, Berkshire;
French Lycee, London; Durham University
*Elected*. . . . . . . . . . . . 1983 MP for Gainsborough and
Horncastle, then (1997) Gainsborough
*Offices Held* . . . . . . . . 1990 - 93 Parliamentary Secretary,
Department of Trade and Industry
2001 - Chairman, Public Accounts Committee,
House of Commons
*Commons Office* . . . . . Tel: (020) 7219 6480 Fax: (020) 7219 4883
E-mail: leighe@parliament.uk
*Constituency Office* . . . . 23 Queen Street, Market Rasen, Lincolnshire,
LN8 3EN
Tel: (01673) 844501 Fax: (01673) 844501
E-mail: gcca@lineone.net
Agent – Mr Martin Vickers
*Parliamentary Interests* . Social Security; Third World;
Development; Moral and Ethical Issues
*Leisure Interests* . . . . . Family; Walking; Music; Reading

**Lepper, David** . . . . Brighton Pavilion
**Labour** . . . . . . . . . . Majority 9,643 over Con
*Born*. . . . . . . . . . . . . 15th September 1945 in Surrey
*Educated* . . . . . . . . . . Gainsborough Road Secondary School,
Richmond;
Wimbledon County Secondary School;
University of Kent; Sussex University;
Polytechnic of Central London
*Elected*. . . . . . . . . . . 1997 MP for Brighton Pavilion
*Offices Held* . . . . . . . . Leader (1986 - 87), Deputy Leader
(1987 - 92) and Mayor (1993 - 94),
Brighton Borough Council
2001 - Chairman, Broadcasting Committee,
House of Commons
*Commons Office* . . . . . Tel: (020) 7219 4421 Fax: (020) 7219 5814
Secretary/Research Assistant –
Mrs Irene Rochester
*Constituency Office* . . . . John Saunders House, 179 Preston Road,
Brighton, BN1 6AG
Tel: (01273) 551532 Fax: (01273) 550617
Office Manager – Mrs Margaret Davis-Brown
Secretary – Mrs Phylis Shippam
*Parliamentary Interests* . Media; Culture; Environment; Town Centre
Regeneration; Leasehold Reform; Cyprus;
English Language Schools
*Leisure Interests* . . . . . . Cinema; Cycling; Visual Arts; Music; Travel

**Leslie, Christopher** Shipley
**Labour** . . . . . . . . . . . Majority 1,428 over Con
*Born*. . . . . . . . . . . . . . 28th June 1972 in Keighley, Yorkshire
*Educated* . . . . . . . . . . Bingley Grammar School; Leeds University
*Elected*. . . . . . . . . . . . 1997 MP for Shipley
*Offices Held* . . . . . . . . 2001 - 02 Parliamentary Secretary,
Cabinet Office
2002 - 03 Parliamentary Secretary,
Office of the Deputy Prime Minister
2003 - Parliamentary Secretary, Department
for Constitutional Affairs
*Constituency Office* . . . . 33 Saltaire Road, Shipley, West Yorkshire,
BD18 3HH
Tel: (01274) 401300 Fax: (01274) 401313
E-mail: lesliec@parliament.uk
Web: http://www.chrisleslie.com
Office Manager – Ms Ann Martin
Research Assistant – Mr Martin Bell
Political Support Officer – Mr Frank Needham
Tel: (01274) 401333
*Parliamentary Interests* . Economic and Industrial Policy;
Environmental Issues; Local Government
*Leisure Interests* . . . . . . Tennis; Film; Art; Travel

# MEMBERS OF THE HOUSE OF COMMONS

**Letwin, Rt Hon Oliver** Dorset West
**Conservative** . . . . . . Majority 1,414 over Lib Dem
*Born* . . . . . . . . . . . . . 19th May 1956
*Educated* . . . . . . . . . . Trinity College, Cambridge
*Elected* . . . . . . . . . . . 1997 MP for Dorset West
*Offices Held* . . . . . . . . 1998 - 99 Opposition Spokesman on
        Constitutional Affairs
        1999 - 2000 Shadow Financial Secretary to
        the Treasury
        2000 - 01 Shadow Chief Secretary to the
        Treasury
        2001 - 03 Shadow Home Secretary
        2003 - Shadow Chancellor of the Exchequer
*Commons Office* . . . . . . Tel: (020) 7219 4192 Fax: (020) 7219 4405
        Chief of Staff – Mr Robert Halfon
        Tel: (020) 7219 5823
        E-mail: halfonr@parliament.uk
*Constituency Office* . . . . Chapel House, Dorchester Road,
        Maiden Newton, Dorset, DT2 0BG
        Tel: (01300) 321188 Fax: (01300) 321233
        Parliamentary Secretary – Mrs Angela Charles
        Tel & Fax: (01308) 456891

**Levitt, Tom** . . . . . . High Peak
**Labour** . . . . . . . . . . . Majority 4,489 over Con
*Born* . . . . . . . . . . . . . 10th April 1954 in Crewe
*Educated* . . . . . . . . . . Westwood High School, Leek;
        Lancaster University; Oxford University
*Elected* . . . . . . . . . . . 1997 MP for High Peak
*Offices Held* . . . . . . . . 1999 - 03 PPS to Barbara Roche
        (successively Minister of State, Home
        Office, Cabinet Office and Office of the
        Deputy Prime Minister)
        2003 - PPS to Baroness Amos (Secretary of
        State for International Development
        and Leader of the House of Lords)
        2003 - PPS to Hilary Benn (Secretary of
        State for International Development)
*Commons Office* . . . . . . Tel: (020) 7219 6599 Fax: (020) 7219 0935
        Pager: 07644 004889
        E-mail: tomlevittmp@parliament.uk
        Web: http://www.tomlevitt.org.uk
        Assistants – Ms Helen Berresford
                Mrs Teresa Levitt
        Tel: (020) 7219 1344
*Constituency Office* . . . . 20 Hardwick Street, Buxton, Derbyshire,
        SK17 6DH
        Tel: (01298) 71111 Fax: (01298) 71522
        Secretaries – Ms Janice Armitt
                Ms Sue Quas-Cohen
*Parliamentary Interests* . Disability; Education; Quarrying;
        Voluntary Sector
*Leisure Interests* . . . . . Cricket; Walking; Theatre

**Lewis, Ivan** . . . . . . Bury South
**Labour** . . . . . . . . . . . Majority 12,772 over Con
*Born* . . . . . . . . . . . . . 4th March 1967 in Manchester
*Educated* . . . . . . . . . . William Hulme Grammar School;
        Stand Sixth Form College;
        Bury College of Further Education
*Elected* . . . . . . . . . . . 1997 MP for Bury South
*Offices Held* . . . . . . . . 1999 - 2001 PPS to Stephen Byers
        (Secretary of State for Trade and Industry)
        2001 - Parliamentary Secretary,
        Department for Education and Skills
*Commons Office* . . . . . . Pager: 07623 523523 (880041)
*Constituency Office* . . . . 381 Bury New Road, Prestwich, Manchester,
        M25 1AW
        Tel: (0161) 773 5500 Fax: (0161) 773 7959
        E-mail: ian.ivanlewis@virgin.net
        Constituency Organiser – Mr Ian Peacock
*Parliamentary Interests* . Health; Crime; Middle East (Israel); Industry;
        Education
*Leisure Interests* . . . . . Football (Manchester City FC)

**Lewis, Dr Julian** . . . New Forest East
**Conservative** . . . . . . Majority 3,829 over Lib Dem
*Born* . . . . . . . . . . . . . 26th September 1951 in Swansea
*Educated* . . . . . . . . . . Dynevor Grammar School, Swansea;
        Balliol College, Oxford;
        St Antony's College, Oxford
*Elected* . . . . . . . . . . . 1997 MP for New Forest East
*Offices Held* . . . . . . . . 2001 - 02 Opposition Whip
        2002 - 04 Opposition Spokesman on
        Defence and International Affairs
        2004 - Shadow Minister for the Cabinet Office
*Constituency Office* . . . . 3 The Parade, Southampton Road, Cadnam,
        Hampshire, SO40 2NG
        Tel: (023) 8081 4905/4817
        Web: http://www.julianlewis.net
        Parliamentary Assistant – Mr Colin Smith
        Parliamentary Caseworker – Mrs Di Brooks
*Parliamentary Interests* . Defence; Foreign Affairs; Europe; Media;
        Mental Health
*Leisure Interests* . . . . . History; Films; Fiction; Music; Photography

**Lewis, Terry** . . . . . . Worsley
**Labour** . . . . . . . . . . . Majority 11,787 over Con
*Born* . . . . . . . . . . . . . 29th December 1935 in Salford, Lancashire
*Educated* . . . . . . . . . . Our Lady of Mount Carmel School, Salford
*Elected* . . . . . . . . . . . 1983 MP for Worsley
*Office Held* . . . . . . . . . 1980 - 83 Deputy Leader, Bolton Metropolitan
        Borough Council
*Commons Office* . . . . . . Tel: (020) 7219 3479 Fax: (020) 7219 4882
*Parliamentary Interests* . Health; Animal Welfare; Local Government
*Leisure Interests* . . . . . Football

# MEMBERS OF THE HOUSE OF COMMONS

**Liddell, Rt Hon Helen**  Airdrie and Shotts
**Labour** . . . . . . . . . . . Majority 12,340 over SNP
*Born*. . . . . . . . . . . . . . 6th December 1950 in Coatbridge
*Educated* . . . . . . . . . . St Patrick's High School, Coatbridge;
University of Strathclyde
*Elected*. . . . . . . . . . . . 1994 MP for Monklands East
(By-election), then (1997) Airdrie and Shotts
*Offices Held* . . . . . . . . 1995 - 97 Opposition Spokesman on Scotland
1997 - 98 Economic Secretary to the Treasury
1998 - 99 Minister of State, Scottish Office
1999 Minister for Transport
1999 - 2001 Minister of State, Department of
Trade and Industry
2001 - 03 Secretary of State for Scotland
*Commons Office* . . . . . Tel: (020) 7219 6507 Fax: (020) 7219 3390
*Constituency Office* . . . . 115 Graham Street, Airdrie, ML6 6DE
Tel: (01236) 748777 Fax: (01236) 748666
E-mail: timmonsj@parliament.uk
Personal Assistant – Mr Jim Timmons
Web: http://www.helenlidellmp.org.uk
*Parliamentary Interests* . Education
*Leisure Interests* . . . . . . Cooking; Walking; Reading


**Liddell-Grainger, Ian**  Bridgwater
**Conservative** . . . . . . . Majority 4,987 over Lib Dem
*Born*. . . . . . . . . . . . . . 23rd February 1959 in Edinburgh
*Educated* . . . . . . . . . . Millfield School, Somerset;
South of Scotland Agricultural College,
Edinburgh
*Elected*. . . . . . . . . . . . 2001 MP for Bridgwater
*Constituency Office* . . . . 16 Northgate, Bridgwater, Somerset, TA6 3EU
Tel: (01278) 458383 Fax: (01278) 433613
E-mail: ianlg@parliament.uk
PA – Miss Claire Gibson
*Parliamentary Interests* . Agriculture; Rural Issues; Defence; Tourism
*Leisure Interests* . . . . . . Walking; Skiing; Tennis


**Lidington, David** . . Aylesbury
**Conservative** . . . . . . . Majority 10,009 over Lib Dem
*Born*. . . . . . . . . . . . . . 30th June 1956 Lambeth, London
*Educated* . . . . . . . . . . Haberdashers' Aske's School, Elstree;
Sidney Sussex College, Cambridge
*Elected*. . . . . . . . . . . . 1992 MP for Aylesbury
*Offices Held* . . . . . . . . 1997 - 99 PPS to William Hague
(Leader of the Opposition)
1999 - 2001 Opposition Spokesman on
Home Affairs
2001 - 02 Opposition Spokesman on
Treasury Matters
2002 - 03 Shadow Secretary for
Environment, Food and Rural Affairs
2003 - Shadow Secretary for Northern
Ireland
*Commons Office* . . . . . Tel: (020) 7219 3432 Fax: (020) 7219 2564
E-mail: davidlidingtonmp@parliament.uk
Personal Assistant – Miss Verity Inge
*Constituency Office* . . . . 100 Walton Street, Aylesbury,
Buckinghamshire, HP21 7QP
Tel: (01296) 482102 Fax: (01296) 398481
Web: http://www.aylesbury.tory.org.uk
Agent – Mrs Jackie Porter
*Parliamentary Interests* . Home Affairs; Education


**Lilley, Rt Hon Peter**  Hitchin and Harpenden
**Conservative** . . . . . . Majority 6,663 over Lab
*Born*. . . . . . . . . . . . . . 23rd August 1943 in Kent
*Educated* . . . . . . . . . . Dulwich College; Clare College, Cambridge
*Elected*. . . . . . . . . . . . 1983 - 97 MP for St Albans
1997 MP for Hitchin and Harpenden
*Offices Held* . . . . . . . . 1987 - 89 Economic Secretary to the Treasury
1989 - 90 Financial Secretary to the Treasury
1990 - 92 Secretary of State for
Trade and Industry
1992 - 97 Secretary of State for
Social Security
1997 - 98 Shadow Chancellor of the
Exchequer
1998 - 99 Deputy Leader of the
Conservative Party
*Commons Office* . . . . . Tel: (020) 7219 4577 Fax: (020) 7219 3840
Web: http://www.peterlilley.co.uk
Secretary – Mrs Christine Percival
E-mail: percivalc@parliament.uk
*Constituency Office* . . . . 1 Place Farm, Wheathampstead,
Hertfordshire, AL4 8SB
Tel: (01582) 834344
Agent – Mrs Geraldine Mitchell


**Linton, Martin** . . . . Battersea
**Labour** . . . . . . . . . . . Majority 5,053 over Con
*Born*. . . . . . . . . . . . . . 11th August 1944 in Stockholm, Sweden
*Educated* . . . . . . . . . . Christ's Hospital; Pembroke College, Oxford
*Elected*. . . . . . . . . . . . 1997 MP for Battersea
*Office Held*. . . . . . . . . 2003 - PPS to Peter Hain
(Leader of the House of Commons)
*Commons Office* . . . . . Tel: (020) 7219 4619 Fax: (020) 7219 5728
E-mail: lintonm@parliament.uk
Web: http://www.martinlinton.org.uk
Researcher– Ms Judith Attar
Tel: (020) 7219 1181
E-mail: attarj@parliament.uk
*Constituency Office* . . . . 177 Lavender Hill, London, SW11 5TE
Tel: (020) 7207 3060
Agent/Organiser – Mr Adam Gray
Tel: (020) 7223 5306
*Parliamentary Interests* . Electoral Reform; Funding of Political Parties;
Housing; Transport; Home Affairs; Arts
*Leisure Interests* . . . . . . Playing Trumpet and Piano; Running;
Football (Fulham FC)

# MEMBERS OF THE HOUSE OF COMMONS

**Lloyd, Tony** . . . . . . Manchester Central
**Labour** . . . . . . . . . . Majority 13,742 over Lib Dem
*Born* . . . . . . . . . . . . . 25th February 1950 in Stretford, Manchester
*Educated* . . . . . . . . . Stretford Grammar School;
                   Nottingham University;
                   Manchester Business School
*Elected* . . . . . . . . . . . 1983 - 97 MP for Stretford, then (1007) for
                   Manchester Central
*Offices Held* . . . . . . . 1987 - 89 Opposition Spokesman on Transport
                   1989 - 94 Opposition Spokesman on
                       Employment
                   1994 - 95 Opposition Spokesman on
                       Environment (Local Government)
                   1995 - 97 Opposition Spokesman on
                       Foreign Affairs
                   1997 - 99 Minister of State, Foreign and
                       Commonwealth Office
*Commons Office* . . . . . Tel: (020) 7219 3488 Fax: (020) 7219 2585
                   E-mail: lloydt@parliament.uk
                   Web: http://www.tonylloydmp.co.uk
                   Research Assistant – Miss Danielle Codd
                   Tel: (020) 7219 6626
                   E-mail: coddd@parliament.uk
*Constituency Office* . . . . 10 Swan Street, Manchester, M4 5JN
                   Tel: (0161) 819 2828  Fax: (0161) 839 6875
                   Personal Assistant – Mr David Carr
                   Caseworker – Mr Aydin Djemal
*Parliamentary Interests* . Trade Unions; Foreign Affairs

**Llwyd, Elfyn** . . . . . . Meirionnydd Nant Conwy
**Plaid Cymru** . . . . . . . Majority 5,684 over Lab
*Born* . . . . . . . . . . . . . . . 26th September 1951 in Betws-y-Coed
*Educated* . . . . . . . . . . Llanrwst Grammar School;
                   Ysgol Dyffryn, Conwy;
                   University College of Wales, Aberystwyth;
                   Chester College of Law
*Elected* . . . . . . . . . . . . 1992 MP for Meirionnydd Nant Conwy
*Offices Held* . . . . . . . . 1997 - 2000 Plaid Cymru Parliamentary Whip
                   2000 - Parliamentary Leader, Plaid Cymru
*Commons Office* . . . . . . Tel: (020) 7219 5021/3555
                   Fax: (020) 7219 3705
                   Mobile: 07831 202047
                   Pager: 07625 245991
                   E-mail: 100571.1006@compuserve.com
                   Secretary – Ms Rhian Medi Roberts
                   Researcher – Miss Gwenllian Griffiths
                   Tel: (020) 7219 6422
                   E-mail: griffithsg@parliament.uk
*Constituency Office* . . . . Ty Glyndwr, Heol Glyndwr, Dolgellau,
                   LL40 1BD
                   Tel: (01341) 422661 Fax: (01341) 423990
                   Personal Assistant/Secretary –
                     Ms Sheila Williams
                   E-mail: sheila@plaid-cymru.org
*Parliamentary Interests* . Home Affairs; Tourism; Agriculture;
                   Children's Issues
*Leisure Interests* . . . . . . Fishing; Choral Singing; Pigeon Breeding

**Lord, Sir Michael** Suffolk Central and Ipswich North
**Conservative** . . . . . . . Majority 3,538 over Lab
*Born* . . . . . . . . . . . . . . 17th October 1938 in Manchester
*Educated* . . . . . . . . . . William Hulme's Grammar School,
                   Manchester;
                   Christ's College, Cambridge
*Elected* . . . . . . . . . . . . 1983 MP for Central Suffolk, then (1997)
                   for Suffolk Central and Ipswich North
*Office Held* . . . . . . . . . 1997 - Second Deputy Chairman of Ways and
                   Means and Deputy Speaker,
                   House of Commons
*Commons Office* . . . . . Tel: (020) 7219 6545 Fax: (020) 7219 2931
                   Private Secretary – Miss Sarah Jeffery
*Constituency Office* . . . . 19 The Business Centre, Earl Soham,
                   Woodbridge, Suffolk, IP13 7SA
                   Tel: (01728) 685148 Fax: (01728) 685157
                   Organising Secretary – Mrs Diane Smith

**Loughton, Tim** . . . . Worthing East and Shoreham
**Conservative** . . . . . . . Majority 6,139 over Lab
*Born* . . . . . . . . . . . . . . 30th May 1962 in Eastbourne
*Educated* . . . . . . . . . . The Priory School, Lewes, Sussex;
                   Warwick University;
                   Clare College, Cambridge
*Elected* . . . . . . . . . . . . 1997 MP for Worthing East and Shoreham
*Offices Held* . . . . . . . . 2000 - 01 Opposition Spokesman on the
                   Regions, Urban Regeneration, Housing
                   and Poverty
                   2001 - 03 Opposition Spokesman on Health
                   2003 - Opposition Spokesman on Children
*Commons Office* . . . . . Tel: (020) 7219 4012 Fax: (020) 7219 0461
                   Mobile: 07956 297007
                   Pager: 07626 801679
                   E-mail: loughtont@parliament.uk
                   Web: http://www.timloughton.com
                   Secretary – Miss Fiona Gunn
                   Tel: (020) 7219 4471
                   E-mail: gunnf@parliament.uk
                   Researcher – Miss Alice Ferrero
                   Tel: (020) 7219 1622
                   E-mail: ferreroa@parliament.uk
*Constituency Office* . . . . Haverfield House, 4 Union Place, Worthing,
                   West Sussex, BN11 1LG
                   Tel: (01903) 235168 Fax: (01903) 219755
                   E-mail: worthing@tory.org
                   Agent – Major Tom Wye
*Parliamentary Interests* . Finance; Environment; Home Affairs; Europe;
                   Disabilities; Animal Welfare; Health
*Leisure Interests* . . . . . . Archaeology; Wine; Skiing; Hockey; Classics

# MEMBERS OF THE HOUSE OF COMMONS

**Love, Andrew** . . . . . Edmonton
**Labour** . . . . . . . . . . Majority 9,772 over Con
*Born* . . . . . . . . . . . . . 21st March 1949 in Greenock
*Educated* . . . . . . . . . Greenock High School; Strathclyde University
*Elected* . . . . . . . . . . . 1997 MP for Edmonton
*Office Held* . . . . . . . . 2001 - PPS to Jacqui Smith
(Minister of State, Department of Health,
then Department of Trade and Industry)
*Commons Office* . . . . . Tel: (020) 7219 6377 Fax: (020) 7219 6623
E-mail: lovea@parliament.uk
Web: http://www.andylovemp.com
Personal Assistant/Researcher –
Ms Victoria Silver
E-mail: silverv@parliament.uk
Case Worker/Assistant – Mr David Grier
E-mail: grierd@parliament.uk
*Constituency Office* . . . . Broad House, 205 Fore Street, Edmonton,
London, N18 2TZ
Tel: (020) 8803 0574 Fax: (020) 8807 1673
E-mail: andylovemp@aol.com
Caseworker – Mr Sean O'Donovan
*Parliamentary Interests* . Mutuality; Health; Housing; Regeneration;
International/European Relations;
Small Businesses
*Leisure Interests* . . . . . . Golf; Reading; Cinema; Art; Travelling

**Lucas, Ian** . . . . . . . . Wrexham
**Labour** . . . . . . . . . . Majority 9,118 over Con
*Born* . . . . . . . . . . . . . 18th September 1960 in Gateshead
*Educated* . . . . . . . . . New College, Oxford; Chester College of Law
*Elected* . . . . . . . . . . . 2001 MP for Wrexham
*Commons Office* . . . . . Tel: (020) 7219 8346 Fax: (020) 7219 1948
Pager: 07626 409553
E-mail: lucasi@parliament.uk
Web: http://www.ianlucas.co.uk
Research Assistant – Mr David Boothroyd
Tel: (020) 7219 4065
E-mail: boothroydd@parliament.uk
*Constituency Office* . . . . 2 Mount Street, Wrexham, LL13 8DN
Tel: (01978) 355743 Fax: (01978) 310051
Personal and Political Assistant –
Mrs Lesley Griffiths
Research Assistant – Mrs Norah Lucas
*Parliamentary Interests* . Trade and Industry; Home Affairs;
Foreign Affairs; United Nations; Environment;
Constitution; Transport; Treasury
*Leisure Interests* . . . . . . History; Painting; Soccer

**Luff, Peter** . . . . . . . . Mid Worcestershire
**Conservative** . . . . . . Majority 10,627 over Lab
*Born* . . . . . . . . . . . . . 18th February 1955 in Windsor
*Educated* . . . . . . . . . Windsor Grammar School;
Corpus Christi College, Cambridge
*Elected* . . . . . . . . . . . 1992 MP for Worcester, then (1997) Mid
Worcestershire
*Offices Held* . . . . . . . . 1997 - 2000 Chairman, Agriculture Select
Committee, House of Commons
2000 - Opposition Whip (Assistant Chief
Whip from 2002)
*Constituency Office* . . . . Tel: (01905) 763952 Fax: (01905) 761808
E-mail: luffpj@parliament.uk
Web: http://www.peterluff.co.uk
Private Secretary – Mrs Julia Luff
*Parliamentary Interests* . Rural Affairs; Transport: Performing Arts;
Overseas Development
*Leisure Interests* . . . . . . Theatre; Photography; Shooting; Driving

**Luke, Iain** . . . . . . . . Dundee East
**Labour** . . . . . . . . . . Majority 4,475 over SNP
*Born* . . . . . . . . . . . . . 8th October, 1951 in Dundee
*Educated* . . . . . . . . . Harris Academy, Dundee; Dundee University;
Edinburgh University;
Jordanhill Teacher Training College
*Elected* . . . . . . . . . . . 2001 MP for Dundee East
*Commons Office* . . . . . Tel: (020) 7219 8165 Fax: (020) 7219 1758
Mobile: 07903 017809
Pager 07626 409569
E-mail: lukei@parliament.uk
Web: http://www.iainluke.labour.co.uk
*Constituency Office* . . . . 57 Blackscroft, Dundee, DD4 6AT
Tel: (01382) 466700 Fax: (01382) 466719
Secretary – Mrs Jane O'Neill
Tel: (01382) 466702
Constituency Assistant – Ms Emma Thomson
Tel: (01382) 466712
Parliamentary Researcher – Mrs Marie Luke
Tel: (01382) 640000 Fax: (01382) 668302
*Parliamentary Interests* . Europe; Middle East; British/Indian/Pakistani
Relations; Economic Development;
Trade and Industry
*Leisure Interests* . . . . . Reading; Cinema; Watching Football;
Swimming

**Lyons, John** . . . . . Strathkelvin and Bearsden
**Labour** . . . . . . . . . . Majority 11,717 over Lib Dem
*Born* . . . . . . . . . . . . . 11th July 1949
*Educated* . . . . . . . . . Woodside Secondary School, Glasgow;
Stirling University;
West Middlesex Polytechnic
*Elected* . . . . . . . . . . . 2001 MP for Strathkelvin and Bearsden
*Commons Office* . . . . . Tel: (020) 7219 8325
E-mail: lyonsj@parliament.uk
*Constituency Office* . . . . 1 Dalrymple Court, Townhead, Kirkintilloch,
Glasgow, G66 3AA
Tel: (0141) 776 5403 Fax: (0141) 776 3239
Office Manager – Mrs Marion Kinley
E-mail: kinleym@parliament.uk
Secretary – Mrs Jane MacGregor
*Parliamentary Interests* . Health Service; Local Government;
Higher Education; Voluntary Sector;
Social Security; Pensions; Employment;
International Development; Minimum Wage
*Leisure Interests* . . . . . . Reading; Hill Walking

# M

**McAvoy, Rt Hon Tommy** Glasgow Rutherglen
**Labour** . . . . . . . . . . Majority 12,625 over SNP
*Born* . . . . . . . . . . . . . 14th December 1943 in Rutherglen
*Educated* . . . . . . . . . St Columbkilles School, Rutherglen
*Elected* . . . . . . . . . . . 1987 MP for Glasgow Rutherglen
*Offices Held* . . . . . . . . 1996 - 97 Opposition Whip
1997 - Government Whip (Comptroller of
H M Household)

# MEMBERS OF THE HOUSE OF COMMONS

**McCabe, Stephen** . . Birmingham Hall Green
**Labour** . . . . . . . . . . . Majority 6,648 over Con
*Born* . . . . . . . . . . . . . 4th August 1955
*Educated* . . . . . . . . . Port Glasgow Secondary School;
Moray House College of Education;
Bradford University
*Elected* . . . . . . . . . . . 1997 MP for Birmingham Hall Green
*Office Held* . . . . . . . . 2003 - PPS to Charles Clarke (Secretary of
State for Education and Skills)
*Commons Office* . . . . . Tel: (020) 7219 3509 Fax: (020) 7219 0367
Secretary – Ms Linda Spencer
Tel: (020) 7219 4842 Fax: (020) 7219 0996
E-mail: spencerl@parliament.uk
*Constituency Office* . . . . 14-16 Bristol Street, Birmingham, B5 7AF
Tel: (0121) 622 6761 Fax: (0121) 622 7322
*Parliamentary Interests* . Transport; Telematics and Vehicle Security;
Care of Elderly; Police and Security Issues;
Northern Ireland; Economy
*Leisure Interests* . . . . . . Cooking; Reading; Hill Walking; Football

**McCafferty, Christine** Calder Valley
**Labour** . . . . . . . . . . . Majority 3,094 over Con
*Born* . . . . . . . . . . . . . 14th October 1945
*Educated* . . . . . . . . . Whalley Range Grammar School;
Footscray High School, Melbourne, Australia
*Elected* . . . . . . . . . . . 1997 MP for Calder Valley
*Commons Office* . . . . . Tel: (020) 7219 5026 Fax: (020) 7219 2769
E-mail: mccaffertyc@parliament.uk
Staff – Mr David Tarlo
E-mail: tarlod@parliament.uk
*Constituency Office* . . . . 15 Heptonstall Road, Hebden Bridge,
West Yorkshire, HX7 6AZ
Tel & Fax: (01422) 843713
E-mail: chris.mccafferty@email.labour.org.uk
*Parliamentary Interests* . International Development;
Sexual and Reproductive Health
*Leisure Interests* . . . . . . Swimming; Gardening; Motor Caravan

**McCartney, Rt Hon Ian** Makerfield
**Labour** . . . . . . . . . . . Majority 17,750 over Con
*Born* . . . . . . . . . . . . . 25th April 1951 in Lennoxtown
*Educated* . . . . . . . . . Lenzie Academy; Langside College
*Elected* . . . . . . . . . . . 1987 MP for Makerfield
*Offices Held* . . . . . . . . 1992 - 94 Opposition Spokesman on Health
1994 - 97 Opposition Spokesman on
Employment
1997 - 99 Minister of State, Department of
Trade and Industry
1999 - 2001 Minister of State, Cabinet Office
2001 - 03 Minister of State, Department for
Work and Pensions (Minister for Pensions)
2003 - Minister without Portfolio and
Chairman of the Labour Party
*Constituency Office* . . . . Gerrard Winstanley House, Crawford Street,
Wigan, WN1 1NJ
Tel: (01942) 824029 Fax: (01942) 492746
E-mail: ian_mccartney@btconnect.com
Personal Assistant – Ms Lynda Birch
Administrative Assistant – Mr Patrick Hunt
*Parliamentary Interests* . Trade and Industry; Pensions
*Leisure Interests* . . . . . . Rugby League

**McDonagh, Siobhain** Mitcham and Morden
**Labour** . . . . . . . . . . . Majority 13,785 over Con
*Born* . . . . . . . . . . . . . 20th February 1960 in London
*Educated* . . . . . . . . . Holy Cross Convent, New Malden;
Essex University
*Elected* . . . . . . . . . . . 1997 MP for Mitcham and Morden
*Commons Office* . . . . . Tel: (020) 7219 4522 Fax: (020) 7219 2697
E-mail: mcdonaghs@parliament.uk
E-mail: allisonm@parliament.uk
Researcher – Mr Mark Allison
*Constituency Office* . . . . 1 Crown Road, Morden, SM4 5DD
Tel: (020) 8542 4835 Fax: (020) 8542 0377
E-mail: contact@mm-clp.new.labour.org.uk
P/A – Ms Vince Romagnnolo
*Parliamentary Interests* . Housing; Benefit Reform; Law and Order
*Leisure Interests* . . . . . . Reading; Cooking; Music

**MacDonald, Calum** Western Isles
**Labour** . . . . . . . . . . . Majority 1,074 over SNP
*Born* . . . . . . . . . . . . . 7th May 1956 on Isle of Lewis
*Educated* . . . . . . . . . Nicolson Institute, Stornoway;
Edinburgh University;
University of California, USA
*Elected* . . . . . . . . . . . 1987 MP for Western Isles
*Office Held* . . . . . . . . 1997 - 99 Parliamentary Secretary,
Scottish Office
*Commons Office* . . . . . Tel: (020) 7219 2780 Fax: (020) 7219 0142
E-mail: macdonaldc@parliament.uk
Web:
http://www.calummacdonald.labour.co.uk
*Constituency Office* . . . . 4 South Beach Street, Stornoway,
Isle of Lewis, HS1 2XY
Tel: (01851) 704684 Fax: (01851) 703048
Secretary – Ms Ann Ross
E-mail: annross@wiclp.freeserve.co.uk

**McDonnell, John** . . Hayes and Harlington
**Labour** . . . . . . . . . . . Majority 13,466 over Con
*Born* . . . . . . . . . . . . . 8th September 1951 in Liverpool
*Educated* . . . . . . . . . Brunel University; Birkbeck College, London
*Elected* . . . . . . . . . . . 1997 MP for Hayes and Harlington
*Contact* . . . . . . . . . . . E-mail: mcdonnellj@parliament.uk
*Constituency Office* . . . . Pump Lane, Hayes, UB3 3NB
Tel: (020) 8569 0010 Fax: (020) 8569 0109
E-mail: office@john-mcdonnellnet
Personal Assistant – Mr Kevin Lockie
E-mail: lockiek@parliament.uk
Personal Assistant/Researcher –
Ms Tracey Beck
Caseworker – Ms Jacquie Connor
*Parliamentary Interests* . Ireland; Environment; Local Government;
Economy; Kenya; Gambia; Tanzania; Asylum
*Leisure Interests* . . . . . . Football; Sailing; Cycling; Gardening

**MacDougall, John** Fife Central
**Labour** . . . . . . . . . . . Majority 10,075 over SNP
*Born* . . . . . . . . . . . . . 8th December 1947 in Dunfermline
*Educated* . . . . . . . . . Templehall Secondary Modern School,
Kirkcaldy; Rosyth Naval Dockyard College;
Glenrothes Technical College
*Elected* . . . . . . . . . . . 2001 MP for Fife Central

# MEMBERS OF THE HOUSE OF COMMONS

**McFall, Rt Hon John**    Dumbarton
*Labour* . . . . . . . . . . . Majority 9,575 over SNP
*Born*. . . . . . . . . . . . . 14th October 1944 in Dumbarton
*Educated* . . . . . . . . . . Glasgow University
*Elected*. . . . . . . . . . . 1987 MP for Dumbarton
*Offices Held* . . . . . . . . 1989 - 92 Opposition Whip
                                1992 - 97 Opposition Spokesman on Scotland
                                1997 - 98 Government Whip
                                  (Lord Commissioner, H M Treasury)
                                1998 - 99 Parliamentary Secretary,
                                  Northern Ireland Office
                                2001 - Chairman, Treasury Select Committee,
                                  House of Commons
*Commons Office* . . . . . Tel: (020) 7219 3521 Fax: (020) 7219 6141
                                E-mail: mcfallj@parliament.uk
                                Web: http://www.john.mcfall.com
*Leisure Interests* . . . . . . Golf; Running; Reading

**McGrady, Eddie**. . . Down South
*SDLP* . . . . . . . . . . . . . Majority 13,858 over Sinn Fein
*Born*. . . . . . . . . . . . . 3rd June 1935 in Northern Ireland
*Educated* . . . . . . . . . . St Patrick's Grammar School, Downpatrick;
                                Belfast Technical College
*Elected*. . . . . . . . . . . 1987 MP for Down South
*Offices Held* . . . . . . . . Formerly Leader, Down District Council
                                1998 - 2003 Member,
                                  Northern Ireland Assembly
*Constituency Office* . . . . 32 Saul Street, Downpatrick, County Down,
                                BT30 6NQ
                                Tel: (028) 4461 2882 Fax: (028) 4461 9574
                                E-mail: e.mcgrady@sdlp.ie
                                Web: http://www.eddiemcgrady.com
                                Researchers/Secretaries – Ms Theresa Doran
                                            Ms Alice O'Hare
*Parliamentary Interests* . Housing; Economy; Inward Investment;
                                Environment; Local Government
*Leisure Interests* . . . . . . Walking; Gardening

**McGuinness, Martin**  Mid Ulster
*Sinn Fein* . . . . . . . . . . Majority 9,953 over DUP
*Born*. . . . . . . . . . . . . 23rd May 1950
*Educated* . . . . . . . . . . Christian Brothers Technical College
*Elected*. . . . . . . . . . . 1997 MP for Mid Ulster
                                *(Note: Has not taken seat at Westminster)*
*Offices Held* . . . . . . . . 1998 - Member, Northern Ireland Assembly
                                  (1999 - 2002 Minister of Education,
                                  Northern Ireland)
*Constituency Office* . . . . 32 Burn Road, Cookstown, Co Tyrone,
                                BT80 8DN
                                Tel: (028) 8676 5830 Fax: (028) 8676 8734
                                Political Advisor – Mr Oliver Molloy
*Leisure Interests* . . . . . . Fishing

**McGuire, Anne**. . . . Stirling
*Labour* . . . . . . . . . . . Majority 6,274 over Con
*Born*. . . . . . . . . . . . . 26th May 1949 in Glasgow
*Educated* . . . . . . . . . . Our Lady and St Francis School, Glasgow;
                                Glasgow University
*Elected*. . . . . . . . . . . 1997 MP for Stirling
*Offices Held* . . . . . . . . 1997 - 98 PPS to Donald Dewer
                                  (Secretary of State for Scotland)
                                1998 - 01 Assistant Government Whip
                                2001 - 02 Government Whip (Lord
                                  Commissioner, H M Treasury)
                                2002 - Parliamentary Secretary,
                                  Scotland Office (also Department of
                                  Constitutional Affairs from 2003)
*Commons Office* . . . . . Tel: (020) 7219 5014
                                E-mail: mcguirea@parliament.uk
*Constituency Office* . . . . 22 Viewfield Street, Stirling, FK8 1UA
                                Tel: (01786) 446515 Fax: (01786) 446513
                                Office Manager – Mr Graham Fraser
                                E-mail: fraserg@parliament.uk
*Parliamentary Interests* . Rural Development; Urban Regeneration;
                                Voluntary Sector; Europe
*Leisure Interests* . . . . . . Walking; Scottish Traditional Music

**McIntosh, Anne** . . . Vale of York
*Conservative* . . . . . . . Majority 12,517 over Lab
*Born*. . . . . . . . . . . . . 20th September 1954 in Edinburgh
*Educated* . . . . . . . . . . Harrogate College; Edinburgh University:
                                Aarhus University, Denmark
*Elected*. . . . . . . . . . . 1997 MP for Vale of York
*Offices Held* . . . . . . . . 1989 - 99 Member of the European Parliament
                                  (for North East Essex, then for
                                  North Essex and South Suffolk)
                                2001 - 02 Opposition Spokesman on
                                  Culture, Media and Sport
                                2003 - Opposition Spokesman on
                                  Environment and Transport
*Commons Office* . . . . . Tel: (020) 7219 3541/4518
                                Fax: (020) 7219 0972
                                Parliamentary Assistants – Mr William Fry
                                            Mr Benedict Reid
                                Parliamentary Secretary – Miss Joy Greenfield
                                E-mails: [surnameinitial]@parliament.uk
*Constituency Office* . . . . Thirsk Conservative Club, Westgate, Thirsk,
                                North Yorkshire, YO7 1QS
                                Tel: (01845) 523835 Fax: (01845) 527507
                                Agent/Secretary – Mrs Diane Clarke
                                Secretary – Ms Jan Laughton
                                Tel: (01845) 527240
*Parliamentary Interests* . Transport; Legal Affairs; Tourism
*Leisure Interests* . . . . . . Swimming; Reading; Cinema

# MEMBERS OF THE HOUSE OF COMMONS

**McIsaac, Shona** . . . Cleethorpes
**Labour** . . . . . . . . . . . Majority 5,620 over Con
*Born.* . . . . . . . . . . . . 3rd April 1960 in Dunfermline
*Educated* . . . . . . . . . . Durham University
*Elected* . . . . . . . . . . . 1997 MP for Cleethorpes
*Office Held* . . . . . . . . 2003 - PPS to Baroness Scotland of
                Asthal (Minister of State, Home Office)
*Commons Office* . . . . . Tel: (020) 7219 5801 Fax: (020) 7219 3047
                E-mail: mcisaacs@parliament.uk
                Researcher – Mr Chris Randell
                Tel: (020) 7219 2526
*Constituency Office* . . . . Immingham Resource Centre, Margaret Street,
                Immingham, DN40 1LE
                Tel: (01469) 574324 Fax: (01469) 510842
                PA/Constituency Co-ordinator –
                Mrs Susan Turner
                Advice Workers – Ms Jo Avison
                            Ms Caroline Sansam
*Parliamentary Interests* . Crime; Leasehold Reform; Tax and Benefits
*Leisure Interests* . . . . . . Cycling; Food; Football; Archaeology

**MacKay, Rt Hon Andrew**    Bracknell
**Conservative** . . . . . . Majority 6,713 over Lab
*Born.* . . . . . . . . . . . . 27th August 1949 in Birmingham
*Educated* . . . . . . . . . . Solihull School
*Elected* . . . . . . . . . . . 1977 - 79 MP for Birmingham Stechford
                (By-election)
                1983 MP for Berkshire East, then (1997)
                for Bracknell
*Offices Held* . . . . . . . . 1992 - 93 Assistant Government Whip
                1993 - 96 Government Whip
                (Lord Commissioner, H M Treasury,
                then Vice-Chamberlain, H M Household)
                1996 - 97 Government Deputy Chief Whip
                (Treasurer, H M Household)
                1997 - 2001 Shadow Northern Ireland
                Secretary
*Commons Office* . . . . . Tel: (020) 7219 2989 Fax: (020) 7219 4123
                E-mail: mackaya@parliament.uk
*Constituency Office* . . . . 10 Milbanke Court, Bracknell,
                Berkshire, RG12 1RP
                Tel: (01344) 868286 Fax: (01344) 868894
                E-mail: bracknellca@tory.org
                Agent – Mrs Mary Ballin
*Leisure Interests* . . . . . . Golf; Squash; Gourmet Food

**McKechin, Ann** . . . Glasgow Maryhill
**Labour** . . . . . . . . . . . Majority 9,888 over SNP
*Born.* . . . . . . . . . . . . 22nd April 1961 in Paisley
*Educated* . . . . . . . . . . Paisley Grammar School;
                Strathclyde University
*Elected* . . . . . . . . . . . 2001 MP for Glasgow Maryhill
*Commons Office* . . . . . Tel: (020) 7219 8239 Fax: (020) 7219 1770
                Mobile: 07751 482722
                Pager: 07626 409531
                E-mail: mckechina@parliament.uk
                Web: http://www.annmckechinmp.net
*Constituency Office* . . . . 154/156 Raeberry Street, Maryhill,
                Glasgow, G20 6EA
                Tel: (0141) 946 1300 Fax: (0141) 946 1412
                E-mail: rhodesm@parliament.uk
                Research Officer – Mr Martin Rhodes
                Secretaries/Caseworkers: –Ms Yvonne Boyle
                            Ms Pat Rice
*Parliamentary Interests* . International Development; Globalisation
*Leisure Interests* . . . . . . Films; Dancing; Art History

**McKenna, Rosemary** CBE Cumbernauld and Kilsyth
**Labour** . . . . . . . . . . . Majority 7,520 over SNP
*Born.* . . . . . . . . . . . . 8th May 1941 in Renfrewshire
*Educated* . . . . . . . . . . St Augustine's Comprehensive, Glasgow;
                Notre Dame College of Education, Glasgow
*Elected* . . . . . . . . . . . 1997 MP for Cumbernauld and Kilsyth
*Offices Held* . . . . . . . . Formerly Leader and Provost, Cumbernauld
                and Kilsyth Council
*Commons Office* . . . . . Tel: (020) 7219 4135 Fax: (020) 7217 2544
                E-mail: mckennar@parliament.uk
                Web:
                http://www.rosemarymckenna.labour.org.uk
*Constituency Office* . . . . Lennox House, Lennox Road, Cumbernauld,
                G67 1LB
                Tel: (01236) 457788 Fax: (01236) 455303
                Parliamentary Assistant – Mr Bob McBean
                Secretarial Assistant – Ms Gillian Dalrymple
*Parliamentary Interests* . Education and Training; Access to Technology
*Leisure Interests* . . . . . . Reading; Travel; Family Gatherings

**Mackinlay, Andrew**    Thurrock
**Labour** . . . . . . . . . . . Majority 9,997 over Con
*Born.* . . . . . . . . . . . . 24th April 1949 in Wembley, London
*Educated* . . . . . . . . . . Salesian College, Chertsey
*Elected* . . . . . . . . . . . 1992 MP for Thurrock
*Commons Office* . . . . . Tel: (020) 7219 6819 Fax: (020) 7219 2539
*Constituency Office* . . . . MPs Office, Civic Square, Tilbury, Essex,
                RM18 8ZZ
                Tel & Fax: (01375) 850359
                Personal Assistant – Mr Carl Morris
                E-mail: morrisc@parliament.uk

**Maclean, Rt Hon David**    Penrith and the Border
**Conservative** . . . . . . Majority 14,677 over Lib Dem
*Born.* . . . . . . . . . . . . 16th May 1953 in Cromarty
*Educated* . . . . . . . . . . Fortrose Academy; Aberdeen University
*Elected* . . . . . . . . . . . 1983 MP for Penrith and the Border
                (By-election)
*Offices Held* . . . . . . . . 1987 - 88 Assistant Government Whip
                1988 - 89 Government Whip
                (Lord Commissioner, H M Treasury)
                1989 - 92 Parliamentary Secretary,
                Ministry of Agriculture, Fisheries and Food
                1992 - 93 Minister of State,
                Department of Environment
                1993 - 97 Minister of State, Home Office
                2001 - Opposition Chief Whip
*Commons Office* . . . . . Tel: (020) 7219 6494
                Private Secretary – Miss Alex Burrell

# MEMBERS OF THE HOUSE OF COMMONS

**McLoughlin, Patrick**  Derbyshire West
**Conservative** . . . . . . Majority 7,370 over Lab
*Born*. . . . . . . . . . . . . . 30th November 1957 in Stafford
*Educated* . . . . . . . . . . Cardinal Griffin RC School, Cannock
*Elected*. . . . . . . . . . . . 1986 MP for Derbyshire West (By-election)
*Offices Held* . . . . . . . . 1989 - 92 Parliamentary Secretary,
    Department of Transport
    1992 - 93 Parliamentary Secretary,
    Department of Employment
    1993 - 94 Parliamentary Secretary,
    Department of Trade and Industry
    1995 - 96 Assistant Government Whip
    1996 - 97 Government Whip (Lord
    Commissioner, H M Treasury)
    1997 - 98 Opposition Pairing Whip
    1998 - Opposition Deputy Chief Whip
*Constituency Office* . . . . Tel: (01322) 558125 Fax: (01322) 541509
    E-mail: mcloughlinp@parliament.uk
    Constituency Administrator –
    Mrs Lynne McLoughlin
*Parliamentary Interests* . Education; Agriculture
*Leisure Interests* . . . . . . Football

**McNamara, Kevin** . Hull North
**Labour** . . . . . . . . . . . Majority 10,721 over Lib Dem
*Born*. . . . . . . . . . . . . . 5th September 1934 in Liverpool
*Educated* . . . . . . . . . St Mary's College, Crosby; Hull University
*Elected*. . . . . . . . . . . . 1966 MP for Hull North (1974 - 83 Hull
    Central)
*Offices Held* . . . . . . . . 1982 - 87 Opposition Spokesman on Defence
    1987 - 94 Shadow Northern Ireland Secretary
    1994 - 96 Opposition Spokesman on
    Civil Service
*Commons Office* . . . . . Tel: (020) 7219 5194 Fax: (020) 7219 3398
    E-mail: kevinmcnamaramp@parliament.uk
    Web: http://www.kevinmcnmara.co.uk
    Personal Assistant – Ms Lorna Rea
    E-mail: real@parliament.uk
    Researcher – Mr Martin Collins
    Tel: (020) 7219 6477
    E-mail: collinsm@parliament.uk
*Constituency Office* . . . . 145 Newland Park, Hull, HU5 2DX
    Tel: (01482) 448170 Fax: (01482) 441505
    E-mail: clarkji@parliament.uk
    Constituency Caseworker – Mrs Janet Clark

**McNulty, Tony** . . . . Harrow East
**Labour** . . . . . . . . . . . Majority 11,124 over Con
*Born*. . . . . . . . . . . . . . 3rd November 1958 in London
*Educated* . . . . . . . . . . Salvatorian College, Harrow;
    Stanmore Sixth Form College;
    Liverpool University;
    Virginia Polytechnic Institute and State
    University
*Elected*. . . . . . . . . . . . 1997 MP for Harrow East
*Offices Held* . . . . . . . . 1999 - 2001 Assistant Government Whip
    2001 - 02 Government Whip (Lord
    Commissioner, H M Treasury)
    2002 Parliamentary Secretary, Department of
    Environment, Transport and the Regions
    2002 - 03 Parliamentary Secretary, Office of
    the Deputy Prime Minister (Minister for
    London)
    2003 - 04 Parliamentary Secretary,
    Department of Transport
    2004 - Minister of State, Department for
    Transport
*Commons Office* . . . . . Tel: (020) 7219 2807 Fax: (020) 7219 2417
    Secretary – Mrs Marjorie Lamb
    Tel: (020) 7219 4108
    E-mail: lambm@parliament.uk
*Constituency Office* . . . . 18-20 Byron Road, Wealdstone, Harrow,
    Middlesex, HA3 7ST
    Tel: (020) 8427 2100 Fax: (020) 8424 2319
    Senior Researcher – Ms Marie-Louise Nolan
    Community Liaison Officer –
    Mrs Diana Hardman
*Parliamentary Interests* . Local Government; Ireland; Germany; Europe;
    London; Education; Regeneration;
    Anti-Racism
*Leisure Interests* . . . . . . Football. Rugby; Literature; Theatre;
    Eating Out

**MacShane, Dr Denis**  Rotherham
**Labour** . . . . . . . . . . . Majority 13,077 over Con
*Born*. . . . . . . . . . . . . . 21st May 1948 in Glasgow
*Educated* . . . . . . . . . . Merton College, Oxford;
    Birkbeck College, London
*Elected*. . . . . . . . . . . . 1994 MP for Rotherham (By-election)
*Offices Held* . . . . . . . . 2001 - 02 Parliamentary Secretary, Foreign
    and Commonwealth Office
    2002 - Minister of State, Foreign and
    Commonwealth Office (Minister for Europe)
*Commons Office* . . . . . Tel: (020) 7219 4060 Fax: (020) 7219 6888
    E-mail: macshaned@parliament.uk
*Constituency Office* . . . . Tel: (01709) 837577 Fax: (01709) 835622
    P/A – Mrs Kath Sims
*Parliamentary Interests* . Steel; Europe

# MEMBERS OF THE HOUSE OF COMMONS

**Mactaggart, Fiona** . Slough
**Labour** . . . . . . . . . . Majority 12,508 over Con
*Born*. . . . . . . . . . . . . 12th September 1953 in London
*Educated* . . . . . . . . . Kings College, London;
         Goldsmiths College, London;
         Institute of Education, London
*Elected*. . . . . . . . . . . 1997 MP for Slough
*Offices Held* . . . . . . . 1997 - 2001 PPS to Chris Smith
         (Secretary of State for Culture, Media
         and Sport)
         2003 - Parliamentary Secretary, Home Office
*Commons Office* . . . . . Tel: (020) 7219 3416 Fax: (020) 7219 0989
         Pager: 07644 006388
         E-mail: mactaggartf@parliament.uk
         Researcher – Ms Sue Shutter
         Tel: (020) 7219 4818
         E-mail: shutters@parliament.uk
*Constituency Office* . . . . 29 Church Street, Slough, SL1 1PL
         Tel: (01753) 518161 Fax: (01753) 550293
         Assistant – Mr Peter Ruhemann
*Parliamentary Interests* . Human Rights; Civil Liberties; Home Affairs;
         Education; Media; The Arts
*Leisure Interests* . . . . . . Conversation; Walking

**McWalter, Tony** . . . Hemel Hempstead
**Labour** . . . . . . . . . . . Majority 3,742 over Con
*Born*. . . . . . . . . . . . . . 20th March 1945 in Worksop,
         Nottinghamshire
*Educated* . . . . . . . . . . University College of Wales, Aberystywth;
         McMaster University, Ontario;
         University College, Oxford
*Elected*. . . . . . . . . . . . 1997 MP for Hemel Hempstead
*Commons Office* . . . . . Tel: (020) 7219 4547 Fax: (020) 7219 0563
         Pager: 07734 604538
         E-mail: mcwaltert@parliament.uk
         Web: http://www.tonymcwaltermp.org.uk
         Secretarial Assistant – Mrs Ryma Howard
         Tel: (020) 7219 2460
         E-mail: howardr@parliament.uk
*Constituency Office* . . . . 7a Marlowes, Hemel Hempstead,
         Hertfordshire, HP1 1LA
         Tel: (01442) 251251 Fax: (01442) 241268
         E-mail: jeffersonp@parliament.uk
         Secretary – Mrs Patricia Jefferson
         Assistants – Mr Clive Brooks
                Mrs Linda Morris
*Parliamentary Interests* . Philosophy; Environmental Issues; Health;
         Economic Policy; Education; Welfare Reform:
         Policing; Science and Technology;
         Development Issues
*Leisure Interests* . . . . . . Tennis; Bridge; Croquet

**McWilliam, John** . . Blaydon
**Labour** . . . . . . . . . . . Majority 7,809 over Lib Dem
*Born*. . . . . . . . . . . . . . 16th May 1941 in Grangemouth
*Educated* . . . . . . . . . . Leith Academy; Heriot Watt College;
         Napier College of Science and Technology
*Elected*. . . . . . . . . . . . 1979 MP for Blaydon
*Offices Held* . . . . . . . . 1981 - 84 Chairman, Education Select
         Committee, House of Commons
         1983 - 84 Deputy Shadow Leader of
         the House
         1984 - 87 Opposition Whip
         1997 - Chairman, Committee of
         Selection, House of Commons
*Commons Office* . . . . . Tel: (020) 7219 4020
         E-mail: jdmblaydon@aol.com
*Constituency Office* . . . . 15 Shibdon Road, Blaydon-on-Tyne,
         NE21 5AF
         Tel: (0191) 414 2488 Fax: (0191) 414 8036
         Office Manager – Mr Frank Earl
         Secretary – Mrs Bernadette Oliphant
*Parliamentary Interests* . IT; Defence; Parliamentary Issues
*Leisure Interests* . . . . . . Fly Fishing; Music; Reading

**Mahmood, Khalid** . Birmingham Perry Barr
**Labour** . . . . . . . . . . . Majority 8,753 over Con
*Born*. . . . . . . . . . . . . . 13th July 1961 in Birmingham
*Educated* . . . . . . . . . . Golden Hillock Comprehensive School,
         Birmingham; Birmingham Polytechnic
*Elected*. . . . . . . . . . . . 2001 MP for Birmingham Perry Barr

**Mahon, Alice**. . . . . . Halifax
**Labour** . . . . . . . . . . . Majority 6,129 over Con
*Born*. . . . . . . . . . . . . . 28th September 1937 in Halifax,
         West Yorkshire
*Educated* . . . . . . . . . . Bradford University
*Elected*. . . . . . . . . . . . 1987 MP for Halifax
*Commons Office* . . . . . Tel: (020) 7219 4464 Fax: (020) 7219 2450
         E-mail: mahona@parliament.uk
         Parliamentary Secretary – Ms Matesha Ababa
*Constituency Office* . . . . 2 West Parade, Halifax,
         West Yorkshire, HX1 2TA
         Tel: (01422) 251800 Fax: (01422) 251888
         Parliamentary and Constituency Assistant –
         Mr Jago Parker
         Senior Secretary – Ms Linda Riordan
*Parliamentary Interests* . Health; Human Rights; Women's Right;
         Foreign Affairs

# MEMBERS OF THE HOUSE OF COMMONS

**Malins, Humfrey** CBE Woking
**Conservative** . . . . . . . Majority 6,759 over Lib Dem
*Born* . . . . . . . . . . . . . . 31st July 1945
*Educated* . . . . . . . . . . St John's School, Leatherhead;
 Brasenose College, Oxford;
 College of Law, Guildford
*Elected* . . . . . . . . . . . . 1982 - 92 MP for Croydon North West
 1997 MP for Woking
*Office Held* . . . . . . . . . 2001 - 03 Opposition Spokesman on
 Home Affairs
 2003 - Opposition Spokesman on Home,
 Constitutional and Legal Affairs
*Commons Office* . . . . . . Tel: (020) 7219 1189 Fax: (020) 7219 2624
 Pager: 07626 801287
 E-mail: malinsh@parliament.uk
 Assistant – Mr David Fowlis
*Constituency Office* . . . . Churchill House, Chobham Road, Woking,
 Surrey, GV21 4AA
 Tel: (01483) 773384 Fax: (01483) 770060
 E-mail: office@wcca.org.uk
*Parliamentary Interests* . Penology; Criminal Law
*Leisure Interests* . . . . . . Golf; Rugby; Football; Cooking; Gardening

**Mallaber, Judy** . . . . Amber Valley
**Labour** . . . . . . . . . . . Majority 7,227 over Con
*Born* . . . . . . . . . . . . . . 10th July 1951
*Educated* . . . . . . . . . . North London Collegiate School;
 St Anne's College, Oxford
*Elected* . . . . . . . . . . . . 1997 MP for Amber Valley
*Commons Office* . . . . . . Tel: (020) 7219 3428 Fax: (020) 7219 0991
 E-mail: j.mallaber@btinternet.com
 Parliamentary Assistant – Miss Joyce Sullivan
 E-mail: sullivanj@parliament.uk
 Research Assistant – Mr Louis Eustace
 E-mail: eustacel@parliament.uk
*Constituency Office* . . . . Prospect House, Nottingham Road, Ripley,
 Derbyshire, DE5 3AZ
 Tel: (01773) 512792 Fax; (01773) 742393
 Constituency Officer – Mrs Margaret Flude
 Constituency Assistant – Mr Tony Munro
*Parliamentary Interests* . Employment; Education

**Mallon, Seamus** . . . Newry and Armagh
**SDLP** . . . . . . . . . . . . Majority 3,576 over Sinn Fein
*Born* . . . . . . . . . . . . . . 17th August 1936 in Northern Ireland
*Educated* . . . . . . . . . . Christian Brothers Grammar School, Newry;
 St Mary's College of Education, Belfast
*Elected* . . . . . . . . . . . . 1986 MP for Newry and Armagh (By-election)
*Offices Held* . . . . . . . . Formerly Deputy Leader, SDLP
 1998 - 2003 Member, Northern Ireland
 Assembly (Deputy First Minister
 1999 - 2001)
*Constituency Office* . . . . 2 Bridge Street, Newry, Co Down, BT35 8AE
 Tel: (028) 3026 7933 Fax: (028) 3026 7828
 Secretary – Mrs Nuala Feehan
*Parliamentary Interests* . Justice Issues
*Leisure Interests* . . . . . . Golf; Fishing

**Mann, John** . . . . . . Bassetlaw
**Labour** . . . . . . . . . . . Majority 9,748 over Con
*Born* . . . . . . . . . . . . . . 10th January 1960
*Educated* . . . . . . . . . . Manchester University
*Elected* . . . . . . . . . . . . 2001 MP for Bassetlaw
*Commons Office* . . . . . Tel: (020) 7219 8345 Fax; (020) 7219 5965
 E-mail: mannj@parliament.uk
 Research Assistant – Ms Sadie Smith
 E-mail: smithsk@parliament.uk
*Constituency Office* . . . . 68A Carlton Road, Worksop,
 Nottinghamshire, SS0 1PH
 Tel: (01909) 506200 Fax: (01909) 532447
 Secretary – Ms Joanna White
 Assistant – Mr John Curry
 E-mail: curryj@parliament.uk

**Maples, John** . . . . . . Stratford-on-Avon
**Conservative** . . . . . . . Majority 11,802 over Lib Dem
*Born* . . . . . . . . . . . . . . 22nd April 1943
*Educated* . . . . . . . . . . Marlborough College;
 Downing College, Cambridge
*Elected* . . . . . . . . . . . . 1983 - 92 MP for Lewisham West
 1997 MP for Stratford-on-Avon
*Offices Held* . . . . . . . . 1990 - 92 Economic Secretary to the Treasury
 1994 - 95 Deputy Chairman,
 Conservative Party
 1997 - 98 Shadow Health Secretary
 1998 - 99 Shadow Defence Secretary
 1999 - 2000 Shadow Foreign Secretary
*Commons Office* . . . . . Tel: (020) 7219 5495 Fax: (020) 7219 2829
 E-mail: maplesj@parliament.uk
*Constituency Office* . . . . 3 Trinity Street, Stratford-on-Avon,
 Warwickshire, CV37 6BL
 Tel: (01789) 292723 Fax: (01789) 415886
 E-mail: stratford.tory@virgin.net
 Agent – Mr James Holloway

# MEMBERS OF THE HOUSE OF COMMONS

**Marris, Robert** .... Wolverhampton South West
**Labour** .......... Majority 3,487 over Con
*Born*. .............. 8th April 1955 in Wolverhampton
*Educated* .......... University of British Columbia
*Elected*. ........... 2001 MP for Wolverhampton South West
*Commons Office* ...... Tel: (020) 7219 8342
E-mail: robmarrismp@wolvessw.fsnet.co.uk
Web: http://www.robmarris.org.uk
*Constituency Office* .... 41 Bath Road, Wolverhampton, WV1 4EW
Tel: (01902) 771166 Fax: (01902) 427628
Caseworker – Mr Bill Smith O'Gorman

**Marsden, Gordon**. . Blackpool South
**Labour** .......... Majority 8,262 over Con
*Born*. .............. 28th November 1953 in Manchester
*Educated* .......... Stockport Grammar School;
New College, Oxford; London University;
Harvard University, USA
*Elected*. ........... 1997 MP for Blackpool South
*Offices Held* ........ 2001 - 02 PPS to Lord Irvine of Laing
(Lord Chancellor)
2003 - PPS to Tessa Jowell (Secretary of
State for Culture, Media and Sport)
*Commons Office* ..... Tel: (020) 7219 1262 Fax: (020) 7219 5859
Research Assistant – Mr Oliver Pauley
E-mail: pauleyo@parliament.uk
*Constituency Office* .... 304 Highfield Road, Blackpool, FY4 3JX
Tel: (01253) 344143 Fax: (01253) 344940
Assistant – Mr John Jones
*Parliamentary Interests*. Education; Tourism; Defence; Foreign Affairs
(especially Central/Eastern Europe);
Disabilities; Legal Affairs
*Leisure Interests* ...... World Music; Medieval Culture;
Heritage Sites and Gardens; Swimming

**Marsden, Paul** .... Shrewsbury and Atcham
**Liberal Democrat** ... Majority 3,579 Lab over Con
*Born*. .............. 18th March 1968 in Frodsham, Cheshire
*Educated* .......... Helsby High School; Teesside Polytechnic;
Open University
*Elected*. ........... 1997 MP for Shrewsbury and Atcham
(Labour 1997 - 2001, Liberal Democrat
from 2001)
*Offices Held* ........ 2002 - 03 Liberal Democrat Spokesman on
Health
2003 - Liberal Democrat Spokesman on
Transport
*Commons Office* ..... Tel: (020) 7219 2300 Fax: (020) 7219 0963
E-mail: marsdenp@parliament.uk
Web: http://www.paulmarsdenmp.com
*Constituency Office* .... 3rd Floor, Talbot House, Market Street,
Shrewsbury, SY1 1LG
Tel: (01743) 341422 Fax: (01743) 341261
Personal Assistant – Mrs Diane Coley
Secretary – Mrs Pam Jones
Administrator – Mrs Diane Holden
*Parliamentary Interests*. Health; Environment; Agriculture;
Rural Development; Economy
*Leisure Interests* ...... Cinema; Reading; Marathon Running;
Gardening; Local History

**Marshall, David** ... Glasgow Shettleston
**Labour** .......... Majority 9,818 over SNP
*Born*. .............. 7th May 1941 in Glasgow
*Educated* .......... Larbert High School; Denny High School;
Falkirk High School;
Woodside Senior Secondary School, Glasgow
*Elected*. ........... 1979 MP for Glasgow Shettleston
*Office Held* ......... 1997 - 2001 Chairman, Scottish Affairs
Select Committee, House of Commons
*Commons Office* ..... Tel: (020) 7219 5134
E-mail: marshallda@parliament.uk
*Leisure Interests* ..... Gardening; Music

**Marshall-Andrews, Robert** QC Medway
**Labour** .......... Majority 3,780 over Con
*Born*. .............. 10th April 1944 in London
*Educated* .......... Mill Hill School, London; Bristol University
*Elected*. ........... 1997 MP for Medway
*Commons Office* ..... Tel: (020) 7219 6920 Fax: (020) 7219 2933
Mobile: 07768 935730
Pager: 07644 006394
E-mail: marshallandrews@parliament.uk
PA – Ms Jill Fennell
Research Assistants –
Mr Stephen Hubbard
Mr Christopher Rumsey
E-mail: [surnameinitial]@parliament.uk
*Constituency Office* .... Moathouse, 1 Castle Hill, Rochester,
Kent, ME1 1OQ
Tel: (01634) 814687 Fax: (01634) 831294
Personal Assistant – Ms Jill Fennell
*Parliamentary Interests*. Law; Environment; Higher Education;
Museums
*Leisure Interests* ...... Writing; Walking; Reading; Rugby; Cricket

**Martin, Rt Hon Michael** Glasgow Springburn
**Speaker** .......... Majority 11,378 over SNP
*Born*. .............. 3rd July 1945 in Glasgow
*Educated* .......... St Patrick's School, Glasgow
*Elected*. ........... 1979 MP for Glasgow Springburn
*Offices Held* ........ 1987 - 97 Chairman, Scottish Grand
Committee, House of Commons
1997 - 2000 First Deputy Chairman of Ways
and Means, House of Commons
2000 - Speaker of the House of Commons
*Commons Office* ..... Tel: (020) 7219 5300 Fax: (020) 7219 6901
Speaker's Secretary – Mr Roger Daw
Tel: (020) 7219 4111
E-mail: dawrk@parliament.uk
*Constituency Office* .... Tel: (0141) 762 2329 Fax: (0141) 762 1519
Secretaries – Mrs Mary Drain
Mrs Georgie Rainey
*Leisure Interests* ...... Hill Walking; Local History; Piping

# MEMBERS OF THE HOUSE OF COMMONS

**Martlew, Eric** ..... Carlisle
**Labour** ........... Majority 5,702 over Con
*Born* .............. 3rd January 1949 in Carlisle, Cumbria
*Educated* .......... Harraby School, Carlisle; Carlisle College
*Elected* ........... 1987 MP for Carlisle
*Offices Held* ........ 1981 - 83 Chairman, Cumbria County Council
　　　　　　　　　　1992 - 95 Opposition Spokesman on Defence
　　　　　　　　　　1995 - 97 Opposition Whip
　　　　　　　　　　1997 - 98 PPS to David Clark (Chancellor of
　　　　　　　　　　　　the Duchy of Lancaster)
　　　　　　　　　　1999 - 2001 PPS to Baroness Jay of
　　　　　　　　　　　　Paddington (Leader, House of Lords)
*Commons Office* ...... Tel: (020) 7219 4114 Fax: (020) 7219 6898
　　　　　　　　　　Mobile: 07977 926311
　　　　　　　　　　E-mail: eric.martlew@email.labour.org.uk
　　　　　　　　　　Web: http://www.ericmartlewmp.co.uk
*Constituency Office* .... 3 Chatsworth Square, Carlisle,
　　　　　　　　　　Cumbria, CA1 1HB
　　　　　　　　　　Tel: (01228) 511395 Fax: (01228) 819798
　　　　　　　　　　Researcher – Ms Elsie Martlew
　　　　　　　　　　Secretary – Ms Shirley Reay
　　　　　　　　　　Admin Assistant – Mrs Christine Potter
*Parliamentary Interests* . Transport; Health; Social Services;
　　　　　　　　　　Agriculture; Defence
*Leisure Interests* ...... Fell Walking; Local History;
　　　　　　　　　　Watching Rugby League


**Mates, Rt Hon Michael** Hampshire East
**Conservative** ....... Majority 8,890 over Lib Dem
*Born* .............. 9th June 1934 in London
*Educated* .......... Salisbury Cathedral School; Blundell's School;
　　　　　　　　　　King's College Cambridge
*Elected* ........... 1974 MP for Petersfield, then (1983) for
　　　　　　　　　　Hampshire East
*Offices Held* ........ 1986 - 92 Chairman, Defence Select
　　　　　　　　　　　　Committee House of Commons
　　　　　　　　　　1992 - 93 Minister of State,
　　　　　　　　　　　　Northern Ireland Office
　　　　　　　　　　2001 - Chairman, Northern Ireland Affairs
　　　　　　　　　　　　Select Committee, House of Commons
*Commons Office* ...... Tel: (020) 7219 5166 Fax: (020) 7219 4884
　　　　　　　　　　Web: http://www.epolitix.com/webminster/
　　　　　　　　　　michael-mates
　　　　　　　　　　Secretary – Mrs Janice Dust
*Constituency Office* .... 14a Butts Road, Alton, Hampshire,
　　　　　　　　　　GU34 1ND
　　　　　　　　　　Tel: (01420) 84122 Fax: (01420) 84925
　　　　　　　　　　Executive Secretary – Ms Beverly Carpenter


**Maude, Rt Hon Francis** Horsham
**Conservative** ....... Majority 13,666 over Lib Dem
*Born* .............. 1953
*Educated* .......... Abingdon School;
　　　　　　　　　　Corpus Christi College, Cambridge;
　　　　　　　　　　College of Law
*Elected* ........... 1983 - 92 MP for North Warwickshire
　　　　　　　　　　1997 MP for Horsham
*Offices Held* ........ 1985 - 87 Government Whip
　　　　　　　　　　1987 - 88 Minister for Corporate and
　　　　　　　　　　　　Consumer Affairs, Department
　　　　　　　　　　　　of Trade and Industry
　　　　　　　　　　1989 - 90 Minister of State, Foreign and
　　　　　　　　　　　　Commonwealth Office
　　　　　　　　　　1990 - 92 Financial Secretary to the Treasury
　　　　　　　　　　1997 - 98 Shadow Secretary for Culture,
　　　　　　　　　　　　Media and Sport
　　　　　　　　　　1998 - 2000 Shadow Chancellor of the
　　　　　　　　　　　　Exchequer
　　　　　　　　　　2000 - 01 Shadow Foreign Secretary
*Commons Office* ...... Tel: (020) 7219 2494 Fax: (020) 7219 2990
　　　　　　　　　　E-mail: francismaudemp@parliament.uk
　　　　　　　　　　Web: http://www.francismaude.com
　　　　　　　　　　Secretaries – Lady Susan Forsyth
　　　　　　　　　　　　　　Miss Pippa Way
*Constituency Office* .... Gough House, Madeira Avenue, Horsham,
　　　　　　　　　　West Sussex, RH12 1AB
　　　　　　　　　　Tel: (01403) 242000 Fax: (01403) 210600
　　　　　　　　　　Agent – Mrs Toni Bradnum
　　　　　　　　　　Secretary – Mrs Anne Walls


**Mawhinney, Rt Hon Sir Brian** Cambridgeshire North West
**Conservative** ....... Majority 8,101 over Lab
*Born* .............. 26th July 1940 in Belfast
*Educated* .......... Royal Belfast Academical Institution;
　　　　　　　　　　Queen's University, Belfast;
　　　　　　　　　　Michigan University, USA; London University
*Elected* ........... 1979 - 97 MP for Peterborough
　　　　　　　　　　1997 MP for Cambridgeshire North West
*Offices Held* ........ 1986 - 90 Parliamentary Secretary,
　　　　　　　　　　　　Northern Ireland Office
　　　　　　　　　　1990 - 92 Minister of State,
　　　　　　　　　　　　Northern Ireland Office
　　　　　　　　　　1992 - 94 Minister of State,
　　　　　　　　　　　　Department of Health
　　　　　　　　　　1994 - 95 Secretary of State for Transport
　　　　　　　　　　1995 - 97 Minister without Portfolio and
　　　　　　　　　　　　Chairman of the Conservative Party
　　　　　　　　　　1997 - 98 Shadow Home Secretary
*Commons Office* ...... Tel: (020) 7219 6205 Fax: (020) 7219 2737
　　　　　　　　　　Secretary – Mrs Kate Hicks
*Constituency Office* .... 18 Peterborough Road, Wansford,
　　　　　　　　　　Cambridgeshire, PE8 6JN
　　　　　　　　　　Tel: (01733) 261868 Fax: (01733) 266887
　　　　　　　　　　Personal Assistant – Mrs Judi Broadhead
*Parliamentary Interests* . Health; Northern Ireland; Transport;
　　　　　　　　　　United States
*Leisure Interests* ...... Sport

# MEMBERS OF THE HOUSE OF COMMONS

**May, Rt Hon Theresa**  Maidenhead
**Conservative** . . . . . . Majority 3,284 over Lib Dem
*Born*. . . . . . . . . . . . . . 1st October 1956 in Eastbourne
*Educated* . . . . . . . . . . Wheatley Park Comprehensive;
St Hugh's College, Oxford
*Elected*. . . . . . . . . . . . 1997 MP for Maidenhead
*Offices Held* . . . . . . . . 1998 - 99 Opposition Spokesman on Schools,
Disabled People and Women
1999 - 2001 Shadow Education and
Employment Secretary
2001 - 02 Shadow Secretary for Transport,
Local Government and the Regions
2002 - 03 Chairman of the Conservative Party
2003 - 04 Shadow Secretary for
Environment and Transport
2004 - Opposition Spokesman on the Family
*Commons Office* . . . . . Tel: (020) 7219 5206 Fax: (020) 7219 1145
E-mail: mayt@parliament.uk
Web: http://www.tmay.co.uk
Secretary – Mrs Jenny Sharkey
E-mail: sharkeyj@parliament.uk
Researcher – Mr Chris Goater
Tel: (020) 7219 1304
E-mail: goaterc@parliament.uk
*Constituency Office* . . . . 2 Castle End Farm, Ruscombe,
Berkshire, RG10 9XA
Tel: (0118) 934 5433 Fax: (0118) 934 5288
E-mail: gillianowen@tory.org
Agent/Secretary – Mrs Gillian Owen
*Parliamentary Interests*. Education; Disability Issues; Transport;
Local Government

**Meacher, Rt Hon Michael**  Oldham West and Royton
**Labour** . . . . . . . . . . . Majority 13,365 over Con
*Born*. . . . . . . . . . . . . . 4th November 1939 in Berkhamsted,
Hertfordshire
*Educated* . . . . . . . . . . Berkhamsted School; New College, Oxford;
London School of Economics
*Elected*. . . . . . . . . . . . 1970 MP for Oldham West, then (1997)
Oldham West and Royton
*Offices Held* . . . . . . . . 1974 - 75 Parliamentary Secretary,
Department of Industry
1975 - 76 Parliamentary Secretary,
Department of Health and Social Security
1976 - 79 Parliamentary Secretary,
Department of Trade
1983 - 87, 1989 - 92 Opposition
Spokesman on Health and Social Security
1987 - 89, 1995 - 96 Opposition
Spokesman on Employment
1992 - 93 Shadow Minister for
Overseas Development
1993 - 94 Shadow Minister for
Citizen's Charter
1994 - 95 Shadow Transport Secretary
1996 - 97 Opposition Spokesman on
Environmental Protection
1997 - 2003 Minister for the Environment
(Minister of State, Department for
Environment, Transport and the Regions,
then Department for Environment,
Food and Rural Affairs)
*Commons Office* . . . . . Tel: (020) 7219 6461 Fax: (020) 7219 5945
E-mail: massonm@parliament.uk
Web: http://www.
epolitix.com/en/mpwebsites/michael-meacher
Parliamentary Assistant – Ms Monica Masson
Tel: (020) 7219 4532
*Constituency Office* . . . . 11 Church Lane, Oldham, OL1 3AN
Tel: (0161) 626 5779 Fax: (0161) 626 8572
Constituency Secretary – Ms Shirley Buckley
E-mail: buckleys@parliament.uk
*Parliamentary Interests*. Environment
*Leisure Interests* . . . . . Reading; Sport

**Meale, Alan** . . . . . . . Mansfield
**Labour** . . . . . . . . . . . Majority 11,038 over Con
*Born*. . . . . . . . . . . . . . 31st July 1949 in Bishop Auckland,
Co Durham
*Educated* . . . . . . . . . . St Joseph's RC School, Bishop Auckland;
Durham University; Ruskin College, Oxford;
Sheffield Hallam University
*Elected*. . . . . . . . . . . . 1987 MP for Mansfield
*Offices Held* . . . . . . . . 1992 - 94 Opposition Whip
1994 - 97 PPS to John Prescott (as
Deputy Leader, Labour Party, then as
Deputy Prime Minister)
1998 - 99 Parliamentary Secretary,
Department of Environment,
Transport and the Regions
*Constituency Office* . . . . 85 Westgate, Mansfield, Nottinghamshire,
NG18 1RT
Tel: (01623) 660531 Fax: (01623) 420495
Secretary – Miss Diahanne Roper
Caseworker/Receptionist –
Mrs Sally Higgins
*Parliamentary Interests*. Human Rights; Drug Misuse; Sports;
European Union; Music; Unemployment;
Media; Transport; Health; Social Security;
Home Affairs; Environment; Animal Welfare
*Leisure Interests* . . . . . . Reading; Writing; Music; Arts; Politics;
Cyprus; Sport; Football (Mansfield Town FC)

# MEMBERS OF THE HOUSE OF COMMONS

**Mercer, Patrick** OBE  Newark
**Conservative** . . . . . . Majority 4,073 over Lab
*Born*. . . . . . . . . . . . . 26th June 1956
*Educated* . . . . . . . . . King's School, Chester;
Exeter College, Oxford;
Royal Military Academy, Sandhurst
*Elected*. . . . . . . . . . . 1997 MP for Newark
*Office Held*. . . . . . . . 2003 - Opposition Spokesman on Homeland
Security
*Commons Office* . . . . . Tel: (020) 7219 8477 Fax: (020) 7219 1961
E-mail: millicanh@parliament.uk
Web: http://www.patrickmercer.org.uk
Parliamentary Assistant –
Mrs Heather Millican
*Constituency Office* . . . . 29A London Road, Newark,
Nottinghamshire, NG24 1TN
Tel: (01636) 703269 Fax; (01636) 676312
E-mail: graysj@parliament.uk
*Parliamentary Interests* . Defence; Homeland Security
*Leisure Interests* . . . . . . History; Country Sports

**Merron, Gillian**. . . . Lincoln
**Labour** . . . . . . . . . . . Majority 8,420 over Con
*Born*. . . . . . . . . . . . . . 12th April 1959
*Educated* . . . . . . . . . . Wanstead High School; Lancaster University
*Elected*. . . . . . . . . . . . 1997 MP for Lincoln
*Offices Held* . . . . . . . . 2001 - 02 PPS to John Reid (Secretary of
State for Northern Ireland)
2002 - Assistant Government Whip
*Commons Office* . . . . . . Tel: (020) 7219 4031/8355
Fax: (020) 7219 0489
E-mail: merrong@parliament.uk
Parliamentary Assistants –  Mr Chris Page
Personal Assistant –  Miss Helen Johnson
E-mail: [surnameinitial]@parliament.uk
*Constituency Office* . . . . Grafton House, 32 Newland,
Lincoln, LN1 1XJ
Tel: (01522) 888688 Fax: (01522) 888686
Constituency Assistant – Mrs Sally Doughty
*Parliamentary Interests* . Economy; Low Pay; Employment;
Business Development; Transport
*Leisure Interests* . . . . . . Walking; Films; Football (Lincoln City FC);
Running

**Michael, Rt Hon Alun**  Cardiff South and Penarth
**Labour** . . . . . . . . . . . Majority 12,287 over Con
*Born*. . . . . . . . . . . . . . 22nd August 1943 in North Wales
*Educated* . . . . . . . . . . Colwyn Bay Grammar School;
Keele University
*Elected*. . . . . . . . . . . . 1987 MP for Cardiff South and Penarth
*Offices Held* . . . . . . . . 1987 - 88 Opposition Whip
1988 - 92 Opposition Spokesman on
Welsh Affairs
1992 - 97 Opposition Spokesman on
Home Affairs
1997 - 98 Minister of State, Home Office
1998 - 99 Secretary of State for Wales
1999 - 2000 Member and First Secretary,
Welsh Assembly
2001 - Minister of State, Department for
Environment, Food and Rural Affairs
(Minister for Rural Affairs)
*Commons Office* . . . . . . Tel: (020) 7219 5980 Fax: (020) 7219 5930
E-mail: alunmichaelmp@parliament.uk
Web: http://www.alunmichael.com
Researcher – Mr Jonathan Cox
E-mail: coxj@parliament.uk
*Constituency Office* . . . . PO Box 453, Cardiff, CF11 9YN
Tel: (029) 2022 3533 Fax: (029) 2022 9936
Senior Caseworker and Office Manager –
Ms Sheryl Edwards
E-mail: edwardss@parliament.uk
Administrative Researcher –
Ms Kristin Vaughan
E-mail: vaughank@parliament.uk
*Parliamentary Interests* . Economic Development; Crime; Police;
Criminal Justice; Voluntary Sector;
Community Development; National Parks
and Access Issues
*Leisure Interests* . . . . . . Hill Walking; Running; Music; Reading

**Milburn, Rt Hon Alan**  Darlington
**Labour** . . . . . . . . . . . Majority 10,384 over Con
*Born*. . . . . . . . . . . . . . 27th January 1958 in Birmingham
*Educated* . . . . . . . . . . John Marlay School, Newcastle-upon-Tyne;
Stokesley Comprehensive School;
Lancaster University; Newcastle University
*Elected*. . . . . . . . . . . . 1992 MP for Darlington
*Offices Held* . . . . . . . . 1995 - 96 Opposition Spokesman on Health
1996 - 97 Opposition Spokesman on Treasury
and Economic Affairs
1997 - 99 Minister of State,
Department of Health
1998 - 99 Chief Secretary to the Treasury
1999 - 2003 Secretary of State for Health
2004 - Chancellor of the Duchy of Lancaster
*Commons Office* . . . . . . Tel: (020) 7219 3594 Fax: (020) 7219 2689
E-mail: forbesv@parliament.uk
Research Assistant – Miss Vicki Forbes
*Constituency Office* . . . . 123 Victoria Road, Darlington,
Co Durham, DL1 5JH
Tel: (01325) 380366 Fax: (01325) 381341
Assistants – Ms Elaine Hope
Mrs Kathryn MacColl
E-mails: [surnameinitial]@parliamennt.uk
*Parliamentary Interests* . Regional Policy; Economic Policy; Health;
Crime;
*Leisure Interests* . . . . . . Family; Films; Music; Football; Cricket

# MEMBERS OF THE HOUSE OF COMMONS

**Miliband, David** ... South Shields
**Labour** ........... Majority 14,090 over Con
*Born*............... 15th July 1965 in London
*Educated* .......... Haverstock Comprehensive School;
    Corpus Christi College, Oxford;
    Massachusetts Institute of Technology
*Elected*............. 2001 MP for South Shields
*Office Held*......... 2002 - Minister of State, Department for
    Education and Skills (Minister for School
    Standards)
*Constituency Office* .... Ede House, 143 Westoe Road,
    South Shields, NE33 3PD
    Tel: (0191) 456 8910/7136
    Fax: (0191) 456 5842
    Assistants – Mr Scott Duffy
        Ms Hannah Reed

**Miller, Andrew** .... Ellesmere Port and Neston
**Labour** ........... Majority 10,861 over Con
*Born*............... 23rd March 1949 in Middlesex
*Educated* .......... Highbury Technical College;
    London School of Economics
*Elected*............. 1992 MP for Ellesmere Port and Neston
*Office Held*......... 2001 - PPS to Department of Trade and
    Industry Ministers
*Commons Office* ..... Tel: (020) 7219 3580 Fax: (020) 7219 3796
    E-mail: millera@parliament.uk
    Web: http://www.andrew-miller-mp.co.uk
    Secretary/Researcher – Ms Julie Spencer
    E-mail: spencerj@parliament.uk
*Constituency Office* .... Whitby Hall Lodge, Stanney Lane,
    Ellesmere Port, Cheshire, CH65 6QY
    Tel: (0151) 357 3019 Fax: (0151) 356 8226
    Secretaries/Researchers –
      Mrs Fran Miller
      Ms Catherine Sherlock
    Clerical Assistant – Mrs Gwynn Cowper
*Parliamentary Interests* . Science and Technology; Communications and
    Information Technology; Regional Economy;
    Industry; Environment
*Leisure Interests* ...... Music; Photography; Tennis; Cricket

**Mitchell, Andrew** .. Sutton Coldfield
**Conservative** ....... Majority 10,104 over Lab
*Born*............... 23rd March 1956
*Educated* .......... Rugby School; Jesus College, Cambridge
*Elected*............. 2001 MP for Sutton Coldfield
*Office Held*......... 2003 - 04 Opposition Spokesman on
    Economic Affairs
    2004 - Opposition Spokesman on
    Home and Constitutional and Legal Affairs
*Commons Office* ..... Tel: (020) 7219 8516
    E-mail: andrewmitchellmp@parliament.uk
    Web: http://www.andrew-mitchell-mp.co.uk
*Constituency Office* .... 36 High Street, Sutton Coldfield, B72 1UP
    Tel: (0121) 354 2229 Fax: (0121) 321 1762
    E-mail: info@sutton-coldfield-tories.org.uk
    Agent – Mr Martyn Punyer
*Parliamentary Interests* . Pensions; Social Services; International
    Development

**Mitchell, Austin** ... Great Grimsby
**Labour** ........... Majority 11,484 over Con
*Born*............... 19th September 1934 in Yorkshire
*Educated* .......... Bingley Grammar School;
    Manchester University;
    Nuffield College, Oxford
*Elected*............. 1977 MP for Grimsby (By-election), then
    (1983) Great Grimsby
*Offices Held* ........ 1980 - 85 Opposition Whip
    1987 - 89 Opposition Spokesman on
    Trade and Industry
*Commons Office* ..... Tel: (020) 7219 4559 Fax: (020) 7219 4843
    Mobile: 07719 764939
    E-mail: mitchellav@parliament.uk
    Web: http://www.austinmitchell.co.uk
    Parliamentary Assistant – Miss Joy Millward
*Constituency Office* .... 15 New Cartergate, Grimsby, DN31 1RB
    Tel: (01472) 342145 Fax: (01472) 251484
    Secretary – Ms Joyce Benton
    Constituency Caseworker – Ms Pat Murray
*Parliamentary Interests* . Accountancy/Insolvency Professions;
    Agriculture; Broadcasting; Consumer Affairs;
    Economy; Electoral/Constitutional Reform;
    Europe (anti-EU); Fishing Industry;
    Legal Reform; Media; Poverty;
    Trade and Industry
*Leisure Interests* ...... Photography

**Moffatt, Laura**...... Crawley
**Labour** ........... Majority 6,770 over Con
*Born*............... 9th April 1954 in London
*Educated* .......... Hazelwick Comprehensive;
    Crawley College of Technology
*Elected*............. 1997 MP for Crawley
*Offices Held* ........ 1989 - 90 Mayor of Crawley
    2002 - 03 PPS to Lord Irvine of Lairg
    (Lord Chancellor)
    2003 - PPS to Lord Falconer (Secretary of
    State for Constitutional Affairs and
    Lord Chancellor)
*Commons Office* ..... Tel: (020) 7219 3619 Fax: (020) 7219 0473
    Pager: 07644 006452
    E-mail: moffattl@parliament.uk
    Web: http://www.lauramoffattmp.co.uk
*Constituency Office* .... 6 The Broadway, Crawley, RH10 1DS
    Tel: (01293) 526005 Fax: (01293) 527610
    Personal Assistant – Ms Denise Clewer
    Researcher – Mrs Alison Cornell
    Caseworker – Mrs Sharon Braes
*Parliamentary Interests* . Defence; Health; Housing; Aviation
*Leisure Interests* ...... Swimming; Reading; Caravanning; Walking

# MEMBERS OF THE HOUSE OF COMMONS

**Mole, Chris** . . . . . . . Ipswich
**Labour** . . . . . . . . . . . Majority 4,087 over Con
*Born*. . . . . . . . . . . . . . 16th March 1958 in Bromley, Kent
*Educated* . . . . . . . . . . Dulwich College; University of Kent
Canterbury
*Elected*. . . . . . . . . . . . 2001 MP for Ipswich (By-election)
*Office Held*. . . . . . . . . 1993 - 2001 Leader, Suffolk County Council
*Commons Office* . . . . . Tel: (020) 7219 4158 Fax: 0870 1305681
Pager: 07693 268320
Parliamentary Researcher – Mr Chris Magee
E-mail: mageec@parliament.uk
*Constituency Office* . . . . 33 Silent Street, Ipswich, IP1 1TF
Tel: (01473) 281559 Fax; (01473) 217489
Office Manager – Ms Sandra Jones
*Parliamentary Interests* . Education; Economic Development; Transport;
Social Care

**Moonie, Dr Lewis** . Kirkcaldy
**Labour** . . . . . . . . . . . Majority 8,963 over SNP
*Born*. . . . . . . . . . . . . . 25th February 1947 in Dundee
*Educated* . . . . . . . . . . Grove Academy, Dundee;
St Andrews University; Edinburgh University
*Elected*. . . . . . . . . . . . 1987 MP for Kirkcaldy
*Offices Held* . . . . . . . . 1989 - 92 Opposition Spokesman on
Trade and Industry
1992 - 94 Opposition Spokesman on
Science and Technology
1995 - 97 Opposition Spokesman on
National Heritage
1997 - 2000 Chairman, Finance and Services
Select Committee, House of Commons
2000 - 03 Parliamentary Secretary,
Ministry of Defence
*Constituency Office* . . . . Wing A, Suite D, Carlyle House,
Carlyle Road, Kirkcaldy, Fife, KY1 1DB
Tel: (01592) 564116 Fax; (01592) 561085
E-mail: lewismoonie@wwmail.co.uk
Assistant – Mr Neil Crooks
Secretary – Mrs Ruby Arnott
*Parliamentary Interests* . Defence; Industry; Science and Technology;
Energy

**Moore, Michael** . . . Tweeddale, Ettrick and Lauderdale
**Liberal Democrat** . . . Majority 5,157 over Lab
*Born*. . . . . . . . . . . . . . 3rd June 1965 in Dundonald,
Northern Ireland
*Educated* . . . . . . . . . . Strathallan School; Jedburgh Grammar School;
Edinburgh University
*Elected*. . . . . . . . . . . . 1997 MP for Tweeddale, Ettrick and
Lauderdale
*Offices Held* . . . . . . . . 1997 - 99, 2001 Liberal Democrat
Spokesman on Scottish Affairs
1999 - 01 Liberal Democrat Spokesman on
Transport
2002 - Liberal Democrat Spokesman
on Foreign Affairs
*Commons Office* . . . . . Tel: (020) 7219 2236 Fax: (020) 7219 0263
E-mail: michaelmoore@parliament.uk
Web: http://www.michaelmoore.org.uk
Researcher – Ms Alexandra Hernandez
E-mail: hernandeza@parliament.uk
*Constituency Office* . . . . 11 Island Street, Galashiels, TD1 1NZ
Tel: (01896) 663650 Fax: (01896) 663655
Caseworker– Mrs Margaret Lundie
Personal Assistant – Mrs Lesley Crozier
E-mail: [surnameinitial]@parliament.uk
*Parliamentary Interests* . Transport; Textiles; Europe; Foreign Affairs:
Corporate Social Responsibility
*Leisure Interests* . . . . . . Hillwalking; Jazz; Rugby

**Moran, Margaret** . . Luton South
**Labour** . . . . . . . . . . . Majority 10,133 over Con
*Born*. . . . . . . . . . . . . . 24th April 1955 in London
*Educated* . . . . . . . . . . St Ursula's High School, Greenwich;
St Mary's College, Twickenham;
Birmingham University
*Elected*. . . . . . . . . . . . 1997 MP for Luton South
*Offices Held* . . . . . . . . Formerly Leader, London Borough of
Lewisham Council
1997 - 2000 PPS to Dr Mo Mowlam
(Secretary of State for Northern Ireland,
then Minister for Cabinet Office)
2003 - Assistant Government Whip
*Commons Office* . . . . . Tel: (020) 7219 5049 Fax: (020) 7219 5094
E-mail: moranm@parliament.uk
*Constituency Office* . . . . 3 Union Street, Luton, LU1 3AN
Tel: (01592) 730764 Fax: (01582) 731885
Personal Assistant – Miss Jeannie Hobart
E-mail: hobartj@parliament.uk
*Parliamentary Interests* . Housing; Transport; New Technology;
Economy; Employment

**Morgan, Julie** . . . . . Cardiff North
**Labour** . . . . . . . . . . . Majority 6,165 over Con
*Born*. . . . . . . . . . . . . . 2nd November 1944 in Cardiff
*Educated* . . . . . . . . . . Howells School; Kings College, London
Manchester University
Cardiff University
*Elected*. . . . . . . . . . . . 1997 MP for Cardiff North
*Commons Office* . . . . . Tel: (020) 7219 6960 Fax: (020) 7219 0960
E-mail: morganj@parliament.uk
*Constituency Office* . . . . 17 Plasnewydd, Whitchurch, Cardiff,
CF14 1NR
Tel: (029) 2062 4166 Fax: (029) 2062 3661
*Parliamentary Interests* . Equal Opportunities; Social Services; Health
*Leisure Interests* . . . . . . Swimming; Walking; Theatre; Reading

# MEMBERS OF THE HOUSE OF COMMONS

**Morley, Elliot** . . . . Scunthorpe
**Labour** . . . . . . . . . . Majority 10,372 over Con
*Born.* . . . . . . . . . . . . 6th July 1952 in Liverpool
*Educated* . . . . . . . . . St Margaret's High School, Liverpool;
Hull College of Education
*Elected.* . . . . . . . . . . 1987 MP for Glanford and Scunthorpe,
then (1997) Scunthorpe
*Offices Held* . . . . . . . 1989 - 97 Opposition Spokesman on
Agriculture, Food and Rural Affairs
1997 - 2003 Parliamentary Secretary,
Ministry of Agriculture, Fisheries and Food;
then (from 2001) Department for
Environment, Food and Rural Affairs
2003 - Minister of State, Department for
Environment, Food and Rural Affairs
(Minister for the Environment)
*Constituency Office* . . . . Kinsley Labour Club, Cole Street, Scunthorpe,
South Humberside, DN15 6QS
Tel: (01724) 842000 Fax: (01724) 281734
E-mail: emorleymp@aol.com
Secretaries – Mrs Pauline Carlile
Mrs Andrea Deas
Research Assistant – Mr John O'Connor
*Leisure Interests* . . . . . . Ornithology; Environment

**Morris, Rt Hon Estelle** Birmingham Yardley
**Labour** . . . . . . . . . . . Majority 2,578 over Lib Dem
*Born.* . . . . . . . . . . . . . 17th June 1952 in Manchester
*Educated* . . . . . . . . . . Whalley Range High School, Manchester;
Coventry College of Education;
Warwick University
*Elected.* . . . . . . . . . . . 1992 MP for Birmingham Yardley
*Offices Held* . . . . . . . . 1994 -95 Opposition Whip
1995- 97 Opposition Spokesman on Education
1997 - 98 Parliamentary Secretary,
Department for Education and Employment
1998 - 2001 Minister of State, Department for
Education and Employment
2001 - 02 Secretary of State for
Education and Skills
2003 - Minister of State, Department for
Culture, Media and Sport
(Minister for the Arts)
*Constituency Office* . . . . Tel: (0121) 706 6418 Fax: (0121) 706 8327
E-mail: morrise@parliament.uk
Personal Assistant – Ms Sheila Brookes
Research Assistant – Mr Peter Griffiths
*Parliamentary Interests* . Education; Housing; Industry; Health

**Moss, Malcolm** . . . . Cambridgeshire North East
**Conservative** . . . . . . . Majority 6,373 over Lab
*Born.* . . . . . . . . . . . . . 6th March 1943 in Audenshaw, Manchester
*Educated* . . . . . . . . . . Audenshaw Grammar School;
St John's College, Cambridge
*Elected.* . . . . . . . . . . . 1987 MP for Cambridgeshire North East
*Offices Held* . . . . . . . . 1994 - 97 Parliamentary Secretary,
Northern Ireland Office
1997 - 99 Opposition Spokesman on
Northern Ireland
1999 - 2001 Opposition Spokesman on
Agriculture, Fisheries and Food
2001 - 02 Opposition Spokesman on
Local Government and the Regions
2002 - 03 Opposition Spokesman on
Culture, Media and Sport
2003 - Opposition Spokesman on Home,
Constitutional and Legal Affairs
*Commons Office* . . . . . . Tel: (020) 7219 6933 Fax: (020) 7219 6840
E-mail: mossm@parliament.uk
Web: http://www.malmoss.easynet.co.uk
Secretary/PA – Mrs Sonya Moss
Tel: (020) 7219 1426 Fax: (020) 7219 1051
E-mail: mosss@parliament.uk
*Constituency Office* . . . . 111 High Street, March, Cambridgeshire,
PE15 9LH
Tel: (01354) 656541 Fax: (01354) 660417
Secretary – Mrs Mary Brownlow
Administrative Assistant – Mrs Debbie Clark
*Parliamentary Interests* . Health; Small Businesses; Foreign Affairs;
Education
*Leisure Interests* . . . . . . Music; Tennis; Skiing; Gardening

**Mountford, Kali** . . . Colne Valley
**Labour** . . . . . . . . . . . Majority 4,639 over Con
*Born.* . . . . . . . . . . . . . 12th January 1954 in Crewe
*Educated* . . . . . . . . . . Crewe County Grammar School for Girls;
Crewe and Alsager College
*Elected.* . . . . . . . . . . . 1997 MP for Colne Valley
*Office Held* . . . . . . . . . 2003 - PPS to Desmond Browne (Minister of
State, Home Office)
*Commons Office* . . . . . . Tel: (020) 7219 4507 Fax: (020) 7219 1256
E-mail: mountfordk@parliament.uk
*Constituency Office* . . . . 23 Carr Lane, Slaithwaite, Huddersfield,
HD7 5AG
Tel: (01484) 840100 Fax: (01484) 840101
Office Manager – Mr Ian Leedham
E-mail: leedhami@parliament.uk
*Parliamentary Interests* . Pensions; Consumers; Banking;
Domestic Violence

**Mudie, George** . . . . Leeds East
**Labour** . . . . . . . . . . . Majority 12,643 over Con
*Born.* . . . . . . . . . . . . . 6th February 1945 in Scotland
*Educated* . . . . . . . . . . Hull University
*Elected.* . . . . . . . . . . . 1992 MP for Leeds East
*Offices Held* . . . . . . . . 1994 - 97 Opposition Whip
1997 - 98 Government Deputy Chief Whip
(Treasurer of H M Household)
1998 - 99 Parliamentary Secretary,
Department for Education and Employment

# MEMBERS OF THE HOUSE OF COMMONS

**Mullin, Chris** . . . . . Sunderland South
**Labour** . . . . . . . . . . Majority 13,667 over Con
*Born*. . . . . . . . . . . . . 12th December 1947 in Essex
*Educated* . . . . . . . . . St Joseph's College, Ipswich; Hull University
*Elected*. . . . . . . . . . . 1987 MP for Sunderland South
*Offices Held* . . . . . . . 1997 - 99, 2001 - 03 Chairman, Home Affairs
    Select Committee, House of Commons
    1999 - 2001 Parliamentary Secretary,
    Department for Environment, Transport
    and the Regions
    2001 Parliamentary Secretary, Department
    for International Development
    2003 - Parliamentary Secretary,
    Foreign and Commonwealth Office
*Constituency Office* . . . . 3, The Esplanade, Sunderland, SR2 7BQ
    Tel: (0191) 567 2848 Fax: (0191) 510 1063
    Assistant – Mr Graham March
    Secretary – Ms Pat Aston
*Parliamentary Interests* . Justice; Democracy; Farm Animal Welfare
*Leisure Interests* . . . . . . Walking; Gardening; Writing

**Munn, Meg**. . . . . . . . Sheffield Heeley
**Labour** . . . . . . . . . . Majority 11,704 over Lib Dem
*Born*. . . . . . . . . . . . . 1959 in Sheffield
*Educated* . . . . . . . . . . Rowlinson Comprehensive School;
    York University; Nottingham University
*Elected*. . . . . . . . . . . . 2001 MP for Sheffield Heeley
*Office Held*. . . . . . . . . 2003 - PPS to Margaret Hodge (Minister of
    State, Department of Education and Skills)
*Commons Office* . . . . . Tel: (020) 7219 8316 Fax: (020) 7219 1793
    E-mail: munnm@parliament.uk
    Web: http://www.megmunnmp.org.uk
    Policy Adviser – Mr Dennis Bates
    Tel: (020) 7219 4398
    E-mail: batesd@parliament.uk
*Constituency Office* . . . . 2nd Floor, Barkers Pool House,
    Burgess Street, Sheffield, S1 2HF
    Tel: (0114) 263 4004 Fax: (0114) 263 4334
    Constituency Assistant – Ms Deborah Stenton
*Parliamentary Interests* . Social Welfare; Europe; Co-operatives:
    Small Business; Children
*Leisure Interests* . . . . . . Tennis; Swimming; Reading; Gardening

**Murphy, Denis** . . . . Wansbeck
**Labour** . . . . . . . . . . Majority 13,101 over Lib Dem
*Born*. . . . . . . . . . . . . 2nd November 1948 in Ashington
*Educated* . . . . . . . . . . St Cuthbert's Grammar School;
    Northumberland College
*Elected*. . . . . . . . . . . . 1997 MP for Wansbeck
*Commons Office* . . . . . Tel: (020) 7219 6474
*Constituency Office* . . . . 94 Station Road, Ashington, NE63 8RN
    Tel: (01670) 523100 Fax; (01670) 813208
    Research Assistant – Mr Peter Moran
    Parliamentary Agent – Mr David Nicholson
*Parliamentary Interests* . Energy; Employment; Health;
    Local Government
*Leisure Interests* . . . . . . Cycling; Walking

**Murphy, Jim** . . . . . . Eastwood
**Labour** . . . . . . . . . . Majority 9,141 over Con
*Born*. . . . . . . . . . . . . 23rd August 1967 in Glasgow
*Educated* . . . . . . . . . . Bellarmine Secondary School, Glasgow;
    Milnerton High School, Cape Town;
    Strathclyde University
*Elected*. . . . . . . . . . . . 1997 MP for Eastwood
*Offices Held* . . . . . . . . 2001 - 02 PPS to Helen Liddell
    (Secretary of State for Scotland)
    2002 - 03 Assistant Government Whip
    2003 - Government Whip (Lord
    Commissioner, HM Treasury)
*Commons Office* . . . . . Tel: (020) 7219 1290 Fax: (020) 7219 6866
    E-mail: murphyj@parliament.uk
*Constituency Office* . . . . 238 Ayr Road, Newtonmearns,
    East Renfrewshire, G77 6AA
    Tel: (0141) 577 0100 Fax: (0141) 616 3613
    Personal Assistant – Ms Marion Anderson
    Researcher/Press Officer –
    Miss Sarah-Anne Munro
    Researcher – Miss Dawn Graham
*Parliamentary Interests* . Sport; Consumer Affairs; Treasury Issues;
    International Issues; Defence
*Leisure Interests* . . . . . . Football; Golf; Cinema; Travelling in Scotland

**Murphy, Rt Hon Paul** Torfaen
**Labour** . . . . . . . . . . Majority 16,280 over Con
*Born*. . . . . . . . . . . . . 25th November 1948 in Usk, Gwent
*Educated* . . . . . . . . . . West Monmouth School, Pontypool;
    Oriel College, Oxford
*Elected*. . . . . . . . . . . . 1987 MP for Torfaen
*Offices Held* . . . . . . . . 1988 - 94 Opposition Spokesman on Wales
    1994 - 95 Opposition Spokesman on
    Northern Ireland
    1995 - 97 Opposition Spokesman on Defence
    1997 - 99 Minister of State,
    Northern Ireland Office
    1999 - 2002 Secretary of State for Wales
    2002 - Secretary of State for Northern Ireland
*Commons Office* . . . . . Tel: (020) 7219 3463
    E-mail: hunta@parliament.uk
    Parliamentary Researcher – Mr Anthony Hunt
*Constituency Office* . . . . 73 Upper Trosnant Street, Pontypool,
    Torfaen, NP4 8AU
    Tel: (01495) 750078 Fax: (01495) 752584
    Constituency Caseworker –
    Mrs Pamela Cameron
    Secretary – Mrs Sian James
*Leisure Interests* . . . . . . Cooking; Classical Music

**Murrison, Dr Andrew** Westbury
**Conservative** . . . . . . Majority 5,294 over Lib Dem
*Born*. . . . . . . . . . . . . 24th April 1961
*Educated* . . . . . . . . . . The Harwich School; Bristol University
    Cambridge University
*Elected*. . . . . . . . . . . . 2001 MP for Westbury
*Office Held*. . . . . . . . . 2003 - Opposition Spokesman on Health
*Constituency Office* . . . . Lovemead House, Roundstone Street,
    Trowbridge, BA14 8DG
    Tel: (01225) 358584 Fax: (01225) 358583
    E-mail: murrisona@parliament.uk
    Web: http://www.andrewmurrison.co.uk
    Parliamentary Assistant – Mrs Gilly Walsh
    E-mail: walshg@parliament.uk
    Researcher – Mr Bob Munden
    Tel: (02392) 370479 Fax; (02392) 326391
*Parliamentary Interests* . Defence; Health
*Leisure Interests* . . . . . . Family; Sailing

# MEMBERS OF THE HOUSE OF COMMONS

## N

**Naysmith, Dr Doug**  Bristol North West
*Labour* . . . . . . . . . . . Majority 11,087 over Con
*Born*. . . . . . . . . . . . . . 1st April 1941 in Musselburgh
*Educated* . . . . . . . . . . Musselburgh School;
George Heriot School; Edinburgh University;
Yale University, USA
*Elected*. . . . . . . . . . . . 1997 MP for Bristol North West
*Commons Office* . . . . . Tel: (020) 7219 4187 Fax: (020) 7219 2602
E-mail: naysmithd@parliament.uk
*Constituency Office* . . . . Unit 6, Greenway Business Centre,
Doncaster Road, Bristol, BS10 5PY
Tel: (0117) 950 2385 Fax: (0117) 950 5302
Researchers – Dr Rosemary Chamberlin
Mr John Loosley
Secretary – Mrs Liz Grace
*Parliamentary Interests* . Health; Co-operative Development;
Ports/Shipping; Science; Higher Education
*Leisure Interests* . . . . . . Cinema; Theatre; Music
Paddle Steamer Preservation


**Norman, Archie** . . . Tunbridge Wells
*Conservative* . . . . . . . Majority 9,730 over Lib Dem
*Born*. . . . . . . . . . . . . . 1st May 1954
*Educated* . . . . . . . . . . Emmanuel College, Cambridge;
Harvard Business School, USA
*Elected*. . . . . . . . . . . . 1997 MP for Tunbridge Wells
*Offices Held* . . . . . . . . 1997 - 98 Vice-Chairman, Conservative Party
1998 - 99 Deputy Chairman and Chief
Executive, Conservative Party
1999 - 2000 Shadow Minister for Europe
2000 - 01 Shadow Secretary for
Environment, Transport and the Regions
*Commons Office* . . . . . Tel: (020) 7219 5156 Fax: (020) 7219 6050
Personal Assistant – Miss Barbara Kyriakou
E-mail: kyriakoub@parliament.uk
*Constituency Office* . . . . 84 London Road, Tunbridge Wells,
Kent, TN1 1EA
Tel: (01892) 522581 Fax: (01892) 522582
*Parliamentary Interests* . Trade and Industry; Agriculture
*Leisure Interests* . . . . . . Music; Tennis; Farming; Football


**Norris, Dan** . . . . . . Wansdyke
*Labour* . . . . . . . . . . . Majority 5,613 over Con
*Born*. . . . . . . . . . . . . . 28th January 1960 in London
*Educated* . . . . . . . . . . Avon Comprehensive; Sussex University
*Elected*. . . . . . . . . . . . 1997 MP for Wansdyke
*Office Held* . . . . . . . . . 2001 - 03 Assistant Government Whip
*Constituency Office* . . . . Tel: (01454) 857406  Fax: (01454) 857382
*Parliamentary Interests* . Child Protection; Animal Welfare; Health

## O

**O'Brien, Bill** . . . . . Normanton
*Labour* . . . . . . . . . . . Majority 9,937 over Con
*Born*. . . . . . . . . . . . . . 25th January 1929 in Castleford, Yorkshire
*Educated* . . . . . . . . . . St Joseph's School, Castleford;
Leeds University
*Elected*. . . . . . . . . . . . 1983 MP for Normanton
*Offices Held* . . . . . . . . 1987 - 92 Opposition Spokesman on
Environment
1992 - 95 Opposition Spokesman on
Northern Ireland
*Commons Office* . . . . . Tel: (020) 7219 3492 Fax: (020) 7219 0301
*Parliamentary Interests* . Transport; Environment; Energy;
Local Government


**O'Brien, Mike** . . . . Warwickshire North
*Labour* . . . . . . . . . . . Majority 9,639 over Con
*Born*. . . . . . . . . . . . . . 19th June 1954 in Worcester
*Educated* . . . . . . . . . . Blessed Edward Oldcorne RC School;
Worcester Technical College;
North Staffordshire Polytechnic;
College of Law
*Elected*. . . . . . . . . . . . 1992 MP for Warwickshire North
*Offices Held* . . . . . . . . 1995 - 97 Opposition Spokesman on
Treasury Matters
1997 - 2001 Parliamentary Secretary,
Home Office
2002 - 03 Parliamentary Secretary,
Foreign and Commonwealth Office
2003 - 04 Minister of State for Trade (Foreign
and Commonwealth Office and Department
of Trade and Industry)
2004 - Minister of State, Department of
Trade and Industry (Minister for
E-commerce and Competitiveness)
*Constituency Office* . . . . 92 King Street, Bedworth,
Warwickshire, CV12 8JF
Tel: (024) 7631 5084 Fax: (024) 7664 0139

# MEMBERS OF THE HOUSE OF COMMONS

**O'Brien, Stephen**. . Eddisbury
**Conservative** . . . . . . Majority 4,568 over Lab
*Born*. . . . . . . . . . . . . . 1st April 1957 in Mtwara, Tanzania
*Educated* . . . . . . . . . . Seabergh School;
    Emmanuel College, Cambridge;
    College of Law
*Elected*. . . . . . . . . . . . 1999 MP for Eddisbury (By-election)
*Offices Held* . . . . . . . . 2000 - 01 PPS to Michael Ancram
    (Chairman, Conservative Party)
    2001 - 03 Opposition Whip and Spokesman
    on Treasury Matters
    2003 - Shadow Secretary for Industry
*Commons Office* . . . . . . Tel: (020) 7219 6315 Fax: (020) 7219 0584
    E-mail: obriens@parliament.uk
    Web: http://www.stephenobrienmp.co.uk
    Personal Assistant/Researcher –
    Mrs Emma Wegoda
    E-mail: wegodae@parliament.uk
    Secretary – Mrs Christine Watts
    Researcher/Press Officer – Mr Craig Jackson
    Tel: (01406) 351393 Fax: (01406) 351605
    E-mail: jacksoncb@parliament.uk
*Constituency Office* . . . . 4 Church Walk, High Street, Tarporley,
    Cheshire, CW6 0AJ
    Tel & Fax: (01829) 733243
    E-mail: eddisbury@callnetuk.com
    Agent – Mr Peter Robinson
    Secretary – Mrs Jenny Owen
*Parliamentary Interests* . Northern Ireland; Trade and Industry;
    Economy; Education; Agriculture; Health;
    Built Environment; Constitution
*Leisure Interests* . . . . . . Fell Walking; Golf; Music (Piano)

**O'Hara, Eddie** . . . . Knowsley South
**Labour** . . . . . . . . . . . Majority 21,316 over Lib Dem
*Born*. . . . . . . . . . . . . . 1st October 1937 in Bootle, Merseyside
*Educated* . . . . . . . . . . Liverpool Collegiate School;
    Magdalen College, Oxford; London University
*Elected*. . . . . . . . . . . . 1990 MP for Knowsley South (By-election)
*Commons Office* . . . . . Tel: (020) 7219 4538 Fax: (020) 7219 4952
    E-mail: oharae@parliament.uk
    Secretary – Ms Susan Utting
*Constituency Office* . . . . Tel: (0151) 489 8021 Fax: (0151) 449 3873
*Parliamentary Interests* . Pensioners' Issues; Animal Welfare;
    Cyprus; Education; Greece
*Leisure Interests* . . . . . . Football; Greek Language and Culture;
    Literature; Music; Visual Arts

**O'Neill, Martin** . . . . Ochil
**Labour** . . . . . . . . . . . Majority 5,349 over SNP
*Born*. . . . . . . . . . . . . . 6th January 1945 in Edinburgh
*Educated* . . . . . . . . . . Trinity Academy; Heriot Watt University;
    Moray House College of Education, Edinburgh
*Elected*. . . . . . . . . . . . 1979 MP for Stirlingshire East and
    Clackmannan, then (1983) Clackmannan
    and (1997) Ochil
*Offices Held* . . . . . . . . 1981 - 84 Opposition Spokesman on Scotland
    1984 - 88 Opposition Spokesman on
    Defence and Disarmament
    1988 - 92 Shadow Defence Secretary
    1992 - 95 Shadow Energy Minister
    1995 - Chairman, Trade and Industry Select
    Committee, House of Commons
*Commons Office* . . . . . Tel: (020) 7219 5059 Fax: (020) 7219 5907
*Constituency Office* . . . . 49 High Street, Alloa,
    Clackmannanshire, FK10 1JF
    Tel: (01259) 721536 Fax: (01259) 216761
    Assistant – Ms Haldis Scott
*Parliamentary Interests* . Energy; Scotland; Trade and Industry
*Leisure Interests* . . . . . . Football; Jazz

**Oaten, Mark** . . . . . . Winchester
**Liberal Democrat** . . . Majority 9,634 over Con
*Born*. . . . . . . . . . . . . . 8th March 1964 in Watford
*Educated* . . . . . . . . . . Queen's Comprehensive School, Watford;
    Hatfield Polytechnic
*Elected*. . . . . . . . . . . . 1997 MP for Winchester (By-election)
*Offices Held* . . . . . . . . 1997 - 99 Liberal Democrat Spokesman on
    Social Security and Welfare
    1999 - 2001 Liberal Democrat Spokesman on
    Foreign Affairs and Defence and PPS to
    Charles Kennedy (Leader of the Liberal
    Democrats)
    2001 - 02 Liberal Democrat Spokesman on
    Cabinet Office
    2002 - 03 Chairman, Liberal Democrat
    Parliamentary Party
    2003 - Liberal Democrat Spokesman on
    Home Affairs
*Commons Office* . . . . . Tel: (020) 7219 2703 Fax: (020) 7219 2389
    E-mail: oatenm@parliament.uk
    Web: http://www.markoaten.com
    Researcher – Mr Olly Kendall
    E-mail: kendallo@parliament.uk
*Constituency Office* . . . . 13 City Road, Winchester, Hampshire,
    SO23 4EH
    Tel: (01962) 622212 Fax: (01962) 863300
    Secretary – Mrs Gill Killmartin
    Constituency Agent – Mr Rodney Sabine
    Tel: (01962) 622210
*Parliamentary Interests* . Election Process; Former POWs (Japan);
    Intercountry Adoption; Human Rights;
    Mobile Phone Masts; Healthcare Funding
*Leisure Interests* . . . . . . Gardening; Football

## MEMBERS OF THE HOUSE OF COMMONS

**Olner, Bill** . . . . . . . Nuneaton
**Labour** . . . . . . . . . . . Majority 7,535 over Con
*Born* . . . . . . . . . . . . . 9th May 1942 in Atherstone, Warwickshire
*Educated* . . . . . . . . . . Atherstone Secondary Modern School;
North Warwickshire Technical College
*Elected* . . . . . . . . . . . 1992 MP for Nuneaton
*Office Held* . . . . . . . . . Formerly Leader and Mayor, Nuneaton and
Bedworth Council
*Commons Office* . . . . . E-mail: olnerb@parliament.uk
Assistant – Mrs Kate Atkinson
*Constituency Office* . . . . 171 Queens Road, Nuneaton, CV11 5NB
Tel: (024) 7664 2222 Fax: (024) 7664 2223
Assistants – Mrs Pat Henry
Mrs June Tandy
*Parliamentary Interests* . Cable and Satellite/Space;
Child Abduction; Transport
*Leisure Interests* . . . . . . Hospice Movement; Walking

**Öpik, Lembit** . . . . . . Montgomeryshire
**Liberal Democrat** . . . Majority 6,234 over Con
*Born* . . . . . . . . . . . . . . 2nd March 1965 in Bangor, Co Down
*Educated* . . . . . . . . . . . Royal Belfast Academical Institution;
Bristol University
*Elected* . . . . . . . . . . . . 1997 MP for Montgomeryshire
*Offices Held* . . . . . . . . 1997 - 2002 Liberal Democrat Spokesman on
Young People
1997 - Liberal Democrat Spokesman on
Northern Ireland and Welsh Affairs
*Commons Office* . . . . . Tel: (020) 7219 1144 Fax: (020) 7219 2210
E-mail: opikl@parliament.uk
Chief Researcher – Mr Simon Milner
E-mail: milners@parliament.uk
Researcher/Press Officer – Ms Suzanna Nagle
E-mail: nagles@parliament.uk
Personal Assistant – Miss Charlotte Williams
E-mail: williamscm@parliament.uk
*Constituency Office* . . . . 3 Park Street, Newtown, Powys, SY16 1EE
Tel: (01686) 625527 Fax: (01686) 628891
E-mail: montgomery ldp@kix.co.uk
Web: http://www.montgomery.libdems.org
Office Manager – Mrs Rhian Selby
Caseworker – Ms Sarah Edwards
Tel: (01686) 625145
*Parliamentary Interests* . Northern Ireland; Agriculture; Rural Affairs;
Aviation; Youth Issues
*Leisure Interests* . . . . . . Aviation; Astronomy; Windsurfing;
Motorcycles; MGB Cars

**Organ, Diana** . . . . . Forest of Dean
**Labour** . . . . . . . . . . . Majority 2,049 over Con
*Born* . . . . . . . . . . . . . . 21st February in West Bromwich
*Educated* . . . . . . . . . . . Church of England College, Edgbaston;
St Hugh's College, Oxford; Bath University
*Elected* . . . . . . . . . . . . 1997 MP for Forest of Dean
*Commons Office* . . . . . Tel: (020) 7219 5498 Fax: (020) 7219 6860
Mobile: 07710 321606
Pager: 07644 007920
E-mail: organd@parliament.uk
Web: http://www.dianaorgan.labour.co.uk
*Constituency Office* . . . . St Annal's House, Belle Vue Centre,
Belle Vue Road, Cinderford, Gloucestershire,
GL14 1AB
Tel: (01594) 826835/826927
Fax: (01594) 827892
PAs/Caseworkers – Ms Cherry Burrow
Ms Annie Lapington
PA/Diary Secretary – Ms Tricia Lawrence
*Parliamentary Interests* . Education; Rural Affairs; Women's Health;
Environmental Protection
*Leisure Interests* . . . . . . Gardening; Theatre; Friends; Swimming

**Osborne, George** . . Tatton
**Conservative** . . . . . . . Majority 8,611 over Lab
*Born* . . . . . . . . . . . . . . 23rd May 1971 in London
*Educated* . . . . . . . . . . Davidson College, North Carolina, USA;
St Paul's School, London;
Magdalen College, Oxford
*Elected* . . . . . . . . . . . . 2001 MP for Tatton
*Offices Held* . . . . . . . . 2003 Opposition Whip
2003 - 04 Opposition Spokesman on
Economic Affairs
2004 - Shadow Chief Secretary, HM Treasury
*Commons Office* . . . . . Tel: (020) 7219 8329
E-mail: osborneg@parliament.uk
Web: http://www.georgeosborne.co.uk
*Constituency Office* . . . . Tel: (01565) 873037
Constituency Secretary – Mrs Jane Robertson
*Parliamentary Interests* . Treasury; Education; Relations with USA
*Leisure Interests* . . . . . . Walking; Cinema; Theatre; Skiing

**Osborne, Sandra** . . Ayr
**Labour** . . . . . . . . . . . Majority 2,545 over Con
*Born* . . . . . . . . . . . . . . 23rd February 1956
*Educated* . . . . . . . . . . Camphill Secondary School, Paisley;
Strathclyde University
Jordanhill College
*Elected* . . . . . . . . . . . . 1997 MP for Ayr
*Office Held* . . . . . . . . . 2002 - 03 PPS to Helen Liddell
(Secretary of State for Scotland)
*Constituency Office* . . . . Damside, Ayr, KA8 8ER
Tel: (01292) 262906 Fax: (01292) 885661
E-mail: osbornes@parliament.uk
Senior Secretary – Ms Lisa Stewart
E-mail: stewartl@parliament.uk
*Parliamentary Interests* . Women's Issues; Housing; Poverty;
International Development

**Ottaway, Richard** . Croydon South
**Conservative** . . . . . . . Majority 8,697 over Lab
*Born* . . . . . . . . . . . . . . 24th May 1945
*Educated* . . . . . . . . . . Backwell School, Somerset;
Britannia Royal Naval College, Dartmouth;
Bristol University
*Elected* . . . . . . . . . . . . 1983 - 87 MP for Nottingham North
1992 MP for Croydon South
*Offices Held* . . . . . . . . 1995 - 96 Assistant Government Whip
1996 - 97 Government Whip
(Lord Commissioner, H M Treasury)
1997 - 98 Opposition Spokesman on London
1998 - 99 Opposition Spokesman on
Local Government, Planning,
Housing and Construction
1999 - 2000 Opposition Spokesman on
Defence
2000 - 01 Opposition Spokesman on
Treasury Matters
2004 - Opposition Spokesman on the
Environment
*Commons Office* . . . . . Tel: (020) 7219 6392 Fax: (020) 7219 2256
E-mail: ottawayrgj@parliament.uk
Web: http://www.richardottaway.com
Parliamentary Assistant – Ms Jane Hill
E-mail: hillj@parliament.uk
Constituency Caseworker – Mrs Lynne Hale
Tel: (020) 7219 1590
E-mail: halel@parliament.uk
*Constituency Office* . . . . 36 Brighton Road, Purley, Surrey, CR8 2LG
Tel: (020) 8660 0491 Fax: (020) 8763 9686
Agent – Mr Ian Parker
*Parliamentary Interests* . Population and Development; London
*Leisure Interests* . . . . . . Jazz; Skiing; Yacht Racing

# MEMBERS OF THE HOUSE OF COMMONS

**Owen, Albert**...... Ynys Môn
**Labour**........... Majority 800 over Plaid Cymru
*Educated* .......... Holyhead Comprehensive School;
York University; Coleg Harlech
*Elected*............ 2001 MP for Ynys Môn
*Commons Office* ..... Tel: (020) 7219 8415 Fax: (020) 7219 1951
E-mail: owena@parliament.uk
*Constituency Office* .... Tel: (01407) 765750 Fax: (01407) 764336
Personal Assistant – Mr Peter Murphy
Research Assistant – Mr Gerwyn Jones
*Parliamentary Interests* . Welsh Affairs; Welfare Issues;
Macro Economics
*Leisure Interests* ...... Cycling; Cooking

# P

**Page, Richard**..... Hertfordshire South West
**Conservative** ....... Majority 8,181 over Lab
*Born*.............. 22nd February 1941 in South Wales
*Educated* .......... Hurstpierpoint College, Sussex;
Luton Technical College
*Elected*............ 1976 - 79 MP for Workington (By-election)
1979 MP for Hertfordshire South West
(By-election)
*Offices Held* ........ 1995 - 97 Parliamentary Secretary,
Department of Trade and Industry
2000 - 2001 Opposition Spokesman on
Trade and Industry
*Commons Office* ...... Tel: (020) 7219 6547
Secretary and Office Administrator –
Mrs Sally Hammond
*Constituency Office* .... Scots Bridge House, Scots Hill,
Rickmansworth, Hertfordshire, WD1 3BB
Tel: (01923) 771781
*Parliamentary Interests* . Trade and Industry; Small Businesses
*Leisure Interests* ...... Horse Racing; Shooting

**Paice, James**...... Cambridgeshire South East
**Conservative** ....... Majority 8,990 over Lib Dem
*Born*.............. 24th April 1949 in Suffolk
*Educated* .......... Framlingham College, Suffolk;
Writtle Agricultural College, Essex
*Elected*............ 1987 MP for Cambridgeshire South East
*Offices Held* ........ 1983 Chairman, Suffolk Coastal District
Council
1994 - 95 Parliamentary Secretary,
Department of Employment
1995 - 97 Parliamentary Secretary,
Department for Education and Employment
1997 - 2001 Opposition Spokesman on
Agriculture, Fisheries and Food
2001 - 04 Opposition Spokesman on Home
Affairs (also Constitutional and Legal
Affairs from 2004)
2004 - Opposition Spokesman on
Agriculture, Fisheries and Food
*Commons Office* ...... Tel: (020) 7219 5063 Fax: (020) 7219 3804
E-mail: paicejet@parliament.uk
Web: http://www.jamespaice.mp.com
Secretary – Mrs Dounie Stanley-Clarke
Researcher/PA –Mr David Scott
*Constituency Office* .... 153 St Neot's Road, Hardwick,
Cambridge, CB3 8QJ
Tel: (01954) 211444 Fax: (01954) 212455
*Parliamentary Interests* . Rural Affairs; Agriculture; Forestry;
Employment and Training
*Leisure Interests* ...... Shooting; Conservation

**Paisley, Rev Ian**... Antrim North
**Democratic Unionist**. Majority 14,224 over Ulster Unionist
*Born*.............. 6th April 1926 in Armagh
*Educated* .......... Ballymena Model School;
Ballymena Technical College;
South Wales Bible College;
Reformed Presbyterian Theological Hall,
Belfast
*Elected*............ 1970 MP for Antrim North
*Offices Held* ........ 1971 - Leader, Democratic Unionist Party
1979 - Member, European Parliament
1998 - Member, Northern Ireland Assembly
*Commons Office* ...... Tel: (020) 7219 5031/3457
Fax: (020) 7219 5854
*Constituency Office* .... 256 Ravenhill Road, Belfast, BT5 8GJ
Tel: (028) 9045 8900 Fax: (028) 9045 7783
*Parliamentary Interests* . Northern Ireland; Constitution; Foreign Policy;
Security; Policing
*Leisure Interests* ...... Reading

# MEMBERS OF THE HOUSE OF COMMONS

**Palmer, Dr Nick** .. Broxtowe
**Labour** . . . . . . . . . . . Majority 5,873 over Con
*Born*. . . . . . . . . . . . . . 5th February 1950 in London
*Educated* . . . . . . . . . . Copenhagen University; London University
*Elected*. . . . . . . . . . . . 1997 MP for Broxtowe
*Office Held*. . . . . . . . . 2003 - PPS to Department of Environment,
  Food and Rural Affairs Ministers
*Commons Office* . . . . . Tel: (020) 7219 4197 Fax: (020) 7219 5205
  Pager: 07644 004912
  E-mail: palmern@parliament.uk
  Assistant –Ms Philipa Coughlan
  Tel: (020) 7219 2553
  E-mail: coughlanp@parliament.uk
  Research Assistant – Dr David Wright
  Tel: (020) 7219 2553
  E-mail: wrightdt@parliament.uk
*Constituency Office* . . . . Harold Wilson House, 23 Barratt Lane,
  Attenborough, Nottingham, NG9 6AD
  Tel: (0115) 943 0721 Fax: (0115) 943 1244
  Web: http://www.broxtowelabour.org
  Assistants – Mr Brian Pollard
   Mr David S Smith
*Parliamentary Interests* . Europe; Science; Animal Welfare;
  Northern Ireland; Treasury
*Leisure Interests* . . . . . . Postal and Computer Games

**Paterson, Owen** . . . Shropshire North
**Conservative** . . . . . . . Majority 6,241 over Lab
*Born*. . . . . . . . . . . . . . 24th June 1956 in Shropshire
*Educated* . . . . . . . . . . Radley School;
  Corpus Christi College, Cambridge
*Elected*. . . . . . . . . . . . 1997 MP for Shropshire North
*Offices Held* . . . . . . . . 2000 - 01 Opposition Whip
  2001 - 03 PPS to Iain Duncan Smith (Leader
   of the Opposition)
  2003 - Opposition Spokesman on
   Environment and Transport
*Commons Office* . . . . . Tel: (020) 7219 5185 Fax: (020) 7219 3955
  Mobile: 07966 234635
  Pager: 07626 802303
  E-mail: patersono@parliament.uk
  Web: http://www.owenpaterson.org.uk
  Parliamentary Assistant/Researcher –
   Miss Claire Ingram
  E-mail: ingramc@parliament.uk
*Constituency Office* . . . . Sambrook House, Noble Street, Wem,
  Shropshire, SY4 5DT
  Tel: (01939) 235222 Fax: (01939) 232220
  Secretary/Researcher – Mrs Rose Paterson
  Tel: (01978) 710667 Fax: (01978) 710073

**Pearson, Ian** . . . . . Dudley South
**Labour** . . . . . . . . . . . Majority 6,817 over Con
*Born*. . . . . . . . . . . . . . 5th April 1959 in Wall Heath, West Midlands
*Educated* . . . . . . . . . . Crestwood Comprehensive;
  Balliol College, Oxford; Warwick University
*Elected*. . . . . . . . . . . . 1994 - MP for Dudley West (By-election),
   then (1997) Dudley South
*Offices Held* . . . . . . . . 2001 - 02 Assistant Government Whip
  2002 Government Whip
   (Lord Commissioner, H M Treasury)
  2002 - Parliamentary Secretary, Northern
   Ireland Office
*Commons Office* . . . . . Tel: (020) 7219 6462 Fax: (020) 7219 0390
  E-mail: pearsoni@parliament.uk
  Web: http://www.ianpearsonmp.org.uk
*Constituency Office* . . . . Suite 1, Grazebrook House, Peartree Lane,
  Dudley, West Midlands, DY2 0XW
  Tel: (01384) 455022 Fax: (01384) 455045
  Office Manager – Mrs Karen Jordan
*Parliamentary Interests* . Economic and Industrial Policy;
  Regional Development;
  Further and Higher Education
*Leisure Interests* . . . . . Rugby; Literature; Architecture

**Perham, Linda** . . . . Ilford North
**Labour** . . . . . . . . . . . Majority 2,115 over Con
*Born*. . . . . . . . . . . . . . 29th June 1947 in London
*Educated* . . . . . . . . . . Mary Datchelor Girls School, Camberwell;
  Leicester University
*Elected*. . . . . . . . . . . . 1997 MP for Ilford North
*Office Held* . . . . . . . . . 1994 - 95 Mayor, London Borough
   of Redbridge
*Commons Office* . . . . . Tel: (020) 7219 5853 Fax: (020) 7219 1161
  Mobile: 07867 538538
  Pager: 07644 008583
  E-mail: lindaperhammp@parliament.uk
  Web: http://www.lindaperham.labour.co.uk
  Parliamentary Assistant – Ms Tessa Jones
  E-mail: jonest@parliament.uk
  Diary Secretary – Mrs Edith Miller
  Researcher – Mr Alex Hilton
  Tel: (020) 7219 5482
  E-mail: hiltona@parliament uk
*Parliamentary Interests* . Age Discrimination; Health; Libraries;
  London Transport
*Leisure Interests* . . . . . . Art; Cinema; Heritage;
  Organising and Participating in Quizzes;

**Picking, Anne** . . . . . East Lothian
**Labour** . . . . . . . . . . . Majority 10,830 over Con
*Born*. . . . . . . . . . . . . . 30th March 1958 in Dunfermline
*Educated* . . . . . . . . . . Woodmill High School
*Elected*. . . . . . . . . . . . 2001 MP for East Lothian
*Commons Office* . . . . . Tel: (020) 7219 8220 Fax: (020) 7219 1760
  Pager: 07693 254848
  E-mail: pickinga@parliament.uk
*Constituency Office* . . . . 65 High Street, Tranent, East Lothian,
  EH33 1LN
  Tel: (01875) 614990 Fax: (01875) 613562
  Personal Assistant – Miss Colette Davie
  E-mail: daviec@parliament.uk
  Parliamentary Assistant – Mr John Russell
*Parliamentary Interests* . Work and Pensions; Health
*Leisure Interests* . . . . . . Sailing; Walking; Reading

# MEMBERS OF THE HOUSE OF COMMONS

**Pickles, Eric** . . . . . . Brentwood and Ongar
**Conservative** . . . . . . Majority 2,821 over Independent
*Born*. . . . . . . . . . . . . . 20th April 1952 in Keighley, Yorkshire
*Educated* . . . . . . . . . . Greenhead Grammar School, Keighley;
Leeds Polytechnic
*Elected*. . . . . . . . . . . . 1992 MP for Brentwood and Ongar
*Offices Held* . . . . . . . . 1998 - 2001 Opposition Spokesman on
Social Security
2001 - 02 Opposition Spokesman
on Transport
2002 - 04 Opposition Spokesman on Local
Government and Regions
2004 Shadow Secretary for Local Government
*Commons Office* . . . . . Tel: (020) 7219 4428 Fax: (020) 7219 2783
E-mail: picklese@parliament.uk
Web: http://www.epickles.com
*Constituency Office* . . . . Tel: (01277) 210725 Fax: (01277) 202221

**Pickthall, Colin** . . . Lancashire West
**Labour** . . . . . . . . . . . Majority 9,643 over Con
*Born*. . . . . . . . . . . . . . 13th September 1944 in Dalton-in-Furness,
Cumbria
*Educated* . . . . . . . . . . Ulverston Grammar School;
University of Wales; Lancaster University
*Elected*. . . . . . . . . . . . 1992 MP for Lancashire West
*Office Held*. . . . . . . . . 1998 - PPS to Jack Straw (as Home Secretary,
then Foreign Secretary)
*Commons Office* . . . . . Tel: (020) 7219 5011 Fax: (020) 7219 2354
E-mail: pickthallc@parliament.uk
Secretary – Miss Aviva Bresky
Tel: (020) 7219 0322
*Constituency Office* . . . . 127 Burscough Street, Ormskirk, Lancashire,
L39 2EP4
Tel: & Fax (01695) 570094
Secretary – Ms Pauline Roughley
Research Assistant – Mr Derek Thompson
*Parliamentary Interests*. Home Affairs; Agriculture; Environment;
Foreign Affairs
*Leisure Interests* . . . . . . Gardening; Theatre; Cricket; Rugby Union;
Fell Walking; Cumbria and Lancashire

**Pike, Peter** . . . . . . . Burnley
**Labour** . . . . . . . . . . . Majority 10,498 over Con
*Born*. . . . . . . . . . . . . . 26th June 1937 in Ware, Hertfordshire
*Educated* . . . . . . . . . . Hinchley Wood Secondary School;
Kingston Technical College
*Elected*. . . . . . . . . . . . 1983 MP for Burnley
*Offices Held* . . . . . . . . 1980 - 83 Leader, Burnley Borough Council
1990 - 92 Opposition Spokesman on
Agriculture, Fisheries and Food
1992 - 94 Opposition Spokesman on
Environment (Housing)
1997 - Chairman, Regulatory Reform
Committee, House of Commons
*Commons Office* . . . . . Tel: (020) 7219 6488  Fax: (020) 7219 3872
Mobile: 07976 891801
Pager: (020) 8345 6789 (807974)
E-mail: peterpikemp@parliament.uk
Web: http://www.epolitix.com/peter-pike
Researcher – Miss Jane Pike
E-mail: pikej@parliament.uk
*Constituency Office* . . . . 2 Victoria Street, Burnley, BB11 1DD
Tel: (01282) 450840 Fax: (01282) 839623
Secretary – Mrs Maureen Martin
Caseworkers – Ms Angela Donovan
Miss Joanne Whitaker
Assistant – Mrs Carole Galbraith
*Parliamentary Interests*. Local Government; Social Services; Housing
and Homelessness; Transport; Pensions
*Leisure Interests* . . . . . . Football (Burnley FC)

**Plaskitt, James** . . . . Warwick and Leamington
**Labour** . . . . . . . . . . . Majority 5,953 over Con
*Born*. . . . . . . . . . . . . . 23rd June 1954 in Grimsby
*Educated* . . . . . . . . . . Pilgrim School, Bedford;
University College, Oxford
*Elected*. . . . . . . . . . . . 1997 MP for Warwick and Leamington
*Office Held*. . . . . . . . . 1990 - 96 Leader, Oxfordshire County Council
*Commons Office* . . . . . Tel: (020) 7219 6207 Fax: (020) 7219 4993
E-mail: plaskittj@parliament.uk
Web: http://www.jamesplaskitt.com
*Constituency Office* . . . . First Floor, 2a Leam Terrace,
Leamington Spa, CV31 1BB
Tel: (01926) 831151 Fax: (01926) 338838
E-mail: mp@jamesplaskitt.com
Personal Assistant – Mr Andy Marshall
*Parliamentary Interests*. Economic Policy; Welfare Reform;
Constitution; European Union
*Leisure Interests* . . . . . . Classical Music; Travel

# MEMBERS OF THE HOUSE OF COMMONS

**Pollard, Kerry** .... St Albans
**Labour** .......... Majority 4,459 over Con
*Born*. .............. 27th April 1944 in Pinner, Middlesex
*Educated* ......... Thornleigh Grammar School, Bolton;
........ Huddersfield Polytechnic; Open University
*Elected*. ........... 1997 MP for St Albans
*Commons Office* ..... Tel: (020) 7219 4537 Fax: (020) 7219 2548
........ Pager: 07644 007804
........ E-mail: pollardk@parliament.uk
........ Web: http://www.kerrypollardmp.co.uk
........ Parliamentary Secretary –
........ Mrs Vivienne Windle
........ Tel: (020) 7219 6423
........ E-mail: windlev@parliament.uk
*Constituency Office* .... 28 Alma Road, St Albans, Hertfordshire,
........ AL1 3BW
........ Tel: (01727) 761031 Fax: (01727) 761032
........ Casework/Press Officer – Ms Anne Dunlop
........ Constituency Assistant – Ms Claire Tilcock
*Parliamentary Interests*. Housing; Social Services; Small Businesses;
........ Industrial Relations; International
........ Development; Alternative Energy
*Leisure Interests* ...... Walking; Swimming

**Pond, Chris** ....... Gravesham
**Labour** .......... Majority 4,862 over Con
*Born*. .............. 25th September 1952
*Educated* ......... Minchenden School, Southgate;
........ Sussex University
*Elected*. ........... 1997 MP for Gravesham
*Office Held* ........ 2003 - Parliamentary Secretary,
........ Department of Work and Pensions
*Commons Office* ..... Tel: (020) 7219 6493 Fax: (020) 7219 0946
........ E-mail: pondc@parliament.uk
........ Parliamentary Assistant – Mrs Lorraine Pond
........ Tel: (020) 7219 2490
*Constituency Office* .... 24 The Overcliffe, Gravesend, Kent,
........ DA11 0EH
........ Tel: (01474) 354725 Fax: (01474) 351679
........ Constituency Assistants –
........ Mrs Carole Bowman
........ Mr Ron Bowman
*Parliamentary Interests*. Economics; Social Policy; Child Protection;
........ River Safety
*Leisure Interests* ...... Running; Reading; Parenthood

**Pope, Greg** ....... Hyndburn
**Labour** .......... Majority 8,219 over Con
*Born*. .............. 29th August 1960 in Blackburn, Lancashire
*Educated* ......... St. Mary's College, Blackburn; Hull University
*Elected*. ........... 1992 MP for Hyndburn
*Offices Held* ........ 1995 - 97 Opposition Whip
........ 1997 - 99 Assistant Government Whip
........ 1999 - 2001 Government Whip
........ (Lord Commissioner, H M Treasury)
*Commons Office* ..... Fax: (020) 7219 0685
........ E-mail: popegj@parliament.uk
........ Web: http://www.gregpop.co.uk
*Constituency Office* .... 149 Blackburn Road, Accrington,
........ Lancashire, BB5 0AA
........ Tel: (01254) 382283 Fax: (01254) 398089
........ Parliamentary Assistant – Ms Doreen Pollitt
........ Office Manager and Personal Assistant –
........ Ms Julie Milligan
........ Caseworker/Administration Assistant –
........ Ms Naveed Akhtar
*Parliamentary Interests*. Foreign Affairs; Education; Northern Ireland
*Leisure Interests* ...... Walking; Football; Chess; Swimming

**Portillo, Rt Hon Michael** Kensington and Chelsea
**Conservative** ....... Majority 8,771 over Lab
*Born*. .............. 26th May 1953 in Hertfordshire
*Educated* ......... Harrow County School,
........ Peterhouse College, Cambridge
*Elected*. ........... 1984 - 97 MP for Enfield Southgate
........ 1999 MP for Kensington and Chelsea
........ (By-election)
*Offices Held* ........ 1986 - 87 Assistant Government Whip
........ 1987 - 88 Parliamentary Secretary,
........ Department of Health and Social Security
........ 1988 - 90 Minister of State,
........ Department of Transport
........ 1990 - 92 Minister of State,
........ Department of Environment
........ 1992 - 94 Chief Secretary to the Treasury
........ 1994 - 95 Secretary of State for Employment
........ 1995 - 97 Secretary of State for Defence
........ 2000 - 01 Shadow Chancellor of the
........ Exchequer
*Commons Office* ..... Tel: (020) 7219 6212 Fax: (020) 7219 1208
........ Web: http://www.michaelportillo.co.uk
........ Private Secretary – Miss Sarah Bridger

**Pound, Stephen** ... Ealing North
**Labour** .......... Majority 11,837 over Con
*Born*. .............. 3rd July 1948 in Hammersmith
*Educated* ......... Hertford Grammar School;
........ London School of Economics
*Elected*. ........... 1997 MP for Ealing North
*Commons Office* ..... Tel: (020) 7219 6238/4312
........ Fax: (020) 7219 5982
........ Mobile: 07976 577735
........ Pager: 07644 002252
........ E-mail: pounds@parliament.uk
........ Web: http://www.stevepound.org.uk
........ Researcher/Office Manager –
........ Ms Sophie Hosking
........ E-mail: hoskings@parliament.uk
........ Caseworker/Diary Secretary –
........ Mr Jonathan Williams
........ Tel: (020) 7219 1140
........ E-mail: williamsjd@parliament.uk
*Parliamentary Interests*. Housing; Ireland; Transport
*Leisure Interests* ...... Playing Cricket; Watching Football

# MEMBERS OF THE HOUSE OF COMMONS

**Prentice, Bridget**.. Lewisham East
**Labour** . . . . . . . . . . . Majority 9,003 over Con
*Born*. . . . . . . . . . . . . . 28th December 1952
*Educated* . . . . . . . . . . Our Lady and St Francis School, Glasgow;
                  Glasgow University; London University;
                  South Bank University
*Elected*. . . . . . . . . . . . 1992 MP for Lewisham East
*Offices Held* . . . . . . . . 1995 - 97 Opposition Whip
                  1997 - 98, 2003 - Assistant Government Whip
                  1999 - 2001 PPS to Lord Irvine of Lairg
                    (Lord Chancellor)
                  2004 - Government Assistant Whip
*Commons Office* . . . . . . Tel: (020) 7219 3503 Fax: (020) 8219 5581
                  Mobile: 07973 894514
                  Pager: 07644 002254
                  E-mail: info@bridgetprenticemp.org.uk
                  Web: http://www.bridgetprenticemp.org.uk
                  Parliamentary Assistant – Mr Simon Benson
                  E-mail: bensons@parliament.uk
                  Caseworker – Mr Paul Boughen
                  Tel: (020) 7219 6994 Fax: (020) 7219 1286
                  E-mail: boughenp@parliament.uk
*Constituency Office*. . . . 82 Lee High Road, London, SE13
                  Tel: (020) 8852 3995 Fax: (020) 8927 5760
                  E-mail: lewishameastclp@email.labour.org.uk
*Parliamentary Interests*. Home Affairs; Constitutional Reform; Training
*Leisure Interests* . . . . . . Reading; Music; Football; Cats

**Prentice, Gordon**.. Pendle
**Labour** . . . . . . . . . . . Majority 4,275 over Con
*Born*. . . . . . . . . . . . . . 28th January 1951 in Edinburgh
*Educated* . . . . . . . . . . George Heriot's School, Edinburgh;
                  Glasgow University
*Elected*. . . . . . . . . . . . 1992 MP for Pendle
*Office Held*. . . . . . . . . Formerly Leader, London Borough of
                  Hammersmith and Fulham Council
*Commons Office* . . . . . . E-mail: prenticeg@parliament.uk
*Constituency Office*. . . . 33 Carr Road, Nelson, Lancashire, BB9 7JS
                  Tel: (01282) 695471 Fax: (01282) 614097
                  E-mail: prenticeg@parliament.uk
                  Assistants – Ms Helen Ingham
                        Ms Ruth Wilkinson
*Leisure Interests* . . . . . . Hill Walking; Cooking; Football

**Prescott Rt Hon John** Hull East
**Labour** . . . . . . . . . . . Majority 15,325 over Con
*Born*. . . . . . . . . . . . . . 31st May 1938 in North Wales
*Educated* . . . . . . . . . . Grange Secondary Modern School,
                  Ellesmere Port; Ruskin College, Oxford;
                  Hull University
*Elected*. . . . . . . . . . . . 1970 MP for Hull East
*Offices Held* . . . . . . . . 1972 - 74 Opposition Spokesman on
                  Merchant Shipping
                  1979 - 81 Opposition Spokesman on Transport
                  1981 - 83 Opposition Spokesman on
                  Regional Affairs
                  1983 - 85, 1988 - 93 Shadow Transport
                  Secretary
                  1985 - 87, 1993 - 94 Shadow
                  Employment Secretary
                  1987 - 88 Shadow Energy Secretary
                  1994 - Deputy Leader, Labour Party
                  1997 - 2001 Deputy Prime Minister and
                  Secretary of State for the Environment,
                  Transport and the Regions
                  2001 - Deputy Prime Minister and First
                  Secretary of State
*Commons Office* . . . . . . Chief of Staff – Ms Joan Hammell
                  E-mail: hammellj@parliament.uk
                  Office Manager – Miss Della Armstrong
                  Office Assistant – Miss Emma Onono

**Price, Adam** . . . . . Carmarthen East and Dinefwr
**Plaid Cymru** . . . . . . . Majority 2,590 over Lab
*Born*. . . . . . . . . . . . . . 23rd September 1968 in Llanelli,
                  Carmarthenshire
*Educated* . . . . . . . . . . Amman Valley Comprehensive School;
                  University of Wales, Cardiff;
                  Saarland University, Germany
*Elected*. . . . . . . . . . . . 2001 MP for Carmarthen East and Dinefwr
*Commons Office* . . . . . . Tel: (020) 7219 8486 Fax: (020) 7219 3705
                  E-mail: pricea@parliament.uk
*Constituency Office*. . . . 37 Wind Street, Ammanford,
                  Carmarthenshire, SA18 3DN
                  Tel: (01269) 597677 Fax: (01269) 591334
                  Caseworker – Mr Alun Lewis
                  Senior Policy and Communications Officer –
                  Mr Jonathon Edwards
*Parliamentary Interests*. Culture; Economic Policy; Education;
                  International Development;
                  Regional Development;
                  Trade and Industry
*Leisure Interests* . . . . . . Contemporary Culture; Food; Friends; Travel

# MEMBERS OF THE HOUSE OF COMMONS

**Primarolo, Rt Hon Dawn** Bristol South
**Labour** . . . . . . . . . . Majority 14,181 over Con
*Born* . . . . . . . . . . . . . 2nd May 1954 in London
*Educated* . . . . . . . . . . Thomas Bennett School Crawley;
University of the West of England;
Bristol University
*Elected* . . . . . . . . . . . 1987 MP for Bristol South
*Offices Held* . . . . . . . . 1992 - 94 Opposition Spokeswoman on Health
1994 - 97 Opposition Spokeswoman on
Treasury and Economic Affairs
1997 - 99 Financial Secretary, H M Treasury
1999 - Paymaster General, H M Treasury
*Constituency Office* . . . . PO Box 1002, Bristol, BS99 1WH
Tel: (0117) 909 0063 Fax: (0117) 909 0064
Secretary/Personal Assistant –
Ms Claire Radford
Clerical Assistant – Ms Margaret Hwang
Research Assistant – Mr Edmund Bramall
*Parliamentary Interests* . Economic Policy; Equal Opportunities;
Housing; Social Security
*Leisure Interests* . . . . . . Gardening; Cooking; Cinema; Opera

**Prisk, Mark** . . . . . . Hertford and Stortford
**Conservative** . . . . . . Majority 5,603 over Lab
*Born* . . . . . . . . . . . . . 12th June 1962
*Educated* . . . . . . . . . . Truro School, Cornwall; Reading University
*Elected* . . . . . . . . . . . 2001 MP for Hertford and Stortford
*Offices Held* . . . . . . . . 2002 - Opposition Spokesman on
Economic Affairs
*Commons Office* . . . . . Tel: (020) 7219 6358 Fax: (020) 7219 3826
Web: http://www.markprisk.com
Personal Assistant – Mrs Joan Hunter
E-mail: hunterj@parliament.uk
Researcher – Mr Jonathan Woodhead
E-mail: woodheadj@parliament.uk
*Constituency Office* . . . . Unit 4a, Swains Mill, Crane Mead, Ware,
Hertfordshire, SG12 9PX
Tel: (01920) 462182 Fax: (01920) 485805
E-mail: hertfordandstortford@tory.org
Constituency Secretary –
Mrs Rosemary Poulton
*Parliamentary Interests* . Defence; Small Businesses
*Leisure Interests* . . . . . . Rugby; Singing; Theatre

**Prosser, Gwyn** . . . . Dover
**Labour** . . . . . . . . . . Majority 5,199 over Con
*Born* . . . . . . . . . . . . . 27th April 1943 in Swansea
*Educated* . . . . . . . . . . Duvant Secondary Modern;
Swansea Technical School;
Swansea College of Technology
*Elected* . . . . . . . . . . . 1997 MP for Dover
*Commons Office* . . . . . Tel: (020) 7219 3704
E-mail: prosserg@parliament.uk
*Constituency Office* . . . 26 Coombe Valley Road,
Dover, Kent, CT17 0EP
Tel: (01304) 214484 Fax: (01304) 214486
Parliamentary Assistant – Ms Jo Knight
Diary Assistant – Mrs Carol Errington
Office Assistant – Mrs Pam Hawkins
*Parliamentary Interests* . Engineering; Shipping; Animal Welfare;
Immigration and Asylum; Transport;
*Leisure Interests* . . . . . . Hill Walking; Swimming; Rugby

**Pugh, Dr John** . . . . Southport
**Liberal Democrat** . . . Majority 3,007 over Con
*Born* . . . . . . . . . . . . . 28th June 1948 in Liverpool
*Educated* . . . . . . . . . . Prescott Grammar School;
Maidstone Grammar School;
Durham University
*Elected* . . . . . . . . . . . 2001 MP for Southport
*Offices Held* . . . . . . . . 2000 - 01 Leader, Sefton Metropolitan
Borough Council
2002 - Liberal Democrat Spokesman,
Education and Skills
*Commons Office* . . . . . . Tel: (020) 7219 8318 Fax: (020) 7219 1794
E-mail: pughj@parliament.uk
Secretary – Mrs Annette Pugh
Tel: (020) 7219 8034
*Constituency Office* . . . . 35 Shakespeare Street, Southport, PR8 5AB
Tel: (01704) 533555 Fax: (01704) 884160
E-mail: hq@southportlibdems.com
Constituency Secretary – Ms Pat Sumner
*Parliamentary Interests* . Transport; Local Government; Hospitals;
IT Procurement
*Leisure Interests* . . . . . . Gym; Music; Films; Computers;
Football (Liverpool FC)

**Purchase, Ken** . . . . Wolverhampton North East
**Labour** . . . . . . . . . . Majority 9,965 over Con
*Born* . . . . . . . . . . . . . 8th January 1939 in Wolverhampton
*Educated* . . . . . . . . . . Springfield Secondary Modern;
Wolverhampton Polytechnic
*Elected* . . . . . . . . . . . 1992 MP for Wolverhampton North East
*Office Held* . . . . . . . . 1997 - 03 PPS to Robin Cook (as Foreign
Secretary, then Leader of the House of
Commons)
*Commons Office* . . . . . Tel: (020) 7219 3602 Fax: (020) 7219 2110
Mobile: 07850 688105
E-mail: ken.purchasemp@parliament.uk
Web: http://www.kenpurchase.co.uk
*Constituency Office* . . . . 492a Stafford Road, Oxley, Wolverhampton,
WV10 6AN
Tel: (01902) 397698 Fax: (01902) 397538
Personal Assistant – Mr George Lockett
IT Manager – Mr Paul Sweet
Secretary – Ms Fay Warrilow
*Parliamentary Interests* . Industry; Exports; Education; Health;
Foreign Affairs
*Leisure Interests* . . . . . . Jazz

**Purnell, James** . . . . Stalybridge and Hyde
**Labour** . . . . . . . . . . Majority 8,859 over Con
*Born* . . . . . . . . . . . . . 2nd March 1970
*Educated* . . . . . . . . . . Lycée International, St Germain-en-Laye,
France; Guildford Royal Grammar School;
Balliol College, Oxford
*Elected* . . . . . . . . . . . 2001 MP for Stalybridge and Hyde
*Office Held* . . . . . . . . 2003 - PPS to Ruth Kelly (Financial
Secretary, HM Treasury)
*Commons Office* . . . . . Tel: (020) 7219 8166 Fax: (020) 7219 1287
E-mail: purnellj@parliament.uk
Parliamentary Assistant –
Miss Amanda Wolthuizer
E-mail: wolthuizera@parliament.uk
*Constituency Office* . . . . Hyde Town Hall, Market Street, Hyde,
Cheshire, SK14 1AL
Tel: (0161) 367 8077 Fax: (0161) 367 0050
Constituency Assistant –
Mr Jonathan Reynolds
E-mail: reynoldsj@parliament.uk
*Parliamentary Interests* . Work and Pensions; Education; Poverty;
Welfare
*Leisure Interests* . . . . . . Football; Music; Cinema

# MEMBERS OF THE HOUSE OF COMMONS

## Q

**Quin, Rt Hon Joyce**   Gateshead East and Washington West
**Labour** . . . . . . . . . . . . Majority 17,904 over Con
*Born.* . . . . . . . . . . . . . . 26th November 1944 in Tynemouth, Tyneside
*Educated* . . . . . . . . . . . Whitley Bay Grammar School;
Newcastle University;
London School of Economics
*Elected.* . . . . . . . . . . . . 1987 MP for Gateshead East and
Washington West
*Offices Held* . . . . . . . . 1989 - 92 Opposition Spokeswoman on
Trade and Industry
1992 - 93 Opposition Spokeswoman on
Employment
1993 - 97 Opposition Spokeswoman on
Foreign and Commonwealth Affairs
1997 - 98 Minister of State, Home Office
1998 - 99 Minister of State, Foreign and
Commonwealth Office (Minister for Europe)
1999 - 2001 Minister of State, Ministry of
Agriculture, Fisheries and Food
*Commons Office* . . . . . Tel: (020) 7219 4009 Fax: (020) 7219 6052
Researcher – Ms Emily Bird
*Constituency Office* . . . . Design Works, Folling, Gateshead, NE10 0JP
Tel: (0191) 469 6006 Fax: (0191) 469 6009
Office Manager/Researcher – Mr Brian Hall
Secretary/PA – Ms Val Henderson
Clerical Assistant – Ms Jane Blakeman
*Parliamentary Interests* . Europe; Regional Policy; Environment
*Leisure Interests* . . . . . . Local History; Walking; Cycling; Music


**Quinn, Lawrie.** . . . . Scarborough and Whitby
**Labour** . . . . . . . . . . . . Majority 3,585 over Con
*Born.* . . . . . . . . . . . . . . 25th December 1956 in Carlisle
*Educated* . . . . . . . . . . Harraby School, Carlisle; Hatfield Polytechnic
*Elected.* . . . . . . . . . . . . 1997 MP for Scarborough and Whitby
*Office Held.* . . . . . . . . 2002 - PPS to Douglas Alexander
(Minister for the Cabinet Office)
*Commons Office* . . . . . Tel: (020) 7219 4170 Fax: (020) 7219 2477
E-mail: quinnl@parliament.uk
Web: http://www.lawrie-quinn.org.uk
Researcher/Diary Secretary – Ms Clare Billing
Tel: (020) 7219 5937
E-mail: billingc@parliament.uk
*Constituency Office* . . . . 53 Westborough, Scarborough, YO11 1TU
Tel: (01723) 507000 Fax: (01723) 507008
E-mail: brittainl@parliament.uk
Office Manager – Mrs Linda Brittain
Casework Assistant – Ms Maggie Hargreaves
Tel: (01947) 821733
*Parliamentary Interests* . Transport; Environment; Devolution;
Health and Safety at Work; Tourism;
Agriculture; Fishing; Trade and Industry;
Regional Assemblies
*Leisure Interests* . . . . . . Photography; Reading; Biographies; Internet

## R

**Rammell, Bill** . . . . Harlow
**Labour** . . . . . . . . . . . . Majority 5,228 over Con
*Born.* . . . . . . . . . . . . . . 10th October 1959
*Educated* . . . . . . . . . . . Burnt Mill Comprehensive School, Harlow;
University College of Wales, Cardiff
*Elected.* . . . . . . . . . . . . 1997 MP for Harlow
*Offices Held* . . . . . . . . 2001 - 02 PPS to Tessa Jowell (Secretary of
State for Culture, Media and Sport)
2002 Assistant Government Whip
2002 - Parliamentary Secretary,
Foreign and Commonwealth Office
*Commons Office* . . . . . Tel: (020) 7219 2828 Fax: (020) 7219 2804
E-mail: rammellb@parliament.uk
Web: http://www.billrammell.labour.co.uk
PA/Caseworker – Ms Emma Nicholson
E-mail: nicholsonel@parliament.uk
Political Officer/Researcher – Ms Ruth Fox
Tel: (020) 7219 3443
E-mail: foxru@parliament.uk
*Constituency Office* . . . . 1st Floor, 4-6 Market House, The High,
Harlow, Essex, CM20 1BL
Tel: (01279) 439706
Constituency Caseworker/Organiser –
Ms Andrea Pattison
E-mail: pattisona@parliament.uk
*Parliamentary Interests* . Europe; Housing; Economy; Electoral Reform;
Health
*Leisure Interests* . . . . . . Cricket; Football; Travel; Family


**Randall, John** . . . . . Uxbridge
**Conservative** . . . . . . . Majority 2,098 over Lab
*Born.* . . . . . . . . . . . . . . 5th August 1955 in Ealing
*Educated* . . . . . . . . . . . Rutland House School, Hillingdon;
Merchant Taylors School, Hertfordshire;
University of London
*Elected.* . . . . . . . . . . . . 1997 MP for Uxbridge (by-election)
*Office Held.* . . . . . . . . . 2000 - Opposition Whip
*Commons Office* . . . . . Tel: (020) 7219 6885 Fax: (020) 7219 2590
E-mail: randallj@parliament.uk
Web: http://www.johnrandallmp.com
Secretary – Mrs Delma Beebe
E-mail: beebed@parliament.uk
*Constituency Office* . . . . Bay Lodge, Harefield Road, Uxbridge,
Middlesex, UB8 1PH
Tel: (01895) 239465 Fax: (01895) 253105
Secretary – Mrs Wendy Mouat
*Parliamentary Interests* . Environment; Wildlife; Eastern Europe;
Foreign Affairs
*Leisure Interests* . . . . . . Bird Watching; Music; Reading; Cricket;
Rugby; Football

# MEMBERS OF THE HOUSE OF COMMONS

**Rapson, Syd** BEM . . Portsmouth North
**Labour** . . . . . . . . . . Majority 5,134 over Con
*Born.* . . . . . . . . . . . . . 17th April 1942 on the Isle of Wight
*Educated* . . . . . . . . . Southsea Modern School;
    Paulsgrove Modern School;
    Portsmouth Dockyard College
*Elected.* . . . . . . . . . . . 1997 MP for Portsmouth North
*Offices Held* . . . . . . . . 1990 - 91 Lord Mayor of Portsmouth
    PPS to Defence Ministers
*Commons Office* . . . . . Tel: (020) 7219 6248 Fax: (020) 7219 0915
    Mobile: 07711 332764
    Pager: 07644 008668
    E-mail: rapsons@parliament.uk
    Personal Secretary – Ms Judith Murray
    Fax: (020) 7219 3415
*Constituency Office* . . . . 79 Washbrook Road, Paulsgrove, Portsmouth,
    Hampshire, PO6 3SB
    Tel & Fax: (023) 9242 1165
    Personal Secretary – Mrs Phyllis Rapson
    Researcher – Ms Sarah McCathy-Fry
    Tel: (023) 9271 3299
    Agent – Mr Geoff Wade
    Tel: (01329) 223043 Fax; (01329) 223045
*Parliamentary Interests* . Defence; Health; Local Government;
    Trade Unions; Culture, Media and Sport;
    Manufacturing Industry; Engineering
*Leisure Interests* . . . . . . Gardening; Swimming

**Raynsford, Rt Hon Nick**  Greenwich and Woolwich
**Labour** . . . . . . . . . . . Majority 13,433 over Con
*Born.* . . . . . . . . . . . . . . 28th January 1945 in Northampton
*Educated* . . . . . . . . . . Repton School;
    Sidney Sussex College, Cambridge;
    Chelsea School of Art
*Elected.* . . . . . . . . . . . 1986 - 87 MP for Fulham (By-election)
    1992 MP for Greenwich, then (1997)
    Greenwich and Woolwich
*Offices Held* . . . . . . . . 1993 - 97 Opposition Spokesman on
    Housing and London
    1997 - 99 Parliamentary Secretary,
    Department of Environment, Transport
    and the Regions
    1999 - 2001 Minister of State, Department of
    Environment, Transport and the Regions
    2001 - Minister of State, Department for
    Transport, Local Government and the
    Regions, then Office of Deputy Prime
    Minister (Minister for Local and
    Regional Government)
*Commons Office* . . . . . . Tel: (020) 7219 2773 Fax: (020) 7219 2619
    Pager: 07644 002258
    E-mail: raynsfordn@parliament.uk
    Parliamentary/Political Assistant –
    Ms Alison Seabeck
    E-mail: seabeckaj@parliament.uk
    Caseworkers – Ms Andrea Aroba
        Ms Elizabeth Gardiner
    Tel: (020) 7219 5895 Fax: (020) 7219 0205
    E-mails: [surnameinitial]@parliament.uk
*Constituency Office* . . . . 32 Woolwich Road, London, SE10 0JU
    Tel: (020) 8853 1261
*Parliamentary Interests* . Housing; Planning; Construction; Transport;
    Environment
*Leisure Interests* . . . . . . Photography; Walking

**Redwood, Rt Hon John**  Wokingham
**Conservative** . . . . . . Majority 5,994 over Lib Dem
*Born.* . . . . . . . . . . . . . 15th June 1951 in Kent
*Educated* . . . . . . . . . . Kent College, Canterbury;
    Magdalen College, Oxford;
    St Antony's College, Oxford
*Elected.* . . . . . . . . . . . 1987 MP for Wokingham
*Offices Held* . . . . . . . . 1989 - 90 Parliamentary Secretary,
    Department of Trade and Industry
    1990 - 92 Minister of State,
    Department of Trade and Industry
    1992 - 93 Minister of State,
    Department of Environment
    1993 - 95 Secretary of State for Wales
    1997 - 99 Shadow Trade and Industry
    Secretary
    1999 - 2000 Shadow Secretary for
    Environment, Transport and the Regions
    2004 - Shadow Secretary for Deregulation
*Commons Office* . . . . . Tel: (020) 7219 4205 Fax: (020) 7219 0377
    PA – Mrs Avril Tawning
    E-mail: pagen@parliament.uk
*Constituency Office* . . . . Tel: (0118) 962 5902
*Parliamentary Interests* . Economy; Europe
*Leisure Interests* . . . . . . Watersports; Cricket

**Reed, Andrew** . . . . . Loughborough
**Labour** . . . . . . . . . . . Majority 6,378 over Con
*Born.* . . . . . . . . . . . . . 17th September 1964 in Kettering
*Educated* . . . . . . . . . . Stonehill High School;
    Longslade Community College, Birstall;
    Leicester Polytechnic
*Elected.* . . . . . . . . . . . 1997 MP for Loughborough
*Office Held* . . . . . . . . 2001 - 03 PPS to Margaret Beckett
        (Secretary of State for Environment, Food
        and Rural Affairs)
*Commons Office* . . . . . Tel: (020) 7219 3529 Fax: (020) 7219 2405
    Parliamentary Assistant – Mr Kerron Cross
*Constituency Office* . . . . Unity House, Fennel Street, Loughborough,
    Leicestershire, LE11 1UQ
    Tel: (01509) 261226 Fax: (01509) 212159
    Caseworker Assistant – Mr Mike Jones
*Parliamentary Interests* . Unemployment; Regeneration; Sport;
    International Development; Transport
*Leisure Interests* . . . . . . Rugby; Football; Running; Volleyball; Tennis

# MEMBERS OF THE HOUSE OF COMMONS

**Reid, Alan** . . . . . . . . Argyll and Bute
**Liberal Democrat** . . . Majority 1,653 over Lab
*Born*. . . . . . . . . . . . . . 7th August 1954
*Educated* . . . . . . . . . . Prestwick Academy; Ayr Academy;
Strathclyde University; Jordanhill College;
Bell College
*Elected*. . . . . . . . . . . . 2001 MP for Argyll and Bute
*Offices Held* . . . . . . . . 2001 - 03 Liberal Democrat Spokesman on
Scottish Fisheries
2003 - Liberal Democrat Whip and
Spokesman for Scotland
*Commons Office* . . . . . Tel: (020) 7219 8127 Fax: (020) 7219 1737
E-mail: reida@parliament.uk
*Constituency Office* . . . . 44 Hillfoot Street, Dunoon, Argyll, PA23 7DT
Tel: (01369) 704840 Fax: (01369) 701212
*Leisure Interests* . . . . . . Chess; Reading; Walking; Watching TV

**Reid, Rt Hon John** Hamilton North and Bellshill
**Labour** . . . . . . . . . . . Majority 13,561 over SNP
*Born*. . . . . . . . . . . . . . 8th May 1947 in Bellshill
*Educated* . . . . . . . . . . St Patrick's Secondary School, Coatbridge;
Stirling University
*Elected*. . . . . . . . . . . . 1987 MP for Motherwell North, then (1997)
Hamilton North and Bellshill
*Offices Held* . . . . . . . . 1990 - 97 Opposition Spokesman on Defence
1997 - 98 Minister of State, Ministry of
Defence
1998 - 99 Minister for Transport, Department
for Environment, Transport and the Regions
1999 - 01 Secretary of State for Scotland
2001 - 02 Secretary of State for
Northern Ireland
2002 - 03 Minister without Portfolio and
Chairman of the Labour Party
2003 Leader of the House of Commons
2003 - Secretary of State for Health
*Commons Office* . . . . . Tel: (020) 7210 5954/5
Special Advisers – Mr Richard Olszewski
Mr Steve Bates
*Constituency Office* . . . . Montrose House, 154 Montrose Crescent,
Hamilton, ML3 6LL
Tel: (01698) 454672 Fax: (01698) 424732
Personal Assistant – Ms Mary McKenna
Fax: (01698) 734118
*Parliamentary Interests* . Defence; Foreign Affairs; The Economy;
Northern Ireland; Health
*Leisure Interests* . . . . . . Crossword Puzzles; Football

**Rendel, David**. . . . Newbury
**Liberal Democrat** . . . Majority 2,415 over Con
*Born*. . . . . . . . . . . . . . 15th April 1949 in Athens
*Educated* . . . . . . . . . . Eton College; Magdalen College, Oxford;
St Cross College, Oxford
*Elected*. . . . . . . . . . . . 1993 MP for Newbury (By-election)
*Offices Held* . . . . . . . . 1993 - 97 Liberal Democrat Spokesman on
Local Government
1997 - 99 Liberal Democrat Spokesman on
Social Security and Welfare
2001 - Liberal Democrat Spokesman on
Education and Skills (Higher and Further
Education)
*Commons Office* . . . . . Tel: (020) 7219 3495 Fax: (020) 7219 2941
E-mail: rendeld@parliament.uk
Web: http://www.davidrendel.org.uk
*Constituency Office* . . . . Kendrick House, Wharf Street, Newbury,
Berkshire, RG14 5AP
Tel: (01635) 581048 Fax: (01635) 581049
E-mail: newburyldp@cix.co.uk
Web: http://www.davidrendel.libdems.org.uk
*Parliamentary Interests* . Benefits; Child Support Agency;
Mobile Homes; Racing Industry;
Animal Welfare; Cycling; Universities
*Leisure Interests* . . . . . . Walking; Travel; Classical Music

**Robathan, Andrew** Blaby
**Conservative** . . . . . . . Majority 6,209 over Lab
*Born*. . . . . . . . . . . . . . 17th July 1951
*Educated* . . . . . . . . . . Merchant Taylors School, Northwood;
Oriel College, Oxford;
Royal Military Academy, Sandhurst;
Army Staff College, Camberley
*Elected*. . . . . . . . . . . . 1992 MP for Blaby
*Offices Held* . . . . . . . . 2002 - 03 Opposition Spokesman on Trade
and Industry
2003 - 04 Opposition Spokesman on
International Development
*Commons Office* . . . . . Tel: (020) 7219 3459 Fax: (020) 7219 0096
Secretary – Mrs Diana Thompson
*Constituency Office* . . . . 35 Lutterworth Road, Blaby, Leicestershire,
LE8 4DW
Tel: (0116) 277 9992 Fax: (0116) 278 6664
Organising Secretary – Mr Len Mitchell
*Parliamentary Interests* . Defence; Environment; Northern Ireland;
International Development
*Leisure Interests* . . . . . . Running; Skiing; Hill Walking; Conservation

# MEMBERS OF THE HOUSE OF COMMONS

**Robertson, Angus** . Moray
**SNP** . . . . . . . . . . . . Majority 1,744 over Lab
*Born.* . . . . . . . . . . . . . 28th September 1969
*Educated* . . . . . . . . . Broughton High School, Edinburgh;
Aberdeen University
*Elected.* . . . . . . . . . . . 2001 MP for Moray
*Office Held* . . . . . . . . . 2001 - SNP Spokesman on
Europe and Defence
*Commons Office* . . . . . Tel: (020) 7219 4182
E-mail: robertsona@parliament.uk
Web: http://www.moraymp.org
Parliamentary Adviser –
Federico Castellani-Kössler
E-mail: castellanikoessler@parliament.uk
*Constituency Office* . . . . 9 Wards Road, Elgin, Moray, IV30 1NL
Tel: (01343) 551111 Fax: (01343) 556355
E-mail: info@moraymp.org
Office Manager – Mr Graham Leadbitter
Parliamentary Assistant –
Ms Carron Anderson
*Parliamentary Interests* . Scottish Independence; Defence;
International and European Affairs; Whisky;
Oil; Fishing; Sustainable Development;
Youth Issues
*Leisure Interests* . . . . . . Football; Rugby; Skiing; Golf; Films; Travel;
Books; Socialising; Music; History

**Robertson, Hugh** . . Faversham and Mid Kent
**Conservative** . . . . . . Majority 4,183 over Lab
*Born.* . . . . . . . . . . . . . 9th October 1962 in Canterbury
*Educated* . . . . . . . . . . King's School, Canterbury;
Royal Military Academy, Sandhurst;
Reading University
*Elected.* . . . . . . . . . . . 2001 MP for Faversham and Mid Kent
*Office Held.* . . . . . . . . 2002 - 04 Opposition Whip (also Spokesman
on Trade and Industry 2002 - 03)
2004 - Shadow Minister for Sport
*Commons Office* . . . . . Tel: (020) 7219 8230 Fax: (020) 7219 1765
E-mail: robertsonh@parliament.uk
Web: http://www.hughrobertson.org
Political Assistant – Miss Charlotte Earl
Tel: (020) 7219 2643
E-mail: earlc@parliament.uk
*Constituency Office* . . . . 8 Faversham Road, Lenham, Maidstone,
Kent, ME17 2PN
Tel: (01622) 850574/851616
Fax: (01622) 890294
E-mail: fmkca@totalise.co.uk
Case Worker – Mrs Angela Stainton-James
*Parliamentary Interests* . Defence; Foreign Affairs; Northern Ireland;
Agriculture
*Leisure Interests* . . . . . . Cricket; Field Sports; Hockey; Skiing

**Robertson, John** . . Glasgow Anniesland
**Labour** . . . . . . . . . . . Majority 11,054 over SNP
*Born.* . . . . . . . . . . . . . 17th April 1952 in Glasgow
*Educated* . . . . . . . . . . Shawlands Academy, Glasgow;
Langside College; Stow College
*Elected.* . . . . . . . . . . . 2000 MP for Glasgow Anniesland (By-election)
*Commons Office* . . . . . Tel: (020) 7219 6964 Fax: (020) 7219 1096
Mobile: 07885 141599
Pager: 07644 070257
E-mail: robertsonjo@parliament.uk
Web: http://www.johnrobertsonmp.co.uk
Researcher – Mr Stuart Hudson
E-mail: hudsons@parliament.uk
*Constituency Office* . . . . 131 Dalstter Avenue, Glasgow, G15 8TE
Tel: (0141) 944 7298 Fax: (0141) 944 7121
Secretary/Caseworker – Ms Rachel Paton
Assistant Secretary/Caseworker –
Mr Alan Cook
Parliamentary Assistant – Mr Steven Purcell
*Parliamentary Interests* . Trade and Industry; Work and Pensions;
International Development
*Leisure Interests* . . . . . . Cricket; Football; Music; Reading

**Robertson, Laurence** Tewkesbury
**Conservative** . . . . . . . Majority 8,663 over Lab
*Born.* . . . . . . . . . . . . . 29th March 1958 in Bolton
*Educated* . . . . . . . . . . St James Secondary School;
Farnworth Grammar School;
Bolton Institute of Technology
*Elected.* . . . . . . . . . . . 1997 MP for Tewkesbury
*Offices Held* . . . . . . . . 2001 - 03 Opposition Whip
2003 - Opposition Spokesman on
Economic Affairs and Industry
*Commons Office* . . . . . Tel: (020) 7219 4196 Fax: (020) 7219 2325
E-mail: larhofc@aol.com
Secretary – Miss Fiona Bryce
*Constituency Office* . . . . Lloyds Bank Chambers, Abbey Terrace,
Winchcombe, Gloucestershire, GL54 5LL
Tel: (01242) 602388 Fax: (01242) 603428
Constituency Assistant – Cllr Mark Calway
*Parliamentary Interests* . Constitution; Education; Economy;
Law and Order; Small Businesses;
The Countryside; Northern Ireland;
International Development
*Leisure Interests* . . . . . . Horseracing; Golf; History; The Countryside

**Robinson, Geoffrey** Coventry North West
**Labour** . . . . . . . . . . . Majority 10,874 over Con
*Born.* . . . . . . . . . . . . . 25th May 1938 in Sheffield, Yorkshire
*Educated* . . . . . . . . . . Emanuel School, London;
Clare College, Cambridge;
Yale University, USA
*Elected.* . . . . . . . . . . . 1976 MP for Coventry North West
(By-election)
*Offices Held* . . . . . . . . 1982 - 87 Opposition Spokesman on
Science, Trade and Industry
1997 - 98 Paymaster General, H M Treasury
*Commons Office* . . . . . Tel: (020) 7219 4083 Fax: (020) 7219 0984
Personal Assistant – Ms Joan Dale
*Constituency Office* . . . . Transport House, Short Street, Coventry,
CV1 2LS
Tel: (024) 7625 7870 Fax: (024) 7625 7813
Assistant – Ms Floraine Eastelow
*Parliamentary Interests* . Economy; Trade and Industry; Gardens
*Leisure Interests* . . . . . . Architecture; Gardens; Reading

# MEMBERS OF THE HOUSE OF COMMONS

**Robinson, Iris** . . . . . Strangford
**Democratic Unionist**. Majority 1,110 over Ulster Unionist
*Born* . . . . . . . . . . . . . . 6th September 1949 in Belfast
*Educated* . . . . . . . . . . Knockbreda Intermediate School;
Castlereagh College
*Elected* . . . . . . . . . . . . 2001 MP for Strangford
*Office Held* . . . . . . . . . 1998 - Member, Northern Ireland Assembly
*Commons Office* . . . . . . E-mail: robinsoni@parliament.uk
Web: http://www.irisrobinson.org
Parliamentary Researcher –
Mr Colin Kennedy
*Constituency Office* . . . . 2b James Street, Newtownards, BT23 4DY
Tel: (028) 9182 7701 Fax: (028) 9182 7703
E-mail: iris.robinson@ukgatewaynet
Web: http://www.dup.org.uk
Secretary – Mr Jonathan Robinson
E-mail: jonathanrobinson@dup.org.uk
Office Manager – Ms Jacqui Louden
Tel: (028) 9182 7702
*Parliamentary Interests* . Health Issues
*Leisure Interests* . . . . . . Walking; Flower Arranging

**Robinson, Peter** . . . Belfast East
**Democratic Unionist**. Majority 7,117 over Ulster Unionist
*Born* . . . . . . . . . . . . . . 29th December 1948 in Belfast
*Educated* . . . . . . . . . . Annadale Grammar School;
Castlereagh College of Further Education
*Elected* . . . . . . . . . . . . 1979 MP for Belfast East
*Offices Held* . . . . . . . . 1980 - Deputy Leader,
Democratic Unionist Party
1985 - 86 Mayor, Castlereagh Borough
Council
1998 - Member, Northern Ireland Assembly
(Minister for Regional Development
1999 - 2000)
*Commons Office* . . . . . . Tel: (020) 7219 3506 Fax: (020) 7219 5590
E-mail: peterrobinson@dup.org.uk
Web: http://www.dup.org.uk
Secretary – Mrs Pat Green
Tel: (020) 7219 5031
*Constituency Office* . . . . Strandtown Hall, 96 Belmont Avenue,
Belfast, BT4 3DE
Tel: (028) 9047 3111 Fax: (028) 9047 1797
E-mail: info@dup.org.uk
Secretary – Mrs Rebekah Robinson-Rowan
Receptionist/Secretary– Mrs Carol Newton
Personal Assistant – Mr Gareth Robinson
Tel: (028) 9052 1351 Fax: (028) 9052 1337
E-mail: grobinson@dup.org.uk
*Parliamentary Interests* . Aerospace; Housing; Shipbuilding;
Community Care; International Terrorism
*Leisure Interests* . . . . . . Breeding Japanese Koi; Bowling; Golf

**Roche, Barbara** . . . Hornsey and Wood Green
**Labour** . . . . . . . . . . . Majority 10,614 over Lib Dem
*Born* . . . . . . . . . . . . . . 13th April 1954 in London
*Educated* . . . . . . . . . . Jewish Free School Comprehensive, Camden;
Lady Margaret Hall, Oxford
*Elected* . . . . . . . . . . . . 1992 MP for Hornsey and Wood Green
*Offices Held* . . . . . . . . 1994 - 95 Opposition Whip
1995 - 97 Opposition Spokesman on
Trade and Industry
1997 - 99 Parliamentary Secretary,
Department of Trade and Industry
1999 Financial Secretary, H M Treasury
1999 - 01 Minister of State, Home Office
2001 - 02 Minister of State, Cabinet Office
2002 - 03 Minister of State, Office of
Deputy Prime Minister
*Constituency Office* . . . . 28 Middle Lane, London, N8 8PL
Tel: (020) 8348 8668 Fax: (020) 8342 8088
Caseworker – Ms Lorfraine Marshall
Parliamentary Assistant/Caseworker -
Mr Aly Mir

**Roe, Dame Marion** Broxbourne
**Conservative** . . . . . . . Majority 8,993 over Lab
*Born* . . . . . . . . . . . . . . 15th July 1936 in London
*Educated* . . . . . . . . . . Bromley High School; Croydon High School;
English School of Languages, Vevey,
Switzerland
*Elected* . . . . . . . . . . . . 1983 MP for Broxbourne
*Offices Held* . . . . . . . . 1986 - 87 PPS to John Moore
(Secretary of State for Transport)
1987 - 88 Parliamentary Secretary,
Department of the Environment
1992 - 97 Chairman, Health Select
Committee, House of Commons
1997 - Chairman, Administration Committee,
House of Commons
*Commons Office* . . . . . . Tel: (020) 7219 3528 Fax: (020) 7219 4992
Secretary – Mrs Karen Woods
*Constituency Office* . . . . 76 High Street, Hoddesdon, Hertfordshire,
EN11 8ET
Tel: (01992) 479972 Fax: (01992) 479973
*Parliamentary Interests* . Health; Family Matters; Horticulture
*Leisure Interests* . . . . . . Theatre

**Rooney, Terry** . . . . Bradford North
**Labour** . . . . . . . . . . . Majority 8,969 over Con
*Born* . . . . . . . . . . . . . . 11th November 1950
*Educated* . . . . . . . . . . Buttershaw Comprehensive School;
Bradford College
*Elected* . . . . . . . . . . . . 1990 MP for Bradford North (By-election)
*Offices Held* . . . . . . . . 1990 - 91 Deputy Leader,
Bradford City Council
2003 - PPS to Keith Hill (Minister of State,
Office of the Deputy Prime Minister)
*Commons Office* . . . . . . Tel: (020) 7219 6407 Fax: (020) 7219 5275
*Constituency Office* . . . . 76 Kirkgate, Bradford, BD1 1SZ
Tel: (01274) 777821 Fax: (01274) 777817
Secretary – Ms Shafina Khaliq
Researcher – Mr David Green
Caseworker – Mr Tony Niland
*Parliamentary Interests* . Social Security; Employment Law; Housing;
Industrial Relations
*Leisure Interests* . . . . . . Crosswords; Football; Cricket; Badminton;
Reading

# MEMBERS OF THE HOUSE OF COMMONS

**Rosindell, Andrew**. Romford
**Conservative** . . . . . . Majority 5,977 over Lab
*Born*. . . . . . . . . . . . 17th March 1966 in Romford
*Educated* . . . . . . . . . Marshalls Park Secondary School, Romford
*Elected*. . . . . . . . . . . 2001 MP for Romford
*Commons Office* . . . . . Tel: (020) 7219 8475 Fax: (020) 7219 1960
    E-mail: andrew@rosindell.com
    Web: http://www.andrew.rosindell.com
*Constituency Office* . . . . Suite One, 85 Western Road, Romford,
    Essex, RM1 3LS
    Tel: (01708) 766700/761583
    Fax: (01705) 707163
    Community Officer – Mr Ray Morgon
    Community Assistant – Miss Ruth Pye
*Parliamentary Interests*. Foreign Affairs; Europe; Overseas Territories;
    Constitutional Reform; Law and Order;
    Defence; Local Government; Elderly People;
    Dog Related Issues
*Leisure Interests* . . . . . . Bull Terriers


**Ross, Ernie** . . . . . . . Dundee West
**Labour** . . . . . . . . . . Majority 6,800 over SNP
*Born*. . . . . . . . . . . . . 27th July 1942 in Dundee
*Educated* . . . . . . . . . St John's Junior Secondary School, Dundee
*Elected*. . . . . . . . . . . 1979 MP for Dundee West
*Commons Office* . . . . . Tel: (020) 7219 3480
    Mobile: 07710 520254
    Pager: 07644 003645
    E-mail: rosse@parliament.uk
*Constituency Office* . . . . 57 Blackscroft, Dundee, DD4 6AT
    Tel: (01382) 466700 Fax: (01382) 466719
    E-mail: griffinv@parliament.uk
    Secretary – Mrs Vivienne Griffin
    Tel: (01382) 466701
    Aide – Mr Colin Rennie
    Tel: (01382) 466705
*Parliamentary Interests*. Foreign Affairs
*Leisure Interests* . . . . . . Football; Cricket


**Roy, Frank** . . . . . . . Motherwell and Wishaw
**Labour** . . . . . . . . . . . Majority 10,956 over SNP
*Born*. . . . . . . . . . . . . 29th August 1958 in Motherwell
*Educated* . . . . . . . . . Our Lady's High School, Motherwell;
    Glasgow Caledonian University
*Elected*. . . . . . . . . . . 1997 MP for Motherwell and Wishaw
*Office Held*. . . . . . . . . 1999 - 2002 PPS to John Reid, then
    Helen Liddell (successive Secretaries
    of State for Scotland)
*Commons Office* . . . . . Tel: (020) 7219 6467 Fax: (020) 7219 6866
    E-mail: royf@parliament.uk
*Constituency Office* . . . . 265 Main Street, Wishaw, Lanarkshire,
    ML2 7NE
    Tel: (01698) 303040 Fax: (01698) 303060
    E-mail: clarkmm@parliament.uk
    Personal Assistant – Mr John Pentland
    Researcher – Mrs Mary Clark
*Parliamentary Interests*. Foreign Affairs; Social Security
*Leisure Interests* . . . . . . Football; Gardening


**Ruane, Chris**. . . . . Vale of Clwyd
**Labour** . . . . . . . . . . Majority 5,761 over Con
*Born*. . . . . . . . . . . . 18th July 1958
*Educated* . . . . . . . . . Blessed Edward Jones Comprehensive, Rhyl;
    University College of Wales, Aberystwyth;
    Liverpool University
*Elected*. . . . . . . . . . . 1997 MP for Vale of Clwyd
*Office Held*. . . . . . . . 2002 - PPS to Peter Hain (as Secretary of
    State for Wales, then also as
    Leader of the House of Commons)
*Commons Office* . . . . . Tel: (020) 7219 6378 Fax: (020) 7219 0916
    E-mail: ruanec@parliament.uk
    Secretary – Mrs Janet Burgess
    Tel: (020) 7219 4007 Fax: (020) 7219 6090
*Constituency Office* . . . . 25 Kinmel Street, Rhyl, LL18 1AH
    Tel: (01745) 354626 Fax: (01745) 334827
    Personal Assistant – Ms Gill Roberts
    Constituency Assistant – Mrs Sherry Edwards


**Ruddock, Joan** . . . . Lewisham Deptford
**Labour** . . . . . . . . . . Majority 15,293 over Con
*Born*. . . . . . . . . . . . . 28th December 1943 in Pontypool
*Educated* . . . . . . . . . Pontypool Girl's Grammar School;
    Imperial College, London
*Elected*. . . . . . . . . . . 1987 MP for Lewisham Deptford
*Offices Held* . . . . . . . . 1989 - 92 Opposition Spokesman on Transport
    1992 - 94 Opposition Spokesman on
    Home Affairs
    1994 - 97 Opposition Spokesman on
    Environmental Protection
    1997 - 98 Parliamentary Secretary,
    Department of Social Security
    (Minister for Women)
*Commons Office* . . . . . Tel: (020) 7219 6206 Fax: (020) 7219 6045
*Parliamentary Interests*. Environment; Equalities; Afghanistan
*Leisure Interests* . . . . . . Gardening; Music; Theatre


**Ruffley, David** . . . . Bury St Edmunds
**Conservative** . . . . . . Majority 2,503 over Lab
*Born*. . . . . . . . . . . . . 18th April 1962
*Educated* . . . . . . . . . Bolton School; Queens' College, Cambridge
*Elected*. . . . . . . . . . . 1997 MP for Bury St Edmunds
*Office Held*. . . . . . . . . 2004 - Opposition Whip
*Commons Office* . . . . . Tel: (020) 7219 2880 Fax: (020) 7219 3998
    Mobile: 07711 768222
    Pager: 07626 801751
    E-mail: davidruffleymp@parliament.uk
    Web: http://www.davidruffleymp.com
    Private Secretary – Mrs Virginia Tuck
    E-mail: tuckv@parliament.uk
    Researcher – Mr Tony Cox
    Tel: (020) 7219 2321
    E-mail: coxt@parliament.uk
*Constituency Office* . . . . 16 Woolpit Business Park, Woolpit,
    Bury St Edmunds, Suffolk, IP30 9UP
    Tel: (01359) 244199 Fax: (01359) 245002
    E-mail: office@bseca.org
    Agent – Mr James Cockram
*Parliamentary Interests*. Broadcasting/Media; Treasury Affairs;
    Schools; Law and Order
*Leisure Interests* . . . . . . Football; Golf; Films

# MEMBERS OF THE HOUSE OF COMMONS

**Russell, Bob** . . . . . . Colchester
**Liberal Democrat** . . . Majority 5,553 over Con
*Born*. . . . . . . . . . . . . . 31st March 1946 in Camberwell
*Educated* . . . . . . . . . . St Helena Secondary Modern, Colchester;
North East Essex Technical College
*Elected*. . . . . . . . . . . . 1997 MP for Colchester
*Offices Held* . . . . . . . . Mayor (1986 - 87) and Leader (1987 - 91),
Colchester Borough Council
1997 - 98 Liberal Democrat Spokesman on
Home Affairs
1998 - Liberal Democrat Whip and
(from 2001) Spokesman on Culture,
Media and Sport
*Commons Office* . . . . . Tel: (020) 7219 5150 Fax: (020) 7219 2365
Pager: 07699 753995
E-mail: russellb@parliament.uk
*Constituency Office* . . . . Magdalen Hall, Wimpole Road,
Colchester, CO1 2DE
Tel: (01206) 506600 Fax: (01206) 506610
Secretary – Mrs Susan Brooks
E-mail: brooksse@parliament.uk
Clerical Assistant – Mrs Carolyn Catney
*Parliamentary Interests*. Local Government; Environment; Sport;
Road Safety
*Leisure Interests* . . . . . Football (Colchester United FC)

**Russell, Christine**. . City of Chester
**Labour** . . . . . . . . . . . Majority 6,894 over Con
*Born*. . . . . . . . . . . . . . 25th March 1945
*Educated* . . . . . . . . . . Spalding High School;
North West London Polytechnic
*Elected*. . . . . . . . . . . . 1997 MP for City of Chester
*Commons Office* . . . . . Tel: (020) 7219 6398 Fax: (028) 7219 0943
Pager: 07644 008309
E-mail: russellcm@parliament.uk
Personal Assistant – Mr Paul Chadwick
E-mail: chadwickp@parliament.uk
*Constituency Office* . . . . York House, York Street, Chester, CH1 3LR
Tel: (01244) 400174 Fax: (01244) 400487
Secretary – Ms Sandra Rudd
E-mail: rudds@parliament.uk
*Parliamentary Interests*. Environment; Transport; Home Affairs;
International Development
*Leisure Interests* . . . . . Films; Football

**Ryan, Joan**. . . . . . . Enfield North
**Labour** . . . . . . . . . . . Majority 2,291 over Con
*Born*. . . . . . . . . . . . . . 8th September 1955 in Warrington
*Educated* . . . . . . . . . . Liverpool College of Higher Education;
South Bank Polytechnic
*Elected*. . . . . . . . . . . . 1997 MP for Enfield North
*Offices Held* . . . . . . . . 2001 - 02 PPS to Andrew Smith
(Chief Secretary to the Treasury)
2002 - 03 Assistant Government Whip
2003 - Government Whip
(Lord Commissioner, HM Treasury)
*Commons Office* . . . . . Tel: (020) 7219 6502/4861
Fax: (020) 7219 2335
E-mail: ryanj@parliament.uk
Web: http://www.joanryan.labour.co.uk
Executive Secretary – Mrs Denyse Morrell
Diary Secretary – Mrs Marilyn Zoha
*Constituency Office* . . . . 180 High Street, Ponders End, Middlesex,
EN3 4EU
Tel: (020) 8805 9470 Fax: (020) 8804 0754
Caseworker – Mrs Jackie Chapman
Caseworker Assistant – Mr Karge Zoha
Manager – Mr James Fitzpatrick
Tel: (020) 8805 8212
*Parliamentary Interests*. Education; Employment; Health; Environment;
Foreign Affairs
*Leisure Interests* . . . . . Reading; Swimming; Historic Buildings;
Tap Dancing

# S

**Salmond, Alex** . . . . Banff and Buchan
**SNP** . . . . . . . . . . . . Majority 10,503 over Con
*Born*. . . . . . . . . . . . . . 31st December 1954 in Linlithgow
*Educated* . . . . . . . . . . Linlithgow Academy; St Andrews University
*Elected*. . . . . . . . . . . . 1987 MP for Banff and Buchan
*Offices Held* . . . . . . . . 1987 - 90 Deputy Leader,
Scottish National Party
1990 - 2000 Leader Scottish National Party
1999 - 2001 Member, Scottish Parliament
2004 - Leader, SNP
*Commons Office* . . . . . Tel: (020) 7219 3494/0074
Fax: (020) 7219 6716
Research Officers – Mr John Fellows
Mr Stephen Gethins
Tel: (020) 7219 0074
*Constituency Office* . . . . 17 Maiden Street, Peterhead, Aberdeenshire,
AB42 1EE
Tel: (01779) 470444 Fax: (01779) 474460
E-mail: mp@alexsalmond.net
Office Manager – Mr Stephen Smith

# MEMBERS OF THE HOUSE OF COMMONS

**Salter, Martin** . . . . . Reading West
**Labour** . . . . . . . . . . . Majority 8,849 over Con
*Born.* . . . . . . . . . . . . . 19th April 1954 in Hampton, Middlesex
*Educated* . . . . . . . . . . . Sussex University
*Elected* . . . . . . . . . . . . 1997 MP for Reading West
*Office Held* . . . . . . . . 1987 - 96 Deputy Leader, Reading Borough
Council
*Commons Office* . . . . . Tel: (020) 7219 5079 Fax: (020) 7219 2749
E-mail: salterm@parliament.uk
Web: http://www.martinsalter.com
Researcher/Assistant – Mr Will Sherlock
E-mail: sherlockw@parliament.uk
*Constituency Office* . . . . 413 Oxford Road, Reading, RG30 1HA
Tel: (0118) 954 6782 Fax: (0118) 954 6784
Caseworker – Ms Viki Lloyd
Secretary – Ms Ann Morgan
*Parliamentary Interests* . Northern Ireland; Human Rights;
Environment; Local Government; Housing
*Leisure Interests* . . . . . . Angling; Walking; Football

**Sanders, Adrian** . . . Torbay
**Liberal Democrat** . . . Majority 6,708 over Con
*Born.* . . . . . . . . . . . . . 25th April 1959
*Educated* . . . . . . . . . . Torquay Boys Grammar School
*Elected* . . . . . . . . . . . . 1997 MP for Torbay
*Offices Held* . . . . . . . . 1997 - 2001 Liberal Democrat Whip
1999 - 2002 Liberal Democrat Spokesman on
Local Government and (from 2001) Housing
2002 - Liberal Democrat Spokesman on
Culture, Media and Sport
*Commons Office* . . . . . Tel: (020) 7219 2390 Fax: (020) 7219 3963
E-mail: sanders@parliament.uk
Web: http://www.adriansanders.org
Researcher – Miss Sally Hooker
E-mail: hookersh@parliament.uk
*Constituency Office* . . . . 69 Belgrave Road, Torquay, Devon, TQ2 5HZ
Tel: (01803) 200036 Fax: (01803) 200031
Head of Office – Mrs Alison Sanders
Casework Officer – Mr Steve Darling
Casework/Administrative Assistant –
Mrs Ruth Pentney
*Parliamentary Interests* . Diabetes
*Leisure Interests* . . . . . . Football; Music; Reading

**Sarwar, Mohammad** Glasgow Govan
**Labour** . . . . . . . . . . . Majority 6,400 over SNP
*Born.* . . . . . . . . . . . . . 18th August 1952 in Pakistan
*Educated* . . . . . . . . . . University of Faisalabad, Pakistan
*Elected* . . . . . . . . . . . . 1997 MP for Glasgow Govan
*Commons Office* . . . . . Tel: (020) 7219 5024 Fax: (020) 7219 5898
*Constituency Office* . . . . 247 Paisley Road West, Glasgow, G51 1NE
Tel: (0141) 427 5250/7047
Fax: (0141) 427 5938
Researchers – Mr Stephen Curran
Ms Caroline Erickson
Assistant – Miss Siobhan McCrone
*Parliamentary Interests* . Shipbuilding; Senior Citizens;
International Development
*Leisure Interests* . . . . . . Relaxing with Family and Friends;
Charitable Work; Abseiling

**Savidge, Malcolm** . . Aberdeen North
**Labour** . . . . . . . . . . . Majority 4,449 over SNP
*Born.* . . . . . . . . . . . . . 9th May 1946 in Redhill, Surrey
*Educated* . . . . . . . . . Wallington County Grammar School;
Aberdeen University;
Aberdeen College of Education
*Elected* . . . . . . . . . . . . 1997 MP for Aberdeen North
*Office Held* . . . . . . . . 1994 - 96 Deputy Leader, Aberdeen City
Council
*Commons Office* . . . . . Tel: (020) 7219 3570 Fax: (020) 7219 2398
Mobile: 07710 891007
Pager: 07644 001748
E-mail: savidgem@parliament.uk
*Constituency Office* . . . . Tel: (01224) 252708 Fax: (01224) 252712
Parliamentary Assistant – Mr Gordon Third
E-mail: thirdg@parliament.uk
Secretary – Mrs Aileen Cooney
Constituency Assistant – Mrs Elaine Taylor
E-mail: taylorel@parliament.uk
*Parliamentary Interests* . Foreign Affairs; International Development;
Defence/Disarmament
*Leisure Interests* . . . . . . Spectator Sports; Crossword Puzzles;
Heraldry; Reading

**Sawford, Phil** . . . . . Kettering
**Labour** . . . . . . . . . . . Majority 665 over Con
*Born.* . . . . . . . . . . . . . 26th June 1950 in Loddington
*Educated* . . . . . . . . . . Kettering Grammar School;
Ruskin College, Oxford; Leicester University
*Elected* . . . . . . . . . . . . 1997 MP for Kettering
*Office Held* . . . . . . . . 1991 - 97 Leader, Kettering Borough Council
*Commons Office* . . . . . Tel: (020) 7219 6213 Fax: (020) 7219 6174
Mobile: 07966 205729
E-mail: philsawfordmp@parliament.uk
Web: http://www.philsawford.labour.co.uk
*Constituency Office* . . . . 1a Headlands, Kettering, Northamptonshire,
NN15 7ER
Tel: (01536) 411900 Fax: (01536) 410742
Administrator – Mrs Rosemary Sawford
Administration Assistant – Mrs Jackie George
*Parliamentary Interests* . Education; Health; Employment
*Leisure Interests* . . . . . . Playing Guitar; Reading; Walking

**Sayeed, Jonathan** . . Mid Bedfordshire
**Conservative** . . . . . . Majority 8,066 over Lab
*Born.* . . . . . . . . . . . . . 20th March 1948 in London
*Educated* . . . . . . . . . . Britannia Royal Naval College, Dartmouth;
Royal Naval Engineering College, Manadon
*Elected* . . . . . . . . . . . . 1997 MP for Mid Bedfordshire
*Office Held* . . . . . . . . 2001 - 03 Opposition Spokesman on
Environment, Food and Rural Affairs
*Commons Office* . . . . . Tel: (020) 7219 2355 Fax: (020) 7219 1670
E-mail: wolffea@parliament.uk
Web: http://www.jsayeed.org.uk
Parliamentary Assistant – Ms Anna Wolffe
*Constituency Office* . . . . St Michael's Close, High Street, Shefford,
Bedfordshire, SG17 5DD
Tel: (01462) 811992 Fax: (01462) 811010
E-mail: admin@midbeds-ca.co.uk
Organising Secretary – Mrs Diane Morris
*Leisure Interests* . . . . . . Tennis; Sailing; Golf; Classical Music

# MEMBERS OF THE HOUSE OF COMMONS

**Sedgemore, Brian** . Hackney South and Shoreditch
**Labour** . . . . . . . . . . . Majority 15,049 over Lib Dem
*Born.* . . . . . . . . . . . . . . 16th March 1937 in Devon
*Educated* . . . . . . . . . . Heles School, Exeter;
                    Corpus Christi College, Oxford
*Elected.* . . . . . . . . . . . 1974 - 79 MP for Luton West
                    1983 MP for Hackney South and Shoreditch
*Office Held.* . . . . . . . . 1977 - 78 PPS to Tony Benn
                    (Secretary of State for Energy)
*Commons Office* . . . . . Tel: (020) 7219 3410 Fax: (020) 7219 5969
                    E-mail: sedgemoreb@parliament.uk
                    Secretary – Mr Peter Watson
                    E-mail: watsonp@parliament.uk
*Constituency Office* . . . . 17 Sutton Square, Urswick Road,
                    London, E9 6EQ
                    Tel: (020) 8533 1305 Fax: (020) 8533 3392
                    Secretary – Ms Audrey Sedgemore
*Parliamentary Interests* . Economics; Civil Liberties; Constitution; Arts
*Leisure Interests* . . . . . . Music; Theatre

**Selous, Andrew** . . . . Bedfordshire South West
**Conservative** . . . . . . Majority 776 over Lab
*Born.* . . . . . . . . . . . . . . 27th April 1962
*Educated* . . . . . . . . . . London School of Economics
*Elected.* . . . . . . . . . . . 2001 MP for Bedfordshire South West
*Office Held.* . . . . . . . . 2004 - PPS to Michael Ancram (Shadow
                    Foreign Secretary)
*Commons Office* . . . . . Tel: (020) 7219 8134 Fax: (020) 7219 1741
                    E-mail: selousa@parliament.uk
                    Web: http://www.andrewselous.org.uk
                    Secretary – Mrs Sue Howat

**Shaw, Jonathan** . . . Chatham and Aylesford
**Labour** . . . . . . . . . . . Majority 4,340 over Con
*Born.* . . . . . . . . . . . . . . 3rd June 1966 in Aylesford
*Educated* . . . . . . . . . . Vinters Boys School, Maidstone;
                    West Kent College;
                    Bromley College of Further Education
*Elected.* . . . . . . . . . . . 1997 MP for Chatham and Aylesford
*Commons Office* . . . . . Tel: (020) 7219 6919 Fax: (020) 7219 0938
                    E-mail: shawj@parliament.uk
*Constituency Office* . . . 411 Hight Street, Chatham, Kent, ME4 4NU
                    Tel: (01634) 811573 Fax: (01634) 815382
                    Constituency Assistant – Mr Phil Hall
                    E-mail: hallpm@parliament.uk
*Parliamentary Interests* . Social Policy; Welfare; Paper Industry

**Sheerman, Barry** . . Huddersfield
**Labour** . . . . . . . . . . . Majority 10,046 over Con
*Born.* . . . . . . . . . . . . . . 17th August 1940 in London
*Educated* . . . . . . . . . . Hampton Grammar School;
                    London School of Economics
*Elected.* . . . . . . . . . . . 1979 MP for Huddersfield East, then (1983)
                    for Huddersfield
*Offices Held* . . . . . . . . 1983 - 88 Opposition Spokesman on Employment
                    1988 - 92 Opposition Spokesman on
                        Home Affairs
                    1992 - 94 Opposition Spokesman on
                        Disabled People's Rights
                    1997 - 2001 Chairman, Education
                        Sub-Committee (Education and
                        Employment Select Committee),
                        House of Commons
                    2001 - Chairman, Education and Skills Select
                        Committee, House of Commons
*Commons Office* . . . . . Tel: (020) 7219 5037 Fax: (020) 7219 2404
                    Mobile: 07767 387104
                    E-mail: sheermanb@parliament.uk
                    Web: http://www.barrysheerman.labour.co.uk
                    Research Assistants – Ms Jo Billingham
                                Miss Matilda Gosling
                    E-mails: [surnameinitial]@parliament.uk
*Constituency Office* . . . . 6 Cross Church Street, Huddersfield, HD1 2PT
                    Tel: (01484) 451382 Fax: (01484) 451334
                    E-mail: sheerman.const@btconnect.com
                    Researcher – Mrs Gill O'Sullivan
                    Secretary – Ms Betty Selkirk
                    Personal Assistant/Diary Manager –
                        Mrs Sue Longbottom
                    Tel & Fax: (01924) 495277
*Parliamentary Interests* . Economy; Higher Education; Home Affairs;
                    Environment
*Leisure Interests* . . . . . . Walking; Music; Social Entrepreneuring

**Shephard, Rt Hon Gillian** Norfolk South West
**Conservative** . . . . . . . Majority 9,366 over Lab
*Born.* . . . . . . . . . . . . . . 22nd January 1940 in Norfolk
*Educated* . . . . . . . . . . North Walsham High School;
                    St Hilda's College, Oxford
*Elected.* . . . . . . . . . . . 1987 MP for Norfolk South West
*Offices Held* . . . . . . . . 1989 - 90 Parliamentary Secretary,
                        Department of Social Security
                    1990 - 92 Minister of State, H M Treasury
                    1992 - 93 Secretary of State for Employment
                    1993 - 94 Minister of Agriculture, Fisheries
                        and Food
                    1994 - 95 Secretary of State for Education
                    1995 - 97 Secretary of State for Education
                        and Employment
                    1997 - 98 Shadow Leader of the
                        House of Commons
                    1998 - 99 Shadow Secretary for
                        Environment, Transport and Regions
                    2002 - Vice-Chairman, Conservative Party
*Commons Office* . . . . . Tel: (020) 7219 2898 Fax: (020) 7219 1438
                    Private Secretary – Mrs Lynn Fox
*Leisure Interests* . . . . . . France; Music; Gardening

# MEMBERS OF THE HOUSE OF COMMONS

**Shepherd, Richard** . . Aldridge-Brownhills
**Conservative** . . . . . . Majority 3,768 over Lab
*Born*. . . . . . . . . . . . . . 6th December 1942 in Aberdeen
*Educated* . . . . . . . . . . Isleworth Grammar School;
London School of Economics;
John Hopkins School of Advanced
International Studies, Bologna, Italy
*Elected*. . . . . . . . . . . . 1979 MP for Aldridge-Brownhills
*Commons Office* . . . . . Tel: (020) 7219 5004 Fax: (020) 7219 0083
E-mail: shepherdr@parliament.uk
Personal Assistants –
Mrs Davida Catleugh
Mrs Margaret MacLennan
E-mail: catleughd@parliament.uk
*Constituency Office* . . . . 82 Walsall Road, Aldridge, West Midlands,
WS9 0JW
Tel & Fax: (01922) 452228
Organising Secretary – Mrs Margaret Salt
E-mail: margaretsalt@tory.org

**Sheridan, James** . . . . Renfrewshire West
**Labour** . . . . . . . . . . . Majority 8,575 over SNP
*Born*. . . . . . . . . . . . . . 1952
*Elected*. . . . . . . . . . . . 2001 MP for Renfrewshire West
*Commons Office* . . . . . Tel: (020) 7219 8314
Pager: 07626 409536
E-mail: jim@james-sheridan-mp.org.uk
Web: http://www.james-sheridan-mp.org.uk
*Constituency Office* . . . . 21 John Wood Street, Port Glasgow,
PA14 5HU
Tel: (01475) 791826 Fax: (01475) 791829
E-mail: enquiries@james-sheridan-mp.org.uk
Personal Assistant –
Mrs Jacqueline Thompson
Researchers/Caseworkers –
Mr Daniel Harris
Miss Joanne Sheridan
Tel: (01475) 791827/8
*Parliamentary Interests* . Employment Legislation; Social Inclusion;
International Development; Foreign Affairs;
Home Affairs
*Leisure Interests* . . . . . Football; Exercise; Current Affairs

**Shipley, Debra** . . . . Stourbridge
**Labour** . . . . . . . . . . . Majority 3,812 over Con
*Born*. . . . . . . . . . . . . . 22nd June 1957
*Educated* . . . . . . . . . . Kidderminster High School;
Oxford Polytechnic; University of London
*Elected*. . . . . . . . . . . . 1997 MP for Stourbridge
*Commons Office* . . . . . Tel: (020) 7219 3053
Researcher – Mr Phil Jones
*Constituency Office* . . . . Tel: (01384) 374356
*Parliamentary Interests* . Protection of Children;
Architecture and Built Environment
*Leisure Interests* . . . . . Walking; Reading; Cooking

**Short, Rt Hon Clare**  Birmingham Ladywood
**Labour** . . . . . . . . . . . Majority 18,143 over Con
*Born*. . . . . . . . . . . . . . 15th February 1946 in Birmingham
*Educated* . . . . . . . . . . St Paul's Grammar School, Birmingham;
Keele University; Leeds University
*Elected*. . . . . . . . . . . . 1983 MP for Birmingham Ladywood
*Offices Held* . . . . . . . . 1985 - 89 Opposition Spokesman on
Employment
1989 - 90 Opposition Spokesman on
Social Security
1992 - 93 Opposition Spokesman on
Environmental Protection
1993 - 95 Opposition Spokesman on
Women's Issues
1995 - 96 Shadow Transport Secretary
1996 - 97 Shadow Overseas Development
Minister
1997 - 2003 Secretary of State for
International Development
*Commons Office* . . . . . Tel: (020) 7219 4264
Secretary – Ms Jessica Drewery
E-mail: dreweryj@parliament.uk
Assistant – Ms Danielle Hamm
Tel: (020) 7219 4148
E-mail: hammd@parliament.uk

**Simmonds, Mark** . . Boston and Skegness
**Conservative** . . . . . . Majority 513 over Lab
*Born*. . . . . . . . . . . . . . 12th April 1964
*Educated* . . . . . . . . . . Worksop College;
Trent University, Nottingham
*Elected*. . . . . . . . . . . . 2001 MP for Boston and Skegness
*Offices Held* . . . . . . . . 2004 Opposition Spokesman on Education
2004 - Opposition Spokesman on
International Affairs
*Commons Office* . . . . . Tel: (020) 7219 6254 Fax: (020) 7219 1746
E-mail: simmondsm@parliament.uk
Parliamentary Assistant –
Miss Helen Cockburn
E-mail: cockburnh@parliament.uk
Researcher – Mr Robert Detheridge
Tel: (020) 7219 8282
E-mail: detheridger@parliament.uk
*Constituency Office* . . . . 16 Main Ridge West, Boston, Lincolnshire,
PE21 6QQ
Tel & Fax: (01205) 751414
Agent – Mr Graham Street
*Parliamentary Interests* . Foreign Affairs; Agriculture; Education
*Leisure Interests* . . . . . Family; Historical Literature;
Watching Rugby; Playing Tennis

# MEMBERS OF THE HOUSE OF COMMONS

**Simon, Siôn**...... Birmingham Erdington
**Labour**........... Majority 9,962 over Con
*Born*.............. 23rd December 1968 in Doncaster
*Educated*.......... Magdalen College, Oxford
*Elected*........... 2001 MP for Birmingham Erdington
*Commons Office*..... Tel: (020) 7219 8140 Fax: (020) 7219 5856
E-mail: simons@parliament.uk
Secretary – Ms Jane Davies
Tel: (020) 7219 6637
E-mail: daviesjd@parliament.uk
*Constituency Office*.... Regent House, 50A Reservoir Road,
Erdington, Birmingham, B23 6DG
Tel: (0121) 373 1147 Fax: (0121) 382 6347
Constituency Assistants – Mr Desmond Hughes
Ms Anita Ward

**Simpson, Alan**..... Nottingham South
**Labour**........... Majority 9,989 over Con
*Born*.............. 20th September 1948 in Bootle, Merseyside
*Educated*.......... Bootle Grammar School;
Nottingham Trent Polytechnic
*Elected*........... 1992 MP for Nottingham South
*Commons Office*..... Tel: (020) 7219 4534 Fax: (020) 7219 4657
E-mail: simpsona@parliament.uk
Web: http://www.alansimpsonmp.co.uk
Senior Parliamentary Assistant –
Ms Caroline Watson
E-mail: watsonca@parliament.uk
*Constituency Office*.... Vernon House, 18 Friar Lane,
Nottingham, NH1 6DQ
Tel: (0115) 956 0460 Fax: (0115) 956 0445
Caseworker – Miss Marcia Watson
Secretary – Ms Carole Bithell
*Parliamentary Interests*. GM Foods; Local Government; Fuel Poverty;
Environmental Sustainability; Globalisation;
Disarmament
*Leisure Interests*...... Tennis; Cricket; Football; Vegetarian Cooking;
Music

**Simpson, Keith**.... Mid Norfolk
**Conservative**....... Majority 4,562 over Lab
*Born*.............. 29th March 1949 in Norwich
*Educated*.......... Thorpe Grammar School, Norfolk;
Hull University; King's College, London
*Elected*........... 1997 MP for Mid Norfolk
*Offices Held*........ 1998 - 99, 2002 - 03 Opposition
Spokesman on Defence
1999 - 2001 Opposition Whip
2001 - 02 Opposition Spokesman on
Agriculture
2004 - Opposition Spokesman on
International Affairs and Defence
*Commons Office*..... Tel: (020) 7219 4053 Fax: (020) 7219 0975
Pager – 07626 802349
E-mail: keithsimpson@parliament.uk
Secretary – Mrs Katy Craven
E-mail: cravenc@parliament.uk
*Constituency Office*.... The Old Smithy, Church Farm, Attlebridge,
Norfolk, NR9 5ST
Tel: (01603) 865763 Fax: (01603) 865762
E-mail: mncanorfolk@aol.com
*Parliamentary Interests*. Education; Foreign Affairs; Defence;
Agriculture
*Leisure Interests*...... Collecting Books; Observing Ambitious People

**Singh, Marsha**.... Bradford West
**Labour**........... Majority 4,165 over Con
*Born*.............. 11th October 1954 in India
*Educated*.......... Belle Vue Grammar School, Bradford;
Loughborough University
*Elected*........... 1997 MP for Bradford West
*Commons Office*..... Tel: (020) 7219 4516 Fax: (020) 7219 0965
Secretary – Miss Charlene McLean
E-mail: mcleanc@parliament.uk
*Constituency Office*.... 2nd Floor, 76 Kirkgate, Bradford, BD1 1SZ
Tel: (01274) 402220 Fax: (01274) 402211
Constituency Secretary –
Ms Anne-Marie Benson
*Parliamentary Interests*. Home Affairs; Foreign Affairs
*Leisure Interests*...... Reading; Current Affairs

**Skinner, Dennis**... Bolsover
**Labour**........... Majority 18,777 over Con
*Born*.............. 11th February 1932 in Clay Cross, Derbyshire
*Educated*.......... Tupton Hall Grammar School;
Ruskin College, Oxford
*Elected*........... 1970 MP for Bolsover
*Commons Office*..... Tel: (020) 7219 5107
E-mail: skinnerd@parliament.uk
*Constituency Office*.... (01773) 863429/581027
*Leisure Interests*...... Tennis; Cycling; Watching Athletics

**Smith, Rt Hon Andrew**  Oxford East
**Labour**........... Majority 10,344 over Lib Dem
*Born*.............. 1st February 1951 in Berkshire
*Educated*.......... Reading Grammar School;
St John's College, Oxford
*Elected*........... 1987 MP for Oxford East
*Offices Held*........ 1988 - 92 Opposition Spokesman on
Education
1992 - 94 Opposition Spokesman on Treasury
and Economic Affairs
1994 - 96 Shadow Chief Secretary to the
Treasury
1996 - 97 Shadow Transport Secretary
1997 - 99 Minister of State, Department for
Education and Employment
1999 - 02 Chief Secretary, H M Treasury
2002 - 04 Secretary of State for
Work and Pensions
*Constituency Office*.... Suite A, 21 Templars Square, Cowley,
Oxford, OX4 3UZ
Tel: (01865) 772893 Fax: (01865) 772916
E-mail: andrewsmithmp@virgin.net
Web: http://www.andrewsmithmp.org.uk
Office Manager – Mrs Val Smith
E-mail: smithv@parliament.uk
Caseworker – Ms Annabel Fleming
E-mail: fleminga@parliament.uk
Assistant – Mr Laurence Baxter
E-mail: baxterl@parliament.uk
*Parliamentary Interests*. Employment; Economy; Education;
Overseas Development
*Leisure Interests*...... Cycling; Walking; Windsurfing

# MEMBERS OF THE HOUSE OF COMMONS

**Smith, Angela** . . . . . Basildon
**Labour** . . . . . . . . . . . Majority 7,738 over Con
*Born.* . . . . . . . . . . . . . 7th January 1959 in Hackney, London
*Educated* . . . . . . . . . . Chalvedon School, Basildon;
Leicester Polytechnic
*Elected.* . . . . . . . . . . . 1997 MP for Basildon
*Offices Held* . . . . . . . . 2001 - 02 Assistant Government Whip
2002 - Parliamentary Secretary,
Northern Ireland Office
*Commons Office* . . . . . Tel: (020) 7219 6273 Fax: (020) 7219 0926
*Constituency Office* . . . . Cornwallis House, Howard Chase, Basildon,
Essex, SS14 3BB
Tel: (01268) 284830 Fax: (01268) 284831
E-mail: gordonl@parliament.uk
*Parliamentary Interests* . Crime and Crime Prevention; Animal Welfare;
International Development
*Leisure Interests* . . . . . Reading (Political Biographies, Oscar Wilde);
Coronation Street

**Smith, Rt Hon Chris**  Islington South and Finsbury
**Labour** . . . . . . . . . . . Majority 7,280 over Lib Dem
*Born.* . . . . . . . . . . . . . 24th July 1951 in North London
*Educated* . . . . . . . . . . George Watson's College, Edinburgh;
Pembroke College, Cambridge;
Harvard University, USA
*Elected.* . . . . . . . . . . . 1983 MP for Islington South and Finsbury
*Offices Held* . . . . . . . . 1986 - 87 Opposition Whip
1987 - 92 Opposition Treasury Spokesman
1992 - 94 Opposition Spokesman on
Environmental Protection
1994 - 95 Shadow National Heritage Secretary
1995 - 96 Shadow Social Security Secretary
1996 - 97 Shadow Health Secretary
1997 - 2001 Secretary of State for Culture,
Media and Sport
*Commons Office* . . . . . Tel: (020) 7219 5119 Fax: (020) 7219 5820
E-mail: barans@parliament.uk
Parliamentary Assistant – Mr Steve Baran
Constituency Assistants – Ms Cathryn Evans
Ms Fran Newell
*Constituency Office* . . . . 65 Barnsbury Street, London, N1 1EJ
E-mail: labour@islington.org.uk
Tel: (020) 7607 8373 Fax: (020) 7607 8299
Agent – Mr John Wyman-White
*Parliamentary Interests* . Culture, Media and Sport; Health;
Social Security; Environment; Economy;
Civil Liberties
*Leisure Interests* . . . . . Mountaineering; Art; Music; Literature;
Theatre

**Smith, Geraldine** . . Morecambe and Lunesdale
**Labour** . . . . . . . . . . . Majority 5,092 over Con
*Born.* . . . . . . . . . . . . . 29th August 1961 in Belfast
*Educated* . . . . . . . . . . Morecambe High School;
Lancaster and Morecambe College
*Elected.* . . . . . . . . . . . 1997 MP for Morecambe and Lunesdale
*Commons Office* . . . . . Tel: (020) 7219 5816 Fax: (020) 7219 0977
Mobile: 07989 895490
E-mail: smithg@parliament.uk
Researcher – Mr Phil Farrell
Fax: (020) 7219 5487
*Constituency Office* . . . . 26/28 Victoria Street, Morecambe, LA4 4DR
Tel: (01524) 411368 Fax; (01524) 411369
Secretary – Ms Rebekah Gerrard
Tel: (01524) 411367
*Parliamentary Interests* . Tourism; Economic Regeneration
*Leisure Interests* . . . . . Chess; Walking

**Smith, Rt Hon Jacqui**  Redditch
**Labour** . . . . . . . . . . . Majority 2,484 over Con
*Born.* . . . . . . . . . . . . . 3rd November 1962 in London
*Educated* . . . . . . . . . . Dyson Perrins High School, Malvern;
Hertford College, Oxford
Worcester College of Higher Education
*Elected.* . . . . . . . . . . . 1997 MP for Redditch
*Offices Held* . . . . . . . . 1999 - 2001 Parliamentary Secretary,
Department for Education and Employment
2001 - 03 Minister of State,
Department of Health
2003 - Minister of State, Department of
Trade and Industry
*Commons Office* . . . . . Tel: (020) 7219 5190 Fax: (020) 7219 4815
E-mail: smithj@parliament.uk
*Constituency Office* . . . . Unit 16, Greenlands Business Centre,
Studley Road, Redditch, Worcestershire,
B98 7HD
Tel & Fax: (01527) 523355
Constituency Assistant – Mr Richard Timney
*Parliamentary Interests* . Economic Policy; Industrial Policy; Education;
Childcare; Leasehold Reform; Social Services
*Leisure Interests* . . . . . Family; Football; Theatre

**Smith, John** . . . . . . Vale of Glamorgan
**Labour** . . . . . . . . . . . Majority 4,700 over Con
*Born.* . . . . . . . . . . . . . 7th March 1951
*Educated* . . . . . . . . . . Gwent College of Higher Education;
University College of Wales, Cardiff
*Elected.* . . . . . . . . . . . 1989 - 92 MP for Vale of Glamorgan
(By-election)
1997 MP for Vale of Glamorgan
*Offices Held* . . . . . . . . Formerly Leader, Vale of Glamorgan Council
1997 - 99 PPS to John Reid (Minister for the
Armed Forces, then Minister for Transport)
*Commons Office* . . . . . Tel: (020) 7219 3589 Fax: (020) 7219 0939
Pager: 07644 008087
*Constituency Office* . . . . 115 High Street, Barry, CF62 7DT
Tel: (01446) 743769 Fax: (01446) 747921
Researchers – Mr James Howard
Miss Cerys Butcher
Mr Philippe Minchin
*Parliamentary Interests* . Economic Development; Defence; Transport;
Flight Related Deep Vein Thrombosis;
Consumer Affairs
*Leisure Interests* . . . . . Boating; Reading; Walking

# MEMBERS OF THE HOUSE OF COMMONS

**Smith, Llew** . . . . . . . Blaenau Gwent
**Labour** . . . . . . . . . . . Majority 19,313 over Plaid Cymru
*Born* . . . . . . . . . . . . . 16th April 1944 in Newbridge
*Educated* . . . . . . . . . . Greenfield Secondary Modern School,
    Newbridge; Coleg Harlech;
    University College of Wales, Cardiff
*Elected* . . . . . . . . . . . 1992 MP for Blaenau Gwent
*Office Held* . . . . . . . . 1984 - 94 Member of the European
    Parliament
*Commons Office* . . . . . Tel: (020) 7219 6342 Fax: (020) 7219 2357
*Constituency Office* . . . 23 Beaufort Street, Brynmawr, Blaenau Gwent,
    NP3 4AQ
    Tel: (01495) 313345 Fax: (01495) 313346
*Parliamentary Interests* . Poverty; Nuclear Weapons/Power

**Smith, Sir Robert** . Aberdeenshire West and Kincardine
**Liberal Democrat** . . . Majority 4,821 over Con
*Born* . . . . . . . . . . . . . 15th April 1958
*Educated* . . . . . . . . . . Merchant Taylors School;
    University of Aberdeen
*Elected* . . . . . . . . . . . 1997 MP for Aberdeenshire West and
    Kincardine
*Offices Held* . . . . . . . 1997 - 99 Liberal Democrat Spokesman on
    Transport and Environment
    1999 - 2001 Liberal Democrat Whip
    and Spokesman on Scottish Affairs
    2001 - Liberal Democrat Deputy Chief Whip
*Commons Office* . . . . . Tel: (020) 7219 3531 Fax: (020) 7219 4526
    Pager: 07699 780564
*Constituency Office* . . . 6 Dee Street, Banchory, Kincardineshire,
    AB31 5ST
    Tel: (01330) 820330 Fax: (01330) 820338
    E-mail: bobsmith@cix.co.uk
    Office Manager – Cllr John Stewart
    Casework Assistant – Mrs Alison Auld
*Parliamentary Interests* . Electoral Reform; Off Shore Industry;
    Rural Affairs
*Leisure Interests* . . . . . Hill Walking; Sailing

**Smyth, Rev Martin** Belfast South
**Ulster Unionist** . . . . . Majority 5,399 over SDLP
*Born* . . . . . . . . . . . . . 15th June 1931 in Belfast
*Educated* . . . . . . . . . . Methodist College, Belfast;
    Magee University, Londonderry;
    Presbyterian College, Belfast;
    San Francisco Theological Seminary
*Elected* . . . . . . . . . . . 1982 - 85 MP for Belfast South (By-election)
    1986 MP for Belfast South (By-election)
*Offices Held* . . . . . . . 2001 - 02 Ulster Unionist Chief Whip
    2002 - Ulster Unionist Spokesman on Foreign
    and Commonwealth Affairs; International
    Development; Health
*Commons Office* . . . . . Tel: (020) 7219 4098 Fax: (020) 7219 2347
    Mobile: 07770 931528
    Pager: 07644 005186
    Assistant – Miss Margaret McKee
    Tel: (020) 7219 5670
    E-mail: mckeem@parliament.uk
*Constituency Office* . . . 117 Cregagh Road, Belfast, BT6 0LA
    Tel: (028) 9045 7009 Fax: (028) 9045 0837
    E-mail: tearleg@parliament.uk
    Secretary – Mrs Margaret Clarke
    Constituency Aide – Mr Jim Clarke
    Personal Assistant – Mr Gary Tearle
*Parliamentary Interests* . World Protestantism; Health; Social Services;
    Education; Foreign Affairs;
    Overseas Development; Human Rights
*Leisure Interests* . . . . . Photography; Reading; Travel

**Soames, Hon Nicholas** Mid Sussex
**Conservative** . . . . . . Majority 6,898 over Lib Dem
*Born* . . . . . . . . . . . . . 12th February 1948 in London
*Educated* . . . . . . . . . . Eton College
*Elected* . . . . . . . . . . . 1983 - 97 MP for Crawley
    1997 MP for Mid Sussex
*Offices Held* . . . . . . . 1992 - 94 Parliamentary Secretary,
    Ministry of Agriculture, Fisheries and Food
    1994 - 97 Minister of State, Ministry of
    Defence (Minister for the Armed Forces)
    2003 - Shadow Secretary for Defence
*Commons Office* . . . . . Tel: (020) 7219 4143 Fax: (020) 7219 2998
    E-mail: soamesn@parliament.uk
    Web: http://www.nicholassoames.org.uk
    Personal Assistant – Miss Claire Barker
    E-mail: barkerc@parliament.uk
*Constituency Office* . . . 5 Hazelgrove Road, Haywards Heath,
    West Sussex, RH16 3PH
    Tel: (01444) 452590 Fax: (01444) 415766
    E-mail: midsussexconassocn@lineone.net
    Secretary – Mrs Virginia Heard
*Parliamentary Interests* . Defence; Foreign and Commonwealth Affairs;
    Business; Agriculture; Middle East
*Leisure Interests* . . . . . Countryside Pursuits; Reading

**Soley, Clive** . . . . . . . Ealing, Acton and Shepherds Bush
**Labour** . . . . . . . . . . . Majority 10,789 over Con
*Born* . . . . . . . . . . . . . 7th May 1939 in Essex
*Educated* . . . . . . . . . . Downshall Secondary Modern School, Ilford;
    Newbattle Abbey Adult Education College;
    Strathclyde University;
    Southampton University
*Elected* . . . . . . . . . . . 1979 MP for Hammersmith North, then
    (1983) Hammersmith, then (1997) Ealing,
    Acton and Shepherds Bush
*Offices Held* . . . . . . . 1981 - 84 Opposition Spokesman on
    Northern Ireland
    1984 - 87 Opposition Spokesman on
    Home Affairs
    1987 - 92 Opposition Spokesman on Housing
    1995 - 97 Chairman, Northern Ireland Affairs
    Select Committee, House of Commons
    1997 - 2001 Chairman, Parliamentary
    Labour Party
*Commons Office* . . . . . Tel: (020) 7219 5490 Fax: (020) 7219 5974
*Parliamentary Interests* . Press and Media; Northern Ireland; Housing;
    House of Lords Reform
*Leisure Interests* . . . . . Photography; Diving; Gardening

**Southworth, Helen** Warrington South
**Labour** . . . . . . . . . . . Majority 7,387 over Con
*Born* . . . . . . . . . . . . . 13th November 1956 in Preston
*Educated* . . . . . . . . . . Larkhill Convent School; Lancaster University
*Elected* . . . . . . . . . . . 1997 MP for Warrington South
*Office Held* . . . . . . . . 2001 - PPS to Paul Boateng (Chief Secretary,
    H M Treasury)
*Commons Office* . . . . . Tel: (020) 7219 6398 Fax: (020) 7219 0943
*Constituency Office* . . . 1A Academy Place, Academy Street,
    Warrington, WA1 2NR
    Tel: (01925) 240002 Fax: (01925) 632614
    Senior Secretary – Ms Hilary Cooksey
    Personal Assistant – Mr Paul Murgatroyd
*Parliamentary Interests* . Small Businesses; Health; Social Cohesion;
    Trade and Industry
*Leisure Interests* . . . . . Music; Books; Gardens; Strategic Planning

# MEMBERS OF THE HOUSE OF COMMONS

**Spellar, Rt Hon John** Warley

| | |
|---|---|
| **Labour** | Majority 11,850 over Con |
| *Born* | 5th August 1947 in Bromley, Kent |
| *Educated* | Dulwich College; St Edmund Hall, Oxford |
| *Elected* | 1982 - 83 MP for Birmingham Northfield (By-election) |
| | 1992 MP for Warley West, then (1997) Warley |
| *Offices Held* | 1992 - 94 Opposition Whip |
| | 1994 - 95 Opposition Spokesman on Northern Ireland |
| | 1995 - 97 Opposition Spokesman on Defence |
| | 1997 - 99 Parliamentary Secretary, Ministry of Defence |
| | 1999 - 01 Minister of State, Ministry of Defence (Minister for the Armed Forces) |
| | 2001 - 03 Minister of State, Department for Transport, Local Government and the Regions, then Department of Transport |
| | 2003 - Minister of State, Northern Ireland Office |
| *Commons Office* | Tel: (020) 7219 5800 Fax: (020) 7219 2113 |
| | Web: http://www.johnspellar.labour.co.uk |
| | Research Officer – Mrs Maggie Cosin |
| | E-mail: cosinm@parliament.uk |
| | Secretary – Mrs Linda Colyer |
| | Tel: (020) 7219 0674 |
| | E-mail: colyerl@parliament.uk |
| *Constituency Office* | Brandhall Labour Club, Tame Road, Oldbury, West Midlands, B68 0BJ |
| | Tel & Fax: (0121) 423 2933 |
| | Secretary – Mrs Carole Silvester |
| | Casework Officer – Mr W Thomas |
| | Tel: (0121) 423 3023 |
| *Leisure Interests* | Gardening |

**Spelman, Caroline** Meriden

| | |
|---|---|
| **Conservative** | Majority 3,784 over Lab |
| *Born* | 4th May 1958 in Bishops Stortford, Hertfordshire |
| *Educated* | Herts and Essex Girls Grammar School; Queen Mary College, London |
| *Elected* | 1997 MP for Meriden |
| *Offices Held* | 1998 - 99 Opposition Whip |
| | 1999 - 2001 Opposition Spokesman on Health and Women's Issues |
| | 2001 - 03 Shadow International Development Secretary and Opposition Spokesman on Women's Issues |
| | 2003 - 04 Shadow Secretary for Environment and Shadow Minister for Women |
| | 2004 - Shadow Secretary for Local and Devolved Government Affairs |
| *Commons Office* | Tel: (020) 7219 4189 Fax: (020) 7219 0378 |
| | Mobile: 07818 400792 |
| | Pager: 07626 802050 |
| | E-mail: caroline@carolinespelman.com |
| | Web: http://www.carolinespelman.com |
| | Secretary – Miss Katy Harbour |
| | E-mail: harbourk@parliament.uk |
| | Chief of Staff – Mr Simon Cawte |
| | Tel: (020) 7219 1439 Fax: (020) 7219 2498 |
| | E-mail: cawtes@parliament.uk |
| *Constituency Office* | 2 Manor Road, Solihull, B91 2BH |
| | Tel & Fax: (0121) 711 2955 |
| | Secretary – Mrs Paula Yates |
| *Parliamentary Interests* | Agriculture; Environment; International Development |
| *Leisure Interests* | Tennis; Gardening; Cooking; Skiing |

**Spicer, Sir Michael** Worcestershire West

| | |
|---|---|
| **Conservative** | Majority 5,374 over Lib Dem |
| *Born* | 22nd January 1943 in Bath |
| *Educated* | Wellington College; Emmanuel College, Cambridge |
| *Elected* | 1974 MP for Worcestershire South, then (1997) Worcestershire West |
| *Offices Held* | 1984 - 87 Parliamentary Secretary, Department of Transport (Minister for Aviation) |
| | 1987 - 90 Parliamentary Secretary, Department of Energy (Minister for Coal and Electricity) |
| | 1990 Minister of State, Department of Environment (Minister for Housing) |
| | 2001 - Chairman, 1922 Committee of Conservative MPs |
| *Commons Office* | Tel: (020) 7219 6250 Fax: (020) 7219 2991 |
| | Web: http://www.sirmichaelspicer.net |
| | Private Secretary – Miss Jessica Stewart |
| *Constituency Office* | 209a Worcester Road, Malvern Link, Worcestershire, WR14 1SP |
| | Tel: (01684) 573469 Fax: (01684) 575280 |
| | Office Administrator– Mrs Barbara Morgan |
| | Agent – Mr Simon Eardley |
| *Parliamentary Interests* | Finance; Economics |
| *Leisure Interests* | Tennis; Bridge; Painting; Writing |

**Spink, Dr Robert** Castle Point

| | |
|---|---|
| **Conservative** | Majority 985 over Lab |
| *Born* | 1st August 1948 |
| *Educated* | Holycroft Secondary Modern School, Keighley; Southall Technical College; Manchester University; Cranfield Institute of Technology; Cranfield School of Management |
| *Elected* | 1992 - 97, 2001 MP for Castle Point |
| *Commons Office* | Tel: (020) 7219 8468 Fax: (020) 7219 1956 |
| | Mobile: 07957 543648 |
| | Pager: 07644 078133 |
| | E-mail: spinkr@parliament.uk |
| | Web: http://www.epolitix.com/bob-spink |
| | PA/Secretary – Miss Rebecca Galloway |
| | Tel: (020) 7219 8302 Fax: (020) 7219 1989 |
| | E-mail: gallowayr@parliament.uk |
| *Constituency Office* | 75 Downer Road, Benfleet, Essex |
| | Fax: (01268) 474455 |
| *Parliamentary Interests* | Education; Trade and Industry; Energy; Human Rights |
| *Leisure Interests* | Gardening; Jogging; Pottery |

# MEMBERS OF THE HOUSE OF COMMONS

**Spring, Richard** . . . Suffolk West
**Conservative** . . . . . . Majority 4,295 over Lab
*Born*. . . . . . . . . . . . . . 24th September 1946
*Educated* . . . . . . . . . Rondebosch, South Africa;
                University of Capetown, South Africa;
                Magdalene College, Cambridge
*Elected*. . . . . . . . . . . 1992 MP for Bury St Edmunds, then (1997)
                Suffolk West
*Offices Held* . . . . . . . 1997 - 2000 Opposition Spokesman on
                Culture Media and Sport
                2000 - 04 Opposition Spokesman on
                International Affairs
                2004 - Opposition Spokesman on
                Economic Affairs
*Commons Office* . . . . . . Tel: (020) 7219 5192
                Web: http://www.richardspringmp.com
                Secretary – Ms Beverley Sandel
*Constituency Office* . . . . 4a Exeter Road, Newmarket, Suffolk,
                CB8 8LT
                Tel: (01638) 669391 Fax: (01638) 669410
                Secretary – Mrs Dorothy Whittaker
*Leisure Interests* . . . . . . Country Pursuits; Tennis; Swimming

**Squire, Rachel** . . . . Dunfermline West
**Labour** . . . . . . . . . . . Majority 10,980 over SNP
*Born*. . . . . . . . . . . . . . 13th July 1954 in Carshalton, Surrey
*Educated* . . . . . . . . . . Godolphin and Latymer Girls' School, London;
                Durham University; Birmingham University
*Elected*. . . . . . . . . . . . 1992 MP for Dunfermline West
*Commons Office* . . . . . . Tel: (020) 7219 5144 Fax: (020) 7219 2866
                Research Assistant – Mr Richard Conway
                Tel: (020) 7219 4005
*Constituency Office* . . . . Music Hall Lane, Dunfermline, Fife,
                KY12 7NG
                Tel: (01383) 622889 Fax: (01383) 623500
                Constituency Assistant –
                Mrs Margaret McCulloch
*Parliamentary Interests* . Defence; Foreign Affairs; Education;
                Employment
*Leisure Interests* . . . . . . Archaeology; Cooking; Reading

**Stanley, Rt Hon Sir John** Tonbridge and Malling
**Conservative** . . . . . . Majority 8,250 over Lab
*Born*. . . . . . . . . . . . . . 19th January 1942 in London
*Educated* . . . . . . . . . . Repton School; Lincoln College, Oxford
*Elected*. . . . . . . . . . . . 1974 MP for Tonbridge and Malling
*Offices Held* . . . . . . . . 1976 - 79 PPS to Margaret Thatcher
                (Leader of the Opposition)
                1979 - 83 Minister of State, Department of
                Environment (Minister for Housing)
                1983 - 87 Minister of State,
                Ministry of Defence
                1987 - 88 Minister of State,
                Northern Ireland Office
*Commons Office* . . . . . . Tel: (020) 7219 5977
                Web: http://www.teamconservatives.co.uk
*Parliamentary Interest* . Foreign Affairs; Korea; Nepal;
                Child Abduction

**Starkey, Dr Phyllis** Milton Keynes South West
**Labour** . . . . . . . . . . . Majority 6,978 over Con
*Born*. . . . . . . . . . . . . . 4th January 1947
*Educated* . . . . . . . . . Perse School for Girls, Cambridge;
                Lady Margaret Hall, Oxford;
                Clare Hall, Cambridge
*Elected*. . . . . . . . . . . . 1997 MP for Milton Keynes South West
*Offices Held* . . . . . . . . 1990 - 93 Leader, Oxford City Council
                2002 - PPS to Dr Denis MacShane
                (Minister of State, Foreign and
                Commonwealth Office)
*Commons Office* . . . . . . Tel: (020) 7219 6427 Fax: (020) 7219 6865
                Mobile: 07702 370043
                Pager: 07644 008750
                Web: http://www.phyllisstarkey.labour.co.uk
                Parliamentary Assistant – Mr Stephen Mutton
                Tel: (020) 7219 0456
                E-mail: muttons@parliament.uk
*Constituency Office* . . . . Labour Hall, Newport Road, New Bradwell,
                Milton Keynes, MK13 0AA
                Tel: (01908) 225522 Fax: (01908) 320731
                E-mail:
                starkeyp@miltonkeynes-sw.demon.co.uk
                Personal Assistant – Ms Veronica Belcher
                Secretarial Assistant – Mrs Clare Megeary
*Parliamentary Interests* . Foreign Policy (particularly Middle East);
                Science; Health
*Leisure Interests* . . . . . . Walking; Gardening; Cinema;

**Steen, Anthony** . . . . Totnes
**Conservative** . . . . . . Majority 3,597 over Lib Dem
*Born*. . . . . . . . . . . . . . 22nd July 1939 in London
*Educated* . . . . . . . . . . Westminster School; Gray's Inn
*Elected*. . . . . . . . . . . . 1974 - 83 MP for Liverpool Wavertree
                1983 MP for South Hams, then (1997)
                Totnes
*Commons Office* . . . . . . Tel: (020) 7219 5045 Fax: (020) 7219 6586
                E-mail: steena@parliament.uk
*Constituency Office* . . . . Totnes Constituency Conservative Association,
                Station Road, Totnes, Devon, TQ9 5HW
                Tel: (01803) 866069 Fax: (01803) 867286
                E-mail: tcca@tory.org
*Parliamentary Interests* . Deregulation; Europe; Environment;
                Rural Affairs
*Leisure Interests* . . . . . . Fell Walking; Swimming; Wine Tasting

**Steinberg, Gerry** . . City of Durham
**Labour** . . . . . . . . . . . Majority 13,441 over Lib Dem
*Born*. . . . . . . . . . . . . . 20th April 1945 in Durham
*Educated* . . . . . . . . . . Whinney Hill Secondary Modern School;
                Durham Johnston Grammar School;
                Sheffield College of Education;
                Newcastle Polytechnic
*Elected*. . . . . . . . . . . . 1987 MP for City of Durham
*Commons Office* . . . . . . Tel: (020) 7219 6909 Fax: (020) 7219 5901
                Web: http://www.gerry-steinberg.org.uk
*Constituency Office* . . . . 4b Millennium Place, Durham, DH1 1WA
                Tel: (0191) 386 0166 Fax: (0191) 383 0047
                Personal Assistant – Mrs Donna Whitfield
*Parliamentary Interests* . Education; Local Government;
                Animal Welfare
*Leisure Interests* . . . . . . Dog Walking; Gym; Music

# MEMBERS OF THE HOUSE OF COMMONS

**Stevenson, George**  Stoke-on-Trent South
**Labour** . . . . . . . . . . Majority 10,489 over Con
*Born.* . . . . . . . . . . . . . 30th August 1938 in Maltby, Yorkshire
*Educated* . . . . . . . . . . . Queensberry Road Secondary Modern School,
    Stoke-on-Trent
*Elected.* . . . . . . . . . . . 1992 MP for Stoke-on-Trent South
*Offices Held* . . . . . . . . Formerly Deputy Leader, Staffordshire
    County Council and Stoke-on-Trent City
    Council; Former Member of the European
    Parliament
*Commons Office* . . . . . Tel: (020) 7219 5012 Fax: (020) 7219 2688
    E-mail: stevensonp@parliament.uk
*Constituency Office* . . . . 2a Stanton Road, Meir, Stoke-on-Trent,
    Staffordshire, ST3 6DD
    Tel: (01782) 593393 Fax: (01782) 593430
    Secretary – Mrs Barbara Betts
    Office Manager/Researcher –
    Mrs Pauline Stevenson
*Parliamentary Interests* . Transport; Education; Manufacturing Industry;
    Local Government
*Leisure Interests* . . . . . . Travel; Reading; Walking; Cinema

**Stewart, David** . . . . Inverness East, Nairn and Lochaber
**Labour** . . . . . . . . . . Majority 4,716 over SNP
*Born.* . . . . . . . . . . . . . 5th May 1956 in Inverness
*Educated* . . . . . . . . . Inverness High School; Paisley College;
    Stirling University;
    Open University Business School
*Elected.* . . . . . . . . . . . 1997 MP for Inverness East, Nairn
    and Lochaber
*Office Held* . . . . . . . . . 2003 - PPS to Alistair Darling,
    (Secretary of State for Transport
    and Secretary of State for Scotland)
*Commons Office* . . . . . Tel: (020) 7219 3586 Fax: (020) 7219 5687
    E-mail: stewartd@parliament.uk
    Web: http://www.davidstewartmp.co.uk
*Constituency Office* . . . . Queensgate Business Centre, Fraser Street,
    Inverness, IN1 1DY
    Tel: (01463) 237441 Fax: (01463) 237661
    Political Researcher – Ms Olivia Bell
    Parliamentary Assistant – Ms Pam Urquhart
*Parliamentary Interests* . International Development; Social Security;
    Diabetic Screening; Oil and Gas Industry;
    Aviation
*Leisure Interests* . . . . . . Fitness; Film; Football; Travel

**Stewart, Ian**. . . . . . . Eccles
**Labour** . . . . . . . . . . Majority 14,528 over Con
*Born.* . . . . . . . . . . . . . 28th August 1950 in Blantyre, Scotland
*Educated* . . . . . . . . . . Irlam High School, Salford;
    Stretford Technical College;
    Manchester Metropolitan University
*Elected.* . . . . . . . . . . . 1997 MP for Eccles
*Offices Held* . . . . . . . . 2001 - 03 PPS to Brian Wilson (Minister
    for Energy and Construction, Department
    for Trade and Industry)
    2003 - PPS to Stephen Timms
    (Minister of State, Department of
    Trade and Industry)
*Commons Office* . . . . . Tel: (020) 7219 6175 Fax: (020) 7219 0903
    E-mail: ianstewartmp@parliament.uk
    Parliamentary Assistant – Ms Teresa Black
*Constituency Office* . . . . Eccles Town Hall, Church Street, Eccles,
    Manchester, M30 0EL
    Tel: (0161) 707 4688 Fax: (0161) 789 8065
    Constituency Assistant –
    Miss Elizabeth Holland
*Parliamentary Interests* . Education and Training; Trade and Industry;
    International Affairs
*Leisure Interests* . . . . . . Art; Sport; Philosophy; Reading; Tai Chi

**Stinchcombe, Paul**  Wellingborough
**Labour** . . . . . . . . . . Majority 2,355 over Con
*Born.* . . . . . . . . . . . . . 25th April 1962 in Haslemere
*Educated* . . . . . . . . . . Royal Grammar School, High Wycombe;
    Trinity College, Cambridge;
    Harvard Law School, USA
*Elected.* . . . . . . . . . . . 1997 MP for Wellingborough
*Commons Office* . . . . . Tel: (020) 7219 4066 Fax: (020) 7219 0923
*Constituency Office* . . . . 48A Oxford Street, Wellingborough,
    Northamptonshire, NN8 4JH
    Tel: (01933) 279022 Fax: (01933) 279025
    Constituency Liaison/Diary Secretary –
    Mrs Suzanne Stinchcombe
    Parliamentary Assistant – Mr Michael O'Leary
    Caseworker – Mrs Jenny Rolfe
*Parliamentary Interests* . Human Rights; Home Affairs; Environment;
    Health
*Leisure Interests* . . . . . . Sports; Literature; Music

**Stoate, Dr Howard**  Dartford
**Labour** . . . . . . . . . . Majority 3,306 over Con
*Born.* . . . . . . . . . . . . . 14th April 1954 in Weymouth
*Educated* . . . . . . . . . . King's College, London
*Elected.* . . . . . . . . . . . 1997 MP for Dartford
*Offices Held* . . . . . . . . 2001 - 03 PPS to John Denham
    (Minister of State, Home Office)
    2003 - PPS to Estelle Morris
    (Minister of State, Department of Culture,
    Media and Sport)
*Commons Office* . . . . . Tel: (020) 7219 4571 Fax: (020) 7219 6820
    Pager: 07644 008753
    Web: http://www.howardstoate.com
*Constituency Office* . . . . Civic Centre, Home Gardens, Dartford,
    Kent, DA1 1DR
    Tel: (01322) 343234 Fax: (01322) 343235
    Constituency Manager – Cllr Deborah Stoate
    E-mail: debstoate@hotmail.com
    Researcher – Cllr Bryan Jones
    Secretary – Mrs Jenny Barlow
*Parliamentary Interests* . Health; Environment; Local Government;
    Home Affairs
*Leisure Interests* . . . . . . Running; Sailing; Reading; Travel;
    Car Building

**Strang, Rt Hon Dr Gavin**  Edinburgh East and Musselburgh
**Labour** . . . . . . . . . . Majority 14,530 over SNP
*Born.* . . . . . . . . . . . . . 10th July 1943 in Dundee
*Educated* . . . . . . . . . . Morrison's Academy, Perthshire;
    Edinburgh University;
    Churchill College, Cambridge
*Elected.* . . . . . . . . . . . 1970 MP for Edinburgh East, then (1997)
    Edinburgh East and Musselburgh
*Offices Held* . . . . . . . . 1974 Parliamentary Secretary,
    Department of Energy
    1974 - 79 Parliamentary Secretary, Ministry of
    Agriculture, Fisheries and Food
    1979 - 83 Opposition Spokesman on
    Agriculture, Fisheries and Food
    1987 - 89 Opposition Spokesman on
    Employment
    1992 - 97 Shadow Minister of Agriculture,
    Food and Rural Affairs
    1997 - 98 Minister for Transport
*Commons Office* . . . . . Tel: (020) 7219 5155 Fax: (020) 7219 5815
*Constituency Office* . . . . 54 Portobello High Street, Edinburgh,
    EH15 1DA
    Tel: (0131) 669 6002 Fax: (0131) 669 9162
    Agent – Ms Angela Gillan
*Parliamentary Interests* . Agriculture; AIDS; Aviation
*Leisure Interests* . . . . . . Watching Football; Swimming; Cycling; Golf

# MEMBERS OF THE HOUSE OF COMMONS

**Straw, Rt Hon Jack**  Blackburn
**Labour** . . . . . . . . . . . Majority 9,249 over Con
*Born* . . . . . . . . . . . . . . 3rd August 1946 in Essex
*Educated* . . . . . . . . . . Brentwood School, Essex; Leeds University;
Inns of Court School of Law
*Elected* . . . . . . . . . . . . 1979 MP for Blackburn
*Offices Held* . . . . . . . . 1973 - 74 Deputy Leader, Inner London
Education Authority
1980 - 83 Opposition Spokesman on
Treasury and Economic Affairs
1983 - 87 Opposition Spokesman on
Environment
1987 - 92 Shadow Education Secretary
1992 - 94 Shadow Environment Secretary
1994 - 97 Shadow Home Secretary
1997 - 2001 Home Secretary
2001 - Foreign Secretary
*Constituency Office* . . . . 1st Floor, Richmond Chambers,
Richmond Terrace, Blackburn, BB1 7AS.
Tel: (01254) 52317 Fax: (01254) 682213
E-mail: blackburnlabour@hotmail.com
Personal Assistant – Mrs Anne Higginson
Constituency Assistants – Mrs Annette Murphy
Mr Damian Talbot
*Parliamentary Interests* . Foreign Affairs; Economic Policy;
Machinery of Government;
Housing and Local Government; Police;
Education; European Union
*Leisure Interests* . . . . . . Walking; Cycling; Cooking Puddings; Music

**Streeter, Gary** . . . . Devon South West
**Conservative** . . . . . . . Majority 7,144 over Lab
*Born* . . . . . . . . . . . . . . 2nd October 1955
*Educated* . . . . . . . . . . Tiverton Grammar School;
King's College, London
*Elected* . . . . . . . . . . . . 1992 MP for Plymouth Sutton, then (1997)
Devon South West
*Offices Held* . . . . . . . . 1995 - 96 Assistant Government Whip
1996 - 97 Parliamentary Secretary,
Lord Chancellor's Department
1997 - 98 Opposition Spokesman on
Foreign Affairs
1998 - 2001 Shadow Secretary of State for
International Development
2001 - 02 Vice-Chairman, Conservative Party
2003 - Opposition Spokesman on International
Affairs
*Commons Office* . . . . . . Tel: (020) 7219 4070 Fax: (020) 7219 2414
Web: http://www.garystreeter.co.uk
Research Assistant – Mrs Janet Streeter
Tel: (020) 7219 5033
*Constituency Office* . . . . Tel: (01752) 335666 Fax: (01752) 338401
E-mail: mail@garystreeter.co.uk
Constituency Manager – Mrs Sally Dean
Secretary – Mrs Michelle Sewell

**Stringer, Graham** . . Manchester Blackley
**Labour** . . . . . . . . . . . Majority 14,464 over Con
*Born* . . . . . . . . . . . . . . 17th February 1950
*Educated* . . . . . . . . . . Moston Brook High School;
Sheffield University
*Elected* . . . . . . . . . . . . 1997 MP for Manchester Blackley
*Offices Held* . . . . . . . . 1984 - 96 Leader, Manchester City Council
1999 - 2001 Parliamentary Secretary,
Cabinet Office
2001 - 02 Government Whip
(Lord Commissioner, H M Treasury)
*Commons Office* . . . . . . Tel: (020) 7219 6055
Researcher – Ms Amanda Ramsay
*Constituency Office* . . . . 4th Floor, Mancat, Moston Campus,
Ashley Lane, Moston, Manchester, M9 4WU
Tel: (0161) 202 6600 Fax: (0161) 202 6626
Assistant – Mr Martin Connolly
*Parliamentary Interests* . House of Lords Reform; Urban Regeneration;
Revitalising Local Democracy;
New Aviation and Airports

**Stuart, Gisela** . . . . . Birmingham Edgbaston
**Labour** . . . . . . . . . . . Majority 4,698 over Con
*Born* . . . . . . . . . . . . . . 26th November 1955
*Educated* . . . . . . . . . . West Germany (State Sector);
Manchester Polytechnic; London University
*Elected* . . . . . . . . . . . . 1997 MP for Birmingham Edgbaston
*Office Held* . . . . . . . . . 1999 - 2001 Parliamentary Secretary,
Department of Health
*Commons Office* . . . . . . Tel: (020) 7219 4853 Fax: (020) 7219 0317
Mobile: 07973 860799
Pager: 07644 007324
E-mail: stuartg@parliament.uk
Staff – Ms Linda Spencer
Fax: (020) 7219 0995
E-mail: spencerl@parliament.uk
*Parliamentary Interests* . Pensions; Manufacturing;
Constitutional Reform; European Union

**Stunell, Andrew** OBE  Hazel Grove
**Liberal Democrat** . . . Majority 8,435 over Con
*Born* . . . . . . . . . . . . . . 24th November 1942
*Educated* . . . . . . . . . . Surbiton Grammar School;
Manchester University; Liverpool Polytechnic
*Elected* . . . . . . . . . . . . 1997 MP for Hazel Grove
*Offices Held* . . . . . . . . 1997 - 2001 Liberal Democrat Deputy Chief
Whip
2001 - Liberal Democrat Chief Whip and
Spokesman on Energy
*Commons Office* . . . . . . Tel: (020) 7219 5223 Fax: (020) 7219 2302
E-mail: stunella@parliament.uk
Web: http://www.stunell.co.uk
Researcher – Miss Stephanie Egbe
E-mail: egbes@parliament.uk
*Constituency Office* . . . . 68a Compstall Road, Romiley, Stockport,
SK6 4DE
Tel: (0161) 406 7070 Fax: (0161) 494 2425
Constituency Office Manager –
Mr Brendon Jones
*Parliamentary Interests* . Modernisation of Commons Procedure;
Energy Policy

# MEMBERS OF THE HOUSE OF COMMONS

**Sutcliffe, Gerry** . . . Bradford South
**Labour** . . . . . . . . . . Majority 9,662 over Con
*Born* . . . . . . . . . . . . . 13th May 1953 in Salford
*Educated* . . . . . . . . . . Cardinal Hinsley Grammar School, Bradford
*Elected* . . . . . . . . . . . 1994 MP for Bradford South (By-election)
*Offices Held* . . . . . . . 1990 - 94 Leader, Bradford Metropolitan
District Council
1999 - 2001 Assistant Government Whip
2001 - 03 Government Whip
(Vice Chamberlain, HM Household)
2003 - Parliamentary Secretary,
Department of Trade and Industry
*Commons Office* . . . . . Tel: (020) 7219 3247 Fax: (020) 7219 1227
E-mail: sutcliffeg@parliament.uk
*Constituency Office* . . . . 76 Kirkgate, Bradford, BD1 1SZ
Tel: (01274) 400007 Fax: (01274) 400020
Constituency Assistant– Ms Alison McLean
E-mail: mcleana@parliament.uk
Research Assistant – Mr Michael Swales
E-mail: swalesm@parliament.uk
*Parliamentary Interests* . Local Government; Social Security; Sport
*Leisure Interests* . . . . . . Football; Music; Theatre

**Swayne, Desmond** . . . New Forest West
**Conservative** . . . . . . Majority 13,191 over Lib Dem
*Born* . . . . . . . . . . . . . . 20th August 1956 in Bern, Switzerland
*Educated* . . . . . . . . . . Bedford School; St Andrews University
*Elected* . . . . . . . . . . . 1997 MP for New Forest West
*Offices Held* . . . . . . . 2001 - 03 Opposition Whip
2001 - 2002 Opposition Spokesman on
Defence
2004 Opposition Spokesman on Local and
Devolved Government and Northern Ireland
2004 - PPS to Michael Howard (Leader of
the Opposition)
*Commons Office* . . . . . Tel: (020) 7219 4886 Fax: (020) 7219 0901
Web: http://www.desmondswaynemp.com
Personal Assistant – Mrs Maria Bower
E-mail: niallm@parliament.uk
Research Assistant – Miss Isabella Sharp
Tel: (020) 7219 2187
E-mail: sharpi@parliament.uk
*Parliamentary Interests* . Constitutional Affairs; Europe
*Leisure Interests* . . . . . . Territorial Army

**Swire, Hugo** . . . . . . Devon East
**Conservative** . . . . . . . Majority 8,195 over Lib Dem
*Born* . . . . . . . . . . . . . . 30th November 1959
*Educated* . . . . . . . . . . Eton College; St Andrew's University;
Royal Military Academy, Sandhurst
*Elected* . . . . . . . . . . . 2001 MP for Devon East
*Offices Held* . . . . . . . 2003 PPS to Theresa May (Party Chairman)
2003 - Opposition Whip
*Commons Office* . . . . . Tel: (020) 7219 8163 Fax: (020) 7219 1895
Web: http://www.hugo.swire.org.uk
Personal Secretary – Mrs Diana Blair
Tel: (020) 7219 8173
Researcher – Mr Andrew Unterhalter
Tel: (020) 7219 1389
*Constituency Office* . . . . 45 Imperial Road, Exmouth, Devon, EX8 1DQ
Tel: (01395) 264251 Fax: (01395) 272205
E-mail: office@eastdevonconservatives.co.uk
Agent – Mr Jon Quinn

**Syms, Robert** . . . . . Poole
**Conservative** . . . . . . Majority 7,166 over Lab
*Born* . . . . . . . . . . . . . 15th August 1956 in Chippenham, Wiltshire
*Educated* . . . . . . . . . . Colston's School, Bristol
*Elected* . . . . . . . . . . . 1997 MP for Poole
*Offices Held* . . . . . . . 1984 - 87 Leader, North Wiltshire
District Council
1999 - 2001 Opposition Spokesman on
Environment, Transport and the Regions
2001 - Vice Chairman, Conservative Party
2003 - Opposition Spokesman on Local and
Devolved Government (Office of the
Deputy Prime Minister)
*Constituency Office* . . . . 38 Sandbanks Road, Poole, Dorset,
PH14 8BX
Tel: (01202) 739922 Fax: (01202) 739944
Web: http://www.robertsymsmp.com
Personal Secretary – Mrs Nicky Edwards
Tel: (01202) 718078
*Parliamentary Interests* . Economy; Constitution; Health;
Local Government
*Leisure Interests* . . . . . . Cycling; Travel

# T

**Tami, Mark** . . . . . . Alyn and Deeside
**Labour** . . . . . . . . . . Majority 9,222 over Con
*Born* . . . . . . . . . . . . . 3rd October 1962
*Educated* . . . . . . . . . . Enfield Grammar School;
University College of Wales, Swansea
*Elected* . . . . . . . . . . . 2001 MP for Alyn and Deeside
*Commons Office* . . . . . Tel: (020) 7219 8174 Fax: (020) 7219 1943
E-mail: tamim@parliament.uk
*Constituency Office* . . . . Deeside Enterprise Centre, Rowleys Drive,
Shotton, Deeside, Flintshire, CH5 1PP
Tel: (01244) 819854 Fax: (01244) 823854
*Parliamentary Interests* . Manufacturing Industry; Aerospace
*Leisure Interests* . . . . . . Antiques; Cricket; Fishing; Football

**Tapsell, Sir Peter** . Louth and Horncastle
**Conservative** . . . . . . . Majority 7,554 over Lab
*Born* . . . . . . . . . . . . . 1st February 1930 in Sussex
*Educated* . . . . . . . . . . Tonbridge School; Merton College, Oxford
*Elected* . . . . . . . . . . . 1959 - 64 MP for Nottingham West
1966 MP for Horncastle, then (1983)
Lindsey East, then (1997) Louth and
Horncastle
*Offices Held* . . . . . . . 1976 - 77 Opposition Spokesman on
Foreign and Commonwealth Affairs
1977 - 78 Opposition Spokesman on
Treasury and Economic Affairs
*Commons Office* . . . . . Tel: (020) 7219 4477 Fax: (020) 7219 0976
*Constituency Office* . . . . Cannon Street House, Cannon Street, Louth,
Lincolnshire, LN11 9NL
Tel: (01507) 603713 Fax: (01507) 602154
*Parliamentary Interests* . Foreign Affairs; Defence; Finance; Economics

# MEMBERS OF THE HOUSE OF COMMONS

**Taylor, Rt Hon Ann** Dewsbury
**Labour** . . . . . . . . . . . Majority 7,449 over Con
*Born* . . . . . . . . . . . . . . 2nd July 1947 in Motherwell
*Educated* . . . . . . . . . . Bolton School; Bradford University;
Sheffield University
*Elected* . . . . . . . . . . . . 1974 - 1983 MP for Bolton West
1987 MP for Dewsbury
*Offices Held* . . . . . . . . 1977 - 79 Assistant Government Whip
1979 - 81 Opposition Spokeswoman on
Education
1981 - 83 Opposition Spokeswoman on
Housing
1987 - 88 Opposition Spokeswoman on
Home Affairs
1988 - 90 Opposition Spokeswoman on
Environment and Water
1990 - 92 Shadow Minister for
Environmental Protection
1992 - 94 Shadow Education Secretary
1994 - 95 Shadow Chancellor of Duchy
of Lancaster
1994 - 97 Shadow Leader of the House
of Commons
1997 - 98 President of the Council and
Leader of the House of Commons
1997 - 98 Chairman, Modernisation of the
House of Commons Select Committee,
House of Commons
1998 - 2001 Government Chief Whip
2001 - Chairman, Intelligence and Security
Committee, House of Commons
*Commons Office* . . . . . . Tel: (020) 7219 4400 Fax: (020) 7219 2510
*Constituency Office* . . . . 2nd Floor, Dewsbury Business and Media
Centre, Wellington Road, Dewsbury,
WF13 1HF
Tel: (01924) 324999 Fax: (01924) 324998
Caseworker – Ms Catherine Wood
Office Manager – Ms Margaret Sheard
E-mail: margaret@dewsbury1597.co.uk

**Taylor, Dari** . . . . . . Stockton South
**Labour** . . . . . . . . . . . Majority 9,086 over Con
*Born* . . . . . . . . . . . . . . 13th December 1944 in Rhondda
*Educated* . . . . . . . . . . Ynyshir Girls School;
Burnley Municipal College;
Nottingham University; Durham University
*Elected* . . . . . . . . . . . . 1997 MP for Stockton South
*Offices Held* . . . . . . . . 2001 - 03 PPS to Lord Bach (Minister for
Defence Procurement) and Dr Lewis Moonie
(Minister for Veterans Affairs)
2003 - PPS to Hazel Blears
(Minister of State, Home Office)
*Commons Office* . . . . . . Tel: (020) 7219 4608 Fax: (020) 7219 6876
Mobile: 07770 482142
Pager: 07693 256804
E-mail:
contact@dari-taylor-mp42.new.labour.org.uk
Web: http://www.daritaylormp.co.uk
Research Assistant – Ms Amanda Webster
E-mail: webstera@parliament.uk
*Constituency Office* . . . . 109 Lanehouse Road, Thornaby-on-Tees,
TS17 8AB
Tel: (01642) 604546 Fax: (01642) 608395
Personal Assistant – Ms Susan Donaghy
*Parliamentary Interests* . Employment; Defence; Education; Health
*Leisure Interests* . . . . . . Walking; Opera; Swimming; Travelling;
Classical Music

**Taylor, David** . . . . Leicestershire North West
**Labour** . . . . . . . . . . . Majority 8,157 over Con
*Born* . . . . . . . . . . . . . . 22nd August 1946
*Educated* . . . . . . . . . . Ashby-de-la-Zouch Grammar School;
Leicester Polytechnic; Lanchester Polytechnic;
Open University
*Elected* . . . . . . . . . . . . 1997 MP for Leicestershire North West
*Commons Office* . . . . . . Tel: (020) 7219 4567 Fax: (020) 7219 6808
Mobile: 07957 336221
E-mail: taylordl@parliament.uk
Parliamentary Researcher – Mr Daniel Crimes
Tel: (020) 7219 2237 Fax: (020) 7219 1082
E-mail: crimesd@parliament.uk
*Constituency Office* . . . . 17 Hotel Street, Coalville, Leicester,
LE67 3EQ
Tel: (01530) 814372 Fax: (01530) 813833
Casework Manager – Miss Alison Harrop
Constituency Assistant – Ms Lauren Otter
*Parliamentary Interests* . Rural Issues; Housing; Local Government
Finance; Environment
*Leisure Interests* . . . . . . Cricket; Cycling; Hill Walking

**Taylor, Ian** MBE . . . Esher and Walton
**Conservative** . . . . . . . Majority 11,538 over Lab
*Born* . . . . . . . . . . . . . . 18th April 1945 in Coventry
*Educated* . . . . . . . . . . Whitley Abbey School; Keele University;
London School of Economics
*Elected* . . . . . . . . . . . . 1987 MP for Esher, then (1997)
Esher and Walton
*Offices Held* . . . . . . . . 1990 - 94 PPS to William Waldegrave
(as Secretary of State for Health and
Minister for the Cabinet Office)
1994 - 97 Parliamentary Secretary,
Department of Trade and Industry
(Minister for Science and Technology)
1997 (May-Oct) Opposition Spokesman on
Northern Ireland
*Commons Office* . . . . . . Tel: (020) 7219 5221 Fax: (020) 7219 5492
Mobile: 07860 327416
E-mail: taylori@parliament.uk
Web: http://www.iantaylormp.com
Secretary – Ms Anne Buckingham
E-mail: buckinghama@parliament.uk
Political Assistant – Mrs Sarah Chilman
Tel: (020) 7219 4490
E-mail: chilmans@parliament.uk
*Constituency Office* . . . . Cheltonian House, Portsmouth Road, Esher,
Surrey, KT10 9AA
Tel: (01372) 469105 Fax: (01372) 469091
E-mail: esherwalton@tory.org
Secretary – Mrs Janet Fuller
Agent – Ms Andrea Knowles
*Parliamentary Interests* . Science; Technology; Engineering; Europe;
Economy
*Leisure Interests* . . . . . . Opera; Biographies; Cigars; Shooting

# MEMBERS OF THE HOUSE OF COMMONS

**Taylor, John** . . . . . . Solihull
**Conservative** . . . . . . Majority 9,407 over Lib Dem
*Born*. . . . . . . . . . . . . 19th August 1941 in Hampton-in-Arden,
Warwickshire
*Educated* . . . . . . . . . Bromsgrove School; College of Law
*Elected*. . . . . . . . . . . 1983 MP for Solihull
*Offices Held* . . . . . . . 1977 - 79 Leader, West Midlands
Metropolitan County Council
1979 - 84 MEP for Midlands East
1988 - 89 Assistant Government Whip
1989 - 92 Government Whip
(Lord Commissioner, H M Treasury, then
Vice-Chamberlain, H M Household)
1992 - 95 Parliamentary Secretary,
Lord Chancellor's Department
1995 - 97 Parliamentary Secretary,
Department of Trade and Industry
1997 - 99 Opposition Whip
1999 - 2003 Opposition Spokesman on
Northern Ireland
*Constituency Office* . . . . Northampton House, Poplar Road, Solihull,
West Midlands, B91 3AW
Tel: (0121) 704 3071 Fax: (0121) 705 6388
Secretary – Ms Paula Barnes

**Taylor, Matthew** . . . Truro and St Austell
**Liberal Democrat** . . . Majority 8,065 over Con
*Born*. . . . . . . . . . . . . 3rd January 1963 in London
*Educated* . . . . . . . . . . Treliske School, Truro;
University College, London;
Lady Margaret Hall, Oxford
*Elected*. . . . . . . . . . . 1987 MP for Truro (By-election), then (1997)
Truro and St Austell
*Offices Held* . . . . . . . 1987 - 88 Liberal Democrat Spokesman on
Energy
1988 - 89 Liberal Democrat Spokesman on
Local Government, Housing, Transport
1990 - 92 Liberal Democrat Spokesman on
Education
1992 - 94 Liberal Democrat Spokesman on
Citizen's Charter
1994 - 99 Liberal Democrat Spokesman on
Environment and Transport
1999 - 2003 Liberal Democrat Spokesman on
Treasury Matters
2003 - Chairman, Liberal Democrat
Parliamentary Party
*Commons Office* . . . . . . Tel: (020) 7219 6686 Fax: (020) 7219 4903
Web: http://www.matthewtaylor.info
Researcher – Mr Simon Bucknall
E-mail: bucknalls@parliament.uk
*Constituency Office* . . . . 10 South Street, St Austell,
Cornwall, PL25 5BH
Tel: (01726) 63443 Fax: (01726) 68457
Senior Secretary – Ms Geraldine Duckworth

**Taylor, Dr Richard** Wyre Forest
**Independent**. . . . . . . Majority 17,630 over Lab
*Born*. . . . . . . . . . . . . 7th July 1934
*Educated* . . . . . . . . . . Leys School, Cambridge;
Clare College, Cambridge;
Westminster Medical School
*Elected*. . . . . . . . . . . 2001 MP for Wyre Forest
*Commons Office* . . . . . Tel: (020) 7219 4598 Fax: (020) 7219 1967
E-mail: pricemah@parliament.uk
Web: http://www.healthconcern.org.uk
Secretary – Mrs Mary Price
*Constituency Office* . . . Gavel House, 137 Franche Road,
Kidderminster, Worcestershire, DY11 5AP
Secretary – Mrs Vicky Constable
Tel: (01562) 753333
*Parliamentary Interests* . National Health Service
*Leisure Interests* . . . . . Family; Ornithology; Trees

**Taylor, Sir Teddy** . Rochford and Southend East
**Conservative** . . . . . . Majority 7,034 over Lab
*Born*. . . . . . . . . . . . . 18th April 1937 in Glasgow
*Educated* . . . . . . . . . . Glasgow High School; Glasgow University
*Elected*. . . . . . . . . . . 1964 - 79 MP for Glasgow Cathcart
1980 MP for Southend East (By-election), then
(1997) Rochford and Southend East
*Offices Held* . . . . . . . 1970 - 71, 1974 Parliamentary Secretary,
Scottish Office
1976 Opposition Spokesman on Trade
1976 - 79 Opposition Spokesman on Scotland
*Commons Office* . . . . . Tel: (020) 7219 3476 Fax: (020) 7219 4828
E-mail: daye@parliament.uksecretary – Mrs
Liz Day
Tel: (020) 7219 5868
*Constituency Office* . . . . Strand House, Southchurch Road,
Southend-on-Sea, Essex, SS1 2PS
Tel & Fax: (01702) 600460
Secretary – Mrs Sue Tuhill
*Leisure Interests* . . . . . . Golf; Chess; Music

**Teather, Sarah** . . . . Brent East
**Liberal Democrat** . . . Majority 1,118 over Lab
*Born*. . . . . . . . . . . . . 1st June 1974
*Elected*. . . . . . . . . . . 2003 MP for Brent East (by-election)
*Office Held* . . . . . . . . 2004 - Liberal Democrat Spokesman
on Health
*Constituency Office* . . . . 1 High Road, Willesden Green, London,
NW10 2TE
Tel: (020) 8459 0455
Fax: (020) 8830 3280
E-mail: teathers@parliament.uk
Web: http://www.sarahteather.libdems.org.uk

**Thomas, Gareth** . . . Clwyd West
**Labour** . . . . . . . . . . Majority 1,115 over Con
*Born*. . . . . . . . . . . . . 25th September 1954 in Bangor, North Wales
*Educated* . . . . . . . . . . Rockferry High School, Birkenhead;
University College of Wales, Aberystwyth
*Elected*. . . . . . . . . . . 1997 MP for Clwyd West
*Office Held* . . . . . . . . 2001 - PPS to Paul Murphy
(as Secretary of State for Wales, then
Secretary of State for Northern Ireland)
*Commons Office* . . . . . Tel: (020) 7219 3516 Fax: (020) 7219 1263
E-mail: thomasg@parliament.uk
Web: http://www.epolitix.com/gareth-thomas
Parliamentary Researcher – Ms Elinor Lewis
Tel: (020) 7219 0365
E-mail: lewisea@parliament.uk
Press Officer – Mr Jamie O'Hara
Tel: (020) 7219 2003
E-mail: oharaj@parliament.uk
*Constituency Office* . . . . 5 Wynnstay Road, Colwyn Bay,
Conwy, LL29 8NB
Tel: (01492) 531154 Fax: (01492) 535731
*Parliamentary Interests* . Welsh Affairs; Legal Affairs; Economy;
Social Security; Agriculture; Broadcasting;
Housing; The Constitution
*Leisure Interests* . . . . . . Walking; Theatre; Music

# MEMBERS OF THE HOUSE OF COMMONS

**Thomas, Gareth R.** Harrow West
**Labour** . . . . . . . . . . . Majority 6,156 over Con
*Born.* . . . . . . . . . . . . . . 15th July 1967 in London
*Educated* . . . . . . . . . . Hatch End High School;
University College of Wales, Aberystwyth;
Kings College, London;
University of Greenwich
*Elected.* . . . . . . . . . . . . 1997 MP for Harrow West
*Offices Held* . . . . . . . . 2001 - 03 PPS to Charles Clarke
(as Minister without Portfolio and
Chairman of Labour Party, then Secretary of
State for Education and Skills)
2003 - Parliamentary Secretary, Department
for International Development
*Commons Office* . . . . . Tel: (020) 7219 4243 Fax: (020) 7219 1154
E-mail: thomasgr@parliament.uk
Personal Assistant – Ms Isabel Campbell
E-mail: campbelli@parliament.uk
Caseworker – Miss Felicity Dawson
Tel: (020) 7219 5988
E-mail: dawsonf@parliament.uk
*Constituency Office* . . . . 132 Blenheim Road, Harrow, HA2 7AA
Tel: (020) 8861 6300
*Parliamentary Interests* . Energy; Co-operative/Mutuals; Health; Police
*Leisure Interests* . . . . . . Canoeing, Running; Rugby Union; Theatre

**Thomas, Simon** . . . Ceredigion
**Plaid Cymru** . . . . . . . Majority 3,944 over Lib Dem
*Born.* . . . . . . . . . . . . . . 28th December 1963
*Elected.* . . . . . . . . . . . . 2000 MP for Ceredigion (By-election)
*Office Held.* . . . . . . . . . 2001 - Plaid Cymru Whip and Spokesman on
Environment, Culture, Transport, Energy
and International Development
*Commons Office* . . . . . Tel: (020) 7219 5021 Fax: (020) 7219 3705
E-mail: thomassi@parliament.uk
Web: http://www.simonthomas.net
Personal Assistant – Ms Rhian Medi Roberts
E-mail: medirobertsr@parliament.uk
Researcher – Ms Ffion Evans
Tel: (020) 7219 6883
E-mail: evansf@parliament.uk
Press Officer/Senior Parliamentary
Researcher – Ms Gwenllian Griffiths
Tel: (020) 7219 6422 Fax: (020) 7219 2633
E-mail: griffithsg@parliament.uk
*Constituency Office* . . . . 32 Pier Street, Aberystwyth, Ceredigion,
SY23 2LN
Tel: (01970) 624516
Fax: (01970) 624473
E-mail: jonesha@parliament.uk
Personal Assistant – Miss Hawen Jones
Assistant – Mrs Carol Rees
Press and Communications Officer –
Mr Mabon ap Gwynfor
*Parliamentary Interests* . Sustainable Development; Environment;
Social Exclusion; Rural Development;
International Development
*Leisure Interests* . . . . . . Cycling; Walking; Family

**Thurso, John**. . . . . Caithness, Sutherland and Easter Ross
**Liberal Democrat** . . . Majority 2,744 over Lab
*Born.* . . . . . . . . . . . . . . 10th September 1953 in Thurso
*Educated* . . . . . . . . . . Eton College
*Elected.* . . . . . . . . . . . . 2001 MP for Caithness, Sutherland and
Easter Ross
*Offices Held* . . . . . . . . 1995 - 99 Member of the House of Lords (as
Viscount Thurso)
2001 - Liberal Democrat Spokesman on
Scotland; also (from 2003) Transport
*Commons Office* . . . . . Tel: (020) 7219 1752/3448 Fax: (020) 7219
3797
E-mail: thursoj@parliament.uk
Staff – Mrs Bridget Beechey
Miss Maggie Harrison
Tel: (020) 7219 3448
E-mail: [surnameinitial]@parliament.uk
*Parliamentary Interests* . Scotland; Tourism; Transport; Lords Reform

**Timms, Stephen** . . . East Ham
**Labour** . . . . . . . . . . . Majority 21,032 over Con
*Born.* . . . . . . . . . . . . . . 29th July 1955
*Educated* . . . . . . . . . . Farnborough Grammar School;
Emmanuel College, Cambridge
*Elected.* . . . . . . . . . . . . 1994 MP for Newham North East
(By-election), then (1997) East Ham
*Offices Held* . . . . . . . . 1990 - 94 Leader, London Borough of
Newham Council
1998 - 99 Parliamentary Secretary,
Department of Social Security
1999 Minister of State,
Department of Social Security
1999 - 2001 Financial Secretary,
H M Treasury
2001 - 02 Minister of State, Department for
Education and Skills
2002 - 04 Minister of State, Department of
Trade and Industry
2004 - Financial Secretary, HM Treasury
*Commons Office* . . . . . (020) 7210 4000 Fax: (020) 7219 2949
E-mail: stephen@stephentimmsmp.org.uk
Web: http://www.stephentimmsmp.org.uk
Personal Assistant – Mr Stewart Gregg
Tel: (020) 7219 2824

**Tipping, Paddy** . . . . Sherwood
**Labour** . . . . . . . . . . . Majority 9,373 over Con
*Born.* . . . . . . . . . . . . . . 24th October 1949 in Halifax, Yorkshire
*Educated* . . . . . . . . . . Hipperholme Grammar School, Halifax;
Nottingham University
*Elected.* . . . . . . . . . . . . 1992 MP for Sherwood
*Office Held.* . . . . . . . . . 1998 - 2001 Parliamentary Secretary,
Privy Council Office
*Commons Office* . . . . . Tel: (020) 7219 5044 Fax: (020) 7219 3641
E-mail: p.tipping@dial.pipex.com
Secretary – Ms Zamira Furtado
Tel: (020) 7219 6484
*Constituency Office* . . . . First Floor, The Council Offices,
Watnall Road, Nottingham, NG15 7LA
Tel: (0115) 964 0314 Fax: (0115) 968 1639
Office Manager – Ms Carol Wright
Caseworker – Ms Carolyn Podmore
*Parliamentary Interests* . Energy; Rural Issues; Local Government;
Environment
*Leisure Interests* . . . . . . Walking; Climbing

## MEMBERS OF THE HOUSE OF COMMONS

**Todd, Mark** . . . . . . Derbyshire South
**Labour** . . . . . . . . . . Majority 7,851 over Con
*Born* . . . . . . . . . . . . 29th December 1954 in Dorchester
*Educated* . . . . . . . . . Emmanuel College, Cambridge
*Elected* . . . . . . . . . . 1997 MP for Derbyshire South
*Offices Held* . . . . . . . 1987 - 90 Leader, Cambridge City Council
2002 - PPS to Baroness Symons of Vernham
Dean (Minister of State, Foreign and
Commonwealth Office)
*Commons Office* . . . . . Tel: (020) 7219 3549 Fax: (020) 7219 4935
E-mail: marktodd@btconnect.com
Web: http://www.marktodd.org.uk
Parliamentary Assistant – Mr Richard Bates
E-mail: batesrl@parliament.uk
*Constituency Office* . . . . 37 Market Street, Church Gresley,
Swadlincote, Derbyshire, DE11 9PR
Tel: (01283) 551573 Fax: (01283) 210640
Constituency Assistants – Mr Doug Haw
Mr John Tuffs
E-mail: [surnameinitial]@parliament.uk
*Parliamentary Interests* . Public Sector Management; Agriculture; IT;
Business; Co-operative Movement

**Tonge, Dr Jenny** . . Richmond Park
**Liberal Democrat** . . . Majority 4,964 over Con
*Born* . . . . . . . . . . . . . 19th February 1941 in West Midlands
*Educated* . . . . . . . . . . Dudley Girls' High School;
University College London;
University College Hospital
*Elected* . . . . . . . . . . . 1997 MP for Richmond Park
*Office Held* . . . . . . . . 1997 - 2004 Liberal Democrat Spokesman on
International Development
*Commons Office* . . . . . Tel: (020) 7219 5563 Fax: (020) 7219 4596
Pager: 07699 734071
E-mail: tonge@cix.co.uk
Web: http://www.jennytonge.org.uk
Researcher – Ms Georgina Banks
Tel: (020) 7219 4596
E-mail: banksg@parliament.uk
*Constituency Office* . . . . The Old Station Works,
119-123 Sandycombe Road, Richmond,
Surrey, TW9 2ER
Tel & Fax: (020) 8332 7919
Head of Office – Mrs Serena Hennessy
Diary Secretary – Ms Kirsty Armstrong
*Parliamentary Interests* . International Development; Women's Health
*Leisure Interests* . . . . . Birdwatching

**Touhig, Don** . . . . . Islwyn
**Labour** . . . . . . . . . . . Majority 15,309 over Lib Dem
*Born* . . . . . . . . . . . . . 5th December 1947 in Abersychan
*Educated* . . . . . . . . . . St Frances School, Abersychan;
East Mon College, Pontypool
*Elected* . . . . . . . . . . . 1995 MP for Islwyn (By-election)
*Offices Held* . . . . . . . . 1999 Assistant Government Whip
2001 - Parliamentary Secretary, Wales Office
(also Constitutional Affairs Department
from 2003)
*Commons Office* . . . . . Tel: (020) 7219 6435 Fax: (020) 7219 2070
*Constituency Office* . . . . 6 Woodfieldside Business Park,
Penmaen Road, Pontllanfraith, Blackwood,
Gwent, NP12 2DG
Tel: (01495) 231990/244990
Fax: (01495) 231959
Secretary – Mrs Lynda Williams
Assistant – Mrs Joanna James
Researcher – Mr Tom Griffin
*Parliamentary Interests* . Health; Education; Economic Affairs
*Leisure Interests* . . . . . Classical Music; Cooking; Walking

**Tredinnick, David** . Bosworth
**Conservative** . . . . . . . Majority 2,280 over Lab
*Born* . . . . . . . . . . . . . 19th January 1950
*Educated* . . . . . . . . . . Eton College; Mons Officer Cadet School;
St John's College, Oxford;
Cape Town University Graduate School of
Business
*Elected* . . . . . . . . . . . 1987 MP for Bosworth
*Office Held* . . . . . . . . 1997 - Chairman, Joint Parliamentary
Committee on Statutory Instruments
*Commons Office* . . . . . Tel: (020) 7219 4514/4474
Fax: (020) 7219 4901
E-mail: tredinnickd@parliament.uk
*Constituency Office* . . . . 10a Priory Walk, Hinckley,
Leicestershire, LE10 1HU
Tel: (01455) 635741 Fax: (01455) 621023
Agent – Mr Stuart Swann
E-mail: stuart@boscons.freeserve.co.uk
*Parliamentary Interests* . Health (particularly Alternative and
Complementary Medicine); Small Businesses

**Trend, Michael** CBE Windsor
**Conservative** . . . . . . . Majority 8,889 over Lib Dem
*Born* . . . . . . . . . . . . . 19th April 1952 in Greenwich, London
*Educated* . . . . . . . . . . Westminster School; Oriel College, Oxford
*Elected* . . . . . . . . . . . 1992 MP for Windsor and Maidenhead, then
(1997) Windsor
*Offices Held* . . . . . . . . 1994 - 95 PPS to Dr Brian Mawhinney
(Secretary of State for Transport)
1998 - 99 Opposition Spokesman on
Foreign and Commonwealth Affairs
1999 - 2000 Opposition Spokesman on
Social Security
*Commons Office* . . . . . Tel: (020) 7219 6929 Fax: (020) 7219 5946
E-mail: trendm@parliament.uk
*Constituency Office* . . . . 87 St Leonard's Road, Windsor,
Berkshire, SL4 3BZ
Tel: (01753) 678693 Fax: (01753) 832774
Agent – Mrs Jackie Porter
E-mail: j.porter@windsor.tory.org.uk
*Leisure Interests* . . . . . . Fishing; Walking; Music

**Trickett, Jon** . . . . . . Hemsworth
**Labour** . . . . . . . . . . . Majority 15,636 over Con
*Born* . . . . . . . . . . . . . 2nd July 1950 in Leeds
*Educated* . . . . . . . . . . Roundhay Grammar School, Leeds;
Hull University; Leeds University
*Elected* . . . . . . . . . . . 1996 MP for Hemsworth (By-election)
*Office Held* . . . . . . . . 1989 - 96 Leader, Leeds Metropolitan
District Council
*Commons Office* . . . . . Tel: (020) 7219 5074 Fax: (020) 7219 0032
E-mail: trickettj@parliament.uk
*Constituency Office* . . . . 18 Market Street, Hemsworth,
Pontefract, WF9 4LB
Tel: (01977) 722291 Fax: (01977) 722290
*Parliamentary Interests* . Regeneration; Energy
*Leisure Interests* . . . . . . Cycling; Windsurfing

# MEMBERS OF THE HOUSE OF COMMONS

**Trimble, Rt Hon David**  Upper Bann
**Ulster Unionist** . . . . . Majority 2,058 over Democratic Unionist
*Born* . . . . . . . . . . . . . . 15th October 1944
*Educated* . . . . . . . . . . Bangor Grammar School, Northern Ireland;
Queen's University, Belfast
*Elected* . . . . . . . . . . . . 1990 MP for Upper Bann (By-election)
*Offices Held* . . . . . . . . 1996 - Leader, Ulster Unionist Party
(First Minister 1999 - 2002)
1998 - Member, Northern Ireland Assembly
(also, from 2002 Ulster Unionist
Spokesman on Constitutional Affairs,
Work and Pensions,
Treasury and Trade and Industry)
*Commons Office* . . . . . . Tel: (020) 7219 6987 Fax: (020) 7219 2489
Parliamentary Assistant – Ms Claire Kirk
Tel: (020) 7219 0505 Fax: (020) 7219 0575
E-mail: kirkc@parliament.uk
*Constituency Office* . . . . 2 Queen Street, Lurgan,
County Armagh, BT66 8BQ
Tel: (028) 3832 8088 Fax: (028) 3832 2343
Secretaries – Mrs Stephanie Roderick
Mrs Daphne Trimble

**Truswell, Paul** . . . . Pudsey
**Labour** . . . . . . . . . . . Majority 5,626 over Con
*Born* . . . . . . . . . . . . . . 17th November 1955
*Educated* . . . . . . . . . . Firth Park Comprehensive School;
Leeds University
*Elected* . . . . . . . . . . . . 1997 MP for Pudsey
*Commons Office* . . . . . . Tel: (020) 7219 3504 Fax: (020) 7219 2252
*Constituency Office* . . . . 10A Greenside, Pudsey,
West Yorkshire, LS28 8PU
Tel: (0113) 229 3553 Fax: (0113) 229 3800
*Parliamentary Interests* . Health; Environment; Local Government
*Leisure Interests* . . . . . . Gardening; Photography; Cinema

**Turner, Andrew** . . . Isle of Wight
**Conservative** . . . . . . Majority 2,826 over Lib Dem
*Born* . . . . . . . . . . . . . . 1953 in Coventry
*Educated* . . . . . . . . . . Rugby School; Keble College, Oxford;
Birmingham University
*Elected* . . . . . . . . . . . . 2001 MP for Isle of Wight
*Commons Office* . . . . . . Tel: (020) 7219 8490 Fax; (020) 7219 0174
Parliamentary Assistant – Miss Carole Dennett
E-mail: dennettc@parliament.uk
Political Adviser – Mr Jonathan Sheppard
E-mail: sheppardj@parliament.uk
Research Assistant – Mr Julian Seymour
E-mail: seymourj@parliament.uk
*Constituency Office* . . . . 24 The Mall, Carisbrooke Road, Newport,
Isle of Wight, PO30 1BW
Tel: (01983) 530808 Fax: (01983) 822266
E-mail: mail@islandmp.com
Web: http://www.islandmp.com
Constituency Assistants –
Mrs Stacey Blackmore
Miss Dawn Snook

**Turner, Dennis** . . . . Wolverhampton South East
**Labour** . . . . . . . . . . . Majority 12,484 over Con
*Born* . . . . . . . . . . . . . . 26th August 1942 in Staffordshire
*Educated* . . . . . . . . . . Stonefield Secondary School, Bilston;
Bilston College of Further Education
*Elected* . . . . . . . . . . . . 1997 MP for Wolverhampton South East
*Offices Held* . . . . . . . . 1994 - 97 Opposition Whip
1997 - Chairman, Catering Committee,
House of Commons
1997 - 2003 PPS to Clare Short (Secretary
of State for International Development)
*Commons Office* . . . . . . Tel: (020) 7219 4120
Secretary – Ms Hilary Davies
Tel: (020) 7219 4036
*Constituency Office* . . . . Springvale Sports and Social Club,
Millfields Road, Bilston, West Midlands,
WV14 0QR
Tel: (01902) 492364
Secretary – Ms Jill Withers
*Parliamentary Interests* . Further Education; Housing; Social Services
*Leisure Interests* . . . . . . Gardening; Reading; Card Games

**Turner, Dr Desmond**  Brighton Kemptown
**Labour** . . . . . . . . . . . Majority 4,922 over Con
*Born* . . . . . . . . . . . . . . 17th July 1939 in Southampton
*Educated* . . . . . . . . . . Imperial College, London;
University College, London;
Brighton Polytechnic
*Elected* . . . . . . . . . . . . 1997 MP for Brighton Kemptown
*Commons Office* . . . . . . Tel: (020) 7219 4024 Fax: (020) 7219 0264
Mobile: 07802 450633
Pager: 07644 008835
E-mail: turnerd@parliament.uk
Web: http://www.desturnermp.co.uk
Researcher – Mr Vaughan Williams
Tel: (020) 7219 2292
E-mail: williamsv@parliament.uk
*Constituency Office* . . . . 179 Preston Road, Brighton, BN1 6AG
Tel: (01273) 330610 Fax: (01273) 500966
Secretary – Mrs Sheila Crafter
Personal Assistant – Mr Simon Burgess
Assistant - Mr Nigel Sweet
*Parliamentary Interests* . Health and Social Services; Employment;
Housing; Science
*Leisure Interests* . . . . . . Classical Music and Jazz; Sailing; Reading;
Fencing

**Turner, Neil** . . . . . . Wigan
**Labour** . . . . . . . . . . . Majority 13,743 over Con
*Born* . . . . . . . . . . . . . . 16th September 1945 in Carlisle
*Educated* . . . . . . . . . . Carlisle Grammar School
*Elected* . . . . . . . . . . . . 1999 MP for Wigan (By-election)
*Office Held* . . . . . . . . . 2001 - PPS to Ian McCartney
(as Minister of State, Department for
Work and Pensions; then as Minister
without Portfolio and Chairman of
Labour Party)
*Constituency Office* . . . . Gerard Winstanley House, Crawford Street,
Wigan, WN1 1NG
Tel: (01942) 242047 Fax: (01942) 828008
E-mail: gerard@labour.u-net.com
Personal Assistant – Ms Judith Pye
Secretary – Ms Pam Gibson
*Parliamentary Interests* . Local Government; Housing
*Leisure Interests* . . . . . . Rugby League, World War II

## M E M B E R S   O F   T H E   H O U S E   O F   C O M M O N S

**Twigg, Derek** . . . . . Halton
**Labour** . . . . . . . . . . . Majority 17,428 over Con
*Born.* . . . . . . . . . . . . . . 9th July 1959 in Widnes
*Educated* . . . . . . . . . . Bankfield High School, Widnes;
Halton College of Further Education, Widnes
*Elected.* . . . . . . . . . . . . 1997 MP for Halton
*Offices Held* . . . . . . . . 2001 - 02 PPS to Stephen Byers
(Secretary of State for Transport, Local
Government and the Regions)
2002 - Assistant Government Whip, then
(from 2003) Government Whip (Lord
Commissioner, HM Treasury)
*Commons Office* . . . . . . Tel: (020) 7219 1039 Fax: (020) 7219 3642
Web: http://www.derektwigg.org.uk
Researcher – Miss Marianna Polanska
E-mail: polanskam@parliament.uk
*Constituency Office* . . . . Unit F2, Moor Lane Business Centre,
Moor Lane, Widnes, Cheshire, WA8 7AQ
Tel: (0151) 424 7030 Fax: (0151) 495 3800
E-mail: derek.twigg@virgin.net
Constituency Assistant – Mr Stan Hill
Secretary – Mrs Mary Twigg
*Parliamentary Interests* . Treasury; Education; Health; Defence
*Leisure Interests* . . . . . . Sport; Hill Walking; Reading Military History

**Twigg, Stephen**. . . . Enfield Southgate
**Labour** . . . . . . . . . . . Majority 5,546 over Con
*Born.* . . . . . . . . . . . . . . 25th December 1966
*Educated* . . . . . . . . . . Southgate Comprehensive School;
Balliol College, Oxford
*Elected.* . . . . . . . . . . . . 1997 MP for Enfield Southgate
*Offices Held* . . . . . . . . 2001 - 02 Parliamentary Secretary, Privy
Council Office
2002 - Parliamentary Secretary, Department
for Education and Skills
*Commons Office* . . . . . Tel: (020) 7219 6554 Fax: (020) 7219 0948
Pager: 07644 003720
E-mail: twiggs@parliament.uk
Web: http://www.stephentwigg.com
Research/Diary Assistant –
Mr Donovan Lambert
E-mail: lambertd@parliament.uk
Constituency Caseworker – Mrs Joan Worker
Tel: (020) 7219 4963
E-mail: workerj@parliament.uk
*Constituency Office* . . . . 3 Chase Side, London, N14 5BP
Tel: (020) 8245 5151 Fax: (0200 8245 0022
E-mail: simpsonp@parliament.uk
Constituency Assistant – Mr Paul Simpson
*Parliamentary Interests* . Constitutional Reform; Young People; Cyprus;
Israel; Middle East; Education;
Crime and Disorder

**Tyler, Paul** CBE. . . . Cornwall North
**Liberal Democrat** . . . Majority 2,832 over Con
*Born.* . . . . . . . . . . . . . . 29th October 1941 in Devon
*Educated* . . . . . . . . . . Mount House School; Sherborne School;
Exeter College, Oxford
*Elected.* . . . . . . . . . . . . 1974 (Feb - Oct) MP for Bodmin
1992 MP for Cornwall North
*Offices Held* . . . . . . . . 1992 - 97 Liberal Democrat Spokesman on
Agriculture and Rural Affairs
1997 - Liberal Democrat Shadow
Leader of the House of Commons
(also Chief Whip 1997 - 2001)
*Commons Office* . . . . . . Tel: (020) 7219 6355 Fax: (020) 7219 4870
E-mail: tylerp@parliament.uk
Web: http://www.paultyler.libdems.org
Parliamentary Assistant – Miss Sarah Hyder
E-mail: hyders@parliament.uk
Parliamentary Assistant – Mr Seth Williams
Tel: (020) 7219 6039
E-mail: williamss@parliament.uk
*Constituency Office* . . . . Church Stile, Launceston, Cornwall,
PL15 8AT
Tel: (01566) 777123 Fax: (01566) 722122
Casework Manager – Mrs Nicky Tyler
Office Manager – Ms Anne Simmonds
Diary Secretary – Mrs Margaret Sanders
*Parliamentary Interests* . Parliamentary and Constitutional Reform;
Rural Affairs; Organic Phosphate
*Leisure Interests* . . . . . . Walking

**Tynan, Bill**. . . . . . . Hamilton South
**Labour** . . . . . . . . . . . Majority 10,775 over SNP
*Born.* . . . . . . . . . . . . . . 18th August 1940
*Elected.* . . . . . . . . . . . . 1999 MP for Hamilton South (By-election)
*Educated* . . . . . . . . . . St Mungo's Academy, Glasgow
*Commons Office* . . . . . Tel: (020) 7219 6285 Fax: (020) 7219 1295
Mobile: 07887 546790
E-mail: tynanb@parliament.uk
Web: http://www.billtynan.labour.co.uk
Research Assistant – Mr Richard Williams
Tel: (020) 7219 0442
E-mail: williamsrj@parliament.uk
*Constituency Office* . . . . Montrose House, 154 Montrose Crescent,
Hamilton, ML3 6LB
Tel: (01698) 454925 Fax: (01698) 454926
Research Assistant – Mrs Jackie Livingstone
Secretary – Mrs Janice Sanderson
*Leisure Interests* . . . . . . Golf; DIY; Gardening

**Tyrie, Andrew** . . . . Chichester
**Conservative** . . . . . . . Majority 11,355 over Lib Dem
*Born.* . . . . . . . . . . . . . . 15th January 1957 in Rochford
*Educated* . . . . . . . . . . Felsted School; Trinity College, Oxford;
College of Europe, Bruges;
Wolfson College, Cambridge
*Elected.* . . . . . . . . . . . . 1997 MP for Chichester
*Office Held.* . . . . . . . . . 2003 - Opposition Spokesman on
Economic Affairs
*Commons Office* . . . . . . Tel: (020) 7219 6371 Fax: (020) 7219 0625
Personal Secretary – Mrs Ann Marsh
E-mail: marsha@parliament.uk
*Constituency Office* . . . . 145 St Pancras, Chichester, West Sussex,
PO19 4LH
Tel: (01243) 783519 Fax: (01243) 536848
Constituency Secretary – Mrs Gina Simpson
*Parliamentary Interests* . Economy; Foreign Affairs
*Leisure Interests* . . . . . . Golf; Theatre

# MEMBERS OF THE HOUSE OF COMMONS

## V

**Vaz, Keith** . . . . . . . . Leicester East
**Labour** . . . . . . . . . . . Majority 13,442 over Con
*Born* . . . . . . . . . . . . . . 26th November 1956 in Aden
*Educated* . . . . . . . . . . . Latymer Upper School, Hammersmith;
   Gonville and Caius College, Cambridge
*Elected* . . . . . . . . . . . . 1987 MP for Leicester East
*Offices Held* . . . . . . . . 1992 - 97 Opposition Spokesman on
   Environment
   1997 - 99 PPS to the Attorney General
   and Solicitor General
   1999 Parliamentary Secretary,
   Lord Chancellor's Department
   1999 - 2001 Minister of State, Foreign and
   Commonwealth Office (Minister for Europe)
*Commons Office* . . . . . . Tel: (020) 7219 4605 Fax: (020) 7219 5743
   E-mail: vazk@parliament.uk
*Constituency Office* . . . . 144 Uppingham Road, Leicester, LE5 0QF
   Tel: (0116) 212 2028 Fax: (0116) 212 2121
*Leisure Interests* . . . . . . Tennis

**Viggers, Peter** . . . . . Gosport
**Conservative** . . . . . . . Majority 2,621 over Lab
*Born* . . . . . . . . . . . . . . 13th March 1938 in Gosport, Hampshire
*Educated* . . . . . . . . . . Portsmouth Grammar School;
   Trinity Hall, Cambridge; College of Law
*Elected* . . . . . . . . . . . . 1974 MP for Gosport
*Office Held* . . . . . . . . 1986 - 89 Parliamentary Secretary,
   Northern Ireland Office
*Commons Office* . . . . . Tel: (020) 7219 4091 Fax: (020) 7219 3985
   Web: http://www.peterviggers.co.uk
   Secretary – Mrs Christine Shaylor
*Constituency Office* . . . . 167 Stoke Road, Gosport, Hampshire,
   PO12 1SE
   Tel: (023) 9258 8400 Fax: (023) 9252 7624
   Administrator – Mrs Kay Stewart
   Personal Assistant – Mrs Debbie Bradshaw
   Tel: (023) 9252 2121
*Parliamentary Interests* . Defence; Finance; Foreign Affairs; Pensions
*Leisure Interests* . . . . . . Beagling; Opera

**Vis, Dr Rudi** . . . . . . Finchley and Golders Green
**Labour** . . . . . . . . . . . Majority 3,716 over Con
*Born* . . . . . . . . . . . . . . 4th April 1941 in Alkmaar, Netherlands
*Educated* . . . . . . . . . . Alkmaar High School, Netherlands;
   Maryland University, USA;
   London School of Economics;
   Brunel University
*Elected* . . . . . . . . . . . . 1997 MP for Finchley and Golders Green
*Commons Office* . . . . . Tel: (020) 7219 4562 Fax: (020) 7219 0565
   E-mail: visr@parliament.uk
   Parliamentary Assistant – Mr David Robinson
   Tel: (020) 7219 4956
*Constituency Office* . . . . 38 Church Lane, East Finchley,
   London, N2 8DT
   Tel & Fax: (020) 8883 0411
   Caseworkers – Ms Katherine McGuirk
      Ms Jacquiline Vis
   Assistant – Mr Nick Guest
*Parliamentary Interests* . Finance; Europe; The Elderly; Human Rights
*Leisure Interests* . . . . . . Walking in Cities

## W

**Walley, Joan** . . . . . . Stoke-on-Trent North
**Labour** . . . . . . . . . . . Majority 11,784 over Con
*Born* . . . . . . . . . . . . . . 23rd January 1949 in Stoke-on-Trent
*Educated* . . . . . . . . . . Biddulph Grammar School; Hull University;
   University College of Wales, Swansea
*Elected* . . . . . . . . . . . . 1987 MP for Stoke-on-Trent North
*Offices Held* . . . . . . . . 1988 - 90 Opposition Spokeswoman on
   Environment
   1990 - 95 Opposition Spokeswoman on
   Transport
*Commons Office* . . . . . Tel: (020) 7219 4524 Fax: (020) 7219 4397
   E-mail: walleyj@parliament.uk
*Constituency Office* . . . . Unit 5, Burslem Enterprise Centre,
   Moorland Road, Burslem,
   Stoke-on-Trent, ST6 1JN
   Tel: (01782) 577900 Fax: (01782) 836462
   Assistants – Ms Adell Landon
      Ms Christine Tennet
*Parliamentary Interests* . Environment
*Leisure Interests* . . . . . . Football; Music; Swimming; Walking

**Walter, Robert** . . . . Dorset North
**Conservative** . . . . . . . Majority 3,797 over Lib Dem
*Born* . . . . . . . . . . . . . . 30th May 1948 in Swansea
*Educated* . . . . . . . . . . Lord Weymouth School; University of Aston
*Elected* . . . . . . . . . . . . 1997 MP for Dorset North
*Office Held* . . . . . . . . 1999 - 2001 Opposition Spokesman on Wales
   and Constitutional Affairs
*Commons Office* . . . . . Tel: (020) 7219 6981 Fax: (020) 7219 2608
   E-mail: walterr@parliament.uk
   Web: http://www.robertwaltermp.com
   Secretary – Miss Susan Hay
   E-mail: hays@parliament.uk
   Research Assistant – Mr Philip Diamond
   Tel: (020) 7219 2742
   E-mail: diamondp@parliament.uk
*Constituency Office* . . . . The Stables, Whitecliff Gardens, Blandford,
   Dorset, DT11 7BU
   Tel: (08451) 232785
   Constituency Support Manager –
   Mrs Diana Mogg
   Constituency Secretary –
   Mrs Barbara Samways
*Parliamentary Interests* . Agriculture; Health; Europe
*Leisure Interests* . . . . . . Sailing

**Ward, Claire** . . . . . . Watford
**Labour** . . . . . . . . . . . Majority 5,555 over Con
*Born* . . . . . . . . . . . . . . 9th May 1972 in North Shields
*Educated* . . . . . . . . . . Loreto College, St Albans;
   Hertfordshire University; Brunel University;
   College of Law
*Elected* . . . . . . . . . . . . 1997 MP for Watford
*Office Held* . . . . . . . . Formerly Mayor, Elstree and Boreham Wood
   2001 - PPS to John Hutton
   (Minister of State, Department of Health)
*Commons Office* . . . . . Tel: (020) 7219 4910 Fax: (020) 7219 0468
   E-mail: wardc@parliament.uk
   Secretary – Mrs Pippa Cracknell
   Caseworker – Mr Steve Benveniste
*Constituency Office* . . . . 270 St Albans Road, Watford, Hertfordshire,
   WD24 6PE
   Tel: (01223) 213579 Fax: (01223) 213595
   Office Manager – Mr Richard Banham
*Parliamentary Interests* . Culture; Media and Sport; Education
*Leisure Interests* . . . . . . Cinema; Eating Out; Football

# MEMBERS OF THE HOUSE OF COMMONS

**Wareing, Robert** .. Liverpool West Derby
**Labour** . . . . . . . . . . Majority 15,853 over Lib
*Born*. . . . . . . . . . . . . . 20th August 1930 in Liverpool
*Educated* . . . . . . . . . . Ranworth Square School, Liverpool;
Alsop High School, Liverpool;
Bolton College of Education;
London University
*Elected*. . . . . . . . . . . . 1983 MP for Liverpool West Derby
*Office Held* . . . . . . . . . 1987 - 92 Assistant Opposition Whip
*Commons Office* . . . . . . Tel: (020) 7219 3482 Fax: (020) 7219 6187
E-mail: wareingr@parliament.uk
Secretary/PA – Miss Katarina Gvozdenovic
Tel: (020) 7219 4592 Fax: (020) 7219 2014
E-mail: gvozdenovick@parliament.uk
*Constituency Office* . . . . 74a Mill Lane, West Derby,
Liverpool, L12 7JB
Tel: (0151) 256 9111 Fax: (0151) 226 0285
E-mail: rowlandsp@parliament.uk
Office Manager – Mr Peter Rowlands
Assistant – Mr Alan Fearnehough
Agent – Mr Wally Edwards
Tel: (0151) 547 2822 Fax: (0151) 226 0880
*Parliamentary Interests*. Health; Foreign Affairs (especially Russia)
*Leisure Interests* . . . . . . Ballet; Soccer; Travel

**Waterson, Nigel** . . . Eastbourne
**Conservative** . . . . . . . Majority 2,154 over Lib Dem
*Born*. . . . . . . . . . . . . . 12th October 1950
*Educated* . . . . . . . . . . Leeds Grammar School;
Queen's College, Oxford
*Elected*. . . . . . . . . . . . 1992 MP for Eastbourne
*Offices Held* . . . . . . . . 1997 - 99 Opposition Whip
1999 - 2001 Opposition Spokesman on
Environment, Transport and the Regions
2001 - 02 Opposition Spokesman on
Trade and Industry
2003 - 04 Opposition Spokesman on Work
and Pensions
2004 – Opposition Spokesman on Economic
Affairs (Pensions and Older People)
*Commons Office* . . . . . . Tel: (020) 7219 4576
Mobile: 07850 377274
E-mail: watersonn@parliament.uk
Secretary – Miss Jean Davy
*Constituency Office* . . . . 179 Victoria Drive, Eastbourne,
East Sussex, BN20 8QJ
Tel: (01323) 720776 Fax: (01323) 410994
Agent – Mr Peter Sabine

**Watkinson, Angela** Upminster
**Conservative** . . . . . . Majority 1,241 over Lab
*Educated* . . . . . . . . . . Wanstead County High School;
Anglia University
*Elected*. . . . . . . . . . . . 2001 MP for Upminster
*Offices Held* . . . . . . . . 2002 - 04 Opposition Whip
2004 - Opposition Spokesman on
Education
*Commons Office* . . . . . Tel: (020) 7219 8267 Fax: (020) 7219 1957
Mobile: 07754 509427
Pager: 07644 003682
E-mail: watkinsona@parliament.uk
Web: http://www.angelawatkinsonmp.com
Personal Secretary – Mrs Jill Brown
E-mail: brownjd@parliament.uk
*Constituency Office* . . . . 23 Butts Green Road, Hornchurch, RM11 2JS
Tel: (01708) 475252 Fax: (01708) 470495
Secretary – Mrs Marjorie Ramsey
E-mail: ramseymf@parliament.uk
*Parliamentary Interests* . Education; Law and Order; Constitution;
Health
*Leisure Interests* . . . . . Family; Reading; Dining; Music

**Watson, Tom** . . . . . West Bromwich East
**Labour** . . . . . . . . . . . Majority 9,763 over Con
*Born*. . . . . . . . . . . . . . 1967 in Sheffield
*Educated* . . . . . . . . . . King Charles I School, Kidderminster
*Elected*. . . . . . . . . . . . 2001 MP for West Bromwich East
*Office Held* . . . . . . . . 2003 - 04 PPS to Dawn Primarolo
(Paymaster General)
2004 - Assistant Government Whip
*Commons Office* . . . . . Tel: (020) 7219 8335 Fax: (020) 7219 1943
E-mail: watsont@parliament.uk
Web: http://www.tom-watson.co.uk
Parliamentary Assistant – Mr Simon Puddick
E-mail: puddicks@parliament.uk
*Constituency Office* . . . . Terry Duffy House, Thomas Street,
West Bromwich, B70 6NT
Tel: (0121) 569 1904 Fax: (0121) 553 1898
Constituency Assistant – Mr Simon Hackett
E-mail: hacketts@parliament.uk
*Parliamentary Interests* . Home Affairs; Industry; Law and Order;
The Economy
*Leisure Interests* . . . . . Play Station; Travel; Gardening

# MEMBERS OF THE HOUSE OF COMMONS

**Watts, Dave**...... St Helens North
**Labour**........... Majority 8985 over Lib Dem
*Born*.............. 26th August 1951 in Liverpool
*Educated*......... Seel Road Secondary Modern School
*Elected*........... 1997 MP for St Helens North
*Offices Held*........ 1993 - 97 Leader, St Helens Metropolitan
　　　　　　　　　　　Borough Council
　　　　　　　　　　2001 - 03 PPS to John Spellar
　　　　　　　　　　　(as Minister of State, Defence, then as
　　　　　　　　　　　Minister for Transport)
　　　　　　　　　　2003 - PPS to John Prescott (Deputy Prime
　　　　　　　　　　　Minister)
*Commons Office*...... Tel: (020) 7219 1644 Fax: (020) 7219 0913
　　　　　　　　　　PA – Ms Sylvia Edkins
　　　　　　　　　　E-mail: edkinss@parliament.uk
*Constituency Office*.... Anne Ward House, 1 Milk Street, St Helens,
　　　　　　　　　　Merseyside, WA10 1PX
　　　　　　　　　　Tel: (01744) 623416 Fax: (01744) 623417
　　　　　　　　　　Research Assistant/Caseworker –
　　　　　　　　　　　Mr Andy Bowden
　　　　　　　　　　Assistant – Ms Pauline Lazenbury
*Parliamentary Interests*. Regional Policy; Europe
*Leisure Interests*...... Football; Reading; Travel

**Webb, Steven**..... Northavon
**Liberal Democrat**... Majority 9,877 over Con
*Born*.............. 18th July 1965 in Birmingham
*Educated*.......... Dartmouth High School, Birmingham;
　　　　　　　　　　Hertford College, Oxford
*Elected*........... 1997 MP for Northavon
*Offices Held*........ 1997 - Liberal Democrat Spokesman on
　　　　　　　　　　Pensions, then Social Security and (from
　　　　　　　　　　2001) Work and Pensions
*Commons Office*...... Tel: (020) 7219 4378 Fax: (020) 7219 1110
　　　　　　　　　　E-mail: steve@winwithwebb.co.uk
　　　　　　　　　　Web: http://www.stevewebb.org.uk
　　　　　　　　　　Researcher – Miss Jo Holland
*Constituency Office*.... Poole Court, Poole Court Drive, Yate,
　　　　　　　　　　Bristol, BS37 5PP
　　　　　　　　　　Tel: (01454) 322100 Fax: (01454) 866515
　　　　　　　　　　Personal Assistant – Mrs Marilyn Palmer
　　　　　　　　　　Caseworker – Mrs Louise Harrison

**Weir, Michael**..... Angus
**SNP**............. Majority 3,611 over Con
*Born*.............. 24th March 1957 in Arbroath
*Educated*.......... Arbroath High School; Aberdeen University
*Elected*........... 2001 MP for Angus
*Commons Office*...... Tel: (020) 7219 8125
　　　　　　　　　　E-mail: weirm@parliament.uk
*Constituency Offices*... 16 Brothock Bridge, Arbroath, Angus
　　　　　　　　　　Tel: (01241) 874522 Fax: (01241) 879350
　　　　　　　　　　E-mail: ocfp@hotmail.com
　　　　　　　　　　Web: http://www.angussnp.org
　　　　　　　　　　Parliamentary Assistant – Mr Donald Morrison
　　　　　　　　　　E-mail: morrisondo@parliament.uk
　　　　　　　　　　Secretary – Mrs Joyce Morrison
　　　　　　　　　　E-mail: morrisonj@parliament.uk
　　　　　　　　　　10A George Street, Montrose
　　　　　　　　　　Tel: (01674) 675743
　　　　　　　　　　Constituency Assistant – Mr Stewart Mowatt
　　　　　　　　　　E-mail: mowatts@parliament.uk
*Parliamentary Interests*. Disability; Rural Affairs; Health;
　　　　　　　　　　Industrial Development; Environment

**White, Brian**..... Milton Keynes North East
**Labour**........... Majority 1,829 over Con
*Born*.............. 5th May 1957 in Isleworth
*Educated*.......... Methodist College, Belfast
*Elected*........... 1997 MP for Milton Keynes North East
*Commons Office*..... Tel: (020) 7219 3435 Fax: (020) 7219 2887
　　　　　　　　　　Pager: 07644 008838
　　　　　　　　　　E-mail: whitebar@parliament.uk
　　　　　　　　　　Web: http://www.brianwhite.org.uk
　　　　　　　　　　Researcher – Ms Kay Withers
　　　　　　　　　　Tel: (020) 7219 2893
　　　　　　　　　　E-mail: withersk@parliament.uk
*Constituency Office*.... Labour Hall, Newport Road, New Bradwell,
　　　　　　　　　　Milton Keynes, MK13 0AA
　　　　　　　　　　Tel: (01908) 313933 Fax: (01908) 311713
　　　　　　　　　　Office Manager – Mrs Leena White
　　　　　　　　　　Caseworker – Mrs Kathleen McLinton
*Parliamentary Interests*. Energy; Competition Policy;
　　　　　　　　　　Environmental Issues; IT Policy;
　　　　　　　　　　Modernising Government

**Whitehead, Dr Alan** Southampton Test
**Labour**........... Majority 11,207 over Con
*Born*.............. 15th September 1950 in Isleworth, Middlesex
*Educated*.......... Isleworth Grammar School;
　　　　　　　　　　Southampton University
*Elected*........... 1997 MP for Southampton Test
*Offices Held*........ 1984 - 92 Leader, Southampton City Council
　　　　　　　　　　2001 - 02 Parliamentary Secretary,
　　　　　　　　　　　Department for Transport, Local
　　　　　　　　　　　Government and the Regions
*Commons Office*...... Tel: (020) 7219 6338 Fax: (020) 7219 0918
　　　　　　　　　　E-mail: whiteheada@parliament.uk
　　　　　　　　　　Web: http://www.alan-whitehead.org.uk
　　　　　　　　　　Researcher – Mr Will Sherlock
　　　　　　　　　　Tel: (020) 7219 5079
　　　　　　　　　　E-mail: sherlockw@parliament.uk
*Constituency Office*.... 20-22 Southampton Street,
　　　　　　　　　　Southampton, SO15 2ED
　　　　　　　　　　Tel: (023) 8023 1942 Fax: (023) 8023 1943
　　　　　　　　　　E-mail: alan@alan-whitehead.org.uk
　　　　　　　　　　Researcher/Constituency Assistant –
　　　　　　　　　　　Mr Sam Goold
　　　　　　　　　　Diary Secretary – Mrs Rosemarie Oxford
　　　　　　　　　　E-mail: rose@alan-whitehead.org.uk
　　　　　　　　　　Office Manager – Mrs Christine Bull
　　　　　　　　　　E-mail: chris@alan-whitehead.org.uk
*Parliamentary Interests*. Environment; Transport; Local and Regional
　　　　　　　　　　Government; Civil Service; Energy; Higher
　　　　　　　　　　Education
*Leisure Interests*...... Football; Films; Writing; Gardening

# MEMBERS OF THE HOUSE OF COMMONS

**Whittingdale, John** OBE  Maldon and Chelmsford East
**Conservative** . . . . . . Majority 8,462 over Lab
*Born.* . . . . . . . . . . . . . 16th October 1959 in Sherborne, Dorset
*Educated* . . . . . . . . . . Sandroyd School, Wiltshire;
Winchester College;
University College, London
*Elected.* . . . . . . . . . . . 1992 MP for Colchester South
and Maldon, then (1997) Maldon and
Chelmsford East
*Offices Held* . . . . . . . . 1997 - 98 Opposition Whip
1998 - 99 Opposition Spokesman on
Treasury Matters
1999 - 2001 PPS to William Hague
(Leader of the Opposition)
2001 - 02 Shadow Secretary for Trade and
Industry
2002 - 03 Shadow Secretary for Culture,
Media and Sport
2003 - 04 Shadow Secretary for Agriculture,
Fisheries and Food
2004 - Shadow Secretary for Culture,
Media and Sport
*Commons Office* . . . . . . Tel: (020) 7219 3557 Fax: (020) 7219 2522
E-mail: jwhittingdale.mp@tory.org.uk
Research Assistant – Mrs Clare Gledhill
*Constituency Office* . . . . 19 High Street, Maldon, Essex, CM9 5PE
Tel: (01621) 855663 Fax: (01621) 855217
E-mail: mecca@tory.org
Organising Secretary – Mrs Eileen Williams
*Parliamentary Interests.* Broadcasting; Media
*Leisure Interests* . . . . . . Cinema; Music

**Wicks, Malcolm** . . . Croydon North
**Labour** . . . . . . . . . . . Majority 16,858 over Con
*Born.* . . . . . . . . . . . . . 1st July 1947 in Hatfield, Hertfordshire
*Educated* . . . . . . . . . . Elizabeth College, Guernsey;
North West London Polytechnic;
London School of Economics
*Elected.* . . . . . . . . . . . 1992 MP for Croydon North West, then
(1997) Croydon North
*Offices Held* . . . . . . . . 1995 - 97 Opposition Spokesman on
Social Security
1998 - 99 Chairman, Select Committee
on Education, House of Commons
1999 - 2001 Parliamentary Secretary,
Department for Education and Employment
2001 - 03 Parliamentary Secretary,
Department for Works and Pensions
2003 - Minister of State, Department for
Work and Pensions (Minister for Pensions)
*Commons Office* . . . . . . Tel: (020) 7219 4418 Fax: (020) 7219 2795
E-mail: wicksm@government.UK
Parliamentary Assistant – Ms Louise Szpera
E-mail: szperal@parliament.uk
*Constituency Office* . . . . 84 High Street, Thornton Heath,
Surrey, CR7 8LF
Tel: (020) 8665 1214 Fax: (020) 8683 0179
Constituency Adviser – Ms Alison Butler
E-mail: butlera@parliament.uk
*Parliamentary Interests.* Social Policy; Education
*Leisure Interests* . . . . . . Gardening; Music; Walking

**Widdecombe, Rt Hon Ann**  Maidstone and the Weald
**Conservative** . . . . . . Majority 10,318 over Lab
*Born.* . . . . . . . . . . . . . 4th October 1947 in Bath
*Educated* . . . . . . . . . . La Sainte Union Convent, Bath;
Birmingham University;
Lady Margaret Hall, Oxford
*Elected.* . . . . . . . . . . . 1987 MP for Maidstone, then (1997)
Maidstone and the Weald
*Offices Held* . . . . . . . . 1990 - 93 Parliamentary Secretary,
Department of Social Security
1993 - 94 Parliamentary Secretary,
Department of Employment
1994 - 95 Minister of State,
Department of Employment
1995 - 97 Minister of State, Home Office
1998 - 99 Shadow Health Secretary
1999 - 2001 Shadow Home Secretary
*Commons Office* . . . . . . Tel: (020) 7219 5091 Fax: (020) 7219 2413
E-mail: widdecombea@parliament.uk
Web: http://www.annwiddecombemp.com
Private Secretary – Mrs Jacqui Gulliver
*Constituency Office* . . . . 3 Albion Place, Maidstone, Kent, ME16 8JB
Tel: (01622) 752463 Fax: (01622) 764427
Secretary – Mrs Sue Dishman
Constituency Caseworker – Mrs Lesley Polley
Tel: (01622) 769898 Fax: (01622) 686606
*Parliamentary Interests.* Home Affairs; Abortion
*Leisure Interests* . . . . . . Writing; Charles II's Escape

**Wiggin, Bill** . . . . . . Leominster
**Conservative** . . . . . . Majority 10,367 over Lib Dem
*Born.* . . . . . . . . . . . . . 4th June 1966 in London
*Educated* . . . . . . . . . . Eton College;
University College of North Wales
*Elected.* . . . . . . . . . . . 2001 MP for Leominster
*Offices Held* . . . . . . . . 2003 Opposition Spokesman on Environment
2003 - Shadow Secretary for Wales
*Commons Office* . . . . . . Tel: (020) 7219 1777
Mobile: 07939 285863
Pager: 07644 006168
E-mail: billwigginmp@parliament.uk
Web: http://www.billwiggin.com
Secretary – Miss Alison Porter
E-mail: portera@parliament.uk
Researcher – Miss Amy Bromfield
Tel: (020) 7219 8175
E-mail: bromfielda@parliament.uk
*Constituency Office* . . . . 8 Corn Square, Leominster, Herefordshire,
HR6 8LR
Tel: (01568) 612565 Fax: (01568) 610320
Agent – Mr Andrew Barrand
*Parliamentary Interests.* Defence; Agriculture; Treasury
*Leisure Interests* . . . . . . Motorcycles; Shooting; Fishing; Fencing

# MEMBERS OF THE HOUSE OF COMMONS

**Wilkinson, John** . . . Ruislip-Northwood
**Conservative** . . . . . . . Majority 7,537 over Lab
*Born*. . . . . . . . . . . . . . 23rd September 1940 in Slough
*Educated* . . . . . . . . . . Eton College; RAF College, Cranwell;
　　　　　　　　　　 Churchill College, Cambridge
*Elected*. . . . . . . . . . . . 1970 - 74 MP for Bradford West
　　　　　　　　　　 1979 MP for Ruislip-Northwood
*Commons Office* . . . . . Tel: (020) 7219 5165 Fax: (020) 7219 4850
　　　　　　　　　　 E-mail: johnwilkinsonmp@parliament.uk
　　　　　　　　　　 PA – Miss Victoria Wheal
　　　　　　　　　　 E-mail: whealv@parliament.uk
*Constituency Office* . . . . 20B High Street, Northwood, Middlesex,
　　　　　　　　　　 HA6 1DU
　　　　　　　　　　 Tel: (01923) 835383
　　　　　　　　　　 Constituency Secretary – Ms Ann Taggart
　　　　　　　　　　 Research Assistant – Mrs Cecilia Wilkinson
*Parliamentary Interests* . Defence; Foreign Affairs; Industry; Aviation;
　　　　　　　　　　 Europe; London Issues; Race Relations;
　　　　　　　　　　 Immigration
*Leisure Interests* . . . . . . Countryside; Travel (Latin America)

**Willetts, David** . . . . Havant
**Conservative** . . . . . . . Majority 4,207 over Lab
*Born*. . . . . . . . . . . . . . 9th March 1956 in Birmingham
*Educated* . . . . . . . . . . King Edward's School, Birmingham;
　　　　　　　　　　 Christ Church, Oxford
*Elected*. . . . . . . . . . . . 1992 MP for Havant
*Offices Held* . . . . . . . . 1994 - 95 Assistant Government Whip
　　　　　　　　　　 1995 Government Whip
　　　　　　　　　　　 (Lord Commissioner, H M Treasury)
　　　　　　　　　　 1995 - 96 Parliamentary Secretary,
　　　　　　　　　　　 Office of Public Service
　　　　　　　　　　 1996 Paymaster General, Office of
　　　　　　　　　　　 Public Service
　　　　　　　　　　 1997 - 99 Opposition Spokesman on
　　　　　　　　　　　 Education and Employment
　　　　　　　　　　 1999 - 01 Shadow Social Security Secretary
　　　　　　　　　　 2001 - Shadow Secretary for Work and
　　　　　　　　　　　 Pensions and Spokesman on
　　　　　　　　　　　 Welfare Reform
*Commons Office* . . . . . Tel: (020) 7219 4570 Fax: (020) 7219 2567
　　　　　　　　　　 E-mail: willettsd@parliament.uk
　　　　　　　　　　 Web: http://www.davidwilletts.org.uk
　　　　　　　　　　 Private Secretary – Mrs Annie Winsbury
　　　　　　　　　　 Researcher – Mr Richard Price
　　　　　　　　　　 Tel: (020) 7219 2234
　　　　　　　　　　 E-mail: pricer@parliament.uk
*Constituency Office* . . . . 19 South Street, Havant, Hampshire,
　　　　　　　　　　 PO9 1BU
　　　　　　　　　　 Tel: (023) 9249 9746 Fax: (023) 9249 8753
　　　　　　　　　　 E-mail: scaddanj@parliament.uk
　　　　　　　　　　 Agent – Mrs Jackie Scaddan
*Parliamentary Interests* . Economic Policy; Pensions; Demography;
　　　　　　　　　　 Social Security; Education
*Leisure Interests* . . . . . . Swimming; Reading; Cycling

**Williams, Rt Hon Alan** Swansea West
**Labour** . . . . . . . . . . . Majority 9,550 over Con
*Born*. . . . . . . . . . . . . . 14th October 1930 in Caerphilly
*Educated* . . . . . . . . . . Cardiff High School;
　　　　　　　　　　 Cardiff College of Technology;
　　　　　　　　　　 University College, Oxford
*Elected*. . . . . . . . . . . . 1964 MP for Swansea West
*Offices Held* . . . . . . . . 1967 - 68 Parliamentary Secretary,
　　　　　　　　　　 Department of Economic Affairs
　　　　　　　　　　 1969 - 70 Parliamentary Secretary,
　　　　　　　　　　 Ministry of Technology and Power
　　　　　　　　　　 1970 - 71 Opposition Spokesman on Industry
　　　　　　　　　　 1970 - 72 Opposition Spokesman on Education
　　　　　　　　　　 1972 - 74 Opposition Spokesman on
　　　　　　　　　　 Consumer Affairs
　　　　　　　　　　 1974 - 76 Minister of State, Department of
　　　　　　　　　　 Prices and Consumer Protection
　　　　　　　　　　 1976 - 79 Minister of State,
　　　　　　　　　　 Department of Industry
　　　　　　　　　　 1979 - 80 Opposition Spokesman on Wales
　　　　　　　　　　 1980 - 83 Opposition Spokesman on
　　　　　　　　　　 Civil Service
　　　　　　　　　　 1983 - 87 Opposition Spokesman on Industry
　　　　　　　　　　 and on House of Commons Affairs
　　　　　　　　　　 1987 - 88 Shadow Secretary of State for Wales
　　　　　　　　　　 1988 - 89 Deputy Shadow Leader of the
　　　　　　　　　　 House of Commons
　　　　　　　　　　 2002 - Chairman, Liaison Committee,
　　　　　　　　　　 House of Commons
*Commons Office* . . . . . Tel: (020) 7219 3449 Fax: (020) 7219 6943
*Constituency Office* . . . . 42 High Street, Swansea, SA1 1LT
　　　　　　　　　　 Tel: (01792) 655097 Fax: (01792) 650766
　　　　　　　　　　 P/As – Mrs Hilary Sullivan
　　　　　　　　　　　 Mr David Thomas
*Parliamentary Interests* The Monarchy
*Leisure Interests* . . . . . . Football (Arsenal Ladies FC)

**Williams, Betty** . . . . Conwy
**Labour** . . . . . . . . . . . Majority 6,219 over Con
*Born*. . . . . . . . . . . . . . 31st July 1944 in North Wales
*Educated* . . . . . . . . . . Ysgol Dyffryn Nantlle; University of Wales
*Elected*. . . . . . . . . . . . 1997 MP for Conwy
*Office Held*. . . . . . . . . 1989 - 90 Mayor, Arfon Borough Council
*Commons Office* . . . . . Tel: (020) 7219 5052 Fax: (020) 7219 2759
　　　　　　　　　　 Secretaries – Mr Paul Jarvis
　　　　　　　　　　　　　 Mr William Neal
*Constituency Office* . . . . Tel: (01248) 680097
*Parliamentary Interests* . Education; Health; Railways;
　　　　　　　　　　 Consumer Affairs
*Leisure Interests* . . . . . . Opera; Eisteddfodau; Sheep Dog Trials

**Williams, Hywel** . . . Caernarfon
**Plaid Cymru** . . . . . . . Majority 3,511 over Labour
*Born*. . . . . . . . . . . . . . 14th May 1953
*Educated* . . . . . . . . . . Ysgol Glan y Mor, Pwllheli, Gwynedd;
　　　　　　　　　　 University of Wales, Cardiff
　　　　　　　　　　 University of Wales, Bangor
*Elected*. . . . . . . . . . . . 2001 MP for Caernarfon
*Commons Office* . . . . . Tel: (020) 7219 5021 Fax: (020) 7219 3705
　　　　　　　　　　 E-mail: williamshy@parliament.uk
　　　　　　　　　　 Secretary – Ms Rhian Medi
*Constituency Office* . . . . 8 Stryd y Castell, Caernarfon, LL55 1SE
　　　　　　　　　　 Tel: (01286) 672076 Fax: (01286) 672003
　　　　　　　　　　 Secretary – Mrs Gwenda Williams
*Parliamentary Interests* . Social Security; Language and Culture Issues;
　　　　　　　　　　 International Development; Health
*Leisure Interests* . . . . . . Reading; Walking; Cinema

## M E M B E R S   O F   T H E   H O U S E   O F   C O M M O N S

**Williams, Roger** . . . Brecon and Radnorshire
**Liberal Democrat** . . . Majority 751 over Con
*Born*. . . . . . . . . . . . . 22nd January 1948
*Educated* . . . . . . . . . . Christ College, Brecon;
                Selwyn College, Cambridge
*Elected*. . . . . . . . . . . . 2001 MP for Brecon and Radnorshire
*Offices Held* . . . . . . . . 2002 - Liberal Democrat Spokesman on
                Rural Affairs and Food and (from 2003) on
                Welsh Affairs
*Commons Office* . . . . . Tel: (020) 7219 8145 Fax: (020) 7219 1747
                E-mail: williamsr@cix.co.uk
                Web: http://www.rogerwilliams.org.uk
                Researcher – Miss Emily Walch
                E-mail: walche@parliament.uk
*Constituency Office* . . . . 4 Watergate, Brecon, Powys, LD3 9AN
                Tel: (01874) 625739 Fax: (01874) 625635
                Secretary – Miss Avril Evans
                Constituency Manager –
                  Mr James Gibson-Watt
                Caseworker – Mr Johnny Pappas
*Parliamentary Interests* . Agriculture; Environment; Wales;
                Special Education
*Leisure Interests* . . . . . Farming; Travel; Poetry; Hillwalking


**Willis, Phil** . . . . . . . Harrogate and Knaresborough
**Liberal Democrat** . . . Majority 8,845 over Con
*Born*. . . . . . . . . . . . . 30th November 1941 in Burnley
*Educated* . . . . . . . . . . Burnley Grammar School;
                City of Leeds College; Birmingham University
*Elected*. . . . . . . . . . . . 1997 MP for Harrogate and Knaresborough
*Offices Held* . . . . . . . . 1990 - 97 Leader, Harrogate Borough Council
                1997 - Liberal Democrat Spokesman on
                Employment and Education, then
                (from 2001) Education and Skills
*Commons Office* . . . . . Tel: (020) 7219 3846 Fax: (020) 7219 0971
                E-mail: info@philwillis.org.uk
                Web: http://www.philwillis.org.uk
                Researchers – Mr John Alker
                   Ms Ruth Brock
                E-mails: [surnameinitial]@parliament.uk
*Constituency Office* . . . . Ashdown House, 75 Station Parade,
                Harrogate, North Yorkshire, HG1 1ST
                Tel: (01423) 528888 Fax: (01423) 505700
                E-mail: kelleyc@parliament.uk
                Constituency Worker – Mrs Claire Kelley
                Constituency Organiser – Mr Michael Newby
*Parliamentary Interests* . Education; Northern Ireland;
                Local Government; Mobile Communications
*Leisure Interests* . . . . . Football (Leeds United FC)


**Wills, Michael** . . . . Swindon North
**Labour** . . . . . . . . . . . Majority 8,105 over Con
*Born*. . . . . . . . . . . . . 20th May 1952 in London
*Educated* . . . . . . . . . . Haberdashers' Askes School, Elstree;
                Clare College, Cambridge
*Elected*. . . . . . . . . . . . 1997 MP for Swindon North
*Offices Held* . . . . . . . . 1999 Parliamentary Secretary,
                Department for Trade and Industry
                1999 - 2001 Parliamentary Secretary,
                Department for Education and Employment
                2001 - 02 Parliamentary Secretary, Lord
                Chancellor's Department
                2002 - 03 Parliamentary Secretary,
                Home Office
*Commons Office* . . . . . Tel: (020) 7219 4399 Fax: (020) 7219 0911
                E-mail: bloorl@parliament.uk
                Assistant – Miss Louise Bloor
*Constituency Office* . . . . Pinehurst People's Centre, Beech Avenue,
                Swindon, SN2 1JT
                Tel: (01793) 481016 Fax: (01793) 524483
                E-mail: andersont@parliament.uk
                Assistant – Mrs Tracy Anderson


**Wilshire, David** . . . Spelthorne
**Conservative** . . . . . . . Majority 3,262 over Lab
*Born*. . . . . . . . . . . . . 16th September 1943 in Bristol
*Educated* . . . . . . . . . . Kingswood School, Bath;
                Fitzwilliam College, Cambridge
*Elected*. . . . . . . . . . . . 1987 MP for Spelthorne
*Offices Held* . . . . . . . . 1981 - 87 Leader, Wansdyke District Council
                2001 - Opposition Whip; (also
                Spokesman on Northern Ireland and
                Treasury 2001 - 03)
*Commons Office* . . . . . Tel: (020) 7219 3534 Fax: (020) 7219 5852
                Secretary – Mrs Ann Palmer
                Tel: (020) 7219 4017
*Constituency Office* . . . . 55 Cherry Orchard, Staines, Middlesex,
                TW18 2DQ
                Tel: (01784) 450822 Fax: (01784) 466109
*Parliamentary Interests* . Foreign Affairs; Northern Ireland; Aviation
*Leisure Interests* . . . . . Gardening; Cider Making


**Wilson, Rt Hon Brian** Cunninghame North
**Labour** . . . . . . . . . . . Majority 8,398 over SNP
*Born*. . . . . . . . . . . . . 13th December 1948 in Dunoon
*Educated* . . . . . . . . . . Dunoon Grammar School; Dundee University;
                University College of Wales, Cardiff
*Elected*. . . . . . . . . . . . 1987 MP for Cunninghame North
*Offices Held* . . . . . . . . 1988 - 92 Opposition Spokesman on
                Scottish Affairs
                1992 Opposition Spokesman on
                Citizen's Charter
                1992 - 94, 1995 - 96 Opposition Spokesman
                on Transport
                1994 - 95 Opposition Spokesman on Industry
                1997 - 98 1999 - 2001 Minister of State,
                Scottish Office
                1998 - 99 Minister of State, Department of
                Trade and Industry (Minister for Trade)
                2001 Minister of State, Foreign and
                Commonwealth Office
                2001 - 03 Minister of State, Department of
                Trade and Industry (Minister for Energy)
*Commons Office* . . . . . Tel: (020) 7219 1053
                Researcher – Mr Mark Hogarth
                E-mail: hogarthm@parliament.uk
*Constituency Office* . . . . 37 Main Street, Kilbirnie, Ayrshire,
                KA25 7BX
                Tel: (01505) 682847 Fax: (01505) 684648
                E-mail: brian@wilsonmp-1.fsnet.co.uk
                Secretaries – Ms Carole Campbell Brown
                   Ms Alison Wilson

# MEMBERS OF THE HOUSE OF COMMONS

**Winnick, David** ... Walsall North
**Labour** . . . . . . . . . . . Majority 9,391 over Con
*Born*. . . . . . . . . . . . . . 26th June 1933 in Brighton, Sussex
*Educated* . . . . . . . . . . London School of Economics
*Elected*. . . . . . . . . . . . 1966 - 70 MP for Croydon South
1979 MP for Walsall North
*Commons Office* . . . . . . Tel: (020) 7219 5003 Fax: (020) 7219 0257
E-mail: winnickd@parliament.uk
Personal Assistant – Ms Jane Richardson
E-mail: richardsonjv@parliament.uk
*Constituency Office*. . . . Bellamy House, Wilkes Street, Willenhall,
West Midlands, WV13 2BS
Tel: (01902) 605020 Fax; (01902) 637372
Constituency Assistant – Mrs Ann Young
*Parliamentary Interests* . Home Affairs; Foreign Policy; Pensioner's
Welfare; Controls on MPs' Financial Interests
*Leisure Interests* . . . . . . Reading; Walking; Cinema; Theatre

**Winterton, Ann** . . . . . Congleton
**Conservative** . . . . . . . Majority 7,134 over Lab
*Born*. . . . . . . . . . . . . . 6th March 1941 in Sutton Coldfield
*Educated* . . . . . . . . . . Erdington Grammar School for Girls
*Elected*. . . . . . . . . . . . 1983 MP for Congleton
*Offices Held* . . . . . . . . 1998 - 2001 Opposition Spokesman on
Drugs Strategy
2001 - 02 Opposition Spokesman on
Agriculture and Fisheries
*Commons Office* . . . . . . Tel: (020) 7219 3585 Fax: (020) 7219 6886
Assistant – Mr Paul Morgan
E-mail: morgandpw@parliament.uk
*Constituency Office*. . . . Riverside, Mountbatten Way, Congleton,
Cheshire, CW12 1DY
Tel: (01260) 278866 Fax: (01260) 271212
E-mail: awinterton@riverside14.fsnet.co.uk
Private Secretary – Mrs Dorothy Littler
*Parliamentary Interests* . Agriculture; Trade and Industry;
Pro-Life Issues; Fisheries
*Leisure Interests* . . . . . . Music; Skiing; Walking; Cycling; Food; Wine

**Winterton, Sir Nicholas** Macclesfield
**Conservative** . . . . . . Majority 7,200 over Lab
*Born*. . . . . . . . . . . . . . 31st March 1938 in Leamington Spa
*Educated* . . . . . . . . . . Rugby School
*Elected*. . . . . . . . . . . . 1971 MP for Macclesfield (By-election)
*Offices Held* . . . . . . . . 1990 - 92 Chairman, Health Select
Committee, House of Commons
1997 - Chairman, Procedure Committee,
House of Commons
*Commons Office* . . . . . . Tel: (020) 7219 6434 Fax: (020) 7219 6886
Secretary – Mrs Diane I'Anson
Assistant – Mr Paul Morgan
Tel: (020) 7219 3585
*Constituency Office*. . . . West Bank Road, Macclesfield, Cheshire,
SK10 3DU
Tel: (01625) 422848 Fax: (01625) 617066
Secretary – Ms Melanie Lewis
*Parliamentary Interests* . Health; Education; Media
*Leisure Interests* . . . . . . Rugby; Football; Tennis; Theatre; Opera;
Reading; Real Ale

**Winterton, Rosie** . . Doncaster Central
**Labour** . . . . . . . . . . . Majority 11,999 over Con
*Born*. . . . . . . . . . . . . . 10th August 1958 in Leicester
*Educated* . . . . . . . . . . Doncaster Grammar School; Hull University
*Elected*. . . . . . . . . . . . 1997 MP for Doncaster Central
*Offices Held* . . . . . . . . 2001 - 03 Parliamentary Secretary, Lord
Chancellor's Department
2003 - Minister of State, Department of Health
*Commons Office* . . . . . . Tel: (020) 7219 0925 Fax: (020) 7219 4581
*Constituency Office*. . . . Guildhall Advice Centre, Old Guildhall Yard,
Doncaster, DN1 1QW
Tel: (01302) 735241 Fax: (01302) 735242
Executive Secretaries –
Mrs Ann Berwick
Mrs Stephanie Faulkner
*Leisure Interests* . . . . . . Sailing; Reading

**Wishart, Peter** . . . . Tayside North
**SNP** . . . . . . . . . . . . . Majority 3,283 over Con
*Born*. . . . . . . . . . . . . . 9th March 1962
*Educated* . . . . . . . . . . Queen Anne High School, Dunfermline;
Moray House College of Education
*Elected*. . . . . . . . . . . . 2001 MP for Tayside North
*Offices Held* . . . . . . . . 2001 - SNP Chief Whip and Spokesman on
Transport, Local Government and Regions
and Culture, Media and Sport
*Commons Office* . . . . . . Tel: (020) 7219 8303
E-mail: wishartp@parliament.uk
*Constituency Office*. . . . 35 Perth Street, Blairgowrie, Perthshire, PH10 6DL
Tel: (01250) 876576 Fax: (01250) 876991
Office Manager – Miss Elaine Wylie
Constituency Assistant – Miss Vari McDonald

**Wood, Mike**. . . . . . . Batley and Spen
**Labour** . . . . . . . . . . . Majority 5,064 over Con
*Born*. . . . . . . . . . . . . . 3rd March 1946 in Crewe
*Educated* . . . . . . . . . . Southampton University; Leeds University;
Leeds Metropolitan University
*Elected*. . . . . . . . . . . . 1997 MP for Batley and Spen
*Office Held*. . . . . . . . . Formerly Deputy Leader, Kirklees
Metropolitan District Council
*Constituency Office*. . . . 9 Cross Crown Street, Cleckheaton, BD19 3HW
Tel: (01274) 335233 Fax: (01274) 335235
E-mail: woodm@parliament.uk
*Parliamentary Interests* . Human Rights; Kashmir; Environment;
Animal Welfare; Education; HIV/AIDS;
Penal Affairs
*Leisure Interests* . . . . . . Walking; Conservation; Reading; Music

# MEMBERS OF THE HOUSE OF COMMONS

**Woodward, Shaun**. St Helens South
**Labour** . . . . . . . . . . Majority 8,985 over Lib Dem
*Born*. . . . . . . . . . . . . . 26th October 1958 in Bristol
*Educated* . . . . . . . . . . Bristol Grammar School;
Jesus College, Cambridge
*Elected*. . . . . . . . . . . . 1997 - 2001 MP for Witney (Con, then Lab)
2001 MP for St Helens South (Lab)
*Commons Office* . . . . . . Tel: (020) 7219 2680 Fax: (020) 7219 0979
E-mail:
shaunwoodwardmp@email.labour.org.uk
Web: http://www.shaunwoodward.com
Parliamentary Assistant – Ms Nathalie Spells
E-mail: spellsn@parliament.uk
*Constituency Office* . . . . 1st Floor, Century House, Hardshaw Street,
St Helens, Merseyside, WA10 1QW
Tel: (01744) 24226 Fax: (01744) 24306
Caseworker – Mr David Holden-Locke
Secretary – Ms Sue Williams
*Parliamentary Interests* . Childrens' Issues; International Affairs;
Equalities; Regeneration
*Leisure Interests* . . . . . . Opera; Tennis; Reading; Gardening;
Architecture

**Woolas, Phil** . . . . . . Oldham East and Saddleworth
**Labour** . . . . . . . . . . Majority 2,726 over Lib Dem
*Born*. . . . . . . . . . . . . . 11th December 1959
*Educated* . . . . . . . . . . Nelson Grammar School;
Nelson and Colne College;
Manchester University
*Elected*. . . . . . . . . . . . 1997 MP for Oldham East and Saddleworth
*Offices Held* . . . . . . . . 2001 - 02 Assistant Government Whip
2002 - 03 Government Whip
(Lord Commissioner, H M Treasury)
2003 - Deputy Leader of the House
of Commons
*Commons Office* . . . . . . Tel: (020) 7219 1149 Fax: (020) 7219 0992
Parliamentary Assistant – Mrs Shona Pinder
*Constituency Office* . . . . Lord Chambers, 11 Church Lane,
Oldham, OL1 3AN
Tel: (0161) 624 4248 Fax: (0161) 626 8572
Constituency Caseworker – Mrs Jean Jones
Agent – Mr John Battye
*Parliamentary Interests* . Employment; Broadcasting; Textiles;
Economy; Higher Education.
*Leisure Interests* . . . . . . Football (Manchester United FC); Photography

**Worthington, Tony** Clydebank and Milngavie
**Labour** . . . . . . . . . . Majority 10,724 over SNP
*Born*. . . . . . . . . . . . . . 11th October 1941 in Hertfordshire
*Educated* . . . . . . . . . . City School, Lincoln;
London School of Economics;
York University
*Elected*. . . . . . . . . . . . 1987 MP for Clydebank and Milngavie
*Offices Held* . . . . . . . . 1989 - 92 Opposition Spokesman on Scotland
1992 - 93 Opposition Spokesman on
Development and Co-operation
1993 - 94 Opposition Spokesman on
Foreign and Commonwealth Affairs
1995 - 97 Opposition Spokesman on
Northern Ireland
1997 - 98 Parliamentary Secretary,
Northern Ireland Office
*Constituency Office* . . . . 24 Cleddans Crescent, Hardgate,
Clydebank, G81 5NW
Tel & Fax: (01389) 873195
E-mail: worthingtont@parliament.uk
Secretary – Ms Joanne McInally
Researcher – Ms Angela Worthington
*Parliamentary Interests* . Overseas Development; Foreign Affairs
*Leisure Interests* . . . . . . Gardening; Reading

**Wray, Jimmy**. . . . . . Glasgow Baillieston
**Labour** . . . . . . . . . . Majority 9,839 over SNP
*Born*. . . . . . . . . . . . . . 28th April 1938 in Glasgow
*Educated* . . . . . . . . . . St Bonaventure Secondary School, Glasgow
*Elected*. . . . . . . . . . . . 1987 MP for Glasgow Provan, then (1997)
MP for Glasgow Baillieston
*Commons Office* . . . . . . Tel: (020) 7219 4606 Fax: (020) 7219 2008
E-mail: wrayj@parliament.uk
*Parliamentary Interests* . Housing; Drug Abuse; Boxing;
Child Protection
*Leisure Interests* . . . . . . Boxing

**Wright, Anthony D** Great Yarmouth
**Labour** . . . . . . . . . . Majority 4,564 over Con
*Born*. . . . . . . . . . . . . . 12th August 1954 in Great Yarmouth
*Educated* . . . . . . . . . . Hospital Secondary Modern School
*Elected*. . . . . . . . . . . . 1997 MP for Great Yarmouth
*Office Held* . . . . . . . . . 1995 - 97 Leader, Great Yarmouth Borough
Council
*Commons Office* . . . . . . Tel: (020) 7219 4832 Fax: (020) 7219 2304
E-mail: wrighta@parliament.uk
Web: http://www.anthonywright.labour.co.uk
Research Assistant – Mr Ian Woodcroft
Tel: (020) 7219 3447
E-mail: woodcrofti@parliament.uk
*Constituency Office* . . . . 21 Euston Road, Great Yarmouth, Norfolk,
NR30 1DZ
Tel: (01493) 332291 Fax: (01493) 332189
Secretary – Mrs Marilyn Higgleton
Caseworker – Mrs Joan Eggleston
Diary Secretary – Mrs Jackie Dixon
*Parliamentary Interests* . ME; Trade and Industry;
Foreign and Commonwealth Affairs
*Leisure Interests* . . . . . . Sport; Horse Racing

# MEMBERS OF THE HOUSE OF COMMONS

**Wright, David** .... Telford
**Labour** ........... Majority 8,383 over Con
*Born* ............... 22nd December 1966 in Telford
*Educated* .......... Wolverhampton Polytechnic
*Elected* ........... 2001 MP for Telford
*Commons Office* ..... Tel: (020) 7219 8331 Fax: (020) 7219 1979
  Mobile: 07866 102101
  Pager: 07626 409608
  E-mail: wrightda@parliament.uk
  Parliamentary Assistant – Ms Sally Grocott
  Tel: (020) 7219 8207
  E-mail: grocotts@parliament.uk
*Constituency Office* .... 35B High Street, Dawley, Telford,
  Shropshire, TF4 2EX
  Tel: (01952) 507747 Fax: (01952) 506064
  E-mail: contact@telford-clp.new.labour.org.uk
  Constituency Assistant – Mr Richard Overton
  Research Assistant – Mr Clive Elliott
*Parliamentary Interests* . Housing; Regeneration Matters
*Leisure Interests* ...... Watching Football; Local History

**Wright, Iain** ...... Hartlepool
**Labour** ........... Majority 2,033 over Lib Dem
*Elected* ............ 2004 MP for Hartlepool *(by-election)*

**Wright, Dr Tony** .. Cannock Chase
**Labour** ........... Majority 10,704 over Con
*Born* ............... 11th March 1948 in Leicester
*Educated* .......... Kettering Grammar School;
  London School of Economics;
  Harvard University, USA;
  Balliol College, Oxford
*Elected* ............ 1992 MP for Cannock and Burntwood, then
  (1997) Cannock Chase
*Office Held* ......... 1999 - Chairman, Public Administration
  Select Committee, House of Commons
*Commons Office* ..... Tel: (020) 7219 5583 Fax: (020) 7219 2665
  E-mail: wrightt@parliament.uk
  Web: http://www.tonywright.labour.co.uk
  Research Assistant – Ms Alice Ripley
*Constituency Office* .... 6a Hallcourt Crescent, Cannock,
  Staffordshire, WS11 0AB
  Tel: (01543) 467810 Fax: (01543) 467811
  Political Assistant – Mrs Susan Woodward

**Wyatt, Derek** ..... Sittingbourne and Sheppey
**Labour** ........... Majority 3,509 over Con
*Born* ............... 4th December 1949 in London
*Educated* .......... Westcliff County High School;
  Colchester Royal Grammar School;
  St Luke's College, Exeter; Open University;
  St Catherine's College, Oxford;
*Elected* ............ 1997 MP for Sittingbourne and Sheppey
*Commons Office* ..... Tel: (020) 7219 5238 Fax: (020) 7219 5520
  E-mail: wyattd@parliament.uk
  Web: http://www.derekwyattmp.co.uk
  Assistant – Mrs Anna Yallop
  E-mail: yallopa@parliament.uk
*Constituency Office* .... 5 London Road, Sittingbourne, Kent
  Tel: (01795) 477277
  E-mail: williamskj@parliament.uk

# Y

**Yeo, Tim** ......... Suffolk South
**Conservative** ....... Majority 5,081 over Lab
*Born* ............... 20th March 1945 in London
*Educated* .......... Charterhouse School;
  Emmanuel College, Cambridge
*Elected* ............ 1983 MP for Suffolk South
*Offices Held* ........ 1988 - 90 PPS to Douglas Hurd
  (Home Secretary and Foreign Secretary)
  1990 - 92 Parliamentary Secretary,
  Department of Environment
  1992 - 93 Parliamentary Secretary,
  Department of Health
  1993 - 94 Minister of State,
  Department of Environment
  1997 - 98 Opposition Spokesman on the
  Environment, Transport and the Regions
  1998 - 2001 Shadow Minister of Agriculture,
  Fisheries and Food
  2001 - 02 Shadow Secretary for Culture,
  Media and Sport Secretary
  2002 - 03 Shadow Secretary for Trade and
  Industry
  2003 - 04 Shadow Secretary for Health and
  Education
  2004 - Shadow Secretary for Environment
  and Transport
*Commons Office* ..... Tel: (020) 7219 6353 Fax: (020) 7219 4857
*Constituency Office* .... Pent House, 43 High Street, Hadleigh,
  Suffolk, IP7 5AB
  Tel: (01473) 823435
  E-mail: ssca@eidosnet.co.uk
  Agent – Mr Peter Burgoyne
*Leisure Interests* ...... Golf; Cricket

## MEMBERS OF THE HOUSE OF COMMONS

**Young, Rt Hon Sir George** Hampshire North West
**Conservative** . . . . . . . Majority 12,009 over Labour
*Born.* . . . . . . . . . . . . . 16th July 1941 in Oxford
*Educated* . . . . . . . . . . Eton College; Christ Church, Oxford;
Surrey University
*Elected.* . . . . . . . . . . . 1974 - 97 MP for Ealing Acton
1997 MP for Hampshire North West
*Offices Held* . . . . . . . . 1976 - 79 Opposition Whip
1979 - 81 Parliamentary Secretary,
Department of Health and Social Security
1981 - 86 Parliamentary Secretary,
Department of Environment
1990 Government Whip
(Comptroller of H M Household)
1990 - 94 Minister of State,
Department of Environment
1994 - 95 Financial Secretary to the Treasury
1995 - 97 Secretary of State for Transport
1997 - 98 Shadow Defence Secretary
1998 - 2000 Shadow Leader of the House and
Spokesman on Constitutional Affairs
2001 - Chairman, Standards and Privileges
Select Committee, House of Commons
*Commons Office* . . . . . Tel: (020) 7219 6665 Fax: (020) 7219 2566
E-mail: sirgeorge@sirgeorgeyoung.org.uk
Web: http://www.sirgeorgeyoung.org.uk
Private Secretary – Ms Camilla Young
E-mail: youngc@parliament.uk
*Constituency Office* . . . . 2 Church Close, Andover, Hampshire,
SP10 1DP
Tel: (01264) 401401 Fax: (01264) 391155
Constituency Secretary –
Mrs Lucinda Henzell-Thomas

**Younger-Ross, Richard** Teignbridge
**Liberal Democrat** . . . Majority 3,011 over Con
*Born.* . . . . . . . . . . . . . 19th January 1953 in Walton-on-Thames,
*Educated* . . . . . . . . . . Walton Secondary School;
Ewell Technical College
*Elected.* . . . . . . . . . . . 2001 MP for Teignbridge
*Office Held* . . . . . . . . . Liberal Democrat Spokesman on Local
Government and the Regions
*Constituency Office* . . . . 70 Queen Street, Newton Abbot, Devon,
TQ12 2ET
Tel: (01626) 202626 Fax: (01626) 202016
E-mail: yrossr@parliament.uk
Office Manager – Miss Sarah Jane Holliday
E-mail: hollidays@parliament.uk
Researcher – Mrs Jan Fitzpatrick
E-mail: fitzpatrickje@parliament.uk
Caseworker – Miss Georgina Watts
E-mail: wattsg@parliament.uk
Constituency Organiser – Miss Helen
Nicholson
Tel: (01626) 363127
E-mail: nicholsonh@parliament.uk
*Parliamentary Interests* . Early Years Learning; Renewable Energy
*Leisure Interests* . . . . . . Cooking; Gardening; Shellfish; Rowing

# MPs – CONSULTANCY/ADVISER POSITIONS

*Note: The following list is based on information supplied by MPs and is not necessarily exhaustive.*

| Member of Parliament | Company / Organisation |
| --- | --- |
| Beith, Rt Hon Alan | Bourne Leisure Group Ltd |
| Berry, Dr Roger | Communications Managers' Association |
| Cameron, David | Carlton Communications plc |
| Chidgey, David | National Federation of Market Traders |
| Cook, Frank | National Federation of Demolition Contractors |
| Cormack, Sir Patrick | Machinery Users' Association |
| Crausby, David | National Union of Labour and Socialist Clubs |
| Cummings, John | National Association of Councillors<br>National Association of Licensed House Managers |
| Davies, Quentin | Chartered Institute of Taxation |
| Evans, Nigel | Mansat Ltd<br>Newsmax.com |
| Foster, Rt Hon Derek | 3Ms |
| Garnier, Edward | British American Bison Breeders Association |
| Greenway, John | Institute of Insurance Brokers<br>Institute of Sales Promotion |
| Hague, Rt Hon William | JCB Group<br>Terrafirma Capital Partners |
| Howarth, George | William Hill |
| Iddon, Dr Brian | Royal Society of Chemistry |
| Illsley, Eric | Caravan Club |
| Key, Robert | Certis Ltd |
| Lamb, Norman | Steeles (Solicitors) |
| Moore, Michael | Norfolk Charitable Trust |
| Murphy, Jim | Scottish Professional Footballers Association |
| Murrison, Dr Andrew | Royal Society of Chemistry |
| O'Brien, Stephen | Institute of Chartered Secretaries and Administrators |
| Palmer, Dr Nick | Novartis |
| Purchase, Ken | British Health Care Association |
| Robertson, Hugh | Schroder Investment Management Ltd |
| Russell, Bob | Royal British Legion |
| Smith, Rt Hon Chris | Walt Disney Company |
| Starkey, Dr Phyllis | Local Government Information Unit<br>Royal College of Midwives<br>Royal College of Nursing |
| Taylor, Ian | Broadband Stakeholders Group |
| Taylor, Sir Teddy | L.A.W. Mining<br>Port of Tilbury Police |
| Widdecombe, Rt Hon Ann | Prison Fellowship |
| Wilkinson, John | London Green Belt Society |

# M P s  –  D I R E C T O R S H I P S

*Note: The following list is based on information supplied by MPs and is not necessarily exhaustive.*

| Member of Parliament | Constituency | Company / Organisation |
|---|---|---|
| Austin, John | Erith and Thamesmead | British Syria Society<br>Crossness Engines' Trust<br>London Marathon Charitable Trust Ltd (unpaid) |
| Barker, Gregory | Bexhill and Battle | Flare View Ltd |
| Baldry, Tony | Banbury | Angel Gate Ltd<br>3DM Europe Ltd<br>Invicta Africa Ltd<br>MMTV plc<br>Transense Technologies plc |
| Baron, John | Billericay | Barons Property Services Ltd<br>JT Investments Ltd |
| Barrett, John | Edinburgh West | ABC Productions |
| Beggs, Roy | Antrim East | Larne Enterprise Development Company (unpaid) |
| Beith, Rt Hon Alan | Berwick-upon-Tweed | Historic Chapels Trust (Chairman, unpaid) |
| Bell, Sir Stuart | Middlesbrough | Spenview Ltd<br>Spenview Communications Ltd<br>Spenview Publications Ltd |
| Bottomley, Rt Hon Virginia | Surrey South West | AKZO Nobel NV<br>Ditchley Foundation<br>Odgers Ray Berndtson Exec Search |
| Burnside, David | Antrim South | DB Associates Ltd<br>NCH Ltd |
| Calton, Patsy | Cheadle | Stockport Cerebral Palsy Society (unpaid) |
| Cameron, David | Witney | Urbium plc |
| Campbell, Anne | Cambridge | Opportunity Links |
| Carmichael, Alistair | Orkney and Shetland | Solicitors Will Aid Scotland (unpaid) |
| Clark, Paul | Gillingham | Groundwork Medway/Swale (unpaid)<br>Thames Gateway Kent Partnership (unpaid) |
| Clarke, Rt Hon Kenneth | Rushcliffe | Alliance Unichem plc (Deputy Chairman)<br>British American Racing Holdings Ltd (Chairman)<br>Foreign and Colonial Investment Trust<br>Independent News and Media<br>Savoy Asset Management plc (Chairman) |
| Clarke, Tony | Northampton South | Northampton Town Football Club |
| Cook, Frank | Stockton North | Lucy Faithful Foundation (unpaid) |
| Corston, Rt Hon Jean | Bristol East | ASDAN (Trustee)<br>Tribune Publications Ltd (unpaid) |
| Cotter, Brian | Weston-super-Mare | The Genesis Foundation Ltd (unpaid) |
| Cunningham, Dr Jack | Copeland | Anderson Macgraw<br>Brinkburn Associates<br>Sovereign Strategy Ltd |
| Curtis-Thomas, Claire | Crosby | Plaza Community Cinema<br>Severn Bridges Trust<br>Venus House |

# MPs – DIRECTORSHIPS

| Member of Parliament | Constituency | Company / Organisation |
|---|---|---|
| Davies, Quentin | Grantham and Stamford | Lloyds of London<br>Vinci plc<br>Vinci SA |
| Dhanda, Parmjit | Gloucester | Gloucester City Football Club |
| Donohoe, Brian | Cunninghame South | 'Thrive' |
| Dorrell, Rt Hon Stephen | Charnwood | Faithful Group Ltd |
| Evans, Nigel | Ribble Valley | Small Business Bureau (unpaid) |
| Fabricant, Michael | Lichfield | Engineering and Technology Board (unpaid) |
| Flight, Howard | Arundel and South Downs | ACM European Enhanced Income Fund (Chairman)<br>Avebury Asset Management (Chairman)<br>Durlacher plc<br>Investec Asset Management (Vice-Chairman) |
| Foster, Rt Hon Derek | Bishop Auckland | Auckland Castle (unpaid)<br>Bishop Auckland Development Co Ltd (Chairman, unpaid)<br>E-Learning Foundation (unpaid)<br>North Regional Electronic Economy Programme<br>(Chairman, unpaid)<br>North Regional Information Society Initiative (Chairman, unpaid)<br>Northern Informatics (unpaid)<br>Pioneering Care Partnership (unpaid)<br>South West Durham Engineering Training Ltd (President) |
| Foulkes, Rt Hon George | Carrick, Cumnock and Doon Valley | Heart of Midlothian FC plc (Chairman) |
| Galloway, George | Glasgow Kelvin | Finjan Ltd |
| Garnier, Edward | Marlborough | Great Britain-China Group |
| George, Andrew | St Ives (Cornwall) | Trelya |
| Gibson, Dr Ian | Norwich North | Institute of Food Research |
| Greenway, John | Ryedale | Smart & Cook Ltd<br>Stewart Title UK Ltd |
| Griffiths, Jane | Reading East | Ectopic Pregnancy Trust (Chair, unpaid)<br>South East Museums, Libraries and Archives Council (unpaid) |
| Gummer, Rt Hon John | Suffolk Coastal | Association of Independent Financial Advisers (Chairman)<br>Catholic Herald<br>Kidde plc<br>Sancroft Group (Chairman)<br>Valpak (Chairman)<br>Veolia UK (Chairman) |
| Hague, Rt Hon William | Richmond (Yorkshire) | AES Engineering, Rotherham |
| Hamilton, David | Midlothian | Cre8te, Midlothian Enterprise Trust |
| Hawkins, Nick | Surrey Heath | Revelfree Ltd |
| Hendry, Charles | Wealden | IncrediBull Ideas Ltd |
| Hesford, Stephen | Wirral West | Arch Initiatives (unpaid)<br>UKPHA (unpaid) |
| Horam, John | Orpington | CRU International Ltd<br>CRU Publishing Ltd |
| Iddon, Dr Brian | Bolton South East | Bolton Technical Innovation Centre Ltd (unpaid) |

# MPs – DIRECTORSHIPS

| Member of Parliament | Constituency | Company / Organisation |
|---|---|---|
| Illsley, Eric | Barnsley Central | Cambridge Online Learning Ltd |
| Jackson, Robert | Wantage | CNIM Escalators UK (Chairman) <br> Martin Engineering Systems (Chairman) |
| Ladyman, Dr Stephen | Thanet South | Kent Innovation Centre (unpaid) <br> Sandwich Sports and Leisure Centre Trust (unpaid) |
| Lepper, David | Brighton Pavilion | ARDIS (unpaid) |
| Lewis, Dr Julian | New Forest East | Policy Research Associates Ltd (unpaid) <br> Policy Research Publications Ltd (unpaid) |
| Lilley, Rt Hon Peter | Hitchin and Harpenden | Claverhouse Investment Trust plc <br> i-documentsystems Group plc |
| Lord, Sir Michael | Suffolk Central and Ipswich North | Palmer Family Trust |
| Love, Andrew | Edmonton | Industrial Common Ownership Finance Ltd (Trustee) |
| McKechin, Ann | Glasgow Maryhill | Mercy Corps Scotland <br> World Development Movement |
| McWilliam, John | Blaydon | Eurim (unpaid) |
| Marsden, Paul | Shrewsbury and Atcham | Shrewsbury Citizens Advice Bureau (unpaid) |
| Maude, Rt Hon Francis | Horsham | Benfield Group plc <br> Incepta Group plc (Chairman) <br> Jubilee Investment Trust plc (Chairman) <br> Prestbury Holdings plc (Chairman) <br> The Spectator (1928) Ltd |
| Mawhinney, Rt Hon Sir Brian | Cambridgeshire North West | Alexander and Alexander Pension Trustees (Chairman) <br> Andras House Ltd (Chairman) <br> The Football League Ltd (Chairman) |
| Meale, Alan | Mansfield | Mansfield Town Football Club Ltd (unpaid) |
| Moffatt, Laura | Crawley | Furni-Aid |
| Moonie, Dr Lewis | Kirkcaldy | AEA Technology plc <br> Mining (Scotland) Ltd |
| Moore, Michael | Tweeddale, Ettrick and Lauderdale | Westminster Foundation for Democracy |
| Norman, Archie | Tunbridge Wells | Energis (Chairman) |
| O'Brien, Stephen | Eddisbury | City of London Sinfonia |
| Oaten, Mark | Winchester | Oasis Radio <br> Westminster Communications |
| Owen, Albert | Ynys Mon | Digartref Ynys Mon (unpaid) |
| Page, Richard | Hertfordshire South West | Page Holdings Ltd |
| Pollard, Kerry | St Albans | Birnbeck Housing Association <br> Cherry Tree Housing Association <br> The Genesis Foundation <br> Open Door Trust <br> Key Promotions, St Albans <br> St Albans into the 21st Century |
| Randall, John | Uxbridge | Randalls of Uxbridge Ltd |
| Robinson, Geoffrey | Coventry North West | Coventry FCC (Holdings) Ltd <br> New Statesman Ltd <br> Smart Technology Ltd <br> Torgram Developments |

## M P s  –  D I R E C T O R S H I P S

| Member of Parliament | Constituency | Company / Organisation |
| --- | --- | --- |
| Ruane, Chris | Vale of Clwyd | Rhyl Football Club<br>Rhyl Foyer Project |
| Ryan, Joan | Enfield North | Riders for Health (Trustee) |
| Sanders, Adrian | Torbay | Southern Association of Voluntary Action Groups for Europe (unpaid) |
| Sheerman, Barry | Huddersfield | National Children's Centre<br>Networking for Industry (Chairman)<br>Urban Mines (Chairman) |
| Shepherd, Richard | Aldridge-Brownhills | Partridges of Sloane Street Ltd<br>Shepherds Foods (London) Ltd |
| Smith, Rt Hon Chris | Islington South and Finsbury | Donmar Warehouse (Chairman)<br>Royal National Theatre (unpaid)<br>The Wordsworth Trust (Chairman, unpaid) |
| Smyth, Rev Martin | Belfast South | Belfast Bible College (unpaid)<br>Ormeau Enterprises (unpaid)<br>Presbyterian Widows of Ministers Fund (unpaid) |
| Spelman, Caroline | Meriden | Spelman, Cormack and Associates |
| Spicer, Sir Michael | Worcestershire West | Association of Electricity Producers (President) |
| Spring, Richard | West Suffolk | British Syrian Society<br>Small Business Bureau (unpaid) |
| Taylor, Ian | Esher and Walton | Fentiman Consultants Ltd<br>Interregnum plc<br>Next Fifteen Communications Group plc<br>Radioscope Ltd<br>Screen plc<br>Speed-trap Ltd |
| Taylor, Sir Teddy | Rochford and Southend East | Shepherd Foods Ltd |
| Thurso, John | Caithness, Sutherland and Easter Ross | International Wine and Spirit Competition Ltd (Chairman)<br>Millennium and Copthorne Hotels plc (Deputy Chairman) |
| Turner, Dennis | Wolverhampton South East | Springvale Cooperative Ltd (unpaid)<br>Springvale Enterprise Ltd (unpaid) |
| Viggers, Peter | Gosport | CETO plc<br>Lloyd's Pension Fund (Chairman) |
| Walter, Robert | Dorset North | Silver Apex Films Ltd |
| Whitehead, Dr Alan | Southampton Test | Southampton Environment Centre |
| Winterton, Sir Nicholas | Macclesfield | Emerson International (non-executive)<br>MSB Ltd (non-executive) |
| Woodward, Shaun | St Helens South | Childline (Trustee) |
| Worthington, Tony | Clydebank and Milngavie | Clydebank Rebuilt (Chairman, unpaid)<br>Parliamentarians Network on World Bank (unpaid) |

# MPs – PROFESSIONAL ASSOCIATION MEMBERSHIP

*Note: The following list is based on information supplied by MPs and is not necessarily exhaustive.*

## Member of Parliament     Association

Baird, Vera . . . . . . . . . . . . . . . . . . . Council of Justice
Criminal Bar Association

Baldry, Tony . . . . . . . . . . . . . . . . . Chartered Institute of Arbitrators (Fellow)

Baron, John . . . . . . . . . . . . . . . . . . Securities Institute

Begg, Anne . . . . . . . . . . . . . . . . . . General Teaching Council for Scotland

Beresford, Sir Paul. . . . . . . . . . . . . British Dental Association

Blears, Hazel . . . . . . . . . . . . . . . . . Law Society

Breed, Colin . . . . . . . . . . . . . . . . . Chartered Institute of Bankers (Associate Member)
General Medical Council (Lay Member)

Browne, Desmond . . . . . . . . . . . . . Faculty of Advocates

Burnside, David. . . . . . . . . . . . . . . Institute of Directors

Campbell, Anne. . . . . . . . . . . . . . . Royal Society of Arts (Fellow)
Royal Statistical Society (Fellow)

Carmichael, Alistair. . . . . . . . . . . . Law Society of Scotland

Chidgey, David . . . . . . . . . . . . . . . Chartered Institute of Transport
Institution of Civil Engineers
Royal Aeronautical Society

Clifton-Brown, Geoffrey . . . . . . . . . Royal Institute of Chartered Surveyors

Connarty, Michael . . . . . . . . . . . . . General Teaching Council for Scotland

Conway, Derek. . . . . . . . . . . . . . . . Institute of Directors

Curtis-Thomas, Claire . . . . . . . . . . . Engineering Council
City and Guilds Institute
Institute of Electrical Engineers
Institute of Mechanical Engineering

Dalyell, Tam . . . . . . . . . . . . . . . . . Royal Society of Edinburgh

Dismore, Andrew. . . . . . . . . . . . . . Law Society

Djanogly, Jonathan. . . . . . . . . . . . . Law Society

Drown, Julia . . . . . . . . . . . . . . . . . Chartered Institute of Public Finance and Accountancy

Ewing, Annabelle. . . . . . . . . . . . . . Law Society of Scotland

Fabricant, Michael. . . . . . . . . . . . . Engineering and Technology Board
Institute of Electrical Engineers (Fellow)

Follett, Barbara . . . . . . . . . . . . . . . Royal Society of Arts (Fellow)

Foster, Rt Hon Derek. . . . . . . . . . . Institution of Lighting Engineers

Foster, Don . . . . . . . . . . . . . . . . . . Institute of Physics

# MPs – PROFESSIONAL ASSOCIATION MEMBERSHIP

## Member of Parliament    Association

Foster, Michael John . . . . . . . . . . . . Chartered Institute of Management Accountants

Francis, Dr Hywel . . . . . . . . . . . . . . Royal Society of Arts (Fellow)

Gardiner, Barry . . . . . . . . . . . . . . . . Chartered Insurance Institute

George, Rt Hon Bruce . . . . . . . . . . . Institute of Security Management
International Institute of Security
International Institute for Strategic Studies

Gibb, Nick. . . . . . . . . . . . . . . . . . . . Institute of Chartered Accountants in England and Wales (Fellow)

Gidley, Sandra. . . . . . . . . . . . . . . . . Royal Pharmaceutical Association of Great Britain

Hawkins, Nick. . . . . . . . . . . . . . . . . Bar Council

Hendrick, Mark . . . . . . . . . . . . . . . . Institute of Electrical Engineers

Hoban, Mark . . . . . . . . . . . . . . . . . . Fruiterers Company
Institute of Chartered Accountants of England and Wales (Associate)
Society of Maritime Industries

Hurst, Alan . . . . . . . . . . . . . . . . . . . Law Society

Iddon, Dr Brian . . . . . . . . . . . . . . . . Royal Society of Chemistry (Fellow)

Jenkin, Hon Bernard . . . . . . . . . . . . Royal United Service Institution

Jones, Martyn . . . . . . . . . . . . . . . . . Institute of Biology

Kidney, David . . . . . . . . . . . . . . . . . Law Society

King, Andy . . . . . . . . . . . . . . . . . . . British Association of Social Workers

Knight, Rt Hon Greg . . . . . . . . . . . . Law Society

Kumar, Dr Ashok. . . . . . . . . . . . . . . Institute of Energy
Institution of Chemical Engineers (Fellow)

Lamb, Norman. . . . . . . . . . . . . . . . . Law Society

Loughton, Tim . . . . . . . . . . . . . . . . . Securities Institute

Love, Andrew . . . . . . . . . . . . . . . . . Chartered Institute of Secretaries (Fellow)

Lucas, Ian . . . . . . . . . . . . . . . . . . . . Law Society

Luff, Peter . . . . . . . . . . . . . . . . . . . . Institute of Public Relations (Fellow)

McGrady, Eddie. . . . . . . . . . . . . . . . Chartered Accountants of Northern Ireland

McIntosh, Anne . . . . . . . . . . . . . . . . Faculty of Advocates

McKechin, Ann . . . . . . . . . . . . . . . . Law Society of Scotland

McWalter, Tony. . . . . . . . . . . . . . . . British Philosophical Association

Marris, Robert . . . . . . . . . . . . . . . . . Law Society

Marsden, Paul . . . . . . . . . . . . . . . . . Institute of Directors
Institute of Management

# MPs – PROFESSIONAL ASSOCIATION MEMBERSHIP

## Member of Parliament    Association

Michael, Rt Hon Alun . . . . . . . . . . . Royal Society of Arts (Fellow)

Moore, Michael . . . . . . . . . . . . . . . Institute of Chartered Accounts of Scotland

Naysmith, Dr Doug . . . . . . . . . . . . . Royal Society of Medicine (Fellow)

O'Brien, Stephen . . . . . . . . . . . . . . Institute of Chartered Secretaries and Administrators (Fellow)
Law Society

Öpik, Lembit . . . . . . . . . . . . . . . . . Royal Aeronautical Society (Fellow)

Perham, Linda . . . . . . . . . . . . . . . . Chartered Institute of Library and Information Professionals

Prisk, Mark . . . . . . . . . . . . . . . . . . Royal Institution of Chartered Surveyors

Quinn, Laurie . . . . . . . . . . . . . . . . Institute of Civil Engineers

Robertson, Hugh . . . . . . . . . . . . . . Royal Geographical Society (Fellow)

Roe, Dame Marion . . . . . . . . . . . . . Institute of Horticulture
Professional Business and Technical Management (Honorary Fellow)

Ruffley, David . . . . . . . . . . . . . . . . Law Society

Russell, Christine . . . . . . . . . . . . . . Library Association
Magistrates Association

Sawford, Phil . . . . . . . . . . . . . . . . . Institute of Personnel and Development

Sheerman, Barry . . . . . . . . . . . . . . Royal Geographical Society (Fellow)
Royal Society of Arts (Fellow)

Smith, Rt Hon Chris . . . . . . . . . . . . Royal Institute of British Architects (Honorary Fellow)

Starkey, Dr Phyllis . . . . . . . . . . . . . Biochemical Society

Stoate, Dr Howard . . . . . . . . . . . . . British Medical Association
Royal College of General Practitioners (Fellow)

Taylor, David . . . . . . . . . . . . . . . . . Chartered Institute of Public Finance and Accountancy
Magistrates Association

Taylor, Ian . . . . . . . . . . . . . . . . . . . UK Society of Investment Professionals (Associate)
Worshipful Company of Information Technologists (Freeman)

Taylor, John . . . . . . . . . . . . . . . . . . The Law Society

Taylor, Dr Richard . . . . . . . . . . . . . British Medical Association
Royal Colleges of Physicians (Fellow)

Thomas, Gareth . . . . . . . . . . . . . . . Chartered Insurance Institute (Associate)

Thurso, John . . . . . . . . . . . . . . . . . Hotel and Catering International Management Association (Fellow)
Tourism Society (Fellow)

Todd, Mark . . . . . . . . . . . . . . . . . . Royal Society of Arts and Manufacture

Tonge, Dr Jenny . . . . . . . . . . . . . . . British Medical Association
Faculty of Family Planning (Fellow)
Royal Institute of Public Health and Hygiene

# MPs – PROFESSIONAL ASSOCIATION MEMBERSHIP

## Member of Parliament    Association

Turner, Andrew . . . . . . . . . . . . . . . . . Royal Society of Arts (Fellow)

Tyler, Paul. . . . . . . . . . . . . . . . . . . . Institute of Public Relations

Viggers, Peter . . . . . . . . . . . . . . . . . Law Society

Waterson, Nigel . . . . . . . . . . . . . . . . Law Society

Weir, Michael . . . . . . . . . . . . . . . . . Law Society of Scotland

Widdecombe, Rt Hon Ann . . . . . . . . Society of Authors

Wilkinson, John. . . . . . . . . . . . . . . . . Royal Aeronautical Society (Companion)

Williams, Roger. . . . . . . . . . . . . . . . . Country Landowner's Association

Wishart, Peter . . . . . . . . . . . . . . . . . Performance Rights Society

Wright, David . . . . . . . . . . . . . . . . . Chartered Institute of Housing

## M P s  –  T R A D E   U N I O N   M E M B E R S H I P

# *AMICUS*

*35 King Street, Covent Garden, London, WC2E 8JG*
*Tel: (020) 7420 8900 Fax: (020) 7420 8998*
*Web: http://www.amicustheunion.org*

Ainsworth, Bob . . . . . . . . . . . . . . . . . . . . . Coventry North East
Armstrong, Rt Hon Hilary . . . . . . . . . . . . . . . Durham North West
Austin, John . . . . . . . . . . . . . . . . . . . . . Erith and Thamesmead
Barnes, Harry . . . . . . . . . . . . . . . . . . Derbyshire North East
Battle, Rt Hon John . . . . . . . . . . . . . . . . . . . . Leeds West
Benn, Rt Hon Hilary . . . . . . . . . . . . . . . . . . . Leeds Central
Berry, Dr Roger . . . . . . . . . . . . . . . . . . . . . . Kingswood
Bradley, Rt Hon Keith . . . . . . . . . . . . . Manchester Withington
Bradley, Peter . . . . . . . . . . . . . . . . . . . . . . The Wrekin
Bryant, Chris . . . . . . . . . . . . . . . . . . . . . . . . Rhondda
Campbell, Anne . . . . . . . . . . . . . . . . . . . . . . Cambridge
Caplin, Ivor . . . . . . . . . . . . . . . . . . . . . . . . . . Hove
Chapman, Ben . . . . . . . . . . . . . . . . . . . . . Wirral South
Clark, Paul . . . . . . . . . . . . . . . . . . . . . . . Gillingham
Clelland, David . . . . . . . . . . . . . . . . . . . . Tyne Bridge
Coaker, Vernon . . . . . . . . . . . . . . . . . . . . . . . Gedling
Coleman, Iain . . . . . . . . . . . . . . Hammersmith and Fulham
Cook, Frank . . . . . . . . . . . . . . . . . . . . . Stockton North
Cousins, Jim . . . . . . . . . . . . . Newcastle-upon-Tyne Central
Crausby, David . . . . . . . . . . . . . . . . . . Bolton North East
Cunningham, Jim . . . . . . . . . . . . . . . . . . Coventry South
Cunningham, Tony . . . . . . . . . . . . . . . . . . . Workington
Curtis-Thomas, Claire . . . . . . . . . . . . . . . . . . . . Crosby
David, Wayne . . . . . . . . . . . . . . . . . . . . . . Caerphilly
Davidson, Ian . . . . . . . . . . . . . . . . . . . Glasgow Pollok
Davies, Rt Hon Denzil . . . . . . . . . . . . . . . . . . . Llanelli
Denham, Rt Hon John . . . . . . . . . . . Southampton Itchen
Dowd, Jim . . . . . . . . . . . . . . . . . . . . . . Lewisham West
Etherington, Bill . . . . . . . . . . . . . . . . . . Sunderland North
Farrelly, Paul . . . . . . . . . . . . . . . Newcastle-under-Lyme
Follett, Barbara . . . . . . . . . . . . . . . . . . . . . Stevenage
Gardiner, Barry . . . . . . . . . . . . . . . . . . . . . Brent North
Gibson, Dr Ian . . . . . . . . . . . . . . . . . . . . . Norwich North
Hanson, David . . . . . . . . . . . . . . . . . . . . . . . . Delyn
Hewitt, Rt Hon Patricia . . . . . . . . . . . . . . . Leicester West
Hood, Jimmy . . . . . . . . . . . . . . . . . . . . . . Clydesdale
Hope, Philip . . . . . . . . . . . . . . . . . . . . . . . . . Corby
Howarth, George . . . . . . . . . Knowsley North and Sefton East
Hoyle, Lindsay . . . . . . . . . . . . . . . . . . . . . . . Chorley
Illsley, Eric . . . . . . . . . . . . . . . . . . . . Barnsley Central
Jones, Dr Lynne . . . . . . . . . . . . . . . Birmingham Selly Oak
Jowell, Rt Hon Tessa . . . . . . . . . Dulwich and West Norwood
Kelly, Ruth . . . . . . . . . . . . . . . . . . . . . . . Bolton West
Kemp, Fraser . . . . . . . . . . . Houghton and Washington East
Khabra, Piara Singh . . . . . . . . . . . . . . . . Ealing Southall
Kidney, David . . . . . . . . . . . . . . . . . . . . . . . Stafford
Knight, Jim . . . . . . . . . . . . . . . . . . . . . . Dorset South
Kumar, Dr Ashok . . . . . . . Middlesbrough South and Cleveland East
Lammy, David . . . . . . . . . . . . . . . . . . . . . Tottenham
Lewis, Ivan . . . . . . . . . . . . . . . . . . . . . . Bury South
Lucas, Ian . . . . . . . . . . . . . . . . . . . . . . . . Wrexham
McCabe, Stephen . . . . . . . . . . . . . . Birmingham Hall Green
McKenna, Rosemary . . . . . . . . . . . Cumbernauld and Kilsyth
McCafferty, Christine . . . . . . . . . . . . . . . . Calder Valley
Martin, Rt Hon Michael . . . . . . . . . . . . Glasgow Springburn
Meale, Alan . . . . . . . . . . . . . . . . . . . . . . . Mansfield
Milburn, Rt Hon Alan . . . . . . . . . . . . . . . . . Darlington

Miller, Andrew . . . . . . . . . . . . . . . . . . Ellesmere Port and Neston
Moonie, Dr Lewis . . . . . . . . . . . . . . . . . . . . . Kirkcaldy
Mullin, Chris . . . . . . . . . . . . . . . . . . . Sunderland South
Olner, Bill . . . . . . . . . . . . . . . . . . . . . . . Nuneaton
Palmer, Dr Nick . . . . . . . . . . . . . . . . . . . . . Broxtowe
Plaskitt, James . . . . . . . . . . . . . . Warwick and Leamington
Pollard, Kerry . . . . . . . . . . . . . . . . . . . . . . St Albans
Purnell, James . . . . . . . . . . . . . . . . Stalybridge and Hyde
Rammell, Bill . . . . . . . . . . . . . . . . . . . . . . . . Harlow
Rapson, Syd . . . . . . . . . . . . . . . . . . . . Portsmouth North
Ross, Ernie . . . . . . . . . . . . . . . . . . . . . . Dundee West
Ryan, Joan . . . . . . . . . . . . . . . . . . . . . . Enfield North
Sheerman, Barry . . . . . . . . . . . . . . . . . . . Huddersfield
Simon, Siôn . . . . . . . . . . . . . . . . . Birmingham Erdington
Smith, Rt Hon Chris . . . . . . . . . . . Islington South and Finsbury
Smith, John . . . . . . . . . . . . . . . . . . . Vale of Glamorgan
Southworth, Helen . . . . . . . . . . . . . . . . Warrington South
Starkey, Dr Phyllis . . . . . . . . . Milton Keynes South West
Stinchcombe, Paul . . . . . . . . . . . . . . . . . Wellingborough
Stoate, Dr Howard . . . . . . . . . . . . . . . . . . . . . Dartford
Stringer, Graham . . . . . . . . . . . . . . Manchester Blackley
Stuart, Gisela . . . . . . . . . . . . . . Birmingham Edgbaston
Thomas, Gareth . . . . . . . . . . . . . . . . . . . Clwyd West
Thomas, Gareth R . . . . . . . . . . . . . . . . . . Harrow West
Timms, Stephen . . . . . . . . . . . . . . . . . . . . East Ham
Todd, Mark . . . . . . . . . . . . . . . . . . . Derbyshire South
Turner, Dr Desmond . . . . . . . . . . . . . . Brighton Kemptown
Turner, Neil . . . . . . . . . . . . . . . . . . . . . . . . . Wigan
Twigg, Stephen . . . . . . . . . . . . . . . . . Enfield Southgate
Tynan, Bill . . . . . . . . . . . . . . . . . . . . . Hamilton South
Vis, Dr Rudi . . . . . . . . . . Finchley and Golders Green
Wareing, Robert . . . . . . . . . . . . . . . Liverpool West Derby
Watson, Tom . . . . . . . . . . . . . . . . . West Bromwich East
Watts, Dave . . . . . . . . . . . . . . . . . . . . . St Helens North
White, Brian . . . . . . . . . . . . . . . . Milton Keynes North East
Woodward, Shaun . . . . . . . . . . . . . . . . . St Helens South
Wright, Anthony D . . . . . . . . . . . . . . . . . Great Yarmouth

# *Association of Teachers and Lecturers*

*7 Northumberland Street, London, WC2N 5RD*
*Tel: (020) 7930 6441  Fax: (020) 7930 1359*
*E-mail: info@atl.org.uk  Web: http://www.askatl.org.uk*

Key, Robert . . . . . . . . . . . . . . . . . . . . . . . . Salisbury
O'Hara, Eddie . . . . . . . . . . . . . . . . . . . Knowsley South

# *Association of University Teachers (AUT)*

*25-31 Tavistock Place, London, WC1H 9UT*
*Tel: (020) 7670 9700 Fax: (020) 7670 9799*
*E-mail: hq@aut.org.uk  Web: http://www.aut.org.uk*

Cranston, Ross . . . . . . . . . . . . . . . . . . . . . Dudley North
Iddon, Dr Brian . . . . . . . . . . . . . . . . . Bolton South East
Mawhinney, Rt Hon Sir Brian . . . . . . . . . Cambridgeshire North West
Naysmith, Dr Doug . . . . . . . . . . . . . . . Bristol North West
Sheerman, Barry . . . . . . . . . . . . . . . . . . . Huddersfield

# M P s  –  T R A D E   U N I O N   M E M B E R S H I P

## Broadcasting, Entertainment, Cinematograph and Theatre Union (BECTU)
*373-377 Clapham Road, London, SW9 9BT*
*Tel: (020) 7346 0900 Fax: (020) 7346 0901*
*E-mail: info@bectu.org.uk  Web: http://www.bectu.org.uk*

Beckett, Rt Hon Margaret . . . . . . . . . . . . . . . . . . . . . Derby South

## Communication Workers Union (CWU)
*CWU House, 150 The Broadway, London, SW19 1RX*
*Tel: (020) 8971 7200 Fax (020) 7971 7300*
*E-mail: info@cwu.org Web: http://www.cwu.org*

Clarke, Tony. . . . . . . . . . . . . . . . . . . . . . . . . . . . Northampton South
Johnson, Rt Hon Alan. . . . . . . . . . . . . . . . . . . Hull West and Hessle
Laxton, Bob . . . . . . . . . . . . . . . . . . . . . . . . . . . . . Derby North
McWilliam, John. . . . . . . . . . . . . . . . . . . . . . . . . . . . Blaydon
Smith, Geraldine . . . . . . . . . . . . . . . . . . Morecombe and Lunesdale

## CONNECT
*30 St Georges Road, Wimbledon, London, SW19 4BD*
*Tel: (020) 8971 6000 Fax: (020) 8971 6002*
*E-mail: union@connectuk.org  Web: http://www.connectuk.org*

Dhanda, Parmjit . . . . . . . . . . . . . . . . . . . . . . . . . . . Gloucester
Mole, Chris . . . . . . . . . . . . . . . . . . . . . . . . . . . . . . . . Ipswich
Robertson, John . . . . . . . . . . . . . . . . . . . . . . Glasgow Anniesland

## Educational Institute of Scotland (EIS)
*46 Moray Place, Edinburgh, EH3 6BH*
*Tel: (0131) 225 3155 Fax: (0131) 220 3151*
*E-mail: enquiries@eis.org.uk  Web: http://www.eis.org.uk*

Begg, Anne . . . . . . . . . . . . . . . . . . . . . . . . . . . Aberdeen South
Connarty, Michael . . . . . . . . . . . . . . . . . . . . . . . . Falkirk, East
Dalyell, Tam . . . . . . . . . . . . . . . . . . . . . . . . . . . . Linlithgow
Luke, Iain . . . . . . . . . . . . . . . . . . . . . . . . . . . . Dundee East
Savidge, Malcolm . . . . . . . . . . . . . . . . . . . . . . Aberdeen North

## Fire Brigades Union (FBU)
*Bradley House, 68 Coombe Road, Kingston-upon-Thames,*
*Surrey, KT2 7AE*
*Tel: (020) 8541 1765 Fax: (020) 8546 5187*
*E-mail: office@fbu.org.uk  Web: http://www.fbu.org.uk*

Fitzpatrick, Jim. . . . . . . . . . . . . . . . . . . . Poplar and Canning Town

## General, Municipal and Boilermakers' Union (GMB)
*22-24 Worple Road, London, SW19 4DD*
*Tel: (020) 8947 3131  Fax: (020) 8944 6552*
*E-mail: kevin.curran@gmb.org.uk  Web: http://www.gmb.org.uk*

Bailey, Adrian . . . . . . . . . . . . . . . . . . . . . . . . . West Bromwich West
Beard, Nigel . . . . . . . . . . . . . . . . . . . Bexleyheath and Crayford
Bell, Sir Stuart . . . . . . . . . . . . . . . . . . . . . . . . . . . . Middlesbrough
Benn, Rt Hon Hilary. . . . . . . . . . . . . . . . . . . . . . . . Leeds Central
Blackman, Liz. . . . . . . . . . . . . . . . . . . . . . . . . . . . . . Erewash
Blizzard, Bob. . . . . . . . . . . . . . . . . . . . . . . . . . . . . . Waveney
Boateng, Rt Hon Paul . . . . . . . . . . . . . . . . . . . . . . Brent South
Bradley, Peter . . . . . . . . . . . . . . . . . . . . . . . . . . . . The Wrekin
Brown, Rt Hon Nick . . . . . . Newcastle-upon-Tyne East and Wallsend
Buck, Karen . . . . . . . . . . . . . . Regent's Park and Kensington North
Cairns, David. . . . . . . . . . . . . . . . . . . . Greenock and Inverclyde
Casale, Roger. . . . . . . . . . . . . . . . . . . . . . . . . . . . Wimbledon
Caton, Martin . . . . . . . . . . . . . . . . . . . . . . . . . . . . . . . Gower
Cawsey, Ian. . . . . . . . . . . . . . . . . . . . . . . . . . Brigg and Goole
Clarke, Rt Hon Tom . . . . . . . . . . . . . . . . Coatbridge and Chryston
Clarke, Tony. . . . . . . . . . . . . . . . . . . . . . . . . . . Northampton South
Colman, Tony . . . . . . . . . . . . . . . . . . . . . . . . . . . . . . Putney
Cranston, Ross . . . . . . . . . . . . . . . . . . . . . . . . . . Dudley North
Cunningham, Rt Hon Dr Jack . . . . . . . . . . . . . . . . . . . . Copeland
Davies, Geraint. . . . . . . . . . . . . . . . . . . . . . . Croydon Central
Dean, Janet. . . . . . . . . . . . . . . . . . . . . . . . . . . . . . . . Burton
Dismore, Andrew . . . . . . . . . . . . . . . . . . . . . . . . . . . . Hendon
Doran, Frank . . . . . . . . . . . . . . . . . . . . . . . . . Aberdeen Central
Dowd, Jim . . . . . . . . . . . . . . . . . . . . . . . . . . . . Lewisham West
Eagle, Maria . . . . . . . . . . . . . . . . . . . . . . . Liverpool Garston
Flint, Caroline . . . . . . . . . . . . . . . . . . . . . . . . . . . Don Valley
Foster, Michael Jabez . . . . . . . . . . . . . . . . . . . Hastings and Rye
Foster, Michael John. . . . . . . . . . . . . . . . . . . . . . . . Worcester
Foulkes, Rt Hon George . . . . . . . Carrick, Cumnock and Doon Valley
Gardiner, Barry . . . . . . . . . . . . . . . . . . . . . . . . . . Brent North
George, Rt Hon Bruce. . . . . . . . . . . . . . . . . . . . Walsall South
Gerrard, Neil. . . . . . . . . . . . . . . . . . . . . . . . . . . Walthamstow
Godsiff, Roger. . . . . . . . . . Birmingham Sparkbrook and Small Heath
Grogan, John . . . . . . . . . . . . . . . . . . . . . . . . . . . . . . . Selby
Hain, Rt Hon Peter. . . . . . . . . . . . . . . . . . . . . . . . . . . . Neath
Heal, Sylvia . . . . . . . . . . . . . . . . . Halesowen and Rowley Regis
Healey, John . . . . . . . . . . . . . . . . . . . . . . . . . . . . Wentworth
Henderson, Douglas. . . . . . . . . . . . . . Newcastle-upon-Tyne North

# MPs – TRADE UNION MEMBERSHIP

## (GMB Continued)

Hendrick, Mark . . . . . . . . . . . . . . . . . . . . . . . . . . . . . . . . . . . Preston
Heppell, John . . . . . . . . . . . . . . . . . . . . . . . . . . . . . Nottingham East
Hesford, Stephen . . . . . . . . . . . . . . . . . . . . . . . . . . . . Wirral West
Hoey, Kate . . . . . . . . . . . . . . . . . . . . . . . . . . . . . . . . . . . . . Vauxhall
Howarth, Rt Hon Alan . . . . . . . . . . . . . . . . . . . . . . Newport East
Hutton, Rt Hon John . . . . . . . . . . . . . . . . . . . Barrow and Furness
Irranca-Davies, Huw . . . . . . . . . . . . . . . . . . . . . . . . . . . Ogmore
Kaufman, Rt Hon Sir Gerald . . . . . . . . . . . Manchester Gorton
Keen, Ann . . . . . . . . . . . . . . . . . . . . . Brentford and Isleworth
Keen, Alan . . . . . . . . . . . . . . . . . . . . . . . Feltham and Heston
King, Oona . . . . . . . . . . . . . . . . . . . . . Bethnal Green and Bow
Leslie, Christopher . . . . . . . . . . . . . . . . . . . . . . . . . . . . . Shipley
Levitt, Tom . . . . . . . . . . . . . . . . . . . . . . . . . . . . . . . . . High Peak
Liddell, Rt Hon Helen . . . . . . . . . . . . . . . . . . Airdrie and Shotts
Linton, Martin . . . . . . . . . . . . . . . . . . . . . . . . . . . . . . Battersea
Luke, Iain . . . . . . . . . . . . . . . . . . . . . . . . . . . . . . . Dundee East
Mactaggart, Fiona . . . . . . . . . . . . . . . . . . . . . . . . . . . . . Slough
Mandelson, Rt Hon Peter . . . . . . . . . . . . . . . . . . . . Hartlepool
Marsden, Gordon . . . . . . . . . . . . . . . . . . . . . . . Blackpool South
Michael, Rt Hon Alun . . . . . . . . . . Cardiff South and Penarth
Martlew, Eric . . . . . . . . . . . . . . . . . . . . . . . . . . . . . . . Carlisle
Mitchell, Austin . . . . . . . . . . . . . . . . . . . . . . . . Great Grimsby
Morley, Elliott . . . . . . . . . . . . . . . . . . . . . . . . . . . . Scunthorpe
Morris, Rt Hon Estelle . . . . . . . . . . . . . . Birmingham Yardley
Mountford, Kali . . . . . . . . . . . . . . . . . . . . . . . . . . Colne Valley
Munn, Meg . . . . . . . . . . . . . . . . . . . . . . . . . . . Sheffield Heeley
Murphy, Jim . . . . . . . . . . . . . . . . . . . . . . . . . . . . . . Eastwood
Norris, Dan . . . . . . . . . . . . . . . . . . . . . . . . . . . . . . . Wansdyke
Pike, Peter . . . . . . . . . . . . . . . . . . . . . . . . . . . . . . . . . Burnley
Prentice, Bridget . . . . . . . . . . . . . . . . . . . . . . . Lewisham East
Raynsford, Rt Hon Nick . . . . . . . . . . Greenwich and Woolwich
Roy, Frank . . . . . . . . . . . . . . . . . . . . . . Motherwell and Wishaw
Russell, Christine . . . . . . . . . . . . . . . . . . . . . . City of Chester
Sawford, Phil . . . . . . . . . . . . . . . . . . . . . . . . . . . . . . Kettering
Shipley, Debra . . . . . . . . . . . . . . . . . . . . . . . . . . . Stourbridge
Stinchcombe, Paul . . . . . . . . . . . . . . . . . . . . . Wellingborough
Straw, Rt Hon Jack . . . . . . . . . . . . . . . . . . . . . . . . . Blackburn
Taylor, Dari . . . . . . . . . . . . . . . . . . . . . . . . . . . Stockton South
Taylor, Rt Hon Ann . . . . . . . . . . . . . . . . . . . . . . . . . Dewsbury
Trickett, Jon . . . . . . . . . . . . . . . . . . . . . . . . . . . . . . Hemsworth
Twigg, Derek . . . . . . . . . . . . . . . . . . . . . . . . . . . . . . . . . Halton
Winnick, David . . . . . . . . . . . . . . . . . . . . . . . . . . Walsall North
Wood, Mike . . . . . . . . . . . . . . . . . . . . . . . . . . . Battley and Spen
Woolas, Phil . . . . . . . . . . . . . . . . . Oldham East and Saddleworth
Worthington, Tony . . . . . . . . . . . . . . . Clydebank and Milngavie
Wright, Anthony D . . . . . . . . . . . . . . . . . . . . . . Great Yarmouth

## *Graphical, Paper and Media Union (GPMU)*

*Keys House, 63-67 Bromham Road, Bedford, MK40 2AG*
*Tel: (01234) 351521 Fax: (01234) 270580*
*E-mail: general@gpmu.org.uk Web: http://www.gpmu.org.uk*

Fitzpatrick, Jim . . . . . . . . . . . . . . . . . . . Poplar and Canning Town
Hamilton, Fabian . . . . . . . . . . . . . . . . . . . . . Leeds North East
Howells, Dr Kim . . . . . . . . . . . . . . . . . . . . . . . . . . Pontypridd
Rooney, Terry . . . . . . . . . . . . . . . . . . . . . . . . . . Bradford North
Sutcliffe, Gerry . . . . . . . . . . . . . . . . . . . . . . . . . Bradford South

## *Iron and Steel Trades Confederation (ISTC)*

*Swinton House, 324 Gray's Inn Road, London, WC1X 8DD*
*Tel: (020) 7239 1200 Fax: (020) 7278 8378*
*E-mail: istc@istc.org.uk*
*Web: http://www.istc-tu.org.uk*

Baird, Vera . . . . . . . . . . . . . . . . . . . . . . . . . . . . . . . . . . . Redcar
Cairns, David . . . . . . . . . . . . . . . . . . . . . Greenock and Inverclyde
Cawsey, Ian . . . . . . . . . . . . . . . . . . . . . . . . . . . Brigg and Goole
Francis, Dr Hywel . . . . . . . . . . . . . . . . . . . . . . . . . . . Aberavon
Mann, John . . . . . . . . . . . . . . . . . . . . . . . . . . . . . . . . . Bassetlaw
Turner, Dennis . . . . . . . . . . . . . . . . . Wolverhampton South East

## *Musicians Union (MU)*

*60-62 Clapham Road, London, SW9 0JJ*
*Tel: (020) 7582 5566 Fax: (020) 7582 9805*
*E-mail: info@musiciansunion.org.uk*
*Web: http://www.musiciansunion.org.uk*

Fisher, Mark . . . . . . . . . . . . . . . . . . . . . . Stoke-on-Trent Central
Wishart, Peter . . . . . . . . . . . . . . . . . . . . . . . . . . . Tayside North

## *National Association of Co-operative Officials (NACO)*

*6a Clarendon Place, Hyde, Cheshire, SK14 2QZ*
*Tel: (0161) 351 7900 Fax (0161) 366 6800*
*E-mail: lwe@nacoco-op.org*

Love, Andrew . . . . . . . . . . . . . . . . . . . . . . . . . . . . . . . Edmonton

## *National Association of School Members and Women Teachers (NASUWT)*

*Hillscourt Education Centre, Rose Hill, Rednal, Birmingham, B45 8RS*
*Tel: (0121) 453 6150 Fax (0121) 457 6208/9*
*Web: http://www.teachersunion.org.uk*

Calton, Patsy . . . . . . . . . . . . . . . . . . . . . . . . . . . . . . . . . Cheadle

## *NATFHE (University and College Lecturers' Union)*

*27 Britannia Street, London, WC1X 9JP*
*Tel: (020) 7837 3636 Fax: (020) 7837 4403*
*E-mail: hq@natfhe.org.uk Web: http://www.natfhe.org.uk*

Drew, David . . . . . . . . . . . . . . . . . . . . . . . . . . . . . . . . . . Stroud
Foster, Michael John . . . . . . . . . . . . . . . . . . . . . . . . . Worcester

# MPs – TRADE UNION MEMBERSHIP

## National Union of Journalists (NUJ)
*308 Gray's Inn Road, London WC1X 8DP*
*Tel: (020) 7278 7916 Fax: (020) 7837 8143*
*E-mail: info@nuj.org.uk  Web: http://www.nuj.org.uk*

| | |
|---|---|
| Atherton, Candy | Falmouth and Camborne |
| Atkins, Charlotte | Staffordshire Moorlands |
| Beckett, Rt Hon Margaret | Derby South |
| Bradshaw, Ben | Exeter |
| Clwyd Ann | Cynon Valley |
| Cryer, John | Hornchurch |
| Farrelly, Paul | Newcastle-under-Lyme |
| Griffiths, Jane | Reading East |
| Healey, John | Wentworth |
| Mitchell, Austin | Great Grimsby |
| Mullin, Chris | Sunderland South |
| Robertson, Angus | Moray |
| Sedgemore, Brian | Hackney South and Shoreditch |
| Simon, Siôn | Birmingham Erdington |

## National Union of Mineworkers (NUM)
*Miners' Offices, 2 Huddersfield Road, Barnsley, S70 2LS*
*Tel: (01226) 215555 Fax: (01226) 215561*

| | |
|---|---|
| Campbell, Ronnie | Blyth Valley |
| Clapham, Michael | Barnsley West and Penistone |
| Cummings, John | Easington |
| Etherington, Bill | Sunderland North |
| Hamilton, David | Midlothian |
| Hood, Jimmy | Clydesdale |
| O'Brien, Bill | Normanton |

## National Union of Rail, Maritime and Transport Workers (RMT)
*Unity House, 39 Chalton Street, London, NW1 1JD*
*Tel: (020) 7387 4771 Fax: (020) 7387 4123*
*E-mail: info@rmt.org.uk Web: http://www.rmt.org.uk*

| | |
|---|---|
| Dalyell, Tam | Linlithgow |
| Dobson, Rt Hon Frank | Holborn and St Pancras |
| Hill, Rt Hon Keith | Streatham |

## National Union of Teachers (NUT)
*Hamilton House, Mabledon Place, London, WC1H 9BD*
*Tel: (020) 7388 6191 Fax: (020) 7387 8458*
*Web: http://www.teachers.org.uk*

| | |
|---|---|
| Bennett, Andrew | Denton and Reddish |
| Blizzard, Bob | Waveney |
| Clark, Helen | Peterborough |
| Coaker, Vernon | Gedling |
| Davey, Valerie | Bristol West |
| Fisher, Mark | Stoke on Trent Central |
| Foster, Rt Hon Derek | Bishop Auckland |
| Jones, Jon Owen | Cardiff Central |
| Lepper, David | Brighton Pavilion |
| Morris, Rt Hon Estelle | Birmingham Yardley |
| Ruane, Chris | Vale of Clwyd |
| Ryan, Joan | Enfield North |
| Steinberg, Gerry | City of Durham |

## Transport and General Workers Union (TGWU)
*Transport House, 128 Theobalds Road, London WC1X 8TN*
*Tel: (020) 7611 2500 Fax: (020) 7611 2555*
*E-mail: webmaster@tgwu.org.uk  Web: http://www.tgwu.org.uk*

| | |
|---|---|
| Ainger, Nick | Carmarthen West and South Pembrokeshire |
| Alexander, Douglas | Paisley South |
| Atherton, Candy | Falmouth and Camborne |
| Baird, Vera | Redcar |
| Beckett, Rt Hon Margaret | Derby South |
| Best, Harold | Leeds North West |
| Betts, Clive | Sheffield Attercliffe |
| Blair, Rt Hon Tony | Sedgefield |
| Blears, Hazel | Salford |
| Bottomley, Peter | Worthing West |
| Brennan, Kevin | Cardiff West |
| Brown, Russell | Dumfries |
| Burden, Richard | Birmingham Northfield |
| Chaytor, David | Bury North |
| Clark, Helen | Peterborough |
| Clwyd, Ann | Cynon Valley |
| Connarty, Michael | Falkirk East |
| Cooper, Yvette | Pontefract and Castleford |
| Corston, Rt Hon Jean | Bristol East |
| Cryer, Ann | Keighley |
| Cryer, John | Hornchurch |
| Curtis-Thomas, Claire | Crosby |
| Donohoe, Brian | Cunninghame South |
| Drown, Julia | Swindon South |
| Ellman, Louise | Liverpool Riverside |
| Ennis, Jeff | Barnsley East and Mexborough |
| Field, Rt Hon Frank | Birkenhead |
| Gapes, Mike | Ilford South |
| Gallaway, George | Glasgow Kelvin |
| Goggins, Paul | Wythenshawe and Sale East |
| Griffiths, Win | Bridgend |
| Hanson, David | Delyn |
| Henderson, Ivan | Harwich |
| Hewitt, Rt Hon Patricia | Leicester West |
| Hodge, Rt Hon Margaret | Barking |
| Humble, Joan | Blackpool North and Fleetwood |
| Ingram, Rt Hon Adam | East Kilbride |
| Jackson, Helen | Sheffield Hillsborough |
| Jones, Martyn | Clwyd South |
| Jowell, Rt Hon Tessa | Dulwich and West Norwood |
| Lazarowicz, Mark | Edinburgh North and Leith |
| Leslie, Christopher | Shipley |
| Love, Andrew | Edmonton |
| McCartney, Rt Hon Ian | Makerfield |
| McKechin, Ann | Glasgow Maryhill |
| McNamara, Kevin | Hull North |
| McWalter, Tony | Hemel Hempstead |
| Marris, Robert | Wolverhampton South West |
| Martlew, Eric | Carlisle |
| Miliband, David | South Shields |
| Mooney, Dr Lewis | Kirkcaldy |
| Morgan, Julie | Cardiff North |

## M P s – T R A D E   U N I O N   M E M B E R S H I P

### *(TGWU Continued)*

Murphy, Rt Hon Paul . . . . . . . . . . . . . . . . . . . . . . . . . . . . Torfaen
Osborne, Sandra. . . . . . . . . . . . . . . . . . . . . . . . . . . . . . . . . Ayr
Pearson, Ian . . . . . . . . . . . . . . . . . . . . . . . . . . . Dudley South
Pond, Chris. . . . . . . . . . . . . . . . . . . . . . . . . . . . Gravesham
Pound, Stephen . . . . . . . . . . . . . . . . . . . . . . . . . Ealing North
Quin, Rt Hon Joyce . . . . . . . . . Gateshead East and Washington West
Purchase, Ken . . . . . . . . . . . . . . . Wolverhampton North East
Reid, Rt Hon John . . . . . . . . . . . Hamilton North and Belshill
Robinson, Geoffrey. . . . . . . . . . . . . . . . . . . Coventry North West
Salter, Martin . . . . . . . . . . . . . . . . . . . . . . . . . . Reading West
Savidge, Malcolm . . . . . . . . . . . . . . . . . . . . . . . Aberdeen North
Sheridan, James . . . . . . . . . . . . . . . . . . . . . Renfrewshire West
Steinberg, Gerry . . . . . . . . . . . . . . . . . . . . . . . City of Durham
Stewart. Ian . . . . . . . . . . . . . . . . . . . . . . . . . . . . . . . . . Eccles
Strang, Rt Hon Gavin . . . . . . . . . Edinburgh East and Musselburgh
Touhig, Don. . . . . . . . . . . . . . . . . . . . . . . . . . . . . . . . Islwyn
Ward, Claire . . . . . . . . . . . . . . . . . . . . . . . . . . . . . . Watford
Wicks, Malcolm. . . . . . . . . . . . . . . . . . . . . . . Croydon North
Wills, Michael. . . . . . . . . . . . . . . . . . . . . . . . . Swindon North
Wright, David . . . . . . . . . . . . . . . . . . . . . . . . . . . . . Telford

## Transport and Salaried Staffs Association (TSSA)

*Walkden House, 10 Melton Street, London, NW1 2EJ*
*Tel: (020) 7387 2101 Fax: (020) 7383 0656*
*E-mail: enquiries@tssa.org.uk  Web: http://www.tssa.org.uk*

Quinn, Laurie. . . . . . . . . . . . . . . . . . Scarborough and Whitby

## Union of Construction, Allied Trades and Technicians (UCATT)

*UCATT House, 177 Abberville Road, London, SW4 9RL*
*Tel: (020) 7622 2442 Fax: (020) 7720 4081*
*E-mail: info@ucatt.org.uk  Web: http://www.ucatt.org.uk*

Clapham, Michael . . . . . . . . . . . . . . . . Barnsley West and Penistone
Cryer, John. . . . . . . . . . . . . . . . . . . . . . . . . . . . . . . Hornchuch
Hamilton, David . . . . . . . . . . . . . . . . . . . . . . . . . . . . Midlothian

## UNISON

*1 Mabledon Place, London, WC1H 9AJ*
*Tel (0845) 355 0845*
*Web: http://www.unison.org.uk*

Atkins, Charlotte . . . . . . . . . . . . . . . . . . . . Staffordshire Moorlands
Borrow, David . . . . . . . . . . . . . . . . . . . . . . . . . . . . . . Ribble South
Bradley, Rt Hon Keith . . . . . . . . . . . . . . . Manchester Withington
Browne, Desmond . . . . . . . . . . . . . . . . . . . Kilmarnock and Loudoun
Burnham, Andrew. . . . . . . . . . . . . . . . . . . . . . . . . . . . . . . Leigh
Chapman, Ben . . . . . . . . . . . . . . . . . . . . . . . . . . . Wirral South
Cohen, Harry. . . . . . . . . . . . . . . . . . . . Leyton and Wanstead
Dawson, Hilton . . . . . . . . . . . . . . . . . . . . Lancaster and Wyre
Drew, David. . . . . . . . . . . . . . . . . . . . . . . . . . . . . . . . Stroud
Drown, Julia . . . . . . . . . . . . . . . . . . . . . . . . . Swindon South
Harris, Tom. . . . . . . . . . . . . . . . . . . . . . . . . Glasgow Cathcart
Heyes, David . . . . . . . . . . . . . . . . . . . . . . . Ashton-under-Lyne
Hinchcliffe, David . . . . . . . . . . . . . . . . . . . . . . . . . . . Wakefield
Johnson, Melanie. . . . . . . . . . . . . . . . . . Welwyn and Hatfield
Joyce, Eric. . . . . . . . . . . . . . . . . . . . . . . . . . . . . Falkirk West
Kennedy, Rt Hon Jane . . . . . . . . . . . . . . Liverpool Wavertree

King, Andy . . . . . . . . . . . . . . . . . . . . . . . . . . . . Rugby and Kenilworth
Mahon, Alice . . . . . . . . . . . . . . . . . . . . . . . . . . . . . . . . . . . Halifax
Mallaber, Judy . . . . . . . . . . . . . . . . . . . . . . . . . . . . Amber Valley
Meacher, Rt Hon Michael . . . . . . . . . . . Oldham West and Royton
Merron, Gillian. . . . . . . . . . . . . . . . . . . . . . . . . . . . . . . . . Lincoln
Moffatt, Laura . . . . . . . . . . . . . . . . . . . . . . . . . . . . . . . . . Crawley
Organ, Diana . . . . . . . . . . . . . . . . . . . . . . . . . . . . Forest of Dean
Perham, Linda . . . . . . . . . . . . . . . . . . . . . . . . . . . . . . Ilford North
Picking, Anne. . . . . . . . . . . . . . . . . . . . . . . . . . . . . East Lothian
Pollard, Kerry . . . . . . . . . . . . . . . . . . . . . . . . . . . . . . St Albans
Primarolo, Rt Hon Dawn. . . . . . . . . . . . . . . . . . . Bristol South
Reed, Andrew . . . . . . . . . . . . . . . . . . . . . . . . . . . Loughborough
Rooney, Terry . . . . . . . . . . . . . . . . . . . . . . . . . . . Bradford North
Short, Rt Hon Clare. . . . . . . . . . . . . . . . . Birmingham Ladywood
Simpson, Alan . . . . . . . . . . . . . . . . . . . . . . . . Nottingham South
Singh, Marsha . . . . . . . . . . . . . . . . . . . . . . . . . . Bradford West
Squire, Rachel . . . . . . . . . . . . . . . . . . . . . . . . . Dunfermline West
Stewart, David . . . . . . . . . . . . . . Inverness East, Nairn and Lochaber
Taylor, David . . . . . . . . . . . . . . . . . . . Leicestershire North West
Tipping, Paddy . . . . . . . . . . . . . . . . . . . . . . . . . . . . . Sherwood
Whitehead, Dr Alan . . . . . . . . . . . . . . . . . . . . Southampton Test

## Union of Shop Distributive & Allied Workers (USDAW)

*188 Wilmslow Road, Fallowfield, Manchester, M14 6LJ*
*Tel: (0161) 224 2804  Fax: (0161) 257 2566*
*E-mail: enquiries@usdaw.org.uk  Web: http://www.usdaw.org.uk*

Coffey, Ann. . . . . . . . . . . . . . . . . . . . . . . . . . . . . . . . Stockport
Davey, Valerie . . . . . . . . . . . . . . . . . . . . . . . . . . . . . Bristol West
Dhanda, Parmjit . . . . . . . . . . . . . . . . . . . . . . . . . . . Gloucester
Hughes, Rt Hon Beverley . . . . . . . . . . . . . Stretford and Urmston
Hughes, Kevin . . . . . . . . . . . . . . . . . . . . . . . . . . Doncaster North
Ladyman, Dr Stephen. . . . . . . . . . . . . . . . . . . . . . Thanet South
McIsaac, Shona . . . . . . . . . . . . . . . . . . . . . . . . . . . Cleethorpes
Pickthall, Colin . . . . . . . . . . . . . . . . . . . . . . . . Lancashire West
Wilson, Rt Hon Brian . . . . . . . . . . . . . . . . . . Cunninghame North

# MPs – LANGUAGES SPOKEN

*Note: Based on information supplied by the MPs concerned.*

## Afrikaans
Murphy, Jim ...............................................................Eastwood

## British Sign
Levitt, Tom ................................................................High Peak

## Cornish
George, Andrew ................................................St Ives (Cornwall)

## Danish
McIntosh, Anne ....................................................Vale of York
Palmer, Dr Nick........................................................Broxtowe

## Dutch
Burnham, Andrew ...........................................................Leigh
Dunwoody, Gwyneth ...............................Crewe and Nantwich
Fabricant, Michael .....................................................Lichfield
Moonie, Dr Lewis ....................................................Kirkcaldy
Vis, Dr Rudi .......................................Finchley and Golders Green

## Esperanto
Blunkett, Rt Hon David.............................Sheffield Brightside

## Estonian
Öpik, Lembit......................................................Montgomeryshire

## French
Allan, Richard...............................................Sheffield Hallam
Ancram, Rt Hon Michael..............................................Devizes
Anderson, Rt Hon Donald ................................Swansea East
Anderson, Janet ..........................Rossendale and Darwen
Baird, Vera .................................................................Redcar
Baker, Norman ..............................................................Lewes
Battle, Rt Hon John ................................................Leeds West
Beard, Nigel ............................Bexleyheath and Crayford
Beggs, Roy ..........................................................Antrim East
Beith, Rt Hon Alan........................Berwick-upon-Tweed
Bell, Sir Stuart ...............................................Middlesbrough
Bellingham, Henry .........................Norfolk North West
Blair, Rt Hon Tony ..............................................Sedgefield
Boateng, Rt Hon Paul.......................................Brent South
Boswell, Tim ..........................................................Daventry
Brake, Thomas ......................Carshalton and Wallington
Bruce, Malcolm .............................................................Gordon
Bryant, Chris ............................................................Rhondda
Butterfill, Sir John .................................Bournemouth West
Calton, Patsy .............................................................Cheadle
Campbell, Anne ...................................................Cambridge
Carmichael, Alistair......................Orkney and Shetland
Cash, Bill....................................................................Stone
Chapman, Ben .........................................Wirral South
Chaytor, David.....................................................Bury North

Chidgey, David....................................................Eastleigh
Clarke, Rt Hon Charles........................Norwich South
Clifton-Brown, Geoffrey ..........................................Cotswold
Connarty, Michael .........................................Falkirk East
Cormack, Sir Patrick.......................Staffordshire South
Curry, Rt Hon David .......................Skipton and Ripon
Dalyell, Tam.......................................................Linlithgow
Davey, Edward.............................Kingston and Surbiton
Davies, Quentin ...................Grantham and Stamford
Dhanda, Parmjit ...................................................Gloucester
Dismore, Andrew.....................................................Hendon
Donaldson, Jeffrey.........................................Lagan Valley
Dorrell, Rt Hon Stephen ..................................Charnwood
Doughty, Sue......................................................Guildford
Dunwoody, Gwyneth...................Crewe and Nantwich
Evans, Nigel...............................................Ribble Valley
Ewing, Annabelle ........................................................Perth
Fabricant, Michael .....................................................Lichfield
Farrelly, Paul.........................Newcastle-under-Lyme
Flight, Howard.......................Arundel and South Downs
Follett, Barbara ..................................................Stevenage
Foster, Rt Hon Derek .........................Bishop Auckland
Foster, Don.................................................................Bath
Foulkes, Rt Hon George ..............Carrick, Cumnock and Doon Valley
Fox, Dr Liam.......................................................Woodspring
Gale, Roger.................................................Thanet North
Gapes, Mike...................................................Ilford South
Gardiner, Barry .............................................Brent North
Garnier, Edward .............................................Harborough
Gibson, Dr Ian................................................Norwich North
Gillan, Cheryl .........................Chesham and Amersham
Gilroy, Linda .......................................Plymouth Sutton
Gray, James ...............................................Wiltshire North
Grayling, Chris ...................................Epsom and Ewell
Green, Damian.............................................................Ashford
Grieve, Dominic...........................................Beaconsfield
Griffiths, Jane .............................................Reading East
Griffiths, Nigel.......................................Edinburgh South
Gummer, Rt Hon John ................................Suffolk Coastal
Hall, Patrick.............................................................Bedford
Hamilton, Fabian...............................Leeds North East
Harris, Dr Evan.......................Oxford West and Abingdon
Hawkins, Nick.........................................Surrey Heath
Heald, Oliver ...........................Hertfordshire North East
Healey, John...................................................Wentworth
Hendry, Charles...................................................Wealden
Hermon, Lady [Sylvia].........................................Down North
Hewitt, Rt Hon Patricia...............................Leicester West
Hodge, Rt Hon Margaret .........................................Barking
Hoon, Rt Hon Geoff..................................................Ashfield
Hughes, Rt Hon Beverley...................Stretford and Urmston
Hughes, Simon..................Southwark North and Bermondsey
Hume, John...................................................................Foyle
Illsley, Eric...................................................Barnsley Central
Jackson, Helen...................................Sheffield Hillsborough
Jackson, Robert.......................................................Wantage

# MPs – LANGUAGES SPOKEN

*French (Continued)*

Jenkin, Hon Bernard...............................................Essex North
Jones, Martyn .......................................................Clwyd South
Kelly, Ruth ...........................................................Bolton West
King, Andy .............................................Rugby and Kenilworth
King, Oona ..............................Bethnal Green and Bow
Knight, Jim ..........................................................Dorset South
Laing, Eleanor .................................................Epping Forest
Leigh, Edward ..................................................Gainsborough
Letwin, Rt Hon Oliver ......................................Dorset West
Levitt, Tom ............................................................High Peak
Liddell, Rt Hon Helen ...............................Airdrie and Shotts
Lilley, Rt Hon Peter ...........................Hitchin and Harpenden
Linton, Martin ........................................................Battersea
Lloyd, Tony ...............................................Manchester Central
McDonnell, John ..............................Hayes and Harlington
McIntosh, Anne.....................................................Vale of York
McIsaac, Shona ....................................................Cleethorpes
MacShane, Dr Denis .............................................Rotherham
McWalter, Tony ...........................................Hemel Hempstead
Marsden, Gordon .........................................Blackpool South
Meacher, Rt Hon Michael......................Oldham West and Royston
Mitchell, Austin .............................................Great Grimsby
Moonie, Dr Lewis ....................................................Kirkcaldy
Moran, Margaret.................................................Luton South
Moss, Malcolm ...........................Cambridgeshire North East
Munn, Meg...............................................Sheffield Heeley
Murphy, Rt Hon Paul ...............................................Torfaen
Naysmith, Dr Doug.....................................Bristol North West
O'Brien, Stephen.....................................................Eddisbury
Organ, Diana ...............................................Forest of Dean
Palmer, Dr Nick......................................................Broxtowe
Paterson, Owen ...........................................Shropshire North
Pickthall, Colin .......................................Lancashire West
Pond, Chris ...........................................................Gravesham
Portillo, Rt Hon Michael......................Kensington and Chelsea
Purnell, James ...............................Stalybridge and Hyde
Quin, Rt Hon Joyce .................Gateshead East and Washington West
Rammell, Bill .........................................................Harlow
Randall, John...........................................................Uxbridge
Raynsford, Rt Hon Nick ...................Greenwich and Woolwich
Redwood, Rt Hon John ......................................Wokingham
Reid, Rt Hon John ...................Hamilton North and Bellshill
Rendel, David .........................................................Newbury
Robathan, Andrew ...................................................Blaby
Robertson, Angus ......................................................Moray
Robinson, Geoffrey ...............................Coventry North West
Robinson, Peter.................................................Belfast East
Roe, Dame Marion ..........................................Broxbourne
Rooney, Terry.................................................Bradford North
Sedgemore, Brian ...............Hackney South and Shoreditch
Selous, Andrew....................................Bedfordshire South West
Sheerman, Barry....................................................Huddersfield
Shephard, Rt Hon Gillian ........................Norfolk South West
Simon, Siôn ..................................Birmingham Erdington
Smith, Rt Hon Chris.......................Islington South and Finsbury
Smith, Rt Hon Jacqui ............................................Redditch
Soames, Hon Nicholas ...................................Mid Sussex
Spelman, Caroline................................................Meriden
Starkey, Dr Phyllis ...........................Milton Keynes South West
Steen, Anthony ........................................................Totnes
Stevenson, George .................................Stoke-on-Trent South

Strang, Rt Hon Gavin .....................Edinburgh East and Musselburgh
Straw, Rt Hon Jack .............................................Blackburn
Taylor, Ian ................................................Esher and Walton
Taylor, Sir Teddy ......................Rochford and Southend East
Thurso, John .................Caithness, Sutherland and Easter Ross
Tonge, Dr Jenny ...........................................Richmond Park
Tredinnick, David...................................................Bosworth
Trickett, Jon.........................................................Hemsworth
Turner, Dr Desmond ...........................Brighton Kemptown
Tyrie, Andrew ....................................................Chichester
Viggers, Peter ........................................................Gosport
Vis, Dr Rudi ...........................Finchley and Golders Green
Waterson, Nigel......................................................Eastbourne
Whitehead, Dr Alan....................................Southampton Test
Wilkinson, John .......................................Ruislip-Northwood

## Gaelic

Gildernew, Michelle ...............................Fermanagh and South Tyrone
MacDonald, Calum..................................................Western Isles

## German

Anderson, Rt Hon Donald ...........................................Swansea East
Anderson, Janet ..................................Rossendale and Darwen
Bacon, Richard........................................................Norfolk South
Baker, Norman ..........................................................Lewes
Boswell, Tim ............................................................Daventry
Bradshaw, Ben .........................................................Exeter
Carmichael, Alistair.................................Orkney and Shetland
Casale, Roger..........................................................Wimbledon
Davey, Edward..................................Kingston and Surbiton
Davies, Quentin ...........................Grantham and Stamford
Dorrell, Rt Hon Stephen...........................................Charnwood
Fabricant, Michael ...............................................Lichfield
Farrelly, Paul .............................Newcastle-under-Lyme
Field, Mark...........................Cities of London and Westminster
Foster, Rt Hon Derek ...............................Bishop Auckland
Hendrick, Mark........................................................Preston
Hendry, Charles ....................................................Wealden
Hodge, Rt Hon Margaret ........................................Barking
Jackson, Robert.......................................................Wantage
Lucas, Ian ..............................................................Wrexham
McIntosh, Anne .......................................................Vale of York
McIsaac, Shona ....................................................Cleethorpes
MacShane, Dr Denis .............................................Rotherham
Marsden, Gordon .........................................Blackpool South
Munn, Meg...............................................Sheffield Heeley
Öpik, Lembit...............................................Montgomeryshire
Palmer, Dr Nick.......................................................Broxtowe
Paterson, Owen ...........................................Shropshire North
Price, Adam .........................Carmarthen East and Dinefwr
Quin, Rt Hon Joyce .................Gateshead East and Washington West
Reed, Andrew ..................................................Loughborough
Robertson, Angus ......................................................Moray
Robinson, Geoffrey ...............................Coventry North West
Rooney, Terry.................................................Bradford North
Smith, Rt Hon Chris.......................Islington South and Finsbury
Spelman, Caroline................................................Meriden
Stuart, Gisela ...........................Birmingham Edgbaston
Taylor, Ian ................................................Esher and Walton
Taylor, Sir Teddy ......................Rochford and Southend East
Timms, Stephen.....................................................East Ham
Walley, Joan .........................................Stoke-on-Trent North
Waterson, Nigel......................................................Eastbourne
Willetts, David.........................................................Havant

# MPs – LANGUAGES SPOKEN

## Greek

Dismore, Andrew .......................................................Hendon
O'Hara, Eddie .......................................Knowsley South

## Hindi

Khabra, Piara Singh ...............................Ealing Southall
Kumar, Dr Ashok...........Middlesbrough South and Cleveland East

## Irish

Adams, Gerry .......................................Belfast West
Hume, John ...............................................Foyle
Mallon, Seamus ...............................Newry and Armagh

## Italian

Ancram, Rt Hon Michael...................................Devizes
Boswell, Tim ..........................................Daventry
Bradshaw, Ben ...........................................Exeter
Cairns, David ......................Greenock and Inverclyde
Casale, Roger......................................Wimbledon
Dunwoody, Gwyneth......................Crewe and Nantwich
Ewing, Annabelle ........................................Perth
Farrelly, Paul......................Newcastle-under-Lyme
Hodge, Rt Hon Margaret ..............................Barking
King, Oona .........................Bethnal Green and Bow
Letwin, Rt Hon Oliver ..........................Dorset West
McIntosh, Anne.................................Vale of York
Munn, Meg.................................Sheffield Heeley
Portillo, Rt Hon Michael..............Kensington and Chelsea
Quin, Rt Hon Joyce ...............Gateshead East and Washington West
Robinson, Geoffrey.......................Coventry North West

## Japanese

Griffiths, Jane ...................................Reading East

## Korean

Griffiths, Jane ...................................Reading East

## Norwegian

Beith, Rt Hon Alan............................Berwick-upon-Tweed

## Punjabi

Dhanda, Parmjit .....................................Gloucester
Khabra, Piara Singh ...............................Ealing Southall
Kumar, Dr Ashok...........Middlesbrough South and Cleveland East
Sarwar, Mohammad....................................Glasgow Govan
Singh, Marsha .................................Bradford West

## Russian

Davies, Quentin.........................Grantham and Stamford
Fabricant, Michael.....................................Lichfield
Gardiner, Barry .................................Brent North
Griffiths, Jane .....................................Reading East
Lloyd, Tony................................Manchester Central
Randall, John......................................Uxbridge
Robinson, Geoffrey.......................Coventry North West

## Serbo-Croat

Randall, John........................................Uxbridge

## Spanish

Allan, Richard.................................Sheffield Hallam
Benton, Joe...........................................Bootle
Bryant, Chris.........................................Rhondda
Burnham, Andrew .........................................Leigh
Corbyn, Jeremy...............................Islington North
Davey, Edward............................Kingston and Surbiton
Foulkes, Rt Hon George ...............Carrick, Cumnock and Doon Valley
Harris, Dr Evan....................Oxford West and Abingdon
Jones, Martyn ...................................Clwyd South
Kidney, David........................................Stafford
McIntosh, Anne...................................Vale of York
MacShane, Dr Denis ...............................Rotherham
Portillo, Rt Hon Michael ...............Kensington and Chelsea
Quin, Rt Hon Joyce .................Gateshead East and Washington West
Redwood, Rt Hon John ...........................Wokingham
Wilkinson, John ...........................Ruislip-Northwood

## Swahili

Armstrong, Rt Hon Hilary ...............Durham North West
Cunningham, Tony....................................Workington

## Swedish

Linton, Martin ......................................Battersea

## Urdu

Khabra, Piara Singh........................................Ealing Southall
Kumar, Dr Ashok.................Middlesbrough South and Cleveland East
Sarwar, Mohammed.........................Glasgow Govan

## Welsh

Beith, Rt Hon Alan.......................Berwick-upon-Tweed
Brennan, Kevin ...................................Cardiff West
Clwyd, Ann...........................................Cynon Valley
Curtis-Thomas, Claire .................................Crosby
Davies, Rt Hon Denzil ..............................Llanelli
Flynn, Paul .......................................Newport West
Francis, Dr Hywel........................................Aberavon
Irranca-Davies, Huw .....................................Ogmore
Jones, Jon Owen ..............................Cardiff Central
Lawrence, Jackie .....................Preseli Pembrokeshire
Llwyd, Elfyn .................Meirionnydd Nant Conwy
Michael, Rt Hon Alun.............Cardiff South and Penarth
Owen, Albert .........................................Ynys Mon
Price, Adam ...................Carmarthen East and Dinefwr
Taylor, Dari ...................................Stockton South
Thomas, Gareth ...................................Clwyd West
Thomas, Simon.......................................Ceredigion
Williams, Betty ......................................Conwy
Williams, Hywel ...............................Caernarfon

# MPs – PUBLICATIONS

| Author | Date Published | Title of Publication |
|---|---|---|
| Adams, Gerry | | Before the Dawn |
| | | The Street and Other Stories |
| | | Falls Memories |
| | | Peace in Ireland - Towards a Lasting Peace in Ireland |
| | | Cage II |
| | | Pathway to Peace |
| | | An Irish Voice |
| | | The Politics of Irish Freedom |
| | | An Irish Journal |
| Alexander, Douglas | 1999 | New Scotland, New Britain |
| Allen, Graham | 1996 | Re-inventing Democracy |
| | 2001 | The Last Prime Minister - Being Honest about the UK Presidency |
| Amess, David | 1995 | Basildon Experience |
| Atkins, Charlotte | 1981 | How to Select or Reselect Your MP (joint author) |
| Baird, Vera | 1992 | The Judiciary (joint author) |
| | 1993 | Economical with the Proof |
| | 1993 | Negotiated Justice (joint author) |
| | 1993 | Response to Runciman (joint author) |
| | 1998 | Rape in Court |
| | 2004 | Defending Battered Women who Kill (joint author) |
| Battle, Rt Hon John | 1997 | Tom Maguire |
| Bayley, Hugh | 1995 | The Nation's Health |
| Beard, Nigel | 1971 | The Practical Use of Linear Programming in Planning and Analysis |
| Beith, Rt Hon Alan | 1983 | Case for Liberal Party and the Alliance (joint author) |
| | 1987 | Faith and Politics (joint author) |
| Bell, Sir Stuart | 1974 | Days That Used to Be |
| | 1988 | When Salam Came to the Boro |
| | 2000 | Tony Really Loves Me |
| | 2002 | Pathway to the Euro |
| | 2002 | Binkie's Revolution |
| | 2003 | The Honoured Society |
| | 2004 | Lara's Theme |
| | 2004 | Softly in the Dusk |
| Beresford, Sir Paul | | The Good Council Guide |
| Blackman, Liz | 1998 | Parliamentary Portions: A Gourmet's Guide to the House of Commons |
| Blunkett, Rt Hon David | 1987 | Democracy in Crisis |
| | 1995 | On a Clear Day |
| | 2001 | Politics and Progress |
| Blunt, Crispin | 1998 | Britain's Place in the World: Time to Decide |
| Brady, Graham | 1991 | Towards an Employees' Charter |
| Bruce, Malcolm | | Local Enterprise |
| | | Rural Development Energy |
| | | Towards a Federal United Kingdom |
| Bryant, Chris | 1993 | Reclaiming the Ground |
| | 1995 | John Smith: An Appreciation |
| | 1996 | Possible Dreams |
| | 1997 | Stafford Cripps: The First Modern Chancellor |
| | 1999 | Glenda Jackson: The Biography |

## M P s  –  P U B L I C A T I O N S

| Author | Date Published | Title of Publication |
|---|---|---|
| Cable, Dr Vincent | 1983 | Protectionism and Industrial Decline |
| | 1994 | The World's New Fissures |
| | 1995 | Global Superhighways |
| | 1995 | The New Giants - China and India (joint author) |
| | 1995 | Regional Blocs (joint author) |
| | 2000 | Globalisation and Global Governance |
| Campbell, Anne | 1972 | Calculation for Commercial Students |
| Campbell, Gregory | 1987 | Discrimination: The Truth |
| | 1993 | Discrimination: Where Now? |
| | 1994 | Ulster's Verdict on the Joint Declaration |
| | 1998 | Working Toward 2000 |
| Cash, Bill | 1991 | Against a Federal Europe |
| | 1992 | Europe: The Crunch |
| | 1995 | Are We Really Winning on Europe? |
| Challen, Colin | 1998 | Price of Power - The Secret Funding of the Tory Party |
| Clifton-Brown, Geoffrey | 1997 | Privatising the State Pension – Secure Funded Provision for All |
| Cormack, Sir Patrick | 1976 | Heritage in Danger |
| | 1978 | Right Turn |
| | 1981 | Westminster, Palace and Parliament |
| | 1983 | Wilberforce |
| | 1984 | British Castles |
| | 1984 | English Cathedrals |
| Cotter, Brian | 2001 | Creating an Entrepreneurial Culture - Unleashing the Potential of Britain's Small Businesses |
| Cranston, Ross | 1979 | Regulating Business |
| | 1985 | Legal Aspects of the Welfare State |
| | 1987 | Law, Government and Public Policy |
| | 1995 | Professional Responsibility and Legal Ethics (editor) |
| | 2000 | Consumers and the Law |
| | 2002 | Principles of Banking Law |
| Cryer, Ann | 1997 | Boldness Be My Friend: Remembering Bob Cryer (joint compiler) |
| Cryer, John | 1997 | Boldness Be My Friend: Remembering Bob Cryer (joint compiler) |
| Dalyell, Tam | 1960 | The Case of Ship-Schools |
| | 1963 | Ship-School Dunera |
| | 1977 | Devolution: The End of Britain? |
| | 1982 | One Man's Falklands |
| | 1983 | A Science Policy for Britain |
| | 1983 | Thatcher's Torpedo |
| | 1987 | Misrule |
| | 1989 | Dick Crossman: A Portrait |
| Davey, Edward | 2000 | Making MPs Work for our Money: Reforming Parliament's Role in Budget Scrutiny |
| Davies, Rt Hon Denzil | 1993 | Minimise Taxes, Maximise Damages |
| | 1995/1999 | Booth on Residence and Domicile and UK Taxation (2nd-7th editions) |
| | 1995 | The World Trade Organisation and Gatt '94 – A Guide to the New International Economic Law |
| Davies, Quentin | 1996 | Britain and Europe: A Conservative View |
| Davis, Rt Hon David | 1988 | How to Turn Round a Company |
| | 1989 | BBC Guide to Parliament |
| Dhanda, Parmjit | | How to Measure Distances Using a Gallium Arsenide Laser |
| Duncan, Alan | 1995 | Saturn's Children: How the State Devours Liberty, Prosperity and Virtue |
| Edwards, Huw | 1978 | Low Pay in Wales |
| | 1996 | Wales in 1990s - Land of Low Pay |
| Farrelly, Paul | 2003 | Hammer of the Left (editor) |

## M P s  –  P U B L I C A T I O N S

| Author | Date Published | Title of Publication |
|---|---|---|
| Field, Rt Hon Frank | 1982 | Poverty and Politics |
| | 1984 | Policies Against Low Pay |
| | 1984 | The Minimum Wage: Its Potential and Dangers |
| | 1987 | Freedom and Wealth in a Socialist Future |
| | 1987 | The Politics of Paradise |
| | 1989 | Losing Out: The Emergence of Britain's Underclass |
| | 1993 | An Agenda for Britain |
| | 1994 | Europe Isn't Working |
| | 1994 | Beyond Punishment: Hard Choices on the Road to Full Employability |
| | 1995 | Making Welfare Work: Reconstructing Welfare for the Millennium |
| | 1996 | How to Pay for the Future: Establishing a Stakeholders' Welfare |
| | 1997 | Reforming Welfare |
| | 1998 | Reflections on Welfare Reform |
| | 2000 | The State of Dependency: Welfare under Labour |
| | 2001 | Making Welfare Work: Reconstructing Welfare for the Millennium |
| | 2003 | Neighbours from Hell: The Politics of Behaviour |
| Fisher, Mark | 1988 | City Centres, City Cultures |
| | 1991 | A New London |
| | 1991 | Whose Cities? |
| Flight, Howard | 1988 | All You Need to Know about Exchange Rates |
| | 2001 | Unlocking Growth: Proposals to Expand Venture Capital Investment and Activity in the UK |
| Flynn, Paul | 1997 | Commons Knowledge: How to be a Backbencher |
| | 1998 | Baglu Mlaen (Staggering Forward) |
| | 1999 | Dragons Led by Poodles |
| Foster, Don | 1979 | Resource Based Learning in Science |
| | 1981 | Science with Gas |
| | 1984 | Aspects of Science (joint author) |
| | 1984 | Reading About Science (joint author) |
| | 1986 | Nuffield Science (joint author) |
| | 2003 | From the Three Rs to the Three Cs: A Personal View of Education |
| Foulkes, Rt Hon George | 1964 | Eighty Years On |
| Francis, Dr Hywel | 1980/1998 | The Fed: A History of the South Wales Miners in the Twentieth Century (joint author) |
| | 1984/2004 | Miners Against Fascism: Wales and the Spanish Civil War |
| | 1999 | Wales: A Learning Country |
| Galloway, George | 1991 | Downfall - The Ceausescus and the Romanian Revolution |
| | 2004 | I'm Not the Only One |
| Gapes, Mike | 1990 | After the Cold War |
| Garnier, Edward | 1991 | Bearing the Standard |
| | 1993 | Facing the Future |
| George, Andrew | 1986 | Planning - A Guide |
| | 1986 | The Natives are Revolting Down in the Cornwall Theme Park |
| | 1987 | Homes for Locals |
| | 1989 | Cornwall at the Crossroads |
| | 1994 | A Vision of Cornwall |
| | 2002 | A View from the Bottom Left Hand Corner |
| George, Rt Hon Bruce | 1989/90, 1991/92 | Janes NATO Handbook (editor) |
| | 1991 | The British Labour Party and Defence |
| | 1993 | The Military Lessons of the Gulf War (joint author) |
| | 1996 | Worth Saving: The Story of the Staffordshire Regiment's Fight for Survival |
| | 2000 | Private Security (joint author) |
| Gibb, Nick | 1982 | Forgotten Closed Shop |
| | 1989 | Duty to Repeal |
| | 1990 | Bucking the Market |
| Gray, James | 1985 | Financial Risk Management |
| | 1987 | Futures and Options for Shipping |
| | 1990 | Shipping Futures |
| Grayling, Chris | 1984 | The Bridgwater Heritage |
| | 1985 | A Land Fit for Heroes? |
| | 1988 | Just Another Star |

# MPs – PUBLICATIONS

| Author | Date Published | Title of Publication |
|---|---|---|
| Green, Damian | 1984, 1986 | ITN Budget Factbook |
| | 1990 | Freedom of the Airwaves |
| | 1991 | A Better BBC |
| | 1997 | Regulating the Media in the Digital Age |
| | 1998 | Do Convergent Media Need Convergent Regulation? |
| | 1998 | The Four Failures of the New Deal |
| | 2002 | Better Learning |
| | 2003 | More Than Markets |
| Griffiths, Jane | 1988 | Bushido (joint author) |
| Griffiths, Nigel | 1981 | Guide to Council Housing in Edinburgh |
| | 1981 | Welfare Rights Survey |
| | 1982 | Council Housing on the Point of Collapse |
| | 1982-86 | Welfare Rights Guide |
| | 1983 | A Guide to DHSS Claims and Appeals |
| | 1983 | Welfare Rights Advice for Doctors, Health Visitors and Social Workers |
| | 1988 | Rights Guide for Mentally Handicapped People |
| | 2000 | 300 Gains from a Labour Government |
| Gummer, Rt Hon John | | Christian Calendar |
| | | The Permissive Society |
| Hague, Rt Hon William | 2004 | William Pitt the Younger |
| Hain, Rt Hon Peter | 1971 | Don't Play with Apartheid |
| | 1987 | A Putney Plot? |
| | 1995 | Peking Connection |
| | 1995 | Ayes to the Left: A Future for Socialism |
| | 1996 | Sing the Beloved Country |
| | 2000 | Plain Speaking on Europe |
| | 2001 | The End of Foreign Policy? |
| | 2002 | Practical Europeanism |
| Haselhurst, Rt Hon Sir Alan | 1999 | Occasionally Cricket |
| | 2001 | Eventually Cricket |
| | 2003 | Incidentally Cricket |
| Hawkins, Nick | 1990 | 1992: The European Single Market in Insurance (joint author) |
| | 1994 | Competitive Sport in Schools |
| | 1995 | Sport and Broadcasting - Responding to Debate |
| | 1997 | Bringing Order to the Law (joint author) |
| | 1999 | Populist Conservatism |
| Heathcoat-Amory, Rt Hon David | 1996 | A Single European Currency - Why the UK Must say NO |
| Hendrick, Mark | | The Euro and Co-operative Enterprise |
| | | Changing States |
| Hewitt, Rt Hon Patricia | 1993 | About Time: The Revolution in Work and Family Life |
| Hinchliffe, David | 2000 | Rugby's Class War |
| | 2002 | A Westminster XIII |
| Hodge, Rt Hon Margaret | 1991 | Quality, Equality and Democracy |
| | 1994 | Beyond the Town Hall |
| | 1997 | Elected Mayors and Democracy |
| Hope, Philip | 1986 | Local Government - Making it Work for You (joint author) |
| | 1987 | Ideas Into Action |
| | 1987 | Making the Break - Choices and Decisions Facing Young People Leaving Home |
| | 1991 | View to Learn |
| | 1992 | On-Line: The Drugs Learning Pack |
| | 1993 | Making Best Use of Consultants |
| | 1993 | Home and Dry |
| | 1993 | Education for Citizenship |
| | 1994 | Good Moves |
| | 1995 | Education for Parenthood |
| | 1995 | Performance Appraisal (joint author) |
| | 1995 | House Nation |
| | 1995 | Analysis and Action on Youth Health |
| | 1995 | Just Us (joint author) |
| | 1997 | Tomorrow's Parents - Developing Parenthood Education in Schools (joint author) |
| Howarth, Rt Hon Alan | 1985 | Monty at Close Quarters (joint author) |

# M P s  –  P U B L I C A T I O N S

| Author | Date Published | Title of Publication |
|---|---|---|
| Hughes, Rt Hon Beverley | 1995 | Community Care and Older People |
| Hunter, Andrew | 2001 | The Betrayal of British Ulster |
| Iddon, Dr Brian | 1974 | Polychloroaromatic Compounds (joint author) |
| | 1985 | The Magic of Chemistry |
| | 1988 | Bromine Compounds: Chemistry and Applications (joint editor) |
| Jackson, Robert | 1978 | The Powers of the European Parliament |
| | 1979 | The Penguin Guide to the European Elections |
| | 1982 | The Tradition and Reality: Conservative Philosophy and European Integration |
| | 1983 | From Boom to Bust? British Farming and CAP Reform |
| | 1984 | Political Ideas in Western Europe Today |
| Johnson, Boris | 2001 | Friends, Voters, Countrymen; Jottings from the Stump |
| | 2003 | Lend Me Your Ears |
| Joyce, Eric | 1997 | Arms and the Man: Renewing the Armed Forces |
| Kaufman, Rt Hon Sir Gerald | 1973 | To Build the Promised Land |
| | 1980, 1997 | How to be a Minister |
| | 1985 | My Life in the Silver Screen |
| | 1986 | Inside the Promised Land |
| | 1994 | Meet Me in St Louis |
| Keeble, Sally | 1984 | Flat Broke |
| | 1985 | Collectors Corner |
| | 1995 | Conceiving Your Baby |
| Kennedy, Rt Hon Charles | 2000 | The Future of Politics |
| Kilfoyle, Peter | 2001 | Left Behind: Lessons from Labour's Heartlands |
| Kirkwood, Sir Archy | 1996 | Long Term Care: A Framework for Reform |
| Knight, Rt Hon Greg | 1988 | Westminster Words |
| | 1990 | Honourable Insults |
| | 1993 | Parliamentary Sauce |
| | 1998 | Right Honourable Insults |
| Lamb, Norman | 1998 | Remedies in the Employment Tribunal |
| Lammy, David | 2002 | Leading Together |
| Lansley, Andrew | 1989 | A Private Route |
| | 1997 | Conservatives and the Constitution |
| | 2002 | Do the Right Thing |
| | 2003 | Extending the Reach |
| Lazarowicz, Mark | 1999 | The Scottish Parliament: An Introduction (joint author) |
| Lepper, David | 1986 | John Wayne |
| Letwin, Rt Hon Oliver | 1985 | Aims of Schooling |
| | 1986 | Ethics, Emotion and the Unity of the Self |
| | 1988 | Privatising the World |
| | 1990 | Drift to Union |
| | 1998 | The Purpose of Politics |
| Levitt, Tom | 1995 | Sound Practice |
| | 1996 | Clear Access |
| Lewis, Dr Julian | 1988, 2003 | Changing Direction: British Military Planning for Post-War Strategic Defence 1942-47 |
| | 1992 | Who's Left? An Index of Labour MPs and Left-Wing Causes, 1986-92 |
| | 1992 | Labour's CND Cover-up |
| | 1992 | Labour's New Left |
| | 1992 | Labour's Constitutional Crisis |
| | 1993 | The Liberal Democrats: The Character of their Politics |
| | 1994 | Who's Left in Europe? |
| | 1996 | What's Liberal? Liberal Democrat Quotations and Facts |
| Liddell, Rt Hon Helen | 1992 | Elite |

# MPs – PUBLICATIONS

| Author | Date Published | Title of Publication |
|---|---|---|
| Lilley, Rt Hon Peter | 1972 | Do You Sincerely Want to Win? – Defeating Terrorism in Ulster |
| | 1974 | Lessons for Power |
| | 1977 | Delusions of Income Policy (joint author) |
| | 1989 | Thatcherism: The Next Generation |
| | 1993 | The Mais Lecture - Benefits and Costs: Securing the Future of Social Security |
| | 2000 | Patient Power |
| | 2001 | Common Sense on Cannabis |
| | 2002 | Taking Liberties |
| | 2003 | Save our Pensions |
| Linton, Martin | 1980 | Get Me Out of Here |
| | 1984 | The Swedish Road to Socialism |
| | 1988 | Labour Can Still Win |
| | 1993 | What's Wrong with First-Past-the-Post |
| | 1994 | Money and Votes |
| | 1995 | Was it the Sun Wot Won It? |
| | 1999 | Beyond 2002: Long-term policies for Labour |
| McWalter, Tony | 1990 | Kant and his Influence (joint editor) |
| Marsden, Gordon | 1990/1998 | Victorian Values: Personalities and Values in 19th Century |
| Marshall-Andrews, Robert | 1990 | Palace of Wisdom |
| | 2002 | A Man Without Guilt |
| Mawhinney, Rt Hon Sir Brian | | Conflict and Christianity in Northern Ireland (joint author) |
| | 1999 | In the Firing Line: Politics, Faith, Power and Forgiveness |
| Meacher, Rt Hon Michael | 1992 | Diffusing Power: The Key to Socialist Revival |
| Mercer, Patrick | 1997 | Give Them a Volley and a Charge |
| Milburn, Rt Hon Alan | 1986 | Jobs and Industry - The North Can Make It |
| | 1987 | Plan for the North |
| | 1989 | The Case for Regional Government |
| | 1989 | Good Health: Labour's Proposals for Health in the North |
| Mitchell, Austin | 1962 | New Zealand Politics in Action |
| | 1966 | Government by Party |
| | 1969 | Whips in Opposition: 1815-1830 |
| | 1970 | Politics and People in New Zealand |
| | 1971, 1988 | Yorkshire Jokes |
| | 1974 | The Half-Gallon Quarter-Acre Pavlova-Paradise |
| | 1979 | Can Labour Win Again? |
| | 1981 | Yes Maggie - There is an Alternative |
| | 1982 | Westminster Man |
| | 1983 | The Case for Labour |
| | 1983 | Four Years in the Death of the Labour Party |
| | 1988 | Teach Thissen Tyke |
| | 1989 | Britain, Beyond the Blue Horizon |
| | 1989 | Competitive Socialism |
| | 1993 | Accounting for Change |
| | 1995 | Election'45 |
| | 1996 | Corporate Governance Matters |
| | 1996 | The Common Fisheries Policy: End or Mend? |
| | 1997 | Last Time: Labour's Lessons from the Sixties |
| | 1997 | Fishermen: The Rise and Fall of Deep Water Trawling |
| | 1999 | Farewell My Lords |
| | 1999 | Parliament in Pictures |
| | 2002 | Pavlova Paradise Revisited |
| | 2003 | They Came to Yorkshire |
| | 2003 | Yorkshire Thoughts |
| Mullin, Chris | 1982 | A Very British Coup |
| | 1986 | The Last Man Out of Saigon |
| | 1986 | Error of Judgement - The Truth About the Birmingham Bombings |
| | 1991 | The Year of the Fire Monkey |

# M P s  –  P U B L I C A T I O N S

| Author | Date Published | Title of Publication |
|---|---|---|
| Paisley, Rev Ian | 1959 | History of the 1859 Revival |
| | 1960 | Christian Foundations |
| | 1966/67 | Ravenhill Pulpit Vol 1 - 2 |
| | 1968 | Exposition of the Epistle to the Romans |
| | 1970 | Billy Graham and the Church of Rome |
| | 1972 | The Massacre of St Bartholomew |
| | 1976 | America's Debt to Ulster (joint author) |
| | 1981 | Ulster - The Facts |
| | 1982 | No Pope Here |
| | 1982 | Dr Kidd |
| | 1983 | Those Flaming Tennents |
| | 1985 | Mr Protestant |
| | 1986 | Be Sure |
| | 1987/90 | Paisley's Pocket Preacher Vol I - IV |
| | 1987 | Jonathan Edwards: The Theologian of Revival |
| | 1989 | Union with Rome |
| | 1990 | The Revised English Bible: An Exposure |
| | 1994 | What a Friend we have in Jesus |
| | 1995 | Understanding Events in Northern Ireland: An Introduction for Americans |
| Palmer, Dr Nick | 1985 | The Comprehensive Guide to Board Wargaming |
| | 1987 | The Best of Board Wargaming |
| | 1990 | Beyond the Arcade |
| | 1998 | Parliamentary Portions: A Gourmet Guide to the new House of Commons |
| Pearson, Ian | 2000 | Universities and Innovation: Meeting the Challenge |
| Perham, Linda | 1971 | Directory of GLC Library Resources |
| | 1973 | Libraries of London |
| | 1977 | How to Find Out in French |
| Plaskitt, James | 1982 | America in Perspective (joint author) |
| | 2000 | Beyond 2002 - Long Term Prospects for Labour |
| Pond, Chris | 1975 | Inflation and Low Incomes |
| | 1976 | Trade Unions and Taxation |
| | 1977 | To Him Who Hath (joint author) |
| | 1978 | The Poverty Trap: A Study in Statistical Sources |
| | 1980 | Taxing Wealth Inequalities |
| | 1981 | Taxation and Social Policy |
| | 1983 | Low Pay: Labour's Response |
| Price, Adam | 1992 | The Welsh Renaissance: The Innovation and Inward Investment in Wales |
| | 1993 | Rebuilding our Communities: A New Agenda for the Valleys |
| | 1994 | Quiet Revolution?: Language, Culture and Economy in the Nineties |
| | 1996 | The Diversity Dividend |
| | 1998 | The Other Wales: The Case for Objective 1 Funding Post 1999 |
| | 1999 | The Collective Entrepreneur |
| Raynsford, Rt Hon Nick | 1982 | A Guide to Housing Benefits |
| Redwood, Rt Hon John | 1975, 1997 | Reason, Ridicule and Religion |
| | 1987 | Popular Capitalism |
| | 1987 | Going for Broke |
| | 1987 | Public Enterprise in Crisis |
| | 1994 | The Global Marketplace |
| | 1997 | Our Currency, Our Country |
| | 1999 | The Death of Britain? |
| | 2001 | Stars and Strife |
| | 2001 | Just Say No |
| | 2002 | Third Way – Which Way? |
| Robinson, Geoffrey | 2000 | The Unconventional Minister |

# M P s  –  P U B L I C A T I O N S

| Author | Date Published | Title of Publication |
|---|---|---|
| Robinson, Peter | 1970 | The North Answers Back |
| | 1978 | Capital Punishment for Capital Crime |
| | 1981 | Self Inflicted |
| | 1981 | Ulster in Peril |
| | 1981 | Savagery and Suffering |
| | 1982 | Ulster - The Facts |
| | 1989 | Their Cry Was "No Surrender" |
| Roe, Dame Marion | 1985 | The Labour Left in London - A Blueprint for a Socialist Britain |
| | 1986 | Fair Comment |
| Rosindell, Andrew | 1993 | Defending Our Great Heritage (joint author) |
| Ruddock, Joan | 1987 | CND Scrapbook |
| Sanders, Adrian | 1991 | Service with a Smile |
| | 1992 | Service Beyond a Smile |
| Sedgemore, Brian | 1977 | Mr Secretary of State |
| | 1978 | The How and Why of Socialism |
| | 1980 | Power Failure |
| | 1990 | Pitiless Pursuit |
| | 1995 | Big Bang 2000 |
| | 1995 | The Insider's Guide to Parliament |
| Sheerman, Barry | 1993 | Harold Laski: A Life on the Left |
| Shephard, Rt Hon Gillian | 1999 | Reform of Local Government |
| | 2000 | Shephard's Watch |
| Simpson, Alan | 1981 | Stacking the Decks - A Study of Race, Inequality and Council Housing |
| | 1988 | Cuckoos in the Nest: Urban Regeneration Policies |
| | 1991 | Against a Rising Tide: Racism and Europe |
| | 1994 | Beyond the Famished Road: New Policies for Common Security |
| Simpson, Keith | 1981 | The Old Contemptibles |
| | 1985 | History of the German Army |
| | 1985 | A Nation in Arms (editor) |
| | 1987 | The War the Infantry Knew (editor) |
| | 1990 | Waffen SS |
| Smith, Rt Hon Chris | 1996 | New Questions for Socialism |
| | 1998 | Creative Britain |
| Smith, Llew | | The Politics of Poverty in Blaenau Gwent |
| | | Bombing Ahead with Disarmament |
| | | Quangos - Not so Much a Bonfire, More a Damp Squib |
| Soley, Clive | 2000 | Regulating the Press (co-author) |
| Spelman, Caroline | 1991 | A Green and Pleasant Land |
| | 1994 | Non-Food Uses of Agricultural Raw Materials |
| Spicer, Sir Michael | 1981 | Final Act |
| | 1986 | Prime Minister Spy |
| | 1989 | Cotswold Manners |
| | 1990 | Cotswold Murders |
| | 1992 | Cotswold Mistress |
| | 1992 | A Treaty Too Far - A New Policy for Europe |
| | 1993 | Cotswold Moles |
| | 1996 | The Challenge from the East and the Rebirth of the West |
| Steen, Anthony | 1980 | P.L.U.M.S |
| | 1982 | New Life for Old Cities |
| | 1993 | Tested Ideas for Political Success |
| Stoate, Dr Howard | 2002 | All's Well that Starts Well; Strategy for Children's Health (joint author) |
| Straw, Rt Hon Jack | 1992 | Policy and Ideology |
| Stuart, Gisela | 2003 | The Making of Europe's Constitution |
| Stunell, Andrew | 1999 | Clean and Green to 2050 |
| | 2001 | Nuclear Waste - Cleaning up the Mess |
| Taylor, Rt Hon Ann | 1991 | Choosing our Future |

| Author | Date Published | Title of Publication |
|---|---|---|
| Taylor, Ian | 1988 | Fair Shares for all the Workers |
| | 1990 | Releasing the Community Spirit |
| | 1992 | A Community of Employee Shareholders |
| | 1993 | The Positive Europe |
| | 1995 | Escaping the Protectionist Trap |
| | 1996 | Networking |
| | 2000 | Restoring the Balance |
| | 2001 | Full Steam Ahead |
| | 2002 | Europe: Our Case |
| | 2002 | Shaping the New Europe - The British Opportunity |
| | 2003 | Twin Towers: Europe and America |
| | 2003 | Corporate Social Responsibility - Should Business be Socially Aware? |
| Taylor, John | 2003 | Please Stay to the Adjournment |
| Taylor, Sir Teddy | 1967 | Hearts of Stone |
| Thomas, Gareth R | 2001 | At the Energy Crossroads: Policies for a Low Carbon Economy |
| | 2002 | From Margins to Mainstream: Making Social Responsibility Part of Corporate Culture |
| Thomas, Simon | 1966 | As Good as Our Words |
| Twigg, Stephen | 1997 | The Cross We Bear - Electoral Reform for Local Government |
| Tyler, Paul | 1996 | Country Lives, Country Landscapes |
| Tyrie, Andrew | 1996 | The Prospects for Public Spending |
| | 1998 | Sense on EMU |
| | 1998 | Reforming the Lords - A Conservative Approach |
| | 2000 | Leviathan at Large: The New Regulator for the Financial Markets (joint-author) |
| | 2000 | Mr Blair's Poodle: An Agenda for Reviving the House of Commons |
| | 2001 | Back from the Brink |
| | 2002 | Statism by Stealth: New Labour, New Collectivism (joint author) |
| | 2003 | Axis of Instability: America, Britain and the New World Order After Iraq |
| Vaz, Keith | 1997 | Law Reform Now |
| Webb, Steven | | Inequality in the UK |
| Whitehead, Dr Alan | 1999 | Beyond 2001: Long Term Policies for Labour (joint author) |
| Whittingdale, John | 1995 | New Policies for the Media |
| Wicks, Malcolm | 1978 | Old and Cold: Hypothermia and Social Policy |
| | 1987 | A Future for All: Do We Need a Welfare State ? |
| Widdecombe, Rt Hon Ann | 2000 | The Clematis Tree |
| | 2002 | An Act of Treachery |
| Wilkinson, John | 1982 | The Uncertain Ally - British Defence 1960-1990 (joint author) |
| | 1987 | British Defence - A Blueprint for Reform (joint author) |
| Willetts, David | 1992 | Modern Conservatism |
| | 1994 | Civic Conservatism |
| | 1996 | Blair's Gurus |
| | 1997 | Why Vote Conservative? |
| | 1997 | Is Conservatism Dead? (joint author) |
| | 1998 | Welfare to Work |
| | 1999 | After the Landslide |
| | 2000 | Browned Off: What's Wrong with Gordon Brown's Social Policy |
| | 2002 | Tax Credits: Do They Add Up? |
| | 2003 | Left Out, Left Behind |
| | 2003 | Old Europe? Demographic Change and Pension Reform |
| Williams, Hywel | 1988 | Geirfa Gwaith Cymdeithasol: A Social Work Vocabulary (editor) |
| | 1993 | Geirfa Gwaith Plant: Child Care Terms (general editor) |
| | 1994 | Llawlyfr Hyfforddi a Hyfforddiant: An Index of Trainers and Training |
| | 1998 | Gofal - A Training and Resource Pack for Community Care in Wales (joint editor) |
| Wilshire, David | 1987 | Scene from the Hill |
| Wilson, Rt Hon Brian | 1988 | Celtic - A Century with Honour |

## M P s  –  P U B L I C A T I O N S

| Author | Date Published | Title of Publication |
|---|---|---|
| Woodward, Shaun | 1983 | Tranquillisers: A Study of Transqulliser Dependency (joint author) |
| | 1984 | Ben: The Story of Ben Hardwick (joint author) |
| | 1985 | Drugwatch: A Study of Hard Drug Addiction (joint author) |
| Wright, Dr Tony | 1997 | Why Vote Labour? |
| | 1997 | The People's Party (joint author) |
| | 1999 | The New Social Democracy (joint editor) |
| | 2000 | The British Political Process (editor) |
| | 2003 | British Politics: A Very Short Introduction |
| Young, Rt Hon Sir George | 1973 | Tourism: Blessing or Blight? |

# M E M B E R S   O F   T H E   H O U S E   O F   L O R D S

*Note: (i) Members of the House of Lords are listed below according to their political affiliation. This list also includes peers of no party affiliation – ie. those who have registered as Cross Benchers and other peers. Peers on Leave of Absence are not included. None of the Lords Spiritual has any political affiliation.*

*(ii) The following abbreviations are used:*

| | | | |
|---|---|---|---|
| *Abp* | *Archbishop* | *E* | *Earl* |
| *Bp* | *Bishop* | *L* | *Lord (Baron)* |
| *Bs* | *Baroness* | *Ly* | *Lady* |
| *C* | *Countess* | *M* | *Marquess* |
| *V* | *Viscount* | *D* | *Duke* |

*(iii) Hereditary Peers (sitting by virtue of an hereditary peerage) are denoted by\*.*

*(iv) Correspondence should be addressed to the House of Lords, Westminster, London, SW1A 0PW. The main switchboard number is Tel: (020) 7219 3000.*

*(v) To contact the House of Lords Information Office, Tel: (020) 7219 3107.*

*(vi) For further information on members of the House of Lords and its procedures, see The Guide to the House of Lords, published annually by Carlton Publishing and Printing Ltd.*

## Conservative

### A

Alexander of Weedon, L
Anelay of St Johns, Bs
Arran, E*
Ashcroft, L
Astor, V*
Astor of Hever, L*
Attlee, E*

### B

Bagri, L
Baker of Dorking, L
Barber, L
Bell, L
Belstead, L
Biffen, L
Black of Crossharbour, L
Blackwell, L
Blaker, L
Blatch, Bs
Blyth of Rowington, L
Bowness, L
Bridgeman, V*
Brigstocke, Bs
Brittan of Spennithorne, L
Brooke of Sutton Mandeville, L
Brougham and Vaux, L*
Burnham, L*
Buscombe, Bs
Buxton of Alsa, L
Byford, Bs

### C

Caithness, E*
Campbell of Alloway, L
Campbell of Croy, L
Carlisle of Bucklow, L
Carnegy of Lour, Bs
Carr of Hadley, L
Carrington, L
Cavendish of Furness, L
Chadlington, L
Chalker of Wallasey, Bs
Chilver, L
Clark of Kempston, L
Cockfield, L

Coe, L
Colwyn, L*
Cope of Berkeley, L
Courtown, E*
Crathorne, L
Crawford and Balcarres, E
Crickhowell, L
Cuckney, L
Cumberlege, Bs

### D

Dean of Harptree, L
Deedes, L
Denham, L*
Dixon-Smith, L
Dundee, E*

### E

Eccles of Moulton, Bs
Eden of Winton, L
Elles, Bs
Elliott of Morpeth, L
Elton, L*

### F

Feldman, L
Ferrers, E*
Flather, Bs
Fookes, Bs
Forsyth of Drumlean, L
Fowler, L
Fraser of Carmyllie, L
Freeman, L

### G

Gardner of Parkes, Bs
Garel-Jones, L
Geddes, L*
Gilmour of Craigmillar, L
Glenarthur, L*
Glentoran, L*
Goschen, V*
Gray of Contin, L
Griffiths of Fforestfach, L

### H

Hanham, Bs
Hanningfield, L
Hanson, L
Harris of Peckham, L
Hayhoe, L.
Henley, L*
Heseltine, L
Higgins, L
Hodgson of Astley Abbotts, L
Hogg, Bs
Home, E*
Hooper, Bs
Howard of Rising, L
Howe, E*
Howe of Aberavon, L
Howell of Guildford, L
Hunt of Wirral, L
Hurd of Westwell, L

### I

Inglewood, L*

### J

James of Holland Park, Bs
Jellicoe, E
Jenkin of Roding, L
Jopling, L

### K

Kalms, L
Keith of Castleacre, L
Kelvedon, L
Kimball, L
King of Bridgwater, L
Kingsland, L
Kirkham, L
Knight of Collingtree, Bs

### L

Laidlaw, L
Laing of Dunphail, L
Lamont of Lerwick, L
Lane of Horsell, L
Lang of Monkton, L
Lawson of Blaby, L
Lindsay, E*
Liverpool, E*
Lloyd-Webber, L

# MEMBERS OF THE HOUSE OF LORDS

## *Conservative (Continued)*

Lucas, L*
Luke, L*
Lyell, L*

### M
McAlpine of West Green, L
McColl of Dulwich, L
Macfarlane of Bearsden, L
MacGregor of Pulham Market, L
Mackay of Clashfern, L
MacLaurin of Knebworth, L
Mancroft, L*
Marlesford, L
Mayhew of Twysden, L
Miller of Hendon, Bs
Monro of Langholm, L
Montagu of Beaulieu, L*
Montrose, D*
Moore of Lower Marsh, L
Morris of Bolton, Bs
Mowbray and Stourton, L*
Moynihan, L*
Murton of Lindisfarne, L

### N
Naseby, L
Newton of Braintree, L
Noakes, Bs
Northbrook, L*
Northesk, E*
Norton of Louth, L

### O
O'Cathain, Bs
Onslow, E*
Oppenheim-Barnes, Bs

### P
Palumbo, L
Park of Monmouth, Bs
Parkinson, L
Patten, L
Peel, E*
Perry of Southwark, Bs
Peyton of Yeovil, L
Pilkington of Oxenford, L
Platt of Writtle, Bs
Plumb, L
Plummer of St Marylebone, L
Prior, L
Pym, L

### Q
Quinton, L

### R
Rawlings, Bs
Rawlinson of Ewell, L
Reay, L*
Rees, L
Renfrew of Kaimsthorn, L
Renton, L

Renton of Mount Harry, L
Roberts of Conwy, L
Rotherwick, L*

### S
Saatchi, L
Sainsbury of Preston Candover, L
St John of Fawsley, L
Sanderson of Bowden, L
Seccombe, Bs
Selborne, E*
Selkirk of Douglas, L
Selsdon, L*
Sharples, Bs
Shaw of Northstead, L
Sheppard of Didgemere, L
Skelmersdale, L*
Soulsby of Swaffham Prior, L
Sterling of Plaistow, L
Stewartby, L
Strathclyde, L*
Swinfen, L*

### T
Taylor of Warwick, L
Tebbit, L
Thatcher, Bs
Thomas of Gwydir, L
Trefgarne, L*
Trenchard, V*
Trumpington, Bs
Tugendhat, L

### U
Ullswater, V*

### V
Vinson, L

### W
Waddington, L
Wade of Chorlton, L
Wakeham, L
Waldegrave of North Hill, L
Walker of Worcester, L
Wilcox, Bs
Windlesham, L
Wolfson, L
Wolfson of Sunningdale, L

### Y
Young of Graffham, L

## *Labour*

### A
Acton, L
Ahmed, L
Alli, L
Amos, Bs
Andrews, Bs
Archer of Sandwell, L
Ashley of Stoke, L

Ashton of Upholland, Bs
Attenborough, L

### B
Bach, L
Barnett, L
Bassam of Brighton, L
Berkeley, L
Bernstein of Craigwell, L
Bhattacharjja, L
Billingham, Bs
Blackstone, Bs
Blood, Bs
Borrie, L
Bragg, L
Brennan, L
Brooke of Alverthorpe, L
Brookman, L
Brooks of Tremorfa, L
Bruce of Donington, L
Burlison, L

### C
Callaghan of Cardiff, L
Campbell-Savours, L
Carter, L
Chandos, V
Christopher, L
Clark of Windermere, L
Clarke of Hampstead, L
Clinton-Davis, L
Cohen of Pimlico, Bs
Corbett of Castle Vale, L
Crawley, Bs

### D
David, Bs
Davies of Coity, L
Davies of Oldham, L
Dean of Thornton-le-Fylde, Bs
Desai, L
Dixon, L
Donoughue, L
Drayson, L
Dubs, L

### E
Eatwell, L
Elder, L
Evans of Parkside, L
Evans of Temple Guiting, L
Evans of Watford, L
Ewing of Kirkford, L

### F
Falconer of Thoroton, L
Falkender, Bs
Farrington of Ribbleton, Bs
Faulkner of Worcester, L
Filkin, L
Fyfe of Fairfield, L

# MEMBERS OF THE HOUSE OF LORDS

## Labour (Continued)

### G

Gale, Bs
Gavron, L
Gibson of Market Rasen, L
Giddens, L
Gilbert, L
Glenamara, L
Golding, Bs
Goldsmith, L
Gordon of Strathblane, L
Goudie, Bs
Gould of Potternewton, Bs
Grabiner, L
Graham of Edmonton, L
Grantchester, L*
Gregson, L
Griffiths of Pembrey and Burry Port
Grocott, L.

### H

Harris of Haringey, L
Harrison, L
Hart of Chilton, L
Haskel, L
Haskins, L
Hattersley, L
Haworth, L
Hayman, Bs
Healey, L
Henig, Bs
Hilton of Eggardon, Bs
Hogg of Cumbernauld, L
Hollick, L
Hollis of Heigham, Bs
Howells of St Davies, Bs
Howie of Troon, L
Hoyle, L
Hughes of Woodside, L
Hunt of Chesterton, L
Hunt of Kings Heath, L

### I

Irvine of Lairg, L

### J

Janner of Braunstone, L
Jay of Paddington, Bs
Jeger, Bs
Jones, L
Jordan, L
Judd, L

### K

Kennedy of The Shaws, Bs
King of West Bromwich, L
Kirkhill, L

### L

Layard, L
Lea of Crondall, L
Leitch, L
Levy, L
Lipsey, L
Lockwood, Bs
Lofthouse of Pontefract, L

### M

McCarthy, L
McDonagh, Bs
Macdonald of Tradeston, L
McIntosh of Haringey, L
McIntosh of Hudnall, Bs
MacKenzie of Culkein, L
Mackenzie of Framwellgate, L
McKenzie of Luton, L
Mallalieu, Bs
Mason of Barnsley, L
Massey of Darwen, Bs
Maxton, L
Merlyn-Rees, L
Mishcon, L
Mitchell, L
Morgan, L
Morgan of Drefelin, Bs
Morgan of Huyton, Bs
Morris of Aberavon, L
Morris of Manchester, L

### N

Nicol, Bs
Northfield, L

### O

Orme, L

### P

Parekh, L
Patel of Blackburn, L
Paul, L
Pendry, L
Peston, L
Pitkeathley, Bs
Plant of Highfield, L
Ponsonby of Shulbrede, L
Prosser, Bs
Prys-Davies, L
Puttnam, L

### R

Radice, L
Ramsay, of Cartvale, Bs
Randall of St Budeaux, L
Rea, L*
Rendell of Babergh, Bs
Renwick of Clifton, L
Richard, L
Robertson of Port Ellen, L
Rogers of Riverside, L
Rooker, L
Rosser, L
Rowlands, L
Royall of Blaisdon, Bs

### S

Sainsbury of Turville, L
Sawyer, L
Scotland of Asthal, Bs
Sewel, L
Sheldon, L
Sheppard of Liverpool, L
Simon, V*
Simon of Highbury, L
Simpson of Dunkeld, L
Smith of Gilmorehill, Bs
Smith of Leigh, L
Snape, L
Stallard, L
Stone of Blackheath, L
Strabolgi, L*
Symons of Vernham Dean, Bs

### T

Taylor of Blackburn, L
Temple-Morris, L
Thomas of Macclesfield, L
Thornton, Bs
Tomlinson, L
Triesman, L
Truscott, L
Tunnicliffe, L
Turnberg, L
Turner of Camden, Bs

### U

Uddin, Bs

### V

Varley, L

### W

Wall of New Barnet, Bs
Warner, L
Warwick of Undercliffe, Bs
Watson of Invergowrie, L
Wedderburn of Charlton, L
Whaddon, L
Whitaker, Bs
Whitty, L
Wilkins, Bs
Williams of Elvel, L
Winston, L
Woolmer of Leeds, L

### Y

Young of Norwood Green, L

## Liberal Democrat

### A

Addington, L*
Alderdice, L
Ashdown of Norton-sub-Hamdon, L
Avebury, L*

# MEMBERS OF THE HOUSE OF LORDS

## *Liberal Democrat (Continued)*

### B
Barker, Bs
Bonham-Carter of Yarnbury, Bs
Bradshaw, L

### C
Carlile of Berriew, L
Clement-Jones, L

### D
Dahrendorf, L
Dholakia, L
Dykes, L

### E
Ezra, L

### F
Falkland, V*
Falkner of Margravine, Bs
Fearn, L

### G
Garden, L
Goodhart, L
Greaves, L

### H
Hamwee, Bs
Harris of Richmond, Bs
Holme of Cheltenham, L
Hooson, L
Hutchinson of Lullington, L

### J
Jacobs, L

### L
Lester of Herne Hill, L
Linklater of Butterstone, Bs
Livsey of Talgarth, L
Ludford, Bs

### M
Mackie of Benshie, L
Maclennan of Rogart, L
McNally, L
Maddock, Bs
Mar and Kellie, E
Methuen, L*
Michie of Gallanach, Bs
Miller of Chilthorne Domer, Bs

### N
Neuberger, Bs
Newby, L
Nicholson of Winterbourne, Bs
Northover, Bs

### O
Oakeshott of Seagrove Bay, L

### P
Phillips of Sudbury, L

### R
Razzall, L
Redesdale, L
Rennard, L
Roberts of Llandudno, L
Rodgers of Quarry Bank, L
Roper, L
Russell, E*
Russell-Johnston, L

### S
Sandberg, L
Scott of Needham Market, Bs
Sharman, L
Sharp of Guildford, Bs
Shutt of Greetland, L
Smith of Clifton, L
Steel of Aikwood, L

### T
Taverne, L
Thomas of Gresford, L
Thomas of Walliswood, Bs
Thomson of Monifieth, L
Tope, L
Tordoff, L

### W
Wallace of Saltaire, L
Walmsley, Bs
Watson of Richmond, L
Wigoder, L
Williams of Crosby, Bs

## *Cross Bench*

### A
Ackner, L
Adebowale, L
Allenby of Megiddo, V*
Allen of Abbeydale, L
Alton of Liverpool, L
Ampthill, L*
Armstrong of Ilminster, L

### B
Baldwin of Bewdley, E*
Ballyedmond, L
Barber of Tewkesbury, L
Best, L
Bhatia, L
Bingham of Cornhill, L
Birt, L
Bledisloe, V*

Boothroyd, Bs
Boston of Faversham, L
Boyce, L
Brabazon of Tara, L*
Bramall, L
Bridge of Harwich, L
Bridges, L*
Briggs, L
Brightman, L
Broers, L
Brookeborough, V*
Brown of Easton-under-Heywood, L
Browne of Madingley, L
Browne-Wilkinson, L
Burns, L
Butler of Brockwell, L

### C
Cameron of Lochbroom, L
Carey of Clifton, L
Carswell, L
Chalfont, L
Chan, L
Chapple, L
Chitnis, L
Cholmondeley, M*
Chorley, L*
Clyde, L
Cobbold, L*
Colville of Culross, V*
Condon, L
Cooke of Islandreagh, L
Cooke of Thorndon, L
Craig of Radley, L
Craigavon, V*
Croham, L
Cullen of Whitekirk, L
Currie of Marylebone, L

### D
Darcy de Knayth, Bs*
Dearing, L
Donaldson of Lymington, L
Dunn, Bs

### E
Eames, L
Elis-Thomas, L
Elystan-Morgan, L
Emerton, Bs
Erroll, E*

### F
Fellowes, L
Finlay of Llandaff, L
Flowers, L
Foster of Thames Bank, L
Freyberg, L*

# MEMBERS OF THE HOUSE OF LORDS

## Cross Bench (Continued)

### G
Goff of Chieveley, L
Greenfield, Bs
Greengross, Bs
Greenway, L*
Griffiths, L
Guthrie of Craigiebank, L

### H
Habgood, L
Hale of Richmond, Bs
Hannay of Chiswick
Hardie, L
Harris of High Cross, L
Hoffman, L
Hope of Craighead, L
Howarth of Breckland, Bs
Howe of Idlicote, Bs
Hunt of Tanworth, L
Hussey of North Bradley, L
Hutton, L
Hylton, L*

### I
Imbert, L
Inge, L

### J
Jauncey of Tullichettle, L
Joffe, L

### K
Kilcooney, L
Kilpatrick of Kincraig, L
Kingsdown, L
Knights, L

### L
Laird, L
Laming, L
Lane, L
Levene of Portsoken, L
Lewis of Newnham, L
Listowel, E*
Lloyd of Berwick, L
Lloyd of Highbury, Bs
Luce, L

### M
McCluskey, L
McFarlane of Llandaff, Bs
Mackay of Drumadoon, L
Maginnis of Drumglass
Mar, C*
Marsh, L
Marshall of Knightsbridge, L
Masham of Ilton, B
May of Oxford, L
Millett, L

Molyneaux of Killead, L
Monson, L*
Moore of Wolvercote, L
Moran, L*
Moser, L
Murphy, Bs
Mustill, L

### N
Neill of Bladen, L
Nicholls of Birkenhead, L
Nickson, L
Nolan, L
Norfolk, D*
Northbourne, L*

### O
Oliver of Aylmerton, L
O'Neill of Bengarve, Bs
Ouseley, L
Owen, L
Oxburgh, L

### P
Palmer, L*
Patel, L
Phillips of Worth Matravers, L
Powell of Bayswater, L
Prashar, Bs

### Q
Quirk, L

### R
Rana, L
Rees-Mogg, L
Richardson, L
Richardson of Calow, Bs
Richardson of Duntisbourne, L
Rix, L
Rodger of Earlsferry, L
Rogan, L
Roll of Ipsden, L
Rosslyn, E*
Ryder of Wensum, L

### S
Saltoun of Abernethy, Ly*
Sandwich, E*
Saville of Newdigate, L
Scarman, L
Scott of Foscote. l
Simon of Glaisdale, L
Skidelsky, L
Slim, V*
Slynn of Hadley, L
Snowdon, E
Stern, Bs
Stevenson of Coddenham, L
Steyn, L
St John of Bletso, L*
Stokes, L
Strange, Bs*
Sutherland of Houndwood, L

### T
Tanlaw, L
Templeman, L
Tenby, V*
Thomas of Swynnerton, L
Tombs, L

### V
Vincent of Coleshill, L

### W
Walker of Gestingthorpe, L
Walpole, L*
Walton of Detchant, L
Warnock, Bs
Waverley, V*
Weatherill, L
Weidenfeld, L
Williamson of Horton, L
Wilson of Dinton, L
Wilson of Tillyorn, L
Woolf, L
Wright of Richmond, L

### Y
Young of Hornsey, Bs

## Others

### A
Archer of Weston-super-Mare, L

### B
Beaumont of Whittey, L

### C
Cox, Bs

### F
Fitt, L

### G
Grenfell, L

### P
Pearson of Rannock, L

### S
Shrewsbury, E
Stevens of Ludgate, L
Stoddart of Swindon, L

### W
Willoughby de Broke, L*

### Y
Young of Old Scone, Bs

# MEMBERS OF THE HOUSE OF LORDS

## *Lords Spiritual*

### *C*
Canterbury, Abp
Chelmsford, Bp
Chester, Bp
Coventry, Bp

### *D*
Derby, Bp
Durham, Bp

### *L*
Leicester, Bp
Liverpool, Bp
London, Bp

### *M*
Manchester, Bp

### *N*
Newcastle, Bp
Norwich, Bp

### *O*
Oxford, Bp

### *P*
Peterborough, Bp
Portsmouth, Bp

### *R*
Rochester, Bp

### *S*
St Albans, Bp
St Edmundsbury and Ipswich, Bp
Salisbury, Bp
Sheffield, Bp
Southwark, Bp
Southwell, Bp

### *T*
Truro, Bp

### *W*
Winchester, Bp
Worcester, Bp

### *Y*
York, Abp

# LEADER OF THE HOUSE OF LORDS' OFFICE

Cabinet Office
70 Whitehall
London, SW1A 2AT
Tel: (020) 7270 0501  Fax: (020) 7270 0491

House of Lords
London SW1A 0PW
Tel: (020) 7219 3201  Fax: (020) 7219 3051

**Leader of the House of Lords and
Lord President of the Council** . . . . . . . . . . . . . . Rt Hon Baroness Amos

Principal Private Secretary . . . . . . . . . . . . . . . . . . . . . Mr Christopher Jacobs . . . . . . . . . . . . . . Tel: (020) 7210 1056

Private Secretary . . . . . . . . . . . . . . . . . . . . . . . . . . . Ms Nicki Daniels . . . . . . . . . . . . . . . . . . . Tel: (020) 7210 1057

Private Secretary (House of Lords) . . . . . . . . . . . . . . Mr Andrew Makower . . . . . . . . . . . . . . . Tel: (020) 7219 3131

Special Advisers . . . . . . . . . . . . . . . . . . . . . . . . . . . . Mr Mark Davies . . . . . . . . . . . . . . . . . . . . Tel: (020) 7210 1066
Mr Matthew Seward . . . . . . . . . . . . . . . . . Tel: (020) 7210 1066
Mr Joe Dancey . . . . . . . . . . . . . . . . . . . . . Tel: (020) 7210 1066

**Deputy Leader of the House of Lords** . . . . . . . . . . Rt Hon Baroness Symons of Vernham Dean
*(also Minister of State, Foreign and Commonwealth Office)*

Press Officer . . . . . . . . . . . . . . . . . . . . . . . . . . . . . . Ms Kasia Reardon . . . . . . . . . . . . . . . . . Tel: (020) 7276 1196

# WHIP'S OFFICES, HOUSE OF LORDS

Government Whips' Office . . . . . . . . . . . . . . . . . . . . . Tel: (020) 7219 3131
*(for further information, see p16 above)*

Conservative Whips' Office . . . . . . . . . . . . . . . . . . . . Tel: (020) 7219 3237

Liberal Democrat Whip's Office . . . . . . . . . . . . . . . . Tel: (020) 7219 3114

*Note: Cross Bench peers do not have a Whip's Office. The convenor of the Cross Bench peers is Lord Craig of Radley, Tel: (020) 7219 2200*

## BRITISH AVIATION

**FOUNDED 1909**

# THE AIR LEAGUE

Broadway House, Tothill Street, London SW1H 9NS

*Telephone:* (020) 7222 8463    *Facsimile:* (020) 7222 8462
*e-mail:* exec@airleague.co.uk    *Web:* http://www.airleague.co.uk

*Contact:* Edward Cox – *The Director*

*The Air League* has been championing the cause of British Aviation since 1909 and is concerned to see that Britain remains strong and competitive in the air.
*A Company Limited by Guarantee No:* 102488

With the *Associate Parliamentary Aerospace Group*, the League draws together members from both Houses of Parliament, a wide cross-section of civil and military aviation, the aerospace industry and other business interests for regular meetings and lectures.

The League promotes air-mindedness in Britain's youth by providing flying scholarships, flying bursaries, and engineering scholarships through the *Air League Educational Trust.*
*Registered Charity No:* 313280

## BRITISH LEGION

# THE ROYAL BRITISH LEGION

48 Pall Mall, London, SW1Y 5JY

*Telephone:* (08457) 725 725
*Facsimile:* (020) 7973 7399
*E-mail:* info@britishlegion.org.uk
*Internet:* http://www.britishlegion.org.uk

*Contact:* I G Townsend – *Secretary-General*

Britain's premier ex-Service organisation for the welfare of ex- Servicemen, women and their dependents. Provides financial assistance, residential and convalescent homes, employment for the disabled, small business advice and loans, resettlement training, free pensions advice and much more, all financed from public donations. Also provides social focus for ex-Service community in branches (2958) and clubs (797) throughout England, Wales and all Ireland.

*Registered Charity No:* 219279

## CHARITIES ASSOCIATION

# ASSOCIATION FOR CHARITIES
83 Priory Gardens, London, N6 5QU

*Telephone* (020) 8348 9114
*Facsimile* (020) 8348 1637
*E-mail* contact@association4charities.org.uk
*Web* http://www.association4charities.org.uk

*Contact* Belinda McKenzie – *AfC Co-ordinator*

The Association for Charities was established in 1999 when a number of charity people, worried about the damaging effects of recent Charity Commission action on certain charities, trustees and beneficiaries, came together to analyse why this had been happening and what could be done about it.

The AfC has an active and committed core membership of past and present trustees, supported by a growing network of associate members and sympathisers throughout England and Wales, and indeed Scotland. We are united by a passion to protect and nurture charity as it is traditionally understood, and for justice.

Our aim is to offer a pastoral service particularly to smaller charities and to build good working relationships with a range of organisations and individuals concerned for standards in public life and/or the health of the charity sector, including the Charity Commission and its appointed Independent Complaints Reviewer. In the wake of the 2002 government report on the charity sector, our efforts are focused on garnering support in Parliament for proposed new legislation, which will make the Commission more accountable and enable charities to appeal against its decisions.

## ETHICS IN TECHNOLOGY AND ENVIRONMENT

# SOCIETY RELIGION AND TECHNOLOGY PROJECT
## CHURCH OF SCOTLAND
**Winner of UK Templeton Prize 1999**

John Knox House, 45 High Street, Edinburgh, EH1 1SR

*Telephone* (0131) 556 2953
*Facsimile* (0131) 556 7478
*E-mail* srtp@srtp.org.uk
*Web* http://www.srtp.org.uk

*Contact* Dr Donald M Bruce – *Director*

SRT is a unique project of the Church of Scotland working at the interface of science and society. It is noted for its balanced non-partisan ethical assessment of current technology, including GM crops, food and animals, cloning and stem cells, science and society, risk, gene patents, climate change, energy policy and globalisation.

*Registered Charity No:* SCO11353

## GREEK CYPRIOT BROTHERHOOD
Britannia Centre, Britannia Road
London, N12 9RU

*Telephone:* (020) 8445 7070  *Facsimile:* (020) 8445 7072

*Contacts:* Haris Sophoclides – *President*
Andreas Karaolis – *Secretary*

The Brotherhood was founded in 1934 with the aims of providing cultural, educational and moral support to the first Cypriot immigrants to Britain and assisting them to settle in their new environment. Its formation provided a focal point for all Cypriots, where they could get help and advice on how to adjust to the conditions of their adopted country. It organised English classes for the community and later the first Greek schools, to assist the younger generation in learning their mother tongue and heritage.

The Brotherhood is the oldest Cypriot association in Britain and has always played a vital role in the life of the Cypriot community. Although its aims have changed with the needs of the community, it continues to initiate and support social and cultural events, in addition to its philanthropic activities. Its history and struggles mirror those of the community itself and it is held with affection by every Cypriot in Britain.

In addition to maintaining close links with Cyprus, it devotes much of its resources to bring to the attention of all freedom and peace loving people the injustice being suffered by all Cypriot people as a result of the Turkish invasion of the island in July 1974 and the need for a just and viable solution to the Cyprus problem, which will bring peace to the island and stability in the region.

## EXECUTIVE SEARCH AND RECRUITMENT

# Hays Executive
## Search & Selection
1 Southampton Street, London, WC2R 0LR

*Telephone* (020) 7520 5960
*Facsimile* (020) 7520 5991
*Web* http://www.hayspersonnel.com

*Contact* Chris McCarthy – *Head of Business, Public Sector*

Hays Personnel Services, listed on the FTSE 100, is the UK's largest specialist recruitment business. In 1991, Hays was the first national consultancy to establish a division concentrating on servicing publicly funded and voluntary/not for profit organisations. Since this time we have built a Public Sector Division which crosses all specialist recruitment disciplines from Executive Search, Advertised Selection to Interim placement. Hays have developed a network of over 200 offices in the UK and Ireland, with another 100 offices in our International Network, where our specialist divisions understand the regional issues and work closely with clients to deliver tangible and bespoke recruitment solutions. Hays are approved Executive Recruiter's & Assessors for both the Cabinet Office and NHS framework agreements as well as listed S-cat suppliers of interim management services. Hays bring an innovative and pro-active approach in assisting each client to address specific areas of under-representation.

*Specialist divisions for multidisciplinary Search and Selection, Interim Managers, Assessment, Training, Advertising, Outplacement, Relocations and Reorganisations.*

*Committed to Quality and Equality*

## GAMBLING CARE

# GAMCARE

Units 2 & 3 Baden Place, Crosby Row, London, SE1 1YW

Telephone (020) 7378 5200  Facsimile (020) 7378 5233
E-mail info@gamcare.org.uk  Web www.gamcare.org.uk
Helpline: 0845 6000 133

Contact Peter Cox – Managing Director

Gambling care centre for the promotion of responsible gambling, provides:
- Helpline and face-to-face counselling
- Information
- Education and training programmes
- Advises gambling industry on social responsibility issues
- Consultant to government on the social impact of gambling.

*Registered Charity Number* 1060005

## OVERSEAS GOVERNMENT

## FALKLAND ISLANDS GOVERNMENT OFFICE

Falkland House, 14 Broadway
London, SW1H 0BH
*Telephone* (020) 7222 2542
*Facsimile* (020) 7222 2375
*E-mail* rep@falklands.gov.fk
*Web* http://www.falklandislands.com

*Contact* Sukey Cameron MBE – *Representative*

The Falkland Islands Government Office represents the interests of the Falkland Islands Government to the UK Government, Members of Parliament, Media and the general public. Promotes Tourism to the Falkland Islands and assists with recruitment and immigration requirements.

## EUROPE

EUROPEAN
MOVEMENT

## EUROPEAN MOVEMENT

85 Frampton Street
London, NW8 8NQ

*Telephone* (020) 7725 4200
*Facsimile* (020) 7799 2817
*E-mail* info@euromove.org.uk
*Web* www.euromove.org.uk

*Contact* Stephen Woodard – *Director*

The European Movement is Britain's leading pro-European campaigning group. It is independent, all-party and non-profit making. Its mission is to explain to the public the benefits of EU membership, to promote a positive approach to the EU and the European single currency and to argue for reform of the EU, its policies and institutions.

## PUBLIC SERVICE

# ASSOCIATION FOR PUBLIC SERVICE EXCELLENCE

2nd Floor, Washbrook House
Lancastrian Office Centre,
Talbot Road, Old Trafford, Manchester, M32 0FP
*Telephone* (0161) 772 1810
*Facsimile* (0161) 772 1811
*E-mail* enquiries@apse.org.uk
*Web* http://www.apse.org.uk

*Contact* Paul O'Brien – *Chief Executive*

The Association for Public Service Excellence (APSE) is a local authority networking organisation promoting high-quality public services and undertaking a lobbying role on key policy issues. APSE provides a number of services to its membership including consultancy, training, seminars, advice, research, publications, Direct News and Performance Networks (the largest local government benchmarking database in the UK).

## SCIENCE

# BIOSCIENCES FEDERATION

c/o 76 Portland Place, London, W1B 1NT

*Telephone* (020) 7299 4431
*Facsimile* (020) 7637 7626
*E-mail* info@bsf.ac.uk
*Web* http://www.bsf.ac.uk

*Contact* Dr Mike Withnall – *Chief Executive*

An umbrella body of major learned societies from across the whole spectrum of the biosciences, including the Institute of Biology, representing some 60,000 biologists. Provides authoritative information and opinion on developments in the biosciences to government, media and educational authorities on behalf of the biosciences community, and promotes liaison and dialogue within this community. Particularly interested in government/public policy matters regarding the biosciences and their funding; education from school to postgraduate stages; careers; and public communication of science.

## SOCIAL WELFARE

# THE ASSOCIATION OF CHARITY OFFICERS

Unicorn House, Station Close, Potters Bar
Hertfordshire, EN6 3JW

*Telephone* (01707) 651777
*Facsimile* (01707) 660477
E-mail: info@aco.uk.net

*Contact* Mrs Valerie J Barrow – *Chief Executive*

A voice for benevolence and personal social welfare charities, with well over 200 members, all serving individuals in need with grants, advice, counselling, residential care, nursing homes and special housing. ACO is concerned with all aspects of legislation affecting the work of charities and the lives of their beneficiaries.

*Registered Charity No:* 299117

# WHITEHALL

# CABINET OFFICE

70 Whitehall, London, SW1A 2AS
Tel: (020) 7270 1234  Fax: (020) 7210 0557
Web: http://www.cabinet-office.gov.uk

## MINISTERS

**Chancellor of the Duchy of Lancaster** . . . . . . . . . . . . . . Rt Hon Alan Milburn MP
**Minister for the Cabinet Office** . . . . . . . . . . . . . . . . . . Ms Ruth Kelly MP
  *Private Secretary* . . . . . . . . . . . . . . . . . . . . . . . . . . . . . . . Ms Georgia Hutchinson . . . . . . . . . . . . . . . . . Tel: (020) 7276 0652

**Minister without Portfolio** . . . . . . . . . . . . . . . . . . . . . Rt Hon Ian McCartney MP
  *Private Secretary* . . . . . . . . . . . . . . . . . . . . . . . . . . . . . . . Mr Sheridan Burnside . . . . . . . . . . . . . . . . . . Tel: (020) 7276 0636
  *Special Advisers* . . . . . . . . . . . . . . . . . . . . . . . . . . . . . . . Mr Blair McDougall . . . . . . . . . . . . . . . . . . . Tel: (020) 7276 1096
                                                                          Mr Martin O'Donovan . . . . . . . . . . . . . . . . . . Tel: (020) 7276 1093

## CIVIL SERVICE

*70 Whitehall London, SW1A 2AS*
**Secretary of the Cabinet and Head of the**
  **Home Civil Service** . . . . . . . . . . . . . . . . . . . . . . . . . Sir Andrew Turnbull KCB CVO
  *Private Secretary* . . . . . . . . . . . . . . . . . . . . . . . . . . . . . . . Ms Penny Ciniewicz . . . . . . . . . . . . . . . . . . . Tel: (020) 7276 0101

**Security and Intelligence Co-ordinator and**
  **Permanent Secretary, Cabinet Office** . . . . . . . . Sir David Omand KCB
  *Private Secretary* . . . . . . . . . . . . . . . . . . . . . . . . . . . . . . . Mr Sebastian Madden . . . . . . . . . . . . . . . . . . Tel: (020) 7276 0191

**Permanent Secretary, Communications** . . . . . . . . . . . . Mr Howell James
  *Private Secretary* . . . . . . . . . . . . . . . . . . . . . . . . . . . . . . . Ms Ingrid Clifford-Jones . . . . . . . . . . . . . . . . Tel: (020) 7276 1234

## SUBJECT RESPONSIBILITIES AND CONTACTS

**Appointments, Public**
  Head, Public Appointments Unit . . . . . . . . . . . . . . . . . . Ms Elaine Webber . . . . . . . . . . . . . . . . . . . . . . Tel: (020) 7276 2492
  Appointments Policy and Practice . . . . . . . . . . . . . . . . . Ms Belinda Brown . . . . . . . . . . . . . . . . . . . . . . Tel: (020) 7276 1043

**Audit, Internal**
*9 Whitehall, London, SW1A 2DD*
  Head, Internal Audit . . . . . . . . . . . . . . . . . . . . . . . . . . . Mr Peter Norris . . . . . . . . . . . . . . . . . . . . . . . Tel: (020) 7276 5220

**Beacon Scheme** (*See below under Charter Mark and Beacon Unit*)

**Ceremonial Secretariat**
*35 Great Smith Street, London, SW1P 3BQ*
  Ceremonial Officer . . . . . . . . . . . . . . . . . . . . . . . . . . . . Mrs Gay Catto . . . . . . . . . . . . . . . . . . . . . . . . Tel: (020) 7276 2770
  Nominations for Honours . . . . . . . . . . . . . . . . . . . . . . . . . . . . . . . . . . . . . . . . . . . . . . . . . . . . . . . . . . . . . . . . Tel: (020) 7276 2775

**Charter Mark and Beacon Unit**
*Kirkland House, 22 Whitehall, London, SW1A 2WH*
  Head, Charter Mark and Beacon Unit . . . . . . . . . . . . . . Mr Roy Stephenson . . . . . . . . . . . . . . . . . . . . Tel: (020) 7276 1741
  Communications and Marketing . . . . . . . . . . . . . . . . . . Mr Mike Rose . . . . . . . . . . . . . . . . . . . . . . . . Tel: (020) 7276 1751
  Policy and Review . . . . . . . . . . . . . . . . . . . . . . . . . . . . . Ms Jane Jones . . . . . . . . . . . . . . . . . . . . . . . . Tel: (020) 7276 1746

**Civil Contingencies Secretariat**
*10 Great George Street, London, SW1P 3AE*
  Head, Civil Contingencies Secretariat . . . . . . . . . . . . . . Ms Susan Schofield . . . . . . . . . . . . . . . . . . . . Tel: (020) 7276 5061
  Deputy Head . . . . . . . . . . . . . . . . . . . . . . . . . . . . . . . . . Dr John Fuller . . . . . . . . . . . . . . . . . . . . . . . . Tel: (020) 7276 5101
  Directors
    Business and Resources . . . . . . . . . . . . . . . . . . . . . . . Mr Keith Tolladay . . . . . . . . . . . . . . . . . . . . . Tel: (020) 7276 5057
    Capability Management . . . . . . . . . . . . . . . . . . . . . . . Mr Richard Jackson . . . . . . . . . . . . . . . . . . . . Tel: (020) 7276 0031
    Contingency Planning . . . . . . . . . . . . . . . . . . . . . . . . Ms Cheryl Plumridge . . . . . . . . . . . . . . . . . . . Tel: (020) 7270 1234
    UK Resilience . . . . . . . . . . . . . . . . . . . . . . . . . . . . . . Ms Sue Ambler-Edwards . . . . . . . . . . . . . . . . . Tel: (020) 7276 0118
  Emergency Planning College . . . . . . . . . . . . . . . . . . . . . Mr Michael Charlton-Weedy . . . . . . . . . . . . . . . Tel: (020) 7270 1234

# CABINET OFFICE

Parliamentary Intelligence and Security
    Committee Secretariat. . . . . . . . . . . . . . . . . . . . . Mr Alistair Corbett. . . . . . . . . . . . . . . . . . . . . Tel: (020) 7270 1234

**Civil Service College**
*Sunningdale Park, Larch Avenue, Ascot, Berkshire, SL5 0QE*
    Director . . . . . . . . . . . . . . . . . . . . . . . . . . . Mr Ewart Wooldridge. . . . . . . . . . . . . . . . . . . . Tel: (01344) 634000
    Deputy Directors
        Finance and Resources. . . . . . . . . . . . . . . . . . Mr Michael Timmis . . . . . . . . . . . . . . . . . . Tel: (01344) 634374
        Government Group . . . . . . . . . . . . . . . . . . . Ms Eleanor Goodison . . . . . . . . . . . . . . . . . . Tel: (01344) 634321
        International Public Service . . . . . . . . . . . . . . . Mr Bob Stephenson . . . . . . . . . . . . . . . . . . Tel: (020) 7276 1682
        Management Development . . . . . . . . . . . . . . . Mr Martin Barnes. . . . . . . . . . . . . . . . . . . . Tel: (01344) 634330
        Specialist Development . . . . . . . . . . . . . . . . . Ms Shenna Matthews . . . . . . . . . . . . . . . . . Tel: (01344) 634348

**Civil Service: Corporate Development Group**
*(includes Centre for Management and Policy Studies (CMPS), Civil Service College, and Public Appointments Unit)*
*Admiralty Arch, The Mall, London, SW1A 2HW*
    Director-General . . . . . . . . . . . . . . . . . . . . . Ms Alice Perkins CB . . . . . . . . . . . . . . . . . . Tel: (020) 7276 1511
    Directors
        Development . . . . . . . . . . . . . . . . . . . . . . . Mr Richard Kornicki CBE . . . . . . . . . . . . . . . Tel: (020) 7276 1312
        Maximising Talent . . . . . . . . . . . . . . . . . . . Mr John Barker CB . . . . . . . . . . . . . . . . . . . Tel: (020) 7276 1616
        Modernising People Management . . . . . . . . . . . Mr Tim Kemp . . . . . . . . . . . . . . . . . . . . . . Tel: (020) 7276 1643
        Performance Directorate. . . . . . . . . . . . . . . . . Mr Richie Furlong . . . . . . . . . . . . . . . . . . . Tel: (020) 7276 1515
    Agencies and Non-Departmental Public Bodies. . . . . . . . Ms Rosemary Banner . . . . . . . . . . . . . . . . . Tel: (020) 7276 2462
                                 Mr Victor Clayton . . . . . . . . . . . . . . . . . . Tel: (020) 7276 1716
                                 Ms Sharon Wort. . . . . . . . . . . . . . . . . . . . Tel: (020) 7276 0269
    Business Management and Private Office . . . . . . . . . . . Ms Ruth Curry. . . . . . . . . . . . . . . . . . . . . . Tel: (020) 7276 1569
    Conditions and Jobs Evaluation Unit. . . . . . . . . . . . . Mr John Whittaker . . . . . . . . . . . . . . . . . . . Tel: (020) 7276 2229
    Diversity . . . . . . . . . . . . . . . . . . . . . . . . . . . Mr Simon Fryer . . . . . . . . . . . . . . . . . . . . . Tel: (020) 7276 1594
    Fast Stream/FSERS . . . . . . . . . . . . . . . . . . . . . Mr Michael Herron. . . . . . . . . . . . . . . . . . . Tel: (020) 7276 1645
    Job Evaluation . . . . . . . . . . . . . . . . . . . . . . . . Mr John Whittaker . . . . . . . . . . . . . . . . . . . Tel: (020) 7276 2229
    Performance and Reward . . . . . . . . . . . . . . . . . . Mr John Whittaker . . . . . . . . . . . . . . . . . . . Tel: (020) 7276 2229
    Recruitment. . . . . . . . . . . . . . . . . . . . . . . . . . Mr Michael Herron. . . . . . . . . . . . . . . . . . . Tel: (020) 7276 1645
    Statistics . . . . . . . . . . . . . . . . . . . . . . . . . . . Mr Michael Herron. . . . . . . . . . . . . . . . . . . Tel: (020) 7276 1645
    Succession Planning. . . . . . . . . . . . . . . . . . . . . Mr Simon Fryer . . . . . . . . . . . . . . . . . . . . . Tel: (020) 7276 1594

**Civil Service Pensions**
*Grosvenor House, Basingstoke, RG21 4EH*
    Head of Division, Civil Service Pensions. . . . . . . . . . . Mr Derek Pain CBE . . . . . . . . . . . . . . . . . . Tel: (01256) 846548

**Civil Service Selection Board**
*57 Tufton Street, London, SW1P 3QS*
    Head, Civil Service Selection Board . . . . . . . . . . . . . Ms Yvette Radford-Foley . . . . . . . . . . . . . . . Tel: (020) 7276 1632

**Communications** *(See under Press and Communications below)*

**Corporate Services** *(see below under Management, Departmental)*

**Defence and Overseas Affairs Secretariat**
    Director . . . . . . . . . . . . . . . . . . . . . . . . . . . Sir Nigel Sheinwald KCMG . . . . . . . . . . . . . . . Tel: (020) 7276 0107
    Deputy Head of Secretariat. . . . . . . . . . . . . . . . . Mr Desmond Bowen CMG . . . . . . . . . . . . . . . Tel: (020) 7276 0050

**Delivery**
*Prime Minister's Delivery Unit, 1 Horseguards, London, SW1A 2HQ*
    Prime Minister's Chief Adviser on Delivery. . . . . . . . . Professor Michael Barber . . . . . . . . . . . . . . . Tel: (020) 7930 5860

# CABINET OFFICE

**E-Commerce and E-Government**

*Office of the E-Envoy, Stockley House, 130 Wilton Road, London, SW1V 1LQ*
*Web:* http://www.e-envoy.gov.uk

| | | |
|---|---|---|
| E-Envoy | Mr Andrew Pinder | Tel: (020) 7276 3300 |
| Director, Communications | Mr Bill Edwards | Tel: (020) 7276 3014 |
| Director, E-Economy | Mr Graham Walker | Tel: (020) 7276 3274 |
| Director, E-Government | Ms Christina Smyth | Tel: (020) 7276 3165 |
| Press Officer | Mr Ryan Heath | Tel: (020) 7276 0393 |

**Economic and Domestic Affairs**

| | | |
|---|---|---|
| Director | Mr Paul Britton CB | Tel: (020) 7276 0240 |
| Deputy Director | Mr Robin Fellgett | Tel: (020) 7276 0189 |

**Estates, Departmental**

| | | |
|---|---|---|
| Management | Mr Chris Zammit | Tel: (020) 7276 5501 |
| Strategy | Mr Ian Dougal | Tel: (020) 7276 5430 |

**Ethics, Ministerial and Civil Service** *(see below under Propriety and Ethics)*

**European Affairs**

| | | |
|---|---|---|
| EU Adviser to the Prime Minister/Head of Secretariat | Sir Stephen Wall KCMG LVO | Tel: (020) 7968 3364 |
| Deputy Head of Secretariat | Ms Katrina Williams | Tel: (020) 7276 0177 |
| Heads of Division | Mr Philip Hall | Tel: (020) 7276 0605 |
| | Ms Alison Rose | Tel: (020) 7276 0059 |

**Government Information and Communication Service (GICS)**

*10 Great George Street, London, SW1P 3AE*

| | | |
|---|---|---|
| Director General, GICS | Mr Mike Granatt CB | Tel: (020) 7276 0014 |
| Deputy Head | Ms Sue Jenkins | Tel: (020) 7276 5090 |

Government News Network (GNN)

| | | |
|---|---|---|
| Head, GNN | Mr Robert Haslam | Tel: (020) 7276 5166 |

Media Monitoring Unit (MMU)

*70 Whitehall, London, SW1A 2AS*

| | | |
|---|---|---|
| Head, MMU | Ms Emma Thwaites | Tel: (020) 7270 1044 |
| News Distribution Service | Mr Barry Johnson | Tel: (020) 7261 8445 |
| Operations Director | Ms Lyn Salisbury | Tel: (020) 7276 5089 |

Staffing - GICS Development Centre (GICSDS)

*67 Tufton Street, London, SW1P 3QS*

| | | |
|---|---|---|
| Director, GICSDS | Mr Tim Dunmore | Tel: (020) 7276 2700 |
| Deputy Directors, GICSDS | Mr Atula Gor | Tel: (020) 7276 2704 |
| | Mr Viv Shaw | Tel: (020) 7276 2703 |

Regional Directors

| | | |
|---|---|---|
| East Midlands | Mr Peter Smith | Tel: (0115) 971 2781 |
| Eastern | Ms Mary Basham | Tel: (01223) 345714 |
| North East | Mr Chris Child | Tel: (0191) 202 3601 |
| North West | Ms Eileen Jones | Tel: (0161) 952 4501 |
| London and South East | Ms Virginia Burdon | Tel: (020) 7261 8762 |
| Scotland | Ms Elaine Ravenscroft | Tel: (0131) 244 9062 |
| South West and Wales | Mr Peter Whitehead | Tel: (0117) 945 6972 |
| West Midlands | Mr Brent Garner | Tel: (0121) 626 2028 |
| Yorkshire and Humberside | Ms Wendy Miller | Tel: (0113) 283 6590 |

**Her Majesty's Stationery Office**

*Admiralty Arch, The Mall, London, SW1A 2WH*

| | | |
|---|---|---|
| Controller | Mrs Carol Tullo | Tel: (020) 7276 2660 |

**Honours** *(see above under Ceremonial Secretariat)*

# CABINET OFFICE

**IT, Departmental** ................................. Mr Brian Peplow ....................... Tel: (020) 7276 2690

**Joint Intelligence Organisation**
    Chairman *(Vacant)* ............................. Mr William Ehrman ................... Tel: (020) 7276 0333
    Chief of Assessment Staff ...................... Mr Julian Miller ...................... Tel: (020) 7276 0370

**Management, Departmental**
    Managing Director and Cabinet Office Accounting Officer. Mr Colin Balmer CB ................ Tel: (020) 7276 0532
    Directors, Managing Director's Office
        Business Development ...................... Mr John Sweetman ........ Tel: (020) 7276 2548
        Financial Management ...................... Ms Jenny Page ............. Tel: (020) 7210 0570
        Infrastructure ............................... Mr Eric Hepburn ........... Tel: (020) 7276 5423
        Personnel ..................................... Ms Claudette Francis ...... Tel: (020) 7276 6266

**Media Monitoring Unit** *(see above under Government Information and Communication Service)*

**Ministerial Code of Conduct** ...................... Ms Sue Gray ......................... Tel: (020) 7276 2470

**Parliamentary Clerk** .............................. Ms Pauline Reece ................... Tel: (020) 7276 0508

**Pensions (Civil Service)** *(See under Civil Service Pensions above)*

**Performance and Innovation Unit**
*Admiralty Arch, The Mall, London, SW1A 2HW*
    Director ......................................... Mr Geoff Mulgan ................. Tel: (020) 7276 1702
    Deputy Directors ............................... Ms Patricia Greer .............. Tel: (020) 7276 1431
                                   Ms Catriona Laing .............. Tel: (020) 7276 1967
                                   Mr Jamie Rentoul .............. Tel: (020) 7276 1468
    Chief Economist ................................ Mr Stephen Aldridge ........... Tel: (020) 7276 1470
    Chief Social Researcher ....................... Ms Sue Duncan .................. Tel: (020) 7276 1327

**Personnel** *(See above under Management, Departmental)*

**Press and Communications**
    Director of Communications .................... Ms Melanie Leech ............. Tel: (020) 7276 0079
    Deputy Director (Head of News) ............... Mr John Bretherton ......... Tel: (020) 7276 0174
    Head of Publicity .............................. Mr Graham Pike .............. Tel: (020) 7276 5587
    Corporate Communication ..................... Mrs Ann Hall ................. Tel: (020) 7276 5582
    Electronic Communication ..................... Mr Daniel de Cruz ........... Tel: (020) 7276 5583
    Internal Communication ....................... Ms Eileen Meara ............. Tel: (020) 7276 5593
    Marketing ...................................... Mr Ian Hampton ............. Tel: (020) 7276 5588
    Press Officer to E-Government Unit ........... Mr Ryan Heath ............... Tel: (020) 7276 0393
    Press Secretary to Douglas Alexander MP ...... Mr Simon Watts .............. Tel: (020) 7276 1203
    Press Secretary to Rt Hon Baroness Amos ...... Ms Kasia Reardon ............ Tel: (020) 7276 1196
    Press Secretary to Rt Hon Peter Hain MP ...... Ms Des McCartan ............. Tel: (020) 7276 1146
    Press Secretary to Rt Hon Ian McCartney MP ... Ms Sameena Khan ............ Tel: (020) 7276 0311
    Press Secretary to Phil Woolas MP ............ Ms Sameena Khan ............ Tel: (020) 7276 0311

**Private Offices Group**
    Head of Private Offices Group ................. Ms Sue Gray ................. Tel: (020) 7276 2470
    Parliamentary Procedure Adviser .............. Ms Philippa Helme ........... Tel: (020) 7276 0351
        Propriety and Ethics ..................... Mr David Hill ............... Tel: (020) 7276 2471

**Procurement**
    Financial Management Division, Head of Procurement ... Mr Nick Luck ........... Tel: (020) 7276 0577

**Propriety and Ethics** .............................. Ms Sue Gray ......................... Tel: (020) 7276 2470

# CABINET OFFICE

**Public Bodies: Appointments**

Head, Public Appointments Unit . . . . . . . . . . . . . . . Ms Elaine Webber . . . . . . . . . . . . . . . . . . . . . . Tel: (020) 7276 2492

Senior Policy Advisers on Public Appointments . . . . . . . Ms Belinda Brown . . . . . . . . . . . . . . . . . . . . . . Tel: (020) 7276 1043

Public Appointments: Cabinet Office NDPBs . . . . . . . . . Mr Mike Lewis . . . . . . . . . . . . . . . . . . . . . . . . Tel: (020) 7210 0340

**Public Service Reform**

*22 Whitehall, London, SW1A 2WH*

Prime Minister's Chief Adviser on Public Service Reform . Ms Wendy Thomson . . . . . . . . . . . . . . . . . . . . . Tel: (020) 7276 3527

**Records**

*Admiralty Arch, The Mall, London, SW1A 2WH*

Head of Historical and Records Section . . . . . . . . . . . . Mrs Tessa Stirling . . . . . . . . . . . . . . . . . . . . . Tel: (020) 7217 6326

**Reform (Civil Service)**

*Ripley Court, 26 Whitehall, London, SW1A 2WH*

Director, Reform Strategy Group . . . . . . . . . . . . . . . . . Mr Paul Kirby . . . . . . . . . . . . . . . . . . . . . . . . Tel: (020) 7276 5861

**Regulatory Impact Unit**

*Kirkland House, 22 Whitehall, London, SW1A 2WH*

Director, Regulatory Impact Unit . . . . . . . . . . . . . . . . Mr Simon Virley . . . . . . . . . . . . . . . . . . . . . . Tel: (020) 7276 2150

Deputy Directors

    Better Regulation . . . . . . . . . . . . . . . . . . . . . . . . Dr Jeanie Cruickshank . . . . . . . . . . . . . . . . . . Tel: (020) 7276 2140

    Business Regulation . . . . . . . . . . . . . . . . . . . . . . . Ms Shelley Grey . . . . . . . . . . . . . . . . . . . . . . . Tel: (020) 7276 2152

    Economics and Europe . . . . . . . . . . . . . . . . . . . . . Mr Mark Courtney . . . . . . . . . . . . . . . . . . . . . . Tel: (020) 7276 2169

    Regulatory Reform Strategy . . . . . . . . . . . . . . . . . Ms Kate Jennings . . . . . . . . . . . . . . . . . . . . . . Tel: (020) 7276 2197

    Scrutiny . . . . . . . . . . . . . . . . . . . . . . . . . . . . . . Ms Karen Hill . . . . . . . . . . . . . . . . . . . . . . . . . Tel: (020) 7276 2178

    Public Sector . . . . . . . . . . . . . . . . . . . . . . . . . . . Dr Philip Rushbrook . . . . . . . . . . . . . . . . . . . . Tel: (020) 7276 2194

**Security and Intelligence**

Security and Intelligence Co-ordinator and

    Permanent Secretary, Cabinet Office . . . . . . . . . . . . . Sir David Omand KCB . . . . . . . . . . . . . . . . . . . . Tel: (020) 7270 0191

Director, Scope Programme . . . . . . . . . . . . . . . . . . . . Dr Michael Taylor . . . . . . . . . . . . . . . . . . . . . . Tel: (020) 7276 0160

Head, Intelligence and Security Secretariat . . . . . . . . . . Mr John Scarlett CMG OBE . . . . . . . . . . . . . . . . . Tel: (020) 7276 0333

Head, Security Policy Division . . . . . . . . . . . . . . . . . . Mr Steve Reinstadtler . . . . . . . . . . . . . . . . . . . . Tel: (020) 7276 5642

## OTHER RELEVANT CONTACTS

**ADVERTISING**

**Advisory Committee on Advertising** . . . . . . . . . . . . . . . Cabinet Office, 67 Tufton Street, London, SW1P 3QS

Chairman . . . . . . . . . . . . . . . . . . . . . . . . . . . . . . . Mr Dick Emery

Secretary . . . . . . . . . . . . . . . . . . . . . . . . . . . . . . . Ms Attula Gorr . . . . . . . . . . . . . . . . . . . . . . . . Tel: (020) 7276 2704

    E-mail: ira.macmull@coi.gsi.gov.uk

**APPOINTMENTS**

**Advisory Committee on Business Appointments** . . . . . . . 35 Great Smith Street, London, SW1P 3BQ

Chairman . . . . . . . . . . . . . . . . . . . . . . . . . . . . . . . Rt Hon Lord Mayhew of Twysden QC

Secretary . . . . . . . . . . . . . . . . . . . . . . . . . . . . . . . Mr Tony Nichols . . . . . . . . . . . . . . . . . . . . . . . Tel: (020) 7276 2610

    E-mail: tony.nichols@cabinet-office.x.gsi.gov.uk

**Commissioner for Public Appointments** . . . . . . . . . . . . 3rd Floor, 35 Great Smith Street, London, SW1P 3BQ

Commissioner . . . . . . . . . . . . . . . . . . . . . . . . . . . . Dame Rennie Fritchie

Secretary . . . . . . . . . . . . . . . . . . . . . . . . . . . . . . . Mr Jim Barron . . . . . . . . . . . . . . . . . . . . . . . . Tel: (020) 7276 2632

    Web: http://www.ocpa.gov.uk

# CABINET OFFICE

**CIVIL SERVICE**

**Civil Service Appeal Board** . . . . . . . . . . . . . . . . . . . . . . . 11 Belgrave Road, London, SW1V 1RB

    Chairman . . . . . . . . . . . . . . . . . . . . . . . . . . . . . . . . . . . . . Mr John Davies

    Secretary . . . . . . . . . . . . . . . . . . . . . . . . . . . . . . . . . . . . . Mr Keith Wright . . . . . . . . . . . . . . . . . . . . . . . Tel: (020) 7273 6500

        E-mail: kwright@cabinet-office.x.gsi.gov.uk

        Web: http://www.civilserviceappealboard.gov.uk

**Civil Service Arbitration Tribunal** . . . . . . . . . . . . . . . . . ACAS, Brandon House, 180 Borough High Street, London, SE1 1LW

    Chairman . . . . . . . . . . . . . . . . . . . . . . . . . . . . . . . . . . . . . Mr Robert Henderson QC

    Secretary . . . . . . . . . . . . . . . . . . . . . . . . . . . . . . . . . . . . . Mr Amik Sen . . . . . . . . . . . . . . . . . . . . . . . . . . Tel: (020) 7210 3929

**Civil Service Commissioners** . . . . . . . . . . . . . . . . . . . . . . 35 Great Smith Street, London, SW1P 3BQ

    First Commissioner . . . . . . . . . . . . . . . . . . . . . . . . . . . . . Baroness Prashar CBE

    Secretary to the Commissioners . . . . . . . . . . . . . . . . . . Mr Jim Barron . . . . . . . . . . . . . . . . . . . . . . . . Tel: (020) 7276 2604

        E-mail: jim.barron@cabinet-office.x.gsi.gov.uk

**CROWN COPYRIGHT**

**Advisory Panel on Crown Copyright** . . . . . . . . . . . . . . . Admiralty Arch, The Mall, London, SW1A 2WH

    Chairman . . . . . . . . . . . . . . . . . . . . . . . . . . . . . . . . . . . . . Professor Richard Susskind . . . . . . . . . . . . . . Tel: (020) 7276 6216

        E-mail: richard.susskind@cabinet-office.x.gsi.gov.uk

**GOVERNMENT CARS / DISTRIBUTION SERVICES**

**Government Car and Despatch Agency** (*Executive Agency*) 46 Ponton Road, London, SW8 5AX

    Chief Executive . . . . . . . . . . . . . . . . . . . . . . . . . . . . . . . . Mr Nicholas Matheson . . . . . . . . . . . . . . . . . Tel: (020) 7217 3839

        Web: http://www.gcda.gov.uk

**HONOURS**

**Honours Scrutiny Committee** . . . . . . . . . . . . . . . . . . . . . Ceremonial Branch, Cabinet Office, 35 Great Smith Street, London, SW1P 3BQ

    Chairman . . . . . . . . . . . . . . . . . . . . . . . . . . . . . . . . . . . . . Rt Hon Lord Thomson of Monifieth KT

    Secretary . . . . . . . . . . . . . . . . . . . . . . . . . . . . . . . . . . . . . Mrs Gay Catto . . . . . . . . . . . . . . . . . . . . . . . . Tel: (020) 7276 2770

        Web: http://www.cabinet-office.gov.uk/ceremonial

**INFORMATION**

**COI Communications** (*Executive Agency*) . . . . . . . . . . . . Hercules Road, London, SE1 7DU

    Chief Executive . . . . . . . . . . . . . . . . . . . . . . . . . . . . . . . . Mr Alan Bishop . . . . . . . . . . . . . . . . . . . . . . . Tel: (020) 7261 8210

        Web: http://www.coi.gov.uk

**LORDS**

**House of Lords Appointments Commission** . . . . . . . . . . 35 Great Smith Street, London, SW1P 3BQ

    Chairman . . . . . . . . . . . . . . . . . . . . . . . . . . . . . . . . . . . . . Lord Stevenson of Coddenham

    Secretary . . . . . . . . . . . . . . . . . . . . . . . . . . . . . . . . . . . . . Mr Jim Barron . . . . . . . . . . . . . . . . . . . . . . . . Tel: (020) 7276 2005

        Web: http://www.lordsappointments.gov.uk

**REGULATION**

**Better Regulation Task Force** . . . . . . . . . . . . . . . . . . . . . 5th Floor, 22 Whitehall, London, SW1P 3BQ

    Chairman . . . . . . . . . . . . . . . . . . . . . . . . . . . . . . . . . . . . . Mr David Arculus

    Secretary . . . . . . . . . . . . . . . . . . . . . . . . . . . . . . . . . . . . . Ms Sara Mason . . . . . . . . . . . . . . . . . . . . . . . Tel: (020) 7276 2139

        E-mail: taskforce@cabinet-office.x.gsi.gov.uk

        Web: http://www.brtf.gov.uk

**SALARIES**

**Senior Salaries Review Body** . . . . . . . . . . . . . . . . . . . . . . Office of Manpower Economics, Oxford House, 76 Oxford Street, London, W1D 1BS

    Chairman . . . . . . . . . . . . . . . . . . . . . . . . . . . . . . . . . . . . . Mr John Baker CBE

    Secretary . . . . . . . . . . . . . . . . . . . . . . . . . . . . . . . . . . . . . Mr Nigel Peace . . . . . . . . . . . . . . . . . . . . . . . Tel: (020) 7467 7239

        Web: http://www.ome.uk.com

# CABINET OFFICE

**SECURITY**

**Security Commission** . . . . . . . . . . . . . . . . . . . . . . . . . . . . 3rd Floor, 2 Little Smith Street, London, SW1P 3DH

    Chairman . . . . . . . . . . . . . . . . . . . . . . . . . . . . . . . . . . . Rt Hon Dame Elizabeth Butler-Sloss

    Secretary . . . . . . . . . . . . . . . . . . . . . . . . . . . . . . . . . . . Mr Stephen Reinstadtler . . . . . . . . . . . . . . . . . . . Tel: (020) 7276 5642

**Security Vetting Appeals Panel** . . . . . . . . . . . . . . . . . . . . 3rd Floor, 2 Little Smith Street, London, SW1P 3DH

    Chairman . . . . . . . . . . . . . . . . . . . . . . . . . . . . . . . . . . . Rt Hon Dame Janet Smith

    Secretary . . . . . . . . . . . . . . . . . . . . . . . . . . . . . . . . . . . Mr Martin Sterling . . . . . . . . . . . . . . . . . . . . . . . Tel: (020) 7276 5645

                              E-mail: martin.sterling@cabinet-office.x.gsi.gov.uk

**STANDARDS IN PUBLIC LIFE**

**Committee on Standards in Public Life** . . . . . . . . . . . . . 35 Great Smith Street, London, SW1P 3BQ

    Chairman . . . . . . . . . . . . . . . . . . . . . . . . . . . . . . . . . . . Sir Nigel Wicks GCB CVO CBE

    Secretary . . . . . . . . . . . . . . . . . . . . . . . . . . . . . . . . . . . Mr Rob Behrens . . . . . . . . . . . . . . . . . . . . . . . . . Tel: (020) 7276 2595

                              E-mail: nigel.wicks@gtnet.gov.uk

                              Web: http://www.public-standards.gov.uk

# DEPARTMENT FOR CONSTITUTIONAL AFFAIRS

Selborne House
54-60 Victoria Street
London, SW1E 6QW
Tel: (020) 7210 8500  Fax: (020) 7210 8501
E-mail: general.queries@dca.gsi.gov.uk
Web: http://www.dca.gov.uk

## MINISTERS

**Secretary of State for Constitutional Affairs**
**and Lord Chancellor** . . . . . . . . . . . . . . . . . . . . Rt Hon Lord Falconer of Thoroton QC
*Private Secretary* . . . . . . . . . . . . . . . . . . . . . . . . . . Mr Mike Anderson . . . . . . . . . . . . . . . . . . . . . . Tel: (020) 7210 8380
*Special Advisers* . . . . . . . . . . . . . . . . . . . . . . . . . Mr Phillip Bassett . . . . . . . . . . . . . . . . . . . . . . . Tel: (020) 7210 8839
                                                              Mr Gary Hart . . . . . . . . . . . . . . . . . . . . . . . . . . . Tel: (020) 7210 8594

**Parliamentary Secretary** . . . . . . . . . . . . . . . . . . . Baroness Ashton of Upholland
*Private Secretary* . . . . . . . . . . . . . . . . . . . . . . . . . . Mr David Liddemore . . . . . . . . . . . . . . . . . . . . . Tel: (020) 7210 8562

**Parliamentary Secretary** . . . . . . . . . . . . . . . . . . . Mr David Lammy MP
*Private Secretary* . . . . . . . . . . . . . . . . . . . . . . . . . . Mr Edward Bowles . . . . . . . . . . . . . . . . . . . . . . . Tel: (020) 7210 0701

**Parliamentary Secretary** . . . . . . . . . . . . . . . . . . . Mr Christopher Leslie MP
*Private Secretary* . . . . . . . . . . . . . . . . . . . . . . . . . . Mr Grant Morris . . . . . . . . . . . . . . . . . . . . . . . . . Tel: (020) 7210 8683

**Parliamentary Secretary (Scotland)** . . . . . . . . . . Ms Anne McGuire MP
*Private Secretary* . . . . . . . . . . . . . . . . . . . . . . . . . . Ms Chloe Squires . . . . . . . . . . . . . . . . . . . . . . . . Tel: (020) 7270 6806

**Parliamentary Secretary (Wales)** . . . . . . . . . . . . Mr Don Touhig MP
*Private Secretary* . . . . . . . . . . . . . . . . . . . . . . . . . . Ms Anna Ruehall . . . . . . . . . . . . . . . . . . . . . . . . Tel: (020) 7270 0569

## CIVIL SERVICE

**Permanent Secretary and**
**Clerk of the Crown in Chancery** . . . . . . . . . . . Mr Alex Allan
*Private Secretary* . . . . . . . . . . . . . . . . . . . . . . . . . . Ms Jade Courtes . . . . . . . . . . . . . . . . . . . . . . . . . Tel: (020) 7219 8395
**Second Permanent Secretary** . . . . . . . . . . . . . . . Mr Ian Magee CB
*Private Secretary* . . . . . . . . . . . . . . . . . . . . . . . . . . Ms Maureen Sullivan . . . . . . . . . . . . . . . . . . . . . Tel: (020) 7219 8001

**Directors-General**
Clients and Policy . . . . . . . . . . . . . . . . . . . . . . . . Mr Jonathan Spencer . . . . . . . . . . . . . . . . . . . . . Tel: (020) 7210 8014
Finance . . . . . . . . . . . . . . . . . . . . . . . . . . . . . . . . . Mr Simon Ball . . . . . . . . . . . . . . . . . . . . . . . . . . Tel: (020) 7210 8005
Legal and International . . . . . . . . . . . . . . . . . . . . Mr Richard Heaton . . . . . . . . . . . . . . . . . . . . . . Tel: (020) 7210 0711
Legal and Judicial Services . . . . . . . . . . . . . . . . . Mr John Lyon . . . . . . . . . . . . . . . . . . . . . . . . . . . Tel: (020) 7210 8007

**Chief Executive, Her Majesty's Court Service** . . . Professor Sir Ronald De Witt . . . . . . . . . . . . . . . Tel: (020) 7210 1373

## SUBJECT CONTACTS AND RESPONSIBILITIES

**Administrative Justice**
Head, Administrative Justice Division . . . . . . . . . Mr Paul Stockton . . . . . . . . . . . . . . . . . . . . . . . . Tel: (020) 7210 8588
Coroner's Reforms . . . . . . . . . . . . . . . . . . . . . . . . Ms Judith Bernstein . . . . . . . . . . . . . . . . . . . . . . Tel: (020) 7210 1487
Council on Tribunals Policy . . . . . . . . . . . . . . . . . Mr David Webb . . . . . . . . . . . . . . . . . . . . . . . . . . Tel: (020) 7210 8273
Tax Tribunals . . . . . . . . . . . . . . . . . . . . . . . . . . . . Ms Leueen Fox . . . . . . . . . . . . . . . . . . . . . . . . . . Tel: (020) 7210 8832
Tribunal Policy . . . . . . . . . . . . . . . . . . . . . . . . . . Mr Chris Lappin . . . . . . . . . . . . . . . . . . . . . . . . . Tel: (020) 7210 8786
Tribunals Reforms . . . . . . . . . . . . . . . . . . . . . . . . Mr Rhys Chesters-Lewis . . . . . . . . . . . . . . . . . . . Tel: (020) 7210 1392
User Focus Team . . . . . . . . . . . . . . . . . . . . . . . . . Mr Tony Wall . . . . . . . . . . . . . . . . . . . . . . . . . . . Tel: (020) 7210 1319

**Appointments** *(see below under Judicial Group and under Magistrates)*

**Asylum and Immigration Policy and Diversity**
Director . . . . . . . . . . . . . . . . . . . . . . . . . . . . . . . . . Mr Nick Smedley . . . . . . . . . . . . . . . . . . . . . . . . Tel: (020) 7210 8809

**Asylum Policy: Programme Delivery** . . . . . . . . . . Ms Mary Shaw . . . . . . . . . . . . . . . . . . . . . . . . . . Tel: (020) 7217 8932

# DEPARTMENT FOR CONSTITUTIONAL AFFAIRS

**Audit: Internal Assurance Division** . . . . . . . . . . . . Mr Alan Rummins . . . . . . . . . . . . . . . . . . . . . . . Tel: (020) 7217 4581/2

**Change**
Director, Change . . . . . . . . . . . . . . . . . . . . . . . . . Ms Bernadette Kenny . . . . . . . . . . . . . . . . . . . . Tel: (020) 7210 8021
Business Change . . . . . . . . . . . . . . . . . . . . . . . . . Ms Julie Fletcher . . . . . . . . . . . . . . . . . . . . . . . . Tel: (020) 7210 8364

**Channel Islands** . . . . . . . . . . . . . . . . . . . . . . . . . . Mr Mark Hughes . . . . . . . . . . . . . . . . . . . . . . . . Tel: (020) 7210 1504

**Children and Family Courts Advisory Support Service**
*8th Floor, Millbank Tower, Millbank, London, SW1P 4QP*
Senior Inspector, CAFCASS Inspection . . . . . . . . . Mr Arran Poyser . . . . . . . . . . . . . . . . . . . . . . . . Tel: (020) 7217 4443
Sponsorship . . . . . . . . . . . . . . . . . . . . . . . . . . . . . Ms Amanda Finlay . . . . . . . . . . . . . . . . . . . . . . . Tel: (020) 7210 0708

**Civil Justice and Legal Services**
Director, Civil Justice and Legal Services . . . . . . . Mr David Nooney . . . . . . . . . . . . . . . . . . . . . . . . Tel: (020) 7210 1305
Civil Enforcement . . . . . . . . . . . . . . . . . . . . . . . . Ms Anne Marie Harrington . . . . . . . . . . . . . . . . . Tel: (020) 7210 0644
Civil Landscape Branch . . . . . . . . . . . . . . . . . . . . Ms Heather Bradbury . . . . . . . . . . . . . . . . . . . . . Tel: (020) 7210 8685
Civil Law Development . . . . . . . . . . . . . . . . . . . . Mr Andrew Frazer . . . . . . . . . . . . . . . . . . . . . . . Tel: (020) 7210 1206
Civil Procedure . . . . . . . . . . . . . . . . . . . . . . . . . . Mr Richard Mortimer . . . . . . . . . . . . . . . . . . . . . Tel: (020) 7210 8530
Civil Structures . . . . . . . . . . . . . . . . . . . . . . . . . . Mrs Andrea Scotland . . . . . . . . . . . . . . . . . . . . . Tel: (020) 7210 8685
Courts and Tribunals . . . . . . . . . . . . . . . . . . . . . . Mr Richard Mortimer . . . . . . . . . . . . . . . . . . . . . Tel: (020) 7210 8530
Public Legal Services . . . . . . . . . . . . . . . . . . . . . . Mr Derek Hill . . . . . . . . . . . . . . . . . . . . . . . . . . Tel: (020) 7210 8591

**Civil Law Development**
Head, Civil Law Development Division . . . . . . . . . Mr Andrew Frazer . . . . . . . . . . . . . . . . . . . . . . . Tel: (020) 7210 1206
Contract Law and Freedom of Expression . . . . . . . Mr David Willink . . . . . . . . . . . . . . . . . . . . . . . . Tel: (020) 7210 1233
Damages and Tort . . . . . . . . . . . . . . . . . . . . . . . . Mrs Janet Howe . . . . . . . . . . . . . . . . . . . . . . . . . Tel: (020) 7210 1221
Land Law . . . . . . . . . . . . . . . . . . . . . . . . . . . . . . . Mr Paul Hughes . . . . . . . . . . . . . . . . . . . . . . . . . Tel: (020) 7210 1228
Succession, Trusts and Law Commission . . . . . . . . Mr Chris Morter . . . . . . . . . . . . . . . . . . . . . . . . . Tel: (020) 7210 1225

**Clients and Policy**
Director-General, Clients and Policy . . . . . . . . . . . Mr Jonathan Spencer . . . . . . . . . . . . . . . . . . . . . Tel: (020) 7210 8014
Information Management . . . . . . . . . . . . . . . . . . . Mr Andy Maultby . . . . . . . . . . . . . . . . . . . . . . . . Tel: (020) 7217 4872
Policy Support Unit . . . . . . . . . . . . . . . . . . . . . . . Mr Laurence Fiddler . . . . . . . . . . . . . . . . . . . . . . Tel: (020) 7210 2622
Research . . . . . . . . . . . . . . . . . . . . . . . . . . . . . . . . Ms Judith Sidaway . . . . . . . . . . . . . . . . . . . . . . . Tel: (020) 7210 1465
Resource and Planning Unit . . . . . . . . . . . . . . . . . Ms Ann Achow . . . . . . . . . . . . . . . . . . . . . . . . . . Tel: (020) 7210 8858

**Commercial**
Director . . . . . . . . . . . . . . . . . . . . . . . . . . . . . . . . Mr Colin Lyne . . . . . . . . . . . . . . . . . . . . . . . . . . Tel: (020) 7210 8019
Head, DISC Programme (IT Recompete) . . . . . . . . Ms Alicia O'Neill . . . . . . . . . . . . . . . . . . . . . . . . Tel: (020) 7210 2052
Head, HQ Estates . . . . . . . . . . . . . . . . . . . . . . . . . Mr Adam Skinner . . . . . . . . . . . . . . . . . . . . . . . . Tel: (020) 7210 8689
Head of Procurement . . . . . . . . . . . . . . . . . . . . . . Mr Ken Cooney . . . . . . . . . . . . . . . . . . . . . . . . . Tel: (020) 7210 8689

**Communications**
Director, Communications . . . . . . . . . . . . . . . . . . *Vacant* . . . . . . . . . . . . . . . . . . . . . . . . . . . . . . . . Tel: (020) 7210 8673
Head of Corporate Communications and Projects . . . Mr Mike Wicksteed . . . . . . . . . . . . . . . . . . . . . . Tel: (020) 7210 8514
Chief Press Officer . . . . . . . . . . . . . . . . . . . . . . . . Mr Rob Smith . . . . . . . . . . . . . . . . . . . . . . . . . . . Tel: (020) 7210 1367
Corporate Communications . . . . . . . . . . . . . . . . . . Ms Gill Haizelden . . . . . . . . . . . . . . . . . . . . . . . . Tel: (020) 7210 8600
Correspondence Unit . . . . . . . . . . . . . . . . . . . . . . Mr Iain Walters . . . . . . . . . . . . . . . . . . . . . . . . . Tel: (020) 7210 0628
Press Enquiries . . . . . . . . . . . . . . . . . . . . . . . . . . *enquiries* . . . . . . . . . . . . . . . . . . . . . . . . . . . . . Tel: (020) 7210 8512
Web Team . . . . . . . . . . . . . . . . . . . . . . . . . . . . . . Mr Phillip Golding . . . . . . . . . . . . . . . . . . . . . . . Tel: (020) 7210 0675

**Constitution**
Director, Constitution Directorate . . . . . . . . . . . . . Mr Andrew McDonald . . . . . . . . . . . . . . . . . . . . Tel: (020) 7210 1440
Head, Constitutional Policy Division . . . . . . . . . . . Ms Judith Simpson . . . . . . . . . . . . . . . . . . . . . . . Tel: (020) 7210 8517
Head, Church, Civic and Marriage Branch . . . . . . . Ms Janet Hawkes . . . . . . . . . . . . . . . . . . . . . . . . Tel: (020) 7210 8522
Channel Islands and Isle of Man . . . . . . . . . . . . . . Mr Mark Hughes . . . . . . . . . . . . . . . . . . . . . . . . Tel: (020) 7210 2603
Constitutional Law Division . . . . . . . . . . . . . . . . . Mr Richard Heaton . . . . . . . . . . . . . . . . . . . . . . . Tel: (020) 7210 1951
Royal and Hereditary Matters . . . . . . . . . . . . . . . . Mr Phillip Goldsmith . . . . . . . . . . . . . . . . . . . . . Tel: (020) 7210 1447

**Coroners** . . . . . . . . . . . . . . . . . . . . . . . . . . . . . . . Ms Judith Bernstein . . . . . . . . . . . . . . . . . . . . . . Tel: (020) 7210 1487

# DEPARTMENT FOR CONSTITUTIONAL AFFAIRS

**Corporate Services**

| | | |
|---|---|---|
| Commercial Director | Mr Colin Lyne | Tel: (020) 7210 8019 |
| E-Delivery | Ms Annette Vernon | Tel: (020) 7189 2002 |
| Equality and Corporate Diversity | Ms Vivienne Hodgson | Tel: (020) 7210 8852 |
| Human Resources Director | Ms Helen Dudley | Tel: (020) 7189 2018 |
| Information Management | Mr Andy Maultby | Tel: (020) 7217 4872 |
| Internal Audit | Mr Alan Rummins | Tel: (020) 7217 4581 |
| IT, Departmental | Ms Annette Vernon | Tel: (020) 7217 2050 |
| Performance Management Unit | Miss Jeanette Martin | Tel: (020) 7210 8823 |
| Resource Planning | Ms Ann Achow | Tel: (020) 7210 8858 |
| Statutory Publications | Mr Tony Hopkins | Tel: (020) 7210 2600 |
| Strategic Unit | Ms Clare Pillman | Tel: (020) 7210 0690 |

**HM Courts Service Inspectorate**

*Millbank Tower, Millbank, London, SW1P 4QU*

| | | |
|---|---|---|
| Chief Inspector | Dr Stella Dixon | Tel: (020) 7217 4342 |

**Criminal Justice Delivery**

Principal Adviser to the Secretary of State on

| | | |
|---|---|---|
| Criminal Justice and Delivery Director | Mr Peter Handcock | Tel: (020) 7210 8011 |
| Heads, Criminal Business Branch | Mr Ron Sargen | Tel: (020) 7210 8641 |
| | Mr Tim Strouts | Tel: (020) 7210 8259 |
| Head, Criminal Justice Delivery | Mr Keith Budgen | Tel: (020) 7210 8897 |
| Community Justice | Ms Debbie Clarke | Tel: (020) 7210 0622 |
| Confidence and Diversity | Ms Gillian Barton | Tel: (020) 7210 8750 |
| Delivery Manager | Ms Bronwen Tumani | Tel: (020) 7210 8253 |
| Performance Management | Mrs Lesley Hopcraft | Tel: (020) 7210 8622 |
| | Miss Jeanette Martin | Tel: (020) 7210 8833 |
| Pubic Service Agreement | Mr Ian Brown | Tel: (020) 7210 8258 |

**Criminal Justice Joint Inspectorate**

*8th Floor, Millbank Tower, Millbank, London, SW1P 4QP*

Director, HM Magistrates Court Service

| | | |
|---|---|---|
| Joint Inspectorate Secretariat | Ms Sharon Davidson | Tel: (020) 7217 4351 |

**Data Protection / Sharing** (*see below under Information Rights*)

**Ecclesiastical Office**

*10 Downing Street, London, SW1A 2AT*

| | | |
|---|---|---|
| Ecclesiastical Secretary | Mr William Chapman | Tel: (020) 7930 4433 |

| | | |
|---|---|---|
| **E-Delivery, Departmental** | Ms Annette Vernon | Tel: (020) 7217 2050 |

**Effective Trial Management Programme**

| | | |
|---|---|---|
| Programme Manager | Mr Arwa'a Abdulla | Tel: (020) 7210 8657 |
| Delivery and Change | Ms Mairead Collins | Tel: (020) 7210 8829 |
| Evaluation and Analysis | Mr Kelvin Launchbury | Tel: (020) 7210 0697 |
| Production | Ms Neelam Sarkaria | Tel: (020) 7210 1315 |

**Elections**

| | | |
|---|---|---|
| Head, Electoral Policy Division | Mr John Sills | Tel: (020) 7210 8218 |
| Electoral Reform Branch | Ms Antonia Romeo | Tel: (020) 7210 8223 |
| Legislation and Administration | Mr Malcolm Rawlings | Tel: (020) 7210 8225 |
| Multi-Channel Elections Branch | Mr Paul Docker | Tel: (020) 7210 8221 |
| Political Parties and Referendums | Ms Pauline Prosser | Tel: (020) 7210 8232 |

**European Convention on Human Rights**

| | | |
|---|---|---|
| Director, Public and Private Rights Directorate | Ms Amanda Finlay | Tel: (020) 7210 0708 |

| | | |
|---|---|---|
| **European Policy Unit** | Mr Edwin Kilby | Tel: (020) 7210 0623 |

**Facilities Management Group**

| | | |
|---|---|---|
| Director | Mr Colin Lyne | Tel: (020) 7210 2013 |

# DEPARTMENT FOR CONSTITUTIONAL AFFAIRS

**Family Justice / Policy**

| | | |
|---|---|---|
| Head, Family Policy Division | Ms Sally Field | Tel: (020) 7210 8649 |
| Adoption and Care | Ms Terry Hunter | Tel: (020) 7210 8325 |
| Divorce, Mediation and Property | Mr Alex Clark | Tel: (020) 7210 1475 |
| International Branch | Mr Paul Ahearn | Tel: (020) 7210 8321 |
| Programme Support | Mr Stuart Moore | Tel: (020) 7210 2651 |
| Relationship Breakdown Branch | Mr John Briden | Tel: (020) 7210 8648 |

**Finance**

| | | |
|---|---|---|
| Director-General, Finance | Mr Simon Ball | Tel: (020) 7210 2801 |
| Budget | Mr Nadeem Ilyas | Tel: (020) 7210 8605 |

**Freedom of Information** *(see below under Information Rights)*

**Gallantry Awards, Civilian / Civic Honours** . . . . . . Ms Janet Hawkes . . . . . . . . . . . . Tel: (020) 7210 8522

**Human Rights**

| | | |
|---|---|---|
| Human Rights Unit | Mr Mark De Pulford | Tel: (020) 7210 8746 |
| Domestic | Mr Paul Zimmermann | Tel: (020) 7210 1483 |
| International | Mr John Kissane | Tel: (020) 7210 0654 |

**House of Lords Reform**

| | | |
|---|---|---|
| Head, Constitutional Policy Division | Ms Judith Simpson | Tel: (020) 7210 8517 |
| Constitutional Law Division | Mr Richard Heaton | Tel: (020) 7210 1951 |

**Human Resources Director** . . . . . . . . . . . . . . Ms Helen Dudley . . . . . . . . . . . . . . Tel: (020) 7189 2018

**Information Rights**

| | | |
|---|---|---|
| Head, Information Rights Division | Mr Paul Boyle | Tel: (020) 7210 0676 |
| Data Protection: Domestic | Mrs Jennifer Flaschner | Tel: (020) 7210 3453 |
| Data Protection: International | Mr Graham Sutton | Tel: (020) 7210 3454 |
| Freedom of Information: Policy | Ms Katherine Fox | Tel: (020) 7210 3468 |
| Freedom of Information: Project Management | Ms Jiwan Raheja | Tel: (020) 7210 3460 |

**Inquiries Policy Division** . . . . . . . . . . . . . . Dr Colin Myerscough . . . . . . . . . . . . . . Tel: (020) 7210 8675

**International Law, Private** . . . . . . . . . . . . . . Mr Alasdair Wallace . . . . . . . . . . . . . . Tel: (020) 7210 0738

**Isle of Man** . . . . . . . . . . . . . . . . . . . . Mr Mark Hughes . . . . . . . . . . . . . . Tel: (020) 7210 2603

**Judicial Appointments / Policy** *(see Legal and Judicial Services Group below)*

**Learning and Development Division** . . . . . . . . . . Ms Joanne Peel . . . . . . . . . . . . . . Tel: (020) 7189 2029

**Legal Advice**

| | | |
|---|---|---|
| Legal Adviser | Mr Richard Heaton | Tel: (020) 7210 1951 |
| Asylum, Civil and Administrative Justice, and Public Legal Services | Miss Emma Robinson | Tel: (020) 7210 0728 |
| Civil Law, Legal Services, EU and Devolution | Mr Alasdair Wallace | Tel: (020) 7210 0738 |
| Constitutional Law, Human Rights and Information Rights | Ms Rowena Collins-Rice | Tel: (020) 7210 0716 |
| Courts and Judiciary | Mr Michael Kron | Tel: (020) 7210 0711 |
| Criminal Procedure Rule Committee (Secretariat) | Mr Jonathan Solly | Tel: (020) 7210 0735 |
| Family and Criminal | Ms Claire Johnston | Tel: (020) 7210 0745 |

**Legal Aid**

| | | |
|---|---|---|
| Public Legal Services Division | Mr Derek Hill | Tel: (020) 7210 8591 |

# DEPARTMENT FOR CONSTITUTIONAL AFFAIRS

**Legal and Judicial Services Group**

| | | |
|---|---|---|
| Director-General | Mr Judith Lyon | Tel: (020) 7210 8007 |
| Director, Judicial Appointments and Legal Services Development | Mr Neil Ward | Tel: (020) 7210 8926 |
| Director, Judicial Policy | Ms Liz Grimsey | Tel: (020) 7210 8706 |
| Judicial Appointments Commission | Mr Alastair Clegg | Tel: (020) 7210 8982 |
| Judicial Appointments Development Division | Mr Anunay Jha | Tel: (020) 7210 0572 |
| Judicial Appointments: Policy and Correspondence | Ms Judeth Killick | Tel: (020) 7210 4887 |
| | Ms Maggy Piggott | Tel: (020) 7210 4887 |
| Judicial Competitions (Courts) Division | Mr Lee Hughes | Tel: (020) 7210 1484 |
| Judicial Competitions (Tribunals) Division | Mr Ray Sams | Tel: (020) 7210 0572 |
| Judicial Pay, Pensions, Terms and Conditions | Mr David Staff | Tel: (020) 7210 8936 |
| Judicial Policy: Courts Division | Mr Alastair Shaw | Tel: (020) 7210 8789 |
| Legal and Constitutional Modernisation Programme (Manager) | Mr Hugh Ind | Tel: (020) 7210 8749 |
| Legal Services Development Division | Ms Anita Bharucha | Tel: (020) 7210 8629 |
| Review of Regulatory Framework for Legal Services (England and Wales) | Ms Sheila Spicer | Tel: (020) 7210 8810 |
| Secretariat | Ms Joan Lewis | Tel: (020) 7210 0135 |
| Supreme Court Policy | Mr Edward Adams | Tel: (020) 7210 8245 |
| Tribunals Appointments | Mr Ray Sams | Tel: (020) 7210 0567 |

**Legal Services**

| | | |
|---|---|---|
| Director-General, Legal and International Group | Mr David Nooney | Tel: (020) 7210 1305 |
| Civil Law Development | Mr Andrew Frazer | Tel: (020) 7210 8699 |
| Criminal Procedure Rules | Mr Jonathan Solly | Tel: (020) 7210 0735 |
| Legal Services Development | Mr Peter Harris | Tel: (020) 7210 8629 |
| Public Legal Services | Mr Derek Hill | Tel: (020) 7210 8591 |

*(see also Unified and Judicial Services Group above)*

**Lords Lieutenant** ... Mr Phillip Goldsmith ... Tel: (020) 7210 1447

**Magistrates**

| | | |
|---|---|---|
| Appointments | Ms Gill Sloan | Tel: (020) 7210 0316 |
| Lay Magistrates | Mr Malcom Watts | Tel: (020) 7210 8989 |

*(see also verified Administration and Magistrates Courts Administration below)*

**Magistrates' Courts Inspectorate**
*Millbank Tower, Millbank, London, SW1P 4QU*

| | | |
|---|---|---|
| Chief Inspector | Dr Stella Dixon | Tel: (020) 7217 4342 |

**Marriage Law** ... Ms Janet Hawkes ... Tel: (020) 7210 8522

**Mental Capacity**

| | | |
|---|---|---|
| Head of Division | Ms Susan Johnson *(Mondays to Wednesdays)* | Tel: (020) 7210 8896 |
| | Ms Rosemary Pratt *(Thursdays and Fridays)* | Tel: (020) 7210 8896 |
| Legislation | Ms Rachel Atkinson | Tel: (020) 7210 2677 |
| Projects | Mrs Chris Walker | Tel: (020) 7210 2653 |

**Open Government** *(see above under Information Rights)*

**Parliamentary Clerk** ... Ms Ann Nixon ... Tel: (020) 7219 8382

**Performance Management Unit** ... Mr Peter Handcock ... Tel: (020) 7210 8011

**Press Office**

| | | |
|---|---|---|
| Chief Press Officer | Mr Rob Smith | Tel: (020) 7210 1367 |

**Public and Private Rights**

| | | |
|---|---|---|
| Director | Ms Amanda Finlay | Tel: (020) 7210 0708 |

**Public Legal Services**

| | | |
|---|---|---|
| Head, Public Legal Services Division | Mr Derek Hill | Tel: (020) 7210 8591 |
| Community Legal Service | | |
| Eligibility, Scope and Supply | Mr Robert Wright | Tel: (020) 7210 8853 |
| Partnership, Innovation and Quality | Mr Robert Gill | Tel: (020) 7210 8710 |
| Criminal Defence Service | Mr Brett Regan | Tel: (020) 7210 0678 |
| Management Information and Analysis | Mr Chris Lancaster | Tel: (020) 7210 8679 |
| Operational Research Unit | Mr Simon Hayllar | Tel: (020) 7210 8850 |

# DEPARTMENT FOR CONSTITUTIONAL AFFAIRS

**Publications**
Head, Statutory Publications Office............. Mr Tony Hopkins......................... Tel: (020) 7210 2600

**Queen's Counsel Branch**..................... Mr Sean Langley ....................... Tel: (020) 7210 1449

**Referendums**............................... Ms Pauline Prosser ..................... Tel: (020) 7210 8232

**Research Unit (Clients and Policy Directorate)** .. Ms Judith Sidaway....................... Tel: (020) 7210 1465

**Royal and Hereditary Matters**................ Mr Phillip Goldsmith ................... Tel: (020) 7210 1447

**Scotland Office** (*see below at p253*)

**Security**
Departmental Security Officer................. Mr Richard Atkinson .................... Tel: (020) 7210 8570

**Strategic Unit, Departmental** ................ Ms Clare Pillman ...................... Tel: (020) 7210 0690

**Supreme Court Policy** ...................... Mr Edward Adams....................... Tel: (020) 7210 8245

**Trans-sexual Legal Issues** ................. Mr Peter Thompson ..................... Tel: (020) 7210 8201

**Tribunals**
Appointments............................... Mr Ray Sams........................... Tel: (020) 7210 0567
Council on Tribunals Policy ................. Mr David Webb......................... Tel: (020) 7210 8273
Tax Tribunals.............................. Ms Leueen Fox ........................ Tel: (020) 7210 8832
Tribunal Policy ........................... Ms Chris Lappin ...................... Tel: (020) 7210 8786
Tribunals Reform........................... Mr Rhys Chesters-Lewis................ Tel: (020) 7210 1392
Tribunals Service Programme ................ Mr Mike Watson ....................... Tel: (020) 7210 0040
User Focus Team ........................... Mr Tony Wall ......................... Tel: (020) 7210 1319

**Unified Administration and Magistrates'**
**Courts Administration**
Director................................... Mr Kevin Sadler....................... Tel: (020) 7210 0010
Head of Criminal Enforcement ............... Mr Paul McGladrigan................... Tel: (020) 7210 0562
Head of Magistrates' Court Administration ....... Mr Jonathan Lane ..................... Tel: (020) 7210 0563
Programme Manager for Unified Courts
   Administration Programme ................ Ms Karen Wheeler...................... Tel: (020) 7210 0014
Director of Tribunals ..................... Mr Martin John ....................... Tel: (020) 7566 1362

**Wales Office** (*see below at p254*)

**Warrants** ................................. Ms Heather Bradbury................... Tel: (020) 7210 8685

# DEPARTMENT FOR CONSTITUTIONAL AFFAIRS

## SCOTLAND OFFICE
Dover House, Whitehall, London, SW1A 2AU
Tel: (020) 7270 6754  Fax: (020) 720 6812

1 Melville Crescent, Edinburgh, EH3 7HW
Tel: (0131) 244 9010

**Secretary of State for Scotland**. . . . . . . . . . . . . . . Rt Hon Alistair Darling MP
*Principal Private Secretary* . . . . . . . . . . . . . . . . . . Ms Jayne Colquhoun . . . . . . . . . . . . . . . . . . . . . Tel: (020) 7270 6740
*Special Advisers* . . . . . . . . . . . . . . . . . . . . . . . . . Mr Iain Gray . . . . . . . . . . . . . . . . . . . . . . . . . . . Tel: (020) 7270 6754
Mr Sam White . . . . . . . . . . . . . . . . . . . . . . . . . . Tel: (020) 7270 6754

**Parliamentary Secretary** . . . . . . . . . . . . . . . . . . Ms Anne McGuire MP
*Private Secretary*. . . . . . . . . . . . . . . . . . . . . . . . . Ms Chloe Squires. . . . . . . . . . . . . . . . . . . . . . . . . Tel: (020) 7270 6806

**Scotland Office Management Group**
Head of Department, Scotland Office . . . . . . . . . . Mr David Crawley . . . . . . . . . . . . . . . . . . . . . . . Tel: (020) 7270 6769
Head of Constitutional Branch . . . . . . . . . . . . . . Mr Hugo Deadman. . . . . . . . . . . . . . . . . . . . . . . Tel: (0131) 244 6788
Head of Parliamentary and Constitutional Division . *Vacant*. . . . . . . . . . . . . . . . . . . . . . . . . . . . . . . . Tel: (020) 7270 6800
Head of Parliamentary Branch . . . . . . . . . . . . . . Mr Kenneth Robbie . . . . . . . . . . . . . . . . . . . . . . Tel: (020) 7270 6753
Briefing Services Division. . . . . . . . . . . . . . . . . . Mr Gerald McHugh . . . . . . . . . . . . . . . . . . . . . . TelL (0131) 244 9071
Finance and Administration:
Principal Finance Officer . . . . . . . . . . . . . . . . Mr Norman Kernohan. . . . . . . . . . . . . . . . . . . . . Tel: (0131) 244 9001

**Parliamentary Clerk**. . . . . . . . . . . . . . . . . . . . . . Mr Ian Stage . . . . . . . . . . . . . . . . . . . . . . . . . . . Tel: (020) 7270 6727

**Chief Press Officer**. . . . . . . . . . . . . . . . . . . . . . . Ms Elizabeth Ravenscroft. . . . . . . . . . . . . . . . . . . Tel: (0131) 244 9053

**Advocate General for Scotland** . . . . . . . . . . . . . . Dr Lynda Clark QC MP
*Private Secretary*. . . . . . . . . . . . . . . . . . . . . . . . . Mr James Johnston. . . . . . . . . . . . . . . . . . . . . . . Tel: (020) 7270 6720

Legal Secretariat to the Advocate
General for Scotland . . . . . . . . . . . . . . . . . . . . Mr Charles Mullin . . . . . . . . . . . . . . . . . . . . . . . Tel: (020) 7270 6810
Assistant Legal Secretaries. . . . . . . . . . . . . . . . . . Mr Andrew Campbell. . . . . . . . . . . . . . . . . . . . . . Tel: (020) 7270 6708
Ms Jane Ferrier . . . . . . . . . . . . . . . . . . . . . . . . . Tel: (020) 7270 6766

**Office of the Solicitor to the Advocate General for Scotland**
*Victoria Quay, Edinburgh, EH6 6QQ*
Solicitor to the Advocate General . . . . . . . . . . . . . Mr Hugh Macdiarmid CB. . . . . . . . . . . . . . . . . . . Tel: (0131) 244 1634

# DEPARTMENT FOR CONSTITUTIONAL AFFAIRS

## WALES OFFICE

Gwydyr House, Whitehall, London, SW1A 2ER
Tel: (020) 7270 0549 Fax (020) 7270 0561
E-mail: office@wales.gsi.gov.uk
Web: http://www.ossw.walesoffice.gov.uk

The National Assembly for Wales
Cardiff Bay, Cardiff, CF99 1NA
Tel: (029) 2082 5111  Fax: (029) 2082 8129

**Secretary of State for Wales** . . . . . . . . . . . . . . . . . Rt Hon Peter Hain MP
   *Private Secretaries* . . . . . . . . . . . . . . . . . . . . . . . . Ms Cherie Jones . . . . . . . . . . . . . . . . . . . . . . . . . Tel: (020) 7270 0538
                                               Mr Simon Morris . . . . . . . . . . . . . . . . . . . . . . . . Tel: (020) 7270 0550
   *Special Advisers* . . . . . . . . . . . . . . . . . . . . . . . . . . Mr Andrew Bold . . . . . . . . . . . . . . . . . . . . . . . . . Tel: (020) 7270 0592
                                               Mr Philip Taylor . . . . . . . . . . . . . . . . . . . . . . . . . Tel: (020) 7270 0532

**Parliamentary Secretary** . . . . . . . . . . . . . . . . . . . . Mr Don Touhig MP
   *Private Secretary* . . . . . . . . . . . . . . . . . . . . . . . . . . Ms Anna Ruehall . . . . . . . . . . . . . . . . . . . . . . . . . Tel: (020) 7270 0569

**Head of Wales Office** . . . . . . . . . . . . . . . . . . . . . . . Mrs Alison Jackson . . . . . . . . . . . . . . . . . . . . . . Tel: (020) 7270 0558
   *Private Secretary* . . . . . . . . . . . . . . . . . . . . . . . . . . Ms Pauline Sterling . . . . . . . . . . . . . . . . . . . . . . Tel: (020) 7270 0559

**Legal Advisers** . . . . . . . . . . . . . . . . . . . . . . . . . . . . . Mr Roger Bonehill . . . . . . . . . . . . . . . . . . . . . . . Tel: (029) 2089 8484
                                               Mr Cedric Longville . . . . . . . . . . . . . . . . . . . . . . Tel: (029) 2089 8484

**Parliamentary Clerk** . . . . . . . . . . . . . . . . . . . . . . . Mr Mike Williams . . . . . . . . . . . . . . . . . . . . . . . . Tel: (020) 7270 0544

**Policy Officers**
   Head of Policy . . . . . . . . . . . . . . . . . . . . . . . . . . . . Ms Anne Stephenson . . . . . . . . . . . . . . . . . . . . . Tel: (020) 7270 0585
   Administration, Constitutional Policy, Finance . . . . Mr John Kilner . . . . . . . . . . . . . . . . . . . . . . . . . . . . . . . Tel: (020) 7270 0557
   Agriculture, Economic Affairs,
      Employment, European Affairs,
      Industry, New Deal, Rural Affairs . . . . . . . . . . Mr Andrew Nicholas . . . . . . . . . . . . . . . . . . . . . Tel: (020) 7270 0554
   Education, Health, Social Affairs . . . . . . . . . . . . . Ms Anne Morrice . . . . . . . . . . . . . . . . . . . . . . . . . Tel: (020) 7270 0587
   Environment, Home Affairs,
      Local Government, Planning and
      Transport . . . . . . . . . . . . . . . . . . . . . . . . . . . . . Mr David Webb . . . . . . . . . . . . . . . . . . . . . . . . . . Tel: (020) 7270 8513

**Press Secretary** . . . . . . . . . . . . . . . . . . . . . . . . . . . Mr Alan Cummins . . . . . . . . . . . . . . . . . . . . . . . . Tel: (020) 7270 0565

# DEPARTMENT FOR CONSTITUTIONAL AFFAIRS

## OTHER RELEVANT CONTACTS - CONSTITUTIONAL AFFAIRS

### APPOINTMENTS (JUDICIAL)
**Commissioner for Judicial**
    **Appointments (England and Wales)** . . . . . . . . 7th Floor, Millbank Tower, Millbank, London, SW1P 4RD
    First Commissioner. . . . . . . . . . . . . . . . . . . . . . . Professor Sir Colin Campbell
    Secretary . . . . . . . . . . . . . . . . . . . . . . . . . . . . . . Mr Jon Casey . . . . . . . . . . . . . . . . . . . . . . . . . . . Tel: (020) 7217 4470

### CIVIL LAW
**Civil Justice Council** . . . . . . . . . . . . . . . . . . . . . . Room E214, Royal Courts of Justice, Strand, London, WC2A 2LL
    Chairman . . . . . . . . . . . . . . . . . . . . . . . . . . . . . . Rt Hon Lord Phillips of Worth Matravers *(Master of the Rolls)*
    Secretary . . . . . . . . . . . . . . . . . . . . . . . . . . . . . . Mr Robert Musgrove . . . . . . . . . . . . . . . Tel: (020) 7947 6670
    Web: http://www.civiljusticecouncil.gov.uk
**Civil Procedure Rule Committee** . . . . . . . . . . . . . Room 3N10,Department for Constitutional Affairs, Southside,
    105 Victoria Street, London, SW1 6QT
    Chairman . . . . . . . . . . . . . . . . . . . . . . . . . . . . . . Rt Hon Lord Phillips of Worth Matravers *(Master of the Rolls)*
    Secretary . . . . . . . . . . . . . . . . . . . . . . . . . . . . . . Mr Michael Collon . . . . . . . . . . . . . . . . . . . . . Tel: (020) 7210 0729

### COURT SERVICES
**Court Service** *(Executive Agency)* . . . . . . . . . . . . . . Southside, 105 Victoria Street, London, SW1E 6QT
    Chief Executive . . . . . . . . . . . . . . . . . . . . . . . . . Professor Sir Ronald De Witt . . . . . . . . . . . . . . . Tel: (020) 7210 2269
    Web: http://www.courtservice.gov.uk

### DATA PROTECTION
**Information Commissioner** . . . . . . . . . . . . . . . . . . Wycliffe House, Water Lane, Wilmslow, Cheshire, SK9 5AF
    Registrar . . . . . . . . . . . . . . . . . . . . . . . . . . . . . . Mr Richard Thomas . . . . . . . . . . . . . . . Tel: (01625) 545700
    Web: http://www.informationcommissioner.gov.uk
**Information Tribunal** . . . . . . . . . . . . . . . . . . . . . . 4th Floor, MWB Business Exchange, 10 Greycoat Place, London, SW1P 1SB
    Chairman . . . . . . . . . . . . . . . . . . . . . . . . . . . . . . Mr David Marks
    Secretary . . . . . . . . . . . . . . . . . . . . . . . . . . . . . . Ms Charlotte Mercer . . . . . . . . . . . . . . . . . . . . . Tel: (020) 7654 4365
    Web: http://www.dca.gov.uk/foi/inftrib.htm

### FAMILY LAW
**Children and Family Court Advisory**
    **Support Service (CAFCASS)** . . . . . . . . . . . . . . 2nd Floor, Newspaper House, 8-16 Great New Street, London, EC4A 3BN
    Chairman . . . . . . . . . . . . . . . . . . . . . . . . . . . . . . Ms Angela Killick
    Chief Executive . . . . . . . . . . . . . . . . . . . . . . . . . Mr Jonathon Tross . . . . . . . . . . . . . . . . . . . . . Tel: (020) 7210 4400
    Web: http://www.cafcass.gov.uk
**Family Proceedings Rule Committee** . . . . . . . . . . . Department for Constitutional Affairs, Southside,
    105 Victoria Street, London, SW1 6QT
    Chairman . . . . . . . . . . . . . . . . . . . . . . . . . . . . . . Dame Elizabeth Butler-Sloss *(President of the Family Division)*
    Secretary . . . . . . . . . . . . . . . . . . . . . . . . . . . . . . Ms Claire Johnston. . . . . . . . . . . . . . . . . . . . . . Tel: (020) 7210 0729

### INCOME TAX
**Advisory Committees on General Commissioners**
    **of Income Tax (England and Wales)** . . . . . . . . Magistrates Branch, Courts Division, Department for Constitutional Affairs,
    Selborne House, 54-60 Victoria Street, London SW1E 6QW
    *Contact* . . . . . . . . . . . . . . . . . . . . . . . . . . . . . . Mr John Nicholson. . . . . . . . . . . . . . . . . . . . . . Tel: (020) 7210 8990
**Advisory Committees on General Commissioners**
    **of Income Tax (Northern Ireland)** . . . . . . . . . Northern Ireland Court Service, Headline Building, 10-14 Victoria Street,
    Belfast, BT1 3GG
    *Contact* . . . . . . . . . . . . . . . . . . . . . . . . . . . . . . Mr Alan Hunter. . . . . . . . . . . . . . . . . . . . . . Tel: (028) 9032 8594
**General Commissioners of Income**
    **Tax (England, Wales and Northern Ireland)** . . Office of the Secretary of Commissions, Department for Constitutional Affairs,
    Selborne House, 54-60 Victoria Street, London SW1E 6QW
    *Contact* . . . . . . . . . . . . . . . . . . . . . . . . . . . . . . Ms Natasha Gardner . . . . . . . . . . . . . . . . . . . . . Tel: (020) 7210 0668

### INSOLVENCY
**Insolvency Rules Committee** . . . . . . . . . . . . . . . . . c/o Insolvency Service, PO Box 203, 21 Bloomsbury Street, London, WC1B 3QW
    Chairman . . . . . . . . . . . . . . . . . . . . . . . . . . . . . . Hon Mr Justice Evans-Lombe
    Secretary . . . . . . . . . . . . . . . . . . . . . . . . . . . . . . Mr Steve Quick . . . . . . . . . . . . . . . . . . . . . Tel: (020) 7291 6747
    E-mail: steve.quick@insolvency.gsi.gov.uk

# DEPARTMENT FOR CONSTITUTIONAL AFFAIRS

*Other Relevant Contacts: Constitutional Affairs (Continued)*

**JPs**
**Advisory Committees on Justices of the**
    **Peace (England and Wales)** . . . . . . . . . . . . . . Magistrates Branch, Courts Division, Constitutional Affairs Department,
                           Selborne House, 54-60 Victoria Street, London SW1E 6QW
    *Contact* . . . . . . . . . . . . . . . . . . . . . . . . . . . . . . Mr John Nicholson . . . . . . . . . . . . . . . . . . . . . . . . . Tel: (020) 7210 8993
                           Web: http://www.cad.gov.uk/magist/advcom/advcoms.htm
**Advisory Committees on Justices of the**
    **Peace (Lancashire)** . . . . . . . . . . . . . . . . . . . . . Duchy of Lancaster Office, County Hall, Preston, Lancashire, PR1 8XJ
    *Contact* . . . . . . . . . . . . . . . . . . . . . . . . . . . . . . Ms Janet Mulligan . . . . . . . . . . . . . . . . . . . . . . . . Tel: (01772) 533542
**Advisory Committees on Justices of the**
    **Peace (Northern Ireland)** . . . . . . . . . . . . . . . . Northern Ireland Court Service, Headline Building, 10-14 Victoria Street,
                           Belfast, BT1 3GG
    *Contact* . . . . . . . . . . . . . . . . . . . . . . . . . . . . . . Mr Alan Hunter . . . . . . . . . . . . . . . . . . . . . . . . . . Tel: (028) 9032 8594

## JUDGE ADVOCATE
**Judge Advocate General of the Forces** . . . . . . . . 81 Chancery Lane, London, WC2A 1BQ
    Judge Advocate General . . . . . . . . . . . . . . . . . . . . *Vacant* . . . . . . . . . . . . . . . . . . . . . . . . . . . . . . . . . . Tel: (020) 7218 8089

## JUVENILE COURTS (NORTHERN IRELAND)
**Advisory Committee on Juvenile Court**
    **Lay Panel (Northern Ireland)** . . . . . . . . . . . . . Northern Ireland Court Service, Headline Building, 10-14 Victoria Street,
                           Belfast, BT1 3GG
    *Contact* . . . . . . . . . . . . . . . . . . . . . . . . . . . . . . Mr Alan Hunter . . . . . . . . . . . . . . . . . . . . . . . . . . Tel: (028) 9032 8594

## LAND
**HM Land Registry** *(Executive Agency)* . . . . . . . . . . . 32 Lincoln's Inn Fields, London, WC2A 3PH
    Chief Land Registrar and Chief Executive . . . . . . . Mr Peter Collis . . . . . . . . . . . . . . . . . . . . . . . . . . Tel: (020) 7917 8888
                           Web: http://www.landreg.gov.uk
**Land Registration Rule Committee** . . . . . . . . . . . . HM Land Registry, 32 Lincoln's Inn Fields, London, WC2A 3PH
    Chairman . . . . . . . . . . . . . . . . . . . . . . . . . . . . . . Sir William Blackburne
    Secretary . . . . . . . . . . . . . . . . . . . . . . . . . . . . . . Ms Christine Adams . . . . . . . . . . . . . . . . . . . . . . . . Tel: (020) 7917 8888 ext 4421
                           Web: http://www.landreg.gsi.gov.uk

## LAW REFORM
**Law Commission** . . . . . . . . . . . . . . . . . . . . . . . . . Conquest House, 37-38 John Street, Theobalds Road, London, WC1N 2BQ
    Chairman . . . . . . . . . . . . . . . . . . . . . . . . . . . . . . Sir Roger Toulson
    Secretary . . . . . . . . . . . . . . . . . . . . . . . . . . . . . . Mr Steve Humphreys . . . . . . . . . . . . . . . . . . . . . . . Tel: (020) 7453 1220
                           Web: http://www.lawcom.gov.uk

## LEGAL SERVICES
**Legal Aid Advisory Committee (Northern Ireland)** Northern Ireland Court Service, 9-15 Bedford Street, Belfast, BT2 7LT
    Chairman . . . . . . . . . . . . . . . . . . . . . . . . . . . . . . His Honour Judge Smyth QC
    Chief Executive . . . . . . . . . . . . . . . . . . . . . . . . . . Mrs Joyce Henderson . . . . . . . . . . . . . . . . . . . . . . . Tel: (028) 9041 2353
**Legal Services Commission (England and Wales)** . 85 Gray's Inn Road, London, WC1X 8TX
    Chairman . . . . . . . . . . . . . . . . . . . . . . . . . . . . . . Mr Philip Ely OBE
    Chief Executive . . . . . . . . . . . . . . . . . . . . . . . . . Ms Clare Dodgson . . . . . . . . . . . . . . . . . . . . . . . . Tel: (020) 7759 0000
                           Web: http://www.legalservices.gov.uk
**Legal Services Consultative Panel** . . . . . . . . . . . . . Selborne House, 54-60 Victoria Street, London, SW1E 6QW
    Chairman . . . . . . . . . . . . . . . . . . . . . . . . . . . . . . Hon Lord Justice Potter
    Secretary . . . . . . . . . . . . . . . . . . . . . . . . . . . . . . Mr Nigel Reeder . . . . . . . . . . . . . . . . . . . . . . . . . . Tel: (020) 7210 8677
                           Web: http://www.dca.co.uk
**Judicial Studies Board** . . . . . . . . . . . . . . . . . . . . . 9th Floor, Millbank Tower, Millbank, London, SW1P 4QU
    Chairman . . . . . . . . . . . . . . . . . . . . . . . . . . . . . . Rt Hon Lord Justice David Keene
    Executive Director . . . . . . . . . . . . . . . . . . . . . . . . Ms Deborah Mathews . . . . . . . . . . . . . . . . . . . . . . Tel: (020) 7217 4708
                           Web: http://www.jsboard.co.uk

## OFFICIAL SOLICITOR
**Official Solicitor's Department** . . . . . . . . . . . . . . . 81 Chancery Lane, London, WC2A 1DD
    Official Solicitor . . . . . . . . . . . . . . . . . . . . . . . . . . Mr Lawrence Oates . . . . . . . . . . . . . . . . . . . . . . . . Tel: (020) 7911 7127
                           Web: http://www.offsol.demon.co.uk

# DEPARTMENT FOR CONSTITUTIONAL AFFAIRS

*Other Relevant Contacts: Constitutional Affairs (Continued)*

## PUBLIC GUARDIANSHIP
**Public Guardianship Office** *(Executive Agency)* . . . . Archway Tower, 2 Junction Road, London, N19 5SZ
    Chief Executive . . . . . . . . . . . . . . . . . . . . . . . . . . . Mr David Lye. . . . . . . . . . . . . . . . . . . . . . . . . . Tel: (0845) 3330 2900
    Web: http://www.guardianship.gov.uk
**Strategic Investment Board**. . . . . . . . . . . . . . . . . . Public Guardianship Office, Archway Tower, 2 Junction Road, London, N19 5SZ
    Chairman. . . . . . . . . . . . . . . . . . . . . . . . . . . . . . Dr Colin Price
    Secretary . . . . . . . . . . . . . . . . . . . . . . . . . . . . . . Mr Alan Palmer . . . . . . . . . . . . . . . . . . . . . . . . . Tel: (020) 7664 7127
    Web: http://www.lcd.gov.uk/family/sib

## PUBLIC RECORDS
**Advisory Council on National Records**
    **and Archives** . . . . . . . . . . . . . . . . . . . . . . . . . National Archives, Kew, Richmond, Surrey, TW9 4DU
    Chairman. . . . . . . . . . . . . . . . . . . . . . . . . . . . . . Rt Hon Lord Phillips of Worth Matravers *(Master of the Rolls)*
    Secretary . . . . . . . . . . . . . . . . . . . . . . . . . . . . . . Mr Tim Padfield. . . . . . . . . . . . . . . . . . . . . . . . . Tel: (020) 8392 5381
    Web: http://www.nationalarchives.gov.uk/advisorycouncil/default.htm
**National Archives** *(Executive Agency)* . . . . . . . . . . . Ruskin Avenue, Kew, Richmond, Surrey, TW9 4DU
    Keeper of Public Records and
        Chief Executive of Public Record Office . . . . . Mrs Sarah Tyacke CB . . . . . . . . . . . . . . . . . . . . . Tel: (020) 8876 3444
    Web: http://www.nationalarchives.gov.uk

## STATUTE LAW
**Advisory Committee on Statute Law** . . . . . . . . . . Statutory Publications Office, 54-60 Victoria Street, London, SW1E 6QW
    Chairman. . . . . . . . . . . . . . . . . . . . . . . . . . . . . . Rt Hon Lord Falconer of Thoroton QC *(Lord Chancellor and Secretary of State)*
    Secretary . . . . . . . . . . . . . . . . . . . . . . . . . . . . . . Mr Norman Hodgett . . . . . . . . . . . . . . . . . . . . . . Tel: (020) 7210 2615

## TRIBUNALS
**Council on Tribunals** . . . . . . . . . . . . . . . . . . . . . 81 Chancery Lane, London, WC2A 1BQ
    Chairman. . . . . . . . . . . . . . . . . . . . . . . . . . . . . . Rt Hon Lord Newton of Braintree OBE DL
    Secretary . . . . . . . . . . . . . . . . . . . . . . . . . . . . . . Mrs Pat Fairbairn. . . . . . . . . . . . . . . . . . . . . . . . Tel: (020) 7855 5200
    E-mail: enquiries@cot.gsi.gov.uk
    Web: http://www.council-on-tribunals.gov.uk
**Immigration Adjudicator** . . . . . . . . . . . . . . . . . . . Taylor House, 88 Roseberry Avenue, London, EC1R 4QU
    President . . . . . . . . . . . . . . . . . . . . . . . . . . . . . . Hon Judge Henry Hodge OBE . . . . . . . . . . . . . . . Tel: (0845) 600 0877
**Immigration Appeals Tribunal** . . . . . . . . . . . . . . Field House, 15 Breams Buildings, London, EC4A 1DZ
    President . . . . . . . . . . . . . . . . . . . . . . . . . . . . . . Hon Mr Justice Ouseley
    Tribunal Manager. . . . . . . . . . . . . . . . . . . . . . . . Mr Peter Fisher . . . . . . . . . . . . . . . . . . . . . . . . . Tel: (0845) 600 0877
**Lands Tribunal** . . . . . . . . . . . . . . . . . . . . . . . . . Procession House, 55 Ludgate Hill, London, EC4M 7JW
    President . . . . . . . . . . . . . . . . . . . . . . . . . . . . . . Mr George Bartlett QC
    Registrar . . . . . . . . . . . . . . . . . . . . . . . . . . . . . . Mr Donald Scanell . . . . . . . . . . . . . . . . . . . . . . . Tel: (020) 7029 9783
    Web: http://www.courtservice.gov.uk/tribunals/lands
**Transport Tribunal**. . . . . . . . . . . . . . . . . . . . . . . Procession House, 55 Ludgate Hill, London, EC4M 7JW
    President . . . . . . . . . . . . . . . . . . . . . . . . . . . . . . Mr Hugh Carlisle QC
    Tribunal Clerk . . . . . . . . . . . . . . . . . . . . . . . . . . Mr Geraint Evans. . . . . . . . . . . . . . . . . . . . . . . . Tel: (020) 7029 9791
    Web: http://www.transporttribunal.gov.uk
**VAT and Duties Tribunal**. . . . . . . . . . . . . . . . . . 15-19 Bedford Avenue, London, WC1B 3AS
    President . . . . . . . . . . . . . . . . . . . . . . . . . . . . . . His Hon Stephen Oliver QC
    Registrar . . . . . . . . . . . . . . . . . . . . . . . . . . . . . . Mr Richard Lester . . . . . . . . . . . . . . . . . . . . . . . Tel: (020) 7612 9700
    Web: http;//www.financeandtaxtribunals.gov.uk

# DEPARTMENT FOR CONSTITUTIONAL AFFAIRS

## OTHER RELEVANT CONTACTS - SCOTLAND

### AGRICULTURE

**Hannah Research Institute** . . . . . . . . . . . . . . . . . . . . . . Hannah Research Park, Ayr, KA6 5HL
    Director *(Acting)* . . . . . . . . . . . . . . . . . . . . . . . . . . . . . Professor Chris Knight . . . . . . . . . . . . . . . . Tel: (01292) 674000
                                                      Web: http://www.hanna.ac.uk

**Hill Farming Advisory Committee for Scotland** . . . . . . . . c/o Room 248, Pentland House, 47 Robb's Loan,
                                                Edinburgh, EH14 1TY
    Chairman . . . . . . . . . . . . . . . . . . . . . . . . . . . . . Mr David Middleton
    Secretary . . . . . . . . . . . . . . . . . . . . . . . . . . . . . Mr Bill Hepburn . . . . . . . . . . . . . . . . . . . . Tel: (0131) 244 5248

**Macaulay Land Use Research Institute** . . . . . . . . . . . . . The Macaulay Institute, Craigiebuckler, Aberdeen, AB15 8QH
    Chairman . . . . . . . . . . . . . . . . . . . . . . . . . . . . . Mr Andrew Raven
    Chief Executive and Director of Research . . . . . . . . . . . . Professor Margaret Gill . . . . . . . . . . . . . . . . Tel: (01224) 498200
                                                      Web: http://www.macaulay.ac.uk

**Scottish Agricultural Science Agency** *(Executive Agency)* . . 82 Craigs Road, East Craigs, Edinburgh, EH12 8NJ
    Chief Executive . . . . . . . . . . . . . . . . . . . . . . . . . . Dr Robert Hay . . . . . . . . . . . . . . . . . . . . . . Tel: (0131) 244 8890
                                                      Web: http://www.sasa.gov.uk

**Scottish Agricultural Wages Board** . . . . . . . . . . . . . . . . Pentland House, 47 Robb's Loan, Edinburgh, EH14 1TY
    Chairman . . . . . . . . . . . . . . . . . . . . . . . . . . . . . Mrs Christine Davis CBE
    Secretary . . . . . . . . . . . . . . . . . . . . . . . . . . . . . Mr Ronnie Grady . . . . . . . . . . . . . . . . . . . Tel: (0131) 244 6392

**Scottish Crop Research Institute** . . . . . . . . . . . . . . . . . Mylnefield, Invergowrie, Dundee, DD2 5DA
    Director . . . . . . . . . . . . . . . . . . . . . . . . . . . . . . Professor John Hillman . . . . . . . . . . . . . . . Tel: (01382) 562731
                                                      Web: http://www.scri.sari.ac.uk

### AMBULANCE

**Scottish Ambulance Service** . . . . . . . . . . . . . . . . . . . . Tipperlinn Road, Edinburgh, EH10 5UU
    Chairman . . . . . . . . . . . . . . . . . . . . . . . . . . . . . Mr William Brackenridge
    Chief Executive . . . . . . . . . . . . . . . . . . . . . . . . . . Mr Adrian Lucas . . . . . . . . . . . . . . . . . . . Tel: (0131) 446 7000
                                                      Web: http://www.scottishambulance.co.uk

### ANCIENT MONUMENTS / HISTORIC BUILDINGS

**Historic Environment Advisory Council for Scotland** . . . Longmore House, Salisbury Place, Edinburgh, EH9 1SH
    Chairman . . . . . . . . . . . . . . . . . . . . . . . . . . . . . Mrs Elizabeth Burns OBE
    Secretary . . . . . . . . . . . . . . . . . . . . . . . . . . . . . Dr Malcolm Bangor-Jones . . . . . . . . . . . . . Tel: (0131) 668 8810

**Historic Scotland** *(Executive Agency)* . . . . . . . . . . . . . . Longmore House, Salisbury Place, Edinburgh, EH9 1SH
    Chief Executive . . . . . . . . . . . . . . . . . . . . . . . . . . Mr Graeme Munro . . . . . . . . . . . . . . . . . . Tel: (0131) 668 8600
                                                      Web: http://www.historic-scotland.gov.uk

**Royal Commission on the Ancient and**
**Historical Monuments of Scotland** . . . . . . . . . . . . . . . John Sinclair House, 16 Bernard Terrace, Edinburgh, EH8 9NX
    Chairman . . . . . . . . . . . . . . . . . . . . . . . . . . . . . Mrs Kathleen Dalyell
    Secretary . . . . . . . . . . . . . . . . . . . . . . . . . . . . . Mr Roger Mercer . . . . . . . . . . . . . . . . . . . Tel: (0131) 662 1456
                                                      Web: http://www.rcahms.gov.uk

### ARTS

**Royal Fine Art Commission for Scotland** . . . . . . . . . . . . Bakehouse Close, 146 Canongate, Edinburgh, EH8 8DD
    Chairman . . . . . . . . . . . . . . . . . . . . . . . . . . . . . Rt Hon Lord Cameron of Lochbroom
    Secretary . . . . . . . . . . . . . . . . . . . . . . . . . . . . . Mr Charles Prosser . . . . . . . . . . . . . . . . . . Tel: (0131) 556 6699
                                                      Web: http://www.royalfineartscomforsco.gov.uk

**Scottish Arts Council** . . . . . . . . . . . . . . . . . . . . . . . . 12 Manor Place, Edinburgh, EH3 7DD
    Chairman . . . . . . . . . . . . . . . . . . . . . . . . . . . . . Mr James Boyle
    Director . . . . . . . . . . . . . . . . . . . . . . . . . . . . . . Mr Graham Berry . . . . . . . . . . . . . . . . . . . Tel: (0131) 226 6051
                                                      Web: http://www.scottisharts.org.uk

### AUDIT

**Accounts Commission Scotland / Audit Scotland** . . . . . . . 110 George Street, Edinburgh, EH2 4LH
    Auditor General . . . . . . . . . . . . . . . . . . . . . . . . . . Mr Robert Black
    Chairman of the Accounts Commission . . . . . . . . . . . . . Mr Alastair MacNish . . . . . . . . . . . . . . . . . Tel: (0131) 477 1234
                                                      E-mail: info@audit-scot.gov.uk
                                                      Web: http://www.audit-scotland.gov.uk

# DEPARTMENT FOR CONSTITUTIONAL AFFAIRS

*Other Relevant Contacts: Scotland (Continued)*

## BANKRUPTCY
**Office of the Accountant in Bankruptcy** . . . . . . . . . . . . . George House, 126 George Street. Edinburgh, EH2 4HH
    Accountant in Bankruptcy . . . . . . . . . . . . . . . . . . . . . . . . Mrs Gillian Thompson . . . . . . . . . . . . . . . . Tel: (0131) 473 4600
    Web: http://www.aib.gov.uk

## BOTANIC GARDEN
**Royal Botanic Garden Edinburgh** . . . . . . . . . . . . . . . . . 20a Inverleith Row, Edinburgh, EH3 5LR
    Chairman of Trustees. . . . . . . . . . . . . . . . . . . . . . . . . . . . Dr Paul Nicholson
    Regius Keeper. . . . . . . . . . . . . . . . . . . . . . . . . . . . . . . . . Professor Stephen Blackmore FRSE . . . . . . . . Tel: (0131) 552 7171
    Web: http://www.rbge.org.uk

## BOUNDARIES
**Boundary Commission for Scotland** . . . . . . . . . . . . . . . . 3 Drumsheugh Gardens, Edinburgh, EH3 7QJ
    Chairman . . . . . . . . . . . . . . . . . . . . . . . . . . . . . . . . . . . . Rt Hon Michael Martin MP (*Speaker of the House of Commons*)
    Secretary. . . . . . . . . . . . . . . . . . . . . . . . . . . . . . . . . . . . . Mr Robert Smith. . . . . . . . . . . . . . . . . . . . . Tel: (0131) 538 7200
    Web: http://www.bcomm-scotland.gov.uk
**Local Government Boundary Commission for Scotland** . 3 Drumsheugh Gardens, Edinburgh, EH3 7QJ
    Chairman . . . . . . . . . . . . . . . . . . . . . . . . . . . . . . . . . . . . Mr John Marjoribanks
    Secretary. . . . . . . . . . . . . . . . . . . . . . . . . . . . . . . . . . . . . Mr Bob Smith. . . . . . . . . . . . . . . . . . . . . . . Tel: (0131) 538 7510
    Web: http://www.lgbc-scotland.gov.uk

## CHILDREN
**Children's Panels** . . . . . . . . . . . . . . . . . . . . . . . . . . . . . . Area 2B South, Victoria Quay, Edinburgh, EH6 6QQ
    *Contact* . . . . . . . . . . . . . . . . . . . . . . . . . . . . . . . . . . . . . . Ms Alexandra Simpson . . . . . . . . . . . . . . . . Tel: (0131) 244 3545
    Web: http:/www.childrens-hearings.co.uk
**Commissioner for Children and**
**Young People in Scotland** . . . . . . . . . . . . . . . . . . . . . . MWB Business Exchange, 9-10 St Andrew's Square, Edinburgh, EH2 2AF
    Commissioner . . . . . . . . . . . . . . . . . . . . . . . . . . . . . . . . . Ms Kathleen Marshall. . . . . . . . . . . . . . . . . Tel: (0131) 348 8500
    E-mail: enquiries@cypcommissioner.org
    Web: http://www.cypcommissioner.org
**Scottish Children's Reporter Administration** . . . . . . . . . Ochil House, Springkerse Business Park, Stirling, FK7 7XE
    Chairman . . . . . . . . . . . . . . . . . . . . . . . . . . . . . . . . . . . . Mr Douglas Bulloch
    Chief Executive. . . . . . . . . . . . . . . . . . . . . . . . . . . . . . . . Mr Alan Miller . . . . . . . . . . . . . . . . . . . . . . Tel: (01786) 459500
    E-mail: info@childrens-reporter.org

## COMMUNICATIONS
**OFCOM, Scotland** . . . . . . . . . . . . . . . . . . . . . . . . . . . . . Sutherland House, 149 St Vincent Street, Glasgow, G2 5NW
    Chief Executive. . . . . . . . . . . . . . . . . . . . . . . . . . . . . . . . Mr Stephen Carter . . . . . . . . . . . . . . . . . . . Tel: (0141) 229 7400
    E-mail: contact@ofcom.org.uk
    Web: http://www.ofcom.org.uk

## CONSTRUCTION
**Building Standards Advisory Committee** . . . . . . . . . . . . . Development Department, Building Standards Division
    2-H Victoria Quay, Edinburgh, EH6 6QQ
    Chairman . . . . . . . . . . . . . . . . . . . . . . . . . . . . . . . . . . . . Dr Sam Thorburn OBE
    Secretary. . . . . . . . . . . . . . . . . . . . . . . . . . . . . . . . . . . . . Mr Alan Murchison. . . . . . . . . . . . . . . . . . . Tel: (0131) 244 7440

## CONSUMERS
**Scottish Consumer Council** . . . . . . . . . . . . . . . . . . . . . . Royal Exchange House, 100 Queen's Street, Glasgow, G1 3DN
    Chairman . . . . . . . . . . . . . . . . . . . . . . . . . . . . . . . . . . . . Mr Graeme Miller
    Director . . . . . . . . . . . . . . . . . . . . . . . . . . . . . . . . . . . . . . Mr Martyn Evans . . . . . . . . . . . . . . . . . . . . Tel: (0141) 226 5261
    Web: http://www.scotconsumer.org.uk

## COUNTRYSIDE AND NATURE
**Advisory Committee on Sites of Special**
    **Scientific Interest** . . . . . . . . . . . . . . . . . . . . . . . . . . . . 3rd Floor, 23 Chester Street, Edinburgh, EH3 7ET
    Chairman . . . . . . . . . . . . . . . . . . . . . . . . . . . . . . . . . . . . Professor Donald Davidson
    Secretary. . . . . . . . . . . . . . . . . . . . . . . . . . . . . . . . . . . . . Ms Sue Bell . . . . . . . . . . . . . . . . . . . . . . . . Tel: (0131) 225 1230
**Scottish Natural Heritage** . . . . . . . . . . . . . . . . . . . . . . . 12 Hope Terrace, Edinburgh, EH9 2AS
    Chairman . . . . . . . . . . . . . . . . . . . . . . . . . . . . . . . . . . . . Dr John Markland CBE
    Chief Executive. . . . . . . . . . . . . . . . . . . . . . . . . . . . . . . . Dr Ian Jardine . . . . . . . . . . . . . . . . . . . . . . Tel: (0131) 447 4784
    Web: http://www.snh.org.uk

# DEPARTMENT FOR CONSTITUTIONAL AFFAIRS

*Other Relevant Contacts: Scotland (Continued)*

**CROFTING**

**Crofters Commission** . . . . . . . . . . . . . . . . . . . . . . . . . . . . . 4-6 Castle Wynd, Inverness, IV2 3EQ
    Chairman . . . . . . . . . . . . . . . . . . . . . . . . . . . . . . . . . . Mr David Green
    Chief Executive . . . . . . . . . . . . . . . . . . . . . . . . . . . . . . Mr Shane Rankin . . . . . . . . . . . . . . . . . . . . . Tel: (01463) 663450
                                            Web: http://www.crofterscommission.org.uk

**DEER**

**Deer Commission for Scotland** . . . . . . . . . . . . . . . . . . . . . Knowsley, 82 Fairfield Road, Inverness, IV3 5LH
    Chairman . . . . . . . . . . . . . . . . . . . . . . . . . . . . . . . . . . Mr Andrew Raven
    Director . . . . . . . . . . . . . . . . . . . . . . . . . . . . . . . . . . . Mr Nick Reiter . . . . . . . . . . . . . . . . . . . . . . Tel: (01463) 231751
                                            Web: http://www.dcs.gov.uk

**DISABILITY**

**Mobility and Access Committee for Scotland** . . . . . . . . . Chevron Suite, Forsyth House, Innova Campus, Rosyth, KY11 2UU
    Convenor. . . . . . . . . . . . . . . . . . . . . . . . . . . . . . . . . . . Ms Margaret Hickish . . . . . . . . . . . . . . . . . Tel: (01383) 428031
                                            Web: http://www.macs-mobility.org

**DRUGS**

**Scottish Advisory Committee on Drug Misuse** . . . . . . . . Substance Misuse Division, Department of Health, St Andrew's House,
                                            Edinburgh, EH1 3DG
    Chairman . . . . . . . . . . . . . . . . . . . . . . . . . . . . . . . . . . Mr Hugh Henry MSP
    Secretary. . . . . . . . . . . . . . . . . . . . . . . . . . . . . . . . . . Mrs Molly Robertson . . . . . . . . . . . . . . . . . Tel: (0131) 244 2496
                                            E-mail: mollyrobertson@scotland.gov.uk
**Scottish Drug Enforcement Agency**. . . . . . . . . . . . . . . . Osprey House, Inchinnan Road, Paisley, PA3 2RE
    Director . . . . . . . . . . . . . . . . . . . . . . . . . . . . . . . . . . . Mr Graham Pearson . . . . . . . . . . . . . . . . . . Tel: (0141) 302 1000

**EDINBURGH CASTLE**

**Edinburgh Castle** . . . . . . . . . . . . . . . . . . . . . . . . . . . . . Edinburgh, EH1 2YT
    Governor. . . . . . . . . . . . . . . . . . . . . . . . . . . . . . . . . . . Major-General Euan Loudon. . . . . . . . . . . . Tel: (0131) 310 2061

**EDUCATION**

**General Teaching Council for Scotland** . . . . . . . . . . . . . Clerwood House, 96 Clermiston Road, Edinburgh, EH12 6UT
    Convener. . . . . . . . . . . . . . . . . . . . . . . . . . . . . . . . . . . Mrs Norma Anne Watson
    Chief Executive / Registrar . . . . . . . . . . . . . . . . . . . . . Mr Matthew MacIver. . . . . . . . . . . . . . . . . Tel: (0131) 314 6000
                                              Web: http://www.gtcs.org.uk
**HM Inspectorate of Education** *(Executive Agency)* . . . . . . . TI Spur, Saughton House, Broomhouse Drive, Edinburgh, EH11 3XD
    HM Senior Chief Inspector . . . . . . . . . . . . . . . . . . . . . Mr Graham Donaldson . . . . . . . . . . . . . . . Tel: (0131) 244 0650
                                            Web: http://www.hmie.gov.uk
**Learning and Teaching Scotland** . . . . . . . . . . . . . . . . . . 74 Victoria Crescent Road, Glasgow, G12 9JN
    Chairman . . . . . . . . . . . . . . . . . . . . . . . . . . . . . . . . . . Professor Tom Wilson OBE
    Chief Executive. . . . . . . . . . . . . . . . . . . . . . . . . . . . . . Mr Bernard McLeary . . . . . . . . . . . . . . . . . Tel: (0141) 337 5000
                                            Web: http://www.itscotland.org.uk
**Scottish Further Education Funding Council** . . . . . . . . . Donaldson House, 97 Haymarket Terrace, Edinburgh, EH12 5HD
    Chairman . . . . . . . . . . . . . . . . . . . . . . . . . . . . . . . . . . Mrs Esther Roberton
    Chief Executive. . . . . . . . . . . . . . . . . . . . . . . . . . . . . . Mr Roger McClure . . . . . . . . . . . . . . . . . . . Tel: (0131) 313 6500
                                            E-mail: info@sfc.ac.uk
                                            Web: http://www.sfc.ac.uk
**Scottish Higher Education Funding Council**. . . . . . . . . . Donaldson House, 97 Haymarket Terrace, Edinburgh, EH12 5HD
    Chairman . . . . . . . . . . . . . . . . . . . . . . . . . . . . . . . . . . Dr Chris Masters
    Chief Executive. . . . . . . . . . . . . . . . . . . . . . . . . . . . . . Mr Roger McClure . . . . . . . . . . . . . . . . . . . Tel: (0131) 313 6500
                                            E-mail: info@sfc.ac.uk
                                            Web: http://www.sfc.ac.uk
**Scottish Qualifications Authority** . . . . . . . . . . . . . . . . . Hanover House, 24 Douglas Street, Glasgow, G2 7NQ
    Chairman . . . . . . . . . . . . . . . . . . . . . . . . . . . . . . . . . . Professor Sir John Ward
    Chief Executive *(Acting)* . . . . . . . . . . . . . . . . . . . . . . . . Mr Anton Corella . . . . . . . . . . . . . . . . . . . . Tel: (0141) 242 2214
                                            Web: http://www.sqa.org.uk
**Student Awards Agency for Scotland** *(Executive Agency)* . . Gyleview House, 3 Redheughs Rigg, Edinburgh, EH12 9HH
    Chief Executive. . . . . . . . . . . . . . . . . . . . . . . . . . . . . . Mr David Stephen. . . . . . . . . . . . . . . . . . . . Tel: (0131) 476 8212
                                            Web: http://www.saas.gov.uk

# DEPARTMENT FOR CONSTITUTIONAL AFFAIRS

*Other Relevant Contacts: Scotland (Continued)*

## EMPLOYMENT
**Jobcentre Plus Scotland** . . . . . . . . . . . . . . . . . . . . . . . . . Argyle House, 3 Lady Lawson Street, Edinburgh, EH3 9SD
   Director . . . . . . . . . . . . . . . . . . . . . . . . . . . . . . . . Mr Kevin Doran . . . . . . . . . . . . . . . . . . . . Tel: (0131) 221 4001
                                  Web: http://www.jobcentreplus.gov.uk

## ENTERPRISE *(see below under Highlands and Islands and under Industry)*

## ENVIRONMENT
**Scottish Environment Protection Agency** . . . . . . . . . . . . Erskine Court, Castle Business Park, Stirling, FK9 4TR
   Chairman . . . . . . . . . . . . . . . . . . . . . . . . . . . . . . . . Sir Ken Collins
   Chief Executive . . . . . . . . . . . . . . . . . . . . . . . . . . . . Dr Campbell Gemmell . . . . . . . . . . . . . . . . Tel: (01786) 457700
                                    E-mail: info@sepa.org.uk
                                    Web: http://www.sepa.org.uk

## EQUAL OPPORTUNITIES
**Equal Opportunities Commission for Scotland** . . . . . . . . St Stephen's House, 279 Bath Street, Glasgow, G2 4JL
   Commissioner for Scotland . . . . . . . . . . . . . . . . . . . . . Mrs Rowena Arshad OBE
   Director . . . . . . . . . . . . . . . . . . . . . . . . . . . . . . . . Mr John Wilkes . . . . . . . . . . . . . . . . . . . . . Tel: (0845) 601 5901
                                    Web: http://www.eoc.org.uk

## FILM
**Scottish Screen** . . . . . . . . . . . . . . . . . . . . . . . . . . . . . 2nd Floor, 249 West George Street, Glasgow, G2 4QE
   Chairman . . . . . . . . . . . . . . . . . . . . . . . . . . . . . . . . Mrs Ray MacFarlane
   Chief Executive . . . . . . . . . . . . . . . . . . . . . . . . . . . . Mr Steve McIntyre . . . . . . . . . . . . . . . . . . Tel: (0141) 302 1700
                                    E-mail: info@scottishscreen.com
                                    Web: http://www.scottishscreen.com

## FISHERIES
**Fisheries (Electricity) Committee** . . . . . . . . . . . . . . . . . Room 408A, Pentland House, 47 Robb's Loan, Edinburgh, EH14 1TY
   Chairman . . . . . . . . . . . . . . . . . . . . . . . . . . . . . . . . Mr James Cockburn
   Secretary . . . . . . . . . . . . . . . . . . . . . . . . . . . . . . . . Mr Richard Gustar . . . . . . . . . . . . . . . . . . Tel: (0131) 244 5245
**Fisheries Research Services** *(Executive Agency)* . . . . . . . . FRS Marine Laboratory, PO Box 101, 375 Victoria Road,
                                    Aberdeen, AB11 9DB
   Chief Executive . . . . . . . . . . . . . . . . . . . . . . . . . . . . Professor Robin Cook . . . . . . . . . . . . . . . . Tel: (01224) 876544
                                    E-mail: enquiries@marlab.ac.uk
                                    Web: http://www.frs-scotland.gov.uk
**Scottish Fisheries Protection Agency** *(Executive Agency)* . . Pentland House, 47 Robb's Loan, Edinburgh, EH14 1TY
   Chief Executive . . . . . . . . . . . . . . . . . . . . . . . . . . . . Mr Paul Du Vivier . . . . . . . . . . . . . . . . . . Tel: (0131) 244 6595

## FORESTRY
**Forest Enterprise Scotland** *(Executive Agency)* . . . . . . . . . 1 Highlander Way, Inverness Business Park, Inverness, IV2 7GB
   Chief Executive . . . . . . . . . . . . . . . . . . . . . . . . . . . . Dr Hugh Insley . . . . . . . . . . . . . . . . . . . . . Tel: (01463) 232811
                                    Web: http://www.forestry.gov.uk
**Forest Research** *(Executive Agency)* . . . . . . . . . . . . . . . . Northern Research Station, Roslin, Midlothian, EH25 9SY
   Chief Executive . . . . . . . . . . . . . . . . . . . . . . . . . . . . Professor Jim Lynch . . . . . . . . . . . . . . . . . Tel: (0131) 445 2176
                                    Web: http://www.forestry.gov.uk/forest_research
**Forestry Commission Scotland** . . . . . . . . . . . . . . . . . . . Silvan House, 231 Corstorphine Road, Edinburgh, EH12 7AT
   Director . . . . . . . . . . . . . . . . . . . . . . . . . . . . . . . . Dr Bob McIntosh . . . . . . . . . . . . . . . . . . . Tel: (0131) 314 6156
                                    Web: http://www.forestry.gov.uk

## GAELIC DEVELOPMENT AGENCY
**Bòrd Gàidhlig na h-alba** . . . . . . . . . . . . . . . . . . . . . . . Ness Horizons Kintail House, Beechwood Park, Inverness, IV2 3BW
   Chairman . . . . . . . . . . . . . . . . . . . . . . . . . . . . . . . . Mr Duncan Ferguson
   Chief Executive . . . . . . . . . . . . . . . . . . . . . . . . . . . . Mr Allan Campbell . . . . . . . . . . . . . . . . . . Tel: (01463) 723570
                                    Web: http://www.bord-na-gaidhlig.org.uk

## HEALTH
**Common Services Authority for the NHS Scotland** . . . . . Trinity Park House, South Trinity Road, Edinburgh, EH5 3SE
   Chairman . . . . . . . . . . . . . . . . . . . . . . . . . . . . . . . . Mr Graeme Millar
   Chief Executive . . . . . . . . . . . . . . . . . . . . . . . . . . . . Mr Stuart Bain . . . . . . . . . . . . . . . . . . . . . Tel: (0131) 552 6255
                                    Web: http://www.show.scot.nhs.uk

# DEPARTMENT FOR CONSTITUTIONAL AFFAIRS

*Other Relevant Contacts: Scotland – Health (Continued)*

**Health Education Board for Scotland** . . . . . . . . . . . . . . . Woodburn House, Canaan Lane, Edinburgh, EH10 4SG
    Chairman . . . . . . . . . . . . . . . . . . . . . . . . . . . . . . . . . . Cllr Leslie Hinds
    Chief Executive . . . . . . . . . . . . . . . . . . . . . . . . . . . . . . Mr Graham Robertson . . . . . . . . . . . . . . . . Tel: (0131) 536 5500
        Web: http://www.hebs.com

**Mental Welfare Commission for Scotland** . . . . . . . . . . . Floor K, Argyle House, 3 Lady Lawson Street, Edinburgh, EH3 9SH
    Chairman . . . . . . . . . . . . . . . . . . . . . . . . . . . . . . . . . . Mr Ian Miller OBE
    Director . . . . . . . . . . . . . . . . . . . . . . . . . . . . . . . . . . . Mt Donald Lyons . . . . . . . . . . . . . . . . . . . Tel: (0131) 222 6111
        Web: http://www.mwcscot.org.uk

**NHS Education for Scotland** . . . . . . . . . . . . . . . . . . . . . 22 Queen Street, Edinburgh, EH2 1NT
    Chairman . . . . . . . . . . . . . . . . . . . . . . . . . . . . . . . . . . Mrs Ann Markham
    Chief Executive . . . . . . . . . . . . . . . . . . . . . . . . . . . . . . Mr Stewart Bain . . . . . . . . . . . . . . . . . . . . Tel: (0131) 225 4365
        Web: http://www.nes.scot.nhs.uk

**NHS Health Scotland** . . . . . . . . . . . . . . . . . . . . . . . . . . Woodburn House, Canaan Lane, Edinburgh, EH10 4SG
    Chairman . . . . . . . . . . . . . . . . . . . . . . . . . . . . . . . . . . Cllr Lesley Hinds
    Chief Executive . . . . . . . . . . . . . . . . . . . . . . . . . . . . . . Mr Graham Robertson . . . . . . . . . . . . . . . . Tel: (0131) 536 5500
        Web: http://www.hebs.com

**NHS 24** . . . . . . . . . . . . . . . . . . . . . . . . . . . . . . . . . . . . . 3rd Floor, Delta House, 50 West Nile Street, Glasgow, G1 2NP
    Chairman . . . . . . . . . . . . . . . . . . . . . . . . . . . . . . . . . . Mrs Christine Lenihan
    Chief Executive . . . . . . . . . . . . . . . . . . . . . . . . . . . . . . Dr Des Bonnar . . . . . . . . . . . . . . . . . . . . . Tel: (0141) 225 0099
        Web: http://www.nhs24.com

**NHS Quality Improvement Scotland** . . . . . . . . . . . . . . . Elliott House, 8-10 Hillside Crescent, Edinburgh, EH7 5EA
    Chairman . . . . . . . . . . . . . . . . . . . . . . . . . . . . . . . . . . Lord Patel
    Chief Executive . . . . . . . . . . . . . . . . . . . . . . . . . . . . . . Dr David Steel . . . . . . . . . . . . . . . . . . . . . Tel: (0131) 623 4300
        Web: http://www.nhshealthquality.org

**NHS Scotland Property and Environment Forum** . . . . . . 4th Floor, Empire House, 131 West Nile Street, Glasgow, G1 2RX
    Chief Executive . . . . . . . . . . . . . . . . . . . . . . . . . . . . . . Mr Ian McLucie . . . . . . . . . . . . . . . . . . . . Tel: (0141) 332 3455
        E-mail: enquiries@pef.scot.nhs.uk
        Web: http://www.scot.nhs.uk/pef

**National Waiting Times Centre** . . . . . . . . . . . . . . . . . . . Golden Jubilee National Hospital, Beardmore Street, Clydebank, G81 4HX
    Chairman of the Trustees . . . . . . . . . . . . . . . . . . . . . . . Dr Lindsay Burley
    Chief Executive . . . . . . . . . . . . . . . . . . . . . . . . . . . . . . Mr Ian McAdam . . . . . . . . . . . . . . . . . . . . Tel: (0141) 951 5000
        E-mail: ian.mcadam@gjnh.scot.nhs.uk

**Rowett Research Institute** . . . . . . . . . . . . . . . . . . . . . . . Greenburn Road, Bucksburn, Aberdeen, AB21 9SB
    Chairman . . . . . . . . . . . . . . . . . . . . . . . . . . . . . . . . . . Dr James Stewart
    Director . . . . . . . . . . . . . . . . . . . . . . . . . . . . . . . . . . . Professor Peter Morgan . . . . . . . . . . . . . . . Tel: (01224) 712751
        Web: http://www.rowett.ac.uk

**Scottish Advisory Committee on Distinction Awards** . . . . Scottish Health Service Centre, Crewe Road South, Edinburgh, EH4 2LF
    Chairman . . . . . . . . . . . . . . . . . . . . . . . . . . . . . . . . . . Professor Colin Suckling
    Secretary . . . . . . . . . . . . . . . . . . . . . . . . . . . . . . . . . . Ms Margaret Brown . . . . . . . . . . . . . . . . . Tel: (0131) 623 2540
        Web: http://www.show.scot.nhs.uk/sacda

**Scottish Advisory Committee on the Medical Workforce** Department of Health, St Andrew's House, Edinburgh, EH1 3DG
    Chairman . . . . . . . . . . . . . . . . . . . . . . . . . . . . . . . . . . Dr Robin Cairncross
    Secretary . . . . . . . . . . . . . . . . . . . . . . . . . . . . . . . . . . Mr Neil Murray . . . . . . . . . . . . . . . . . . . . Tel: (0131) 244 2486

**Scottish Hospital Endowments Research Trust** . . . . . . . . Princes Exchange, 1 Earl Grey Street, Edinburgh, EH3 9EE
    Chairman . . . . . . . . . . . . . . . . . . . . . . . . . . . . . . . . . . Professor Moira Brown . . . . . . . . . . . . . . . Tel: (0131) 659 8800
        Web: http://www.shert.org.uk

**Scottish Medical Practices Committee** . . . . . . . . . . . . . . Scottish Health Service Centre, Crewe Road South, Edinburgh, EH4 2LF
    Chairman . . . . . . . . . . . . . . . . . . . . . . . . . . . . . . . . . . Dr Graham McIntosh MBE
    Secretary . . . . . . . . . . . . . . . . . . . . . . . . . . . . . . . . . . Ms Julie Anderson . . . . . . . . . . . . . . . . . . Tel: (0131) 623 2540
        Web: http://www.show.scot.nhs/shsc

**State Hospitals Board for Scotland** . . . . . . . . . . . . . . . . . The State Hospital, Carstairs, Lanarkshire, ML11 8RP
    Chairman . . . . . . . . . . . . . . . . . . . . . . . . . . . . . . . . . . Mr Gordon Craig
    Chief Executive . . . . . . . . . . . . . . . . . . . . . . . . . . . . . . Mrs Andreana Adamson . . . . . . . . . . . . . . Tel: (01555) 840293
        Web: http://www.show.scot.nhs.uk

## HIGHLANDS AND ISLANDS

**Highlands and Islands Enterprise** . . . . . . . . . . . . . . . . . . Cowan House, Inverness Retail and Business Park, Inverness, IV2 7GF
    Chairman . . . . . . . . . . . . . . . . . . . . . . . . . . . . . . . . . . Dr James Hunter CBE
    Chief Executive . . . . . . . . . . . . . . . . . . . . . . . . . . . . . . Mr Sandy Cumming CBE . . . . . . . . . . . . . . Tel: (01463) 234171
        Web: http://www.hie.co.uk

# DEPARTMENT FOR CONSTITUTIONAL AFFAIRS

*Other Relevant Contacts: Scotland (Continued)*

## HOUSING AND REGENERATION

**Communities Scotland** *(Executive Agency)* . . . . . . . . . . . . . Thistle House, 91 Haymarket Terrace, Edinburgh, EH12 5HE
  Chief Executive *(Acting)* . . . . . . . . . . . . . . . . . . . . . . . . . . Ms Angiolina Foster . . . . . . . . . . . . . . . . . . . . Tel: (0131) 313 0044
  Web: http://www.communitiesscotland.gov.uk
**Rent Assessment Committee** . . . . . . . . . . . . . . . . . . . . . . . 3rd Floor, 140 West Campbell Street, Glasgow, G2 4TZ
  President. . . . . . . . . . . . . . . . . . . . . . . . . . . . . . . . . . . . . . . Mrs Isabel Montgomery
  Secretary. . . . . . . . . . . . . . . . . . . . . . . . . . . . . . . . . . . . . . Mrs Sara James . . . . . . . . . . . . . . . . . . . . . Tel: (0141) 572 1170
  E-mail: admin@rapc.org
**Scottish Homes**. . . . . . . . . . . . . . . . . . . . . . . . . . . . . . . . . . Thistle House, 91 Haymarket Terrace, Edinburgh, EH12 5HE
  Chief Executive. . . . . . . . . . . . . . . . . . . . . . . . . . . . . . . . . . Ms Angelina Foster . . . . . . . . . . . . . . . . . . . . Tel: (0131) 313 0044
  Web: http://www.communitiesscotland.gov.uk

## INDUSTRY

**Scottish Enterprise** . . . . . . . . . . . . . . . . . . . . . . . . . . . . . . 150 Broomielaw, Atlantic Quay, Glasgow, G2 8LU
  Chairman . . . . . . . . . . . . . . . . . . . . . . . . . . . . . . . . . . . . . . Sir Ian Robinson
  Chief Executive. . . . . . . . . . . . . . . . . . . . . . . . . . . . . . . . . . Dr Robert Crawford . . . . . . . . . . . . . . . . . . . Tel: (0141) 248 2700
  Web: http://www.scottish-enterprise.com
**Scottish Industrial Development Advisory Board** . . . . . . Meridian Court, 5 Cadogan Street, Glasgow, G2 6AT
  Chairman . . . . . . . . . . . . . . . . . . . . . . . . . . . . . . . . . . . . . . Mr Vikram Lall
  Secretary. . . . . . . . . . . . . . . . . . . . . . . . . . . . . . . . . . . . . . Mr Peter Ford. . . . . . . . . . . . . . . . . . . . . . . . . Tel: (0141) 242 5674
  Web: http://www.rsascotland.gov.uk

## LAND

**Lands Tribunal for Scotland**. . . . . . . . . . . . . . . . . . . . . . . Scottish Land Court, 1 Grosvenor Crescent, Edinburgh, EH12 5ER
  Chairman and Principal Clerk . . . . . . . . . . . . . . . . . . . . . . Hon Lord McGhie. . . . . . . . . . . . . . . . . . . . . . Tel: (0131) 225 7996
  Clerk. . . . . . . . . . . . . . . . . . . . . . . . . . . . . . . . . . . . . . . . . Mr Neil Tainsh
  Web: http://www.lands-tribunal-scotland.org.uk
**Registers of Scotland** *(Executive Agency)* . . . . . . . . . . . . . Meadowbank House, 153 London Road, Edinburgh, EH8 7AU
  Chief Executive. . . . . . . . . . . . . . . . . . . . . . . . . . . . . . . . . . Mr Jim Meldrum. . . . . . . . . . . . . . . . . . . . . . . Tel: (0131) 659 6111
  Web: http://www.ros.gov.uk
**Scottish Land Court**. . . . . . . . . . . . . . . . . . . . . . . . . . . . . . 1 Grosvenor Crescent, Edinburgh, EH12 5ER
  Chairman . . . . . . . . . . . . . . . . . . . . . . . . . . . . . . . . . . . . . . Hon Lord McGhie QC
  Clerk. . . . . . . . . . . . . . . . . . . . . . . . . . . . . . . . . . . . . . . . . Mr Neil Tainsh. . . . . . . . . . . . . . . . . . . . . . . . Tel: (0131) 225 3595

## LEGAL SERVICES

**Central Advisory Committee on Justices
of the Peace (Scotland)**. . . . . . . . . . . . . . . . . . . . . . . 1st Floor West, St Andrews House, Edinburgh, EH1 3DG
  Chairman . . . . . . . . . . . . . . . . . . . . . . . . . . . . . . . . . . . . . . Rt Hon Lord Gill
  Secretary. . . . . . . . . . . . . . . . . . . . . . . . . . . . . . . . . . . . . . Mr Hugh Dignon . . . . . . . . . . . . . . . . . . . . . . Tel: (0131) 244 2691
  E-mail: hugh.dignon@scotland.gsi.gov.uk
**Scottish Court Service** *(Executive Agency)* . . . . . . . . . . . . . Hayweight House, 23 Lauriston Street, Edinburgh, EH3 9DQ
  Chief Executive. . . . . . . . . . . . . . . . . . . . . . . . . . . . . . . . . . Mr John Ewing. . . . . . . . . . . . . . . . . . . . . . . . Tel: (0131) 229 9200
  Web: http://www.scotcourts.gov.uk
**Scottish Criminal Cases Review Commission** . . . . . . . . . 5th Floor, Portland House, 17 Renfield Street, Glasgow, G2 5AH
  Chairman . . . . . . . . . . . . . . . . . . . . . . . . . . . . . . . . . . . . . . Very Rev Graham Forbes
  Chief Executive. . . . . . . . . . . . . . . . . . . . . . . . . . . . . . . . . . Mr Gerard Sinclair . . . . . . . . . . . . . . . . . . . . Tel: (0141) 270 7030
  E-mail: info@sccrc.co.uk
  Web: http://www.sccrc.org.uk
**Scottish Law Commission** . . . . . . . . . . . . . . . . . . . . . . . . 140 Causewayside, Edinburgh, EH9 1PR
  Chairman . . . . . . . . . . . . . . . . . . . . . . . . . . . . . . . . . . . . . . Hon Lord Eassie
  Secretary. . . . . . . . . . . . . . . . . . . . . . . . . . . . . . . . . . . . . . Miss Jane McLeod . . . . . . . . . . . . . . . . . . . . . Tel: (0131) 668 2131
  E-mail: info@scotlawcom.gov.uk
  Web: http://www.scotlawcom.gov.uk
**Scottish Legal Aid Board** . . . . . . . . . . . . . . . . . . . . . . . . 44 Drumsheugh Gardens, Edinburgh, EH3 7SW
  Chairman . . . . . . . . . . . . . . . . . . . . . . . . . . . . . . . . . . . . . . Mrs Jean Couper
  Chief Executive. . . . . . . . . . . . . . . . . . . . . . . . . . . . . . . . . . Mr Lindsay Montgomery. . . . . . . . . . . . . . . . . Tel: (0131) 226 7061
  Web: http://www.slab.org.uk
**Scottish Legal Services Ombudsman** . . . . . . . . . . . . . . . 17 Waterloo Place, Edinburgh, EH1 3DL
  Ombudsman . . . . . . . . . . . . . . . . . . . . . . . . . . . . . . . . . . . Ms Linda Costelloe Baker. . . . . . . . . . . . . . . . Tel: (0131) 556 9123
  Web: http://www.slso.org.uk
**Secretary of Commissions for Scotland** . . . . . . . . . . . . . 1st Floor, St Andrew's House, Regent Road, Edinburgh, EH1 3DG
  Secretary of Commissions . . . . . . . . . . . . . . . . . . . . . . . . Mr Charles Coull . . . . . . . . . . . . . . . . . . . . . . Tel: (0131) 244 2793
  E-mail: alan.oliver@scotland.gov.uk

# DEPARTMENT FOR CONSTITUTIONAL AFFAIRS

*Other Relevant Contacts: Scotland – Legal Services (Continued)*

**Supreme Courts of Scotland**. . . . . . . . . . . . . . . . . . . . . . Court of Session, Parliament Square, Edinburgh, EH1 1RQ
Lord Justice General and
    Lord President of the Court of Session. . . . . . . . . . . . . Rt Hon Lord Cullen of Whitekirk . . . . . . . . Tel: (0131) 225 2595
                        Web: http://www.scotcourts.gov.uk

## LIBRARY
**National Library of Scotland** . . . . . . . . . . . . . . . . . . . . . George IV Bridge, Edinburgh, EH1 1EW
    Chairman of the Trustees. . . . . . . . . . . . . . . . . . . . . . . Professor Michael Anderson
    Librarian and Secretary to the Board . . . . . . . . . . . . . . Mr Martyn Wade . . . . . . . . . . . . . . . . . . . . . Tel: (0131) 226 4531
                        E-mail: enquiries@nls.uk
                        Web: http://www.nls.uk

## LIGHTHOUSES
**Northern Lighthouse Board** . . . . . . . . . . . . . . . . . . . . . . 84 George Street, Edinburgh, EH2 3DA
    Chairman . . . . . . . . . . . . . . . . . . . . . . . . . . . . . . . . . . Sheriff Principal Edward Bowen QC
    Chief Executive. . . . . . . . . . . . . . . . . . . . . . . . . . . . . . Mr James Taylor. . . . . . . . . . . . . . . . . . . . . . . Tel: (0131) 473 3100
                        Web: http://www.nlb.org.uk

## MOBILITY AND ACCESS
**Mobility and Access Committee for Scotland** . . . . . . . . . Forsyth House, Innova Campus, Rosyth Europarc,
                        Rosyth, KY11 2UU
    Chairman . . . . . . . . . . . . . . . . . . . . . . . . . . . . . . . . . . Ms Margaret Hickish . . . . . . . . . . . . . . . . . . Tel: (01383) 428031
                        E-mail: macs@ednet.co.uk  Web: http://www.macs-mobility.org

## MUSEUMS AND GALLERIES
**National Galleries of Scotland** . . . . . . . . . . . . . . . . . . . . The Mound, Edinburgh, EH2 2EZ
    Chairman . . . . . . . . . . . . . . . . . . . . . . . . . . . . . . . . . . Mr Brian Ivory CBE FRSE
    Director-General . . . . . . . . . . . . . . . . . . . . . . . . . . . . . Sir Timothy Clifford FRSE . . . . . . . . . . . . . . Tel: (0131) 624 6200
    Director, National Gallery of Scotland . . . . . . . . . . . . . . Mr Michael Clarke
    Director, Scottish National Gallery of Modern Art. . . . . . . Mr Richard Calvorcoressi
    Director, Scottish National Portrait Gallery. . . . . . . . . . . Mr James Holloway
                        Web: http://www.nationalgalleries.org
**National Museums of Scotland** . . . . . . . . . . . . . . . . . . . . Chambers Street, Edinburgh, EH1 1JF
    Chairman of the Trustees. . . . . . . . . . . . . . . . . . . . . . . Lord Wilson of Tillyorn
    Director . . . . . . . . . . . . . . . . . . . . . . . . . . . . . . . . . . . Dr Gordon Rintoul . . . . . . . . . . . . . . . . . . . Tel: (0131) 225 7534
                        E-mail: info@nms.ac.uk
                        Web: http://www.nms.ac.uk

## NATIONAL LOTTERY
**Community Fund (Scotland)**. . . . . . . . . . . . . . . . . . . . . . Highlander House, 58 Waterloo Street, Glasgow, G2 7DB
    Director . . . . . . . . . . . . . . . . . . . . . . . . . . . . . . . . . . . *Vacant* . . . . . . . . . . . . . . . . . . . . . . . . . . . . Tel: (0141) 223 8600
                        Web: http://www.community-fund.org.uk

## NATIONAL PARKS
**Cairngorms National Park Authority**. . . . . . . . . . . . . . . 14 The Square, Grantown-on-Spey, Moray, PH26 3HG
    Chairman . . . . . . . . . . . . . . . . . . . . . . . . . . . . . . . . . . Mr Andrew Thinn
    Chief Executive *(Acting)* . . . . . . . . . . . . . . . . . . . . . . . Mrs Jane Ispen. . . . . . . . . . . . . . . . . . . . . . Tel: (01479) 873535
                        E-mail: enquiries@cairngorms.prestel.co.uk
                        Web: http://www.cairngorms.co.uk
**Loch Lomond and the Trossachs**
    **National Park Authority** . . . . . . . . . . . . . . . . . . . . . The Old Station, Balloch Road, Balloch, Dunbartonshire, G83 8SS
    Chairman . . . . . . . . . . . . . . . . . . . . . . . . . . . . . . . . . . Cllr Gillie Thomson
    Chief Executive. . . . . . . . . . . . . . . . . . . . . . . . . . . . . . Mr William Dalrymple . . . . . . . . . . . . . . . . Tel: (01389) 722600
                        E-mail: info@lochlomond-trossachs.org.
                        Web: http://www.lochlomond-trossachs.org

## OMBUDSMAN
**Scottish Public Services Ombudsman** . . . . . . . . . . . . . . . 4 Melville Street, Edinburgh, EH3 7NS
    Commissioner . . . . . . . . . . . . . . . . . . . . . . . . . . . . . . . Professor Alice Brown . . . . . . . . . . . . . . . . Tel: (0870) 011 5378
                        Web: http://www.scottishombudsman.org.uk

# DEPARTMENT FOR CONSTITUTIONAL AFFAIRS

*Other Relevant Contacts: Scotland (Continued)*

## PAROLE

**Parole Board for Scotland** . . . . . . . . . . . . . . . . . . . . . . . Room Y1/9, Saughton House, Broomhouse Drive, Edinburgh, EH11 3XD
    Chairman . . . . . . . . . . . . . . . . . . . . . . . . . . . . . . . . . Dr James McManus
    Secretary . . . . . . . . . . . . . . . . . . . . . . . . . . . . . . . . . Mr Hugh Boyle . . . . . . . . . . . . . . . . . . . . . . . Tel: (0131) 244 8473
                    Web: http://www.scottishparoleboard.gov.uk

## PENSIONS

**Pensions Appeal Tribunals for Scotland** . . . . . . . . . . . . . 20 Walker Street, Edinburgh, EH3 7HS
    President . . . . . . . . . . . . . . . . . . . . . . . . . . . . . . . . . Mr Colin McEachran QC
    Secretary . . . . . . . . . . . . . . . . . . . . . . . . . . . . . . . . . Mr William Barclay . . . . . . . . . . . . . . . . . . . Tel: (0131) 220 1404
                    E-mail: info@patscotland.org.uk
**Scottish Public Pensions Agency** *(Executive Agency)* . . . . . 7 Tweedside Park, Tweedbank, Galashiels, TD1 3TE
    Chief Executive . . . . . . . . . . . . . . . . . . . . . . . . . . . . Mr Ralph Garden . . . . . . . . . . . . . . . . . . . . . Tel: (01896) 893000
                    Web: http://www.scotland.gov.uk/sppa

## POLICE

**Police Advisory Board of Scotland** . . . . . . . . . . . . . . . . . St Andrew's House, Regent Road, Edinburgh, EH1 3DG
    Chairman . . . . . . . . . . . . . . . . . . . . . . . . . . . . . . . . . Ms Cathy Jamieson MSP
    Secretary . . . . . . . . . . . . . . . . . . . . . . . . . . . . . . . . . Mr George Vine . . . . . . . . . . . . . . . . . . . . . . Tel: (0131) 244 2160
**Scottish Police College** . . . . . . . . . . . . . . . . . . . . . . . . . Tulliallan Castle, Kincardnie, Fife, FK10 4BE
    Director . . . . . . . . . . . . . . . . . . . . . . . . . . . . . . . . . . Mr David Garbutt
    Secretariat . . . . . . . . . . . . . . . . . . . . . . . . . . . . . . . . Mrs M Henderson . . . . . . . . . . . . . . . . . . . . Tel: (01259) 732000
                    Web: http://www.tulliallan.police.uk

## POSTAL SERVICE

**Postwatch (Scotland)** . . . . . . . . . . . . . . . . . . . . . . . . . . Queen Margaret University College, Clerwood Terrace, Edinburgh, EH12 8TS
    Chairman . . . . . . . . . . . . . . . . . . . . . . . . . . . . . . . . . Dr Thomas Begg
    Director . . . . . . . . . . . . . . . . . . . . . . . . . . . . . . . . . . Ms Tricia Dow . . . . . . . . . . . . . . . . . . . . . . . Tel: (0131) 334 3969
                    E-mail: info@postwatch.co.uk
                    Web: http://www.postwatch.co.uk

## PRISONS

**Scottish Prison Service** *(Executive Agency)* . . . . . . . . . . . Calton House, 5 Redheughs Rigg, Edinburgh, EH12 9HW
    Chief Executive . . . . . . . . . . . . . . . . . . . . . . . . . . . . Mr Tony Cameron . . . . . . . . . . . . . . . . . . . . Tel: (0131) 244 8745
                    Web: http://www.sps.gov.uk

## PUBLIC RECORDS

**General Register Office for Scotland** . . . . . . . . . . . . . . . Ladywell House, Ladywell Road, Edinburgh, EH12 7TF
    Registrar General . . . . . . . . . . . . . . . . . . . . . . . . . . . Mr Duncan Macniven . . . . . . . . . . . . . . . . . Tel: (0131) 334 0380
                    Web: http://www.gro-scotland.gov.uk
**National Archives of Scotland** *(Executive Agency)* . . . . . . HM General Register House, 2 Princes Street, Edinburgh, EH1 3YY
    Keeper of the Records of Scotland and Chief Executive . . . Mr George MacKenzie . . . . . . . . . . . . . . . . Tel: (0131) 535 1314
                    E-mail: enquiries@nas.gov.uk
                    Web: http://www.nas.gov.uk
**Scottish Records Advisory Council** . . . . . . . . . . . . . . . . . HM General Register House, 2 Princes Street, Edinburgh, EH1 3YY
    Chairman . . . . . . . . . . . . . . . . . . . . . . . . . . . . . . . . . Professor Hector MacQueen
    Secretary . . . . . . . . . . . . . . . . . . . . . . . . . . . . . . . . . Dr Alison Rosie . . . . . . . . . . . . . . . . . . . . . . Tel: (0131) 535 1403
                    Web: http://www.nas.gov.uk

## SCIENTIFIC RESEARCH

**Moredun Research Institute** . . . . . . . . . . . . . . . . . . . . . . International Research Centre, Pentlands Science Park, Bush Loan, Penicuik, EH26 0PZ
    Chairman . . . . . . . . . . . . . . . . . . . . . . . . . . . . . . . . . Mr John Ross
    Director . . . . . . . . . . . . . . . . . . . . . . . . . . . . . . . . . . Professor Quintin McKellar . . . . . . . . . . . . Tel: (0131) 445 5111
                    E-mail: info@mri.sari.ac.uk
                    Web: http://www.mri.sari.ac.uk

# DEPARTMENT FOR CONSTITUTIONAL AFFAIRS

*Other Relevant Contacts: Scotland (Continued)*

## SCOTTISH PARLIAMENT AND EXECUTIVE

**Scottish Parliament** . . . . . . . . . . . . . . . . . . . . . Edinburgh, EH99 1SP
    Presiding Officer . . . . . . . . . . . . . . . . . . . . . . . . . . Mr George Reid MSP
    Clerk and Chief Executive . . . . . . . . . . . . . . . . . Mr Paul Grice . . . . . . . . . . . . . . . . . . . . . Tel: (0131) 348 5000
                       Web: http://www.scottish.parliament.uk
**Scottish Executive** . . . . . . . . . . . . . . . . . . . . . . . St Andrew's House, Regent Road,
                       Edinburgh, EH1 3DG . . . . . . . . . . . . . . . . Tel: (08457) 741741
                       Web: http://www.scotland.gov.uk
    First Minister . . . . . . . . . . . . . . . . . . . . . . . . . . . Rt Hon Jack McConnell MSP
    Deputy First Minister and Minister for Justice . . . . . . . . . Rt Hon Jim Wallace QC MSP
    Ministers
        Communities . . . . . . . . . . . . . . . . . . . . . . . . . . . Ms Margaret Curran MSP
        Education and Young People . . . . . . . . . . . . . . . . . . Mr Peter Peacock MSP
        Environment and Rural Development . . . . . . . . . . . . . . Mr Ross Finnie MSP
        Finance and Public Services . . . . . . . . . . . . . . . . . . Mr Andrew Kerr MSP
        Health and Community Care . . . . . . . . . . . . . . . . . . Mr Malcolm Chisholm MSP
        Justice . . . . . . . . . . . . . . . . . . . . . . . . . . . . . . . . Ms Cathy Jamieson MSP
        Parliamentary Business . . . . . . . . . . . . . . . . . . . . . Ms Patricia Ferguson MSP
        Tourism, Culture and Sport . . . . . . . . . . . . . . . . . . Mr Frank McAveety MSP
        Transport . . . . . . . . . . . . . . . . . . . . . . . . . . . . . . Ms Nicol Stephen MSP
    Lord Advocate . . . . . . . . . . . . . . . . . . . . . . . . . . . Mr Colin Boyd QC
    Permanent Secretary, Scottish Executive . . . . . . . . . . . . Mr John Elvidge
**Development Department** . . . . . . . . . . . . . . . . . . . Victoria Quay, Edinburgh, EH6 6QQ
    Head of Department . . . . . . . . . . . . . . . . . . . . . . . Mrs Nicola Munro . . . . . . . . . . . . . . . . . . . . Tel: (0131) 244 0759
**Education Department** . . . . . . . . . . . . . . . . . . . . Victoria Quay, Edinburgh, EH6 6QQ
    Secretary and Head of Department . . . . . . . . . . . . . . . Mr Mike Ewart . . . . . . . . . . . . . . . . . . . . . . Tel: (0131) 556 8400
**Enterprise and Lifelong Learning Department** . . . . . . . . Meridian Court, 5 Cadogan Street, Glasgow, G2 6AT
    Department Secretary . . . . . . . . . . . . . . . . . . . . . . Mr Eddie Frizell CB . . . . . . . . . . . . . . . . . . . Tel: (0141) 242 5704
**Environment and Rural Affairs Department** . . . . . . . . . Pentland House, 47 Robb's Loan, Edinburgh, EH14 1TY
    Department Secretary . . . . . . . . . . . . . . . . . . . . . . Mr John Graham . . . . . . . . . . . . . . . . . . . . . Tel: (0131) 556 8400
**Finance and Central Services Department** . . . . . . . . . . St Andrews House, Edinburgh, EH1 3DG
    Head of Department . . . . . . . . . . . . . . . . . . . . . . . Mr John Elvidge . . . . . . . . . . . . . . . . . . . . . Tel: (0131) 556 8400
**Health Department** . . . . . . . . . . . . . . . . . . . . . . St Andrews House, Edinburgh, EH1 3DG
    Chief Executive . . . . . . . . . . . . . . . . . . . . . . . . . . Mr Trevor Jones . . . . . . . . . . . . . . . . . . . . . Tel: (0131) 556 8400
**Justice Department** . . . . . . . . . . . . . . . . . . . . . . St Andrews House, Regent Road, Edinburgh, EH1 3DG
    Department Secretary . . . . . . . . . . . . . . . . . . . . . . Mr Jim Gallagher . . . . . . . . . . . . . . . . . . . . Tel: (0131) 556 8400

## SOCIAL SERVICES

**Scottish Commission for the Regulation of Care** . . . . . . . Compass House, 11 Riverside Drive, Dundee, DD1 4NY
    Convener . . . . . . . . . . . . . . . . . . . . . . . . . . . . . . Ms Mary Hartnoll
    Chief Executive . . . . . . . . . . . . . . . . . . . . . . . . . . Ms Jacquie Roberts . . . . . . . . . . . . . . . . . Tel: (01382) 207100
                       Web: http://www.carecommission.com
**Scottish Social Services Council** . . . . . . . . . . . . . . . Compass House, 11 Riverside Drive, Dundee, DD1 4NY
    Convener . . . . . . . . . . . . . . . . . . . . . . . . . . . . . . Mrs Morag Alexander
    Chief Executive . . . . . . . . . . . . . . . . . . . . . . . . . . Ms Carole Wilkinson . . . . . . . . . . . . . . . . . Tel: (01382) 207101
                       E-mail: enquiries@sssc.uk.com
                       Web: http://www.sssc.uk.com

## SPORTS

**Sport Scotland** (The Scottish Sports Council) . . . . . . . . . Caledonia House, South Gyle, Edinburgh, EH12 9DQ
    Chairman . . . . . . . . . . . . . . . . . . . . . . . . . . . . . Mr Alastair Dempster
    Chief Executive . . . . . . . . . . . . . . . . . . . . . . . . . . Mr Ian Robson . . . . . . . . . . . . . . . . . . . . . . Tel: (0131) 317 7200
                       Web: http://www.sportsscotland.org.uk

## STANDARDS IN PUBLIC LIFE

**The Standards Commission for Scotland** . . . . . . . . . . . Forsyth House, Innova Campus, Rosyth Europarc,
                       Rosyth, KY1 2UU
    Convener . . . . . . . . . . . . . . . . . . . . . . . . . . . . . . Professor Lorne Crerar . . . . . . . . . . . . . . . . Tel: (01383) 428061
                       Web: http://www.standardscommissionscotland.org.uk

# DEPARTMENT FOR CONSTITUTIONAL AFFAIRS

*Other Relevant Contacts: Scotland (Continued)*

**TOURISM**

**VisitScotland** . . . . . . . . . . . . . . . . . . . . . . . . . . . . . . . . 23 Ravelston Terrace, Edinburgh, EH4 3TP
    Chairman . . . . . . . . . . . . . . . . . . . . . . . . . . . . . . . . . . Mr Peter Lederer OBE
    Chief Executive . . . . . . . . . . . . . . . . . . . . . . . . . . . . . . Mr Philip Riddle . . . . . . . . . . . . . . . . . . . . . Tel: (0131) 332 2433
                                           Web: http://www.visitscotland.com

**TRANSPORT**

**Bus Users Complaints Tribunal** . . . . . . . . . . . . . . . . . . . . PO Box 23556, Edinburgh, EH3 9YS
    Convener . . . . . . . . . . . . . . . . . . . . . . . . . . . . . . . . . . . Mr Malcolm Stewart . . . . . . . . . . . . . . . . . . Tel: (0131) 228 5478
**Caledonian MacBrayne Ltd** . . . . . . . . . . . . . . . . . . . . . . The Ferry Terminal, The Pier, Gourock, PA19 1QP
    Chairman . . . . . . . . . . . . . . . . . . . . . . . . . . . . . . . . . . Dr Harold Mills CB
    Managing Director . . . . . . . . . . . . . . . . . . . . . . . . . . . . Mr Lawrie Sinclair . . . . . . . . . . . . . . . . . . . Tel: (01475) 650100
                                           Web: http://www.calmac.co.uk
**Highlands and Islands Airports Ltd** . . . . . . . . . . . . . . . . Inverness Airport, Inverness, IV2 7JB
    Chairman . . . . . . . . . . . . . . . . . . . . . . . . . . . . . . . . . . Mr Sandy Mattheson OBE
    Managing Director . . . . . . . . . . . . . . . . . . . . . . . . . . . . Mr Robert Macleod . . . . . . . . . . . . . . . . . . Tel: (01667) 462445
                                           Web: http://www.hial.co.uk
**Rail Passengers Committee for Scotland** . . . . . . . . . . . . . 5th Floor, Corunna House, 29 Cadogan Street, Glasgow, G2 7AB
    Convenor . . . . . . . . . . . . . . . . . . . . . . . . . . . . . . . . . . . Mr Mike Lunan
    Director . . . . . . . . . . . . . . . . . . . . . . . . . . . . . . . . . . . . Mr Robert Samson . . . . . . . . . . . . . . . . . . . Tel: (0141) 221 7760
                                           Web: http://www.railpassengers.org.uk

**TRIBUNALS**

**Council on Tribunals (Scottish Committee)** . . . . . . . . . . 44 Palmerston Place, Edinburgh, EH12 5BJ
    Chairman . . . . . . . . . . . . . . . . . . . . . . . . . . . . . . . . . . Mr John Elliott DKS
    Secretary . . . . . . . . . . . . . . . . . . . . . . . . . . . . . . . . . . . Mrs Marjorie MacRae . . . . . . . . . . . . . . . . Tel: (0131) 220 1236
                                           Web: http://www.council-on-tribunals.gov.uk

**WATER**

**Scottish Water** . . . . . . . . . . . . . . . . . . . . . . . . . . . . . . . . Castle House, 6 Castle Drive, Carnegie Campus, Dumfermline, KY11 8GG
    Chairman . . . . . . . . . . . . . . . . . . . . . . . . . . . . . . . . . . Professor Alan Alexander
    Chief Executive . . . . . . . . . . . . . . . . . . . . . . . . . . . . . . Dr Jon Hargreaves . . . . . . . . . . . . . . . . . . . Tel: (01383) 848200
                                           Web: http://www.scottishwater.co.uk
**Water Industry Commissioner for Scotland** . . . . . . . . . . Ochil House, Springkerse Business Park, Stirling, FK7 7XE
    Commissioner . . . . . . . . . . . . . . . . . . . . . . . . . . . . . . . . Mr Alan Sutherland . . . . . . . . . . . . . . . . . . Tel: (01786) 430200
                                           E-mail: enquiries@watercommissioner.co.uk
                                           Web: http://www.watercommissioner.co.uk

# DEPARTMENT FOR CONSTITUTIONAL AFFAIRS

## OTHER RELEVANT CONTACTS – WALES

### AGRICULTURE

**Agricultural Land Tribunal (Wales)** . . . . . . . . . . . . . . . .Government Buildings, Spa Road East, Llandrindod Wells, LD1 5HA
    Chairman . . . . . . . . . . . . . . . . . . . . . . . . . . . . . . . . . . . . .Mr John Owen
    Secretary . . . . . . . . . . . . . . . . . . . . . . . . . . . . . . . . . . . . .Mrs Cath Davies . . . . . . . . . . . . . . . . . . . . . Tel: (01597) 828281
                    Web: http://www.countryside.wales.gov.uk
**Hill Farming Sub-Committee for Wales** . . . . . . . . . . . . .APD1, National Assembly for Wales, Cathays Park,
                    Cardiff, CF10 3NQ . . . . . . . . . . . . . . . . . . . Tel: (029) 2082 5735
**Independent Appeal Panel for Farmers** . . . . . . . . . . . . .Government Buildings, Spa Road East, Llandrindod Wells, LD1 5HA
    Secretary . . . . . . . . . . . . . . . . . . . . . . . . . . . . . . . . . . . . .Ms Margaret Watson . . . . . . . . . . . . . . . . . . Tel: (01597) 828226

### ANCIENT/HISTORIC MONUMENTS

**Ancient Monuments Board for Wales** . . . . . . . . . . . . . . .CADW, Crown Buildings, Cathays Park, Cardiff, CF10 3NQ
    Chairman . . . . . . . . . . . . . . . . . . . . . . . . . . . . . . . . . . . . .Professor Robert Rees Davies
    Secretary . . . . . . . . . . . . . . . . . . . . . . . . . . . . . . . . . . . . .Mrs Jean Booker . . . . . . . . . . . . . . . . . . . . . Tel: (029) 2082 6376
**CADW: Welsh Historic Monuments** *(Executive Agency)* . . .Crown Buildings, Cathays Park, Cardiff, CF10 3NQ
    Chief Executive . . . . . . . . . . . . . . . . . . . . . . . . . . . . . . .Mr Tom Cassidy . . . . . . . . . . . . . . . . . . . . . Tel: (029) 2050 0200
                    Web: http://www.cadw.wales.gov.uk
**Historic Buildings Council for Wales** . . . . . . . . . . . . . . .Crown Buildings, Cathays Park, Cardiff, CF10 3NQ
    Chairman . . . . . . . . . . . . . . . . . . . . . . . . . . . . . . . . . . . . .Mr Thomas Lloyd
    Secretary . . . . . . . . . . . . . . . . . . . . . . . . . . . . . . . . . . . . .Mrs Jean Booker . . . . . . . . . . . . . . . . . . . . . Tel: (029) 2050 0200
                    Web: http://www.cadw.wales.gov.uk
**Royal Commission on the Ancient and Historical**
    **Monuments of Wales** . . . . . . . . . . . . . . . . . . . . . . . . .Crown Building, Plas Crug, Aberystwyth, Ceredigion, SY23 1NJ
    Chairman . . . . . . . . . . . . . . . . . . . . . . . . . . . . . . . . . . . . .Professor Ralph A Griffiths
    Secretary . . . . . . . . . . . . . . . . . . . . . . . . . . . . . . . . . . . . .Mr Peter White . . . . . . . . . . . . . . . . . . . . . Tel: (01970) 621200
                    Web: http://www.rcahmw.org.uk

### ARTS

**Arts Council of Wales** . . . . . . . . . . . . . . . . . . . . . . . . . . .9 Museum Place, Cardiff, CF10 3NX
    Chairman . . . . . . . . . . . . . . . . . . . . . . . . . . . . . . . . . . . . .Mr Geraint Talfan Davies
    Chief Executive . . . . . . . . . . . . . . . . . . . . . . . . . . . . . . .Mr Peter Tyndall . . . . . . . . . . . . . . . . . . . . . Tel: (029) 2037 6500
                    Web: http://www.artswales.org.uk

### ASSEMBLY

**National Assembly for Wales** . . . . . . . . . . . . . . . . . . . . .Pierhead Street, Cardiff, CF99 1NA
    Presiding Officer . . . . . . . . . . . . . . . . . . . . . . . . . . . . . .Lord Elis Thomas AM
    First Minister . . . . . . . . . . . . . . . . . . . . . . . . . . . . . . . . .Rt Hon Rhodri Morgan AM
    Ministers
        Assembly Business . . . . . . . . . . . . . . . . . . . . . . . . . .Ms Karen Sinclair AM
        Culture, Welsh Language and Sport . . . . . . . . . . . . . .Mr Alan Pugh AM
        Economic Development and Transport . . . . . . . . . . . .Mr Andrew Davies AM
        Education and Life-Long Learning . . . . . . . . . . . . . .Ms Jane Davidson AM
        Environment, Planning and Countryside . . . . . . . . . .Mr Carwyn Jones AM
        Finance, Local Government and Public Services . . . . .Ms Suse Essex AM
        Health and Social Services . . . . . . . . . . . . . . . . . . . .Ms Jane Hutt AM
        Social Justice and Regeneration . . . . . . . . . . . . . . . .Ms Edwina Hart MBE AM
    Clerk to the Assembly . . . . . . . . . . . . . . . . . . . . . . . . . .Mr Paul Silk . . . . . . . . . . . . . . . . . . . . . . . . . Tel: (029) 2089 8705
                    Web: http://www.assembly.wales.gov.uk

# DEPARTMENT FOR CONSTITUTIONAL AFFAIRS

*Other Relevant Contacts: Wales – Welsh Assembly (Continued)*

**Welsh Executive** . . . . . . . . . . . . . . . . . . . . . . . . . . . . . . . .Cathays Park, Cardiff, CF10 3NQ
    Permanent Secretary . . . . . . . . . . . . . . . . . . . . . . .Sir John Shortridge KCB . . . . . . . . . . . . . . Tel: (029) 2082 5111
    Senior Directors
        Human Resources Group . . . . . . . . . . . . . . . . . . .Mr Bernard Galton . . . . . . . . . . . . . . . . Tel: (029) 2082 5111
        Policy . . . . . . . . . . . . . . . . . . . . . . . . . . . . . . . . . .Mr Derek Jones . . . . . . . . . . . . . . . . . . . Tel: (029) 2082 5111
**Economic Development and Transport Department**
    Director . . . . . . . . . . . . . . . . . . . . . . . . . . . . . . . . .Mr David Pritchard . . . . . . . . . . . . . . . . . Tel: (029) 2082 5111
**Environment Planning and Countryside Department**
    Head of Department . . . . . . . . . . . . . . . . . . . . . . . .Mr Gareth Jones . . . . . . . . . . . . . . . . . . Tel: (029) 2082 5111
**Finance Group**
    Principal Finance Officer . . . . . . . . . . . . . . . . . . . .Mr David Richards . . . . . . . . . . . . . . . . . Tel: (029) 2082 5111
**NHS**
    Director, NHS Wales . . . . . . . . . . . . . . . . . . . . . . .Ms Ann Lloyd . . . . . . . . . . . . . . . . . . . . Tel: (029) 2082 5111
    Chief Medical Officer . . . . . . . . . . . . . . . . . . . . . . .Dr Ruth Hall . . . . . . . . . . . . . . . . . . . . . Tel: (029) 2082 5111
**Office of the Counsel General**
    Counsel General . . . . . . . . . . . . . . . . . . . . . . . . . . .*Vacant* . . . . . . . . . . . . . . . . . . . . . . . . . Tel: (029) 2082 5111
**Public Service and Culture Department**
    Director . . . . . . . . . . . . . . . . . . . . . . . . . . . . . . . . .Dr Hugh Rowlings . . . . . . . . . . . . . . . . . Tel: (029) 2082 5111
**Public Service Group**
    Head of Group . . . . . . . . . . . . . . . . . . . . . . . . . . .Mrs Barbara Wilson . . . . . . . . . . . . . . . Tel: (029) 2082 5111
**Regulation/Inspection Review**
    Head of Group . . . . . . . . . . . . . . . . . . . . . . . . . . .Ms Helen Thomas . . . . . . . . . . . . . . . . . Tel: (029) 2082 5111
**Social Justice and Regeneration Department**
    Director . . . . . . . . . . . . . . . . . . . . . . . . . . . . . . . . .Mr John Bader . . . . . . . . . . . . . . . . . . . Tel: (029) 2082 5111
**Strategy and Communications Directorate**
    Director . . . . . . . . . . . . . . . . . . . . . . . . . . . . . . . . .Mr Huw Brodie . . . . . . . . . . . . . . . . . . . Tel: (029) 2082 5111
**Training and Education Department**
    Director . . . . . . . . . . . . . . . . . . . . . . . . . . . . . . . . .Mr Richard Davies . . . . . . . . . . . . . . . . . Tel: (029) 2082 5111

**AUDIT**
**Auditor General for Wales** . . . . . . . . . . . . . . . . . . . . .3-4 Park Place, Cardiff, CF10 3DP
    Auditor General . . . . . . . . . . . . . . . . . . . . . . . . . . .Sir John Bourn
    Secretary . . . . . . . . . . . . . . . . . . . . . . . . . . . . . . . . .Ms Helen Kirkby . . . . . . . . . . . . . . . . . . Tel: (029) 2067 8545
                                 Web: http://www.agw.wales.gov.uk

**BOUNDARIES**
**Local Government Boundary Commission for Wales** . . .1st Floor, Caradog House, 1-6 Saint Andrew's Place, Cardiff, CF10 3BE
    Chairman . . . . . . . . . . . . . . . . . . . . . . . . . . . . . . . .Mrs Susan Smith
    Secretary . . . . . . . . . . . . . . . . . . . . . . . . . . . . . . . . .Mr Edward Lewis . . . . . . . . . . . . . . . . . . Tel: (029) 2039 5031
                                 Web: http://www.lgbc-wales.gov.uk
**Parliamentary Boundary Commission for Wales** . . . . . .1st Floor, Caradog House, 1-6 Saint Andrew's Place, Cardiff, CF10 3BE
    Chairman . . . . . . . . . . . . . . . . . . . . . . . . . . . . . . . .Rt Hon Michael Martin MP *(Speaker of the House of Commons)*
    Joint Secretaries . . . . . . . . . . . . . . . . . . . . . . . . . . .Mr Mark Barnett
                                 Mr Edward Lewis . . . . . . . . . . . . . . . . . . Tel: (029) 2039 5031
                                 E-mail: bcomm.wales@wales.gsi.gov.uk

**CHILDREN'S COMMISSIONER**
**Children's Commissioner for Wales** . . . . . . . . . . . . . . .Oystermouth House, Phoenix Way, Swansea Enterprise Park, Llansamlet,
                                 Swansea, SA7 9FS
    Commissioner . . . . . . . . . . . . . . . . . . . . . . . . . . . .Mr Peter Clark . . . . . . . . . . . . . . . . . . . Tel: (01792) 765600
                                 Web: http://www.childcomwales.org.uk

**COMMUNICATIONS**
**OFCOM, Wales** . . . . . . . . . . . . . . . . . . . . . . . . . . . . . .2 Caspian Point, Caspian Way, Cardiff, CF120 4DQ
    Chief Executive . . . . . . . . . . . . . . . . . . . . . . . . . . . . Mr Stephen Carter . . . . . . . . . . . . . . . . . Tel: (029) 2046 7200

**CONSUMER COUNCIL**
**Welsh Consumer Council** . . . . . . . . . . . . . . . . . . . . . .5th Floor, Longcross Court, 47 Newport Road, Cardiff, CF24 OWL
    Chairman . . . . . . . . . . . . . . . . . . . . . . . . . . . . . . . .Ms Vivienne Sugar
    Director . . . . . . . . . . . . . . . . . . . . . . . . . . . . . . . . .Dr Nick Pearson . . . . . . . . . . . . . . . . . . Tel: (029) 2025 5454
                                 Web: http://www.wales-consumer.org.uk

# DEPARTMENT FOR CONSTITUTIONAL AFFAIRS

*Other Relevant Contacts: Wales (Continued)*

**COUNTRYSIDE**

**Countryside Council for Wales** . . . . . . . . . . . . . . . . . . . . . .Maes y Ffynnon, Penrhosgarnedd, Bangor, Gwynedd, LL57 2DN
    Chairman . . . . . . . . . . . . . . . . . . . . . . . . . . . . . . . . . . . . . .Mr John Lloyd Jones OBE
    Chief Executive . . . . . . . . . . . . . . . . . . . . . . . . . . . . . . . .Mr Roger Thomas . . . . . . . . . . . . . . . . . . . . . . Tel: (01248) 385500
            Web: http://www.ccw.gov.uk

**DEVELOPMENT**

**Welsh Development Agency** . . . . . . . . . . . . . . . . . . . . . . .Plas Glyndwr, Kingsway, Cardiff, CF10 3AH
    Chairman . . . . . . . . . . . . . . . . . . . . . . . . . . . . . . . . . . . . . .Mr Roger Jones OBE
    Chief Executive . . . . . . . . . . . . . . . . . . . . . . . . . . . . . . . .*Vacant* . . . . . . . . . . . . . . . . . . . . . . . . . . . . . Tel: (0845) 777 5577
            Web: http://www.wda.co.uk

**Welsh Industrial and Development Advisory Board** . . . .c/o Investment and Corporate Management Division,
            National Assembly for Wales, Cathays Park, Cardiff, CF10 3NQ
    Chairman . . . . . . . . . . . . . . . . . . . . . . . . . . . . . . . . . . . . . .*Vacant*
    Secretary . . . . . . . . . . . . . . . . . . . . . . . . . . . . . . . . . . . . .Mr Ian Shuttleworth. . . . . . . . . . . . . . . . . . Tel: (029) 2082 3681
            E-mail: rsa.sewales@wales.gsi.gov.uk

**DRUGS MISUSE**

**Advisory Panel on Substance Misuse** . . . . . . . . . . . . . . .Crown Buildings, Cathays Park, Cardiff, CF10 3NQ
    Chairman . . . . . . . . . . . . . . . . . . . . . . . . . . . . . . . . . . . . . .Mr Richard Pates
    Chief Executive . . . . . . . . . . . . . . . . . . . . . . . . . . . . . . . .Ms Laura Tranter . . . . . . . . . . . . . . . . . . . . Tel: (029) 2082 5481

**EDUCATION**

**ELWa (National Council for**
  **Education and Learning Wales)** . . . . . . . . . . . . . . . . .Ty-rafon Bedwas Road, Bedwas, Caerphilly, CF83 8WT
    Chairman . . . . . . . . . . . . . . . . . . . . . . . . . . . . . . . . . . . . . .Mrs Sheila Dury
    Chief Executive . . . . . . . . . . . . . . . . . . . . . . . . . . . . . . . .Ms Elizabeth Raikes . . . . . . . . . . . . . . . . . Tel: (0829) 2076 1861
            Web: http://www.elwa.org.uk

**Higher Education Funding Council for Wales** . . . . . . . .Linden Court, The Orchards, Ilex Close, Llanishen, Cardiff, CF14 5DZ
    Chairman . . . . . . . . . . . . . . . . . . . . . . . . . . . . . . . . . . . . . .Professor Roger Williams
    Chief Executive . . . . . . . . . . . . . . . . . . . . . . . . . . . . . . . .Mr Steve Martin . . . . . . . . . . . . . . . . . . . . . Tel: (029) 2076 1861
            Web: http://www.hefcw.ac.uk

**HM Inspectorate for Education and Training**
  **in Wales (ESTYN)** . . . . . . . . . . . . . . . . . . . . . . . . . . . .Anchor Court, Keen Road, Cardiff, CF24 5JW
    Chief Inspector . . . . . . . . . . . . . . . . . . . . . . . . . . . . . . . .Miss Susan Lewis . . . . . . . . . . . . . . . . . . . Tel: (029) 2044 6446
            E-mail: enquiries@estyn.gov.uk

**Qualifications, Curriculum and Assessment Authority**
  **for Wales (ACCAC)** . . . . . . . . . . . . . . . . . . . . . . . . . . .Castle Buildings, Womanby Street, Cardiff, CF10 1SX
    Chairman . . . . . . . . . . . . . . . . . . . . . . . . . . . . . . . . . . . . . .Mr Brian Connolly OBE
    Chief Executive . . . . . . . . . . . . . . . . . . . . . . . . . . . . . . . .Mr John Valentine Williams . . . . . . . . . . . Tel: (029) 2037 5400
            E-mail: info@accac.org.uk
            Web: http://www.accac.org.uk

**Registered Inspectors of Schools**
  **Appeals Tribunal (Wales)** . . . . . . . . . . . . . . . . . . . . . .Standards and Performance Division, National Assembly for Wales,
            Cathays Park, Cardiff, CF10 3NQ. . . . . . . . Tel:(029) 2082 6013
            Web: http://www.learning.wales.gov.uk

**ENVIRONMENT**

**Environment Agency Wales** . . . . . . . . . . . . . . . . . . . . . . .Cambria House, 29 Newport Road, Cardiff, CF24 0TP
    Director Wales . . . . . . . . . . . . . . . . . . . . . . . . . . . . . . . . .Dr Helen Phillips . . . . . . . . . . . . . . . . . . . Tel: (029) 2077 0088
            Web: http://www.environment-agency.gov.uk

**EQUAL OPPORTUNITIES**

**Equal Opportunities Commission** . . . . . . . . . . . . . . . . .Windsor House, Windsor Lane, Cardiff, CF10 3GE
    Commissioner for Wales . . . . . . . . . . . . . . . . . . . . . . . . .Mr Neil Wooding
    Director (Wales) . . . . . . . . . . . . . . . . . . . . . . . . . . . . . . . .Ms Kate Bennett . . . . . . . . . . . . . . . . . . . . Tel: (029) 2034 3552
            Web: http://www.eoc.org.uk

# DEPARTMENT FOR CONSTITUTIONAL AFFAIRS

*Other Relevant Contacts: Wales (Continued)*

## EUROPEAN FUNDING

**Welsh European Funding Office** . . . . . . . . . . . . . . . . . .Cwm Cynon Business Park, Mountain Ash, CF45 4ER

    Chief Executive . . . . . . . . . . . . . . . . . . . . . . . . . . . . .Mr Emyr Roberts. . . . . . . . . . . . . . . . . . . . . *Tel: (01443) 471100*

                      *Web: http://www.wefo.wales.gov.uk*

## FOOD

**Food Standards Agency** . . . . . . . . . . . . . . . . . . . . . . . .*1st Floor, Southgate House, Wood Street, Cardiff, CF10 1EW*

    *Director Wales* . . . . . . . . . . . . . . . . . . . . . . . . . . . . . . .*Mrs Joy Whinney. . . . . . . . . . . . . . . . . . . . Tel: (029) 2067 8999*

                      *E-mail: wales@foodstandards.gsi.gov.uk*

                      *Web: http://www.foodstandards.gov.uk*

## FORESTRY

**Forest Research**

    *(Executive Agency)* . . . . . . . . . . . . . . . . . . . . . . . . . . .*Forest Research Station, Cefn Gethiniog, Tallybont-on-Usk, Brecon, LD3 7YN*

    *Forest Officer* . . . . . . . . . . . . . . . . . . . . . . . . . . . . . .*Mr Chris Jones. . . . . . . . . . . . . . . . . . . . . Tel: (01874) 676444*

                      *Web: http://www.forestry.gov.uk*

**Forestry Commission Wales** *(Executive Agency)* . . . . . . . . .*Victoria House, Victoria Terrace, Aberystwyth, SY23 2DQ*

    *Director, Wales* . . . . . . . . . . . . . . . . . . . . . . . . . . . . .*Mr Simon Hewitt . . . . . . . . . . . . . . . . . . . Tel: (01970) 625866*

                      *E-mail: fcwales@forestry.gsi.gov.uk*

                      *Web: http://www.forestry.gov.uk*

## HEALTH

**All Wales Medicines Strategy Group** . . . . . . . . . . . . . . . .*UWCM, Department of Pharmacology, Therapeutics and Toxicality, Heath Park, Cardiff, CF14 4XN*

    *Chairman* . . . . . . . . . . . . . . . . . . . . . . . . . . . . . . . . .*Professor Roger Walker*

    *Secretary* . . . . . . . . . . . . . . . . . . . . . . . . . . . . . . . . .*Mrs Ruth Lang . . . . . . . . . . . . . . . . . . . . . Tel: (029) 2074 5466*

                      Web: http://www.wales.nhs.uk/awmsg

**Health Commission Wales** *(Executive Agency)* . . . . . . . . . .The Stables, Henson Castle, Pontyclun, CF72 8YS

    Chief Executive . . . . . . . . . . . . . . . . . . . . . . . . . . . . .Mr Stuart Fletcher. . . . . . . . . . . . . . . . . . Tel: (01656) 753693

**Health Professions Wales** . . . . . . . . . . . . . . . . . . . . . . .2nd Floor, Golate House, 101 St Mary Street, Cardiff, CF10 1DX

    Chief Executive *(Acting)* . . . . . . . . . . . . . . . . . . . . . . .Dr Barbara Bale

    Secretary . . . . . . . . . . . . . . . . . . . . . . . . . . . . . . . . .Ms Meriel Baldwin . . . . . . . . . . . . . . . . . . Tel: (029) 2026 1400

                      E-mail: info@hpw.org.uk

                      Web: http://www.hpw.ac.uk

**Joint Professional Forum on Health and Well Being** . . .National Assembly for Wales, Cathays Park, Cardiff, CF10 3NQ

    Chairman . . . . . . . . . . . . . . . . . . . . . . . . . . . . . . . . .Dr Ruth Hall

    Secretary . . . . . . . . . . . . . . . . . . . . . . . . . . . . . . . . .Mr Steve Harris. . . . . . . . . . . . . . . . . . . . Tel: (029) 2082 3777

**Mental Health Review Tribunal for Wales** . . . . . . . . . . .4th Floor, Crown Buildings, Cathays Park, Cardiff, CF10 3NQ

    Chairman . . . . . . . . . . . . . . . . . . . . . . . . . . . . . . . . .Mrs Carolyn Kirby

    Secretary . . . . . . . . . . . . . . . . . . . . . . . . . . . . . . . . .Miss Sally Butterworth. . . . . . . . . . . . . . . . Tel: (029) 2082 5328

**NHS Counter Fraud Service (Wales)** . . . . . . . . . . . . . .Mamhilad House, Mamhilad Park Estate, Pontypool. Gwent, NP4 0YP

    Director . . . . . . . . . . . . . . . . . . . . . . . . . . . . . . . . . .Mr Jim Gee. . . . . . . . . . . . . . . . . . . . . . . Tel: (01495) 745844

**Welsh Centre for Post-Graduate Pharmaceutical**

    **Education** . . . . . . . . . . . . . . . . . . . . . . . . . . . . . . . .8 North Road, Cathays park, Cardiff, CF10 3NQ

    Director . . . . . . . . . . . . . . . . . . . . . . . . . . . . . . . . . .Dr David Temple. . . . . . . . . . . . . . . . . . . Tel: (029) 2087 4784

**Welsh Dental Committee** . . . . . . . . . . . . . . . . . . . . . .PHP3, National Assembly for Wales, Cathays Park, Cardiff, CF10 3NQ

    Chairman . . . . . . . . . . . . . . . . . . . . . . . . . . . . . . . . .Mr Keith Silvester

    Secretary . . . . . . . . . . . . . . . . . . . . . . . . . . . . . . . . .Mr Richard Norman. . . . . . . . . . . . . . . . . . Tel: (029) 2082 3430

                      E-mail: richard.norman@wales.gsi.gov.uk

**Welsh Medical Committee** . . . . . . . . . . . . . . . . . . . . . .PHP3, National Assembly for Wales, Cathays Park, Cardiff, CF10 3NQ

    Chairman . . . . . . . . . . . . . . . . . . . . . . . . . . . . . . . . .Dr Hefin Jones

    Secretary. . . . . . . . . . . . . . . . . . . . . . . . . . . . . . . . . .Ms Tracey Moore . . . . . . . . . . . . . . . . . . .Tel: (029) 2082 5201

                      E-mail: tracey.moore@wales.gsi.gov.uk

## DEPARTMENT FOR CONSTITUTIONAL AFFAIRS

*Other Relevant Contacts: Wales – Health (Continued)*

**Welsh Nursing and Midwifery Committee** . . . . . . . . . . . .PHP3, National Assembly for Wales, Cathays Park, Cardiff, CF10 3NQ
    Chairman . . . . . . . . . . . . . . . . . . . . . . . . . . . . . . . . . . . .Ms Mary Cooksey
    Secretary . . . . . . . . . . . . . . . . . . . . . . . . . . . . . . . . . . . .Ms Jan Tester . . . . . . . . . . . . . . . . . . . . Tel: (029) 2082 5417
                 E-mail: janet.tester@wales.gsi.gov.uk

**Welsh Optometric Committee** . . . . . . . . . . . . . . . . . . . .PHP3, National Assembly for Wales, Cathays Park, Cardiff, CF10 3NQ
    Chairman . . . . . . . . . . . . . . . . . . . . . . . . . . . . . . . . . . . .Mr Lionel Davies
    Secretary . . . . . . . . . . . . . . . . . . . . . . . . . . . . . . . . . . . .Mr Andrew Foyle . . . . . . . . . . . . . . . . . . Tel: (029) 2082 5201
                 E-mail: andrew.foyle@wales.gsi.gov.uk

**Welsh Pharmaceutical Committee** . . . . . . . . . . . . . . . . .PHP3, National Assembly for Wales, Cathays Park, Cardiff, CF10 3NQ
    Chairman . . . . . . . . . . . . . . . . . . . . . . . . . . . . . . . . . . . .Mr Jeremy Savage
    Secretary . . . . . . . . . . . . . . . . . . . . . . . . . . . . . . . . . . . .Ms Jan Tester . . . . . . . . . . . . . . . . . . . . Tel: (029) 2082 5038
                 E-mail: janet.tester@wales.gsi.gov.uk

**Welsh Scientific Advisory Committee** . . . . . . . . . . . . . .PHP3, National Assembly for Wales, Cathays Park, Cardiff, CF10 3NQ
    Chairman . . . . . . . . . . . . . . . . . . . . . . . . . . . . . . . . . . . .Professor Geraint Williams
    Secretary . . . . . . . . . . . . . . . . . . . . . . . . . . . . . . . . . . . .Ms Jan Tester . . . . . . . . . . . . . . . . . . . . Tel: (029) 2082 5201
                 E-mail: janet.tester@wales.gsi.gov.uk

### HOUSING
**Rent Assessment Panel for Wales** . . . . . . . . . . . . . . . . . .1st Floor (West Wing), Southgate House, Wood Street, Cardiff, CF10 1EW
    President . . . . . . . . . . . . . . . . . . . . . . . . . . . . . . . . . . . .Mr Gareth Morgan. . . . . . . . . . . . . . . . . . . Tel: (029) 2023 1687
    Vice-President . . . . . . . . . . . . . . . . . . . . . . . . . . . . . . . .Mr David Rhys Davies

### LIBRARY
**National Library of Wales** . . . . . . . . . . . . . . . . . . . . . . . .Aberystwyth, Ceredigion, SY23 3BU
    President . . . . . . . . . . . . . . . . . . . . . . . . . . . . . . . . . . . .Dr Brinley Jones
    Librarian . . . . . . . . . . . . . . . . . . . . . . . . . . . . . . . . . . . .Mr Andrew Green . . . . . . . . . . . . . . . . . . Tel: (01970) 632800
                 Web: http://www.llgc.org.uk

### MARITIME
**Maritime and Coastguard Agency**
    *(Executive Agency)* . . . . . . . . . . . . . . . . . . . . . . . . . . . . .Tutt Head, Mumbles, Swansea, SA3 4EX
    Regional Director . . . . . . . . . . . . . . . . . . . . . . . . . . . . . .Mr Frank Duffin . . . . . . . . . . . . . . . . . . . Tel: (0870) 600 6505
                 Web: http://www.mcga.gov.uk

### MEAT HYGIENE
**Meat Hygiene Service** *(Executive Agency)* . . . . . . . . . . . . .3rd Floor, Caradog House, 1-6 St Andrew's Place, Cardiff, CF10 3SE
    Regional Director . . . . . . . . . . . . . . . . . . . . . . . . . . . . . .Mr Stephen Mulholland. . . . . . . . . . . . . . Tel: (029) 2064 7810

### MUSEUMS/GALLERIES
**National Museums and Galleries of Wales** . . . . . . . . . . . .Cathays Park, Cardiff, CF10 3NP
    President . . . . . . . . . . . . . . . . . . . . . . . . . . . . . . . . . . . .Mr Paul Lovelock CBE
    Director-General . . . . . . . . . . . . . . . . . . . . . . . . . . . . . .Mr Michael Houlihan . . . . . . . . . . . . . . . . Tel: (029) 2039 7951
                 Web: http://www.nmgw.ac.uk

### NATIONAL LOTTERY
**Community Fund (Wales)** . . . . . . . . . . . . . . . . . . . . . . . .2nd Floor, Ladywell House, Newtown, Powys, SY16 1JB
    Chairman . . . . . . . . . . . . . . . . . . . . . . . . . . . . . . . . . . . .Mr Jeff Carroll
    Director . . . . . . . . . . . . . . . . . . . . . . . . . . . . . . . . . . . . .Ms Ceri Doyle . . . . . . . . . . . . . . . . . . . . . Tel: (01686) 611700
                 Web: http://www.community-fund.org.uk

### PLANNING
**Planning Inspectorate** . . . . . . . . . . . . . . . . . . . . . . . . . .Crown Buildings, Cathays Park, Cardiff, CF10 3NQ
    Director, Wales . . . . . . . . . . . . . . . . . . . . . . . . . . . . . . . .Mr Alan Langton. . . . . . . . . . . . . . . . . . . Tel: (029) 2082 3861
                 Web: http://www.planning-inspectorate.gov.uk

# DEPARTMENT FOR CONSTITUTIONAL AFFAIRS

*Other Relevant Contacts: Wales (Continued)*

## POSTAL SERVICE
**Postwatch Wales** . . . . . . . . . . . . . . . . . . . . . . . . . . . . . 2nd Floor, Hayward House South, Dumfries place, Cardiff, CF10 3GA
    Chairman . . . . . . . . . . . . . . . . . . . . . . . . . . . . . . . . . Mr Eifion Pritchard
    Manager . . . . . . . . . . . . . . . . . . . . . . . . . . . . . . . . . . Ms Ceri Cryer . . . . . . . . . . . . . . . . . . . . . .Tel: (029) 2034 9920
        Web: http://www.postwatch.co.uk

## RAILWAYS
**Rail Passengers Committee for Wales** . . . . . . . . . . . . . . St David's House, East Wing, Wood Street, Cardiff, CF10 1ES
    Chairman . . . . . . . . . . . . . . . . . . . . . . . . . . . . . . . . . Mr Colin Foxall
    Director . . . . . . . . . . . . . . . . . . . . . . . . . . . . . . . . . . Mr Clive Williams . . . . . . . . . . . . . . . . . .Tel: (029) 2022 7247
        Web: http://www.railpassengers.org.uk

## SOCIAL SERVICES
**Care Council for Wales** . . . . . . . . . . . . . . . . . . . . . . . . 6th Floor, West Wing, South Gate House, Wood Street, Cardiff, CF10 1EW
    Chairman . . . . . . . . . . . . . . . . . . . . . . . . . . . . . . . . . Ms Mutale Nyoni
    Chief Executive. . . . . . . . . . . . . . . . . . . . . . . . . . . . . Miss Rhian Huws Williams . . . . . . . . . . . .Tel: (029) 2022 6257
        Web: http://www.ccwales.org.uk
**Social Services Inspectorate for Wales Advisory Group** c/o National Assembly for Wales, Cathays Park, Cardiff, CF10 3NQ
    Chairman . . . . . . . . . . . . . . . . . . . . . . . . . . . . . . . . . *Vacant*
    Secretary. . . . . . . . . . . . . . . . . . . . . . . . . . . . . . . . . . Mr Richard Tebboth . . . . . . . . . . . . . . . . .Tel: (029) 2082 3197

## SPORT
**Sports Council for Wales** . . . . . . . . . . . . . . . . . . . . . . .Welsh Institute of Sport, Sophia Gardens, Cardiff, CF11 9SW
    Chairman *(Acting)* . . . . . . . . . . . . . . . . . . . . . . . . . .Mr Philip Carling
    Chief Executive . . . . . . . . . . . . . . . . . . . . . . . . . . . . .Dr Huw Jones . . . . . . . . . . . . . . . . . . . . . . . Tel: (029) 2030 0500
        E-mail: scw@scw.co.uk
        Web: http://www.sports-council-wales.co.uk

## TELECOMMUNICATIONS
**Welsh Advisory Committee on Telecommunications** . . . .4 The Science Park, Aberystwyth, SY23 3AH
    Chairman . . . . . . . . . . . . . . . . . . . . . . . . . . . . . . . . .Professor Mike Tedd
    Secretary . . . . . . . . . . . . . . . . . . . . . . . . . . . . . . . . .Mr Joey Hughes . . . . . . . . . . . . . . . . . . . . . Tel: (01970) 636413
        Web: http://www.acts.org.uk

## TOURISM
**Wales Tourist Board** . . . . . . . . . . . . . . . . . . . . . . . . . . .Brunel House, 2 Fitzalan Road, Cardiff, CF24 0UY
    Chairman . . . . . . . . . . . . . . . . . . . . . . . . . . . . . . . . .Mr Philip Evans
    Chief Executive . . . . . . . . . . . . . . . . . . . . . . . . . . . . .Mr Jonathan Jones. . . . . . . . . . . . . . . . . . . Tel: (029) 2049 9909
        Web: http://www.visitwales.com

## VALUATION
**Valuation Tribunals (Wales)** . . . . . . . . . . . . . . . . . . . . . Local Government Finance Division, Cathays Park, Cardiff, CF10 3NQ
    Administrative Officer. . . . . . . . . . . . . . . . . . . . . . . . . Mr Paul Harrison . . . . . . . . . . . . . . . . . . .Tel: (029) 2082 5301
        Web: http://www.valuation-tribunals.gov.uk

## WATER
**WaterVoice Wales** . . . . . . . . . . . . . . . . . . . . . . . . . . . . Room 140, Caradog House, 1-6 St Andrew's Place, Cardiff, CF10 3BE
    Chairman . . . . . . . . . . . . . . . . . . . . . . . . . . . . . . . . .Dr John Ford CBE
    Regional Manager . . . . . . . . . . . . . . . . . . . . . . . . . . . .Mr Clive Sterl . . . . . . . . . . . . . . . . . . . . . . . Tel: (029) 2023 9852
        E-mail: wales@watervoice.gov.uk

# DEPARTMENT FOR CONSTITUTIONAL AFFAIRS

*Other Relevant Contacts: Wales (Continued)*

**WELSH LANGUAGE**

**Welsh Language Board** . . . . . . . . . . . . . . . . . . . . . . . . . . .Market Chambers, 5-7 St Mary Street, Cardiff, CF10 1AT

    Chairman . . . . . . . . . . . . . . . . . . . . . . . . . . . . . . . . .Mr Rhodri Williams

    Chief Executive . . . . . . . . . . . . . . . . . . . . . . . . . . . . .Mr John Walter Jones . . . . . . . . . . . . . . . . Tel: (029) 2087 8000

                    Web: http://www.welsh-language-board.org.uk

**YOUTH**

**Wales Youth Agency** . . . . . . . . . . . . . . . . . . . . . . . . . . . .Leslie Court, Lôn-y-Llyn, Caerphilly, CF83 1BQ

    Chairman . . . . . . . . . . . . . . . . . . . . . . . . . . . . . . . . .Mr Gerald Davies

    Chief Executive . . . . . . . . . . . . . . . . . . . . . . . . . . . . .Mr Brian Williams. . . . . . . . . . . . . . . . . . . Tel: (029) 2085 5700

                    Web: http://www.wya.org.uk

# DEPARTMENT FOR CULTURE, MEDIA AND SPORT

2-4 Cockspur Street, London, SW1Y 5DH
Tel: (020) 7211 6000  Fax: (020) 7211 6210
E-mail: [firstname.surname]@culture.gov.uk
Web: http://www.culture.gov.uk

## MINISTERS

**Secretary of State** . . . . . . . . . . . . . . . . . . . . . . . . . . . . . Rt Hon Tessa Jowell MP
   *Private Secretary*. . . . . . . . . . . . . . . . . . . . . . . . . . . . . Mr Hugh Ind . . . . . . . . . . . . . . . . . . . . . . . . . . Tel: (020) 7211 6243
   *Special Advisers* . . . . . . . . . . . . . . . . . . . . . . . . . . . . Mr Nick Bent. . . . . . . . . . . . . . . . . . . . . . . . . . Tel: (020) 7211 6010
                                          Mr Bill Bush . . . . . . . . . . . . . . . . . . . . . . . . . . Tel: (020) 7211 6515

**Minister of State** *(Minister for Sport and Tourism)* . . . . . Rt Hon Richard Caborn MP
   *Private Secretary*. . . . . . . . . . . . . . . . . . . . . . . . . . . . . Mr Graeme Cornell . . . . . . . . . . . . . . . . . . . . Tel: (020) 7211 6246

**Minister of State** *(Minister for the Arts)* . . . . . . . . . . . . Rt Hon Estelle Morris MP
   *Private Secretary*. . . . . . . . . . . . . . . . . . . . . . . . . . . . . Mr David McLaren. . . . . . . . . . . . . . . . . . . . . . Tel: (020) 7211 6252

**Parliamentary Secretary**
   *(Media and Heritage)* . . . . . . . . . . . . . . . . . . . . . . . Rt Hon Lord McIntosh of Haringey
   *Private Secretary*. . . . . . . . . . . . . . . . . . . . . . . . . . . . . Mr Gareth Maybury . . . . . . . . . . . . . . . . . . . . Tel: (020) 7211 6303

## CIVIL SERVICE

**Permanent Secretary** . . . . . . . . . . . . . . . . . . . . . . . . . . . Ms Sue Street
   *Private Secretary*. . . . . . . . . . . . . . . . . . . . . . . . . . . . . Ms Eleanor Street. . . . . . . . . . . . . . . . . . . . . . Tel: (020) 7211 6256

**Group Directors**
   Arts and Culture. . . . . . . . . . . . . . . . . . . . . . . . . . . . . Mr Alex Stewart. . . . . . . . . . . . . . . . . . . . . . . . Tel: (020) 7211 6122
   Corporate Services . . . . . . . . . . . . . . . . . . . . . . . . . . . Mr Nicholas Kroll KB . . . . . . . . . . . . . . . . . . . Tel: (020) 7211 6189
   Creative Industries, Broadcasting and Gambling . . . . Mr Andrew Ramsay . . . . . . . . . . . . . . . . . . . . Tel: (020) 7211 6410
   Legal Adviser. . . . . . . . . . . . . . . . . . . . . . . . . . . . . . . Ms Isabel Letwin . . . . . . . . . . . . . . . . . . . . . . . Tel: (020) 7211 2230
   Sports and Lottery . . . . . . . . . . . . . . . . . . . . . . . . . . Mr Alec McGivan. . . . . . . . . . . . . . . . . . . . . . . Tel: (020) 7211 6193
   Strategy and Communications. . . . . . . . . . . . . . . . . . Ms Siobhan Kenny. . . . . . . . . . . . . . . . . . . . . . Tel: (020) 7211 6277
   Tourism, Libraries and Community . . . . . . . . . . . . . Mr Brian Leonard. . . . . . . . . . . . . . . . . . . . . . . Tel: (020) 7211 6384

## SUBJECT RESPONSIBILITIES AND CONTACTS

**Alcohol and Entertainment Licensing**
   Policy . . . . . . . . . . . . . . . . . . . . . . . . . . . . . . . . . . . Mr Andrew Cunningham. . . . . . . . . . . . . . . . . Tel: (020) 7211 6344

**Analytical Services**
   Chief Statistician, Head of Analytical Services . . . . . . Ms Vanessa Brand . . . . . . . . . . . . . . . . . . . . . . Tel: (020) 7211 2190

**Appointments**
   Head, Public Appointments, Honours and
      Modernisation Division . . . . . . . . . . . . . . . . . . . . Ms Janet Evans . . . . . . . . . . . . . . . . . . . . . . . . Tel: (020) 7211 2301
   Appointments Processes. . . . . . . . . . . . . . . . . . . . . . . Mr Stuart Roberts. . . . . . . . . . . . . . . . . . . . . . . Tel: (020) 7211 2303

**Archaeology**. . . . . . . . . . . . . . . . . . . . . . . . . . . . . . . . . . Ms Ilynn Masson . . . . . . . . . . . . . . . . . . . . . . Tel: (020) 7211 2347

**Architecture and Historic Environment**
   Head, Architecture and Historic Environment Division Mr Michael Seeney . . . . . . . . . . . . . . . . . . . . . . Tel: (020) 7211 2330
   Access. . . . . . . . . . . . . . . . . . . . . . . . . . . . . . . . . . . . Mr Gerard Wheeldon MVO. . . . . . . . . . . . . . . . Tel: (020) 7211 2378
   Architecture, Education and World Heritage Branch. . Ms Sheelah Evans . . . . . . . . . . . . . . . . . . . . . . Tel: (020) 7211 2335
   European Union and International . . . . . . . . . . . . . . Ms Sheelah Evans . . . . . . . . . . . . . . . . . . . . . . Tel: (020) 7211 2335
   Flag Flying Rules. . . . . . . . . . . . . . . . . . . . . . . . . . . Mr Gerard Wheeldon MVO. . . . . . . . . . . . . . . . Tel: (020) 7211 2378
   Heritage Open Days . . . . . . . . . . . . . . . . . . . . . . . . Ms Frances MacLeod . . . . . . . . . . . . . . . . . . . Tel: (020) 7211 2371
   Heritage Taxation. . . . . . . . . . . . . . . . . . . . . . . . . . . Ms Frances MacLeod . . . . . . . . . . . . . . . . . . . Tel: (020) 7211 2371
   Heritage Tourism . . . . . . . . . . . . . . . . . . . . . . . . . . Ms Frances MacLeod . . . . . . . . . . . . . . . . . . . Tel: (020) 7211 2371
   Historic Environment Designation Branch. . . . . . . . . Ms Ilynn Masson . . . . . . . . . . . . . . . . . . . . . . Tel: (020) 7211 2347
   Iraq Support Project. . . . . . . . . . . . . . . . . . . . . . . . . Ms Sheelah Evans . . . . . . . . . . . . . . . . . . . . . . Tel: (020) 7211 2335
   National Trust / Historic Houses Association Liaison . Ms Frances MacLeod . . . . . . . . . . . . . . . . . . . Tel: (020) 7211 2371
   Policy . . . . . . . . . . . . . . . . . . . . . . . . . . . . . . . . . . . Ms Frances MacLeod . . . . . . . . . . . . . . . . . . . Tel: (020) 7211 2371
   September 11 Memorial Garden . . . . . . . . . . . . . . . Ms Sheelah Evans . . . . . . . . . . . . . . . . . . . . . . Tel: (020) 7211 2335

# DEPARTMENT FOR CULTURE, MEDIA AND SPORT

*Architecture and Horticultural Environment (Continued)*

| | | |
|---|---|---|
| Stonehenge | Ms Sheelah Evans | Tel: (020) 7211 2335 |
| Taxation | Ms Frances MacLeod | Tel: (020) 7211 2371 |
| UNESCO, World Heritage Convention | Ms Sheelah Evans | Tel: (020) 7211 2335 |

**Arts**

| | | |
|---|---|---|
| Head, Arts Division | Mr Phil Clapp | Tel: (020) 7211 6205 |
| Access | Mr David Fitzgerald | Tel: (020) 7211 6369 |
| Arts Council | Ms Grace Carley | Tel: (020) 7211 6138 |
| Artsmark | Mr David Fitzgerald | Tel: (020) 7211 6369 |
| Business Sponsorship | Mr David Fitzgerald | Tel: (020) 7211 6369 |
| Crafts Council | Ms Grace Carley | Tel: (020) 7211 6138 |
| Creative Partnerships | Mr David Fitzgerald | Tel: (020) 7211 6369 |
| Culture Online | Mr Jonathan Druri | Tel: (020) 7273 8706 |
| Development | Mr David Fitzgerald | Tel: (020) 7211 6369 |
| Education | Mr David Fitzgerald | Tel: (020) 7211 6369 |
| European Union and International | Mr Alan Simpson | Tel: (020) 7211 6403 |
| Funding | Ms Grace Carley | Tel: (020) 7211 6138 |
| Literature | Ms Patricia Terry | Tel: (020) 7211 6197 |
| Lottery Funding Monitoring | Ms Grace Carley | Tel: (020) 7211 6138 |
| National Foundation of Youth Music | Mr David Fitzgerald | Tel: (020) 7211 6369 |
| National Companies | Mr Alan Simpson | Tel: (020) 7211 6403 |
| Neighbourhood Renewal | Ms Patricia Terry | Tel: (020) 7211 6197 |
| Policy: National | Mr Alan Simpson | Tel: (020) 7211 6403 |
| Regional Issues | Ms Grace Carley | Tel: (020) 7211 6138 |
| Sector Skills Council | Mr David Fitzgerald | Tel: (020) 7211 6369 |
| Social Inclusion | Ms Patricia Terry | Tel: (020) 7211 6197 |
| Theatre Licensing | Mr Philip Baker | Tel: (020) 7211 6353 |
| Volunteering | Ms Patricia Terry | Tel: (020) 7211 6197 |

| | | |
|---|---|---|
| **Bingo** | Mr Gideon Hoffman | Tel: (020) 7211 6479 |

**Broadcasting** *(See below under Creative Industries and Broadcasting)*

| | | |
|---|---|---|
| **Casinos** | Mr Gideon Hoffman | Tel: (020) 7211 6479 |
| **Children and DCMS Functions** | Ms Anne Marie Andreali | Tel: (020) 7211 6331 |
| **Churches, Conservation** | Ms Frances Malleod | Tel: (020) 7211 2371 |
| **Cinema Licensing** | Mr Andrew Cunningham | Tel: (020) 7211 6344 |

**Corporate Services**

| | | |
|---|---|---|
| Head, Corporate Services Group | Mr Nicholas Kroll | Tel: (020) 7211 6189 |

**Creative Industries and Broadcasting**

| | | |
|---|---|---|
| Head, Creative Industries, Broadcasting and Gambling Group | Mr Andrew Ramsay | Tel: (020) 7211 6410 |
| Head, Broadcasting Policy Division | Mr Jon Zeff | Tel: (020) 7211 6463 |
| Head, Creative Industries Division | Mr Mark Ferrero | Tel: (020) 7211 6424 |
| Advertising and Sponsorship | *Vacant* | Tel: (020) 7211 6488 |
| Appointments to Public Bodies | *Vacant* | Tel: (020) 7211 6488 |
| Audiovisual | Mr Mark Ferrero | Tel: (020) 7211 6424 |
| BBC | Mr Stephen Rosser | Tel: (020) 7211 6468 |
| British Film | Mr Mark Ferrero | Tel: (020) 7211 6424 |
| Broadcasting Policy | | |
| General | *Vacant* | Tel: (020) 7211 6488 |
| European | Mr Chris Bone | Tel: (020) 7211 6444 |
| Cable and Satellite Broadcasting | Ms Catherine Smadja | Tel: (020) 7211 6456 |
| Channel 4 Policy Issues | Mr Stephen Rosser | Tel: (020) 7211 6468 |
| Cinema Licensing | Mr Andrew Cunningham | Tel: (020) 7211 6344 |
| Commercial | Ms Catherine Smadja | Tel: (020) 7211 6456 |
| Complaints: Broadcasting | *Vacant* | Tel: (020) 7211 6488 |

# DEPARTMENT FOR CULTURE, MEDIA AND SPORT

*Creative Industries and Broadcasting (Continued)*

| | | |
|---|---|---|
| Creative Industries Strategy Group | Ms Gail Robinson | Tel: (020) 7211 6376 |
| Digital Terrestrial Broadcasting | Ms Catherine Smadja | Tel: (020) 7211 6456 |
| Exports | Ms Gail Robinson | Tel: (020) 7211 6376 |
| Film Industry | | |
|    Certification | Mr Paul Candler | Tel: (020) 7211 6434 |
|    Classification | Mr Paul Alsey | Tel: (020) 7211 6432 |
|    Policy | Mr Paul Candler | Tel: (020) 7211 6424 |
|    Sponsorship | Mr Paul Candler | Tel: (020) 7211 6434 |
| Frequencies (Allocation of) | Ms Catherine Smadja | Tel: (020) 7211 6456 |
| Independent Television | Ms Catherine Smadja | Tel: (020) 7211 6456 |
| International Broadcasting | Mr Chris Bone | Tel: (020) 7211 6444 |
| Legislation | Mr Chris Dawes OBE | Tel: (020) 7211 6461 |
| Licensing, TV | Mr Stephen Rosser | Tel: (020) 7211 6468 |
| Media Ownership | Mr Stuart Brand | Tel: (020) 7211 6416 |
| Music Industry | | |
|    Policy | Mr Mark Ferrero | Tel: (020) 7211 6424 |
|    Sponsorship | Mr Paul Alsey | Tel: (020) 7211 6432 |
| New Technology | Ms Catherine Smadja | Tel: (020) 7211 6456 |
| News | Mr Stuart Brand | Tel: (020) 7211 6416 |
| Ownership Issues (Cross-Media) | Mr Stuart Brand | Tel: (020) 7211 6416 |
| Public Service Broadcasting | Mr Stephen Rosser | Tel: (020) 7211 6468 |
| Press Freedom and Regulation | Mr Paul Alsey | Tel: (020) 7211 6432 |
| Radio | Mr Stuart Brand | Tel: (020) 7211 6416 |
| Regions | *Vacant* | Tel: (020) 7211 6488 |
| Regulation | Mr Chris Dawes OBE | Tel: (020) 7211 6461 |
| Religious Broadcasting | Mr Stuart Brand | Tel: (020) 7211 6416 |
| S4C | Mr Stephen Rosser | Tel: (020) 7211 6468 |
| Spectrum Management | Ms Catherine Smadja | Tel: (020) 7211 6456 |
| Sponsorship: Broadcasting and Audiovisual | *Vacant* | Tel: (020) 7211 6488 |
| Sports Broadcasting | *Vacant* | Tel: (020) 7211 6488 |
| Standards and Policy (Broadcasting) | Mr Chris Dawes OBE | Tel: (020) 7211 6461 |
| Television | Ms Catherine Smadja | Tel: (020) 7211 6456 |
| Video | Mr Paul Alsey | Tel: (020) 7211 6432 |

**Cultural Property**

| | | |
|---|---|---|
| Head, Cultural Property Unit | Ms Hilary Bauer | Tel: (020) 7211 6102 |

**Culture Online** | Mr Jonathan Drori | Tel: (020) 7273 8706

**Economics**

| | | |
|---|---|---|
| Chief Economist | Mr Stephen Criegh-Tyte | Tel: (020) 7211 2181 |

**Education and Social Policy**

| | | |
|---|---|---|
| Head of Education and Social Unit | Mr Kevin Byrne | Tel: (020) 7211 6117 |
| Big Lottery Fund | Ms Liz Ager | Tel: (020) 7211 6510 |
| Post-16 Education | Ms Deirdre Wells | Tel: (020) 7211 6360 |
| Pre-16 Education | Ms Anne Marie Andreoli | Tel: (020) 7211 6331 |

**Entertainment Licensing** | Mr Andrew Cunningham | Tel: (020) 7211 6344

**European Union, Departmental Issues** | Mr Michael Helston | Tel: (020) 7211 6169

**Export Licenses (Works of Art)** | Ms Hilary Bauer | Tel: (020) 7211 6102

**Film** *(see above under Creative Industries, Broadcasting)*

**Finance**

| | | |
|---|---|---|
| Head, Finance and Planning Division | Mr Keith Smith | Tel: (020) 7211 6217 |
| Accountancy | Miss Kathy Hosker | Tel: (020) 7211 6348 |
| Audit (Internal) | Mr Michael Kirk | Tel: (020) 7273 8712 |
| Financial Management and Accounting | Mr Robert Wright FCCA | Tel: (020) 7211 6229 |
| Planning and Performance | Mr Adrian Reid | Tel: (020) 7211 6459 |

# DEPARTMENT FOR CULTURE, MEDIA AND SPORT

**Galleries** *(see below under Museums and Galleries)*

**Gambling**

| | | |
|---|---|---|
| Head, Gambling and National Lottery Licensing Division | Mr Elliot Grant | Tel: (020) 7211 6465 |
| Bingo | Mr Gideon Hoffman | Tel: (020) 7211 6479 |
| Betting and Racing | Mr Clive Hawkswood | Tel: (020) 7211 6473 |
| Gambling and Lotteries | Mr Gideon Hoffman | Tel: (020) 7211 6479 |
| Gaming Machines | Mr Gideon Hoffman | Tel: (020) 7211 6479 |
| Horserace Betting Levy Board, Abolition | Mr Clive Hawkswood | Tel: (020) 7211 6473 |
| Legislation | Mr Greig Chalmers | Tel: (020) 7211 6453 |
| National Lottery Licensing | Mr Colin Perry | Tel: (020) 7211 6535 |
| Online Gambling | Mr Clive Hawkswood | Tel: (020) 7273 6473 |

**Government Art Collection**

*Queen's Yard, 179A Tottenham Court Road, London, W1P 0BE*

| | | |
|---|---|---|
| Director | Ms Penny Johnson | Tel: (020) 7580 9120 |

| | | |
|---|---|---|
| **Greyhound Racing Industry** | Mr Clive Hawkswood | Tel: (020) 7211 6473 |
| **Horseracing Industry** | Mr Clive Hawkswood | Tel: (020) 7211 6473 |
| **Human Remains, Working Group on** | Mr James Dowline | Tel: (020) 7211 6158 |

**Information**

| | | |
|---|---|---|
| News | Mr Paddy Feeny | Tel: (020) 7211 6273 |
| Information Centre | Ms Abigail Humber | Tel: (020) 7211 6200 |
| Publicity | Ms Penny Dolby | Tel: (020) 7211 6275 |

| | | |
|---|---|---|
| **International Unit** | Mr Michael Helston | Tel: (020) 7211 6169 |
| **IT (Departmental)** | Mr Mark O'Neill | Tel: (020) 7211 2063 |
| **Legal Adviser (Departmental)** | Ms Isabel Letwin | Tel: (020) 7211 2230 |

**Libraries**

| | | |
|---|---|---|
| Head, Libraries and Communities Division | Mr Nigel Pittman | Tel: (020) 7211 6132 |
| Head, Museums and Libraries Sponsorship Division | Mr Richard Hartman | Tel: (020) 7211 6179 |
| Chief Librarian | Mr Peter Beauchamp | Tel: (020) 7211 6134 |
| Archives Policy | Ms Henrietta Lidchi | Tel: (020) 7211 6175 |
| Copyright | Ms Henrietta Lidchi | Tel: (020) 7211 6175 |
| Education | Mr Keith Nichol | Tel: (020) 7211 6123 |
| Historical Manuscripts | Ms Henrietta Lidchi | Tel: (020) 7211 6175 |
| International | Mr Michael Helston | Tel: (020) 7211 6169 |
| IT | Mr Keith Gibbins | Tel: (020) 7211 6392 |
| Librarianship Training | Ms Henrietta Lidchi | Tel: (020) 7211 6175 |
| Local Authority Libraries | Mr Roger Stratton Smith | Tel: (020) 7211 6481 |
| Lottery Issues | Mr Keith Gibbins | Tel: (020) 7211 6392 |
| Private Finance Initiative and Local Authorities | Mr Roger Stratton Smith | Tel: (020) 7211 6481 |
| Public Lending Right | Ms Henrietta Lidchi | Tel: (020) 7211 6175 |
| Public Libraries | Mr Keith Gibbins | Tel: (020) 7211 6392 |
| Resource, Sponsorship | Mr Keith Gibbins | Tel: (020) 7211 6392 |
| Royal Commission on Historical Manuscripts | Ms Henrietta Lidchi | Tel: (020) 7211 6175 |
| School Libraries | Mr Keith Gibbins | Tel: (020) 7211 6392 |

**Liquor**

| | | |
|---|---|---|
| Liquor Licensing | Mr Andrew Cunningham | Tel: (020) 7211 6344 |

| | | |
|---|---|---|
| **Listed Places of Worship Grants** | Ms Frances Macleod | Tel: (020) 7211 2371 |
| **Literature** | Ms Patricia Terry | Tel: (020) 7211 6197 |
| **Local Government Unit** | Mr Roger Stratton-Smith | Tel: (020) 7211 6481 |

# DEPARTMENT FOR CULTURE, MEDIA AND SPORT

**Media** *(see above under Creative Industries and Broadcasting)*

**Millennium Legacy** . . . . . . . . . . . . . . . . . . . . . . . . . . Mr Andrew Robson . . . . . . . . . . . . . . . . . . . . . Tel: (020) 7211 6354

**Museums and Galleries**

Head, Museums and Cultural Property Division . . . . . Mr Nigel Pittman . . . . . . . . . . . . . . . . . . . . . . . Tel: (020) 7211 6132
Head, Museums and Libraries Sponsorship Division . . Mr Richard Hartman . . . . . . . . . . . . . . . . . . . . Tel: (020) 7211 6179
Access to Museums . . . . . . . . . . . . . . . . . . . . . . . . Mr Alan Sutherland . . . . . . . . . . . . . . . . . . . . . Tel: (020) 7211 6173
Appointments of Trustees . . . . . . . . . . . . . . . . . . . . Ms Janet Evans . . . . . . . . . . . . . . . . . . . . . . . . Tel: (020) 7211 2301
Cultural Property . . . . . . . . . . . . . . . . . . . . . . . . . . Ms Hilary Bauer. . . . . . . . . . . . . . . . . . . . . Tel: (020) 7211 6102 / 6153
Culture on Line Initiative . . . . . . . . . . . . . . . . . . . . Mr Jonathan Drori . . . . . . . . . . . . . . . . . . . . . Tel: (020) 7273 8706
Education. . . . . . . . . . . . . . . . . . . . . . . . . . . . . . . Mr Keith Nichol. . . . . . . . . . . . . . . . . . . . . . . Tel: (020) 7211 6123
European Union . . . . . . . . . . . . . . . . . . . . . . . . . . Mr Alun Sutherland . . . . . . . . . . . . . . . . . . Tel: (020) 7211 6173 / 6123
Expenditure Policy. . . . . . . . . . . . . . . . . . . . . . . . . Mr Richard Hartman . . . . . . . . . . . . . . . . . . . . Tel: (020) 7211 6179
Export Licences (Works of Art). . . . . . . . . . . . . . . . Ms Hilary Bauer. . . . . . . . . . . . . . . . . . . . Tel: (020) 7211 6102 / 6166
Financing. . . . . . . . . . . . . . . . . . . . . . . . . . . . . . . Mr Richard Hartman . . . . . . . . . . . . . . . . . . . . Tel: (020) 7211 6179
Heritage Taxation. . . . . . . . . . . . . . . . . . . . . . . . . . Ms Hilary Bauer. . . . . . . . . . . . . . . . . . . . Tel: (020) 7211 6102 / 6153
Independent Museums . . . . . . . . . . . . . . . . . . . . . . Mr Richard Hartman . . . . . . . . . . . . . . . . . . . . Tel: (020) 7211 6179
International . . . . . . . . . . . . . . . . . . . . . . . . . . . . . Mr Alun Sutherland . . . . . . . . . . . . . . . . . . Tel: (020) 7211 6173 / 6123
Local Authorities . . . . . . . . . . . . . . . . . . . . . . . . . . Mr Richard Hartman . . . . . . . . . . . . . . . . . . . . Tel: (020) 7211 6179
Policy, National Museums. . . . . . . . . . . . . . . . . . . . Ms Henrietta Lidchi . . . . . . . . . . . . . . . . . . . . Tel: (020) 7211 6175
Regional . . . . . . . . . . . . . . . . . . . . . . . . . . . . . . . Ms Moira Goatley. . . . . . . . . . . . . . . . . . . . . . Tel: (020) 7211 6316
Resource, Sponsorship . . . . . . . . . . . . . . . . . . . . . . Mr Alun Sutherland . . . . . . . . . . . . . . . . . . Tel: (020) 7211 6173 / 6123
Museum Training . . . . . . . . . . . . . . . . . . . . . . . . . . Ms Henrietta Lidchi . . . . . . . . . . . . . . . . . . . . Tel: (020) 7211 6175
Sponsorship . . . . . . . . . . . . . . . . . . . . . . . . . . . . . Mr Richard Hartman . . . . . . . . . . . . . . . . . . . . Tel: (020) 7211 6179

**National Lottery**

Head, Gambling and National Lottery
   Licensing Division . . . . . . . . . . . . . . . . . . . . . . Mr Elliot Grant . . . . . . . . . . . . . . . . . . . . . . . Tel: (020) 7211 6465
Head, National Lottery Distribution and
   Communities Division . . . . . . . . . . . . . . . . . . . . Mr Simon Broadley . . . . . . . . . . . . . . . . . . . . Tel: (020) 7211 6526
Active Community Initiative . . . . . . . . . . . . . . . . . . Ms Liz Ager . . . . . . . . . . . . . . . . . . . . . . . . . Tel: (020) 7211 6510
Big Lottery Fund . . . . . . . . . . . . . . . . . . . . . . . . . Ms Liz Ager . . . . . . . . . . . . . . . . . . . . . . . . . Tel: (020) 7211 6510
Distribution Policy . . . . . . . . . . . . . . . . . . . . . . . . Ms Rachel Miller . . . . . . . . . . . . . . . . . . . . . . Tel: (020) 7211 6538
Licensing and Regulation, National Lottery . . . . . . . Mr Colin Perry . . . . . . . . . . . . . . . . . . . . . . . Tel: (020) 7211 6535
Monitoring of Awards . . . . . . . . . . . . . . . . . . . . . . Mr Andrew Robson . . . . . . . . . . . . . . . . . . . . Tel: (020) 7211 6354
New Millennium Experience Company, Legacy Issues . Mr Andrew Robson . . . . . . . . . . . . . . . . . . . . Tel: (020) 7211 6354
New Opportunities Fund. . . . . . . . . . . . . . . . . . . . . Ms Liz Ager . . . . . . . . . . . . . . . . . . . . . . . . . Tel: (020) 7211 6510

**Olympic Bid, London**

Head, Olympic Games Unit . . . . . . . . . . . . . . . . . . Mr Paul Bolt . . . . . . . . . . . . . . . . . . . . . . . . . Tel: (020) 7211 6503
Legislation . . . . . . . . . . . . . . . . . . . . . . . . . . . . . . Ms Ruth Shaw . . . . . . . . . . . . . . . . . . . . . . . Tel: (020) 7211 6493
Project Management . . . . . . . . . . . . . . . . . . . . . . . . Ms Helen MacNamara . . . . . . . . . . . . . . . . . . Tel: (020) 7211 6194

**Parliamentary Clerk** . . . . . . . . . . . . . . . . . . . . . . . Mr Harvey Vasey . . . . . . . . . . . . . . . . . . . . . . Tel: (020) 7211 6288

**Personnel and Central Services**

Head, Personnel and Central Services. . . . . . . . . . . . Mr Shaun Cove . . . . . . . . . . . . . . . . . . . . . . . Tel: (020) 7211 2032
Information Systems . . . . . . . . . . . . . . . . . . . . . . . . Mr Mark O'Neill. . . . . . . . . . . . . . . . . . . . . . Tel: (020) 7211 2063
Personnel Operations . . . . . . . . . . . . . . . . . . . . . . . Mr Shaun Cove . . . . . . . . . . . . . . . . . . . . . . . Tel: (020) 7211 2032
Personnel Policy. . . . . . . . . . . . . . . . . . . . . . . . . . . Ms Emma Cockell . . . . . . . . . . . . . . . . . . . . . Tel: (020) 7211 2027
Procurement and Property Services . . . . . . . . . . . . . . Mr Barry Cotterill. . . . . . . . . . . . . . . . . . . . . . Tel: (020) 7211 2023

**Press and Publicity**

Director, Strategy and Communications. . . . . . . . . . . Ms Siobhan Kenny . . . . . . . . . . . . . . . . . . . . . Tel: (020) 7211 6277
Head, Communications. . . . . . . . . . . . . . . . . . . . . . Ms Penny Dolby. . . . . . . . . . . . . . . . . . . . . . . Tel: (020) 7211 6275
Head, News . . . . . . . . . . . . . . . . . . . . . . . . . . . . . Mr Paddy Feeny. . . . . . . . . . . . . . . . . . . . . . . Tel: (020) 7211 6273
Ministerial Briefings and Speeches . . . . . . . . . . . . . . Mr Paddy Feeny. . . . . . . . . . . . . . . . . . . . . . . Tel: (020) 7211 6273

**Public Bodies: Appointments**

Head, Public Appointments, Honours and
   Modernisation Division . . . . . . . . . . . . . . . . . . . Ms Janet Evans . . . . . . . . . . . . . . . . . . . . . . . Tel: (020) 7211 2301
Appointments Processes . . . . . . . . . . . . . . . . . . . . . Ms Linda Dworowski . . . . . . . . . . . . . . . . . . . Tel: (020) 7211 2303

# DEPARTMENT FOR CULTURE, MEDIA AND SPORT

**Public Enquiry Unit** . . . . . . . . . . . . . . . . . . . . . . . . . Ms Abigail Humber . . . . . . . . . . . . . . . . . . Tel: (020) 7211 6200

**Regional Policy** . . . . . . . . . . . . . . . . . . . . . . . . . . . . Mr Dominic Tambling . . . . . . . . . . . . . . . . Tel: (020) 7211 6316

**Sport and Recreation**
    Director, Sports . . . . . . . . . . . . . . . . . . . . . . . . . Ms Nicky Roche. . . . . . . . . . . . . . . . . . . . . Tel: (020) 7211 6193
    Head, Sports Division. . . . . . . . . . . . . . . . . . . . . Mr Paul Heron . . . . . . . . . . . . . . . . . . . . . Tel: (020) 7211 6078
    British Chess Federation. . . . . . . . . . . . . . . . . . Mr Steve Hodgson . . . . . . . . . . . . . . . . . . Tel: (020) 7211 6150
    Broadcasting Rights . . . . . . . . . . . . . . . . . . . . . . Mr Mark Cavey . . . . . . . . . . . . . . . . . . . . Tel: (020) 7211 6506
                                 Mr Mark Balcar . . . . . . . . . . . . . . . . . . . . Tel: (020) 7211 6081
    Children's Playgrounds. . . . . . . . . . . . . . . . . . . . Ms Anne-Marie Andreuli . . . . . . . . . . . . Tel: (020) 7211 6331
    Coaching . . . . . . . . . . . . . . . . . . . . . . . . . . . . . . . Mr Steve Hodgson . . . . . . . . . . . . . . . . . . Tel: (020) 7211 6150
    Coaching . . . . . . . . . . . . . . . . . . . . . . . . . . . . . . . Mr Matthew Conway. . . . . . . . . . . . . . . . Tel: (020) 7211 6088
                                 Ms Susan Shaw . . . . . . . . . . . . . . . . . . . . Tel: (020) 7211 6084
    Community Sport . . . . . . . . . . . . . . . . . . . . . . . . . Ms Debbie Lye. . . . . . . . . . . . . . . . . . . . . . Tel: (020) 7211 6013
                                 Ms Rae Whittaker . . . . . . . . . . . . . . . . . . Tel: (020) 7211 6091
    Disability. . . . . . . . . . . . . . . . . . . . . . . . . . . . . . . . Mr Steve Hodgson . . . . . . . . . . . . . . . . . . Tel: (020) 7211 6150
    Drugs. . . . . . . . . . . . . . . . . . . . . . . . . . . . . . . . . . . Mr Steve Hodgson . . . . . . . . . . . . . . . . . . Tel: (020) 7211 6150
    Elite. . . . . . . . . . . . . . . . . . . . . . . . . . . . . . . . . . . . Mr Steve Hodgson . . . . . . . . . . . . . . . . . . Tel: (020) 7211 6150
    European Union . . . . . . . . . . . . . . . . . . . . . . . . . Mr Steve Hodgson . . . . . . . . . . . . . . . . . . Tel: (020) 7211 6150
    Facilities . . . . . . . . . . . . . . . . . . . . . . . . . . . . . . . . Mr Mark Balcar . . . . . . . . . . . . . . . . . . . . Tel: (020) 7211 6081
    Finance and Funding . . . . . . . . . . . . . . . . . . . . . Mr Mark Cavey . . . . . . . . . . . . . . . . . . . . Tel: (020) 7211 6506
    Fitness Promotion. . . . . . . . . . . . . . . . . . . . . . . . Mr Rae Whitaker . . . . . . . . . . . . . . . . . . Tel: (020) 7211 6091
    Football . . . . . . . . . . . . . . . . . . . . . . . . . . . . . . . . Mr Mark Ballar . . . . . . . . . . . . . . . . . . . . Tel: (020) 7211 6081
    Football Licensing . . . . . . . . . . . . . . . . . . . . . . . Mr Mark Ballar . . . . . . . . . . . . . . . . . . . . Tel: (020) 7211 6081
    Funding of Facilities . . . . . . . . . . . . . . . . . . . . . Mr Mark Ballar . . . . . . . . . . . . . . . . . . . . Tel: (020) 7211 6081
    International . . . . . . . . . . . . . . . . . . . . . . . . . . . . Mr Steve Hodgson . . . . . . . . . . . . . . . . . . Tel: (020) 7211 6150
    Local Authority Issues . . . . . . . . . . . . . . . . . . . . Mr Mark Ballar . . . . . . . . . . . . . . . . . . . . Tel: (020) 7211 6081
    Lottery Funding . . . . . . . . . . . . . . . . . . . . . . . . . Ms Rachel Miller . . . . . . . . . . . . . . . . . . . Tel: (020) 7211 6538
    Olympic Bid. . . . . . . . . . . . . . . . . . . . . . . . . . . . . Mr Paul Bolt . . . . . . . . . . . . . . . . . . . . . . Tel: (020) 7211 6503
    Playing Fields . . . . . . . . . . . . . . . . . . . . . . . . . . . Mr Mark Ballar . . . . . . . . . . . . . . . . . . . . Tel: (020) 7211 6081
    Professional Sport. . . . . . . . . . . . . . . . . . . . . . . . Mr Mark Ballar . . . . . . . . . . . . . . . . . . . . Tel: (020) 7211 6081
    Safety
        Community Facilities . . . . . . . . . . . . . . . . . . . Ms Debbie Lye. . . . . . . . . . . . . . . . . . . . . . Tel: (020) 7211 6013
        Sports Grounds . . . . . . . . . . . . . . . . . . . . . . Ms Anne Henderson. . . . . . . . . . . . . . . . . Tel: (020) 7211 6076
    School Sports, Club Links and Coaching Project . . . . . *Vacant* . . . . . . . . . . . . . . . . . . . . . . . . . . . . Tel: (020) 7211 6088
                                   Ms Susan Shaw . . . . . . . . . . . . . . . . . . . . Tel: (020) 7211 6084
    Sport England, Sponsorship . . . . . . . . . . . . . . . . Mr Mark Lavey . . . . . . . . . . . . . . . . . . . . Tel: (020) 7211 6506
    Sports Councils . . . . . . . . . . . . . . . . . . . . . . . . . . Mr Steve Hodgson . . . . . . . . . . . . . . . . . . Tel: (020) 7211 6150
    Sports Medicine . . . . . . . . . . . . . . . . . . . . . . . . . Mr Steve Hodgson . . . . . . . . . . . . . . . . . . Tel: (020) 7211 6150
    Sports Sponsorship. . . . . . . . . . . . . . . . . . . . . . . Mr Mark Ballar . . . . . . . . . . . . . . . . . . . . Tel: (020) 7211 6081
    Stadiums . . . . . . . . . . . . . . . . . . . . . . . . . . . . . . . Ms Anne Henderson. . . . . . . . . . . . . . . . . Tel: (020) 7211 6076
    UK Sports Institute. . . . . . . . . . . . . . . . . . . . . . . Mr Steve Hodgson . . . . . . . . . . . . . . . . . . Tel: (020) 7211 6150
    Women . . . . . . . . . . . . . . . . . . . . . . . . . . . . . . . . Ms Rae Whittaker . . . . . . . . . . . . . . . . . . Tel: (020) 7211 6091
    Young People, Schools . . . . . . . . . . . . . . . . . . . . Ms Debbie Lye. . . . . . . . . . . . . . . . . . . . . . Tel: (020) 7211 6013

**Statistics**
    Chief Statistician, Head of Analytical Services . . . . . . *Vacant* . . . . . . . . . . . . . . . . . . . . . . . . . . . . Tel: (020) 7211 2190

**Strategy, Departmental**
    Director, Strategy and Communications. . . . . . . . . . Ms Siobhan Kenny . . . . . . . . . . . . . . . . . Tel: (020) 7211 6277
    Head, Strategy Policy and Delivery. . . . . . . . . . . . . Mr David Roe. . . . . . . . . . . . . . . . . . . . . . Tel: (020) 7211 6026
    Delivery. . . . . . . . . . . . . . . . . . . . . . . . . . . . . . . . Mr Tim Freathy . . . . . . . . . . . . . . . . . . . Tel: (020) 7211 6047
    Education and Social Policy Unit . . . . . . . . . . . . . . Mr Kevin Byrne . . . . . . . . . . . . . . . . . . . Tel: (020) 7211 6117
    Post-16 Education . . . . . . . . . . . . . . . . . . . . . . . . Ms Deirdre Wells. . . . . . . . . . . . . . . . . . . Tel: (020) 7211 6360
    Pre-16 Education. . . . . . . . . . . . . . . . . . . . . . . . . Ms Anne-Marie Andreuli . . . . . . . . . . . . Tel: (020) 7211 6331
    Project Centre . . . . . . . . . . . . . . . . . . . . . . . . . . . Mr Alan Ferries . . . . . . . . . . . . . . . . . . . . Tel: (020) 7211 6035
    Risk Management. . . . . . . . . . . . . . . . . . . . . . . . . Mr Simon Cooper . . . . . . . . . . . . . . . . . . Tel: (020) 7211 6023
    Regulatory Impact . . . . . . . . . . . . . . . . . . . . . . . . Mr Simon Cooper . . . . . . . . . . . . . . . . . . Tel: (020) 7211 6023

**Theatre Licensing** . . . . . . . . . . . . . . . . . . . . . . . . . Mr Andrew Cunningham. . . . . . . . . . . . . . . Tel: (020) 7211 6344

# DEPARTMENT FOR CULTURE, MEDIA AND SPORT

**Tourism**

| | | |
|---|---|---|
| Head, Tourism Division | Mr Harry Reeves | Tel: (020) 7211 6324 |
| Accessibility | Ms Susannah Wiltshire | Tel: (020) 7211 6387 |
| Accommodation Grading Scheme | Mr Sean Coster | Tel: (020) 7211 6312 |
| Board Appointments | Mr Paul Blaker | Tel: (020) 7211 6389 |
| Devolution Issues | Ms Susannah Wiltshire | Tel: (020) 7211 6387 |
| E-Commerce and Tourism | Mr Paul Blaker | Tel: (020) 7211 6389 |
| Emergency Response Group, Tourism Industry | Mr Paul Blaker | Tel: (020) 7211 6389 |
| European Union | Ms Valerie Curtis | Tel: (020) 7211 6318 |
| Heritage Tourism | Ms Frances MacLeod | Tel: (020) 7211 2371 |
| Inward | Mr Paul Blaker | Tel: (020) 7211 6389 |
| Language Schools | Ms Valerie Curtis | Tel: (020) 7211 6318 |
| Local Authorities / Regional Issues | Ms Susannah Wiltshire | Tel: (020) 7211 6387 |
| Publicity | Mr Paul Blaker | Tel: (020) 7211 6389 |
| Rural Tourism | Ms Susannah Wiltshire | Tel: (020) 7211 6387 |
| Seaside Resorts | Mr Sean Coster | Tel: (020) 7211 6312 |
| Sector Skills | Mr Sean Coster | Tel: (020) 7211 6312 |
| Statistics | Mr Gavin Sayer | Tel: (020) 7211 6072 |
| Sustainability | Ms Susannah Wiltshire | Tel: (020) 7211 6387 |
| Visit Britain | Mr Paul Blaker | Tel: (020) 7211 6389 |

| | | |
|---|---|---|
| **Treasure Trove** | Ms Hillary Bauer | Tel: (020) 7211 6102 / 6181 |

| | | |
|---|---|---|
| **Wrecks, Designation** | Mr Chris Smith | Tel: (020) 7211 2350 |

## OTHER RELEVANT CONTACTS

**ALCOHOL**
**Alcohol Education and Research Council** . . . . . . . . Room 408, Horseferry House, Dean Ryle Street, London, SW1P 2AW
Chairman . . . . . . . . . . . . . . . . . . . . . . . . . . . . . . . . . Dr Noel Olsen
Director . . . . . . . . . . . . . . . . . . . . . . . . . . . . . . . . . . Professor Ray Hodgson . . . . . . . . . . . . . . . . . Tel: (020) 7217 8896
E-mail: info@aerc.org.uk
Web: http://www.aerc.org.uk

**ARCHITECTURE**
**Commission for Architecture and the**
**Built Environment** . . . . . . . . . . . . . . . . . . . . . . . The Tower Building, 11 York Road, London, SE1 7NX
Chairman . . . . . . . . . . . . . . . . . . . . . . . . . . . . . . . . . Sir Stuart Lipton
Chief Executive . . . . . . . . . . . . . . . . . . . . . . . . . . . . Mr Jon Rouse . . . . . . . . . . . . . . . . . . . . . . . . Tel: (020) 7960 2400
E-mail: enquiries@cabe.olg.uk
Web: http://www.cabe.org.uk

**ARTS**
**Advisory Committee on the**
**Government Art Collection** . . . . . . . . . . . . . . . . . Queen's Yard, 179a Tottenham Court Road, London, W1T 7PA
Chairman . . . . . . . . . . . . . . . . . . . . . . . . . . . . . . . . . Ms Julia Somerville
Secretary . . . . . . . . . . . . . . . . . . . . . . . . . . . . . . . . . Mr Malcolm Steer . . . . . . . . . . . . . . . . . . . . Tel: (020) 7580 9120
E-mail: gac@culture.gov.uk
Web: http://www.gac.culture.gov.uk
**Arts and Humanities Research Board** . . . . . . . . . . Whitefriars, Lewins Mead, Bristol, BS1 2AE
Chairman . . . . . . . . . . . . . . . . . . . . . . . . . . . . . . . . . Professor Sir Brian Follett
Chief Executive . . . . . . . . . . . . . . . . . . . . . . . . . . . . Professor Geoffrey Crossick . . . . . . . . . . . . . Tel: (0117) 987 6500
Web: http://www.ahrb.ac.uk
**Arts Council England** . . . . . . . . . . . . . . . . . . . . . . . 14 Great Peter Street, London, SW1P 3NQ
Chairman . . . . . . . . . . . . . . . . . . . . . . . . . . . . . . . . . Professor Sir Christopher Frayling
Chief Executive . . . . . . . . . . . . . . . . . . . . . . . . . . . . Mr Peter Hewitt . . . . . . . . . . . . . . . . . . . . . . Tel: (020) 7333 0100
Web: http://www.artscouncil.org.uk
**National Endowment for Science,**
**Technology and the Arts** . . . . . . . . . . . . . . . . . . . Fishmongers' Chambers, 110 Upper Thames Street, London, EC4R 3TJ
Chairman . . . . . . . . . . . . . . . . . . . . . . . . . . . . . . . . . Mr Chris Powell
Chief Executive . . . . . . . . . . . . . . . . . . . . . . . . . . . . Mr Jeremy Newton . . . . . . . . . . . . . . . . . . . Tel: (020) 7645 9500
E-mail: nesta@nesta.org.uk
Web: http://www.nesta.org.uk

# DEPARTMENT FOR CULTURE, MEDIA AND SPORT

*Other Relevant Contacts (Continued)*

**Reviewing Committee on the Export of Works of Art** . 2-4 Cockspur Street, London, SW1Y 5DH
Chairman . . . . . . . . . . . . . . . . . . . . . . . . . . . . . . . . . Lord Inglewood
Secretaries . . . . . . . . . . . . . . . . . . . . . . . . . . . . . . . Ms Nicki Fox
Ms Helen Loughlin. . . . . . . . . . . . . . . . . . . . . . Tel: (020) 7211 6160
Web: http://www.culture.gov.uk

## BROADCASTING

**British Broadcasting Corporation**. . . . . . . . . . . . . . Broadcasting House, Portland Place, London, W1A 1AA
Chairman . . . . . . . . . . . . . . . . . . . . . . . . . . . . . . . . . Mr Michael Grade
Director-General . . . . . . . . . . . . . . . . . . . . . . . . . . Mr Mark Byford . . . . . . . . . . . . . . . . . . . . . . . . Tel: (020) 7580 4468
Web: http://www.bbc.co.uk

**Channel 4 Television Corporation** . . . . . . . . . . . . . . 124 Horseferry Road, London, SW1P 2TX
Chief Executive . . . . . . . . . . . . . . . . . . . . . . . . . . . Mr Andy Duncan . . . . . . . . . . . . . . . . . . . . . . . Tel: (020) 7396 4444
Web: http://www.channel4.com

**OFCOM** . . . . . . . . . . . . . . . . . . . . . . . . . . . . . . . . . . Riverside House, 2A Southwark Bridge Road, London, SE1 9HA
Chairman . . . . . . . . . . . . . . . . . . . . . . . . . . . . . . . . . Lord Currie
Chief Executive . . . . . . . . . . . . . . . . . . . . . . . . . . . Mr Stephen Carter . . . . . . . . . . . . . . . . . . . . . . Tel: (020) 7981 3000
Web: http://www.ofcom.org.uk

**Sianel Pedwar Cymru (S4C)** . . . . . . . . . . . . . . . . . . Parc Ty Glas, Llanishen, Cardiff, CF14 5DU
Chairman . . . . . . . . . . . . . . . . . . . . . . . . . . . . . . . . . Mrs Elan Closs Stephens CBE
Chief Executive . . . . . . . . . . . . . . . . . . . . . . . . . . . Mr Huw Jones . . . . . . . . . . . . . . . . . . . . . . . . . Tel: (029) 2074 7444
Web: http://www.s4c.co.uk

## CULTURAL CONSORTIUMS

**East of England Cultural Consortium**
**Living East**. . . . . . . . . . . . . . . . . . . . . . . . . . . . . . . Government Office for the East of England, Shaftesbury Road, Cambridge, CB2 2DF
Chairman . . . . . . . . . . . . . . . . . . . . . . . . . . . . . . . . . Mr Graham Creelman
*Contact* . . . . . . . . . . . . . . . . . . . . . . . . . . . . . . . . . . Ms Jane Edwards . . . . . . . . . . . . . . . . . . . . . . . Tel: (01223) 372610
Web: http://www.livingeast.org.uk

**East Midlands Cultural Consortium**
**Culture East Midlands** . . . . . . . . . . . . . . . . . . . . . Government Office for the East Midlands, Apex House, City Link, Nottingham, NG2 4LA
Chairman . . . . . . . . . . . . . . . . . . . . . . . . . . . . . . . . . Mr Ted Cassidy
Executive Director . . . . . . . . . . . . . . . . . . . . . . . . . Ms Sukhy Johal . . . . . . . . . . . . . . . . . . . . . . . . Tel: (0115) 988 8449
Web: http://www.go-em.gov.uk

**North East Cultural Consortium**
**Culture North East** . . . . . . . . . . . . . . . . . . . . . . . . Government Office for the North East, Wellbar House, Gallowgate, Newcastle-upon-Tyne, NE1 4TD
Chairman . . . . . . . . . . . . . . . . . . . . . . . . . . . . . . . . . Ms Olivia Grant OBE
Executive Director . . . . . . . . . . . . . . . . . . . . . . . . . Ms Pauline Beaumont. . . . . . . . . . . . . . . . . . . . Tel: (0191) 202 3917
E-mail: cne.gone@go-regions.gsi.gov.uk
Web: http://www.culturenortheast.org

**North West Cultural Consortium** . . . . . . . . . . . . . . Giants Basin, Potato Wharf, Castlefield, Manchester, M3 4ND
Chairman . . . . . . . . . . . . . . . . . . . . . . . . . . . . . . . . . Ms Felicity Goodey
Executive Director . . . . . . . . . . . . . . . . . . . . . . . . . Ms Libby Raper . . . . . . . . . . . . . . . . . . . . . . . . Tel: (0161) 817 7421
Web: http://www.culturenorthwest.org.uk

**South East England Cultural Consortium** . . . . . . . . Government Office for the South East, Bridge House, 1 Walnut Tree Close, Guildford, GU1 4GA
Chairman . . . . . . . . . . . . . . . . . . . . . . . . . . . . . . . . . Mr Kalwant Ajimal
Chief Executive . . . . . . . . . . . . . . . . . . . . . . . . . . . Mr Charles Freeman. . . . . . . . . . . . . . . . . . . . . Tel: (01483) 882275
E-mail: info@culturesoutheast.org.uk
Web: http://www.culturesoutheast.org.uk

**South West Cultural Consortium**
**Culture South West** . . . . . . . . . . . . . . . . . . . . . . . . Stirling House, Dix's Field, Exeter, EX1 1QA
Chairman . . . . . . . . . . . . . . . . . . . . . . . . . . . . . . . . . Mr Adrian Vinken
Executive Director . . . . . . . . . . . . . . . . . . . . . . . . . Ms Sue Kay . . . . . . . . . . . . . . . . . . . . . . . . . . . Tel: (01392) 229587
E-mail: culturesw@southwestrda.org.uk
Web: http://www.culturesouthwest.org.uk

# DEPARTMENT FOR CULTURE, MEDIA AND SPORT

*Other Relevant Contacts (Continued)*

**West Midlands Cultural Consortium**
**West Midlands Life** . . . . . . . . . . . . . . . . . . . . . . . . Government Office for the West Midlands, 77 Paradise Circus,
Queensway, Birmingham, B1 2DT
Chairman . . . . . . . . . . . . . . . . . . . . . . . . . . . . . . . Mr Brian Woods-Scawen
Executive Director . . . . . . . . . . . . . . . . . . . . . . . . Mr Steve Trow . . . . . . . . . . . . . . . . . . . . . . . . Tel: (0121) 245 0150
E-mail: jhammond.gowm@go-regions.gsi.gov.uk
Web: http://www.westmidlandslife.org.uk
**Yorkshire Cultural Consortium** . . . . . . . . . . . . . . . . Room 59, County Hall, Bond Street, Wakefield, WF1 2QW
Chairman . . . . . . . . . . . . . . . . . . . . . . . . . . . . . . . Mr Clive Leach CBE
Chief Executive . . . . . . . . . . . . . . . . . . . . . . . . . . Mr Gary Topp . . . . . . . . . . . . . . . . . . . . . . . . Tel: (01924) 306978
E-mail: rchandler@wakefield.gov.uk
Web: http://www.yorkshire-culture.co.uk

## CRAFTS
**Crafts Council** . . . . . . . . . . . . . . . . . . . . . . . . . . . . 44a Pentonville Road, London, N1 9BY
Chairman . . . . . . . . . . . . . . . . . . . . . . . . . . . . . . . Sir Nicholas Goodison
Director . . . . . . . . . . . . . . . . . . . . . . . . . . . . . . . . Ms Louise Taylor . . . . . . . . . . . . . . . . . . . . . . . . Tel: (020) 7278 7700
Web: http://www.craftscouncil.org.uk

## FILMS
**National Film and Television School** . . . . . . . . . . . . Station Road, Beaconsfield, Buckinghamshire, HP9 1LG
Chairman of Governors . . . . . . . . . . . . . . . . . . . . . Mr Michael Kuhn
Director . . . . . . . . . . . . . . . . . . . . . . . . . . . . . . . . Mr Nick Powell . . . . . . . . . . . . . . . . . . . . . . . . Tel: (01494) 671234
E-mail: admin@nftsfilm-tv.ac.uk
Web: http://www.nftsfilm-tv.ac.uk
**National Film Theatre** . . . . . . . . . . . . . . . . . . . . . . Belvedere Road, South Bank, Waterloo, London, SE1 8XT
Chief Executive . . . . . . . . . . . . . . . . . . . . . . . . . . Ms Amanda Neville . . . . . . . . . . . . . . . . . . . . . . . . Tel: (020) 7928 3535
Web: http://www.bfi.org.uk/nft
**UK Film Council** . . . . . . . . . . . . . . . . . . . . . . . . . . 10 Little Portland Street, London, W1W 7JG
Chairman . . . . . . . . . . . . . . . . . . . . . . . . . . . . . . . Sir Alan Parker
Chief Executive . . . . . . . . . . . . . . . . . . . . . . . . . . Mr John Woodward . . . . . . . . . . . . . . . . . . . . . Tel: (020) 7861 7861
Web: http://www.filmcouncil.org.uk

## GAMING
**Gaming Board for Great Britain** . . . . . . . . . . . . . . . Berkshire House, 168-173 High Holborn, London, WC1V 7AA
Chairman . . . . . . . . . . . . . . . . . . . . . . . . . . . . . . . Mr Peter Dean CBE
Chief Executive . . . . . . . . . . . . . . . . . . . . . . . . . . Mr Tom Kavanagh CBE . . . . . . . . . . . . . . . . . . Tel: (020) 7306 6200
E-mail: enqs@gbgb.org.uk
Web: http://www.gbgb.org.uk

## HISTORIC BUILDINGS / SITES
**English Heritage** . . . . . . . . . . . . . . . . . . . . . . . . . . 23 Saville Row, London, W1S 2ET
Chairman . . . . . . . . . . . . . . . . . . . . . . . . . . . . . . . Sir Neil Cossons
Chief Executive . . . . . . . . . . . . . . . . . . . . . . . . . . Dr Simon Thurley . . . . . . . . . . . . . . . . . . . . . . . . Tel: (020) 7973 3000
E-mail: customers@english-heritage.org.uk
Web: http://www.english-heritage.org.uk
**Historic Royal Palaces** . . . . . . . . . . . . . . . . . . . . . Hampton Court Palace, East Molesley, Surrey, KT8 9AU
Chairman . . . . . . . . . . . . . . . . . . . . . . . . . . . . . . . Sir Nigel Mobbs
Chief Executive . . . . . . . . . . . . . . . . . . . . . . . . . . Mr Michael Day . . . . . . . . . . . . . . . . . . . . . . . . Tel: (020) 8781 9750
Web: http://www.hrp.org.uk
**National Heritage Memorial Fund** . . . . . . . . . . . . . 7 Holbein Place, London, SW1W 8NR
Chairman . . . . . . . . . . . . . . . . . . . . . . . . . . . . . . . Ms Liz Forgan OBE
Director . . . . . . . . . . . . . . . . . . . . . . . . . . . . . . . . Mrs Carole Souter . . . . . . . . . . . . . . . . . . . . . . . . Tel: (020) 7591 6000
E-mail: enquiries@hlf.org.uk
Web: http://www.hlf.org.uk

# DEPARTMENT FOR CULTURE, MEDIA AND SPORT

*Other Relevant Contacts (Continued)*

## HORSERACE BETTING
**Horserace Totalisator Board**.................... Tote House, 74 Upper Richmond Road, London, SW15 2SU
    Chairman................................... Mr Peter Jones
    Chief Executive ............................ Mr John Heaton....................... Tel: (020) 8874 6411
         E-mail: htb@tote.co.uk
         Web: http://www.tote.co.uk

## LIBRARIES
**Advisory Council on Libraries**.................. 5th Floor, 2-4 Cockspur Street, London, SW1Y 5DH
    Chairman................................... Mr Bill Macnaught
    Secretary ................................. Mr Dempster Marples................. Tel: (020) 7211 6287
         E-mail: dempster.marples@culture.gsi.uk
**British Library** ............................. 96 Euston Road, London, NW1 2DB
    Chairman................................... Lord Eatwell
    Chief Executive ........................... Mrs Lynn Brindley.................... Tel: (020) 7412 7000
         Web: http://www.bl.uk

*(See also Resource, under Museums and Galleries below)*

## LOTTERY
**Big Lottery Fund** ............................ 1 Plough Place, Fetter Lane, London, EC4A 1DE
    Chairman................................... Sir Clive Booth
    Chief Executive ........................... Mr Stephen Dunmore.................. Tel: (020) 7747 5299
         Web: http://www.biglotteryfund.org.uk
**Millennium Commission**........................ Portland House, Stag Place, London, SW1E 5EZ
    Chairman................................... Rt Hon Tessa Jowell MP
         *(Secretary of State for Culture, Media and Sport)*
    Director................................... Mr Michael O'Connor CBE ............ Tel: (020) 7880 2001
         E-mail: info@millennium.gov.uk
         Web: http://www.millennium.gov.uk
**National Lottery Commission** .................. 2nd Floor, 101 Wigmore Street, London, W1U 1QU
    Chairman................................... Ms Moira Black
    Chief Executive ........................... Mr Mark Harris ..................... Tel: (020) 7016 3400
         Web: http://www.natlotcomm.gov.uk

## MUSEUMS AND GALLERIES
**British Museum**.............................. Great Russell Street, London, WC1B 3DG
    Chairman of Trustees ...................... Sir John Boyd KCMG
    Director................................... Mr Neil MacGregor .................. Tel: (020) 7323 8000
         E-mail: information@thebritishmuseum.ac.uk
         Web: http://www.thebritishmuseum.ac.uk
**Geffrye Museum** ............................. Kingsland Road, London, E2 8EA
    Chairman of Trustees ...................... Mr Richard Hunting
    Director................................... Mr David Dewing .................... Tel: (020) 7739 9893
         E-mail: info@geffrye-museum.org.uk
         Web: http://www.geffrye-museum.org.uk
**Horniman Museum and Gardens**................. 100 London Road, Forest Hill, London, SE23 3PQ
    Chairman of Trustees ...................... Mr Donald Kirkham CBE
    Director................................... Ms Janet Vitmayer ................. Tel: (020) 8699 1872
         E-mail: enquiry@horniman.demon.co.uk
         Web: http://www.horniman.ac.uk
**Imperial War Museum** ........................ Lambeth Road, London, SE1 6HZ
    Chairman of Trustees ...................... Admiral Sir Jock Slater GCB LVO
    Director-General .......................... Mr Robert Crawford CBE ............. Tel: (020) 7416 5000
         E-mail: mail@iwm.org.uk
         Web: http://www.iwm.org.uk
**Museum of London**........................... 150 London Wall, London, EC2Y 5HN
    Chairman of Trustees ...................... Mr Rupert Hambro
    Director................................... Professor Jack Lohman................ Tel: (0870) 444 3852
         E-mail: info@museumoflondon.org.uk
         Web: http://www.museumoflondon.org.uk

# DEPARTMENT FOR CULTURE, MEDIA AND SPORT

*Other Relevant Contacts (Continued)*

**Museum of Science and Industry, Manchester** . . . . . Liverpool Road, Castlefield, Manchester, M3 4FP
Chairman of Trustees . . . . . . . . . . . . . . . . . . . . . . . . Professor Laurie Wood
Director *(Acting)* . . . . . . . . . . . . . . . . . . . . . . . . . Mr Bob Scott . . . . . . . . . . . . . . . . . . . . . . . . . Tel: (0161) 832 2244
Web: http://www.msim.org.uk

**National Gallery** . . . . . . . . . . . . . . . . . . . . . . . . . . Trafalgar Square, London, WC2N 5DN
Chairman of Trustees . . . . . . . . . . . . . . . . . . . . . . . . Mr Peter Scott QC
Director . . . . . . . . . . . . . . . . . . . . . . . . . . . . . . . . Mr Charles Saumarez Smith . . . . . . . . . . . . . . . Tel: (020) 7747 2885
E-mail: information@ng-london.org.uk
Web: http://www.nationalgallery.org.uk

**National Maritime Museum** . . . . . . . . . . . . . . . . . . . Park Row, Greenwich, London, SE10 9NF
Chairman of Trustees . . . . . . . . . . . . . . . . . . . . . . . . Sir David Hardy
Director . . . . . . . . . . . . . . . . . . . . . . . . . . . . . . . . Mr Roy Clare . . . . . . . . . . . . . . . . . . . . . . . . . Tel: (020) 8858 4422
Web: http://www.nmm.ac.uk

**National Museum of Science and Industry** . . . . . . . . Exhibition Road, South Kensington, London, SW7 2DD
Chairman of Trustees . . . . . . . . . . . . . . . . . . . . . . . . Rt Hon Lord Waldegrave
Director . . . . . . . . . . . . . . . . . . . . . . . . . . . . . . . . Dr Lindsay Sharp . . . . . . . . . . . . . . . . . . . . . . Tel: (0870) 870 4868
E-mail: sciencemuseum@nmsi.ac.uk
Web: http://www.sciencemuseum.org.uk

**National Museums Liverpool** . . . . . . . . . . . . . . . . . . 127 Dale Street, Liverpool, L69 3LA
Chairman of Trustees . . . . . . . . . . . . . . . . . . . . . . . . Mr David McDonnell
Director . . . . . . . . . . . . . . . . . . . . . . . . . . . . . . . . Dr David Flemming OBE . . . . . . . . . . . . . . . . . Tel: (0151) 207 0001
E-mail: stephen.guy@nmgm.org
Web: http://www.nmgm.org.uk

**National Portrait Gallery** . . . . . . . . . . . . . . . . . . . . St Martin's Place, London, WC2H 0HE
Chairman of Trustees . . . . . . . . . . . . . . . . . . . . . . . . Sir David Scholey
Director . . . . . . . . . . . . . . . . . . . . . . . . . . . . . . . . Mr Sandy Nairne . . . . . . . . . . . . . . . . . . . . . . Tel: (020) 7306 0055
Web: http://www.npg.org.uk

**Natural History Museum** . . . . . . . . . . . . . . . . . . . . Cromwell Road, South Kensington, London, SW7 5BD
Chairman . . . . . . . . . . . . . . . . . . . . . . . . . . . . . . . Professor Sir Keith O'Nions
Director . . . . . . . . . . . . . . . . . . . . . . . . . . . . . . . . Sir Neil Chalmers . . . . . . . . . . . . . . . . . . . . . Tel: (020) 7942 5000
E-mail: press@nhm.ac.uk
Web: http://www.nhm.ac.uk

**Resource: The Council for Museums, Archives
and Libraries** . . . . . . . . . . . . . . . . . . . . . . . . . . . . 16 Queen Anne's Gate, London, SW1H 9AA
Chairman *(Acting)* . . . . . . . . . . . . . . . . . . . . . . . . . Mr Mark Wood
Chief Executive . . . . . . . . . . . . . . . . . . . . . . . . . . . Mr Chris Batt . . . . . . . . . . . . . . . . . . . . . . . . . Tel: (020) 7273 1444
Web: http://www.resource.gov.uk

**Royal Armouries** . . . . . . . . . . . . . . . . . . . . . . . . . . Armouries Drive, Leeds, LS10 1LT
Chairman of Trustees . . . . . . . . . . . . . . . . . . . . . . . . Ms Ann Green
Master of the Armouries . . . . . . . . . . . . . . . . . . . . . . Mr Paul Evans . . . . . . . . . . . . . . . . . . . . . . . . Tel: (0113) 220 1916
E-mail: enquiries@armouries.org.uk
Web: http://www.armouries.org.uk

**Sir John Soane's Museum** . . . . . . . . . . . . . . . . . . . . 13 Lincoln's Inn Fields, London, WC2A 3BP
Chairman of Trustees . . . . . . . . . . . . . . . . . . . . . . . . Mr Richard Griffiths
Curator . . . . . . . . . . . . . . . . . . . . . . . . . . . . . . . . . Mrs Margaret Richardson . . . . . . . . . . . . . . . . . Tel: (020) 7405 2107
Web: http://www.soane.org

**Tate** . . . . . . . . . . . . . . . . . . . . . . . . . . . . . . . . . . Millbank, London, SW1P 4RG
Chairman of Trustees . . . . . . . . . . . . . . . . . . . . . . . . Mr Paul Myners
Director of Tate . . . . . . . . . . . . . . . . . . . . . . . . . . . Sir Nicholas Serota . . . . . . . . . . . . . . . . . . . . . Tel: (020) 7887 8000
E-mail: information@tate.org.uk
Web: http://www.tate.org.uk

**Victoria and Albert Museum** . . . . . . . . . . . . . . . . . Cromwell Road, South Kensington, London, SW7 2RL
Chairman of Trustees . . . . . . . . . . . . . . . . . . . . . . . . Mrs Paula Ridley OBE
Director . . . . . . . . . . . . . . . . . . . . . . . . . . . . . . . . Mr Mark Jones . . . . . . . . . . . . . . . . . . . . . . . . Tel: (020) 7942 2000
E-mail: vanda@vam.ac.uk
Web: http://www.vam.ac.uk

**Wallace Collection** . . . . . . . . . . . . . . . . . . . . . . . . Hertford House, Manchester Square, London, W1U 3BN
Chairman of Trustees . . . . . . . . . . . . . . . . . . . . . . . . Mr John Lewis
Director . . . . . . . . . . . . . . . . . . . . . . . . . . . . . . . . Miss Rosalind Saville CBE FSA . . . . . . . . . . . . . Tel: (020) 7563 9500
E-mail: enquiries@wallace-collection.org.uk
Web: http://www.the-wallace-collection.org.uk

# DEPARTMENT FOR CULTURE, MEDIA AND SPORT

*Other Relevant Contacts (Continued)*

## PUBLIC LENDING RIGHT
**Advisory Committee for the Public Lending Right** . . Richard House, Sorbonne Close, Stockton-on-Tees, Cleveland, TS17 6DA
    Chairman . . . . . . . . . . . . . . . . . . . . . . . . . . . . . . . . Mr Simon Brett
    Registrar . . . . . . . . . . . . . . . . . . . . . . . . . . . . . . . . Dr James Parker OBE . . . . . . . . . . . . . . . . . . . . Tel: (01642) 604699
            E-mail: corporateservices@plr.uk.com
            Web: http://www.plr.uk.com

## ROYAL PARKS
**Royal Parks** *(Executive Agency)* . . . . . . . . . . . . . . . . . The Old Police House, Hyde Park, London, W2 2UH
    Chief Executive . . . . . . . . . . . . . . . . . . . . . . . . . . . . Mr William Weston . . . . . . . . . . . . . . . . . . . . . Tel: (020) 7298 2000
            E-mail: hq@royalparks.gsi.gov.uk
            Web: http://www.royalparks.gsi.gov.uk

## SPOILATION
**Spoilation Advisory Panel** . . . . . . . . . . . . . . . . . . . . . 2-4 Cockspur Street, London, SW1Y 5DH
    Chairman . . . . . . . . . . . . . . . . . . . . . . . . . . . . . . . . Rt Hon Sir David Hirst
    Secretary . . . . . . . . . . . . . . . . . . . . . . . . . . . . . . . . Ms Hillary Bauer . . . . . . . . . . . . . . . . . . . . . . Tel: (020) 7211 6157
            E-mail: spoilationadvisorypanel@culture.gsi.gov.uk

## SPORT
**Football Foundation** . . . . . . . . . . . . . . . . . . . . . . . . . 25 Soho Square, London, W1D 4FF
    Chairman . . . . . . . . . . . . . . . . . . . . . . . . . . . . . . . . Mr Dave Richards
    Chief Executive . . . . . . . . . . . . . . . . . . . . . . . . . . . . Mr Peter Lee . . . . . . . . . . . . . . . . . . . . . . . . . Tel: (020) 7534 4210
            E-mail: enquiries@footballfoundation.org.uk
            Web: http://www.footballfoundation.org.uk
**Football Licensing Authority** . . . . . . . . . . . . . . . . . . . 27 Harcourt House, 19 Cavendish Square, London, W1G 0PL
    Chairman . . . . . . . . . . . . . . . . . . . . . . . . . . . . . . . . Mr Anthony Speed
    Chief Executive . . . . . . . . . . . . . . . . . . . . . . . . . . . . Mr John de Quidt . . . . . . . . . . . . . . . . . . . . . Tel: (020) 7491 7191
            Web: http://www.flaweb.org.uk/fla
**Independent Football Commission** . . . . . . . . . . . . . . . University of Teesside, Middlesbrough, TS1 3BA
    Chairman . . . . . . . . . . . . . . . . . . . . . . . . . . . . . . . . Professor Derek Fraser
    Company Secretary . . . . . . . . . . . . . . . . . . . . . . . . . . Dr Chris Gamble . . . . . . . . . . . . . . . . . . . . . . Tel: (01642) 342750
            E-mail: contact@theifc.co.uk
            Web: http://www.theifc.co.uk
**Sport England** . . . . . . . . . . . . . . . . . . . . . . . . . . . . . 3rd Floor, Victoria House, Bloomsbury Square, London, WC1B 4SE
    Chairman . . . . . . . . . . . . . . . . . . . . . . . . . . . . . . . . Mr Patrick Carter
    Chief Executive . . . . . . . . . . . . . . . . . . . . . . . . . . . . Mr Roger Draper . . . . . . . . . . . . . . . . . . . . . . Tel: (020) 7273 1500
            E-mail: info@sportengland.org
            Web: http://www.sportengland.org
**UK Sport** . . . . . . . . . . . . . . . . . . . . . . . . . . . . . . . . . 40 Bernard Street, London, WC1N 1ST
    Chairman . . . . . . . . . . . . . . . . . . . . . . . . . . . . . . . . Ms Sue Campbell
    Chief Executive . . . . . . . . . . . . . . . . . . . . . . . . . . . . Mr Richard Callicott . . . . . . . . . . . . . . . . . . . Tel: (020) 7211 5100
            E-mail: info@uksport.gov.uk
            Web: http://www.uksport.gov.uk

## THEATRES
**National Theatre** . . . . . . . . . . . . . . . . . . . . . . . . . . . Upper Ground, London, SE1 9PX
    Artistic Director . . . . . . . . . . . . . . . . . . . . . . . . . . . . Mr Nicholas Hytner . . . . . . . . . . . . . . . . . . . . Tel: (020) 7452 3333
            Web: http://www.nationaltheatre.org.uk
**Theatres Trust** . . . . . . . . . . . . . . . . . . . . . . . . . . . . . 22 Charing Cross Road, London, WC2H 0QL
    Chairman . . . . . . . . . . . . . . . . . . . . . . . . . . . . . . . . Mr Rupert Rhymes OBE
    Director . . . . . . . . . . . . . . . . . . . . . . . . . . . . . . . . . Mr Peter Longman . . . . . . . . . . . . . . . . . . . . . Tel: (020) 7836 8591
            Web: http://www.theatrestrust.org.uk

## TOURISM
**Visit Britain** . . . . . . . . . . . . . . . . . . . . . . . . . . . . . . Thames Tower, Black's Road, Hammersmith, London, W6 9EL
    Chairman . . . . . . . . . . . . . . . . . . . . . . . . . . . . . . . . Sir Michael Lickiss
    Chief Executive . . . . . . . . . . . . . . . . . . . . . . . . . . . . Mr Tom Wright . . . . . . . . . . . . . . . . . . . . . . . Tel: (020) 8846 9000
            E-mail: enquirydesk@bta.org.uk
            Web: http://www.visitbritain.com

## TREASURE VALUATION
**Treasure Valuation Committee** . . . . . . . . . . . . . . . . . c/o Department for Culture, Media and Sport, 2-4 Cockspur Street,
            London, SW1Y 5DH
    Chairman . . . . . . . . . . . . . . . . . . . . . . . . . . . . . . . . Professor Norman Palmer
    Secretary . . . . . . . . . . . . . . . . . . . . . . . . . . . . . . . . Ms Caiti Marsh . . . . . . . . . . . . . . . . . . . . . . . Tel: (020) 7211 6181
            E-mail: caiti.marsh@culture.gsi.uk
            Web: http://www.culture.gov.uk

## WRECKS
**Advisory Committee on Historic Wreck Sites** . . . . . . c/o English Heritage Secretariat, 23 Saville Row, London W1S 2ETB
    Chairman . . . . . . . . . . . . . . . . . . . . . . . . . . . . . . . . Mr Tom Hassall OBE
    Secretary . . . . . . . . . . . . . . . . . . . . . . . . . . . . . . . . Ms Sue Mellish . . . . . . . . . . . . . . . . . . . . . . . Tel: (020) 7973 3000

# sports coach UK - improving the future of coaching

**sports coach UK (scUK)** works with coaches and sporting organisations to develop and improve British sport. It is a registered charity, receiving funding from Sport England and UK Sport as well as a covenant from its own trading subsidiary Coachwise.

2004 is an Olympic and Paralympic year and going on the figures from Sydney 2000, four fifths* of the UK population will invite sport into their living rooms, welcome stories on the training preparations of Britain's hopefuls and support our athletes in their quest for success. During August and September we are given an insight into the lives of those at the highest level in sport.
*United Kingdom's Sporting Preferences, April 2001 –
UK Sport publication*

Coaches figure highly in the general appreciation of performance level sport. Coaching figures Clive Woodward, Alex Ferguson, Charles van Commenée, Amanda Kirby and Jürgen Grobler, for example, occupy well-recognised roles in their respective sports. But sports coaching goes beyond elite level sport. Indeed, coaching is integral to sport at every level.

The profile that coaching has received at Government level through the *Cunningham Review* and the DCMS Coaching Task Force has been carried forward by **scUK**. The commitment of £28 million by DCMS between March 2003 and March 2006 has given **scUK** clear targets towards delivering a coaching workforce that is *fit for purpose*.

**scUK** has taken a lead on developing the role of coaching in sport in the UK. Programmes such as *Paralympians into Coaching* and *Women into High Performance Coaching* reflect **scUK**'s aim to make coaching an inclusive opportunity for all. Addressing the shortage of voluntary and professional coaches, establishing accredited coaching qualifications, and building on the national strategy for PE, school sport and club links (PESSCL) are areas that are receiving attention and action from **scUK**. The considered outcomes of these efforts are closely linked to the *Game Plan* vision of increasing participation and enhancing international success.

The first of four workstrands to be progressed by **scUK** is the development of the UK Coaching Certificate (UKCC). The concept of developing existing coach education systems by endorsing sport-specific qualifications has been positively and widely received.

Extensive consultation is on-going with NGBs and other partners to establish an endorsement that is wholly accepted and bought into by the industry. Thirty one sports have signed up to the UKCC; with the first 6 sports being the *trailblazers*, athletics, cricket, rowing, rugby union, swimming and triathlon. It is expected that 2006 will bring the advent of the UKCC within these six sports, to be quickly followed by the remaining 25.

The need for recruitment, education, deployment and management of coaches at the local level was recognised in the Coaching Task Force. In implementing the recommendations of this report, **scUK** has committed to employing 45 Coach Development Officers (CDOs) by April 2005. In line with the targets set by the Coaching Task Force, the first 30 CDOs commenced in their new posts on 1 April 2004. They will improve access to high-quality, initial and post-qualification coach education and development opportunities for coaches who have been identified locally via County Sports Partnerships as best servicing demand from local sporting communities. The final 15 CDOs will be employed from April 2005.

The Community Sports Coach (CSC) scheme aims to establish 3,000 paid, qualified CSCs working at the local level to increase the number and range of coaching opportunities according to strategic and local needs by 2006. **scUK** is working closely with Sport England who is leading on this area.

**scUK** is developing a coaching system that supports the commitments of those at high level sport, and makes sport more accessible to those who may otherwise only watch on in admiration from the sidelines.

With the UK looking to establish itself as a world leader in sport at all levels, **scUK** is committed to contributing to this aim.

For more information on coaching in the UK contact Melanie Parker, Head of Communications at **sports coach UK**:

www.sportscoachuk.org
Tel: 0113 274 4802
coaching@sportscoachuk.org

**sports coach UK** *will ensure that it has professional and ethical values and that all its practices are inclusive and equitable.*

## CLAY PIGEON SHOOTING – A SPORT FOR ALL

# CLAY PIGEON SHOOTING ASSOCIATION

Edmonton House, Bisley Camp, Brookwood, Woking, Surrey, GU24 0NP

*Telephone* (01483) 485400
*E-mail* info@cpsa.co.uk
*Web* http://www.cpsa.co.uk

*Contact:* Zoë Kolesar – *Communications Manager*

Shooting's recent popularity with celebrities and high profile figures of both sexes is not surprising. It is arguably the one sport that offers something for all. While it is the big names that grab the headlines, from Madonna to Kiri Te Kiwana, and Vinnie Jones to the Royals, it is perhaps those who don't make the headlines on a regular basis who deserve the attention.

It was 27-year-old Richard Faulds who took Olympic Gold at Double Trap in Sydney, a tremendously demanding form of clay target shooting. And again in the same discipline 17-year-old Sussex schoolgirl Charlotte Kerwood won the women's gold medal with a thrilling display at the 2002 Commonwealth Games. Every year the number achievers, within shooting, grows and this year we look forward to seeing five of our top shooters at the Athens 2004 Olympics and look forward to them bringing the gold medals home. Meanwhile Lewis Balmer of Northern Ireland, who lost his legs in a dreadful accident, is one of many disabled shooters who turn in magnificent performances at clays. And let's not forget the veterans…the CPSA's membership magazine PULL! Features may veterans including 90-year-old war veteran Verden Bettinson who is still shooting clays regularly at his local club.

Shooting grounds have now become much more sophisticated with facilities for disabled.

It really is a sport for all. Age, sex and size are irrelevant. An increasing number of married couples and partners are also enjoying the sport together. Indeed whole families can enjoy a great day out for less than the cost of a Premiership football match. Youngsters in particular have a tendency to quickly outshine their older mentors.

The sport teaches the benefits of self-discipline and concentration while at the same time offers the rewards of performance in a warm and friendly social environment. It is not a loner's game. Little wonder that it is so popular.

Moreover shotgun certificate holders are the most law-abiding sector of our community - they have to be in order to retain possession their shotgun certificates. They, more than any other, would like to see gun crime tackled properly – banning and a tightening of controls is not the answer, as the pistol ban has proven. The government has pledged to leave our gun laws alone, which has to be good news for anyone who likes to call "PULL!" at a weekend, not to mention those who like to bring home the medals for Britain.

## SPORT AND PLAY INDUSTRIES

## THEATRE TRUST

# THE SPORTS INDUSTRIES FEDERATION

Federation House, Stoneleigh Park,
Warwickshire, CV8 2RF

*Telephone* (024) 7641 4999
*Facsimile* (024) 7641 4990
*Web* http://www.sports-life.com

*Contact:* Christopher Tuffley LVO – *Director General*

The Sports Industries Federation is Europe's largest sports trade body, representing over 20 autonomous trade associations across many sectors of the sporting goods and play industries.

The Federation plays a strategic role in the support, promotion and protection of the industry with activities ranging from the promotion of free and fair trade to lobbying on issues such as increasing participation in sport.

The Sports Industries Federation

# AGE EXCHANGE THEATRE TRUST

Age Exchange Reminiscence Centre
11 Blackheath Village
London, SE3 9LA

*Telephone* (020) 8318 9105 / 3504
*Facsimile* (020) 8318 0060
*E-mail* administrator@age-exchange.org.uk
*Web:* http://www.age-exchange.org.uk

*Contact* Suzanne Lockett – *Administrator*

Age Exchange houses a museum, exhibition space, library and training facilities. We produce publications, exhibitions and theatre. We offer a variety of training courses for carers wishing to use reminiscence.

*Registered Charity No:* 326899

# MINISTRY OF DEFENCE

Old War Office, London, SW1A 2EU
Tel: (020) 7218 9000
Ensleigh, Bath, BA1 5AB
Tel: (01225) 884884
Web: http://www.mod.uk

## MINISTERS

**Secretary of State for Defence** . . . . . . . . . . . . . . . . . . . . .Rt Hon Geoff Hoon MP
*Private Secretary* . . . . . . . . . . . . . . . . . . . . . . . . . . . . . . . . .Mr Christopher Baker . . . . . . . . . . . . . . . . . . . . .Tel: (020) 7218 2111
*Special Advisers* . . . . . . . . . . . . . . . . . . . . . . . . . . . . . . . . .Mr Michael Dugher . . . . . . . . . . . . . . . . . . . . . . . .Tel: (020) 7218 2911
. . . . . . . . . . . . . . . . . . . . . . . . . . . . . . . . . . . . . . . . . . . . . . . .Mr James Connal . . . . . . . . . . . . . . . . . . . . . . . . . .Tel: (020) 7218 2911

**Minister of State** *(Minister for the Armed Forces)* . . . . . . . . . .Rt Hon Adam Ingram MP
*Private Secretary* . . . . . . . . . . . . . . . . . . . . . . . . . . . . . . . . .Mr Geoff Dean . . . . . . . . . . . . . . . . . . . . . . . . . . . .Tel: (020) 7218 6385

**Parliamentary Secretary** *(Veterans Affairs)* . . . . . . . . . . . . .Mr Ivor Caplin MP
*Private Secretary* . . . . . . . . . . . . . . . . . . . . . . . . . . . . . . . . .Mr Jeremy Williams . . . . . . . . . . . . . . . . . . . . . . . .Tel: (020) 7218 2452

**Parliamentary Secretary** *(Defence Procurement)* . . . . . . . . . .Lord Bach
*Private Secretary* . . . . . . . . . . . . . . . . . . . . . . . . . . . . . . . . .Mr Ben Palmer . . . . . . . . . . . . . . . . . . . . . . . . . . . .Tel: (020) 7218 6621

## CIVIL SERVICE/DEFENCE STAFF

**Permanent Secretary** . . . . . . . . . . . . . . . . . . . . . . . . . . . . . .Sir Kevin Tebbit
*Private Secretary* . . . . . . . . . . . . . . . . . . . . . . . . . . . . . . . . .Mr D Wilson . . . . . . . . . . . . . . . . . . . . . . . . . . . . . .Tel: (020) 7218 2839

**Second Permanent Secretary** . . . . . . . . . . . . . . . . . . . . . . . .Mr Ian Andrews . . . . . . . . . . . . . . . . . . . . . . . . . . . .Tel: (020) 7218 6014

**Chief of the Defence Staff** . . . . . . . . . . . . . . . . . . . . . . . . . .General Sir Michael Walker . . . . . . . . . . . . . . . . . .Tel: (020) 7218 3353
*Principal Staff Officer* . . . . . . . . . . . . . . . . . . . . . . . . . . . . . .Colonel George Zambellas . . . . . . . . . . . . . . . . . . .Tel: (020) 7218 2116

**Vice-Chief of the Defence Staff** . . . . . . . . . . . . . . . . . . . . . .Air Chief Marshal Sir
. . . . . . . . . . . . . . . . . . . . . . . . . . . . . . . . . . . . . . . . . . . . . . . .Anthony Bagnall KCB OBE . . . . . . . . . . . . . . . . . .Tel: (020) 7218 7657

**Chief of the Air Staff** . . . . . . . . . . . . . . . . . . . . . . . . . . . . . .Air Chief Marshal
. . . . . . . . . . . . . . . . . . . . . . . . . . . . . . . . . . . . . . . . . . . . . . . .Sir Jock Stirrup KCB AFC ADC . . . . . . . . . . . . . . .Tel: (020) 7218 6314

**Chief of the General Staff** . . . . . . . . . . . . . . . . . . . . . . . . . . .General Sir Mike Jackson . . . . . . . . . . . . . . . . . . . .Tel: (020) 7218 7873

**Chief of the Naval Staff and First Sea Lord** . . . . . . . . . . . .Admiral Sir Alan West KCB DSC . . . . . . . . . . . . . .Tel: (020) 7218 6193 / 2214

**Chief of Defence Procurement** . . . . . . . . . . . . . . . . . . . . . . .Sir Peter Spencer KCB ADC . . . . . . . . . . . . . . . . . .Tel: (0117) 913 0002

**Chief Scientific Adviser** . . . . . . . . . . . . . . . . . . . . . . . . . . . .Professor Sir Keith O'Nions . . . . . . . . . . . . . . . . .Tel: (020) 7218 3560

**Secretariat, Chief of Staffs Committee** . . . . . . . . . . . . . . . .Captain A Moll . . . . . . . . . . . . . . . . . . . . . . . . . . . .Tel: (020) 7218 2321

# MINISTRY OF DEFENCE

## SUBJECT RESPONSIBILITIES AND CONTACTS

*Note: Area telephone codes relate to bases as follows:*

| Area Code | Base |
|---|---|
| Tel: (0141) | *Glasgow* |
| Tel: (01189) | *Aldermaston* |
| Tel: (01225) | *Bath and Corsham* |
| Tel: (01252) | *Clayton Barracks and Wigram House, Aldershot* |
| Tel: (01258) | *Blandford Camp* |
| Tel: (01264) | *Andover* |
| Tel: (01276) | *Sandhurst* |
| Tel: (01400) | *RAF Cranwell, Sleaford* |
| Tel: (01452) | *RAF Innsworth* |
| Tel: (01480) | *RAF Brampton and RAF Wyton, Huntingdon* |
| Tel: (01752) | *Devonport* |
| Tel: (01793) | *Shrivenham* |
| Tel: (01923) | *Northwood* |
| Tel: (01929) | *Bovingdon Camp, Wareham* |
| Tel: (01935) | *Yeovil* |
| Tel: (01980) | *Larkhill, Salisbury and Trenchard Lines, Upavon, Pewsey* |
| Tel: (01985) | *Warminster* |
| Tel: (020) 8838 | *RAF Bentley Priory, Stanmore* |
| Tel: (023) 9272 | *HM Naval Base, Portsmouth* |

### Adjutant-General's Department
*Trenchard Lines, Upavon, Pewsey, Wiltshire, SN9 6BE*

| | | |
|---|---|---|
| Adjutant-General | Lieutenant-General Alistair Irwin KCB CBE | Tel: (01980) 615406 |
| Deputy Adjutant-General | Major-General A P N Currie OBE | Tel: (01980) 615404 |
| Command Secretary | Ms Elizabeth McLoughlin | Tel: (01980) 615412 |

### Air Force

| | | |
|---|---|---|
| Chief of the Air Staff | Air Chief Marshal Sir Jock Stirrup KCB AFC ADC | Tel: (020) 7218 6314 |
| Assistant Chief of the Air Staff | Air Vice-Marshal Philip Sturley CBE MBE | Tel: (020) 7218 6314 |
| Air Space Policy | | |
| Director, Air Space Policy | Air Vice-Marshal J D Arscott | Tel: (020) 7832 6503 |
| Chaplain General | Venerable R D Hesketh QHC | Tel: (01452) 712612 ext 5031 |

Community Relations, British-American
*4 Gloucester Road, RAF Brampton, Huntingdon, PE18 8QL*

| | | |
|---|---|---|
| Co-ordinator, British-American Relations | Air Marshal (Retd) Sir John Kemball KCB CBE | Tel: (01480) 52151 Ext 7636 / 7101 |

Defence Aviation Safety Centre
*Building 268, RAF Bentley Priory, Stanmore, Middlesex, HA7 3HH*

| | | |
|---|---|---|
| Director | Air Commodore A T Hudson | Tel: (020) 838 7602 |
| **Equipment Support** | | |
| Director General Equipment Support (Air) | Air Vice-Marshal M P Liddell | Tel: (01480) 52151 ext 2915 |
| History, RAF | Mr Sebastian Cox | Tel: (020) 8838 7828 |
| **Judge Advocate** | | |
| Vice-Judge Advocate General of the Forces | Mr Moelwyn Hughes | Tel: (020) 7218 8089 |
| Legal Services | Air Vice-Marshal R A Charles LLV | Tel: (01452) 712612 ext 5264 |

Personnel and Training Headquarters
*RAF Innsworth, Gloucestershire, GL3 1EZ* .... Web: http://www.raf.mod.uk/ptc/units.html

| | | |
|---|---|---|
| Air Officer Commanding-in-Chief and Air Member for Personnel | Air Marshal Sir Christopher Colville | Tel: (01452) 712612 ext 5005 |
| Chief of Staff, Air Member for Personnel | Air Vice-Marshal R V Morris CBE | Tel: (01452) 712612 ext 5012 |

RAF College
*RAF Cranwell, Sleaford, Lincolnshire, NG34 8HB*

| | | |
|---|---|---|
| Commandant | Air Vice-Marshal Thomas Rimmer | Tel: (01400) 261201 |
| **Resources and Plans** | | |
| Director, Resources and Plans (Air) | Air Commodore K J Leeson | Tel: (020) 7218 2899 |
| **Sport** | | |
| Director, Sports Board (RAF) | Mr Robert Honey | Tel: (01452) 712612 ext 5442 |

# MINISTRY OF DEFENCE

*Air Force (Continued)*
    Staff
        Director, Air Staff ............................. Air Commodore H Moran OBE .............. Tel: (020) 7218 6259
        Secretariat, Air Staff ........................ Mr R Howard ........................ Tel: (020) 7218 6930
    Strike Command Headquarters
    *RAF High Wycombe, Buckinghamshire, HP14 4UE* ....... Web: http://www.raf.mod.uk
        Air Officer Commanding-in-Chief .............. Air Chief Marshal Sir John Day ............. Tel: (01494) 461461

## Air Traffic
    Chief Executive, National Air Traffic Services .......... Mr Richard Everitt .................... Tel: (01489) 615708
    Chairman, .................................... Dr Chris Gibson-Smith ................. Tel: (020) 7309 8666

## Army
    Chief of the General Staff ...................... General Sir Mike Jackson ................. Tel: (020) 7218 7873
    Assistant Chief of the General Staff ................. Major-General F R Dannatt .............. Tel: (020) 7218 7191
    Adjutant-General
    *Bray House, Worthy Down, Winchester, Hampshire, SO21 2RG*
        Adjutant General, Training Group ................. Lieutenant-General A Irwin ............... Tel: (01980) 615406
    Artillery *(see below under Royal Artillery)*
    Chaplaincy
    *Trenchard Lines, Upavon, Pewsey, Wiltshire, SN9 6BE*
        Chaplain General ........................... Rev Dr Victor Dobbin .................... Tel: (01980) 615801
    Education and Training Services
    *Trenchard Lines, Upavon, Wiltshire, SN5 6BE*
        Director, Education and Training Services .......... Brigadier P S Purves ..................... Tel: (01980) 618730
    Engineering
    *Cloutman Block, Gibraltar Barracks, Blackwater, Camberley, GU7 9LP*
        Engineer-in-Chief ......................... Brigadier D Innes ....................... Tel: (01252) 863534
        Engineering Services ......................... *enquiries* ............................ Tel: (01722) 433165
    Equipment Support (Land)
    *Portway, Monxton Road, Andover, Hampshire, SP11 8HT*
        Director-General, Equipment Support (Army) ........ Major-General D Judd .................... Tel: (01264) 382431
        Director, Armoured Systems Support .............. Brigadier B W J C Campbell ............. Tel: (01264) 382740
        Director, Electronic Systems Support .............. Brigadier S G Middleton ............... Tel: (01264) 382363
        Director, Support Systems ..................... Brigadier B W J C Steer ................. Tel: (01264) 382564
        Director, Technical ......................... Brigadier Richard Rickard ............... Tel: (01264) 382435
    Gurkhas *(see separate entry below)*
    Infantry
    *Warminster, Wiltshire, BA12 0DJ*
        Director, Infantry .......................... Brigadier M J Strudwick CBE .............. Tel: (01985) 214000 ext 2329
    Information
        Director, Information (Army) .................. Brigadier M S J Griffin .................. Tel: (020) 7340 92375
    Judge Advocate
        Judge Advocate General of the Forces ............. *Vacant* ............................... Tel: (020) 7218 8089
    Legal Services
        Director, Army Legal Services .................. Major-General G Risius ................. Tel: (01980) 615966
    Manning
        Director, Manning (Army) ..................... Brigadier  K H Cima ................... Tel: (01980) 615490
    Medical
        Director-General, Army Medical Services .......... Major-General D S Jolliffe ................ Tel: (0117) 913 0261
    Personal Services
        Head, Personal Services (Army) ................ Brigadier N Cottam .................... Tel: (01980) 615939
    Personnel
        Director, Staff and Personnel Support ............ Brigadier R Leighton .................. Tel: (01962) 887617
    Provost Marshal (Army) ....................... Brigadier I W Fulton .................. Tel: (01980) 615653
    Resources and Plans
        Director, Resources and Plans (Army) ............ Brigadier A J N Graham ................. Tel: (020) 7218 7568
    Royal Armoured Corps
    *Bovington Camp, Wareham, Dorset, BH20 6JA*
        Director ................................. Brigadier M Rutlidge OBE ADC ............. Tel: (01929) 403550

# MINISTRY OF DEFENCE

*Army (Continued)*

Royal Artillery
*HQDRA, Stirling Barracks, Larkhill, Salisbury, Wiltshire, SP4 8QT*
    Director .................................Brigadier C C Wilson ADC ...................Tel: (01980) 675902

Royal Military Academy
*Sandhurst, Camberley, Surrey, GU15 4PQ*
    Commander ...............................Major-General Arthur Denaro OBE ............Tel: (01276) 63344 ext 2206

Royal Military College of Science
*Shrivenham, Swindon, SN6 8LA*
    Commandant ..............................Major-General J C B Sutherell CBE ............Tel: (01793) 785438

Signals
*Blandford Camp, Blandford Forum, Dorset, DT11 8RH*
    Signals Officer-in-Chief .......................Brigadier D McDowall MBE ADC ..............Tel: (01258) 482151

Sport
*Clayton Barracks, Aldershot, Hampshire, GU11 2BG*
    Director, Sport Control Board ....................Major-General (Retd) S W St John Lyttle CBE ....Tel: (01252) 244351 ext 3570

Staff Duties
    Director, Army Staff Duties .....................Brigadier B Davidson-Houston CBE ............Tel: (020) 7218 7618

Territorial Army *(see below under Reserve Forces)*

Training
    Director, Individual Training (Army) ...............Brigadier R M Wilde ......................Tel: (01980) 615373

Veterinary Services
*Wigram House, Galway Road, Aldershot, Hampshire, GU11 2DQ*
    Director, Army Veterinary and Remount Services .....Mr Andrew Roache ......................Tel: (01252) 348534

## Atomic Weapons
Atomic Weapons Establishment
*Aldermaston, Reading, Berkshire, RG7 4PR*
    Managing Director ...........................Mr Bill Haight ..........................Tel: (01189) 814111

## Balkans
    Head, Balkans Secretariat ......................Mr John Tesh ..........................Tel: (020) 7218 1953
    Director of Joint Commitment, Balkans Assistant Director ..Mrs Fiona White .....................Tel: (020) 7218 1948

## Business Improvement Team, Departmental ..........Mr M Preston .........................Tel: (020) 7218 8158

## Buildings
    MoD Main Building Redevelopment ................Mr Jonathon Hoyle ......................Tel: (020) 7218 6677

## Capability
    Director, Capability (Manoeuvre) ..................Major General A C Figgures CBE ............Tel: (020) 7218 2706
    Director, Capability (Strike) ......................Air Vice-Marshal N J Day ................Tel: (020) 7218 7480

## Civilian Management
    Director-General, Civilian Personnel Policy ...........Mr J Pitt Brooke ......................Tel: (020) 7218 4527
    Director-General, Management and Organisation ........Mr Nick Evans ........................Tel: (020) 7218 4095
    Personnel Director ...........................Mr Richard Hatfield CBE ..................Tel: (020) 7218 6832
    Business Improvement Team, Departmental ...........Mr M Preston .........................Tel: (020) 7218 8158
    Civilian Management .........................Mr Chris Furlong ......................Tel: (020) 7218 3882
    Data Base Learning ..........................Mr D Laughrin ........................Tel: (020) 7305 3882
    Employee Relations ..........................Mr Chris Baker ........................Tel: (020) 7218 0018
    HR Strategy ...............................Mr Stephen Smith ......................Tel: (020) 7218 9141
    Management and Consultancy Services .............Mr D K A Reynolds ....................Tel: (020) 7218 4083
    Organisation and Management Development .........Mr Gary Lewitt ........................Tel: (020) 7218 1900
    Pay and Allowances .........................Mr C Baker ..........................Tel: (020) 7218 0018
    Senior Staff Management ......................Dr Frank Price ........................Tel: (020) 7218 0381

## Commitments
    Deputy Chief of the Defence Staff (Commitments) .......Major General Sir Robert Fry ..............Tel: (020) 7218 6297
    Director, Strategic Support ......................Commodore P Eberly ....................Tel: (020) 7218 7412

## 'D' Notices
    Defence Press and Broadcasting Advisory Committee ......Rear-Admiral Nick Wilkinson CB ............Tel: (020) 7218 3820

# MINISTRY OF DEFENCE

**Defence Services Secretary** ..........................Major-General C H Elliot CBE ...............Tel: (020) 7218 6186

**Doctrine**

 Director-General, Development and Doctrine ...........Major General J B A Bailey ...............Tel: (01980) 615119

 Director-General, Doctrine and Concepts .............Air Vice-Marshal I W McNicoll CBE ..........Tel: (01793) 784203

**Economics**

 Senior Economic Adviser ........................Mr Neil Davies ..........................Tel: (020) 7218 2653

**Enquiry Office (Public)** ..........................*enquiries* .........................Tel: (0870) 607 4455

**Equipment**

 Deputy Chief of the Defence Staff (Equipment Capability) ..Lieutenant-General Sir Robert Fulton RM ......Tel: (020) 7218 2531

 Director-General, Equipment .......................Mr Stephen French .........................Tel: (020) 7218 2838

 Director-General, Equipment Support (Air) .............Air Vice-Marshal M P Liddell .............Tel: (01480) 52151 ext 2915

 Director, Acquisition *(Broadening Smart)* .............Ms Kathy Makin ........................Tel: (020) 7218 8659

 Director, Equipment Capability *(Indirect*

  *Battlefield Management)* ......................Brigadier D T A Applegate ................Tel: (020) 7218 1228

 Director, Equipment Capability *(Strategic*

  *Deployment)* .............................Commodore R Finlayson ................Tel: (020) 7218 8255

 Director, Equipment Plan .......................Commodore D A Cooke ................Tel: (020) 7218 7789

 Director, Scrutiny and Analysis, (Air) ..............Mr I Barnett ........................Tel: (020) 7218 6761

 Director, Scrutiny and Analysis, (Land) .............Mr N Barnett ........................Tel: (020) 7218 2945

 Director, Scrutiny and Analysis, (Policy and Programmes) ..Mr A Everett ......................Tel: (020) 7218 2945

 Director, Scrutiny and Analysis, (Sea) ..............Dr Anthony Sinden ..................Tel: (020) 7218 2945

 Investment Appraisal Board ......................Mr J Thatcher .....................Tel: (020) 7218 2076

**Europe**

 Director for Europe ...........................Ms Sarah Beaver .....................Tel: (020) 7218 2558

**Exports**

*St Christopher House, Southwark Street, London, SE1 0TD*

 Director-General, Defence Exports Services ............Ms Gloria Craig ......................Tel: (020) 7305 2555

 Head, Defence Export Services ...................Mr A Garwood ......................Tel: (020) 7305 2560

 Export Services Policy ..........................Mr John Mullen .....................Tel: (020) 7305 2529

**Finance**

 Director-General, Central Budget ...................Mr Carl Mantell .....................Tel: (020) 7218 7524

 Director-General, Financial Management ..............Mr Bruce Mann ......................Tel: (020) 7218 6188

 Director-General, Resources and Plans ..............Mr Tom McKane .....................Tel: (020) 7218 2292

 Director, Acquisition (Broadening Smart) .............Ms Kathy Makin .....................Tel: (020) 7218 8659

 Director, Capability, Resources and Scrutiny ..........Mr David Williams ...................Tel: (020) 7218 6069

 Directors, Finance ...........................Mr Colin Balmer ....................Tel: (020) 7218 6216

                Mr Trevor Woolley ..................Tel: (020) 7218 6216

 Director, Finance (Policy) .......................Mr Bill Davis .....................Tel: (020) 7218 2739

 Director, Resources and Plans ....................Mr Guy Lester .....................Tel: (020) 7218 3927

 Financial Controller ..........................Mr John Thornton / Mr David Dick .........Tel: (020) 7218 6749

 Investment Appraisal Board ......................Mr J Thatcher .....................Tel: (020) 7218 2076

**Fire Service**

*St Giles Court, 1-13 St Giles High Street, London, WC2H 8LD*

 Chief Fire Officer ...........................Mr M Reed ........................Tel: (020) 7218 8219

**Force Development**

 Director, Force Development .....................Commodore A Richards .................Tel: (020) 7218 2726

**General Staff** *(see above under Army)*

**Gulf Veterans Illnesses Unit** .......................Mr Daniel Applegate ..................Tel: (020) 7218 2410

**Gurkhas**

*HQBG, Airfield Camp, Netheravon, Salisbury, SP4 9SF*

 Brigade of Gurkhas ...........................*enquiries* .....................Tel: (01980) 678562

# M I N I S T R Y   O F   D E F E N C E

**Health and Safety**
*St Giles Court, 1-13 St Giles High Street, London, WC2H 8LD*
    Director, Safety Environment and Fire Policy . . . . . . . . . . .Dr Geoff Hooper . . . . . . . . . . . . . . . . . . . . . . . .Tel: (020) 7218 9083

**Infantry**
*Warminster, Wiltshire, BA12 0DJ*
    Director, Infantry . . . . . . . . . . . . . . . . . . . . . . . . . . .Brigadier M J Strudwick CBE . . . . . . . . . . . . . . .Tel: (01985) 214000 ext 2329

**Information and Communications Services**
    Capability Manager, Information Superiority . . . . . . . . . . . .Air Vice-Marshal S Dalton . . . . . . . . . . . . . . . .Tel: (020) 7218 7445

**Intelligence**
    Chief of Defence Intelligence . . . . . . . . . . . . . . . . . . . . . .Air Marshal Joe French CBE . . . . . . . . . . . . . . .Tel: (020) 7218 9000
    Director-General. Intelligence Collection . . . . . . . . . . . . .Major General M Laurie CBE . . . . . . . . . . . . . . .Tel: (020) 7218 9000

**Joint Service Command and Staff College**
*Bracknell, Berkshire, RG12 9DD*
    Commandant . . . . . . . . . . . . . . . . . . . . . . . . . . . . . . . .Air Vice-Marshal B K Burridge CBE . . . . . . . . . .Tel: (01344) 454593 ext 7002

**Land Warfare**
*Trenchard Lines, Upavon, Pewsey, Wiltshire, SN9 6BE*
    Director, Land Warfare . . . . . . . . . . . . . . . . . . . . . . . . .Brigadier Robert Mungo Melvin . . . . . . . . . . . . .Tel: (01980) 615119

**Legal Services**
    Legal Adviser . . . . . . . . . . . . . . . . . . . . . . . . . . . . . . . .Mr Martin Hemmings . . . . . . . . . . . . . . . . . . . . .Tel: (020) 7218 4691
    Legal Services and Claims (Finance and Secretariat) . . . . . .Mrs Jane Alexander . . . . . . . . . . . . . . . . . . . . . .Tel: (020) 7218 4201

**Library**
*3-5 Great Scotland Yard, London, SW1A 2HW* . . . . . . . . . . . . . .*enquiries* . . . . . . . . . . . . . . . . . . . . . . . . . . . .Tel: (020) 7218 4445

**Logistics**
    Deputy Chief, Defence Logistics . . . . . . . . . . . . . . . . . . .Mr J Flescher . . . . . . . . . . . . . . . . . . . . . . . . . .Tel: (020) 7218 2330
    Director-General, Defence Logistics (Operations) . . . . . . . .Rear Admiral Michael Wood . . . . . . . . . . . . . . . .Tel: (01225) 467789
    Director-General, Resources Defence Logistics Organisation Mr C Mace . . . . . . . . . . . . . . . . . . . . . . . . . . . . .Tel: (01225) 467036
    Director-General, Supply Chain Defence Logistics
        Organisation . . . . . . . . . . . . . . . . . . . . . . . . . . . . .Major-General T Cross . . . . . . . . . . . . . . . . . . . .Tel: (01264) 382998

**Management, Departmental** *(see above under Civilian Management)*

**Marines** *(see below under Royal Marines)*

**Medical**
    Defence Medical Services Directorate
        Surgeon-General . . . . . . . . . . . . . . . . . . . . . . . . . . . .Surgeon Vice-Admiral Ian Jenkins CVO . . . . . . . .Tel: (020) 7807 8807
        Chief of Staff, Surgeon-General's Department . . . . . . . .Air Vice-Marshal T Couzens . . . . . . . . . . . . . . . .Tel: (020) 7807 8832
        Director, Medical Operational Capacity . . . . . . . . . . . .Surgeon Commodore P F R Tolley . . . . . . . . . . . .Tel: (020) 7217 8771

**NATO**
    Director, NATO European Policy Group . . . . . . . . . . . . . .Air Commodore R Lacey . . . . . . . . . . . . . . . . . .Tel: (020) 7218 2492

**Navy**
*Web: http://www.royal-navy.mod.uk*
    Chief of the Naval Staff and First Sea Lord . . . . . . . . . . . .Admiral Sir Alan West KCB DSC . . . . . . . . . . . . . .Tel: (020) 7218 6193 / 2214
    Assistant Chief of the Naval Staff . . . . . . . . . . . . . . . . . .Rear-Admiral A J Johns . . . . . . . . . . . . . . . . . . .Tel: (020) 7218 6534
    Second Sea Lord and Chief of Naval Home Command . . . .Vice-Admiral James Burnell-Nugent . . . . . . . . . .Tel: (023) 9272 7003
        Chief of Staff to Second Sea Lord . . . . . . . . . . . . . . . .Rear-Admiral R G Lockwood . . . . . . . . . . . . . . . .Tel: (023) 9272 7105
    Commander in Chief, Fleet . . . . . . . . . . . . . . . . . . . . . . .Admiral Sir Jonathan Bland . . . . . . . . . . . . . . . .Tel: (020) 7218 9000
    Aircraft
        Director-General, Aircraft (Navy) . . . . . . . . . . . . . . . .Rear-Admiral J A Burch . . . . . . . . . . . . . . . . . . .Tel: (01225) 72056
    Aviation Support
        *RNAS Yeovilton, Yeovil, Somerset, BA22 8HJ*
        Director, Naval Aviation Support . . . . . . . . . . . . . . . . .Commodore M Brougham . . . . . . . . . . . . . . . . . .Tel: (01935) 452831
    Bases
        Chief Executive, Naval Bases and Supply Agency . . . . .Rear-Admiral B Perowne . . . . . . . . . . . . . . . . . .Tel: (01225) 67707

# MINISTRY OF DEFENCE

*Navy (Continued)*

Catering
    Director, Defence Catering Group ................Air Commodore S Wood .................Tel: (01225) 677477
Chaplaincy Service
*Room 203, Victory Building, H M Naval Base, Portsmouth, PO1 3LS*
    Director-General, Naval Chaplaincy Service
    and Principal Anglican Chaplain ..............The Ven Barry Hammett QHC MA .............Tel: (023) 9272 7900
    Principal Church of Scotland and Free Churches
    Chaplain ....................................Rev Terry Maze .....................Tel: (023) 9272 7903
    Principal Roman Catholic Chaplain .............Rev Monsignor Richard Madders ...........Tel: (023) 9272 7903
Communications
    Director, Communications and Information Systems ....Commodore Peter Swan ...................Tel: (020) 7218 6630
Devonport
    Base Commander .........................Commodore A Matthews .................Tel: (01752) 553829
Duties
    Director, Naval Staff Duties .................Commodore M Kimmons .................Tel: (020) 7218 6135
Engineering
    Director, Logistics Engineering ..............*enquiries* ..................Tel: (01225) 813302
    Director, Marine Engineering ................Mr Anthony Jenkins .................Tel: (01225) 883057
Fishery Protection .............................Commodore B A L Goldman .............Tel: (01225) 726341
Helicopters
    Director, Helicopter Support Authority ............Commodore P J Kidner ...............Tel: (01935) 453550
Judge Advocate
*The Court Service, Concorde House, 10-12 London Road, Maidstone, Kent, ME16 8QA*
    Chief Naval Judge Advocate ..................His Honour Judge H J Sessions ............Tel: (01622) 200120
Marine Engineering
    Director, Marine Engineering ................Mr Anthony Jenkins .................Tel: (01225) 883057
Medical Director-General, Navy .................Rear-Admiral Ian Jenkins CVO .............Tel: (020) 7807 8807
Munitions
    Director, Defence Munitions ..................Mr A Blair .................Tel: (01225) 67611
Operations, Staff
    Chief of Staff Operations ....................Rear-Admiral N S Kilgour ...............Tel: (01923) 87260
Personnel
    Director, Fleet Support, Personnel ..............Mr S Penfold .................Tel: (01225) 68138
    Director, Naval Personnel Corporate Programming .....Commodore D A H Smith ...............Tel: (023) 9272 7151
    Director, Naval Personnel Family Service .........Commodore P J Wilkinson .............Tel: (023) 9272 7241
    Command Personnel, Second Sea Lord ............Mr P Hatt .................Tel: (023) 9272 7301
    Head, Naval Personnel Secretariat ...............Mr J P Read .................Tel: (023) 9272 7311
Portsmouth
    Base Commander .........................Commodore R P Boissier .................Tel: (023) 9272 2835
Resources
    Director, Resources and Plans (Navy) ............Commodore T Laurence .................Tel: (020) 7218 3539
Royal Fleet Auxiliary
*Naval Base, Portsmouth, Hampshire, PO1 3NH*
    Commodore of the Royal Auxiliary ...............Commodore P J Lannin .................Tel: (023) 9272 6048
Safety
    Chief Environment and Safety Officer .............Mr Jim McLay .................Tel: (01225) 467267
Secretariat, Naval Staffs ........................*enquiries* .................Tel: (020) 7218 7613
Security
    Director, Finance, Safety, Estate and Security .......Mr Martin Piper .................Tel: (01225) 467087
Staff Duties
    Director Naval Staff Duties ..................Commodore T A Soare .................Tel: (020) 7218 6135
Training
    Flag Officer, Naval Training and Recruiting .........Rear-Admiral P R Davis CBE .............Tel: (023) 9272 7603

## Nuclear

Director, Chemical, Biological and Nuclear Policy .......Commodore M P Fitzgerald .................Tel: (020) 7218 6706
Director, Strategic Technologies .....................Mr P W Taylor .................Tel: (020) 7218 7348
Nuclear Weapons Safety Adviser ....................Rear Admiral Frederick Scourse ............Tel: (020) 7218 9167
*(See also above under Atomic Weapons)*

# MINISTRY OF DEFENCE

## Operational Requirements

Capability Manager, Manoeuvre . . . . . . . . . . . . . . . . . . . . .Major-General Dick Applegate OBE . . . . . . . . . .Tel: (020) 7218 2706
Capability Manager, Strategic Deployment . . . . . . . . . . . . .Rear-Admiral C R Style . . . . . . . . . . . . . . . . .Tel: (020) 7218 6070
Capability Manager, Strike . . . . . . . . . . . . . .Air Vice-Marshal N J Day . . . . . . . . . . . . . . .Tel: (020) 7218 6516
Director, Equipment Capability (Strategic
    Deployment) . . . . . . . . . . . . . . . . . . . . . . . . . . . .Commodore R Finlayson . . . . . . . . . . . . . . . . .Tel: (020) 7218 8255
Director, Equipment Capability
    (Direct Battlefield Engagement) . . . . . . . . . . . . . . . . .Brigadier Ian Rodley . . . . . . . . . . . . . . . . . .Tel: (020) 7218 3001
Director, Equipment Capability (Deep Strike) . . . . . . . . . .Air Commodore A Hudson . . . . . . . . . . . . . . . . .Tel: (020) 7218 7486 / 7202

## Operations

Assistant Chief of Defence Staff (Operations) . . . . . . . . . . .Air Vice-Marshal C R Loader . . . . . . . . . . . . . .Tel: (020) 7218 1389
Director-General, Operational Policy . . . . . . . . . . . . . . . . .Mr D Bowen . . . . . . . . . . . . . . . . . . . . . . . .Tel: (020) 7218 6280
Director, Chemical, Biological and Nuclear Policy . . . . . .Commodore M P Fitzgerald . . . . . . . . . . . . . . . .Tel: (020) 7218 6706
Director, Defence Commitments (Joint Warfare) . . . . . . . . .Commodore A Nance OBE . . . . . . . . . . . . . . . . .Tel: (020) 7218 7412
Director, Military Operations . . . . . . . . . . . . . . . . . . . . .Brigadier W E R Rollo . . . . . . . . . . . . . . . . .Tel: (020) 7218 2561
Director, Naval Operations . . . . . . . . . . . . . . . . . . . . . .Commodore Peter Eberle . . . . . . . . . . . . . . . . .Tel: (020) 7218 0014
Director, Operational Capability . . . . . . . . . . . . . . . . . . .Air Commodore C Parry . . . . . . . . . . . . . . . . .Tel: (020) 7218 6493
Director, Overseas Military Activity . . . . . . . . . . . . . . . .Brigadier A R E de C Stewart . . . . . . . . . . . . . .Tel: (020) 7218 2855

## Outplacement Services

Director, Outplacement Services . . . . . . . . . . . . . . . . . . .*Vacant* . . . . . . . . . . . . . . . . . . . . . . . . . . .Tel: (020) 7215 3950

## Overseas

Head, Overseas Secretariat . . . . . . . . . . . . . . . . . . . . . .Mr Stephen Pollard . . . . . . . . . . . . . . . . . . .Tel: (020) 7218 6347

## Parliamentary Clerk . . . . . . . . . . . . . . . . . .Mrs Patricia Parkin . . . . . . . . . . . . . . . . . . .Tel: (020) 7218 1991

## Performance and Analysis

Director, Performance and Analysis . . . . . . . . . . . . . . . . .Mr Ian Woodman . . . . . . . . . . . . . . . . . . . . . .Tel: (020) 7218 6178

## Personnel Policies (all Services)
*St Giles Court, 1-13 St Giles High Street, London, WC2H 8LD*

Deputy Chief of the Defence Staff (Personnel) . . . . . . . . .Lieutenant-General A Palmer . . . . . . . . . . . . . .Tel: (020) 7218 4026
Director-General, Service Personnel Policy . . . . . . . . . . . .Mr Julian Miller / Ms Elizabeth McLoughlin . . . .Tel: (020) 7218 3024
Director, Personnel (Departmental) . . . . . . . . . . . . . . . . .Mr R P Hatfield . . . . . . . . . . . . . . . . . . . . .Tel: (020) 7218 6833
Directors, Service Personnel Policy
    Pay and Allowances . . . . . . . . . . . . . . . . . . . . . . . .Commodore Kim Hemsworth
                                                                    Air Commodore D Pocock MBE . . . . . . . . . . . . . .Tel: (020) 7807 8310
    Service Conditions . . . . . . . . . . . . . . . . . . . . . . . .Mr Martin Fuller . . . . . . . . . . . . . . . . . . . .Tel: (020) 7218 9634

## Pensions (Service Personnel)

Director . . . . . . . . . . . . . . . . . . . . . . . . . . . . . . . . .Mr J L Iremonger . . . . . . . . . . . . . . . . . . . .Tel: (020) 7218 5165

## Policy

Assistant Chief of the Defence Staff (Policy) . . . . . . . . . . .Air Vice-Marshal D A Hobart . . . . . . . . . . . . . .Tel: (020) 7218 2917
Policy Director . . . . . . . . . . . . . . . . . . . . . . . . . . . . .Mr Simon Webb . . . . . . . . . . . . . . . . . . . . . .Tel: (020) 7218 3830
Director, Defence Policy Planning . . . . . . . . . . . . . . . . . .Mr Gavin Barlow . . . . . . . . . . . . . . . . . . . . .Tel: (020) 7218 2617

## Press and Publicity

Director-General, Media and Communications . . . . . . . . . .Mr Ian Lee . . . . . . . . . . . . . . . . . . . . . . . .Tel: (020) 7218 0546
Director, Communication and Planning Management . . . . . .Mr David Howard . . . . . . . . . . . . . . . . . . . . .Tel: (020) 7218 7670
Director, Community and Internal Communications . . . . . .Mr Chris Williams . . . . . . . . . . . . . . . . . . . .Tel: (020) 7218 6181
Director, Corporate Communications (Army) . . . . . . . . . . .*Vacant* . . . . . . . . . . . . . . . . . . . . . . . . . .Tel: (020) 7218 2500
Director, Corporate Communications (Navy) . . . . . . . . . . .Commodore Allan Adair . . . . . . . . . . . . . . . . .Tel: (020) 7218 7906
Director, Corporate Communications (RAF) . . . . . . . . . . .Group Captain David Prowse . . . . . . . . . . . . . . .Tel: (020) 7218 3559
Director, Defence Publicity . . . . . . . . . . . . . . . . . . . . .Air Commodore Mike Lloyd . . . . . . . . . . . . . . . .Tel: (020) 7218 3559
Director, News . . . . . . . . . . . . . . . . . . . . . . . . . . . . .Ms Pam Teare . . . . . . . . . . . . . . . . . . . . . . .Tel: (020) 7218 2717
Defence Press and Broadcasting Advisory Committee . . . . .Rear-Admiral Nick Wilkinson CB . . . . . . . . . . . .Tel: (020) 7218 3820
Duty Press Officer . . . . . . . . . . . . . . . . . . . . . . . . . .*enquiries (outside normal working hours)* . . . . . .Tel: (020) 7218 7907
                                                                    Web: http://www.news.mod.uk

# MINISTRY OF DEFENCE

**Procurement** *(See Other Relevant Contacts – Procurement)*

**Protocol** . . . . . . . . . . . . . . . . . . . . . . . . . . . . . . . . . . . . .*enquiries* . . . . . . . . . . . . . . . . . . . . . . . . . . .Tel: (020) 7218 6608

**Public Appointments** . . . . . . . . . . . . . . . . . . . . . . . . .Mr Nick Darms . . . . . . . . . . . . . . . . . . . . . . . .Tel: (020) 7218 5851

**Resettlement**
*St Giles Court, 1-13 St Giles High Street, London, WC2H 8LD*
    Director, Resettlement Services . . . . . . . . . . . . . . . . . . . . .Commodore A Picton . . . . . . . . . . . . . . . . . . . .Tel: (020) 7215 3950

**Reserve Forces**
*St Giles Court, 1-13 St Giles High Street, London, WC2H 8LD*
    Director, Reserve Forces and Cadets . . . . . . . . . . . . . . . .Brigadier, the Duke of Westminster . . . . . . . . .Tel: (020) 7218 5702
    Inspector-General, Territorial Army . . . . . . . . . . . . . . . . .Major-General J F Deverell . . . . . . . . . . . . . . .Tel: (01722) 433235

**Resident Clerks** . . . . . . . . . . . . . . . . . . . . . . . . . . . . . . . .*enquiries* . . . . . . . . . . . . . . . . . . . . . . . . . . .Tel: (020) 7218 6002
    *(Note: The Resident Clerks' duty hours are weekdays 6.30pm-9am; weekends 6.30pm Friday to 9am Monday)*

**Resources and Plans**
    Assistant Chief of the Defence Staff, Resources and Plans . .Rear-Admiral R I A McLean . . . . . . . . . . . . . .Tel: (020) 7218 2188
    Director-General, Resources and Plans . . . . . . . . . . . . . . .Mr Tom McKane . . . . . . . . . . . . . . . . . . . . . . .Tel: (020) 7218 2292
    Director, Capability, Resources and Scrutiny . . . . . . . . . . .Mr David Williams . . . . . . . . . . . . . . . . . . . . .Tel: (020) 7218 3129
    Director, Resources and Plans . . . . . . . . . . . . . . . . . . . . .Mr Guy Lester . . . . . . . . . . . . . . . . . . . . . . . . .Tel: (020) 7218 3927
    Resources and Plans (Air) . . . . . . . . . . . . . . . . . . . . . . . .Air Commodore K J Leeson . . . . . . . . . . . . . . .Tel: (020) 7218 2899
    Resources and Plans (Army) . . . . . . . . . . . . . . . . . . . . . .Brigadier A J N Graham . . . . . . . . . . . . . . . . .Tel: (020) 7218 7568
    Resources and Plans (Navy) . . . . . . . . . . . . . . . . . . . . . . .Commodore T Laurence . . . . . . . . . . . . . . . . .Tel: (020) 7218 3539

**Royal Air Force** *(see above under Air Force)*

**Royal Armoured Corps**
*Bovington Camp, Wareham, Dorset, BH20 6JA*
    Director . . . . . . . . . . . . . . . . . . . . . . . . . . . . . . . . . . . . .Brigadier M J Rutledge OBE ADC . . . . . . . . . . . . .Tel: (01929) 403550

**Royal Artillery**
*HQ DA, Larkhill, Salisbury, Wiltshire, SP4 8QT*
    Director . . . . . . . . . . . . . . . . . . . . . . . . . . . . . . . . . . . . .Brigadier Jonathan Bailey MBE ADC . . . . . . . . . . .Tel: (01980) 675902

**Royal Marines**
*DERA, Portsdown West, Portsdown Hill Road, Fareham, Hampshire, PO17 6AD*
    Commandant, Royal Marines . . . . . . . . . . . . . . . . . . . . . .Major-General R H G Fulton . . . . . . . . . . . . . .Tel: (023) 9233 7051

**Royal Military Academy, Sandhurst** *(see above under Army)*

**Royal Navy** *(see above under Navy)*

**Science**
    Chief Scientific Adviser . . . . . . . . . . . . . . . . . . . . . . . . . .Professor Sir Keith O'Nions FRS . . . . . . . . . . . .Tel: (020) 7218 3560
    Science and Technology Director . . . . . . . . . . . . . . . . . . .Mr Graham Jordan . . . . . . . . . . . . . . . . . . . . .Tel: (020) 7218 2482
    Director-General, Research and Technology . . . . . . . . . . .Dr M Markin . . . . . . . . . . . . . . . . . . . . . . . . . .Tel: (020) 7218 6237
    Director-General, Scrutiny and Analysis . . . . . . . . . . . . . .Mr N J Bennett . . . . . . . . . . . . . . . . . . . . . . . .Tel: (020) 7218 2034
    Director, Research (Corporate) . . . . . . . . . . . . . . . . . . . . .Professor P Sutton . . . . . . . . . . . . . . . . . . . . .Tel: (020) 7218 2683
    Director, Research (Systems and Technology) . . . . . . . . . .Dr P Simpson . . . . . . . . . . . . . . . . . . . . . . . . .Tel: (020) 7218 3508
    Director, Science (Ballistic Missile Defence) . . . . . . . . . . .Dr R W Jeffrey . . . . . . . . . . . . . . . . . . . . . . . .Tel: (020) 7218 4239
    Director, Science (Manoeuvre) . . . . . . . . . . . . . . . . . . . . .Dr D J Ferbrache . . . . . . . . . . . . . . . . . . . . . .Tel: (020) 7218 6263
    Director, Science (Strategic Deployment) . . . . . . . . . . . . .Dr J B Johns . . . . . . . . . . . . . . . . . . . . . . . . . .Tel: (020) 7218 2711
    Director, Technical Strategy . . . . . . . . . . . . . . . . . . . . . . .Mr P W Taylor . . . . . . . . . . . . . . . . . . . . . . . .Tel: (020) 7218 7348
    Head, Finance and Secretariat, Science and Technology . . .Mr R Mansell . . . . . . . . . . . . . . . . . . . . . . . . .Tel: (020) 7218 2376

# MINISTRY OF DEFENCE

**Security**

Headquarters Security . . . . . . . . . . . . . . . . . . . . . . . . . . . . . .Mr Andy Gray . . . . . . . . . . . . . . . . . . . . . . . . . . .Tel: (020) 7218 0991

Director, Safety, Estate and Security . . . . . . . . . . . . . . . .Mr Martin Piper . . . . . . . . . . . . . . . . . . . . . . . . .Tel: (01225) 467087

**Territorial Army** *(see above under Reserve Forces)*

**Works, Defence** *(see below under Other Relevant Contacts - Estates)*

**Yugoslavia (former)** *(see above under Balkans)*

## OTHER RELEVANT CONTACTS

### ACCOUNTING SERVICES

**Defence Bills Agency** *(Executive Agency)* . . . . . . . . . . . . . .Mersey House, Drury Lane, Liverpool, L2 7PX

Chief Executive . . . . . . . . . . . . . . . . . . . . . . . . . . . . . . . . .Mr Norman Swanney . . . . . . . . . . . . . . . . . . . . . .Tel: (0151) 242 2519

E-mail: heocorp@dba.mod.uk

Web: http://www.defencebills.gov.uk

### AIR FORCE

**RAF Personnel Management Agency** *(Executive Agency)* . . .Building 182, RAF Innsworth, Gloucester, GL3 1EZ

Chief Executive . . . . . . . . . . . . . . . . . . . . . . . . . . . . . . . . .Air Vice-Marshal Dusty Miller . . . . . . . . . . . . . .Tel: (01452) 712612

**RAF Training Group Defence Agency** *(Executive Agency)* . .HQ Personnel and Training Command, RAF Innsworth,

Gloucestershire, GL3 1EZ

Chief Executive . . . . . . . . . . . . . . . . . . . . . . . . . . . . . . . . .Air Vice-Marshal David Allan Walker OBE MVO . . .Tel: (01452) 712612

E-mail: ca@tgda.gov.uk

Web: http://www.tgda.gov.uk

### ANIMALS

**Animal Welfare Advisory Committee** . . . . . . . . . . . . . . . .Building A3, Dstl, Fort Halstead, Sevenoaks, Kent, TN14 7BP

Chairman . . . . . . . . . . . . . . . . . . . . . . . . . . . . . . . . . . . . .Dr Brian Hoskins

Secretary . . . . . . . . . . . . . . . . . . . . . . . . . . . . . . . . . . . . . .Ms Jacqui Whyte . . . . . . . . . . . . . . . . . . . . . . . . .Tel: (01959) 892105

### ARMY

**ABRO** *(Executive Agency)* . . . . . . . . . . . . . . . . . . . . . . . . .Monxton Road, Andover, Hampshire, SP11 8HT

Chief Executive . . . . . . . . . . . . . . . . . . . . . . . . . . . . . . . . .Mr Mike Hayle . . . . . . . . . . . . . . . . . . . . . . . . . .Tel: (01264) 383295

Web: http://www.abro.mod.uk

**Army Personnel Centre** *(Executive Agency)* . . . . . . . . . . . .Kentigern House, 65 Brown Street, Glasgow, G2 8EX

Chief Executive . . . . . . . . . . . . . . . . . . . . . . . . . . . . . . . . .Major-General Freddie Viggers . . . . . . . . . . . . . .Tel: (0141) 224 2023

**Army Training and Recruiting Agency** *(Executive Agency)* . .HQ ATRA, Building 370, Trenchard Lines, Upavon, Pewsey, Wiltshire, SN9 6BE

Chief Executive . . . . . . . . . . . . . . . . . . . . . . . . . . . . . . . . .Major-General David Leakey CBE . . . . . . . . . . . . .Tel: (01980) 615001

### AVIATION

**Defence Aviation Repair Agency** *(Executive Agency)* . . . . . .St Athan, Barry, Vale of Glamorgan, CF62 4WA

Chief Executive . . . . . . . . . . . . . . . . . . . . . . . . . . . . . . . . .Mr Archie Hughes . . . . . . . . . . . . . . . . . . . . . . . .Tel: (01446) 798834

Web: http://www.dara.mod.uk

### BROADCASTING

**Services Sound and Vision Corporation** . . . . . . . . . . . . . .Chalfont Grove, Narcot Lane, Gerrards Cross, Buckinghamshire, SL9 8TN

Managing Director . . . . . . . . . . . . . . . . . . . . . . . . . . . . . . .Air Vice-Marshal David Crwys-Williams CB . . . . .Tel: (01494) 878239

Web: http://www.ssvc.com

### CARTOGRAPHY/SURVEY

**Defence Geographic and Imagery**

**Intelligence Agency** *(Executive Agency)* . . . . . . . . . . . . . .Watson Building, Elmwood Avenue, Feltham, Middlesex, TW13 7AH

Chief Executive . . . . . . . . . . . . . . . . . . . . . . . . . . . . . . . . .Air Commodore Martin Hallam . . . . . . . . . . . . . .Tel: (020) 8818 2422

### CODIFICATION

**UK National Codification Bureau** . . . . . . . . . . . . . . . . . .Kentigern House, 65 Brown Street, Glasgow, G2 8EX

Head of Bureau . . . . . . . . . . . . . . . . . . . . . . . . . . . . . . . . .Mr John Clark . . . . . . . . . . . . . . . . . . . . . . . . . . .Tel: (0141) 224 2164

Web: http://www.ncb.mod.uk

# MINISTRY OF DEFENCE

*Other Relevant Contacts (Continued)*

## COMMUNICATIONS
**Defence Communications Services**
    **Agency** *(Executive Agency)* . . . . . . . . . . . . . . . . . . . . . .Building 111, Basil Hill Site, Park Lane, Corsham, Wiltshire, SN13 9NR
    Chief Executive . . . . . . . . . . . . . . . . . . . . . . . . . . . . . .Rear-Admiral Rees G J Ward CB . . . . . . . . . . . .Tel: (01225) 814785
        E-mail: dcsa-ce@defence.mod.uk
        Web: http://www.mod.uk/dlo/dcsa

## CONSCIENTIOUS OBJECTORS
**Advisory Committee on Conscientious Objectors** . . . . . . .C&L (F&S) Legal 1, Room 606, St Giles Court, 1-13 St Giles High Street, London, WC2H 8LD
    Chairman . . . . . . . . . . . . . . . . . . . . . . . . . . . . . . . .Judge Harris
    Secretary . . . . . . . . . . . . . . . . . . . . . . . . . . . . . . . .Mr Richard Chandler . . . . . . . . . . . . . . . . . . .Tel: (020) 7218 0509

## CONTRACTS
**Review Board for Government Contracts** . . . . . . . . . . . . .c/o Deloitte & Touche, 180 Strand, London, WC2R 1BL
    Chairman . . . . . . . . . . . . . . . . . . . . . . . . . . . . . . . .Mr George Staple
    Secretariat . . . . . . . . . . . . . . . . . . . . . . . . . . . . . . .Mr Pommy Sarwal . . . . . . . . . . . . . . . . . . . .Tel: (020) 7007 1512

## CORRECTIVE TRAINING CENTRES
**Independent Board of Visitors for Military**
    **Corrective Training Centres** . . . . . . . . . . . . . . . . . . . .MCTC, Berechurch Hall Camp, Colchester, Essex, CO2 9NU
    Chairman . . . . . . . . . . . . . . . . . . . . . . . . . . . . . . . .Mr Jim Bond . . . . . . . . . . . . . . . . . . . . . . . .Tel: (01206) 783473

## DARTMOOR
**Dartmoor Steering Group** . . . . . . . . . . . . . . . . . . . . . . .Army Training Estate (South West), Building 7, Wyvern Barracks, Exeter, EX2 6AR
    Chairman . . . . . . . . . . . . . . . . . . . . . . . . . . . . . . . .Mr Jim Woolcombe CBE
    Secretaries . . . . . . . . . . . . . . . . . . . . . . . . . . . . . . .Lieutenant-Colonel Charlie Nutting
        Dr Nick Atkinson . . . . . . . . . . . . . . . . . . . . .Tel: (01392) 492462

## DENTISTRY
**Defence Dental Agency** *(Executive Agency)* . . . . . . . . . . .HQ DDA, RAF Halton, Aylesbury, Buckinghamshire, HP22 5PG
    Chief Executive . . . . . . . . . . . . . . . . . . . . . . . . . . . .Major-General John Gamon CBE QHDS . . . . . . . . .Tel: (01296) 623535

## DISPOSALS
**Disposal Services Agency** *(Executive Agency)* . . . . . . . . . . .2nd Floor, St George's Court, 2-12 Bloomsbury Way, London WC1A 2SH
    Chief Executive . . . . . . . . . . . . . . . . . . . . . . . . . . . .Mr Sym Taylor CBE . . . . . . . . . . . . . . . . . . . .Tel: (020) 7305 3072
        E-mail: disposalservices@dial.pipex.com
        Web: http://www.disposalservices.agency.mod.uk

## EDUCATION
**Duke of York's Royal Military School** *(Executive Agency)* . .Dover, Kent, CT15 5EQ
    Headmaster . . . . . . . . . . . . . . . . . . . . . . . . . . . . . . .Mr John Cummings . . . . . . . . . . . . . . . . . . . .Tel: (01304) 245029
        E-mail: headmaster@doyrms.com
        Web: http://www.dyrmsfriends.org.uk
**Queen Victoria School** *(Executive Agency)* . . . . . . . . . . . .Dunblane, Perthshire, FK15 0JY
    Headmaster . . . . . . . . . . . . . . . . . . . . . . . . . . . . . . .Mr Brian Raine . . . . . . . . . . . . . . . . . . . . . .Tel: (01786) 822288
        E-mail: enquiries@qvs.org.uk
        Web: http://www.qvs.org.uk
**Service Children's Education** *(Executive Agency)* . . . . . . . .HQ SCE, Building 5, Wegberg Military Complex, BFPO 40
    Chief Executive . . . . . . . . . . . . . . . . . . . . . . . . . . . .Mr David Wadsworth . . . . . . . . . . . . . . . . . . .Tel: (0049) 2161 908 2295
        E-mail: sce.hq@bfgnet.de
        Web: http://www.children-education.org

## ESTATES
**Defence Estates** *(Executive Agency)* . . . . . . . . . . . . . . . . .St George's House, Kingston Road, Sutton Coldfield, West Midlands, B75 7RL
    Chief Executive . . . . . . . . . . . . . . . . . . . . . . . . . . . .Vice-Admiral Peter Dunt . . . . . . . . . . . . . . . . .Tel: (0121) 311 2140
        Web: http://www.defence-estates.mod.uk

# M I N I S T R Y   O F   D E F E N C E

*Other Relevant Contacts (Continued)*

## HOUSING
**Defence Housing Executive** *(Executive Agency)* . . . . . . . . .6th Floor, Ibex House, 42-47 Minories, London, EC3N 1DY
   Chief Executive . . . . . . . . . . . . . . . . . . . . . . . . . . . . . . . .Mr John Wilson . . . . . . . . . . . . . . . . . . . . . . . . . .Tel: (020) 7423 4801
                                      E-mail: corporate.services@dhe.mod.uk

## HYDROGRAPHY
**UK Hydrographic Office** *(Executive Agency)* . . . . . . . . . . . .Admiralty Way, Taunton, Somerset, TA1 2DN
   Chief Executive . . . . . . . . . . . . . . . . . . . . . . . . . . . . . . . .Dr Wyn Williams . . . . . . . . . . . . . . . . . . . . . .Tel: (01823) 337900
                E-mail: generalenquiries@ukho.gov.uk
                Web: http://www.ukho.gov.uk

## INTELLIGENCE *(see below under Security and Intelligence)*

## LOGISTICS
**Defence Logistics Organisation** . . . . . . . . . . . . . . . . . . . . . .DLO HQ, Spur 4, E Block, Ensleigh, Bath, BA1 5AB
   Chief of Defence Logistics . . . . . . . . . . . . . . . . . . . . . . . . .Air Chief Marshal
                Sir Malcolm Pledger KCB OBE AFC . . . . . . . . . . .Tel: (01225) 467717
                E-mail: cdlo.comms@gtnet.gov.uk

## MEDICAL
**Advisory Group on Medical Countermeasures** . . . . . . . . .Room 740 St Giles Court, 1-13 St Giles High Street, London, WC2H 8LD
   Secretary . . . . . . . . . . . . . . . . . . . . . . . . . . . . . . . . . . . . .*Vacant* . . . . . . . . . . . . . . . . . . . . . . . . . . . . . . . .Tel: (020) 7807 8780
**Defence Medical and Education**
  **Training Organisation** *(Executive Agency)* . . . . . . . . . . .HQDMETA, Fort Blockhouse, Gosport, Hampshire, PO12 2AB
   Chief Executive . . . . . . . . . . . . . . . . . . . . . . . . . . . . . . . .Rear-Admiral Peter Kidner . . . . . . . . . . . . . . . .Tel: (023) 9276 5243
                Web: http://www.mod.uk/forces/medical/dmto
**Medical Supplies Agency** *(Executive Agency)* . . . . . . . . . . .Drummond Barracks, Ludgershall, Andover, Hampshire, SP11 9RU
   Chief Executive . . . . . . . . . . . . . . . . . . . . . . . . . . . . . . . .Mr Peter Jones . . . . . . . . . . . . . . . . . . . . . . . . .Tel: (01264) 798502

## METEOROLOGY
**Met Office** *(Executive Agency)* . . . . . . . . . . . . . . . . . . . . . . .Fitzroy Road, Exeter, EX1 3PB
   Chief Executive . . . . . . . . . . . . . . . . . . . . . . . . . . . . . . . .Mr Peter Ewins CB . . . . . . . . . . . . . . . . . . . . . .Tel: (0870) 900 0100
                E-mail: enquiries@metoffice.com
                Web: http://www.metoffice.com

## MUSEUMS
**Fleet Air Arm Museum** . . . . . . . . . . . . . . . . . . . . . . . . . . .Box D6, RNAS Yeovilton, Ilchester, Somerset, BA22 8HT
   Chairman . . . . . . . . . . . . . . . . . . . . . . . . . . . . . . . . . . . . .Rear-Admiral Scott Lidbetter
   Director . . . . . . . . . . . . . . . . . . . . . . . . . . . . . . . . . . . . . .Mr Graham Mottram . . . . . . . . . . . . . . . . . . . .Tel: (01935) 840565
                E-mail: info@fleetairarm.com
                Web: http://www.fleetairarm.com
**National Army Museum** . . . . . . . . . . . . . . . . . . . . . . . . . . .Royal Hospital Road, London, SW3 4HT
   Chairman . . . . . . . . . . . . . . . . . . . . . . . . . . . . . . . . . . . . .General Sir John Waters GCB CBE
   Director *(Acting)* . . . . . . . . . . . . . . . . . . . . . . . . . . . . . . .Dr Alan Guy . . . . . . . . . . . . . . . . . . . . . . . . . . .Tel: (020) 7730 0717
                E-mail: info@national-army-museum.ac.uk
                Web: http://www.national-army-museum.ac.uk
**Royal Air Force Museum** . . . . . . . . . . . . . . . . . . . . . . . . . .Grahame Park Way, Hendon, London, NW9 5LL
   Chairman . . . . . . . . . . . . . . . . . . . . . . . . . . . . . . . . . . . . .Air Chief Marshal Sir Richard Johns
   Director . . . . . . . . . . . . . . . . . . . . . . . . . . . . . . . . . . . . . .Dr Michael Fopp . . . . . . . . . . . . . . . . . . . . . . . .Tel: (020) 8205 2266
                E-mail: info@rafmuseum.org
                Web: http://www.rafmuseum.com
**Royal Marines Museum** . . . . . . . . . . . . . . . . . . . . . . . . . . .Eastney Esplande, Southsea, Hampshire, PO4 9PX
   Chairman . . . . . . . . . . . . . . . . . . . . . . . . . . . . . . . . . . . . .Lieutenant-General Sir Henry Beverley KCB OBE
   Director . . . . . . . . . . . . . . . . . . . . . . . . . . . . . . . . . . . . . .Mr Chris Newbery . . . . . . . . . . . . . . . . . . . . . .Tel: (023) 9281 9385
                Web: http://www.royalmarinesmuseums.co.uk
**Royal Naval Museum** . . . . . . . . . . . . . . . . . . . . . . . . . . . . .HM Naval Base, Portsmouth, PO1 3NH
   Chairman . . . . . . . . . . . . . . . . . . . . . . . . . . . . . . . . . . . . .Admiral Sir Peter Abbott KCB CBE
   Director . . . . . . . . . . . . . . . . . . . . . . . . . . . . . . . . . . . . . .Dr H Campbell McMurray OBE . . . . . . . . . . . .Tel: (023) 9272 7562
                Web: http://www.royalnavalmuseum.org
**Royal Navy Submarine Museum** . . . . . . . . . . . . . . . . . . . .Haslar Jetty Road, Gosport, Hampshire, PO12 2AS
   Chairman . . . . . . . . . . . . . . . . . . . . . . . . . . . . . . . . . . . . .Vice-Admiral Sir Roy Newman KCB
   Director . . . . . . . . . . . . . . . . . . . . . . . . . . . . . . . . . . . . . .Commander Jeff Tall OBE . . . . . . . . . . . . . . . .Tel: (023) 9251 0354
                E-mail: director@rnsubmus.co.uk
                Web: http://www.rnsubmus.co.uk

# MINISTRY OF DEFENCE

*Other Relevant Contacts (Continued)*

## NAVY

**Naval Manning Agency** *(Executive Agency)* . . . . . . . . . . . . .Victory Building, HM Naval Base, Portsmouth, PO1 3LS
    Chief Executive . . . . . . . . . . . . . . . . . . . . . . . . . . . . . .Rear-Admiral Mark Kerr . . . . . . . . . . . . . . . . . .Tel: (023) 9272 2351
**Naval Recruiting and Training Agency** *(Executive Agency)* .Victory Building, HM Naval Base, Portsmouth, PO1 3LS
    Chief Executive . . . . . . . . . . . . . . . . . . . . . . . . . . . . . .Rear-Admiral Peter Davies CBE . . . . . . . . . . . . .Tel: (023) 9272 7600
**Warship Support Agency** *(Executive Agency)* . . . . . . . . . . .3131, Birch 1, Abbey Wood, Bristol, BS34 8JH
    Chief Executive . . . . . . . . . . . . . . . . . . . . . . . . . . . . . .Mr John Coles . . . . . . . . . . . . . . . . . . . . . . . . . .Tel: (0117) 913 7503
                                       Web: http://www.mod.uk/dlo/wsa

## NUCLEAR SAFETY

**Defence Nuclear Safety Committee** . . . . . . . . . . . . . . . . .D Strat Tech Secretariat, Room 5/24, Metropole Building,
                                       Northumberland Avenue, London, WC2N 5BP
    Chairman . . . . . . . . . . . . . . . . . . . . . . . . . . . . . . . . . . .Dr Samuel Harbison CB
    Secretary . . . . . . . . . . . . . . . . . . . . . . . . . . . . . . . . . . .Dr Alwyn Davies . . . . . . . . . . . . . . . . . . . . . . . .Tel: (020) 7218 2442
                                       E-mail: dstrattech@gtnet.gov.uk
**Nuclear Research Advisory Committee** . . . . . . . . . . . . . . .D Strat Tech (Sec-a), Room 5/24, Metropole Building,
                                       Northumberland Avenue, London, WC2N 5BP
    Chairman . . . . . . . . . . . . . . . . . . . . . . . . . . . . . . . . . . .*Vacant*
    Secretary . . . . . . . . . . . . . . . . . . . . . . . . . . . . . . . . . . .Dr John Paddy . . . . . . . . . . . . . . . . . . . . . . . . .Tel: (020) 7218 9433

## PATRIOTIC FUND

**Royal Patriotic Fund** . . . . . . . . . . . . . . . . . . . . . . . . . . .40 Queen Anne's Gate, London, SW1H 9AP
    Secretary . . . . . . . . . . . . . . . . . . . . . . . . . . . . . . . . . . .Colonel Richard Sandy . . . . . . . . . . . . . . . . . . .Tel: (020) 7233 1894

## PAY AND PERSONNEL (General)

**Armed Forces Pay Review Body** . . . . . . . . . . . . . . . . . . .Office of Manpower Economics, Oxford House,
                                       76 Oxford Street, London, W1N 9FD
    Chairman . . . . . . . . . . . . . . . . . . . . . . . . . . . . . . . . . . .Baroness Dean of Thornton-le-Fylde
    Secretary . . . . . . . . . . . . . . . . . . . . . . . . . . . . . . . . . . .Mrs Christine Haworth . . . . . . . . . . . . . . . . . . .Tel: (020) 7467 7214
                                       Web: http://www.mod.uk
**Armed Forces Personnel**
    **Administration Agency** *(Executive Agency)* . . . . . . . . . . .Central Office, Building 182, RAF Innsworth, Gloucester, GL3 1HW
    Chief Executive . . . . . . . . . . . . . . . . . . . . . . . . . . . . . .Rear Admiral Trevor Spires . . . . . . . . . . . . . . . .Tel: (01452) 712612
**Pay and Personnel Agency** *(Executive Agency)* . . . . . . . . . .Ministry of Defence, PO Box 99, Bath, BA1 1YT
    Chief Executive . . . . . . . . . . . . . . . . . . . . . . . . . . . . . .Mr David Ball . . . . . . . . . . . . . . . . . . . . . . . . . .Tel: (01225) 828108

## PIPELINES

**Oil and Pipelines Agency** . . . . . . . . . . . . . . . . . . . . . . . .35-38 Portman Square, London, W1H 6EU
    Chairman . . . . . . . . . . . . . . . . . . . . . . . . . . . . . . . . . . .Dr John Hastie
    Chief Executive . . . . . . . . . . . . . . . . . . . . . . . . . . . . . .Dr John Vardon . . . . . . . . . . . . . . . . . . . . . . . . .Tel: (020) 7935 2585

## POLICE

**Ministry of Defence Police** *(Executive Agency)* . . . . . . . . . .MDP HQ, Wethersfield, Braintree, Essex, CM7 4AZ
    Chief Constable . . . . . . . . . . . . . . . . . . . . . . . . . . . . . .Mr Lloyd Clarke QPM . . . . . . . . . . . . . . . . . . . .Tel: (01371) 854000
                                        Web: http://www.mdp.mod.uk

## POSTAL SERVICES

**British Forces Post Office** *(Executive Agency)* . . . . . . . . . . .BFPO 777, Inglis Barracks, Mill Hill, London, NW7 1PX
    Chief Executive . . . . . . . . . . . . . . . . . . . . . . . . . . . . . .Brigadier Peter JT Maggs CBE . . . . . . . . . . . . . . .Tel: (020) 8818 6315
                                        E-mail: bfpo@compuserve.com
                                        Web: http://www.bfpo.org.uk

## PROCUREMENT

**Defence Procurement Agency** *(Executive Agency)* . . . . . . .Maple 2C #2219, Ministry of Defence, Abbey Wood, Bristol, BS34 8JH
    Chief of Defence Procurement and Chief Executive . . . . . .Sir Peter Spencer KCB . . . . . . . . . . . . . . . . . . . .Tel: (0117) 913 0249
                                        Web: http://www.mod.uk/dpa

## RESERVES

**National Employers Advisory Board** . . . . . . . . . . . . . . . .Floor 1, Zone D, St George's Court, 2-12 Bloomsbury Way, London, WC1A 2SH
    Chairman . . . . . . . . . . . . . . . . . . . . . . . . . . . . . . . . . . .Lord Glenarthur
    Secretary . . . . . . . . . . . . . . . . . . . . . . . . . . . . . . . . . . .Lieutenant-Colonel Tim Corry . . . . . . . . . . . . . .Tel: (020) 7305 3180
                                        E-mail: info@sabre.mod.uk
                                        Web: http://www.sabre.mod.uk

# MINISTRY OF DEFENCE

*Other Relevant Contacts (Continued)*

## SCIENCE AND TECHNOLOGY
**Defence Science and Technology**
**Laboratory** *(Executive Agency)* . . . . . . . . . . . . . . . . . .Porton Down, Salisbury, Wiltshire, SP4 0JQ
Chief Executive . . . . . . . . . . . . . . . . . . . . . . . . . . . . . . . . . .Mr Martin Earwicker . . . . . . . . . . . . . . . . . . . . . .Tel: (01980) 613121
E-mail: central-enquiries@dstl.gov.uk
Web: http://www.dstl.gov.uk

**Defence Scientific Advisory Council** . . . . . . . . . . . . . . .Room 513, MOD Metropole Building, Northumberland Avenue,
London, WC2N 5BP
Chairman . . . . . . . . . . . . . . . . . . . . . . . . . . . . . . . . .Dr Julia King CBE
Secretary . . . . . . . . . . . . . . . . . . . . . . . . . . . . . . . . . . .Dr Alex Churchill . . . . . . . . . . . . . . . . . . . . . .Tel: (020) 7218 0333
Web: http://www.mod.uk/dsac.htm

## SECURITY AND INTELLIGENCE
**Defence Intelligence and Security Centre** *(Executive Agency)* .Chicksands, Shefford, Bedfordshire, SG17 5PR
Chief Executive . . . . . . . . . . . . . . . . . . . . . . . . . . . . . .Brigadier P F Everson OBE . . . . . . . . . . . . . . . . .Tel: (01462) 752000

## STATISTICS
**Defence Analytical Services Agency** *(Executive Agency)* . . .Zone 16, St George's Court, 2-12 Bloomsbury Way, London, WC1A 2SH
Chief Executive . . . . . . . . . . . . . . . . . . . . . . . . . . . . . .Mr Colin Youngston . . . . . . . . . . . . . . . . . .Tel: (020) 7305 2199
Web: http://www.dasa.mod.uk

## STORAGE AND DISTRIBUTION
**Defence Storage and**
**Distribution Agency** *(Executive Agency)* . . . . . . . . . . . . .Ploughley Road, Lower Arncott, Bicester, Oxfordshire, OX25 2LD
Chief Executive . . . . . . . . . . . . . . . . . . . . . . . . . . . . . .Mr Peter Foxton CBE . . . . . . . . . . . . . . . . . . . . .Tel: (01869) 256840
Web: http://www.dsda.org.uk

## TRANSPORT
**Defence Transport and Movements Agency**
*(Executive Agency)* . . . . . . . . . . . . . . . . . . . . . . . . . . . . .Building 400, DLO Andover, Monxton Road, Andover,
Hampshire, SP11 8HJ
Chief Executive . . . . . . . . . . . . . . . . . . . . . . . . . . . . . .Brigadier Chris Steirn CBE . . . . . . . . . . . . . . . . .Tel: (01264) 381993

## VETTING
**Defence Vetting Agency** *(Executive Agency)* . . . . . . . . . . . .Ministry of Defence Building, 107 Fulford Road,
Fulford Road, York, YO10 4AS
Chief Executive . . . . . . . . . . . . . . . . . . . . . . . . . . . . . .Mr Michael Wilson . . . . . . . . . . . . . . . . . . . . . .Tel: (01904) 662485
Web: http://www.dva.mod.uk

## WAR GRAVES
**Commonwealth War Graves Commission** . . . . . . . . . . . . . .2 Marlow Road, Maidenhead, Berkshire, SL6 7DX
Director-General . . . . . . . . . . . . . . . . . . . . . . . . . . . . . .Mr Richard Kellaway . . . . . . . . . . . . . . . . . . . .Tel: (01628) 634221
E-mail: casualty@cwgw.org
Web: http://www.cwgc.org

## WAR VETERANS
**Central Advisory Committee on War Pensions** . . . . . . . .c/o Veterans Agency, Tomlinson House, Norcross, Blackpool, FY5 3WP
Secretary . . . . . . . . . . . . . . . . . . . . . . . . . . . . . . . . . . .Ms Sandra Lloyd . . . . . . . . . . . . . . . . . . . . . . .Tel: (01253) 333076
E-mail: sandra.lloyd@veteransagency.gsi.gov.uk
Web: http://www.veteransagency.mod.uk
**Veterans Agency** *(Executive Agency)* . . . . . . . . . . . . . . . . . .Tomlinson House, Norcross, Blackpool, FY5 3WP
Chief Executive . . . . . . . . . . . . . . . . . . . . . . . . . . . . . .Mr Alan Burnham . . . . . . . . . . . . . . . . . . . . . . .Tel: (0800) 169 2277
E-mail: help@veteransagency.mod.uk
Web: http://www.veteransagency.mod.uk

# OFFICE OF THE DEPUTY PRIME MINISTER

26 Whitehall, London, SW1A 2WH
Tel: (020) 7944 4400
E-mail: [firstname.lastname]@odpm.gsi.gov.uk
Web: http://www.odpm.gov.uk

**Deputy Prime Minister and Secretary of State**
**for Local Government and the Regions** . . . . . . . . . . Rt Hon John Prescott MP
*Principal Private Secretary* . . . . . . . . . . . . . . . . . . . . . . . Mr Peter Betts . . . . . . . . . . . . . . . . . . . . . . . . . . . . Tel: (020) 7944 8604
*Special Advisers* . . . . . . . . . . . . . . . . . . . . . . . . . . . . . . . Mr Paul Hackett . . . . . . . . . . . . . . . . . . . . . . . . . . Tel: (020) 7944 8944
. . . . . . . . . . . . . . . . . . . . . . . . . . . . . . . . . . . . . . . . . . . . Ms Joan Hammell . . . . . . . . . . . . . . . . . . . . . . . . . Tel: (020) 7944 8616
. . . . . . . . . . . . . . . . . . . . . . . . . . . . . . . . . . . . . . . . . . . . Mr Ian McKenzie . . . . . . . . . . . . . . . . . . . . . . . . . Tel: (020) 7944 8617

**Minister of State** *(Minister for Housing and Planning)* . . . . . Rt Hon Keith Hill MP
*Private Secretary* . . . . . . . . . . . . . . . . . . . . . . . . . . . . . . . Mr Mark Livesey . . . . . . . . . . . . . . . . . . . . . . . . . . Tel: (020) 7944 8951

**Minister of State** *(Minister for Local*
*and Regional Government* . . . . . . . . . . . . . . . . . . . . . . Rt Hon Nick Raynsford MP
*Private Secretary* . . . . . . . . . . . . . . . . . . . . . . . . . . . . . . . Ms Angela Kerr . . . . . . . . . . . . . . . . . . . . . . . . . . . Tel: (020) 7944 4344

**Minister of State** *(Minister for Regeneration and Regional*
*Development)* . . . . . . . . . . . . . . . . . . . . . . . . . . . . . . . . . Rt Hon Lord Rooker
*Private Secretary* . . . . . . . . . . . . . . . . . . . . . . . . . . . . . . . Ms Jenny Mainland . . . . . . . . . . . . . . . . . . . . . . . . Tel: (020) 7944 4488

**Parliamentary Secretary** . . . . . . . . . . . . . . . . . . . . . . . Ms Yvette Cooper MP
*Private Secretary* . . . . . . . . . . . . . . . . . . . . . . . . . . . . . . . Mr Patrick Owen . . . . . . . . . . . . . . . . . . . . . . . . . . Tel: (020) 7944 4533

**Parliamentary Secretary** . . . . . . . . . . . . . . . . . . . . . . . Mr Philip Hope MP
*Private Secretary* . . . . . . . . . . . . . . . . . . . . . . . . . . . . . . . Ms Karen Abbott . . . . . . . . . . . . . . . . . . . . . . . . . . Tel: (020) 7944 4334

**CIVIL SERVICE**
**Permanent Secretary** . . . . . . . . . . . . . . . . . . . . . . . . . . Dame Mavis McDonald DCB
*Private Secretary* . . . . . . . . . . . . . . . . . . . . . . . . . . . . . . . Mr Andrew Vaughan . . . . . . . . . . . . . . . . . . . . . . . Tel: (020) 7944 8965

**Senior Directors / Directors-General**
Central Strategy and Resources . . . . . . . . . . . . . . . . . . . Mr Peter Unwin . . . . . . . . . . . . . . . . . . . . . . . . . . . Tel: (020) 7944 8940
Communications . . . . . . . . . . . . . . . . . . . . . . . . . . . . . . . Mr Derek Plews . . . . . . . . . . . . . . . . . . . . . . . . . . . Tel: (020) 7944 4645
Legal . . . . . . . . . . . . . . . . . . . . . . . . . . . . . . . . . . . . . . . . Ms Sandra Unerman . . . . . . . . . . . . . . . . . . . . . . . Tel: (020) 7944 6090
Local Government and Fire Group . . . . . . . . . . . . . . . . . Mr Neil Kingham . . . . . . . . . . . . . . . . . . . . . . . . . . Tel: (020) 7944 4040
Regional Development Group . . . . . . . . . . . . . . . . . . . . . Mr Rob Smith . . . . . . . . . . . . . . . . . . . . . . . . . . . . . Tel: (020) 7217 3550
Social Exclusion . . . . . . . . . . . . . . . . . . . . . . . . . . . . . . . Ms Claire Tyler . . . . . . . . . . . . . . . . . . . . . . . . . . . . Tel: (020) 7944 3160
Tackling Disadvantage Group . . . . . . . . . . . . . . . . . . . . . Mr Joe Montgomery . . . . . . . . . . . . . . . . . . . . . . . . Tel: (020) 7944 8310

## SUBJECT RESPONSIBILITIES AND CONTACTS
*Note: Staff on (020) 7944 numbers are based either at:*
*26 Whitehall, London, SW1A 2WH*
*Ashdown House, 123 Victoria Street, London, SW1E 6DE*
*Eland House, Bressenden Place, London, SW1E 6DU*
*Portland House, Stag Place, London, SW1E 5LP*

**Accounting (Departmental)**
Manager, Financial Accounting Services . . . . . . . . . . . . . Mr Alan Beard . . . . . . . . . . . . . . . . . . . . . . . . . . . . Tel: (020) 7944 2681
*(see also under Corporate Strategy and Resources)*

**Beacon Councils** . . . . . . . . . . . . . . . . . . . . . . . . . . . . . . Miss Jeanette Henderson . . . . . . . . . . . . . . . . . . . . Tel: (020) 7944 5191

**Boundaries, Local Authority** . . . . . . . . . . . . . . . . . . . . Mr Mark Barnett . . . . . . . . . . . . . . . . . . . . . . . . . . Tel: (020) 7944 4086

**Building Regulations**
Manager, Building Regulations Division . . . . . . . . . . . . . Mr Paul Everall . . . . . . . . . . . . . . . . . . . . . . . . . . . Tel: (020) 7944 5720
Appeals . . . . . . . . . . . . . . . . . . . . . . . . . . . . . . . . . . . . . . Mr Alec Custerson . . . . . . . . . . . . . . . . . . . . . . . . . Tel: (020) 7944 5738
Changes to Regulations . . . . . . . . . . . . . . . . . . . . . . . . . . Mr Ian Drummond . . . . . . . . . . . . . . . . . . . . . . . . . Tel: (020) 7944 4821
Charges . . . . . . . . . . . . . . . . . . . . . . . . . . . . . . . . . . . . . . Mr Alec Custerson . . . . . . . . . . . . . . . . . . . . . . . . . Tel: (020) 7944 5738
Competent Persons . . . . . . . . . . . . . . . . . . . . . . . . . . . . . Mr Ian Drummond . . . . . . . . . . . . . . . . . . . . . . . . . Tel: (020) 7944 4821
Construction Products . . . . . . . . . . . . . . . . . . . . . . . . . . . Mr Tariq Nawaz . . . . . . . . . . . . . . . . . . . . . . . . . . . Tel: (020) 7944 5710
Determinations . . . . . . . . . . . . . . . . . . . . . . . . . . . . . . . . Mr Alec Custerson . . . . . . . . . . . . . . . . . . . . . . . . . Tel: (020) 7944 5738

# OFFICE OF THE DEPUTY PRIME MINISTER

Disability and Building Regulations . . . . . . . . . . . . . . . . Mr Tariq Nawaz . . . . . . . . . . . . . . . . . . . . . Tel: (020) 7944 5710
Exemptions . . . . . . . . . . . . . . . . . . . . . . . . . . . . . . Mr Ian Drummond. . . . . . . . . . . . . . . . . . . . Tel: (020) 7944 4821
Fees / Charges . . . . . . . . . . . . . . . . . . . . . . . . . . . . Mr Alec Custerson . . . . . . . . . . . . . . . . . . . Tel: (020) 7944 5738
Inspectors . . . . . . . . . . . . . . . . . . . . . . . . . . . . . . . Mr John Thompson . . . . . . . . . . . . . . . . . . Tel: (020) 7944 5752
Party Wall Act . . . . . . . . . . . . . . . . . . . . . . . . . . . . Mr John Thompson . . . . . . . . . . . . . . . . . . Tel: (020) 7944 5752
Self Certification . . . . . . . . . . . . . . . . . . . . . . . . . . Mr Ian Drummond. . . . . . . . . . . . . . . . . . . . Tel: (020) 7944 4821
Standards Policy. . . . . . . . . . . . . . . . . . . . . . . . . . . Mr Tariq Nawaz . . . . . . . . . . . . . . . . . . . . . Tel: (020) 7944 5710
Statutory Undertakers. . . . . . . . . . . . . . . . . . . . . . . Mr Ian Drummond. . . . . . . . . . . . . . . . . . . . Tel: (020) 7944 4821

**Business Leases: Policy Advice** . . . . . . . . . . . . . . . . . . Mr Patrick Martin . . . . . . . . . . . . . . . . . . . . . . Tel: (020) 7944 5567

**By-laws, Local Authority** . . . . . . . . . . . . . . . . . . . . . . . Mr Mark Barnett. . . . . . . . . . . . . . . . . . . . . . . . Tel: (020) 7944 4086

**Cemeteries and Burials** . . . . . . . . . . . . . . . . . . . . . . . . Mrs Judith-Anne MacKenzie. . . . . . . . . . . . . . . Tel: (020) 7944 4789

**Churchyards, Closing of.** . . . . . . . . . . . . . . . . . . . . . . . Mrs Judith-Anne MacKenzie . . . . . . . . . . . . . . . Tel: (020) 7944 4789

**Civil Resilience**
Director, Civil Resilience . . . . . . . . . . . . . . . . . . . . . Mr Alun-Evans . . . . . . . . . . . . . . . . . . . . . . Tel: (020) 7944 0052
Manager, Civil Resilience. . . . . . . . . . . . . . . . . . . . . Mr Richard Bruce . . . . . . . . . . . . . . . . . . . Tel: (020) 7944 3150
Building Decontamination . . . . . . . . . . . . . . . . . . . . Mr Christopher Bowden. . . . . . . . . . . . . . . . . Tel: (020) 7944 2650
Special Projects . . . . . . . . . . . . . . . . . . . . . . . . . . . Mr Keith Phillips . . . . . . . . . . . . . . . . . . . . Tel: (020) 7944 5684

**Coalfields** . . . . . . . . . . . . . . . . . . . . . . . . . . . . . . . . . Ms Jane McLauchlan . . . . . . . . . . . . . . . . . . . Tel: (020) 7944 3748

**Codes of Conduct, Local Government** . . . . . . . . . . . . . . Mr Paul Downie . . . . . . . . . . . . . . . . . . . . . . . Tel: (020) 7944 4266

**Corporate Strategy and Resources**
Director, Corporate Strategy and Resources. . . . . . . . . . Mr Peter Unwin. . . . . . . . . . . . . . . . . . . . . . Tel: (020) 7944 8940
Deputy Director, Corporate Strategy and
    Head, Finance Division . . . . . . . . . . . . . . . . . . . Mr Andrew Lean. . . . . . . . . . . . . . . . . . . . . Tel: (020) 7944 6880
Deputy Director, Strategy and Resources. . . . . . . . . . . . Mr Mike Bailey. . . . . . . . . . . . . . . . . . . . . . Tel: (020) 7944 3200
Manager, Accounting Services . . . . . . . . . . . . . . . . . Mr Alan Beard . . . . . . . . . . . . . . . . . . . . . . Tel: (020) 7944 2681
Manager, Corporate Business and Delivery . . . . . . . . . . Mr Stuart Hoggan . . . . . . . . . . . . . . . . . . . . Tel: (020) 7944 4360
Manager, Human Resources, Departmental . . . . . . . . . . Ms Janet Fortune . . . . . . . . . . . . . . . . . . . . Tel: (020) 7944 3390

*Corporate Strategy and Resources (Continued)*
Manager, Information Management, Departmental . . . . . . Mr David Smith. . . . . . . . . . . . . . . . . . . . . . Tel: (020) 7944 5820
Manager, Infrastructure Services, Departmental. . . . . . . . Mr Simon Barnes. . . . . . . . . . . . . . . . . . . . . Tel: (020) 7944 5709
Manager, International and Central Policy. . . . . . . . . . . . Mr Matt Leach . . . . . . . . . . . . . . . . . . . . . . Tel: (020) 7944 8946
Accountancy
    Departmental Manager, Accounting Services. . . . . . . Mr Alan Beard . . . . . . . . . . . . . . . . . . . . . . Tel: (020) 7944 2681
    Accountancy Adviser . . . . . . . . . . . . . . . . . . . . . Mr Jim Wager . . . . . . . . . . . . . . . . . . . . . . Tel: (020) 7944 6534
    ASSAP Project. . . . . . . . . . . . . . . . . . . . . . . . . Ms Ruth Hemington . . . . . . . . . . . . . . . . . . Tel: (020) 7944 2725
    Business Warehouse. . . . . . . . . . . . . . . . . . . . . . Mr Tim Keegan . . . . . . . . . . . . . . . . . . . . . Tel: (020) 7944 6903
    Corporate and Customer Support. . . . . . . . . . . . . . Mr David Hemington. . . . . . . . . . . . . . . . . . Tel: (020) 7944 2682
    Finance Helpdesk . . . . . . . . . . . . . . . . . . . . . . . Mr Nick Mellors . . . . . . . . . . . . . . . . . . . . Tel: (020) 7944 2680
    Go-Sap Project. . . . . . . . . . . . . . . . . . . . . . . . . Mr Steve Brown. . . . . . . . . . . . . . . . . . . . . Tel: (020) 7944 8039
    Resource Accountancy . . . . . . . . . . . . . . . . . . . . Mr Chano Khosla . . . . . . . . . . . . . . . . . . . . Tel: (020) 7944 6906
Building Management. . . . . . . . . . . . . . . . . . . . . . . . Mr David Foster . . . . . . . . . . . . . . . . . . . . . Tel: (0191) 202 2816
Business Planning . . . . . . . . . . . . . . . . . . . . . . . . . Mr Stephen Putman. . . . . . . . . . . . . . . . . . . Tel: (020) 7944 5014
Central Secretariat . . . . . . . . . . . . . . . . . . . . . . . . . Ms Fiona Willis . . . . . . . . . . . . . . . . . . . . . . Tel: (0191) 202 3208
Consultancy Services: Departmental and Agencies . . . . . . Mr John Fitzpatrick. . . . . . . . . . . . . . . . . . . Tel: (020) 7944 4548
Corporate Secretariat . . . . . . . . . . . . . . . . . . . . . . . Mrs Helen Kelly . . . . . . . . . . . . . . . . . . . . . Tel: (020) 7944 4311
Counselling and Support Services. . . . . . . . . . . . . . . . Mr David Buttress. . . . . . . . . . . . . . . . . . . . Tel: (020) 7944 4474
Customer Services . . . . . . . . . . . . . . . . . . . . . . . . . Mr Peter Sheridan. . . . . . . . . . . . . . . . . . . . Tel: (020) 7944 3156
Electronic Document Management . . . . . . . . . . . . . . . Mr Tim Murray. . . . . . . . . . . . . . . . . . . . . . Tel: (020) 7944 8438
Enquiry Services . . . . . . . . . . . . . . . . . . . . . . . . . . Mr Peter Harris. . . . . . . . . . . . . . . . . . . . . . Tel: (020) 7944 5822
Estates and Property Management,
    Departmental Branch Head. . . . . . . . . . . . . . . . . Mr Dave Hill. . . . . . . . . . . . . . . . . . . . . . . Tel: (020) 7944 5870
    Building Services . . . . . . . . . . . . . . . . . . . . . . . Mr David Foster . . . . . . . . . . . . . . . . . . . . . Tel: (020) 7944 2816

# OFFICE OF THE DEPUTY PRIME MINISTER

**Finance, Departmental**
Manager, Finance Division . . . . . . . . . . . . . . . . . . Mr Andrew Lean . . . . . . . . . . . . . . . . . . . . Tel: (020) 7944 6880
Agencies: Finance . . . . . . . . . . . . . . . . . . . . . . . . Mr Ken Swan . . . . . . . . . . . . . . . . . . . . . . Tel: (020) 7944 4370
Audit Committee . . . . . . . . . . . . . . . . . . . . . . . . Mr Arni Narain . . . . . . . . . . . . . . . . . . . . Tel: (020) 7944 6844
Audit Services, Internal . . . . . . . . . . . . . . . . . . Mr Steve Simmonds . . . . . . . . . . . . . . . . Tel: (020) 7944 6521
Better Budget Management . . . . . . . . . . . . . . . . Ms Amanda McFeeters . . . . . . . . . . . . . . Tel: (020) 7944 6927
Business Risk Management . . . . . . . . . . . . . . . . Mr Arni Narain . . . . . . . . . . . . . . . . . . . . Tel: (020) 7944 6844
Capital Planning . . . . . . . . . . . . . . . . . . . . . . . . Mr Chris Smith . . . . . . . . . . . . . . . . . . . . Tel: (020) 7944 6933
Data Management . . . . . . . . . . . . . . . . . . . . . . . Mr Larry Honeysett . . . . . . . . . . . . . . . . Tel: (020) 7944 6974
Expenditure Administration . . . . . . . . . . . . . . . Ms Alison Harris . . . . . . . . . . . . . . . . . . Tel: (020) 7944 6346
Goods and Services . . . . . . . . . . . . . . . . . . . . . Mr Steve Rolfe . . . . . . . . . . . . . . . . . . . . Tel: (020) 7944 2498
Programme Management . . . . . . . . . . . . . . . . . Mr John Auger . . . . . . . . . . . . . . . . . . . . Tel: (020) 7944 6673
'Quangos': Finance . . . . . . . . . . . . . . . . . . . . . Mr Ken Swan . . . . . . . . . . . . . . . . . . . . . Tel: (020) 7944 4370
Resources Management . . . . . . . . . . . . . . . . . . Mr Jey Jeyaraj . . . . . . . . . . . . . . . . . . . . Tel: (020) 7944 6853
Training: Finance
Development . . . . . . . . . . . . . . . . . . . . . . . Mr Tim Nolan . . . . . . . . . . . . . . . . . . . . Tel: (020) 7944 4541
Management . . . . . . . . . . . . . . . . . . . . . . . Mr Andy Armstrong . . . . . . . . . . . . . . . . Tel: (020) 7944 2895
Human Resources *(see below under separate Human Resources entry)*
Information Sources and Services . . . . . . . . . . . Ms Sue Westcott . . . . . . . . . . . . . . . . . . Tel: (020) 7944 5830
IT, Departmental
Manager, Information Management, Departmental . . . . Mr David Smith . . . . . . . . . . . . . . . . . . Tel: (020) 7944 5820
Electronic Document Management . . . . . . . . . . . Mr Tim Murray . . . . . . . . . . . . . . . . . . . Tel: (020) 7944 8438
E-Procurement . . . . . . . . . . . . . . . . . . . . . . . . *Vacant* . . . . . . . . . . . . . . . . . . . . . . . . . Tel: (020) 7944 8796
Financial Expertise Centre . . . . . . . . . . . . . . . . Mr Tony Evans . . . . . . . . . . . . . . . . . . . Tel: (020) 7944 4936
Internet . . . . . . . . . . . . . . . . . . . . . . . . . . . . . Ms Sue Westcott . . . . . . . . . . . . . . . . . . Tel: (020) 7944 5830
Strategy and Information Management . . . . . . . . Mr Richard Smith . . . . . . . . . . . . . . . . . Tel: (020) 7944 3146
Pay, Departmental . . . . . . . . . . . . . . . . . . . . . . Mr Ron Nash . . . . . . . . . . . . . . . . . . . . . Tel: (020) 7944 3193
Records Management, Departmental . . . . . . . . . . Mr Ron Bennett . . . . . . . . . . . . . . . . . . Tel: (020) 7944 8442
Regulatory Impact Unit . . . . . . . . . . . . . . . . . . Mr David Plant . . . . . . . . . . . . . . . . . . . Tel: (020) 7944 3009
Security, Departmental . . . . . . . . . . . . . . . . . . Mr Peter Usher . . . . . . . . . . . . . . . . . . . Tel: (020) 7944 4794
Strategy and Management, Information Management . . . . Mr Richard Smith . . . . . . . . . . . . . . . . Tel: (020) 7944 3146
Targets and Delivery Plans . . . . . . . . . . . . . . . . Mr Jonathan Capstick . . . . . . . . . . . . . . Tel: (020) 7944 3014
Workforce Planning, Departmental . . . . . . . . . . Mrs Miranda Abrey . . . . . . . . . . . . . . . . Tel: (020) 7944 3700

**Commission for New Towns** . . . . . . . . . . . . . . Mr Robert Gilchrist . . . . . . . . . . . . . . . . Tel: (020) 7944 3738

**Communications** *(see below under Press and Publicity)*

**Conservation Areas** . . . . . . . . . . . . . . . . . . . . Mr Graham Davis . . . . . . . . . . . . . . . . . Tel: (020) 7944 3952

**Crematoria** . . . . . . . . . . . . . . . . . . . . . . . . . . Mrs Judith-Anne MacKenzie . . . . . . . . . . Tel: (020) 7944 4789

**Cross Cutting Issues (Deputy Prime Minister's Responsibilities)**
Cabinet Committees . . . . . . . . . . . . . . . . . . . . . Ms Ciara Mulligan . . . . . . . . . . . . . . . . . Tel: (020) 7944 8611
European Union . . . . . . . . . . . . . . . . . . . . . . . . Mr Timothy Morgan . . . . . . . . . . . . . . . . Tel: (020) 7944 8916
Public Services . . . . . . . . . . . . . . . . . . . . . . . . Ms Margaret Davies . . . . . . . . . . . . . . . . Tel: (020) 7944 5397
Regulatory Impact Unit . . . . . . . . . . . . . . . . . . Mr David Plant . . . . . . . . . . . . . . . . . . . Tel: (020) 7944 3009

**Departmental Business Services** *(see above under Corporate Strategy and Resources )*

**Devolved Administrations (Scotland and Wales),**
**Relations with** . . . . . . . . . . . . . . . . . . . . . . . Mr Mark Barnett . . . . . . . . . . . . . . . . . . Tel: (020) 7944 4086

**Dome Sale** . . . . . . . . . . . . . . . . . . . . . . . . . . . Mr David Liston-Jones . . . . . . . . . . . . . . Tel: (020) 7944 3750

**Economics**
Senior Economic Adviser . . . . . . . . . . . . . . . . . Mr Michael Kell . . . . . . . . . . . . . . . . . . Tel: (020) 7944 8040
Fire Services . . . . . . . . . . . . . . . . . . . . . . . . . . Miss Hazel Granger . . . . . . . . . . . . . . . . Tel: (020) 7944 3020
Housing
Private . . . . . . . . . . . . . . . . . . . . . . . . . . . . Mr Chris Nicholls . . . . . . . . . . . . . . . . . Tel: (020) 7944 3285
Social . . . . . . . . . . . . . . . . . . . . . . . . . . . . . Mr Ben Ridehalgh . . . . . . . . . . . . . . . . . Tel: (020) 7944 3266

# OFFICE OF THE DEPUTY PRIME MINISTER

| | | |
|---|---|---|
| Methodology | Mr Nick Haigh | Tel: (020) 7944 1463 |
| Planning, Town and Country | Mr Gareth Arthur | Tel: (020) 7944 3174 |
| Regeneration | Mr Giovanni Razzu | Tel: (020) 7944 3274 |
| Regional | Mr Charles Tarvin | Tel: (020) 7944 3629 |
| Risk | Miss Hazel Granger | Tel: (020) 7944 3020 |
| Taxation | Miss Hazel Granger | Tel: (020) 7944 3020 |
| Urban Policy | Mr John Curnow | Tel: (020) 7944 3327 |

**Elections: Local Election Pilots** ... Mr Paul Downie ... Tel: (020) 7944 4266

**English Partnerships: Sponsorship** ... Mr Robert Gilchrist ... Tel: (020) 7944 3738

**Enquiry Service** ... Mr Peter Harris ... Tel: (020) 7944 5822

**Equality and Diversity, Departmental** ... Ms Shelagh Prosser ... Tel: (020) 7944 2618

**Estates, Departmental** ... Mr Dave Hill ... Tel: (020) 7944 5870

**European Union** ... Mr Timothy Morgan ... Tel: (020) 7944 8916

**E-voting** ... Mr Paul Downie ... Tel: (020) 7944 4266

**Finance, Departmental** *(see above under Corporate Strategy and Resources)*

**Finance, Local Government** *(see below under Local Government Finance)*

**Fire**

| | | |
|---|---|---|
| Director, Fire and Rescue Service Directorate | Mr Clive Norris CB | Tel: (020) 7944 3990 |
| Manager, Fire Legislation, Safety and Pensions Division | Ms Diana Kahn | Tel: (020) 7944 5530 |
| Manager, Fire Research | Dr David Peace | Tel: (020) 7944 5670 |
| Manager, Fire Service Effectiveness | Ms Marie Winckler | Tel: (020) 7944 6060 |
| Manager, Fire Service Improvement | Mr Dave Lawrence | Tel: (020) 7944 5560 |
| Arson | | |
|     Reduction | Dr Teresa Clay | Tel: (020) 7944 8897 |
|     Research | Ms Lorraine Watson | Tel: (020) 7944 8898 |
| Best Value | Mr David Harper | Tel: (020) 7944 3690 |
| Community Fire Safety Policy | Dr Teresa Clay | Tel: (020) 7944 8897 |
| Contingencies Liaison | Mr David Harper | Tel: (020) 7944 3690 |
| Control Rooms | Mr Dermot Paddon | Tel: (020) 7944 3238 |
| Cover | Mr David Steer | Tel: (020) 7944 5672 |
| Crown Premises Inspection | Mr Martin Finch | Tel: (020) 7944 5592 |
| Discipline | Ms Gill McManus | Tel: (020) 7944 8640 |
| Economics | Miss Hazel Granger | Tel: (020) 7944 3020 |
| Equal Opportunities | Ms Gill McManus | Tel: (020) 7944 8640 |
| Equipment Research | Mr Martin Thomas | Tel: (01608) 650004 |
| Financing | | |
|     Co-ordination | Ms Margaret Bell | Tel: (020) 7944 8651 |
| Fire Authorities | Mr Matthew Bailes | Tel: (020) 7944 4778 |
| Fire Service Cover | Mr David Steer | Tel: (020) 7944 5242 |
| Honours | Mr Martin Hill | Tel: (020) 7944 8641 |
| Inspectorate | | |
|     HM Chief Inspector, Fire Service | Sir Graham Meldrum CBE QFSM | Tel: (020) 7944 5610 |
|     Senior Inspector, Fire Service | Mr Peter Morphew CBE QFSM | Tel: (020) 7944 5787 |
| Leadership | Mr Richard Twyman | Tel: (020) 7944 6192 |
| Modernisation and Improvement | Mr Dave Lawrence | Tel: (020) 7944 5560 |
| Operations | Mr Martin Hill | Tel: (020) 7944 8641 |
| Pensions | Mr Martin Hill | Tel: (020) 7944 8641 |
| Personnel and Administration | Ms Gill McManus | Tel: (020) 7944 8640 |
| Recruitment | Ms Christine Symes | Tel: (020) 7944 3578 |

# OFFICE OF THE DEPUTY PRIME MINISTER

Research
Manager, Fire Research. . . . . . . . . . . . . . . . . . . . . . Dr David Peace. . . . . . . . . . . . . . . . . . . . . . . Tel: (020) 7944 5670
    Arson . . . . . . . . . . . . . . . . . . . . . . . . . . . . . . . . Ms Lorraine Watson . . . . . . . . . . . . . . . . . . . . Tel: (020) 7944 8898
    Equipment . . . . . . . . . . . . . . . . . . . . . . . . . . . . Mr Martin Thomas. . . . . . . . . . . . . . . . . . . . . Tel: (01608) 650004
    Resources. . . . . . . . . . . . . . . . . . . . . . . . . . . . . Mr Brian Nash . . . . . . . . . . . . . . . . . . . . . . . . Tel: (020) 7944 5620
    Operational. . . . . . . . . . . . . . . . . . . . . . . . . . . Ms Cath Reynolds. . . . . . . . . . . . . . . . . . . . . . Tel: (020) 7944 5669
Retained Firefighters . . . . . . . . . . . . . . . . . . . . . Ms Gill McManus . . . . . . . . . . . . . . . . . . . . . Tel: (020) 7944 8640
Safety: Community Fire Prevention . . . . . . . . . . . . . . Dr Teresa Clay . . . . . . . . . . . . . . . . . . . . . . . Tel: (020) 7944 8897
Statistics
    Data Input . . . . . . . . . . . . . . . . . . . . . . . . . . . Ms Lorraine Watson . . . . . . . . . . . . . . . . . . . . Tel: (020) 7944 5242
    Dissemination . . . . . . . . . . . . . . . . . . . . . . . . Mr David Champion . . . . . . . . . . . . . . . . . . . Tel: (020) 7944 8898
Strike Cover. . . . . . . . . . . . . . . . . . . . . . . . . . . . Mr David Steer . . . . . . . . . . . . . . . . . . . . . . . Tel: (020) 7944 5242
Training. . . . . . . . . . . . . . . . . . . . . . . . . . . . . . . Ms Gill McManus . . . . . . . . . . . . . . . . . . . . . Tel: (020) 7944 8640
Vehicles. . . . . . . . . . . . . . . . . . . . . . . . . . . . . . . Mr Dermot Paddon . . . . . . . . . . . . . . . . . . . . Tel: (020) 7944 3238

**Gardens, Urban; Green Spaces**. . . . . . . . . . . . . . . Mr Tim Pope. . . . . . . . . . . . . . . . . . . . . . . . . Tel: (020) 7944 2638

**Gypsies: Policy and Site Management** . . . . . . . . . . . Ms Maria Stasiak . . . . . . . . . . . . . . . . . . . . . . Tel: (020) 7944 3676

**Hedges** . . . . . . . . . . . . . . . . . . . . . . . . . . . . . . . Ms Julie Richardson . . . . . . . . . . . . . . . . . . . . Tel: (020) 7944 5624

**Homelessness**
Director, Homelessness . . . . . . . . . . . . . . . . . . . . Mr Terrie Alafat . . . . . . . . . . . . . . . . . . . . . . Tel: (020) 7944 3600
Deputy Director, Homelessness. . . . . . . . . . . . . . . . Mr Gordon Campbell. . . . . . . . . . . . . . . . . . . Tel: (020) 7944 3633
Manager, Bed and Breakfast . . . . . . . . . . . . . . . . . Mr Ashley Horsey. . . . . . . . . . . . . . . . . . . . . . Tel: (020) 7944 8782
Manager, Homelessness Legislation and Policy . . . . . . . Mr Neil O'Connor . . . . . . . . . . . . . . . . . . . . . Tel: (020) 7944 3477
Manager, Rough Sleeping Policy and Services. . . . . . . . *Vacant* . . . . . . . . . . . . . . . . . . . . . . . . . . . . Tel: (020) 7944 3675
Communications and Strategic Policy . . . . . . . . . . . . Mr Charlie Chappell . . . . . . . . . . . . . . . . . . . Tel: (020) 7944 3469
Homelessness Strategies. . . . . . . . . . . . . . . . . . . . . Ms Sarah Phillips . . . . . . . . . . . . . . . . . . . . . Tel: (020) 7944 5912
Research . . . . . . . . . . . . . . . . . . . . . . . . . . . . . . Ms Jan White . . . . . . . . . . . . . . . . . . . . . . . . Tel: (020) 7944 3264

**Honours** . . . . . . . . . . . . . . . . . . . . . . . . . . . . . . Mrs Lynda Jones. . . . . . . . . . . . . . . . . . . . . . Tel: (020) 7944 4317

**Housing**
Director, Housing. . . . . . . . . . . . . . . . . . . . . . . . . Mr Neil McDonald . . . . . . . . . . . . . . . . . . . . Tel: (020) 7944 3260
Manager, Affordable Housing . . . . . . . . . . . . . . . . Mr Peter Ruback. . . . . . . . . . . . . . . . . . . . . . Tel: (020) 7944 3560
Manager, Decent Homes Finance and Co-ordination . . . . Ms Anne Kirkham. . . . . . . . . . . . . . . . . . . . . Tel: (020) 7944 3525
Manager, Housing Care and Support . . . . . . . . . . . . . Mr Bert Provan . . . . . . . . . . . . . . . . . . . . . . . Tel: (020) 7944 8010
Manager, Housing Data and Statistics . . . . . . . . . . . . Mr Bruce Oelman . . . . . . . . . . . . . . . . . . . . . Tel: (020) 7944 3269
Manager, Housing Management . . . . . . . . . . . . . . . Ms Dawn Eastmead. . . . . . . . . . . . . . . . . . . . Tel: (020) 7944 3630
Manager, Local Authority Housing . . . . . . . . . . . . . . MrChris Woolf . . . . . . . . . . . . . . . . . . . . . . . Tel: (020) 7944 3574
Manager, Private Sector Housing . . . . . . . . . . . . . . . Mr Jeff Hollingworth . . . . . . . . . . . . . . . . . . . Tel: (020) 7944 3447
Allocations. . . . . . . . . . . . . . . . . . . . . . . . . . . . . Mr Selvin Brown . . . . . . . . . . . . . . . . . . . . . Tel: (020) 7944 3478
Anti-Social Neighbours. . . . . . . . . . . . . . . . . . . . . Ms Leona Patterson. . . . . . . . . . . . . . . . . . . . Tel: (020) 7944 3476
Asylum Seekers . . . . . . . . . . . . . . . . . . . . . . . . . Ms Leona Patterson . . . . . . . . . . . . . . . . . . . . Tel: (020) 7944 3476
Best Value. . . . . . . . . . . . . . . . . . . . . . . . . . . . . Miss Emma Preece . . . . . . . . . . . . . . . . . . . . Tel: (020) 7944 8092
Commonhold . . . . . . . . . . . . . . . . . . . . . . . . . . Ms Charlotte Sewell . . . . . . . . . . . . . . . . . . . Tel: (020) 7944 3464
Community Care. . . . . . . . . . . . . . . . . . . . . . . . . Ms Lorraine Regan . . . . . . . . . . . . . . . . . . . . Tel: (01457) 851040
Co-operatives . . . . . . . . . . . . . . . . . . . . . . . . . . Miss Emma Preece . . . . . . . . . . . . . . . . . . . . Tel: (020) 7944 8092
Decent Homes Delivery . . . . . . . . . . . . . . . . . . . . Mr Terence Powell . . . . . . . . . . . . . . . . . . . . Tel: (020) 7944 3120
Disabled Facilities Grants. . . . . . . . . . . . . . . . . . . . Mr Jeff Hollingworth . . . . . . . . . . . . . . . . . . . Tel: (020) 7944 3447
Economics
    Housing Needs Indices. . . . . . . . . . . . . . . . . . . Mr Giovanni Razzu . . . . . . . . . . . . . . . . . . . . Tel: (020) 7944 3274
    Public Private Partnerships / Private
        Finance Initiative . . . . . . . . . . . . . . . . . . . . Mr Chris Nicholls . . . . . . . . . . . . . . . . . . . . . Tel: (020) 7944 3285
    Social. . . . . . . . . . . . . . . . . . . . . . . . . . . . . . Mr Ben Ridehalgh. . . . . . . . . . . . . . . . . . . . . Tel: (020) 7944 3266
Empty Property . . . . . . . . . . . . . . . . . . . . . . . . . Mr John Daniels . . . . . . . . . . . . . . . . . . . . . . Tel: (020) 7944 3553
Estate Renewal Challenge Fund . . . . . . . . . . . . . . . Mr Simon Llewellyn . . . . . . . . . . . . . . . . . . . Tel: (020) 7944 3608
Freehold Purchase . . . . . . . . . . . . . . . . . . . . . . . Ms Charlotte Sewell . . . . . . . . . . . . . . . . . . . Tel: (020) 7944 3464
Grants. Private Sector. . . . . . . . . . . . . . . . . . . . . . Mr Jeff Hollingworth . . . . . . . . . . . . . . . . . . . Tel: (020) 7944 3447
Gypsy Sites . . . . . . . . . . . . . . . . . . . . . . . . . . . . Ms Leona Patterson. . . . . . . . . . . . . . . . . . . . Tel: (020) 7944 3476
Home Improvement Agencies . . . . . . . . . . . . . . . . . Mr David Scott . . . . . . . . . . . . . . . . . . . . . . . Tel: (020) 7944 3467
Home Ownership . . . . . . . . . . . . . . . . . . . . . . . . Mr David Woodward . . . . . . . . . . . . . . . . . . . Tel: (020) 7944 3418
Home Ownership Taskforce . . . . . . . . . . . . . . . . . . Ms Ruth Bloomfield . . . . . . . . . . . . . . . . . . . Tel: (020) 7944 3645

# OFFICE OF THE DEPUTY PRIME MINISTER

*Housing (Continued)*

| | | |
|---|---|---|
| Homebuyers / Sellers Packs | Mr David Woodward | Tel: (020) 7944 3418 |
| Homelessness *(see above under separate entry)* | | |
| Homesteading | Mr Simon Llewellyn | Tel: (020) 7944 3608 |
| House Renovation Grants | Mr Jeff Hollingworth | Tel: (020) 7944 3447 |
| Houseboats | Mr John Daniels | Tel: (020) 7944 3553 |
| Housing Action Trusts | Mr Mike Wilkinson | Tel: (020) 7944 3712 |
| Housing Associations | | |
|    Estate and Land Policy | Mr Simon Llewellyn | Tel: (020) 7944 3608 |
|    Finance | Ms Ruth Bloomfield | Tel: (020) 7944 3645 |
|    Housing Corporation: Sponsorship | Miss Emma Preece | Tel: (020) 7944 8092 |
|    Private Finance | Ms Julie Pearce | Tel: (020) 7944 3607 |
| Housing Inspectorate | Miss Emma Preece | Tel: (020) 7944 8092 |
| Housing Taskforce, Community | Ms Hilary Bartle | Tel: (020) 7944 5760 |
| Infrastructure: Housing Growth Areas | Ms Jessie Hughes | Tel: (020) 7944 6833 |
| Key Workers' Housing | Mr Kevin Taylor | Tel: (020) 7944 3636 |
| Landlords, Licensing | Mr John Daniels | Tel: (020) 7944 3553 |
| Leasehold Reform | Ms Charlotte Sewell | Tel: (020) 7944 3464 |
| Local Authority | | |
|    Manager, Local Authority Housing | Mr Chris Woolf | Tel: (020) 7944 3574 |
|    Arms Length Management | Mr Mike Wilkinson | Tel: (020) 7944 3712 |
|    Economics | Mr Raymond Kershaw | Tel: (020) 7944 3588 |
|    Finance | Ms Helen Giles | Tel: (020) 7944 4432 |
|    Housing Investment Programmes | Mr Chris Woolf | Tel: (020) 7944 3574 |
|    Housing Revenue | Mr Subroto Duttaroy | Tel: (020) 7944 3586 |
|    Major Repairs Allowance | Mr Subroto Duttaroy | Tel: (020) 7944 3586 |
|    Rents | Ms Caroline Jackson | Tel: (020) 7944 3587 |
|    Stock | Mr Raymond Kershaw | Tel: (020) 7944 3588 |
| Local Housing Companies | Mr Simon Llewellyn | Tel: (020) 7944 3608 |
| Management, Housing | Mr Mike Wilkinson | Tel: (020) 7944 3712 |
| Mortgages | Mr David Woodward | Tel: (020) 7944 3418 |
| Multiple Occupation | Mr John Daniels | Tel: (020) 7944 3553 |
| Neighbours, Unsociable and Nuisance | Ms Leona Patterson | Tel: (020) 7944 3476 |
| Performance, Housing | Ms Anne Kirkham | Tel: (020) 7944 3525 |
| Private Housing Grants | Mr Jeff Hollingworth | Tel: (020) 7944 3447 |
| Private Rented Housing | Mr John Daniels | Tel: (020) 7944 3553 |
| Publication and Information | Ms Nicola Hughes | Tel: (020) 7944 3149 |
| Refugees | Ms Leona Patterson | Tel: (020) 7944 3476 |
| Registered Social Landlords | Miss Emma Preece | Tel: (020) 7944 8092 |
| Research | | |
|    English House Conditions Survey | | |
|       Dissemination of Results | Ms Barbara Rose | Tel: (020) 7944 3526 |
|       Survey Operation | Ms Lesley Smith | Tel: (020) 7944 3522 |
|    House Purchase Reforms | Mr Gavin Smart | Tel: (020) 7944 3473 |
|    Housing Management | Mr Keith Kirby | Tel: (020) 7944 3263 |
|    Housing Stock | Ms Anne Kirkham | Tel: (020) 7944 3525 |
|    Needs | Mr Jonathan Hanton | Tel: (020) 7944 3283 |
|    Private Sector | Mr Terry McIntyre | Tel: (020) 7944 3523 |
|    Regeneration Research Programme | Mr Jonathan Hanton | Tel: (020) 7944 3283 |
|    Standards | Ms Tina Golton | Tel: (020) 7944 3517 |
|    Tenant Participation | Mr Keith Kirby | Tel: (020) 7944 3263 |
| Right to Buy | Mr Chris Meader | Tel: (020) 7944 3422 |
| Right to Manage | Mr Mike Wilkinson | Tel: (020) 7944 3712 |
| Right to Repair | Mr Jeff Hollingworth | Tel: (020) 7944 3447 |
| Self Build Housing | Mr Simon Llewellyn | Tel: (020) 7944 3608 |
| Sellers Packs | Mr Gavin Smart | Tel: (020) 7944 3473 |
| Shared Ownership | Mr David Woodward | Tel: (020) 7944 3418 |
| Social Care and Housing | | |
|    Manager, Housing Care and Support | Mr Bert Provan | Tel: (020) 7944 8010 |
|    Community Care | Ms Lorraine Regan | Tel: (01457) 851040 |
|    Community Housing Task Force | Ms Hilary Bartle | Tel: (020) 7944 5760 |
|    Finance | Ms Cecilia Anto-Awuakye | Tel: (020) 7944 3482 |
|    Older People | Miss Kate Noble | Tel: (020) 7944 4289 |

# OFFICE OF THE DEPUTY PRIME MINISTER

*Housing (Continued)*

| | | |
|---|---|---|
| Special Needs | Ms Hilary Bartle | Tel: (020) 7944 5760 |
| Speed of Housebuilding | Ms Canda Smith | Tel: (020) 7944 5561 |
| Standards | Mr David Scott | Tel: (020) 7944 3467 |
| Starter Homes Initiative | Mr Kevin Taylor | Tel: (020) 7944 3636 |

Statistics

| | | |
|---|---|---|
| Manager, Housing Data and Statistics | Mr Bruce Oelman | Tel: (020) 7944 3269 |
| Collection of Statistics | Mr Andrew Davies | Tel: (0117) 372 8909 |
| Homelessness | Mrs Sarah Phillips | Tel: (020) 7944 5912 |
| House Building and Dwellings | Mr Bob Garland | Tel: (020) 7944 3265 |
| House Prices | Mr David Wall | Tel: (020) 7944 3306 |
| Household Projections | Mr Bob Garland | Tel: (020) 7944 3265 |
| Housing Associations | Mr David Wall | Tel: (020) 7944 3306 |
| Housing Needs | Mr Jonathan Hanton | Tel: (020) 7944 3283 |
| International | Mr Oscar Yau | Tel: (020) 7944 3332 |
| IT Development | Mr Dale Ridley | Tel: (020) 7944 3295 |
| Land Prices | Mr David Wall | Tel: (020) 7944 3306 |
| Local Authority | Mr Trevor Steeples | Tel: (020) 7944 3270 |
| Mortgages | Mr David Wall | Tel: (020) 7944 3306 |
| Neighbourhood | Mr Mick Johnston | Tel: (020) 7944 3302 |
| Private Rented Sector | Mr Ed Kafka | Tel: (020) 7944 3301 |
| Survey of English Housing | Mr Ed Kafka | Tel: (020) 7944 3301 |
| Tenure | Mr Andrew Davies | Tel: (020) 7944 8909 |
| Strategy, Housing | Ms Nicola Hughes | Tel: (020) 7944 3149 |
| Sustainable Communities *(see below under separate Sustainable Communities entry)* | | |
| Tenants' Interests, Privately Rented | Mr John Daniels | Tel: (020) 7944 3553 |
| Tenants' Rights | Ms Linda Oliver | Tel: (020) 7944 3486 |
| Tied Cottages | Mr John Daniels | Tel: (020) 7944 3553 |
| Transfers of Stock | Ms Hilary Bartle | Tel: (020) 7944 5760 |

## Human Resources, Departmental

| | | |
|---|---|---|
| Manager, Human Resources | Ms Janet Fortune | Tel: (020) 7944 3390 |
| Counselling Service | Mr David Buttress | Tel: (020) 7944 4474 |
| Employee Relations | Mr Guy Points | Tel: (020) 7944 3194 |
| Pay, Departmental | Mr Ron Nash | Tel: (020) 7944 3193 |
| Personnel Support | Mr Peter Sheridan | Tel: (0191) 202 3156 |
| Senior Civil Service and Fast Stream | Ms Michelle Cameron | Tel: (020) 7944 3172 |
| Workforce Planning | Mrs Miranda Abrey | Tel: (020) 7944 3700 |

## Information *(see below under Press and Publicity)*

## Information Management (Departmental) *(see above under Corporate Strategy and Resources)*

## Inner Cities *(see below under Urban Policy)*

## International Responsibilities, Deputy Prime Minister's

| | | |
|---|---|---|
| Manager, International and Central Policy | Mr Matt Leach | Tel: (020) 7944 3726 |
| Cross- Departmental Issues | Mrs Claire Cooper | Tel: (020) 7944 8970 |
| Euro Preparations | Mr Nick Nash | Tel: (020) 7944 2153 |
| European Union | Mr Timothy Morgan | Tel: (020) 7944 8916 |

## Land

| | | |
|---|---|---|
| Manager, Land and Property | Mr David Edwards | Tel: (020) 7944 5540 |
| Manager, Planning and Land Use Statistics | Mr Peter Capell | Tel: (020) 7944 5520 |
| Commercial Leasing | Mr Patrick Martin | Tel: (020) 7944 5567 |
| Housing and Land, Legal | Mr John Wright | Tel: (020) 7944 4840 |
| Housing Associations, Estate and Land Policy | Mr Simon Llewellyn | Tel: (020) 7944 3608 |
| Land Acquisition, Local Authority / Housing | Ms Caroline Jackson | Tel: (020) 7944 3587 |
| Land Charges, Local | Mr David Woodward | Tel: (020) 7944 3418 |
| Land Contamination | Dr David Brook | Tel: (020) 7944 3842 |
| Land Prices | Mr David Wall | Tel: (020) 7944 3306 |
| Land Stabilisation | Ms Jane McLauchlan | Tel: (020) 7944 3748 |
| Land Use Planning | Mr Adam Davies | Tel: (020) 7944 8792 |

# OFFICE OF THE DEPUTY PRIME MINISTER

**Legal**

| | | |
|---|---|---|
| Director-General, Legal Services | Miss Sandra Unerman CB | Tel: (020) 7944 6090 |
| Director, Legislative Unit | Ms Judith-Anne MacKenzie | Tel: (020) 7944 4789 |
| Constitutional and Regional Government | Ms Donatella Phillips | Tel: (020) 7944 4810 |
| Employment and Commercial | Mr Fred Croft | Tel: (020) 7944 4760 |
| Fire and Safety | Mr David Jordan | Tel: (020) 7944 5213 |
| Housing and Land | Mr John Wright | Tel: (020) 7944 4840 |
| Legal Support Services | Mr Malay Dutta | Tel: (020) 7944 6601 |
| Local Government Finance | Ms Pamela Conlon | Tel: (020) 7944 4769 |
| Planning | Ms Gloria Hedley-Dent | Tel: (020) 7944 4819 |

**Library** ... Ms Sue Westcott ... Tel: (020) 7944 5830

**Listed Buildings** ... Mr Graham Davis ... Tel: (020) 7944 3952

**Local Government: Finance**

| | | |
|---|---|---|
| Director, Local Government Finance | Miss Lindsay Bell | Tel: (020) 7944 4060 |
| Manager, Capital Finance and Accountancy Advice | Mrs Pam Williams | Tel: (020) 7944 4240 |
| Manager, Local Government Modernisation and Grant Distribution | Mr Robert Davies | Tel: (020) 7944 4050 |
| Managers, Local Government Statistics, Payments and IT | Mrs Meg Green | Tel: (020) 7944 4200 |
| | Mr Jon McGinty | Tel: (020) 7944 4200 |
| Manager, Taxation, Valuation and General Policy | Mr Andrew Allberry | Tel: (020) 7944 4220 |
| Accounting, Local Authority | Mr Graham Fletcher | Tel: (020) 7944 4235 |
| Audit and Accountancy | Ms Margaret Lees | Tel: (020) 7944 4418 |
| Borrowing, Local Authority | Mr Trevor Emmott | Tel: (020) 7944 4226 |
| Business Rates | Mr Andrew Allberry | Tel: (020) 7944 4220 |
| Capital Allocations: Local Authorities (England) | Miss Joanne Mctavy | Tel: (020) 7944 3370 |
| Capital Finance Systems | Mr Trevor Emmott | Tel: (020) 7944 4226 |
| Capital Transactions: Monitoring | Mr Richard Job | Tel: (020) 7944 4076 |
| Central Rating List | Mr Nic Suggit | Tel: (020) 7944 2524 |
| Charging, Discretionary Services | Mr Stephen Benton | Tel: (020) 7944 4263 |
| Companies, Local Authority | Mr Melvin Hughes | Tel: (020) 7944 4147 |
| Council Tax Policy | Mr Stephen Benton | Tel: (020) 7944 4263 |
| Council Tax Revaluation | Mr Tim Fairclough | Tel: (020) 7944 6061 |
| Crown Property Rating | Mr Nic Suggit | Tel: (020) 7944 2524 |
| Data Collection | Mr Steve Greenhill | Tel: (020) 7944 4157 |
| Discretionary Spending Powers | Ms Jane Cockerill | Tel: (020) 7944 4248 |
| IT Support | Mr Tim McSweeney | Tel: (020) 7944 4038 |
| Local Authority Companies | Mr Trevor Emmott | Tel: (020) 7944 4226 |
| Private Finance Initiatives | Mr Trevor Emmott | Tel: (020) 7944 4226 |
| Procurement | Mr Melvin Hughes | Tel: (020) 7944 4147 |
| Rate Relief | Mr Nic Suggit | Tel: (020) 7944 2524 |
| Revaluation, Council Tax | Mr Tim Fairclough | Tel: (020) 7944 6061 |
| Revenue Expenditure and Grants | Mr Nick Allan | Tel: (020) 7944 4015 |
| Revenue Grant Distribution Review | Ms Nicki Hinde | Tel: (020) 7944 8837 |
| Revenue Support Grant | Mr Mike Cook | Tel: (020) 7944 4055 |
| Sports Clubs Rating | Mr Nic Suggit | Tel: (020) 7944 2524 |
| Standard Spending Assessments | | |
| Capital Finance | Mr Mike Cook | Tel: (020) 7944 4055 |
| Data | Ms Karen Sussex | Tel: (020) 7944 4053 |
| Education, EPCS | Mr Stephan Herten | Tel: (020) 7944 4062 |
| Fire | Ms Emma Foulds | Tel: (020) 7944 4048 |
| General | Ms Karen Sussex | Tel: (020) 7944 4053 |
| Social Services | Ms Sarah Horne | Tel: (020) 7944 4066 |
| Statistics | | |
| Data Collection | Mr Steve Greenhill | Tel: (020) 7944 4157 |
| Local Authority Borrowing and Investment | Mr Mark Chaplin | Tel: (020) 7944 4167 |
| Local Taxation | Mr Andrew Presland | Tel: (020) 7944 4166 |
| Trading | Mr Melvin Hughes | Tel: (020) 7944 4147 |
| Valuation Office Agency: Liaison | Mr Nic Suggit | Tel: (020) 7944 2524 |
| Valuation Tribunals | Mr Stephen Benton | Tel: (020) 7944 4263 |
| Vote Manager | Mr Tony Finnegan | Tel: (020) 7944 4017 |

# OFFICE OF THE DEPUTY PRIME MINISTER

**Local Government: General**

| | | |
|---|---|---|
| Director-General, Local and Regional Government | Mr Neil Kingham | Tel: (020) 7944 4040 |
| Director, Local Government Performance and Practice Directorate | Mr John O'Brien | Tel: (020) 7944 2576 |
| Director, Regional Policy | Mr Richard Allan | Tel: (020) 7944 4990 |
| Manager, Democracy and Local Leadership | Mr Paul Rowsell | Tel: (020) 7944 4230 |
| Manager, Local Government Capacity and Modernisation | Mr Geoff Tierney | Tel: (020) 7944 8760 |
| Manager, Local Government Legislation | Mr Kevin Lloyd | Tel: (020) 7944 3774 |
| Manager, Local Government Modernisation | Mr Geoff Tierney | Tel: (020) 7944 8760 |
| Manager, Local Government Quality and Performance | Mr John O'Brien | Tel: (020) 7944 2576 |
| Manager, Local Public Service Agreements | Mr Richard Gibson | Tel: (020) 7944 4031 |
| Access to Information | Mr Ashley Pottier | Tel: (020) 7944 4191 |
| Audit Commission Sponsorship | Miss Margaret Lees | Tel: (020) 7944 4418 |
| Beacon Councils | Miss Jeannette Henderson | Tel: (020) 7944 5191 |
| Best Value | | |
|     Performance Indicators | Mr Paul McCafferty | Tel: (020) 7944 4103 |
|     Policy, Legislation and Guidance | Mr Tony Hatch | Tel: (020) 7944 8813 |
| Boundaries | Mr Mark Barnett | Tel: (020) 7944 4086 |
| By-laws | Mr Mark Barnett | Tel: (020) 7944 4086 |
| Cabinets | Mr Ashley Pottier | Tel: (020) 7944 4191 |
| Central / Local Government Relations | Mr Paul Downie | Tel: (020) 7944 4266 |
| City Status | Mr Ashley Pottier | Tel: (020) 7944 4191 |
| Community Strategies | Ms Jane Cockerill | Tel: (020) 7944 4248 |
| Companies | Mr Paul McCafferty | Tel: (020) 7944 4103 |
| Conduct of Business | Mr Paul Downie | Tel: (020) 7944 4266 |
| Councillors' Allowances/Pecuniary Interests | Mr Paul Downie | Tel: (020) 7944 4266 |
| Councillors' National Code of Conduct | Mr Paul Downie | Tel: (020) 7944 4266 |
| Councillors, Role of | Mr Ashley Pottier | Tel: (020) 7944 4191 |
| Discretionary Spending | Ms Jane Cockerill | Tel: (020) 7944 4248 |
| Elections | Mr Ashley Pottier | Tel: (020) 7944 4191 |
| Electoral Commission Liaison | Mr Mark Barnett | Tel: (020) 7944 4086 |
| E-Government Programme | | |
|     Delivery | Miss Jeanette Henderson | Tel: (020) 7944 5191 |
|     Programme Development | Mr Julian Bowrey | Tel: (020) 7944 4218 |
| E-voting | Mr Paul Downie | Tel: (020) 7944 4266 |
| European Union | Mr Robert Lowenstein | Tel: (020) 7944 4267 |
| Finance *(see above under: Local Government: Finance)* | | |
| Inspection Policy | Mr Stephen Edwards | Tel: (020) 7944 4115 |
| International | Mr Robert Lowenstein | Tel: (020) 7944 4267 |
| Intervention | Mr Robert Whittaker | Tel: (020) 7944 4233 |
| Legislation | Ms Anne Hemming | Tel: (020) 7944 4867 |
| Local Authority Standards Committees | Mr Paul Downie | Tel: (020) 7944 4266 |
| Local Democratic Renewal | Mr Ashley Pottier | Tel: (020) 7944 4191 |
| Local Government International Bureau | Mr Robert Lowenstein | Tel: (020) 7944 4267 |
| Local Legislation | Mr Mark Barnett | Tel: (020) 7944 4086 |
| Local Public Service Agreements | Mr Richard Gibson | Tel: (020) 7944 4031 |
| Local Strategic Partnerships | Mr Mark Mason | Tel: (020) 7944 4022 |
| Mayors, Elected | Mr Ashley Pottier | Tel: (020) 7944 4191 |
| Officers, Role of | Mr Ashley Pottier | Tel: (020) 7944 4191 |
| Parishes | Mr Mark Barnett | Tel: (020) 7944 4086 |
| Pensions *(see below under Local Government: Pensions)* | | |
| Performance Delivery Framework | Ms Caroline Eagle | Tel: (020) 7944 2449 |
| Performance Framework | Ms Hilary Morse | Tel: (020) 7944 4978 |
| Performance Targets, Standards and Indicators | Mr Colin Cotmore | Tel: (020) 7944 4023 |
| Poorly Performing Authorities | | |
|     Advice | Ms Caroline Eagle | Tel: (020) 7944 2449 |
|     Intervention | Mr Robert Whittaker | Tel: (020) 7944 4233 |
|     Policy | Ms Hilary Morse | Tel: (020) 7944 4978 |
| Powers and Duties | Ms Jane Cockerill | Tel: (020) 7944 4248 |
| Private Bills | Mr Mark Barnett | Tel: (020) 7944 4086 |
| Procurement and Trading | Mr Melvin Hughes | Tel: (020) 7944 4147 |
| Referendums | Mr Ashley Pottier | Tel: (020) 7944 4191 |

# OFFICE OF THE DEPUTY PRIME MINISTER

*Local Government: General (Continued)*

| | | |
|---|---|---|
| Regional Data | Mr Paul McCafferty | Tel: (020) 7944 4103 |
| Research | Mr Paul McCafferty | Tel: (020) 7944 4103 |
| Section 28 | Ms Jane Cockerill | Tel: (020) 7944 4248 |
| Service Delivery Innovation | Mr Mark Holder | Tel: (020) 7944 4450 |
| Standards of Local Governance | Mr Paul Downie | Tel: (020) 7944 4266 |
| Surcharge | Mr Paul Downie | Tel: (020) 7944 4266 |
| Town Twinning | Mrs Pat Collins | Tel: (020) 7944 3797 |

**Local Government: Pensions**

| | | |
|---|---|---|
| Manager, Local Government Pensions | Mr Terry Crossley | Tel: (020) 7944 5970 |
| Equality Issues | Mr Keith Bloomfield | Tel: (020) 7944 6002 |
| Ill Health / Retirement Review | Mr Robert Holloway | Tel: (020) 7944 5998 |
| Mis-selling and Buyback | Mr Robert Holloway | Tel: (020) 7944 5998 |
| Pensions (General) | Mr Brian Town | Tel: (020) 7944 6015 |
| Schemes and Appeals | Mr Keith Bloomfield | Tel: (020) 7944 6002 |

**Mayors, Elected** ......... Mr Ashley Pottier ......... Tel: (020) 7944 4191

**Millennium Dome Sale** ......... Mr David Liston-Jones ......... Tel: (020) 7944 3750

**Minerals** (*see below under Planning*)

**New Towns** ......... Ms Jane McLauchlan ......... Tel: (020) 7944 3748

**Parishes** ......... Mr Mark Barnet ......... Tel: (020) 7944 4086

**Parliamentary Clerk** ......... Mr Selvin Brown ......... Tel: (020) 7944 8967

**Planning**

| | | |
|---|---|---|
| Director, Planning | Mr Brian Hackland | Tel: (020) 7944 3900 |
| Deputy Director, Planning | Mr Mike Ash | Tel: (020) 7944 3890 |
| Manager, Development Control | Mr John Stambollouian | Tel: (020) 7944 3940 |
| Manager, Minerals and Waste Planning | Mr Lester Hicks | Tel: (020) 7944 3870 |
| Manager, Planning and Land Use Statistics | Mr Peter Capell | Tel: (020) 7944 5520 |
| Manager, Planning Central Casework | Ms Joan Bailey | Tel: (020) 7944 8700 |
| Manager, Planning Inspectorate Review | Mr Alan Gray | Tel: (020) 7944 3880 |
| Manager, Planning Legislation and Implementation | Mr Bob Ledsome | Tel: (020) 7944 8770 |
| Manager, Planning Policies | Ms Joan Bailey | Tel: (020) 7944 3860 |
| Manager, Plans, Compensation and International | Ms Lisette Simcock | Tel: (020) 7944 3700 |
| Advertisements | Mr Steve Marshall-Camm | Tel: (020) 7944 3966 |
| Aggregates Guidance | Dr Brian Marker | Tel: (020) 7944 3851 |
| Agriculture | Mr David Wilkes | Tel: (020) 7944 3977 |
| Airports / Airfields | Ms Katy Collins | Tel: (020) 7944 3942 |
| Appeals and Call Ins | Ms Katy Collins | Tel: (020) 7944 3942 |
| Applications | Miss Helen Smith | Tel: (020) 7944 3952 |
| Best Value | Mr Richard Neville-Carle | Tel: (020) 7944 3938 |
| Blight | Mrs Jean Nowak | Tel: (020) 7944 3958 |
| Business Parks | Mr Michael Bach | Tel: (020) 7944 3976 |
| Casework | | |
|    Northern England and Midlands | Ms Rebecca Carpenter | Tel: (020) 7944 8721 |
|    Southern England | Mr Peter Bates | Tel: (020) 7944 8720 |
| Cement Industry | Dr Brian Marker | Tel: (020) 7944 3851 |
| Channel Tunnel Rail Link | Mr Tony Baden | Tel: (020) 7944 3918 |
| Coal | Mr Andrew Routh | Tel: (020) 7944 3878 |
| Coastal Planning | Dr David Brook | Tel: (020) 7944 3842 |
| Commercial Development | Mr Michael Bach | Tel: (020) 7944 3976 |
| Completion Notices | Mrs Jean Nowak | Tel: (020) 7944 3958 |
| Compulsory Purchase and Compensation | Mrs Jean Nowak | Tel: (020) 7944 3958 |
| Conservation Areas | Miss Helen Smith | Tel: (020) 7944 3952 |
| Control of Major Accident Hazards | Mr Roger Gebbels | Tel: (020) 7944 3903 |
| Countryside | Mr David Wilkes | Tel: (020) 7944 3977 |
| Crichel Down Rules | Mrs Jean Nowak | Tel: (020) 7944 3958 |
| Crime, Planning Out | Mr Peter Ellis | Tel: (020) 7944 3912 |

# OFFICE OF THE DEPUTY PRIME MINISTER

*Planning (Continued)*

| | | |
|---|---|---|
| Crown Developments | Mrs Jean Nowak | Tel: (020) 7944 3958 |
| Deemed Consents | Mrs Jean Nowak | Tel: (020) 7944 3958 |
| Design Quality | Mr Peter Ellis | Tel: (020) 7944 3912 |
| Development Plans | Mr Tony Baden | Tel: (020) 7944 3918 |
| Disused Mines | Mr Andrew Routh | Tel: (020) 7944 3878 |
| Electromagnetic Fields (Planning) | Ms Katy Collins | Tel: (020) 7944 3942 |
| Enforcement | Mr Steve Marshall-Camm | Tel: (020) 7944 3966 |
| Energy, Renewable | Ms Katy Collins | Tel: (020) 7944 3942 |
| Environmental Assessments | Mr Roger Gebbels | Tel: (020) 7944 3903 |
| European Spatial Development Perspective | Ms Christabel Myers | Tel: (020) 7944 3911 |
| Factories | Mr Michael Bach | Tel: (020) 7944 3976 |
| Flooding and Development | Dr David Brook | Tel: (020) 7944 3842 |
| General Consent Orders | Mrs Jean Nowak | Tel: (020) 7944 3958 |
| Geographic Information Strategy | | |
|     Digital Mapping | Ms Liz Hobman | Tel: (020) 7944 5522 |
|     Interdepartmental Strategy | Mr Jonathan Rhind | Tel: (020) 7944 5536 |
| Green Belts | Mr David Wilkes | Tel: (020) 7944 3977 |
| Gypsy Sites, Planning Control | Mr Steve Marshall-Camm | Tel: (020) 7944 3966 |
| Housing Design | Mr Peter Ellis | Tel: (020) 7944 3912 |
| Industrial Development | Mr Michael Bach | Tel: (020) 7944 3976 |
| International Planning | Ms Christabel Myers | Tel: (020) 7944 3911 |
| INTERREG | Ms Christabel Myers | Tel: (020) 7944 3911 |
| Information Technology (Planning) | Mr Steve Peters | Tel: (020) 7944 5542 |
| Land Contamination | Dr David Brook | Tel: (020) 7944 3842 |
| Land Use | Ms Liz Ketch | Tel: (020) 7944 8792 |
| Lawful Development Certificates | Mr Steve Marshall-Camm | Tel: (020) 7944 3966 |
| Legal Advice | Ms Gloria Hedley-Dent | Tel: (020) 7944 4819 |
| Leisure | Mr David Wilkes | Tel: (020) 7944 3977 |
| Listed Buildings | Miss Helen Smith | Tel: (020) 7944 3952 |
| Local Authority Development | Mrs Jean Nowak | Tel: (020) 7944 3958 |
| Local Planning Authority Performance | Mr Richard Neville-Carle | Tel: (020) 7944 3938 |
| Marine Dredging Policy and Restoration | Mr Tom Simpson | Tel: (020) 7944 3868 |
| Marine Dredging Regulations | Dr Brian Marker | Tel: (020) 7944 3851 |
| Minerals | | |
|     Energy Minerals, Legislation and IDO/OMP Casework | Mr Andrew Routh | Tel: (020) 7944 3878 |
|     Non Energy Minerals and General Casework | Dr Brian Marker | Tel: (020) 7944 3851 |
| Nature Conservation | Mr David Wilkes | Tel: (020) 7944 3977 |
| Noise | Ms Katy Collins | Tel: (020) 7944 3942 |
| Offices | Mr Michael Bach | Tel: (020) 7944 3976 |
| Open Cast Coal Mining | Mr Andrew Routh | Tel: (020) 7944 3878 |
| Planning Inspectorate | | |
|     Review | Mr Alan Gray | Tel: (020) 7944 3880 |
|     Sponsorship | Ms Lillian Birch | Tel: (020) 7944 3937 |
| Pollution Control | Dr David Brook | Tel: (020) 7944 3842 |
| Power Stations | Ms Katy Collins | Tel: (020) 7944 3942 |
| Public Inquiry Procedures | Ms Katy Collins | Tel: (020) 7944 3942 |
| Regional and Development Plans | Mr Tony Baden | Tel: (020) 7944 3918 |
| Renewable Energy Schemes | Ms Katy Collins | Tel: (020) 7944 3942 |
| Research Programme, Management and Finance | Mr Peter Bide | Tel: (020) 7944 3904 |
| Retailing | Mr Michael Bach | Tel: (020) 7944 3976 |
| Retrospective Permissions | Mr Steve Marshall-Camm | Tel: (020) 7944 3966 |
| Show People | Mr Steve Marshall-Camm | Tel: (020) 7944 3966 |
| Silica Sand | Dr Brian Marker | Tel: (020) 7944 3851 |
| Sport and Recreation | Mr David Wilkes | Tel: (020) 7944 3977 |
| Statistics | | |
|     Manager, Planning and Land Use Statistics | Mr Peter Capell | Tel: (020) 7944 5520 |
|     Applications and Development Control | Mr Chris Morrey | Tel: (020) 7944 5507 |
|     Land Use | Mr Denis Down | Tel: (020) 7944 5533 |
|     Regional | Mr Mike Haslam | Tel: (020) 7944 5135 |
|     Town Centre | Mr Peter Wilding | Tel: (020) 7944 5501 |
| Statutory Undertakers | Mrs Jean Nowak | Tel: (020) 7944 3958 |
| Sustainable Development | Mr David Wilkes | Tel: (020) 7944 3977 |
| Telecommunications | Ms Katy Collins | Tel: (020) 7944 3942 |

# OFFICE OF THE DEPUTY PRIME MINISTER

*Planning (Continued)*

| | | |
|---|---|---|
| Tourism | Mr David Wilkes | Tel: (020) 7944 3977 |
| Town Centres | Mr Peter Ellis | Tel: (020) 7944 3912 |
| Transport | Ms Liz Ketch | Tel: (020) 7944 8792 |
| Urban Design | Mr Peter Ellis | Tel: (020) 7944 3912 |
| Use Classes | Ms Katy Collins | Tel: (020) 7944 3942 |
| Warehouses | Mr Michael Bach | Tel: (020) 7944 3976 |
| Waste | Mr Tom Simpson | Tel: (020) 7944 3868 |
| Wind Farms | Ms Katy Collins | Tel: (020) 7944 3942 |

**Policy Co-ordination** .... Ms Shona Dunn .... Tel: (020) 7944 4360

**Press and Publicity**

| | | |
|---|---|---|
| Director of Communications | Mr Derek Plews | Tel: (020) 7944 4645 |
| Deputy Director of Communications | Mr Jane Groom | Tel: (020) 7944 4651 |
| Head of Marketing and Corporate Communications *(Acting)* | Ms Coral Hill | Tel: (020) 7944 4645 |
| Press Secretary to the Deputy Prime Minister | Mr Alan Schofield | Tel: (020) 7944 4651 |
| Building Regulations | Mr Ian Sear | Tel: (020) 7944 4607 |
| E-Communications | Mr Graham Noad | Tel: (020) 7944 5846 |
| Fire | Mr Ian Sear | Tel: (020) 7944 4607 |
| Housing, Planning and Regeneration | Ms Helen Egar | Tel: (020) 7944 5274 |
| Internal Communications | Ms Carol Hill | Tel: (020) 7944 4666 |
| Local Government and Regions | Mr Ian Sear | Tel: (020) 7944 4607 |
| London | Mr Ian Sear | Tel: (020) 7944 4607 |
| Neighbourhood Renewal | Ms Sara Tuck | Tel: (020) 7944 4613 |
| New Media, Print and Publishing | Mr Andy Seal | Tel: (020) 7944 4665 |
| Publicity | Mr Richard Meakin | Tel: (020) 7944 3397 |
| Regional Co-ordination | Ms Sara Tuck | Tel: (020) 7944 4613 |
| Resource Management | Mr Barry Hart | Tel: (020) 7944 4643 |
| Social Exclusion | Ms Sara Tuck | Tel: (020) 7944 4613 |
| Strategic Planning | Ms Jennie Hay | Tel: (020) 7944 8631 |
| Women | Ms Sara Tuck | Tel: (020) 7944 4613 |

**Private Bills** .... Mr Mark Barnett .... Tel: (020) 7944 4086

**Regeneration** *(see above under Housing and below under Urban Policy)*

**Regional Assemblies**

| | | |
|---|---|---|
| Manager, Regional Assemblies | Mr Ian Scotter | Tel: (020) 7944 4570 |
| Legislation | Ms Claire Brialey | Tel: (020) 7944 5154 |
| Local Government Reviews before Referendums | Ms Jessica Matthews | Tel: (020) 7944 4956 |
| Membership | Ms Jessica Matthews | Tel: (020) 7944 4956 |
| Powers and Functions | Ms Claire Brialey | Tel: (020) 7944 5154 |
| Referendums, Regional Assemblies | Ms Jessica Matthews | Tel: (020) 7944 4956 |

*(see also Regional Policy below)*

**Regional Co-ordination**

*Riverwalk House, 157 Millbank, London, SW1P 4RP*

| | | |
|---|---|---|
| Director-General, Regional Co-ordination Unit | Mr Rob Smith | Tel: (020) 7217 3550 |
| Director, Regional Co-ordination | Ms Teresa Vokes | Tel: (020) 7217 3189 |
| Director, Strategy and Resources | Ms Lynn Dikies | Tel: (0191) 202 3824 |
| Business Co-ordination | Mr Mark Savigar | Tel: (020) 7217 3141 |
| Business Development | Mr Vince Brady | Tel: (020) 7217 3555 |
| Corporate Business | Mr Clive Mills | Tel: (020) 7217 3363 |
| Corporate Communications | Mr Ian Jones | Tel: (020) 7217 3394 |
| Cross-Department Integration | Ms Louise Stitson | Tel: (020) 7217 3562 |
| Finance | Mr James McKendrick | Tel: (020) 7217 3410 |
| Human Resources | Ms Janina Gammans | Tel: (020) 7217 3647 |
| Information and Communication Technology | Mr Andy Bentley | Tel: (020) 7217 3012 |
| Knowledge Management | Mr Joe Fowler | Tel: (020) 7217 3599 |
| Pay Policy | Mr Paul Arkell | Tel: (020) 7217 3565 |
| Personnel Policy | Ms Jane Bishop | Tel: (020) 7217 3587 |
| Strategy | Mr Nick Dexter | Tel: (020) 7217 3583 |

*(For Government Offices for the Regions, see separate section on pp445-460)*

# OFFICE OF THE DEPUTY PRIME MINISTER

**Regional Policy**

| | | |
|---|---|---|
| Director, Regional Policy | Mr Richard Allan | Tel: (020) 7944 4990 |
| Economic Issues | Mr Charles Tarvin | Tel: (020) 7944 3629 |
| Economic Performance, Regional | Mr Philip Cox | Tel: (020) 7944 3380 |
| European Regional Development Fund (ERDF) | | |
|     Finance | Mr Chris Hubbard | Tel: (020) 7944 3804 |
|     Grants, Policy and Programme Management | Mrs Pat Collins | Tel: (020) 7944 3797 |
| Labour Mobility | Mr Charles Tarvin | Tel: (020) 7944 3629 |
| Regional Chambers | Mr Ian Scotter | Tel: (020) 7944 4570 |
| Regional and Development Plans | Mr Tony Baden | Tel: (020) 7944 3918 |
| Regional Development Agencies | | |
|     Delivery / Finance | Ms Hilary Davies | Tel: (020) 7944 6851 |
|     Policy | Mr David Liston-Jones | Tel: (020) 7944 3750 |
| Statistics | Mr Mike Haslam | Tel: (020) 7944 5135 |

**Research Analysis**

| | | |
|---|---|---|
| Chief Social Scientist, Research Analysis and Evaluation *(Acting)* | Ms Jan White | Tel: (020) 7944 3110 |
| Deputy Manager, Research Analysis and Evaluation | Ms Anne Kirkham | Tel: (020) 7944 3525 |
| Gypsies and Other Travellers | Mr Keith Kirby | Tel: (020) 7944 3263 |
| Homelessness | Ms Jan White | Tel: (020) 7944 3264 |
| Housing | | |
|     English House Conditions Survey | | |
|         Dissemination of Results | Ms Barbara Rose | Tel: (020) 7944 3526 |
|         Survey Operation | Ms Lesley Smith | Tel: (020) 7944 3522 |
|     House Purchase | Mr Gavin Smart | Tel: (020) 7944 3264 |
|     Management | Mr Keith Kirby | Tel: (020) 7944 3263 |
|     Needs | Mr Jonathan Hanton | Tel: (020) 7944 3283 |
|     Private Sector | Mr Terry McIntyre | Tel: (020) 7944 3523 |
|     Regeneration Research Programme | Mr Jonathan Hanton | Tel: (020) 7944 3283 |
|     Standards | Ms Tina Golton | Tel: (020) 7944 3517 |
|     Tenant Participation | Mr Keith Kirby | Tel: (020) 7944 3263 |
| Urban Research Programme | Ms Sarah Fielder | Tel: (020) 7944 3524 |

**Rough Sleepers** *(see above under Homelessness)*

**Science**

| | | |
|---|---|---|
| Chief Scientist | Mr David Fisk | Tel: (020) 7944 6980 |

**Social Exclusion Unit**

| | | |
|---|---|---|
| Director, Social Exclusion Unit | Ms Claire Tyler | Tel: (020) 7944 3160 |
| Business Development | Ms Vanessa Scarborough | Tel: (020) 7944 3320 |
| Children in Care | Ms Cath Shaw | Tel: (020) 7944 8010 |
| Communications | Mr Jos Joures | Tel: (020) 7944 2600 |
| Employment and Enterprise | Mr Marcus Bell | Tel: (020) 7944 8170 |
| Ex-Prisoners | Ms Louise Dominian | Tel: (020) 7276 2054 |
| Implementation | Mr Jos Joures | Tel: (020) 7944 2600 |
| Mental Health and | Ms Ruth Stanier | Tel: (020) 7944 2208 |
| Research | Ms Sally Burlington | Tel: (020) 7944 3320 |
| | Ms Vanessa Scarborough | Tel: (020) 7944 3320 |
| Transport | Mr Marcus Bell | Tel: (020) 7944 8170 |
| Young Runaways | Ms Ruth Stanier | Tel: (020) 7944 2208 |

**Statistics**

| | | |
|---|---|---|
| Fire | Mr David Champion | Tel: (020) 7944 8898 |
| Housing | | |
|     Manager, Housing Data and Statistics | Mr Bruce Oelman | Tel: (020) 7944 3269 |
|     Best Value Performance Indicators | Mr Trevor Steeples | Tel: (020) 7944 3324 |
|     Collection of Housing Statistics | Mr Andrew Davies | Tel: (0117) 372 8909 |
|     Homelessness | Mr Trevor Steeples | Tel: (020) 7944 3324 |
|     House Prices | Mr David Wall | Tel: (020) 7944 3306 |
|     Housebuilding | Mr Bob Garland | Tel: (020) 7944 3265 |

# OFFICE OF THE DEPUTY PRIME MINISTER

*Statistics (Continued)*

| | | |
|---|---|---|
| Household Projections | Mr Bob Garland | Tel: (020) 7944 3265 |
| Housing Associations | Mr David Wall | Tel: (020) 7944 3306 |
| International | Mr Oscar Yau | Tel: (020) 7944 3332 |
| IT Development | Mr Dale Ridley | Tel: (020) 7944 3295 |
| Land Prices | Mr David Wall | Tel: (020) 7944 3306 |
| Local Authority | Mr Trevor Steeples | Tel: (020) 7944 3324 |
| Mortgages | Mr David Wall | Tel: (020) 7944 3306 |
| Neighbourhood | Mr Mick Johnston | Tel: (020) 7944 3302 |
| Private Rented Sector | Mr Ed Kafka | Tel: (020) 7944 3301 |
| Survey of English Housing | Mr Ed Kafka | Tel: (020) 7944 3301 |
| Tenure | Mr Andrew Davies | Tel: (020) 7944 8909 |

Local Authorities

| | | |
|---|---|---|
| Manager, Local Government Finance Statistics | Mrs Meg Green | Tel: (020) 7944 4200 |
| Borrowing and Investment | Mr Mark Chaplin | Tel: (020) 7944 4167 |
| Data Collection | Mr Steve Greenhill | Tel: (020) 7944 4157 |
| Local Taxation | Mr Andrew Presland | Tel: (020) 7944 4166 |

Planning

| | | |
|---|---|---|
| Manager, Planning and Land Use Statistics | Mr Peter Capell | Tel: (020) 7944 5520 |
| Applications and Development Control | Mr Chris Morrey | Tel: (020) 7944 5507 |
| International | Mr Oscar Yau | Tel: (020) 7944 3332 |
| Land Use | Mr Denis Down | Tel: (020) 7944 5533 |
| Retail | Mr Peter Wilding | Tel: (020) 7944 5501 |
| Town Centre | Mr Peter Wilding | Tel: (020) 7944 5501 |
| Regional | Mr Mike Haslam | Tel: (020) 7944 5135 |

## Sustainable Communities

| | | |
|---|---|---|
| Director, Sustainable Communities | Mr Andrew Wells | Tel: (020) 7217 3025 |
| Briefing and Overview | Mr Mark Hamshar | Tel: (020) 7944 3435 |
| Communications | Ms Jackie Jowett | Tel: (020) 7944 5657 |
| Delivery | Mr Mark Coulshed | Tel: (020) 7944 8127 |
| Finance, Sustainable Communities | Ms Marie Ching | Tel: (020) 7944 6785 |
| Growth Areas and Housing Supply | Mr Henry Cleary | Tel: (020) 7944 8850 |
| Low Deman Housing Market Renewal | Mr Martin Townsend | Tel: (020) 7944 3136 |
| Market Renewal | Mr Duncan Campbell | Tel: (020) 7944 8091 |
| Market Restructuring | | |
| Market Restructuring Initiative | Ms Stephanie Couchman | Tel: (020) 7944 3991 |
| Policy | Ms Anna Lewis | Tel: (020) 7944 3136 |
| Ministerial Reporting | Mr Robert Cayzer | Tel: (020) 7944 7804 |

## Tackling Disadvantage Group

| | | |
|---|---|---|
| Director-General, Tackling Disadvantage Group | Mr Joe Montgomery | Tel: (020) 7944 8310 |
| Director, Neighbourhood Strategy | *Vacant* | Tel: (020) 7944 5756 |
| Deputy Director, Neighbourhood Renewal | Mr Alan Riddell | Tel: (020) 7944 8370 |
| Manager, Communications | Mr Martin Joseph | Tel: (020) 7944 8364 |
| Manager, Neighbourhood Renewal Implementation | Mr Jon Bright | Tel: (020) 7944 3784 |
| Manager, Neighbourhood Renewal Programme | Mr Allan Bowman | Tel: (020) 7944 3848 |
| Manager, Research | Ms Carol Hayden | Tel: (020) 7944 4439 |
| Asylum Seekers Policy | Miss Christina Bankes | Tel: (020) 7944 4616 |
| Community Cohesion | Miss Christina Bankes | Tel: (020) 7944 4616 |
| Community Participation | Ms Hulya Mustafa | Tel: (020) 7944 6894 |
| Drugs Policy | Miss Christina Bankes | Tel: (020) 7944 4616 |
| Education Department Liaison | Mrs Siobhan Larking | Tel: (020) 7944 8656 |
| Finance, Neighbourhood Renewal Unit | Mr Andy Armstrong | Tel: (020) 7944 2895 |
| Government Office Interface Team | Mr Colin Jones | Tel: (020) 7944 8320 |
| Health Department Liaison | Mr Tony Armstrong | Tel: (020) 7944 8377 |
| Home Office Liaison | Miss Emma Lord | Tel: (020) 7944 8357 |
| Knowledge and Good Practice Team | Mrs Gillian Houslin | Tel: (020) 7944 8024 |
| Local Strategic Partnerships Development | Mrs Julie Wyeth | Tel: (020) 7944 8371 |
| Neighbourhood and Street Wardens | Ms Susan King | Tel: (020) 7944 2532 |
| Neighbourhood Management | Mr Richard Longman | Tel: (020) 7944 8347 |
| Neighbourhood Renewal Fund | Mr Jonathan Tear | Tel: (020) 7944 3678 |

# OFFICE OF THE DEPUTY PRIME MINISTER

*Tackling Disadvantaged Group (Continued)*

New Deal for Communities

| | | |
|---|---|---|
| Implementation and Support | Mr Allan Bowman | Tel: (020) 7944 3848 |
| Programme Evaluation | Mr Oliver Cowan | Tel: (020) 7944 3258 |
| Programme Management | Ms June Dawes | Tel: (020) 7944 3603 |
| Partnerships, Development | Mrs Julie Wyeth | Tel: (020) 7944 8371 |
| Performance Analysis | Mr Anthony Campbell-Butler | Tel: (020) 7944 2886 |

Policy Co-ordination

| | | |
|---|---|---|
| Cross- Departments | Mr Richard Watson | Tel: (020) 7944 8697 |
| General | Mr Martin Joseph | Tel: (020) 7944 8364 |
| Policy Strategy | Mr Neil Witney | Tel: (020) 7944 8307 |
| Post Office Fund | Mr Colin Jones | Tel: (020) 7944 8320 |
| Race Equality Action Plan | Mr Deepak Rawal | Tel: (020) 7944 8302 |
| Research Local Economic Development | Mr Andrew Maggin | Tel: (020) 7944 8369 |
| Renewal Advice | Ms Carol Hayden | Tel: (020) 7944 4439 |
| Resource Management (Neighbourhood Renewal Unit) | Mr Patrick Allen | Tel: (020) 7944 8107 |
| Statistical Advice | Ms Jane Todorovic | Tel: (020) 7944 3105 |
| Strategic Initiatives and Foresight | Mr Andrew Maginn | Tel: (020) 7944 8369 |
| Trade and Industry Department Liaison | Mr Robert Mason | Tel: (020) 7944 8698 |
| Work and Pensions Department Liaison | Mr Robert Mason | Tel: (020) 7944 8698 |

| | | |
|---|---|---|
| **Thames Gateway** | Ms Pam Temple | Tel: (020) 7944 3680 |
| **Trees and Hedges** | Ms Julie Richardson | Tel: (020) 7944 5624 |

## Urban Policy

| | | |
|---|---|---|
| Director, Urban Policy | Mr David Lunts | Tel: (020) 7944 3770 |
| Chief Social Scientist, Research Analysis and Evaluation | Ms Jan White | Tel: (020) 7944 3110 |
| Manager, Central Economics Advice | Mr Michael Kell | Tel: (020) 7944 8040 |
| Manager, International Urban Policy | Mr Mitesh Dhanak | Tel: (020) 7944 8109 |
| Manager, Land and Property | Mr Martin Leigh-Pollitt | Tel: (020) 7944 5540 |
| Manager, Regeneration and Sponsorship | Mr David Liston-Jones | Tel: (020) 7944 3750 |
| Manager, Thames Gateway | Ms Pam Temple | Tel: (020) 7944 3680 |
| Allotments | Mr Alan Brown | Tel: (020) 7944 3736 |
| Brownfield Land | Ms Jane McLauchlan | Tel: (020) 7944 3748 |
| CABE, Sponsorship | Mr Peter Matthew | Tel: (020) 7944 3780 |
| Coalfields | Ms Jane McLauchlan | Tel: (020) 7944 3748 |
| Communications | Ms Maureen Holkham | Tel: (020) 7944 3707 |
| Community Enablers | Mr Peter Matthew | Tel: (020) 7944 3780 |
| Community Participation | Mr David Rayner | Tel: (020) 7944 3704 |
| Core Cities Working Group | Mr Alan Brown | Tel: (020) 7944 3736 |
| Derelict Land | Mr Peter Matthew | Tel: (020) 7944 3780 |
| Design Work Co-ordination, Urban | Ms Canda Smith | Tel: (020) 7944 5561 |
| Economic Development and Future Challenges | Mr Keith Thorpe | Tel: (020) 7944 3701 |

English Partnerships

| | | |
|---|---|---|
| English Partnerships and CNT Matters | Mr Robert Gilchrist | Tel: (020) 7944 3738 |
| Enterprise Zones | Ms Jane McLauchlan | Tel: (020) 7944 3748 |

European Regional Development Fund (ERDF)

| | | |
|---|---|---|
| Finance | Mr Chris Hubbard | Tel: (020) 7944 3804 |
| Policy and Programme Management | Mrs Pat Collins | Tel: (020) 7944 3797 |
| Good Practice | Ms Maureen Holkham | Tel: (020) 7944 3707 |
| Greenwich Peninsula | Mr Chris Stendall | Tel: (020) 7944 3746 |
| Groundwork, Sponsorship | Mr Peter Matthew | Tel: (020) 7944 3780 |
| Housing *(see above under Housing)* | | |
| Land Stabilisation | Ms Jane McLauchlan | Tel: (020) 7944 3748 |
| Liveability Fund | Mr Alan Brown | Tel: (020) 7944 3736 |
| New Towns | Ms Jane McLauchlan | Tel: (020) 7944 3748 |
| Millennium Dome | Mr Chris Stendall | Tel: (020) 7944 3746 |
| Parks | Mr Tim Pope | Tel: (020) 7944 2638 |
| Policy and Regeneration, Urban Environmental | Mr Peter Matthew | Tel: (020) 7944 3780 |
| Public Space | Mr Tim Pope | Tel: (020) 7944 2638 |
| Quality Services | Mr Alan Brown | Tel: (020) 7944 3736 |

# OFFICE OF THE DEPUTY PRIME MINISTER

*Urban Policy (Continued)*

| | | |
|---|---|---|
| Religious Council, Inner Cities | Mr David Rayner | Tel: (020) 7944 3704 |

Research

| | | |
|---|---|---|
| Chief Social Scientist, Research Analysis and Evaluation | Mr Waqar Ahmad | Tel: (020) 7944 3110 |
| Deputy Manager, Research Analysis and Evaluation | Ms Anne Kirkham | Tel: (020) 7944 3525 |
| Housing and Regeneration Research Programme | Mr Jonathan Hanton | Tel: (020) 7944 3283 |
| Urban Policy Research | Ms Sarah Fielder | Tel: (020) 7944 3524 |
| Skills Review - Built Environment | Ms Maureen Holkham | Tel: (020) 7944 3707 |
| Special Grants Programme | Mr David Rayner | Tel: (020) 7944 3704 |
| State Aids | Mr Stephen Stringer | Tel: (020) 7944 3754 |
| Trees and Hedges | Ms Julie Richardson | Tel: (020) 7944 5624 |
| Urban Design | Ms Canda Smith | Tel: (020) 7944 5561 |
| Urban Green Spaces | Mr Peter Matthew | Tel: (020) 7944 3780 |
| Urban Regeneration Companies | Mr Chris Stendall | Tel: (020) 7944 3746 |
| Urban Regeneration Economics | Mr John Curnow | Tel: (020) 7944 3327 |
| Urban Renaissance Reward | Ms Maureen Holkham | Tel: (020) 7944 3707 |
| Volunteering | Mr David Rayner | Tel: (020) 7944 3704 |

*(see also above under Housing and under Planning)*

| | | |
|---|---|---|
| **Valuation Tribunals** | Ms Margaret Lees | Tel: (020) 7944 4418 |
| **Wardens, Neighbourhood and Street** | Ms Susan King | Tel: (020) 7944 2532 |

## OTHER RELEVANT CONTACTS

**AUDIT**

| | | |
|---|---|---|
| **Audit Commission** | 1 Vincent Square, London, SW1P 2PN | |
| Chairman | Mr James Strachan | |
| Controller of Audit | Mr Steve Bundred | Tel: (020) 7828 1212 |
| | Web: http://www.audit-commission.gov.uk | |
| **District Audit** | 33 Greycoat Street, London, SW1P 2QF | |
| Chief Executive | Mr Alan Meekings | Tel: (020) 7828 4690 |
| | Web: http://www.district-audit.gov.uk | |

**BEACON COUNCILS**

| | | |
|---|---|---|
| **Advisory Committee on Beacon Councils** | 5/A3, Eland House, Bressenden Place, London, SW1E 5DU | |
| Chairman | Ms Marianne Hood | |
| Policy Official | Ms Soley Estat | Tel: (020) 7944 4400 |

**BOUNDARIES**

| | | |
|---|---|---|
| **Parliamentary Boundary Commission for** | | |
| **England** | Room B1/3, 1 Drummond Gate, London, SW1V 2QQ | |
| Chairman | Rt Hon Michael Martin MP *(Speaker of the House of Commons)* | |
| Joint Secretaries | Mr Robert Farrance | Tel: (020) 7533 5177 |
| | Mr Mark Barnett | Tel: (020) 7533 5177 |
| | Web: http://www.statistics.gov.uk/pbc | |

**BUILDING/CONSTRUCTION**

| | | |
|---|---|---|
| **Building Regulations Advisory Committee** | Portland House, Stag Place, London, SW1E 5LP | |
| Chairman | Mr Michael Finn | |
| Secretary | Mr Alec Custerson | Tel: (020) 7944 5738 |
| | Web: http://www.odpm.gov.uk/bregs/brac | |

**COMMUNITY FORUM**

| | | |
|---|---|---|
| **Community Forum** | 6/J2, Eland House, Bressenden Place, London, SW1E 5DU | |
| Chairman | Mr Joe Montgomery | Tel: (020) 7944 8306 |

**CONFERENCE CENTRE**

| | | |
|---|---|---|
| **Queen Elizabeth II Conference Centre** | | |
| *(Executive Agency)* | Broad Sanctuary, London, SW1P 3EE | |
| Chief Executive | Mr Ernest Vincent | Tel: (020) 7222 5000 |
| | E-mail: info@qeiicc.co.uk | |
| | Web: http://www.qeiicc.co.uk | |

# OFFICE OF THE DEPUTY PRIME MINISTER

*Other Relevant Contacts (Continued)*

## CROWN ESTATES
**The Crown Estate** . . . . . . . . . . . . . . . . . . . . . . . . . . . . . 16 Carlton House Terrace, London, SW1Y 5AH
    First Commissioner and Chairman . . . . . . . . . . . . . . . . Mr Ian Grant CBE
    Second Commissioner. . . . . . . . . . . . . . . . . . . . . . . . . . Mr Roger Bright . . . . . . . . . . . . . . . . . . . . . . . Tel: (020) 7210 4377
                                      Web: http://www.thecrownestate.co.uk

## ENGLISH PARTNERSHIPS
**English Partnerships**. . . . . . . . . . . . . . . . . . . . . . . . . . . 110 Buckingham Palace Road, London, SW1W 9SA
    Chairman . . . . . . . . . . . . . . . . . . . . . . . . . . . . . . . . . . Ms Margaret Ford
    Chief Executive . . . . . . . . . . . . . . . . . . . . . . . . . . . . . Mr David Higgins . . . . . . . . . . . . . . . . . . . . . . Tel: (020) 7881 1600
                                        Web: http:/:www.englishpartnerships.co.uk

## FIRE SERVICE
**Fire Service College** *(Executive Agency)* . . . . . . . . . . . . . . Moreton-in-Marsh, Gloucestershire, GL56 0RH
    Chief Executive *(Acting)*. . . . . . . . . . . . . . . . . . . . . . . . Ms Maggie Heart. . . . . . . . . . . . . . . . . . . . . . . Tel: (01608) 650831
                                        Web: http://www.fireservicecollege.ac.uk

## HOUSING
**Housing Action Trusts**
    *Castle Vale* . . . . . . . . . . . . . . . . . . . . . . . . . . . . . . . . 220 Farnborough Road, Birmingham, B35 7NL
        Chairman . . . . . . . . . . . . . . . . . . . . . . . . . . . . . . . . Mr Richard Temple-Cox CBE
        Chief Executive . . . . . . . . . . . . . . . . . . . . . . . . . . . . Mr Angus Kennedy . . . . . . . . . . . . . . . . . . . . . . Tel: (0121) 776 6784
                                        Web: http://www.cvhat.org.uk
    *Liverpool* . . . . . . . . . . . . . . . . . . . . . . . . . . . . . . . . . 2nd Floor, Cunard Building, Water Street, Liverpool, L3 1EG
        Chairman . . . . . . . . . . . . . . . . . . . . . . . . . . . . . . . . Ms Paula Ridley OBE
        Chief Executive . . . . . . . . . . . . . . . . . . . . . . . . . . . . Mr David Green . . . . . . . . . . . . . . . . . . . . . . . . Tel: (0151) 227 1099
                                        Web: http://www.liverpoolhat.org.uk
    *Stonebridge* . . . . . . . . . . . . . . . . . . . . . . . . . . . . . . . Kassinga House, 37-41 Winchelsea Road, London, NW10 8UN
        Chairman . . . . . . . . . . . . . . . . . . . . . . . . . . . . . . . . Ms Caroline Pickering
        Chief Executive . . . . . . . . . . . . . . . . . . . . . . . . . . . . Mr Ian McDermott. . . . . . . . . . . . . . . . . . . . . . Tel: (020) 8961 0278
                                        Web: http://www.stonebridgehat.org.uk
    *Tower Hamlets* . . . . . . . . . . . . . . . . . . . . . . . . . . . . . 542-544 Roman Road, Bow, London, E3 5ES
        Chairman . . . . . . . . . . . . . . . . . . . . . . . . . . . . . . . . Ms Sheila Drew-Smith
        Chief Executive . . . . . . . . . . . . . . . . . . . . . . . . . . . . Ms Jackie Odunoye . . . . . . . . . . . . . . . . . . . . . Tel: (020) 8983 5280
                                        Web: http://www.thhat.co.uk
**Housing Corporation** . . . . . . . . . . . . . . . . . . . . . . . . . . 149 Tottenham Court Road, London, W1T 7BN
    Chairman . . . . . . . . . . . . . . . . . . . . . . . . . . . . . . . . . Mr Peter Dixon
    Chief Executive . . . . . . . . . . . . . . . . . . . . . . . . . . . . . Mr Jon Rouse . . . . . . . . . . . . . . . . . . . . . . . . . Tel: (020) 7393 2000
                                        E-mail: enquiries@housingcorp.gsx.gov.uk
                                        Web: http://www.housingcorp.gov.uk
**The Rent Service** *(Executive Agency)*. . . . . . . . . . . . . . . . 5 Welbeck Street, London, W1G 9YQ
    Chief Executive . . . . . . . . . . . . . . . . . . . . . . . . . . . . . Ms Charlotte Copeland . . . . . . . . . . . . . . . . . Tel: (020) 7023 6000
                                        Web: http://www.therentservice.gov.uk

## LOCAL GOVERNMENT
**Electoral Commission**. . . . . . . . . . . . . . . . . . . . . . . . . . Trevelyan House, 30 Great Peter Street, London, SW1P 2HW
    Chairman . . . . . . . . . . . . . . . . . . . . . . . . . . . . . . . . . Mr Sam Younger
    Chief Executive . . . . . . . . . . . . . . . . . . . . . . . . . . . . . Mr Roger Creedon. . . . . . . . . . . . . . . . . . . . . . Tel: (020) 7271 0500
                                        Web: http//:www.electoralcommission.org.uk
**Local Government Commission for England** . . . . . . . . . Dolphyn Court, 10/11 Great Turnstile, London, WC1V 7JU
    Chairman . . . . . . . . . . . . . . . . . . . . . . . . . . . . . . . . . Professor Malcolm Grant
    Chief Executive . . . . . . . . . . . . . . . . . . . . . . . . . . . . . Ms Barbara Stephens. . . . . . . . . . . . . . . . . . . . Tel: (020) 7430 8400
                                        Web: http//:www.lgce.gov.uk
**Standards Boards for England** . . . . . . . . . . . . . . . . . . . 1st Floor, Cottons Centre, Cottons Lane, London, SE1 2QG
    Chairman . . . . . . . . . . . . . . . . . . . . . . . . . . . . . . . . . Sir Anthony Holland
    Chief Executive . . . . . . . . . . . . . . . . . . . . . . . . . . . . . Mr David Prince . . . . . . . . . . . . . . . . . . . . . . . Tel: (08450) 788181
                                        E-mail: enquiries@standardsboard.co.uk
                                        Web: http://www.standardsboard.co.uk

## OFFICE OF THE DEPUTY PRIME MINISTER

*Other Relevant Contacts (Continued)*

**LONDON**
**Greater London Authority** . . . . . . . . . . . . . . . . . . . . . . . City Hall, The Queen's Walk, London, SE1 2AA
   Mayor of London . . . . . . . . . . . . . . . . . . . . . . . . . . . Mr Ken Livingstone
   Chairman, London Assembly . . . . . . . . . . . . . . . . . . . . Baroness Hamwee GLA
   Chief Executive . . . . . . . . . . . . . . . . . . . . . . . . . . . . . Mr Anthony Mayer . . . . . . . . . . . . . . . . . . . . . Tel: (020) 7983 4000
                             Web: http://www.london.gov.uk

**ORDNANCE SURVEY**
**Ordnance Survey** *(Executive Agency)* . . . . . . . . . . . . . . . . Romsey Road, Southampton, SO16 4GU
   Chief Executive . . . . . . . . . . . . . . . . . . . . . . . . . . . . . Ms Vanessa Lawrence . . . . . . . . . . . . . . . . . . . . Tel: (023) 8030 5030
                             E-mail: customerservices@ordnancesurvey.co.uk
                             Web: http://www.ordnancesurvey.co.uk

**PLANNING**
**Advisory Panel on Standards for the**
   **Planning Inspectorate**. . . . . . . . . . . . . . . . . . . . . . . Floor 4 E/2, Eland House, Bressenden Place, London, SW1E 5DU
   Chairman . . . . . . . . . . . . . . . . . . . . . . . . . . . . . . . . Ms Corrine Swain OBE
   Secretary . . . . . . . . . . . . . . . . . . . . . . . . . . . . . . . . Ms Rebecca Simpson . . . . . . . . . . . . . . . . . . . Tel: (020) 7944 3933
                             E-mail: rebecca.simpson@odpm.gsi.gov.uk
**Planning Inspectorate** *(Executive Agency)* . . . . . . . . . . . . Temple Quay House, 2 The Square, Temple Quay, Bristol, BS1 6PN
   Chief Planning Inspector and Chief Executive . . . . . . . . Ms Katrine Sporle . . . . . . . . . . . . . . . . . . . . . Tel: (0117) 372 6372
                             Web: http//www.planning.gov.uk

**PROPERTY**
**Residential Property Tribunal Service** . . . . . . . . . . . . . . 10 Alfred Place, London, WC1E 7LR
   Senior President . . . . . . . . . . . . . . . . . . . . . . . . . . . Mrs Siobhan McGrath . . . . . . . . . . . . . . . . . . . Tel: (020) 7446 7756
                             Web: http://www.rpts.gov.uk

**REGIONAL DEVELOPMENT AGENCIES** *(See under Department of Trade and Industry)*

**VALUATION TRIBUNALS**
**Valuation Tribunal Service** . . . . . . . . . . . . . . . . . . . . . Block 1, 1 Torrens Street, Angel Square, London, EC1V 1NY
   Chief Executive . . . . . . . . . . . . . . . . . . . . . . . . . . . . Mr Laurence Barnes . . . . . . . . . . . . . . . . . . . . Tel: (020) 7841 8700
                             Web: http://www.valuation-tribunalservice.gov.uk

## HOUSE BUILDING

# THE HOUSE BUILDERS FEDERATION
### 56-64 Leonard Street, London EC2A 4JX

*Telephone* (020) 7608 5100
*Facsimile* (020) 7608 5101

*Contact:* John Slaughter – Director of Public Affairs
*E-mail:* john.slaughter@hbf.co.uk
*Web:* http://www.hbf.co.uk

The House Builders Federation (HBF) is the voice of the house building industry in England and Wales. Its membership ranges from large, multi-national companies to small locally-based businesses, which together build over 80% of all new homes in England and Wales each year.

# DEPARTMENT FOR EDUCATION AND SKILLS

Sanctuary Buildings, Great Smith Street, London, SW1P 3BT
Switchboard: Tel: (0870) 001 2345  Enquiries: Tel: (0870) 000 2288
E-mail: info@dfes.gsi.gov.uk
Web: http://www.dfes.gov.uk

## MINISTERS

**Secretary of State for Education and Skills** . . . . . . . . . . . Rt Hon Charles Clarke MP
    *Principal Private Secretary* . . . . . . . . . . . . . . . . . . . . . . . Mr Chris Wormald . . . . . . . . . . . . . . . . . . . . . Tel: (020) 7925 5963
    *Special Advisers* . . . . . . . . . . . . . . . . . . . . . . . . . . . . Ms Lisa Tremble . . . . . . . . . . . . . . . . . . . . . . . Tel: (020) 7925 6874
                              Mr Robert Hill . . . . . . . . . . . . . . . . . . . . . . . . . Tel: (020) 7925 6873

**Minister of State** *(Minister for Children, Young People*
    *and Families)* . . . . . . . . . . . . . . . . . . . . . . . . . . . . . . Rt Hon Margaret Hodge MBE MP
    *Private Secretary* . . . . . . . . . . . . . . . . . . . . . . . . . . . Ms Claire Carroll . . . . . . . . . . . . . . . . . . . . . . . Tel: (020) 7925 6951

**Minister of State** *(Minister for Lifelong Learning,*
    *Further and Higher Education).* . . . . . . . . . . . . . . . . Dr Kim Howells MP
    *Private Secretary* . . . . . . . . . . . . . . . . . . . . . . . . . . . Ms Jo Ware . . . . . . . . . . . . . . . . . . . . . . . . . . . Tel: (020) 7925 3707

**Minister of State** *(Minister for School Standards)* . . . . . . . . . Mr David Miliband MP
    *Private Secretary* . . . . . . . . . . . . . . . . . . . . . . . . . . . Mr Nick Carson . . . . . . . . . . . . . . . . . . . . . . . . Tel: (020) 7925 6254

**Parliamentary Secretary** *(Skills and Vocational Education)* . . Mr Ivan Lewis MP
    *Private Secretary* . . . . . . . . . . . . . . . . . . . . . . . . . . . Ms Jo Bewley . . . . . . . . . . . . . . . . . . . . . . . . . Tel: (020) 7925 5870

**Parliamentary Secretary** *(Schools)* . . . . . . . . . . . . . . . . . Mr Stephen Twigg MP
    *Private Secretary* . . . . . . . . . . . . . . . . . . . . . . . . . . . Mr Charles Deighton-Fox . . . . . . . . . . . . . . . . . . Tel: (020) 7925 6341

**Parliamentary Secretary**
    *(Sure Start, Early Years and Child Care)* . . . . . . . . . . . . . Lord Filkin
    *Private Secretary* . . . . . . . . . . . . . . . . . . . . . . . . . . . Ms Rebecca Beeton . . . . . . . . . . . . . . . . . . . . . Tel: (020) 7925 6391

## CIVIL SERVICE

**Permanent Secretary** . . . . . . . . . . . . . . . . . . . . . . . . . . Mr David Normington CB
    *Private Secretary* . . . . . . . . . . . . . . . . . . . . . . . . . . . Mr Paul Price . . . . . . . . . . . . . . . . . . . . . . . . . Tel: (020) 7925 6937

**Heads of Directorates**
    Director-General, Children, Young People and Families . . . . Mr Tom Jeffrey . . . . . . . . . . . . . . . . . . . . . . . . . Tel: (020) 7925 5486
    Director-General, Corporate Services and Development . . . . Mrs Susan Thomas . . . . . . . . . . . . . . . . . . . . . . Tel: (020) 7273 4864
    Director-General, Finance and Analytical Services . . . . . . . Mr Peter Makeham . . . . . . . . . . . . . . . . . . . . . . Tel: (020) 7925 5486
    Director-General, Higher Education . . . . . . . . . . . . . . . . Sir Alan Wilson . . . . . . . . . . . . . . . . . . . . . . . . Tel: (020) 7925 6584
    Director-General, Lifelong Learning . . . . . . . . . . . . . . . . Ms Janice Shiner . . . . . . . . . . . . . . . . . . . . . . . Tel: (020) 7925 6210
    Director-General, Schools . . . . . . . . . . . . . . . . . . . . . Mr Peter Housden . . . . . . . . . . . . . . . . . . . . . . Tel: (020) 7925 6504
    Director, Strategy and Communications . . . . . . . . . . . . . Mr Michael Stevenson . . . . . . . . . . . . . . . . . . . . Tel: (020) 7925 5092
    Legal Adviser . . . . . . . . . . . . . . . . . . . . . . . . . . . . Mr Jonathan Jones . . . . . . . . . . . . . . . . . . . . . . Tel: (020) 7273 5865

## SUBJECT RESPONSIBILITIES AND CONTACTS

*Notes:  (020) 7273 numbers refer to staff based at Caxton House, Tothill Street, London, SW1H 9NA*
       *(0114) numbers refer to staff based at Moorfoot, Sheffield, S1 4PQ*
       *(01325) numbers refer to staff based at Mowden Hall, Straindrop Road, Darlington, DL3 9BG*
       *(01928) numbers refer to staff based at East Lane, Runcorn, WA7 2GJ*

**Adoption** . . . . . . . . . . . . . . . . . . . . . . . . . . . . . . . Mr David Holmes . . . . . . . . . . . . . . . . . . . . . . . Tel: (020) 7972 4629

**Adult Learning and Skills**
    Director-General, Lifelong Learning . . . . . . . . . . . . . . . . Ms Janice Shiner . . . . . . . . . . . . . . . . . . . . . . . Tel: (020) 7925 6210
    Director, Adult Learning Group . . . . . . . . . . . . . . . . . . Mr Stephen Marston . . . . . . . . . . . . . . . . . . . . . Tel: (0114) 259 1250
    Director, Adult Basic Skills Strategy Unit . . . . . . . . . . . . Ms Susan Pember . . . . . . . . . . . . . . . . . . . . . . Tel: (020) 7273 4755
    Director, Learning, Delivery and Standards Group . . . . . . . Mr Peter Lauener . . . . . . . . . . . . . . . . . . . . . . . Tel: (0114) 259 3735
    Deputy Director, Skills Strategy, Policy and Support Unit,
        Adult Learning Group . . . . . . . . . . . . . . . . . . . . . Ms Madeline Dunie . . . . . . . . . . . . . . . . . . . . . . Tel: (020) 7273 5145

    Access to Learning / Learner Support . . . . . . . . . . . . . . Mr Tim Down . . . . . . . . . . . . . . . . . . . . . . . . . Tel: (0114) 259 3328

# DEPARTMENT FOR EDUCATION AND SKILLS

| | | |
|---|---|---|
| Lifelong Learning and Technologies | Ms Margaret Bennett | Tel: (0114) 259 3328 |
| Offenders Learning and Skills Unit | Mr Chris Barnham | Tel: (020) 7925 5985 |
| Planning and Delivery | Mr Mark Dawe | Tel: (0870) 001 2345 |
| Regional Skills | Ms Jane Mark-Lawson | Tel: (0114) 259 4923 |
| Sector Skills | Mr Simon Perryman | Tel: (0114) 259 3913 |
| Skills for Employment | Mr Simon Perryman | Tel: (0114) 259 3913 |
| Standards and Achievements | Mr Barry Brooks | Tel: (020) 7273 1397 |
| Strategy and Funding (Lifelong Learning) | Mr John Temple | Tel: (020) 7925 6210 |
| Workforce Development | Ms Jane Mark-Lawson | Tel: (0114) 259 4923 |
| | Ms Barbara Roberts | Tel: (020) 7925 5573 |
| Workplace Learning | Mr Hugh Tollyfield | Tel: (0114) 259 3737 |

## Analytical Services

| | | |
|---|---|---|
| Director-General, Finance and Analytical Services | Mr Peter Makeham | Tel: (020) 7925 5486 |
| Director, Analytical Services | Mr Paul Johnson | Tel: (020) 7925 7313 |
| Adults | Dr Bob Butcher | Tel: (0114) 259 3667 |
| Central Economics and International | Mr John Elliott | Tel: (0114) 259 3523 |
| | Mr Steve Leman | Tel: (0114) 259 3523 |
| Data Agency Project | Mr Alan Cranston | Tel: (020) 7925 3727 |
| Higher Education | Ms Karen Hancock | Tel: (020) 7925 7487 |
| Qualifications, Pupil Assessment and IT | Mr Malcolm Britton | Tel: (020) 7925 7315 |

## Careers Service *(see below under Connexions Service National Unit)*

## Children and Families Group

| | | |
|---|---|---|
| Director-General, Children, Young People and Families | Mr Tom Jeffrey | Tel: (020) 7925 5486 |
| Director, Children's Workforce Unit | Ms Jeanette Pugh | Tel: (020) 7925 5490 |
| Director, Local Transformation Group | Ms Sheila Scales | Tel: (020) 7273 1396 |
| Director, Safeguarding Children Group | Ms Althea Efunshile | Tel: (020) 7273 1396 |
| Director, Sure Start Unit | Ms Naomi Eisenstadt | Tel: (020) 7273 4717 |
| Change and Innovation | Ms Jenny Wright | Tel: (020) 7925 6076 |
| Child Protection | Mr Colin Green | Tel: (020) 7972 4507 |
| Children in Care | Mr David Holmes | Tel: (020) 7972 4507 |
| Children's Commissioner | Ms Anne Jackson | Tel: (020) 7925 6076 |
| Children's Fund | Ms Kathy Bundred | Tel: (020) 7273 1228 |
| Children's Trusts, Placement and Permanence | Mr David Holmes | Tel: (020) 7972 4507 |
| Cross Policy Group | Mr Gordon McKenzie | Tel: (0114) 259 4835 |
| Cross Whitehall Policy | Mr Marcus Bell | Tel: (0114) 259 4835 |
| Families | Ms Ruth Kennedy | Tel: (020) 7273 1396 |
| Finance | Ms Janet Grauberg | Tel: (020) 7925 6076 |
| Information Sharing | Mr Peter Mucklow | Tel: (0114) 259 3905 |
| Local Implementation | Mr Richard Blows | Tel: (0114) 259 3905 |
| Special Educational Needs | Ms Ann Gross | Tel: (020) 7925 5511 |
| Strategy and Performance | Ms Christina Bienkowska | Tel: (020) 7925 6076 |
| Vulnerable Children | Mr Bruce Clark | Tel: (020) 7273 1396 |
| Workforce, Children's | | |
|     Children's Workforce Reform | Mr Chris Wells | Tel: (020) 7925 5490 |
|     Information Sharing Assessment | Mr Peter Mucklow | Tel: (020) 7925 5490 |

**Communications** *(see below under Press and Communications)*

## Connexions Service National Unit

| | | |
|---|---|---|
| Director, Supporting Children and Young People and Head of Connexions Services | Ms Anne Weinstock | Tel: (0114) 259 3595 |
| Delivery and Quality | Mr Steve Jackson | Tel: (0114) 259 3681 |
| Operational Policy | Mr Gordon McKenzie | Tel: (0114) 259 4835 |
| Regions | Mr Steve Jackson | Tel: (0114) 259 3681 |
| Strategy and Communications | Ms Jeanette Pugh | Tel: (020) 7925 5490 |
| Volunteering and Activities for Young People | Ms Jane Haywood | Tel: (0114) 259 1165 |

## Corporate Services and Development

| | | |
|---|---|---|
| Director-General, Corporate Services and Development | Mrs Susan Thomas | Tel: (020) 7273 4864 |
| Change | Mr Mike Daly | Tel: (020) 7273 5921 |
| Commercial Services | Mr Paul Neill | Tel: (01928) 794601 |
| E-Delivery | Mr Kevin McLean | Tel: (020) 7273 5278 |
| Equality and Diversity | Ms Dawn Jarvis | Tel: (020) 7273 4742 |
| | Ms Jan Stockwell | Tel: (020) 7273 4742 |
| Information Services | Mr Colin Moore | Tel: (0114) 259 3736 |
| Leadership and Personnel | Mr Graham Archer | Tel: (020) 7273 6796 |
| Learning Academy | Mr Graham Holley | Tel: (020) 7273 4738 |

# DEPARTMENT FOR EDUCATION AND SKILLS

**E-Learning**

| | | |
|---|---|---|
| Director, Primary Education and E-Learning Group | Ms Helen Williams | Tel: (020) 7273 5273 |
| E-Learning Strategy Unit, Departmental | Ms Diana Laurillard | Tel: (020) 7273 4892 |
| ICT in Schools | Mr Doug Brown | Tel: (020) 7273 4915 |
| School Curriculum | Ms Mela Watts | Tel: (020) 7273 5821 |

**European Union** *(see below under International)*

**Finance**

| | | |
|---|---|---|
| Director-General, Finance and Analytical Services | Mr Peter Makeham | Tel: (020) 7925 5486 |
| Director, Finance | Mr Stephen Kershaw | Tel: (020) 7925 5486 |
| Corporate Planning and Performance | Ms Marion Maddox | Tel: (020) 7925 7463 |
| Financial Accounting | Mr Peter Connor CBE | Tel: (01928) 794203 |
| Internal Audit | Ms Suzanne Orr | Tel: (020) 7273 5762 |
| Programme and Project Management | Mr Ray Hinchcliffe | Tel: (020) 7925 6407 |
| Strategy | Mr Peter Houten | Tel: (0114) 259 4846 |

**Further Education Strategy** ... Mr Trevor Tucknutt ... Tel: (0114) 259 3205

**Higher Education**

| | | |
|---|---|---|
| Director-General, Higher Education | Sir Alan Wilson | Tel: (020) 7925 6584 |
| Director, Higher Education Strategy and Implementation Group | Ms Ruth Thompson | Tel: (020) 7925 6584 |
| Access and Modernisation | Mr Martin Williams | Tel: (020) 7925 7455 |
| Finance *(see below under Student Finance)* | | |
| Foundation Degrees, Employability and Progression | Mr Steve Geary | Tel: (0114) 259 3109 |
| Funding and Research | Ms Rachel Green | Tel: (020) 7925 5458 |
| Higher Education Admissions Review | Ms Linda Dale | Tel: (0114) 259 3539 |
| Higher Education Policy | Mr Nick Sanders | Tel: (020) 7925 6584 |
| Legislation | Ms Lesley Longstone | Tel: (020) 7925 6584 |
| Strategy and Performance Overview | Ms Elaine Hendry | Tel: (020) 7925 5985 |

**International Directorate** *(Joint Group with Department for Work and Pensions)*
*Caxton House, Tothill Street, London, SW1H 9NA*

| | | |
|---|---|---|
| Director, International | Mr Clive Tucker | Tel: (020) 7340 4021 |
| European Social Fund | Mr Gordon Pursglove | Tel: (01442) 677281 |
| European Union | Ms Jane Evans | Tel: (01442) 677281 |
| International Relations | Ms Marie Niven | Tel: (020) 7340 4023 |

**Learning Delivery and Standards**

| | | |
|---|---|---|
| Director, Learning Delivery and Standards | Mr Peter Lauener | Tel: (0114) 259 3735 |
| Director, Teaching and Learning Standards Unit | Mrs Jane Williams | Tel: (0114) 259 3945 |
| Further Education Strategy | Mr Trevor Tucknutt | Tel: (0114) 259 3205 |
| Individual Learning Accounts Projects | Mr Norman White | Tel: (0114) 259 1125 |
| Learning and Skills Partnership Unit | Mr James Turner | Tel: (0114) 259 1125 |
| Programme Management | Mr David Taylor | Tel: (0114) 259 4687 |
| Quality Improvement | Mr Jon Ashe | Tel: (0114) 259 1125 |

**Legal Advice / Services**

| | | |
|---|---|---|
| Legal Adviser | Mr Jonathan Jones | Tel: (020) 7273 5865 |
| Children's Services | Ms Sandra Walker | Tel: (020) 7273 4758 |
| Effectiveness and Admissions | Mr Francis Clarke | Tel: (020) 7273 4758 |
| Equality, Establishments and European Union | Ms Carol Davies | Tel: (020) 7273 6053 |
| Governance and Finance | Mr Patrick Kilgarriff | Tel: (020) 7273 5873 |
| Higher Education and Student Support | Ms Carola Geist-Divver | Tel: (020) 7273 6051 |
| Lifelong Learning and School Workforce | Mr Dudley Aries | Tel: (020) 7273 5903 |
| Special Needs and Curriculum | Mr Nic Ash | Tel: (020) 7273 5885 |

**Lifelong Learning** *(see under Adult Learning and Skills, Higher Education, and under Learning Delivery and Standards)*

**Offenders' Learning and Skills Unit** ... Mr Chris Barnham ... Tel: (020) 7925 5985

**Parliamentary Clerk** ... Mr Jonathon Duff ... Tel: (020) 7925 6343

**Press and Communications**

| | | |
|---|---|---|
| Director, Strategy and Communications | Mr Michael Stevenson | Tel: (020) 7925 5092 |
| Head of News | Mr David Collins | Tel: (020) 7925 5132 |

# DEPARTMENT FOR EDUCATION AND SKILLS

| | | |
|---|---|---|
| Head of Press Office | Mr Trevor Cook | Tel: (020) 7925 5134 |
| Corporate Communications | Ms Yasmin Diamond | Tel: (020) 7925 6157 |
| E-Learning Strategy | Ms Diana Laurillard | Tel: (020) 7273 4892 |
| Marketing and Publicity | Mr John Ross | Tel: (020) 7925 6720 |
| Regions, Delivery Support and Regeneration | Mr Mohammad Haroon | Tel: (0114) 259 3259 |

## Qualifications

| | | |
|---|---|---|
| Director, Qualifications and Young People | Mr Rob Hull | Tel: (020) 7925 5890 |
| Examinations System | Ms Jane Benham | Tel: (020) 7273 5475 |
| 14-19 Programmes | Ms Carol Hunter | Tel: (020) 7925 5890 |
| Higher Education Admissions Review | Ms Linda Dale | Tel: (0114) 259 3539 |
| Learner Support, Young People | Mr Trevor Fellowes | Tel: (020) 7925 5890 |
| Qualifications for Work | Ms Sara Marshall | Tel: (0114) 259 4225 |
| School and College Qualifications | Ms Celia Johnson | Tel: (020) 7925 5722 |

## Schools

| | | |
|---|---|---|
| Director-General, Schools Analysis and Research Division | Mr Peter Housden | Tel: (020) 7925 6504 |
| Director, Primary Education and E-Learning Group | Ms Helen Williams | Tel: (020) 7273 5274 |
| Director, Resources, Infrastructure and Governance | Mr Stephen Crowne | Tel: (020) 7925 5664 |
| Director, School Workforce Unit | Mr Stephen Hillier | Tel: (020) 7925 5642 |
| Director, Secondary Education Group | Mr Peter Wanless | Tel: (020) 7925 6095 |
| Director, Standards and Effectiveness | Professor David Hopkins | Tel: (020) 7925 5380 |
| Director, Sure Start Unit | Ms Naomi Eisenstadt | Tel: (020) 7273 1396 |
| Academies | Mr Neil Flint | Tel: (020) 7925 6354 |
| Admissions, Organisation and Governance | Ms Shan Scott | Tel: (020) 7925 5610 |
| Advisers | Ms Hilary Emery | Tel: (020) 7925 5610 |
| Attendance - Improvement | Mr Alan Sevier | Tel: (020) 7925 5390 |
| Behaviour of Pupils | Mr Alan Sevier | Tel: (020) 7925 5390 |
| Behaviour of Pupils, Primary Schools | Mr Nick Baxter | Tel: (020) 7925 5264 |
| Buildings and Design Unit | Mr Mukund Patel | Tel: (020) 7273 6151 |
| Capital and Buildings | Ms Sally Brooks | Tel: (020) 7925 6325 |
| Children and Young People's Unit | Ms Althea Efunshile | Tel: (020) 7273 1396 |
| Curriculum (Primary Education and E-Learning) | Ms Mela Watts | Tel: (020) 7273 5821 |
| Diversity | Ms Susanna Todd | Tel: (0870) 001 2345 |
| Ethnic Minority Achievement Project | Ms Annabel Burns | Tel: (020) 7925 6514 |

## Schools (Continued)

| | | |
|---|---|---|
| Governance | Mr Shan Scott | Tel: (020) 7925 5610 |
| Independent Schools / Pupil Support | Ms Penny Jones | Tel: (020) 7925 6872 |
| Information and Communications Technology | Mr Doug Brown | Tel: (020) 7273 4915 |
| Innovation | Mr Mike Gibbons | Tel: (020) 7925 5380 |
| LEA Funding | Mr Andrew Wye | Tel: (020) 7925 5775 |
| Leadership and Teacher Development | Mr Richard Harrison | Tel: (0870) 001 2345 |
| Local Authority Performance | Mr Robert Wood | Tel: (020) 7925 6246 |
| Local Partnerships | Ms Kathy Bundred | Tel: (020) 7273 1228 |
| Local Partnerships | Mr Andrew Sargent | Tel: (020) 7273 1228 |
| London Challenge Programme | Mr Jon Coles | Tel: (020) 7925 6246 |
| Performance and Accountability | Mr Nick Baxter | Tel: (020) 7925 5264 |
| Physical Education and Sport | Mr Matthew Conway | Tel: (020) 7925 5000 |
| Policy and Strategy (Children and Young People) | Ms Sue Lewis | Tel: (020) 7273 5597 |
| Pupil Standards | Mr Andrew McCully | Tel: (0870) 001 2345 |
| School Diversity | Ms Susanna Todd | Tel: (0870) 001 2345 |
| Special Educational Needs | Ms Ann Gross | Tel: (020) 7925 5511 |
| Sport in Schools | Mr Matthew Conway | Tel: (020) 7925 5000 |
| Standards and Effectiveness | | |
|     Local Authority Standards | Mr Robert Woods | Tel: (020) 7925 6442 |
|     Local Implementation | Mr Richard Blows | Tel: (01325) 391371 |
|     Pupil Standards | Mr Andy McCully | Tel: (020) 7925 6676 |
|     School Improvement and Excellence | Mr Barnaby Shaw | Tel: (020) 7925 5745 |
| Strategy and Performance | Ms Christina Bienkowska | Tel: (020) 7925 6076 |
| Transport, Schools | Ms Penny Jones | Tel: (020) 7925 6872 |
| Workforce Unit (Schools), Director | Mr Stephen Hillier | Tel: (020) 7925 5573 |
| Youth | Mr John Elliott | Tel: (020) 7925 3523 |
| | Mr Phil Emmott | Tel: (020) 7925 6269 |
| | Mr Tony Moody | Tel: (0114) 259 4601 |

# DEPARTMENT FOR EDUCATION AND SKILLS

**Skills and Lifelong Learning** *(see above under Adult Learning and under Learning Delivery and Standards)*

**Special Educational Needs** . . . . . . . . . . . . . . . . . . . . . . . . . . Ms Ann Gross . . . . . . . . . . . . . . . . . . . . . . . . . . Tel: (020) 7925 5511

**Statistics** *(see above under Analytical Services)*
Children and Families . . . . . . . . . . . . . . . . . . . . . . . . . . . . Mr Richard Bartholomew . . . . . . . . . . . . . . . . . . . . Tel: (020) 7925 7492
Ms Audrey Brown . . . . . . . . . . . . . . . . . . . . . . . . Tel: (020) 7925 7489

**Student Finance**
Director, Student Finance Group . . . . . . . . . . . . . . . . . . . . Mr Michael Hipkins . . . . . . . . . . . . . . . . . . . . . . . . Tel: (020) 7925 6134
Funding Delivery . . . . . . . . . . . . . . . . . . . . . . . . . . . . . . . . Mr Ian Morrison . . . . . . . . . . . . . . . . . . . . . . . . . . . Tel: (020) 7925 6538
Funding Modernisation . . . . . . . . . . . . . . . . . . . . . . . . . . . Ms Noreen Graham . . . . . . . . . . . . . . . . . . . . . . . . Tel: (020) 7925 5372
Funding Policy . . . . . . . . . . . . . . . . . . . . . . . . . . . . . . . . . . Mr Peter Swift . . . . . . . . . . . . . . . . . . . . . . . . . . . . Tel: (020) 7925 6128

**Sure Start**
Director, Sure Start Unit . . . . . . . . . . . . . . . . . . . . . . . . . . Ms Naomi Eisenstadt . . . . . . . . . . . . . . . . . . . . . . . Tel: (020) 7273 4717
Infrastructure, Director . . . . . . . . . . . . . . . . . . . . . . . . . . . Mr Nick Tooze . . . . . . . . . . . . . . . . . . . . . . . . . . . . Tel: (020) 7273 5386
Planning and Performance . . . . . . . . . . . . . . . . . . . . . . . . . Ms Sue lewis . . . . . . . . . . . . . . . . . . . . . . . . . . . . . Tel: (020) 7273 5597
Programme Delivery . . . . . . . . . . . . . . . . . . . . . . . . . . . . . . Ms Jackie Doughty . . . . . . . . . . . . . . . . . . . . . . . . . Tel: (020) 7273 5735
Quality and Standards . . . . . . . . . . . . . . . . . . . . . . . . . . . . Mr David Jeffrey . . . . . . . . . . . . . . . . . . . . . . . . . . Tel: (020) 7273 1318
Strategy . . . . . . . . . . . . . . . . . . . . . . . . . . . . . . . . . . . . . . . Ms Tamara Finkelstein . . . . . . . . . . . . . . . . . . . . . . Tel: (020) 7273 5725

**Statistics** *(see above under Analytical Services)*

**Teachers**
Director, School Workforce Unit . . . . . . . . . . . . . . . . . . . . Mr Stephen Hillier . . . . . . . . . . . . . . . . . . . . . . . . . Tel: (020) 7925 5573
Fast Track Teachers . . . . . . . . . . . . . . . . . . . . . . . . . . . . . . Ms Sarah Read . . . . . . . . . . . . . . . . . . . . . . . . . . . . Tel: (020) 7925 5565
Pay and Performance . . . . . . . . . . . . . . . . . . . . . . . . . . . . . Mr Ian Whitehouse . . . . . . . . . . . . . . . . . . . . . . . . . Tel: (020) 7925 5573
Pensions and Medical Fitness . . . . . . . . . . . . . . . . . . . . . . Mr Paul Bleasdale . . . . . . . . . . . . . . . . . . . . . . . . . Tel: (020) 7925 5573
Recruitment and Training . . . . . . . . . . . . . . . . . . . . . . . . . Mr Graham Holley . . . . . . . . . . . . . . . . . . . . . . . . . Tel: (020) 7925 5573
Workforce Development . . . . . . . . . . . . . . . . . . . . . . . . . . . Ms Barbara Roberts . . . . . . . . . . . . . . . . . . . . . . . . Tel: (020) 7925 5573
Workforce Remodelling . . . . . . . . . . . . . . . . . . . . . . . . . . . Mr Heath Monk . . . . . . . . . . . . . . . . . . . . . . . . . . . Tel: (020) 7925 5573
Workload . . . . . . . . . . . . . . . . . . . . . . . . . . . . . . . . . . . . . . Mr Stuart Edwards . . . . . . . . . . . . . . . . . . . . . . . . . Tel: (020) 7925 5573

**Volunteering and Activities for Young People** . . . . . . . . . Ms Jane Haywood . . . . . . . . . . . . . . . . . . . . . . . . . . Tel: (0114) 259 1165

**Youth / Young People**
Learning Support . . . . . . . . . . . . . . . . . . . . . . . . . . . . . . . . Mr Trevor Fellowes . . . . . . . . . . . . . . . . . . . . . . . . Tel: (0114) 259 3976
Policy . . . . . . . . . . . . . . . . . . . . . . . . . . . . . . . . . . . . . . . . . Mr Alan Davies . . . . . . . . . . . . . . . . . . . . . . . . . . . . Tel: (0114) 259 4790

## OTHER RELEVANT CONTACTS

### ADULT LEARNING
**Adult Learning Inspectorate** . . . . . . . . . . . . . . . . . . . . . . Spring Place, Coventry Business Park, Herald Avenue, Coventry, CV5 6UD
Chairman . . . . . . . . . . . . . . . . . . . . . . . . . . . . . . . . . . . . . . Mr Richard Handover
Chief Inspector . . . . . . . . . . . . . . . . . . . . . . . . . . . . . . . . . Mr David Sherlock . . . . . . . . . . . . . . . . . . . . . . . . . Tel: (0870) 240 7744
E-mail: enquiries@ali.gov.uk
Web: http://www.ali.gov.uk
**Basic Skills Agency** . . . . . . . . . . . . . . . . . . . . . . . . . . . . . 7th Floor, Commonwealth House, 1-19 New Oxford Street, London, WC1A 1NU
Chairman . . . . . . . . . . . . . . . . . . . . . . . . . . . . . . . . . . . . . . Mr Garry Hawkes OBE
Director . . . . . . . . . . . . . . . . . . . . . . . . . . . . . . . . . . . . . . . Mr Alan Wells OBE . . . . . . . . . . . . . . . . . . . . . . . . . Tel: (020) 7405 4017
E-mail: enquiries@basic-skills.co.uk
Web: http://www.basic-skills.co.uk

### HIGHER EDUCATION
**Higher Education Funding Council for England** . . . . . . . . Northavon House, Coldharbour Lane, Frenchay, Bristol, BS16 1QD
Chairman . . . . . . . . . . . . . . . . . . . . . . . . . . . . . . . . . . . . . . Mr David Young
Chief Executive . . . . . . . . . . . . . . . . . . . . . . . . . . . . . . . . . Sir Howard Newby . . . . . . . . . . . . . . . . . . . . . . . . . Tel: (0117) 931 7317
E-mail: hefc@hefc.ac.uk
Web: http://www.hefc.ac.uk

# DEPARTMENT FOR EDUCATION AND SKILLS

*Other Relevant Contacts (Continued)*

**Quality Assurance Agency for Higher Education** . . . . . . . Southgate House, Southgate Street, Gloucester, GL1 1UB
    Chairman . . . . . . . . . . . . . . . . . . . . . . . . . . . . . . . . . . Mr Sam Younger
    Chief Executive . . . . . . . . . . . . . . . . . . . . . . . . . . . . Mr Peter Williams . . . . . . . . . . . . . . . . . . . . . . . . . . Tel: (01452) 557000
                  E-mail: qaa.ac.uk
                  Web: http://www.qaa.ac.uk

## INVESTORS IN PEOPLE
**Investors in People (IIP-UK)** . . . . . . . . . . . . . . . . . . . 4th Floor, 7-10 Chandos Street, London, W1G 9DQ
    Chairman . . . . . . . . . . . . . . . . . . . . . . . . . . . . . . . . . . Mr Tim Melville-Ross
    Chief Executive . . . . . . . . . . . . . . . . . . . . . . . . . . . . Ms Ruth Spellman . . . . . . . . . . . . . . . . . . . . . . . . . . . Tel: (020) 7467 1900
                  E-mail: information@iipuk.co.uk
                  Web: http://www.investorsinpeople.co.uk

## LANGUAGE TEACHING
**National Centre for Languages** . . . . . . . . . . . . . . . . . . 20 Bedfordbury, Covent Garden, London, WC2N 4LB
    Chairman . . . . . . . . . . . . . . . . . . . . . . . . . . . . . . . . . . Professor Leo Murray
    Director . . . . . . . . . . . . . . . . . . . . . . . . . . . . . . . . . . . Mr Peter Boaks . . . . . . . . . . . . . . . . . . . Tel: (020) 7379 5101
                  Web: http://www.cilt.org.uk

## QUALIFICATIONS
**Qualifications and Curriculum Authority** . . . . . . . . . . . 83 Piccadilly, London, W1J 8QA
    Chairman . . . . . . . . . . . . . . . . . . . . . . . . . . . . . . . . . . Sir Anthony Greener
    Chief Executive . . . . . . . . . . . . . . . . . . . . . . . . . . . . Dr Ken Boston . . . . . . . . . . . . . . . . . . . . . . . . . . . . . Tel: (020) 7509 5555
                  Web: http://www.qca.org.uk

## RESEARCH
**Arts and Humanities Research Board** . . . . . . . . . . . . . . Whitefriars, Lewins Mead, Bristol, BS1 2AE
    Chairman . . . . . . . . . . . . . . . . . . . . . . . . . . . . . . . . . . Professor Sir Brian Follett
    Chief Executive . . . . . . . . . . . . . . . . . . . . . . . . . . . . Professor Geoffrey Crossick . . . . . . . . . . . . . . . . . . . Tel: (0117) 987 6500
                  Web: http://www.ahrb.ac.uk

## SCHOOLS
**Office for Standards in Education (OFSTED)** . . . . . . . . . Alexandra House, 33 Kingsway, London, WC2B 6SE
    Chief Inspector of Schools . . . . . . . . . . . . . . . . . . . . . Mr David Bell . . . . . . . . . . . . . . . . . . . . . . . . . . . . . . Tel: (020) 7421 6800
                  E-mail: geninfo@ofsted.gov.uk
                  Web: http://www.ofsted.gov.uk
**Office of the Schools Adjudicator** . . . . . . . . . . . . . . . . Ground Floor, Mowden Hall, Staindrop Road, Darlington, DL3 9BG
    Chief Adjudicator . . . . . . . . . . . . . . . . . . . . . . . . . . . Professor Philip Hunter
    Secretary . . . . . . . . . . . . . . . . . . . . . . . . . . . . . . . . . . Mrs Holly Turner . . . . . . . . . . . . . . . . . . . . . . . . . . . Tel: (0870) 0012468
                  E-mail: offschl.adj@dses.gsi.gov.uk
                  Web: http://www.schoolsadjudicator.gov.uk
**Partnership for Schools** . . . . . . . . . . . . . . . . . . . . . . . Golden Cross House, Duncannon Street, London, WC2N 4JF
    Chief Executive . . . . . . . . . . . . . . . . . . . . . . . . . . . . Mr David Goldstone . . . . . . . . . . . . . . . . . . . . . . . . . Tel: (020) 7484 5062
**Registered Inspectors of Schools Appeals Tribunal** . . . . . Sanctuary Buildings, Great Smith Street, London SW1P 3BT
    Secretariat . . . . . . . . . . . . . . . . . . . . . . . . . . . . . . . . . Mr Kevin Atchinson . . . . . . . . . . . . . . . . . . . . . . . . . Tel: (020) 7925 5309
                  Web: http://www.dfes.gov.uk

## SECTOR SKILLS
**Sector Skills Development Agency** . . . . . . . . . . . . . . . . 3 Callflex Business Park, Golden Smithies Lane, Wath-upon-Dearne, S63 7ER
    Chairman . . . . . . . . . . . . . . . . . . . . . . . . . . . . . . . . . . Ms Margaret Salmon
    Chief Executive . . . . . . . . . . . . . . . . . . . . . . . . . . . . Mr Christopher Duff . . . . . . . . . . . . . . . . . . . . . . . . . Tel: (01709) 765444
                  E-mail: info@ssda.org.uk
                  Web: http://www.ssda.org.uk

## SPECIAL NEEDS
**Special Educational Needs and Disability Tribunal** . . . . . Upper Ground West, Procession House, 55 Ludgate Hill, London, EC4M 7JW
    President . . . . . . . . . . . . . . . . . . . . . . . . . . . . . . . . . . Lady [Rosemary] Hughes
    Secretariat . . . . . . . . . . . . . . . . . . . . . . . . . . . . . . . . . Mr Kevin Mullany . . . . . . . . . . . . . . . . . . . . . . . . . . . Tel: (020) 7029 9702
                  Web: http://www.sendist.gov.uk

## STUDENT LOANS
**Student Loans Company** . . . . . . . . . . . . . . . . . . . . . . . 100 Bothwell Street, Glasgow, G2 7JD
    Executive Chairman . . . . . . . . . . . . . . . . . . . . . . . . . . Mr Keith Bedell-Pierce
    Chief Executive . . . . . . . . . . . . . . . . . . . . . . . . . . . . Mr Ralph Seymour-Jackson . . . . . . . . . . . . . . . . . . . . Tel: (0141) 248 8000
                  E-mail: info@slc.co.uk
                  Web: http://www.slc.co.uk

# DEPARTMENT FOR EDUCATION AND SKILLS

*Other Relevant Contacts (Continued)*

## TEACHERS / TEACHING

**General Teaching Council**...........................344-354 Gray's Inn Road, London, WC1X 8BP
    Chairman.............................................Mr John Beattie
    Chief Executive..................................Ms Carol Adams ............................... Tel: (0870) 001 0308
        E-mail: info@gtce.org.uk
        Web: http://www.gtce.org.uk

**National College for School Leadership** ..............Triumph Road, Nottingham, NG8 1DH
    Chairman of the Governing Council .................Mr Richard Greenhalgh
    Director and Chief Executive.....................Ms Heather Du Quesnay ...................... Tel: (0870) 001 1155
        Web: http://www.ncsl.org.uk

**School Teachers' Review Body** .....................Office of Manpower Economics, Oxford House, 76 Oxford Street,
        London, W1D 1BS
    Chairman.............................................Mr Bill Cockburn CBE
    Secretary .............................................Ms Pat Carty ................................. Tel: (020) 7467 7215
        Web: http://www.ome.uk.com

**Teacher Training Agency** .......................Portland House, Stag Place, London, SW1E 5TT
    Chairman.............................................Professor Sir Bryan Follett
    Chief Executive..................................Mr Ralph Tabberer ........................... Tel: (020) 7925 3700
        E-mail: enquiry@tta.gov.uk
        Web: http://www.tta.gov.uk

## TECHNOLOGY

**British Educational Communications and**
  **Technology Agency**..........................Science Park, Milburn Hill Road, Coventry, CV4 7JJ
    Chairman.............................................Professor David Hargreaves
    Chief Executive..................................Mr Owen Lynch ............................. Tel: (024) 7641 6994
        E-mail: becta@becta.org.uk
        Web: http://www.becta.org.uk

## TEENAGE PREGNANCY

**Independent Advisory Group on Teenage Pregnancy** ....DFES, Ground Floor, Caxton House, 6-12 Tothill Street, London, SW1H 9NA
    Chairman.............................................Lady [Winifred] Tumim OBE
    Secretary .............................................Ms Michelle Warne ......................... Tel: (020) 7273 4923
        Web: http://www.teenagepregnancyunit.gov.uk

## TRAINING

**Construction Industry Training Board** ...............Bircham Newton, Kings Lynn, Norfolk, PE31 6RH
    Chairman.............................................Sir Michael Latham
    Chief Executive..................................Mr Peter Lobban ........................... Tel: (01485) 577577
        E-mail: call.centre@citb.co.uk
        Web: http://www.citb.cc.uk

**Engineering Construction Industry Training**
  **Board (ECITB)**..............................Blue Court, Church Lane, Kings Langley, Hertfordshire, WD4 8JP
    Chairman.............................................Mr Jim Rowland CBE
    Chief Executive..................................Mr David Edwards......................... Tel: (01923) 260000
        E-mail: ecitb@ecitb.org.uk
        Web: http://www.ecitb.org.uk

**Learning and Skills Council** .....................Cheylesmore House, Quinto Road, Coventry, CV1 2WT
    Chairman.............................................Mr Bryan Sanderson CBE
    Chief Executive..................................Mr Mark Haysom ......................... Tel: (0845) 019 4170
        Web: http://www.lsc.gov.uk

**Learning and Skills Development Agency** ............Regent Arcade House, 19-25 Argyll Street, London, W1F 7LS
    Chairman.............................................Sir Geoffrey Holland
    Chief Executive..................................Mr Chris Hughes ......................... Tel: (020) 7297 9000
        E-mail: enquiries@lsda.org.uk
        Web: http://www.lsda.org.uk

**Sector Skills Development Agency (SSDA)**...........3 Calflex Business Park, Golden Smithies Lane, Wath-upon-Dearne, S63 7ER
    Chairman.............................................Ms Margaret Salmon
    Chief Executive..................................Mr Christopher Duff......................... Tel: (01709) 765444
        E-mail: info@ssda.org.uk
        Web: http://www.ssdauk.co.uk

# BERKHAMSTED COLLEGIATE SCHOOL

*(Independent Day for ages 3+ to 18 and*
*boarding for ages 11 to 18)*

## INTO THE 21ST CENTURY

**1541**

**1888**

Berkhamsted Collegiate School, the original foundation dating back to 1541, has a long and distinguished tradition of offering educational excellence for boys and girls.

◆ *SIXTH FORM*  The successful co-educational Sixth Form has excellent facilities and a choice of 27 'A' level subjects to meet the diverse demands of our students.

◆ *SENIOR SCHOOLS*  Recognising the advantages of single-sex teaching between the ages of 11 and 16, boys and girls achieve the best results by studying separately for GCSE, while sharing the benefits of extra-curricular activities.

◆ *PREPARATORY SCHOOL*  The co-educational school for pupils 3+ to 11 years includes a new multi-purpose hall, modern dining facilities, specialist classrooms and a purpose-built nursery.

◆ *BOARDING*  The School offers a boarding option for boys and girls aged 11 to 18. Boarders may be "full", "weekly" or "flexible" depending on parents' preference and feasibility.

Under the leadership of Dr. Priscilla Chadwick, an outstanding educationalist with a distinguished career in secondary and primary educational management, the highly experienced and qualified team of staff have enhanced the School's international reputation for academic excellence. Berkhamsted Collegiate School offers:

◆ *HIGH ACADEMIC ACHIEVEMENT*

◆ *A BROAD AND CHALLENGING CURRICULUM*

◆ *WIDE-RANGING EXTRA-CURRICULAR PROGRAMME OF SPORTS AND OTHER ACTIVITIES*

◆ *A STRONG SYSTEM OF PASTORAL CARE*

**For more information please telephone: 01442 358000 Fax: 01442 358003**
**E-mail: info@bcschool.org  Website: Berkhamstedcollegiateschool.org.uk**
**Berkhamsted Collegiate School, 6 Chesham Road, Berkhamsted,**
**Hertfordshire, HP4 3AA**
*A Charitable Trust in the field of Junior and Senior Education*
*Registered Charity Number 311056*

# Universities UK

The essential voice of our universities

# Speaking up for universities

Universities UK represents the heads of 122 UK higher education institutions.

We are the essential voice of UK universities, speaking on behalf of a dynamic sector which is rapidly growing and diversifying. At this critical juncture for Higher Education, Universities UK is seeking to ensure that Westminster, Whitehall and the general public recognise the vital role played by universities and the need to invest in them to ensure that the sector is fit for the future, and accessible to all who can benefit.

Universities UK does this by:

- speaking up for a thriving higher education sector which creates benefits for all;
- providing and disseminating essential information; and
- bringing people together to share knowledge and good practice.

For more information, please contact:

**Vivienne Stern, Senior Public Affairs Officer, on 020 74195413
or e-mail vivienne.stern@UniversitiesUK.ac.uk
www.UniversitiesUK.ac.uk**

## BASIC SKILLS

## CHILDREN – HEALTH & EDUCATION

### THE BASIC SKILLS AGENCY

Commonwealth House, 1-19 New Oxford Street,
London, WC1A 1NU

*Telephone* (020) 7405 4017
*Facsimile* (020) 7440 6626
*E-mail* enquiries@basic-skills.co.uk
*Web* http://www.basic-skills.co.uk

*Contact* Helen Vaughan-Jones – *Press Officer*

The Basic Skills Agency is the national development organisation for literacy, numeracy and related basic skills in England and Wales. Our main aims are to raise the awareness of the importance of basic skills and to promote continuing improvement in basic skills.
The Agency is committed to offering support for the development of effective basic skills programmes for children and adults – by providing advice and materials; developing new programmes and learning opportunities; improving the quality of existing provision; and commissioning key research into the impact of poor basic skills.

*Registered Charity No:* 1003969

### THE HYPERACTIVE CHILDREN'S SUPPORT GROUP

71 Whyke Lane, Chichester
West Sussex, PO19 7PD

*Telephone* (01243) 551313
*Facsimile* (01243) 552019
*E-mail* hyperactive@hacsg.org.uk
*Web* http://www.hacsg.org.uk

*Contact* Sally Bunday – *Founder*

The HACSG offers information, advice and literature to parents, carers and professionals concerned about Hyperactive/ADHD children. We focus on Dietary and Nutritional treatments.

*Registered Charity No:* 277643

## EDUCATIONAL RESOURCES

**The British National Temperance League**

Westbrook Court, 2 Sharrow Vale Road
Sheffield, S11 8YZ

*Telephone* (0114) 267 9976 (24 Hours)
*Facsimile* (0114) 267 9976
*E-mail* bntl@bntl.org
*Web* http://www.bntl.org

*Contact:* Barbara Briggs – *Chief Executive*

BNTL 'Freeway' is a modern organisation that offers children and young people the option to not drink alcohol or take illegal drugs, solvents and other addictive substances. This is done by producing resources and information to help teachers educate children and young people about the effect of alcohol and other drugs on themselves and people around them.

## EDUCATION CHARITY

# education extra

EDUCATION EXTRA – THE CHARITY THAT SUPPORTS OUT-OF-SCHOOL-HOURS LEARNING

St Margaret's House, 17 Old Ford Rd,
Bethnal Green, London, E2 9PL

*Telephone* (020) 8709 9900
*Facsimile* (020) 8709 9933
*E-mail* info@educationextra.org.uk
*Web* http://www.educationextra.org.uk

Out-of-school-hours learning activities is one of the most exciting and powerful elements in the drive to raise achievement and promote life-long learning for everyone.

The aim of Education Extra is to put extra activities within the reach of every child by stimulating, supporting and promoting these activities in schools, so that young people of all ages and abilities have that extra chance to succeed – whether that is in music, maths or mountaineering. In doing so, our work helps to raise achievement, celebrate creativity, improve schools and build stronger and safer communities.

Education Extra is known as a 'can do' charity, promoting innovation and good practice through its Schools Extra Award and Network of schools, publications and exemplary projects. It has played a key role in promoting summer literacy and family learning.

## EARLY YEARS CARE & EDUCATION/PLAYWORK

# CACHE

The only Awarding Body which specialises in qualifications for early years care, education and playwork

CACHE is the only specialist awarding body that exclusively develops courses and qualifications to provide the underpinning knowledge and practical training for people who work, or plan to work with children and young people. It strives through its qualifications to raise the quality of Child Care and Education and Playwork in Great Britain and beyond.

Originating from the merger of the NNEB (National Nursery Examination) and CEYA (Council for Early Years Awards) in 1994, its expertise has greatly influenced the practice and understanding of the care and education of young children since 1945.

*Chief Executive Dr Richard Dorrance*

Patron: Her Majesty the Queen
Council for Awards in Children's Care and Education
8 Chequer Street, St Albans, Hertfordshire, AL1 3XZ
Tel: 01727 847636  Fax: 01727 867609

## INSPECTORS, ADVISERS & EDUCATIONAL CONSULTANTS

# NATIONAL ASSOCIATION OF EDUCATIONAL INSPECTORS, ADVISERS AND CONSULTANTS
## (NAEIAC)
Woolley Hall, Woolley, Wakefield
West Yorkshire, WF4 2JR

*Telephone* (01226) 383428/0
*Facsimile* (01226) 383427
*E-mail* naeiac@gemsoft.co.uk
*Web* http://www.naeiac.org

*Contact* John Chowcat – *General Secretary*

NAEIAC, the professional body and TUC affiliated trade union representing inspectors, advisers and educational consultants, is the voice of school improvement professionals in this country. It works to influence national policy on key educational and professional matters; to represent members on employment issues; and to provide members with up-to-date information, training and professional development.

## RELIGIOUS BOOK SHOPS

# CHURCH HOUSE BOOKSHOP
31 Great Smith Street, London, SW1P 3BN

*Telephone* (020) 7898 1304
*Mail Order Lines* (020) 7898 1301/2
*Facsimile* (020) 7898 1305
*Email* bookshop@c-of-e.org.uk
*Web* www.chbookshop.co.uk

*Contact* Mark Clifford – *Retail Co-ordinator*

Visit one of London's largest religious bookshops for a wide range of books and Bibles for all occasions. Specialists in official publications/reports of the Church of England. Bulk purchase discounts available.

*Registered Charity No:* 248711

# DEPARTMENT FOR ENVIRONMENT, FOOD AND RURAL AFFAIRS

Nobel House, 17 Smith Square London, SW1P 3JR
Tel: (020) 7238 6000  Fax: (020) 7270 8125
*Information Helpline:* (01645) 335577
Web: http://www.defra.gov.uk

## MINISTERS

**Secretary of State for Environment,**
**Food and Rural Affairs** . . . . . . . . . . . . . . . . . . . . . . Rt Hon Margaret Beckett MP
*Private Secretary* . . . . . . . . . . . . . . . . . . . . . . . . . . . . . Mr Gavin Ross. . . . . . . . . . . . . . . . . . . . . . . . . . . . . . Tel: (020) 7238 5339
*Special Advisers* . . . . . . . . . . . . . . . . . . . . . . . . . . . . . Ms Nicci Collins . . . . . . . . . . . . . . . . . . . . . . . . . . . . Tel: (020) 7238 537
. . . . . . . . . . . . . . . . . . . . . . . . . . . . . . . . . . . . . . . . . . . Mr Stephen Hale . . . . . . . . . . . . . . . . . . . . . . . . . . . Tel: (020) 7238 5375
. . . . . . . . . . . . . . . . . . . . . . . . . . . . . . . . . . . . . . . . . . . Ms Sheila Watson . . . . . . . . . . . . . . . . . . . . . . . . . . Tel: (020) 7238 5373/
. . . . . . . . . . . . . . . . . . . . . . . . . . . . . . . . . . . . . . . . . . . . . . . . . . . . . . . . . . . . . . . . . . . . . . . . . . . . . . . . . . . . . . . 5378

**Minister of State** *(Minister for Rural Affairs and*
*Local Environmental Equality)* . . . . . . . . . . . . . . . . . Rt Hon Alun Michael MP
*Private Secretary* . . . . . . . . . . . . . . . . . . . . . . . . . . . . . Mr Tim Higginson . . . . . . . . . . . . . . . . . . . . . . . . . . . Tel: (020) 7238 5379

**Minister of State** *(Minister for the Environment)*. . . . . . . . . . Mr Elliot Morley MP
*Private Secretary* . . . . . . . . . . . . . . . . . . . . . . . . . . . . . Mr Bradley Bates. . . . . . . . . . . . . . . . . . . . . . . . . . . . Tel: (020) 7238 5404

**Parliamentary Secretary**
*(Nature Conservation and Fisheries)* . . . . . . . . . . . . . . . Mr Ben Bradshaw MP
*Private Secretary* . . . . . . . . . . . . . . . . . . . . . . . . . . . . . Ms Kathleen Cameron . . . . . . . . . . . . . . . . . . . . . . . Tel: (020) 7238 5421

**Parliamentary Secretary**
*(Food, Farming and Sustainable Energy)* . . . . . . . . . . . . Lord Whitty
*Private Secretary* . . . . . . . . . . . . . . . . . . . . . . . . . . . . . Ms Charlotte Middleton . . . . . . . . . . . . . . . . . . . . . . Tel: (020) 7238 5386

## CIVIL SERVICE

**Permanent Secretary** . . . . . . . . . . . . . . . . . . . . . . . . . . Sir Brian Bender KCB
*Private Secretary* . . . . . . . . . . . . . . . . . . . . . . . . . . . . . Ms Claire Lewis. . . . . . . . . . . . . . . . . . . . . . . . . . . . . Tel: (020) 7238 5446

**Directors-General**
Animal Health and Welfare (Chief Veterinary Officer) . . . . Ms Debby Reynolds. . . . . . . . . . . . . . . . . . . . . . . . . . Tel: (020) 7082 6139
Environmental Protection . . . . . . . . . . . . . . . . . . . . . . . . Mr Bill Stow . . . . . . . . . . . . . . . . . . . . . . . . . . . . . . . Tel: (020) 7082 8130
Food, Farming and Fisheries . . . . . . . . . . . . . . . . . . . . . Mr Andrew Lebrecht . . . . . . . . . . . . . . . . . . . . . . . . . Tel: (020) 7238 5581
Land Use and Rural Affairs . . . . . . . . . . . . . . . . . . . . . . Ms Anna Walker CB . . . . . . . . . . . . . . . . . . . . . . . . . . Tel: (020) 7238 5600
Legal Adviser and Solicitor . . . . . . . . . . . . . . . . . . . . . . Mr Donald Macrae . . . . . . . . . . . . . . . . . . . . . . . . . . Tel: (020) 7238 3064
Operations and Service Delivery . . . . . . . . . . . . . . . . . . Mr Mark Addison . . . . . . . . . . . . . . . . . . . . . . . . . . . Tel: (020) 7238 3208

## SUBJECT RESPONSIBILITIES AND CONTACTS

**Abattoirs** . . . . . . . . . . . . . . . . . . . . . . . . . . . . . . . . . . . . Dr Nafees Meah. . . . . . . . . . . . . . . . . . . . . . . . . . . . . Tel: (020) 7238 3139

**Agricultural Dwelling House Advisory Committees** . . . . . Mr Geoffrey Webdale. . . . . . . . . . . . . . . . . . . . . . . . . Tel: (020) 7238 5755

**Agricultural Competitiveness** . . . . . . . . . . . . . . . . . . . . . Mr Jeremy Cowper. . . . . . . . . . . . . . . . . . . . . . . . . . . Tel: (020) 7238 6117

**Agriculture, Sustainable**
Director, Sustainable Agriculture and Livestock Products . . Ms Sonia Phippard. . . . . . . . . . . . . . . . . . . . . . . . . . . Tel: (020) 7238 3062
Sustainable Agriculture . . . . . . . . . . . . . . . . . . . . . . . . . Mr Nigel Atkinson . . . . . . . . . . . . . . . . . . . . . . . . . . . Tel: (020) 7238 3119

# DEPARTMENT FOR ENVIRONMENT,
# FOOD AND RURAL AFFAIRS

## Air Quality

| | | |
|---|---|---|
| Director, Climate, Energy and Environmental Risk | Mr Henry Derwent | Tel: (020) 7944 6210 |
| Air and Environment Quality | Dr Martin Williams | Tel: (020) 7944 6270 |
| CFCs | Ms Sarah Hendry | Tel: (020) 7944 5220 |
| Economics | Mr Simon Harding | Tel: (020) 7238 3233 |
| Global | Ms Sarah Hendry | Tel: (020) 7944 5220 |
| Incineration | Ms Lindsay Cornish | Tel: (020) 7944 5809 |
| Kyoto Protocol | Ms Sarah Hendry | Tel: (020) 7944 5220 |
| Local Authority Pollution Control | Dr Martin Williams | Tel: (020) 7944 6270 |
| Ozone | Ms Sarah Hendry | Tel: (020) 7944 5220 |
| Sulphur Content | Dr Martin Williams | Tel: (020) 7944 6270 |
| Technical Policy | Dr Martin Williams | Tel: (020) 7944 6270 |
| Transboundary Air Pollution | Dr Martin Williams | Tel: (020) 7944 6270 |

## Animal Health: General
*1a Page Street, London, SW1P 4PQ*

| | | |
|---|---|---|
| Director, Animal Health Group Directorate | Mr David Dawson | Tel: (020) 7904 6129 |
| Director, TSE | Dr Peter Nash | Tel: (020) 7904 6089 |
| Animal Disease Control Division | Ms Sue Eades | Tel: (020) 7904 8184 |
| Animal Health and Welfare Strategy and Delivery Division | Ms Diana Linskey | Tel: (020) 7904 6367 |
| Animal Movements and Exotic Diseases | Mr Simon Hewitt | Tel: (020) 7904 6019 |
| Animal Welfare Division | Mr John Bourne | Tel: (020) 7904 6179 |
| BSE and Spongiform Encephalopathies | Dr Mandy Bailey | Tel: (020) 7904 6805 |
| Economics | Mr John Watson | Tel: (020) 7238 3285 |
| Encephalopathies (TSE) Directorate | Dr Peter Nash | Tel: (020) 7904 6231 |
| International Animal Health, | Dr Nigel Gibbens | Tel: (020) 7904 6169 |
| Livestock Identification Division | Mr Malcolm Hunt | Tel: (020) 7904 6260 |
| Planning, Animal Health, and Welfare | Mr Dave Bench | Tel: (020) 7904 6234 |
| Rabies and Equine Division | Ms Alison Reeves | Tel: (020) 7904 6769 |
| Sheep TSE Division | Mr Francis Marlow | Tel: (020) 7904 6492 |
| Tuberculosis | Ms Sue Eades | Tel: (020) 7904 8184 |
| Veterinary Notifiable TSE Diseases | Dr Peter Soul | Tel: (020) 7904 6039 |
| Veterinary Welfare | Mr David Pritchard | Tel: (020) 7904 6464 |

**Arable Area Payments, European Union** .......... Mr Andrew Kuyk ........... Tel: (020) 7238 6494

**Arable Crops** .......... Mr Andrew Kuyk ........... Tel: (020) 7238 6494

**Atmosphere, Global** .......... Ms Sarah Hendry ........... Tel: (020) 7944 5220

**Badgers and TB** .......... Ms Sue Eades ........... Tel: (020) 7904 8184

**Bananas** .......... Mr David Jones ........... Tel: (020) 7238 1038

**Beans** .......... Mr David Jones ........... Tel: (020) 7238 1038

**Bee Keeping** .......... Mr David Jones ........... Tel: (020) 7238 1038

## Beef

| | | |
|---|---|---|
| European Union Beef Regime | Mr Ivor Llewelyn | Tel: (020) 7270 8565 |
| Labelling, EU Rules | Mr Ivor Llewelyn | Tel: (020) 7270 8060 |
| Over 30 Months Slaughter | Mr Ivor Llewelyn | Tel: (020) 7270 8959 |

## Biodiversity

| | | |
|---|---|---|
| Policy | Mr John Osmond | Tel: (020) 7238 6024 |
| Promotion | Mr Martin Capstick | Tel: (0117) 372 8233 |

**Biofuels** .......... Mr Andrew Perrins ........... Tel: (020) 7238 1113

**Birds** .......... Mr John Osmond ........... Tel: (020) 7238 6907

# DEPARTMENT FOR ENVIRONMENT,
## FOOD AND RURAL AFFAIRS

**Broads Authority** . . . . . . . . . . . . . . . . . . . . . . . . . . . . . . Ms Susan Carter . . . . . . . . . . . . . . . . . . . . . . . . . . . . . Tel: (0117) 372 8178

**Brucellosis**
    Policy . . . . . . . . . . . . . . . . . . . . . . . . . . . . . . . . . . . . Ms Sue Eades . . . . . . . . . . . . . . . . . . . . . . . . . . . . . . Tel: (020) 7904 8184
    Veterinary . . . . . . . . . . . . . . . . . . . . . . . . . . . . . . . . . Mr Alick Simmons . . . . . . . . . . . . . . . . . . . . . . . . . . . Tel: (020) 7904 6049

**BSE**
    Director, TSE . . . . . . . . . . . . . . . . . . . . . . . . . . . . . . Mr Peter Nash . . . . . . . . . . . . . . . . . . . . . . . . . . . . . Tel: (020) 7904 6089
    Director, BSE Division. . . . . . . . . . . . . . . . . . . . . . . . Dr Mandy Bailey . . . . . . . . . . . . . . . . . . . . . . . . . . . Tel: (020) 7904 8054
    Contingency Planning- BSE in Sheep . . . . . . . . . . . . . . Dr Nafees Meah. . . . . . . . . . . . . . . . . . . . . . . . . . . . Tel: (020) 7238 3139
    General . . . . . . . . . . . . . . . . . . . . . . . . . . . . . . . . . . . Dr Mandy Bailey . . . . . . . . . . . . . . . . . . . . . . . . . . . Tel: (020) 7904 8054
    SEAC Secretariat. . . . . . . . . . . . . . . . . . . . . . . . . . . . Dr Catherine Boyle . . . . . . . . . . . . . . . . . . . . . . . . . Tel: (020) 7904 6556
    Sheep and TSE . . . . . . . . . . . . . . . . . . . . . . . . . . . . . Mr Francis Marlow. . . . . . . . . . . . . . . . . . . . . . . . . . Tel: (020) 7904 6492
    Veterinary Notifiable TSE  Diseases. . . . . . . . . . . . . . . Dr Peter Soul. . . . . . . . . . . . . . . . . . . . . . . . . . . . . . Tel: (020) 7904 6039

**Building and Estate Management (Departmental)** . . . . . . Mr Tony Nickson . . . . . . . . . . . . . . . . . . . . . . . . . . . Tel: (020) 7238 6677

**Burning of Crop Residues**. . . . . . . . . . . . . . . . . . . . . . . . Mr John Osmond . . . . . . . . . . . . . . . . . . . . . . . . . . . Tel: (020) 7238 6907

**Business and the Environment**
    Awareness. . . . . . . . . . . . . . . . . . . . . . . . . . . . . . . . . Mr Jeremy Eppel . . . . . . . . . . . . . . . . . . . . . . . . . . . Tel: (020) 7944 6688
    Eco-labelling. . . . . . . . . . . . . . . . . . . . . . . . . . . . . . . Mr Bob Ryder . . . . . . . . . . . . . . . . . . . . . . . . . . . . . Tel: (020) 7944 6582
    Energy; Labelling . . . . . . . . . . . . . . . . . . . . . . . . . . . Mr Jeremy Eppel . . . . . . . . . . . . . . . . . . . . . . . . . . . Tel: (020) 7944 6688
    Going for Green. . . . . . . . . . . . . . . . . . . . . . . . . . . . . Mr Jeremy Eppel . . . . . . . . . . . . . . . . . . . . . . . . . . . Tel: (020) 7944 6688
    Joint Environmental Markets Unit . . . . . . . . . . . . . . . . Mr Duncan Prior . . . . . . . . . . . . . . . . . . . . . . . . . . . Tel: (020) 7215 1624
    Packaging . . . . . . . . . . . . . . . . . . . . . . . . . . . . . . . . . Mr Bob Ryder . . . . . . . . . . . . . . . . . . . . . . . . . . . . . Tel: (020) 7944 6582

**By-Laws, Countryside** . . . . . . . . . . . . . . . . . . . . . . . . . . Ms Susan Carter . . . . . . . . . . . . . . . . . . . . . . . . . . . . Tel: (0117) 372 8178

**Camping and Caravanning** . . . . . . . . . . . . . . . . . . . . . . . Ms Susan Carter . . . . . . . . . . . . . . . . . . . . . . . . . . . . Tel: (0117) 372 8178

**Cattle Identification / Movement** . . . . . . . . . . . . . . . . . . Mr Malcolm Hunt . . . . . . . . . . . . . . . . . . . . . . . . . . Tel: (020) 7904 6260

**Cattle Movement Service, British**
*Curwen Road, Workington, Cumbria, CA14 2DD*
    Head, British Cattle Movement Service . . . . . . . . . . . . . Mr David Evans . . . . . . . . . . . . . . . . . . . . . . . . . . . . Tel: (01900) 702001

**Cereals**. . . . . . . . . . . . . . . . . . . . . . . . . . . . . . . . . . . . . Mr Andrew Kuyk. . . . . . . . . . . . . . . . . . . . . . . . . . . . Tel: (020) 7238 6494

**CFCs**. . . . . . . . . . . . . . . . . . . . . . . . . . . . . . . . . . . . . . Dr Martin Williams . . . . . . . . . . . . . . . . . . . . . . . . . Tel: (020) 7944 6270

**Chemicals** . . . . . . . . . . . . . . . . . . . . . . . . . . . . . . . . . . Mr Colin Church . . . . . . . . . . . . . . . . . . . . . . . . . . . Tel: (020) 7944 5231

**Climate**
    Director, Climate, Energy and Environmental Risk. . . . . . Mr Henry Derwent . . . . . . . . . . . . . . . . . . . . . . . . . . Tel: (020) 7944 6210

**Common Agricultural Policy (CAP)**
    Director, European Union and International Policy. . . . . . . Mr David Hunter . . . . . . . . . . . . . . . . . . . . . . . . . . . Tel: (020) 7238 3003
    Agriculture Council. . . . . . . . . . . . . . . . . . . . . . . . . . . Mr Andrew Lawrence. . . . . . . . . . . . . . . . . . . . . . . . . Tel: (020) 7238 3048
    Agrimonetary Arrangements. . . . . . . . . . . . . . . . . . . . . Mr Andrew Lawrence. . . . . . . . . . . . . . . . . . . . . . . . . Tel: (020) 7238 3055
    Devolution. . . . . . . . . . . . . . . . . . . . . . . . . . . . . . . . . Mr Andrew Lawrence. . . . . . . . . . . . . . . . . . . . . . . . . Tel: (020) 7238 3028
    Enlargement . . . . . . . . . . . . . . . . . . . . . . . . . . . . . . . Mr Andrew Lawrence. . . . . . . . . . . . . . . . . . . . . . . . . Tel: (020) 7238 3039
    European Parliament Relations . . . . . . . . . . . . . . . . . . . Mr Andrew Lawrence. . . . . . . . . . . . . . . . . . . . . . . . . Tel: (020) 7238 3039
    External Trade. . . . . . . . . . . . . . . . . . . . . . . . . . . . . . Mr Andrew Lawrence. . . . . . . . . . . . . . . . . . . . . . . . . Tel: (020) 7238 3005
    Financial Aspects, Price Fixing . . . . . . . . . . . . . . . . . . . Mr Andrew Lawrence. . . . . . . . . . . . . . . . . . . . . . . . . Tel: (020) 7238 3050
    Integrated Administrative Control System. . . . . . . . . . . . Mr Andrew Lawrence. . . . . . . . . . . . . . . . . . . . . . . . . Tel: (020) 7238 3028
    Parliamentary Scrutiny. . . . . . . . . . . . . . . . . . . . . . . . Mr Andrew Lawrence. . . . . . . . . . . . . . . . . . . . . . . . . Tel: (020) 7238 3039
    Rural Development Expenditure . . . . . . . . . . . . . . . . . . Mr Martin Nesbit . . . . . . . . . . . . . . . . . . . . . . . . . . . Tel: (020) 7238 6286
    State Aids . . . . . . . . . . . . . . . . . . . . . . . . . . . . . . . . . Mr Andrew Lawrence. . . . . . . . . . . . . . . . . . . . . . . . . Tel: (020) 7238 3054
    World Trade Organisation . . . . . . . . . . . . . . . . . . . . . . Mr Andrew Lawrence. . . . . . . . . . . . . . . . . . . . . . . . . Tel: (020) 7238 3005

# DEPARTMENT FOR ENVIRONMENT, FOOD AND RURAL AFFAIRS

**Coastal Defence** . . . . . . . . . . . . . . . . . . . . . . . . . . . . Ms Sarah Nason . . . . . . . . . . . . . . . . . . . . . . . . . Tel: (020) 7238 6115

**Coffee and Cocoa** . . . . . . . . . . . . . . . . . . . . . . . . . Mr Callton Young . . . . . . . . . . . . . . . . . . . . . . . Tel: (020) 7238 3174

**Commission on the Future of Farming** . . . . . . . . . . . . . . Mr Mike Segal . . . . . . . . . . . . . . . . . . . . . . . . . Tel: (020) 7238 3066

**Commons** . . . . . . . . . . . . . . . . . . . . . . . . . . . . . . Ms Susan Carter . . . . . . . . . . . . . . . . . . . . . . . . Tel: (0117) 372 8178

**Communications** (*see below under Press and Communication*)

**Community Forests** . . . . . . . . . . . . . . . . . . . . . . . . Mr Ray Anderson . . . . . . . . . . . . . . . . . . . . . . . . Tel: (020) 7238 1115

**Co-operatives, Agricultural** . . . . . . . . . . . . . . . . . . . . Mr Jeremy Cowper . . . . . . . . . . . . . . . . . . . . . . . Tel: (020) 7238 6117

**Contaminated Land** . . . . . . . . . . . . . . . . . . . . . . . . Ms Sheila McCabe . . . . . . . . . . . . . . . . . . . . . . . Tel: (020) 7238 3316

**Corporate Services**
    Director, Corporate Services . . . . . . . . . . . . . . . . . . . Mr Richard Allen . . . . . . . . . . . . . . . . . . . . . . . . Tel: (020) 7270 8194
    Director, E-Business . . . . . . . . . . . . . . . . . . . . . . . Mr David Rossington . . . . . . . . . . . . . . . . . . . . . Tel: (01483) 563295
    Information Management Division . . . . . . . . . . . . . . . Ms Caroline Smith . . . . . . . . . . . . . . . . . . . . . . . Tel: (020) 7238 2097

**Corporate Strategy Unit, Departmental** . . . . . . . . . . . . . Ms Francesca Okosi . . . . . . . . . . . . . . . . . . . . . . Tel: (020) 7238 1681

**Cotorou Agreement** . . . . . . . . . . . . . . . . . . . . . . . . Mr Andrew Lawrence . . . . . . . . . . . . . . . . . . . . . Tel: (020) 7238 3005

**Countryside** (*see also below under Rural Development and under Wildlife*)
    Director, Rural Economics and Communities . . . . . . . . . Mr Paul Elliott . . . . . . . . . . . . . . . . . . . . . . . . . Tel: (020) 7238 5700
    Director, Wildlife , Countryside, Land Use and
        Better Regulation . . . . . . . . . . . . . . . . . . . . . . . Mr Brian Harding . . . . . . . . . . . . . . . . . . . . . . . Tel: (020) 7238 1175
    Agri-Environment Schemes Review . . . . . . . . . . . . . . Mr John Osmond . . . . . . . . . . . . . . . . . . . . . . . Tel: (020) 7238 6907
    Bridleways and Byways . . . . . . . . . . . . . . . . . . . . . Ms Susan Carter . . . . . . . . . . . . . . . . . . . . . . . . Tel: (0117) 372 8178
    Caravanning and Camping . . . . . . . . . . . . . . . . . . . Ms Susan Carter . . . . . . . . . . . . . . . . . . . . . . . . Tel: (0117) 372 8178
    Coast . . . . . . . . . . . . . . . . . . . . . . . . . . . . . . . Mr Martin Capstick . . . . . . . . . . . . . . . . . . . . . . Tel: (0117) 372 8233
    Forestry and Woods . . . . . . . . . . . . . . . . . . . . . . . Mr Ray Anderson . . . . . . . . . . . . . . . . . . . . . . . . Tel: (020) 7238 1115
    Hedgerows . . . . . . . . . . . . . . . . . . . . . . . . . . . . Mr John Osmond . . . . . . . . . . . . . . . . . . . . . . . Tel: (020) 7238 6907
    Landscape Protection . . . . . . . . . . . . . . . . . . . . . . Ms Susan Carter . . . . . . . . . . . . . . . . . . . . . . . . Tel: (0117) 372 8178
    National Parks . . . . . . . . . . . . . . . . . . . . . . . . . . Ms Susan Carter . . . . . . . . . . . . . . . . . . . . . . . . Tel: (0117) 372 8178
    Rights of Way Policy . . . . . . . . . . . . . . . . . . . . . . Ms Susan Carter . . . . . . . . . . . . . . . . . . . . . . . . Tel: (0117) 372 8178
    Right to Roam . . . . . . . . . . . . . . . . . . . . . . . . . . Ms Susan Carter . . . . . . . . . . . . . . . . . . . . . . . . Tel: (0117) 372 8178
    Rural Communities . . . . . . . . . . . . . . . . . . . . . . . Mr Chris Dunabin . . . . . . . . . . . . . . . . . . . . . . . Tel: (020) 7238 6141
    SSIs . . . . . . . . . . . . . . . . . . . . . . . . . . . . . . . . Mr Martin Capstick . . . . . . . . . . . . . . . . . . . . . . Tel: (0117) 372 8233
    Stewardship . . . . . . . . . . . . . . . . . . . . . . . . . . . Mr John Osmond . . . . . . . . . . . . . . . . . . . . . . . Tel: (020) 7238 6907
    Tourism . . . . . . . . . . . . . . . . . . . . . . . . . . . . . . Mr Graham Cory . . . . . . . . . . . . . . . . . . . . . . . . Tel: (020) 7238 6442
    Wetlands . . . . . . . . . . . . . . . . . . . . . . . . . . . . . Mr John Roberts . . . . . . . . . . . . . . . . . . . . . . . . Tel: (020) 7944 5260
    Wildlife Conservation Policy . . . . . . . . . . . . . . . . . . Mr John Osmond . . . . . . . . . . . . . . . . . . . . . . . Tel: (020) 7238 6907

**Covent Garden Market Authority, Sponsorship** . . . . . . . Mr David Jones . . . . . . . . . . . . . . . . . . . . . . . . . Tel: (020) 7238 1038

**Crops**
    Director, Food Industry and Crops . . . . . . . . . . . . . . Mr John Robbs . . . . . . . . . . . . . . . . . . . . . . . . . Tel: (020) 7238 3170
    GM Crops . . . . . . . . . . . . . . . . . . . . . . . . . . . . Mr Colin Church . . . . . . . . . . . . . . . . . . . . . . . . Tel: (020) 7944 5231

**Dangerous Pathogens** . . . . . . . . . . . . . . . . . . . . . . . Dr Fred Landeg . . . . . . . . . . . . . . . . . . . . . . . . . Tel: (020) 7904 6185

**Dangerous Substances (Discharge into Water)** . . . . . . . . Mr Daniel Instone . . . . . . . . . . . . . . . . . . . . . . . Tel: (020) 7944 5360

**Dangerous Wild Animals Act** . . . . . . . . . . . . . . . . . . . Mr Martin Brasher . . . . . . . . . . . . . . . . . . . . . . . Tel: (0117) 372 8277

**Deer (Farmed)** . . . . . . . . . . . . . . . . . . . . . . . . . . . Mr Andrew Slade . . . . . . . . . . . . . . . . . . . . . . . . Tel: (020) 7270 8462

# DEPARTMENT FOR ENVIRONMENT, FOOD AND RURAL AFFAIRS

**Delivery Strategy, Departmental - Overview**

Director, Delivery Strategy Team . . . . . . . . . . . . . . . . . Mr George Trevelyan . . . . . . . . . . . . . . . . . . . . . . . Tel: (020) 7238 6462

**Dioxins** . . . . . . . . . . . . . . . . . . . . . . . . . . . . . . . . . Ms Sue Ellis . . . . . . . . . . . . . . . . . . . . . . . . . . . . . Tel: (020) 7944 6410

**Disposal at Sea** . . . . . . . . . . . . . . . . . . . . . . . . . . . Mr John Roberts . . . . . . . . . . . . . . . . . . . . . . . . . Tel: (020) 7944 5260

**Drink Industry** . . . . . . . . . . . . . . . . . . . . . . . . . . . Mr Callton Young . . . . . . . . . . . . . . . . . . . . . . . . Tel: (020) 7238 3174

**Drinking Water Inspectorate** . . . . . . . . . . . . . . . . . Professor Jeni Colbourne MBE . . . . . . . . . . . . . . . . Tel: (020) 7944 5990

**E-Business**

*DEFRA, Government Buildings, Epsom Road, Guildford, GU1 2LD*

Director, E-Business . . . . . . . . . . . . . . . . . . . . . . . . Mr David Rossington . . . . . . . . . . . . . . . . . . . . . . Tel: (01483) 563295
E-nabling Defra Programme . . . . . . . . . . . . . . . . . . Mr David Myers . . . . . . . . . . . . . . . . . . . . . . . . . . Tel: (01483) 404521
IT Procurement . . . . . . . . . . . . . . . . . . . . . . . . . . . Mr Alan Hill . . . . . . . . . . . . . . . . . . . . . . . . . . . . Tel: (01483) 403424
Workstream Enabling Defra Programme . . . . . . . . . . Ms Pearl Scrivener . . . . . . . . . . . . . . . . . . . . . . . . Tel: (01483) 403313

**Eco-labelling** . . . . . . . . . . . . . . . . . . . . . . . . . . . . . Mr Bob Ryder . . . . . . . . . . . . . . . . . . . . . . . . . . . Tel: (020) 7944 6582

**Economics**

Director, Economics and Statistics Directorate . . . . . . . . Mr David Thompson . . . . . . . . . . . . . . . . . . . . . . . Tel: (020) 7238 3292
Agri-environment . . . . . . . . . . . . . . . . . . . . . . . . . . Mr Simon Harding . . . . . . . . . . . . . . . . . . . . . . . . Tel: (020) 7238 3233
Air Quality . . . . . . . . . . . . . . . . . . . . . . . . . . . . . . Mr Bob Davies . . . . . . . . . . . . . . . . . . . . . . . . . . Tel: (020) 7944 6420
Animal Health and Welfare . . . . . . . . . . . . . . . . . . . Mr John Watson . . . . . . . . . . . . . . . . . . . . . . . . . Tel: (020) 7238 3285
Climate Policies and Energy Efficiency . . . . . . . . . . . Mr Bob Davies . . . . . . . . . . . . . . . . . . . . . . . . . . Tel: (020) 7944 6420
Common Agricultural Policy . . . . . . . . . . . . . . . . . . Mr Peter Muriel . . . . . . . . . . . . . . . . . . . . . . . . . . Tel: (020) 7238 3237
Commodities Statistics and Surveys . . . . . . . . . . . . . Mr Stuart Platt . . . . . . . . . . . . . . . . . . . . . . . . . . Tel: (01904) 455557
Environment Protection . . . . . . . . . . . . . . . . . . . . . Mr Bob Davies . . . . . . . . . . . . . . . . . . . . . . . . . . Tel: (020) 7944 6420
European Union . . . . . . . . . . . . . . . . . . . . . . . . . . Mr Peter Muriel . . . . . . . . . . . . . . . . . . . . . . . . . . Tel: (020) 7238 3237
Farm Business . . . . . . . . . . . . . . . . . . . . . . . . . . . . Mr John Watson . . . . . . . . . . . . . . . . . . . . . . . . . Tel: (020) 7238 3285
Fisheries . . . . . . . . . . . . . . . . . . . . . . . . . . . . . . . . Mr Simon Harding . . . . . . . . . . . . . . . . . . . . . . . . Tel: (020) 7238 3233
Food and Drink . . . . . . . . . . . . . . . . . . . . . . . . . . . Mr Peter Muriel . . . . . . . . . . . . . . . . . . . . . . . . . . Tel: (020) 7238 3237
International Economics . . . . . . . . . . . . . . . . . . . . . Mr Peter Muriel . . . . . . . . . . . . . . . . . . . . . . . . . . Tel: (020) 7238 3237
Noise . . . . . . . . . . . . . . . . . . . . . . . . . . . . . . . . . . Mr Bob Davies . . . . . . . . . . . . . . . . . . . . . . . . . . Tel: (020) 7944 6420
Resource Use . . . . . . . . . . . . . . . . . . . . . . . . . . . . . Mr Bob Davies . . . . . . . . . . . . . . . . . . . . . . . . . . Tel: (020) 7944 6420
Rural Regeneration . . . . . . . . . . . . . . . . . . . . . . . . . Mr Simon Harding . . . . . . . . . . . . . . . . . . . . . . . . Tel: (020) 7238 3233
Waste . . . . . . . . . . . . . . . . . . . . . . . . . . . . . . . . . . Mr Bob Davies . . . . . . . . . . . . . . . . . . . . . . . . . . Tel: (020) 7944 6420
Water . . . . . . . . . . . . . . . . . . . . . . . . . . . . . . . . . . Mr Bob Davies . . . . . . . . . . . . . . . . . . . . . . . . . . Tel: (020) 7944 6420

**Eggs** . . . . . . . . . . . . . . . . . . . . . . . . . . . . . . . . . . . Mr Andrew Slade . . . . . . . . . . . . . . . . . . . . . . . . . Tel: (020) 7270 8492

**Endangered Species: Native** . . . . . . . . . . . . . . . . . . . Mr Martin Capstick . . . . . . . . . . . . . . . . . . . . . . . Tel: (0117) 372 8233

**Energy and Environment**

Director-General, Environmental Protection . . . . . . . . . Mr Bill Stow . . . . . . . . . . . . . . . . . . . . . . . . . . . . Tel: (020) 7082 8130
Director, Environment Quality and Waste . . . . . . . . . . *Vacant* . . . . . . . . . . . . . . . . . . . . . . . . . . . . . . . . . Tel: (020) 7944 6660
Business and Sustainable Development . . . . . . . . . . . . Mr Bob Ryder . . . . . . . . . . . . . . . . . . . . . . . . . . . Tel: (020) 7944 6582
Climate Change Levy . . . . . . . . . . . . . . . . . . . . . . . Mr Jeremy Eppel . . . . . . . . . . . . . . . . . . . . . . . . . Tel: (020) 7944 6688
Combined Heat and Power . . . . . . . . . . . . . . . . . . . . Mr Duncan Prior . . . . . . . . . . . . . . . . . . . . . . . . . Tel: (020) 7215 1624
Community Heating . . . . . . . . . . . . . . . . . . . . . . . . Mr Jeremy Eppel . . . . . . . . . . . . . . . . . . . . . . . . . Tel: (020) 7944 6688
Energy and Environment Awareness . . . . . . . . . . . . . Mr Jeremy Eppel . . . . . . . . . . . . . . . . . . . . . . . . . Tel: (020) 7944 6688
Energy Saving Trust . . . . . . . . . . . . . . . . . . . . . . . . Mr Jeremy Eppel . . . . . . . . . . . . . . . . . . . . . . . . . Tel: (020) 7944 6688
Environmental Action Fund . . . . . . . . . . . . . . . . . . . Mr Jeremy Eppel . . . . . . . . . . . . . . . . . . . . . . . . . Tel: (020) 7944 6688
European Union: Energy Labelling . . . . . . . . . . . . . . . Mr Bob Ryder . . . . . . . . . . . . . . . . . . . . . . . . . . . Tel: (020) 7944 6582
Going for Green . . . . . . . . . . . . . . . . . . . . . . . . . . . Mr Jeremy Eppel . . . . . . . . . . . . . . . . . . . . . . . . . Tel: (020) 7944 6688
Green Consumer Policy . . . . . . . . . . . . . . . . . . . . . . Mr Bob Ryder . . . . . . . . . . . . . . . . . . . . . . . . . . . Tel: (020) 7944 6582
Home Energy Efficiency Scheme . . . . . . . . . . . . . . . . Mr Jeremy Eppel . . . . . . . . . . . . . . . . . . . . . . . . . Tel: (020) 7944 6688
Industry and Energy Efficiency . . . . . . . . . . . . . . . . . Mr Bob Ryder . . . . . . . . . . . . . . . . . . . . . . . . . . . Tel: (020) 7944 6582
International Issues . . . . . . . . . . . . . . . . . . . . . . . . . Mr Duncan Prior . . . . . . . . . . . . . . . . . . . . . . . . . Tel: (020) 7215 1624
Local Authorities . . . . . . . . . . . . . . . . . . . . . . . . . . Mr Jeremy Eppel . . . . . . . . . . . . . . . . . . . . . . . . . Tel: (020) 7944 6688
Policy Analysis . . . . . . . . . . . . . . . . . . . . . . . . . . . . Mr Jeremy Eppel . . . . . . . . . . . . . . . . . . . . . . . . . Tel: (020) 7944 6688

# DEPARTMENT FOR ENVIRONMENT, FOOD AND RURAL AFFAIRS

*Energy and Environment (Continued)*

| | | |
|---|---|---|
| Sustainable Energy Policy | Mr Jeremy Eppel | Tel: (020) 7944 6688 |
| Technology Partnership Initiatives | Mr Duncan Prior | Tel: (020) 7215 1624 |
| Waste, Energy from | Ms Sue Ellis | Tel: (020) 7944 6410 |

| | | |
|---|---|---|
| **Energy Crops** | Mr Andrew Perrins | Tel: (020) 7238 1113 |

| | | |
|---|---|---|
| **Environment Agency, Sponsorship** | Mr Stephen Claughton | Tel: (020) 7944 5911 |

**Environmental Protection**

| | | |
|---|---|---|
| Director-General, Environmental Protection | Mr Bill Stow | Tel: (020) 7082 8130 |
| Director, Climate, Energy and Environmental Risk | Mr Henry Derwent | Tel: (020) 7944 6210 |
| Director, Environment Quality and Waste | *Vacant* | Tel: (020) 7944 6660 |
| Director, Environment Protection Strategy | Mr Robert Lowson | Tel: (020) 7944 6450 |
| Agricultural Impact | Ms Lindsay Harris | Tel: (020) 7238 6540 |
| Agri--environment Schemes, Review | Mr John Osmond | Tel: (020) 7238 6907 |
| Air Quality *(see separate entry above)* | | |
| CFCs | Dr Martin Williams | Tel: (020) 7944 6270 |
| Conservation Management | Mr John Osmond | Tel: (020) 7238 6907 |
| Countryside Stewardship Campaign | Mr John Osmond | Tel: (020) 7238 6907 |
| Darwin Initiative for the Survival of the Species | Mr Martin Brasher | Tel: (0117) 372 8277 |
| Eastern Europe, Environmental Aid | Mr Duncan Prior | Tel: (020) 7215 1624 |
| Eco-labelling | Mr Bob Ryder | Tel: (020) 7944 6582 |
| Economics | Mr Bob Davies | Tel: (020) 7944 64205 |
| Environmental Assessment | Mr John Osmond | Tel: (020) 7238 6907 |
| Environmental Liability | Mr Stephen Claughton | Tel: (020) 7944 5911 |
| Europe Environment | Ms Helen Marquard | Tel: (020) 7944 6570 |
| Fertilisers | Dr Sue Popple | Tel: (01904) 455921 |
| Greenhouse Gas Emissions: Control | Dr Martin Williams | Tel: (020) 7944 6270 |
| Integrated Product Policy | Mr Bob Ryder | Tel: (020) 7944 6582 |
| International | Mr Roy Hathaway | Tel: (020) 7944 6220 |
| Making a Corporate Commitment Campaign | Mr Bob Ryder | Tel: (020) 7944 6582 |
| Marine Environment, Protection of | Mr John Roberts | Tel: (020) 7944 5260 |
| Noise | Dr Martin Williams | Tel: (020) 7944 6270 |
| Ozone Layer | Ms Sarah Hendry | Tel: (020) 7944 5220 |
| Packaging Waste | Mr Bob Ryder | Tel: (020) 7944 6582 |
| Pesticides | Dr Sue Popple | Tel: (01904) 455921 |
| Statistics | Mr John Custance | Tel: (020) 7944 6440 |
| Sustainable Development Commission | Mr Scott Ghagan | Tel: (020) 7944 4965 |
| Sustainable Development Unit | Ms Caroline Smith | Tel: (020) 7944 6230 |
| | Ms Andrea Young | Tel: (020) 7944 6230 |
| UN Biodiversity Convention | Mr Martin Brasher | Tel: (0117) 372 8277 |
| Waste *(see below under separate entry)* | | |
| World Trade Organisation | Mr Andrew Lawrence | Tel: (020) 7238 3005 |

| | | |
|---|---|---|
| **Environmentally Sensitive Areas** | Mr John Osmond | Tel: (020) 7238 6907 |

| | | |
|---|---|---|
| **Equal Opportunities, Departmental** | Ms Caroline Smith | Tel: (020) 7238 5786 |

**Estate Management, Departmental**
*30-34 Albert Embankment, London, SE1 7TL*

| | | |
|---|---|---|
| Director, Building and Estate Management | Mr Tony Nickson | Tel: (020) 7238 6677 |

# DEPARTMENT FOR ENVIRONMENT, FOOD AND RURAL AFFAIRS

**European Union and International Policy**

Director, European Union and
International Policy Directorate . . . . . . . . . . . . . . . . . Mr David Hunter . . . . . . . . . . . . . . . . . . . . . . . . . . Tel: (020) 7238 3003

Agriculture / Food: European Union and
International Coordination . . . . . . . . . . . . . . . . . . . . Ms Sarah Thomas. . . . . . . . . . . . . . . . . . . . . . . . . . . Tel: (020) 7238 3024

Agriculture / Food: European Union and
International Agriculture . . . . . . . . . . . . . . . . . . . . Mr Andrew Lawrence. . . . . . . . . . . . . . . . . . . . . . . . Tel: (020) 7238 3005

Economics. . . . . . . . . . . . . . . . . . . . . . . . . . . . . . . . Mr Peter Muriel . . . . . . . . . . . . . . . . . . . . . . . . . . . . Tel: (020) 7238 3237

Enlargement: Departmental Policy Co-ordination . . . . . . . Mr Andrew Lawrence. . . . . . . . . . . . . . . . . . . . . . . . Tel: (020) 7238 3005

European Environment Agency Management
Board: UK Representative . . . . . . . . . . . . . . . . . . . . Mr John Custance . . . . . . . . . . . . . . . . . . . . . . . . . Tel: (020) 7944 6440

Protected Food Names . . . . . . . . . . . . . . . . . . . . . . . Mr Jeremy Cowper. . . . . . . . . . . . . . . . . . . . . . . . . Tel: (020) 7238 6117

Waste Strategy. . . . . . . . . . . . . . . . . . . . . . . . . . . . . Ms Sue Ellis. . . . . . . . . . . . . . . . . . . . . . . . . . . . . . Tel: (020) 7944 6410

Wildlife. . . . . . . . . . . . . . . . . . . . . . . . . . . . . . . . . . Mr Martin Capstick . . . . . . . . . . . . . . . . . . . . . . . . . Tel: (0117) 372 8233

**Executive Agencies - Overview.** . . . . . . . . . . . . . . . . . Mr George Trevelyan . . . . . . . . . . . . . . . . . . . . . . . . Tel: (020) 7238 6462

**Exotic Diseases, Emergency Planning**

Policy . . . . . . . . . . . . . . . . . . . . . . . . . . . . . . . . . . Mr Simon Hewitt . . . . . . . . . . . . . . . . . . . . . . . . . . Tel: (020) 7904 6019

Veterinary . . . . . . . . . . . . . . . . . . . . . . . . . . . . . . . Dr Fred Landeg . . . . . . . . . . . . . . . . . . . . . . . . . . . Tel: (020) 7904 6185

**Exports, Animals / Meat**

Certification . . . . . . . . . . . . . . . . . . . . . . . . . . . . . . Mr Nigel Gibbens . . . . . . . . . . . . . . . . . . . . . . . . . . Tel: (020) 7904 6169

Export Promotion. . . . . . . . . . . . . . . . . . . . . . . . . . . Mr Jeremy Cowper. . . . . . . . . . . . . . . . . . . . . . . . . Tel: (020) 7238 6117

Live Animals. . . . . . . . . . . . . . . . . . . . . . . . . . . . . . Mr Nigel Gibbens . . . . . . . . . . . . . . . . . . . . . . . . . . Tel: (020) 7904 6169

Meat and Meat Products . . . . . . . . . . . . . . . . . . . . . Mr Nigel Gibbens . . . . . . . . . . . . . . . . . . . . . . . . . . Tel: (020) 7904 6169

**FAO.** . . . . . . . . . . . . . . . . . . . . . . . . . . . . . . . . . . . Mr Andrew Lawrence . . . . . . . . . . . . . . . . . . . . . . . . Tel: (020) 7238 3005

**Farm Animal Welfare Council** . . . . . . . . . . . . . . . . . . Mr John Bourne. . . . . . . . . . . . . . . . . . . . . . . . . . . Tel: (020) 7904 6179

**Farm Business Advice Scheme** . . . . . . . . . . . . . . . . . . Ms Julie Hitchcock . . . . . . . . . . . . . . . . . . . . . . . . . Tel: (020) 7238 5792

**Farm Diversification** . . . . . . . . . . . . . . . . . . . . . . . . Mr Martin Nesbit . . . . . . . . . . . . . . . . . . . . . . . . . . Tel: (020) 7238 5672

**Farm Focus.** . . . . . . . . . . . . . . . . . . . . . . . . . . . . . . Mr Alan Taylor . . . . . . . . . . . . . . . . . . . . . . . . . . . . Tel: (020) 7238 6315

**Farm Machinery (Supply)** . . . . . . . . . . . . . . . . . . . . . Ms Lindsay Harris . . . . . . . . . . . . . . . . . . . . . . . . . . Tel: (020) 7238 6540

**Farmers' Markets.** . . . . . . . . . . . . . . . . . . . . . . . . . . Mr Jeremy Cowper. . . . . . . . . . . . . . . . . . . . . . . . . Tel: (020) 7238 6117

**Farming Regulation Strategy** . . . . . . . . . . . . . . . . . . Ms Andrea Young . . . . . . . . . . . . . . . . . . . . . . . . . . Tel: (020) 7238 3321

**Farmland Conservation Policy** . . . . . . . . . . . . . . . . . Mr John Osmond . . . . . . . . . . . . . . . . . . . . . . . . . . Tel: (020) 7238 6907

**Fertilisers** . . . . . . . . . . . . . . . . . . . . . . . . . . . . . . . Dr Sue Popple . . . . . . . . . . . . . . . . . . . . . . . . . . . . Tel: (01904) 455921

**Fibre Crops.** . . . . . . . . . . . . . . . . . . . . . . . . . . . . . . Mr Andrew Perrins. . . . . . . . . . . . . . . . . . . . . . . . . . Tel: (020) 7238 1114

# DEPARTMENT FOR ENVIRONMENT, FOOD AND RURAL AFFAIRS

**Finance**

| | | |
|---|---|---|
| Finance Director | Mr Andrew Burchell | Tel: (020) 7238 5015 |
| Deputy Director, Finance | Mr Ian Grattidge | Tel: (020) 7238 5012 |

Accounting Services
*Foss House, King's Pool, 1-2 Peasholme Green, York, YO1 7PX*

| | | |
|---|---|---|
| Head, Accounting Services | Mr Roger Atkinson | Tel: (01904) 455336 |
| Emergencies - Planning | Mr David Littler | Tel: (020) 7904 6548 |
| Financial Management and Information Division | Mr Richard Wilkinson | Tel: (020) 7270 5042 |
| Financial Strategy | Mrs Julie Flint | Tel: (020) 7270 5074 |

Internal Audit
*19-29 Woburn Place, London, WC1H 0LU*

| | | |
|---|---|---|
| Head, Internal Audit and Accountancy Profession | *Vacant* | Tel: (020) 7273 8889 |

Procurement and Contracts Division
*Room 817, 19-29 Woburn Place, London, WC1H 0LU*

| | | |
|---|---|---|
| Director, Purchasing and Supply | Mr David Rabey | Tel: (020) 7273 8910 |

**Fish/Fisheries**

| | | |
|---|---|---|
| Director, Fisheries | Mr Rodney Anderson | Tel: (020) 7270 8295 |
| Catches; Conservation; CFP and TAC Negotiations | Mr Chris Ryder | Tel: (020) 7270 8217 |
| Conservation | Mr Lindsay Harris | Tel: (020) 7270 8295 |
| Fleet Capacity | Mr Peter Boyling | Tel: (020) 7270 8018 |
| Grants | Mr Peter Boyling | Tel: (020) 7270 8018 |
| Decommissioning | Mr Peter Boyling | Tel: (020) 7270 8018 |
| Economics | Ms Katrina Mullan | Tel: (020) 7238 3263 |
| Enforcement | Ms Anne Sharp | Tel: (020) 7270 8144 |
| Fish Farming and Freshwater Fish | Mr Richard Cowan CBE | Tel: (020) 7270 8188 |
| Licensing of Vessels | Ms Anne Sharp | Tel: (020) 7270 8144 |
| Marine Environment, Protection of | Mr John Roberts | Tel: (020) 7944 5260 |
| Marketing | Mr Peter Boyling | Tel: (020) 7270 8018 |
| Quotas, UK | Ms Anne Sharp | Tel: (020) 7270 8144 |
| Salmon | Mr Richard Cowan CBE | Tel: (020) 7270 8188 |
| Science | Dr John Lock | Tel: (020) 7238 1581 |
| Sea Fisheries Committees | Mr Lindsay Harris | Tel: (020) 7270 8295 |
| Sea Fisheries Inspectorate: Chief Inspector | Mr Nigel Gooding | Tel: (020) 7270 8311 |
| Shellfish | Mr Richard Cowan CBE | Tel: (020) 7270 8188 |
| State Aids | Mr Peter Boyling | Tel: (020) 7270 8018 |
| Statistics, UK | Mr Kevin Williamson | Tel: (020) 7270 8070 |
| Whales | Mr Richard Cowan CBE | Tel: (020) 7270 8188 |

**Flood and Coastal Defence**

| | | |
|---|---|---|
| Head, Flood Management | Ms Sarah Nason | Tel: (020) 7238 6115 |
| Chief Engineer | Mr Reg Purnell | Tel: (020) 7238 6355 |

**Flowers**

| | | |
|---|---|---|
| Flowers | Mr David Jones | Tel: (020) 7238 1038 |

**Fodder**

| | | |
|---|---|---|
| Crops | Mr Andrew Kuyk | Tel: (020) 7238 6494 |
| Dried | Mr David Jones | Tel: (020) 7238 1038 |

# DEPARTMENT FOR ENVIRONMENT, FOOD AND RURAL AFFAIRS

**Food (General)**

| | | |
|---|---|---|
| Director-General, Food, Farming and Fisheries | Mr Andy Lebrecht | Tel: (020) 7238 5581 |
| Director, Food Industry and Crops | Mr John Robbs | Tel: (020) 7238 3170 |
| Aid | Mr Andrew Lawrence | Tel: (020) 7238 3005 |
| Assurance Schemes | Mr Jeremy Cowper | Tel: (020) 7238 6117 |
| Competition | Mr Jeremy Cowper | Tel: (020) 7238 6117 |
| Expenditure and Food Survey | Mr Stuart Platt | Tel: (01904) 455054 |
| Export Promotion | Mr Jeremy Cowper | Tel: (020) 7238 6117 |
| Food and Drink Industry | Mr Callton Young | Tel: (020) 7238 3174 |
| Food Assurance Schemes | Mr Jeremy Cowper | Tel: (020) 7238 6117 |
| International Trade | Mr Andrew Lawrence | Tel: (020) 7238 3005 |
| Marketing/Manufacturing | Mr Callton Young | Tel: (020) 7238 3174 |
| Producer Organisations | Mr David Jones | Tel: (020) 7238 1044 |
| Protected Names, European Union | Mr Jeremy Cowper | Tel: (020) 7238 6117 |
| Regional Specialities | Mr Jeremy Cowper | Tel: (020) 7238 6601 |

| | | |
|---|---|---|
| **Forestry** | Mr Ray Anderson | Tel: (020) 7238 1115 |
| **Forms (Agricultural), Design** | Ms Lindsay Harris | Tel: (020) 7238 6540 |
| **Fruit** | Mr David Jones | Tel: (020) 7238 1038 |
| **Gangmasters** | Ms Lindsay Harris | Tel: (020) 7238 6540 |
| **General Scheme of Preferences (GSP)** | Mr Andrew Lawrence | Tel: (020) 7238 3005 |
| **GM Crops / Vaccines** | Mr Colin Church | Tel: (020) 7944 5231 |
| **Goats** | Mr Ivor Llewelyn | Tel: (020) 7270 8565 |
| **Greenhouse Gas Emissions: Domestic Policy** | Dr Martin Williams | Tel: (020) 7944 6270 |
| **Habitats Directive** | Mr Martin Capstick | Tel: (0117) 372 8233 |
| **Hazardous Substances** | Dr Martin Williams | Tel: (020) 7944 6270 |
| **Health and Safety, Farming** | Ms Lindsay Harris | Tel: (020) 7238 6540 |
| **Hedgerows: Preservation / High Hedges** | Mr John Osmond | Tel: (020) 7238 6907 |
| **Herbs and Spices** | Mr Callton Young | Tel: (020) 7238 3174 |
| **Hill Farming** | Mr John Osmond | Tel: (020) 7238 6907 |
| **Hops** | Mr David Jones | Tel: (020) 7238 1038 |
| **Horses** | Dr Fred Landeg | Tel: (020) 7904 6185 |
| **Horticulture** | Mr David Jones | Tel: (020) 7238 1038 |

**Human Resources, Departmental**

| | | |
|---|---|---|
| Director, Corporate Services | Mr Richard Allen | Tel: (020) 7270 8194 |
| Equal Opportunities | Ms Caroline Smith | Tel: (020) 7238 5786 |
| Health and Safety | Ms Caroline Smith | Tel: (020) 7238 5786 |
| Pay and Rewards | Ms Teresa Newell | Tel: (020) 7270 8169 |
| Promotions | Ms Wendy Cartwright | Tel: (020) 7270 8259 |
| Recruitment | Ms Wendy Cartwright | Tel: (020) 7270 8259 |
| Training | Ms Teresa Newell | Tel: (020) 7270 8169 |

| | | |
|---|---|---|
| **Hunting** | Mr Chris Braun | Tel: (020) 7273 6444 |
| **IACS (Integrated Administrative Control Scheme)** | Mr Tom Eddy CBE | Tel: (020) 7238 3048 |

# DEPARTMENT FOR ENVIRONMENT, FOOD AND RURAL AFFAIRS

**Imports: Meat and Meat Products** . . . . . . . . . . . . . . . Mr Nigel Gibbens . . . . . . . . . . . . . . . . . . . . . . . . . Tel: (020) 7904 6169

**International Relations and Agricultural Exports** . . . . . Mr Jeremy Cowper. . . . . . . . . . . . . . . . . . . . . . . . . Tel: (020) 7238 6117

**IT**
*Government Buildings, Epsom Road, Guildford, Surrey, GU1 2LD*
    Director, IT . . . . . . . . . . . . . . . . . . . . . . . . . . . . . . Mr Shaun Soper. . . . . . . . . . . . . . . . . . . . . . . . . . Tel: (01483) 563285
    Director, E-Business . . . . . . . . . . . . . . . . . . . . . . . . Mr David Rossington . . . . . . . . . . . . . . . . . . . . . . Tel: (01483) 563295
    Applications . . . . . . . . . . . . . . . . . . . . . . . . . . . . . Mr Peter Barber. . . . . . . . . . . . . . . . . . . . . . . . . . Tel: (01483) 403757
    E-Business . . . . . . . . . . . . . . . . . . . . . . . . . . . . . . Mr Alan Hill . . . . . . . . . . . . . . . . . . . . . . . . . . . . Tel: (01483) 403424
    E-nabling DEFRA Programme
        Human Resources . . . . . . . . . . . . . . . . . . . . . . . Ms Pearl Scrivener. . . . . . . . . . . . . . . . . . . . . . . . Tel: (01483) 403313
        Programme Director . . . . . . . . . . . . . . . . . . . . . Mr David Myers . . . . . . . . . . . . . . . . . . . . . . . . . Tel: (01483) 404521
    Infrastructure. . . . . . . . . . . . . . . . . . . . . . . . . . . . Mr David Brown . . . . . . . . . . . . . . . . . . . . . . . . . Tel: (01483) 403800
    IT Procurement . . . . . . . . . . . . . . . . . . . . . . . . . . Mr Alan Hill . . . . . . . . . . . . . . . . . . . . . . . . . . . . Tel: (01483) 403424
    Workstream Enabling DEFRA Programme . . . . . . . . . . Ms Pearl Scrivener. . . . . . . . . . . . . . . . . . . . . . . . Tel: (01483) 403313

**Joint Environmental Markets Unit**
*151 Buckingham Palace Road, London, SW1W 9SS*
    Manager . . . . . . . . . . . . . . . . . . . . . . . . . . . . . . . Mr Duncan Prior . . . . . . . . . . . . . . . . . . . . . . . . . Tel: (020) 7215 1624

**Kyoto Protocol** . . . . . . . . . . . . . . . . . . . . . . . . . . . Ms Sarah Hendry . . . . . . . . . . . . . . . . . . . . . . . . . Tel: (020) 7944 5220

**Land Use**
    Director, Land Management and
        Rural Development. . . . . . . . . . . . . . . . . . . . . . Ms Jane Brown . . . . . . . . . . . . . . . . . . . . . . . . . . Tel: (020) 7238 5699
    Conservation Management . . . . . . . . . . . . . . . . . . Mr John Osmond . . . . . . . . . . . . . . . . . . . . . . . . Tel: (020) 7238 6907
    Hill Farming Policy . . . . . . . . . . . . . . . . . . . . . . . . Mr John Osmond . . . . . . . . . . . . . . . . . . . . . . . . Tel: (020) 7238 6907
    Nutrient Loss from Agriculture, Science . . . . . . . . . . . Mr Peter Costigan . . . . . . . . . . . . . . . . . . . . . . . . Tel: (020) 7238 1533
    Organic Forestry and Industrial Crops . . . . . . . . . . . Mr Andrew Perrins . . . . . . . . . . . . . . . . . . . . . . . Tel: (020) 7238 1114
    Science . . . . . . . . . . . . . . . . . . . . . . . . . . . . . . . . Mr Peter Costigan . . . . . . . . . . . . . . . . . . . . . . . . Tel: (020) 7238 1533
    Sustainable . . . . . . . . . . . . . . . . . . . . . . . . . . . . . Ms Sheila McCabe. . . . . . . . . . . . . . . . . . . . . . . . Tel: (020) 7238 3316

**Landfills**. . . . . . . . . . . . . . . . . . . . . . . . . . . . . . . . Ms Lindsay Cornish . . . . . . . . . . . . . . . . . . . . . . . Tel: (020) 7944  8799

**Landscape Conservation** . . . . . . . . . . . . . . . . . . . . . Ms Susan Carter . . . . . . . . . . . . . . . . . . . . . . . . . Tel: (0117) 372 8178

**Lead in the Environment** . . . . . . . . . . . . . . . . . . . . . Ms Sue Ellis . . . . . . . . . . . . . . . . . . . . . . . . . . . . Tel: (020) 7944 6410

**Legal Services**
*Nobel House, 17 Smith Square, London, SW1P 3JR*
    Legal Adviser and Solicitor . . . . . . . . . . . . . . . . . . Mr Donald Macrae . . . . . . . . . . . . . . . . . . . . . . . Tel: (020) 7238 3299
    Head, Legal Directorate A . . . . . . . . . . . . . . . . . . . Ms Frances Nash . . . . . . . . . . . . . . . . . . . . . . . . . Tel: (020) 7238 5365
    Head Legal Directorate B. . . . . . . . . . . . . . . . . . . . Mr Robert Humm. . . . . . . . . . . . . . . . . . . . . . . . . Tel: (020) 7238 5313
    Animal Health and Welfare . . . . . . . . . . . . . . . . . . Ms Clare Sylvester . . . . . . . . . . . . . . . . . . . . . . . . Tel: (020) 7238 3337
    Civil Litigation. . . . . . . . . . . . . . . . . . . . . . . . . . . Ms Linda Dann . . . . . . . . . . . . . . . . . . . . . . . . . . Tel: (020) 7238 6085
    Climate Change and Air Quality Planning . . . . . . . . . Mr Jonathan Robinson . . . . . . . . . . . . . . . . . . . . . Tel: (020) 7238 3343
    Commercial. . . . . . . . . . . . . . . . . . . . . . . . . . . . . Ms Susan Spence . . . . . . . . . . . . . . . . . . . . . . . . . Tel: (020) 7238 3346
    Countryside and Nature Conservation. . . . . . . . . . . . Ms Gisela Davis. . . . . . . . . . . . . . . . . . . . . . . . . . Tel: (020) 7238 5477
    Farming and Rural Affairs . . . . . . . . . . . . . . . . . . . Mr Nigel Lefton . . . . . . . . . . . . . . . . . . . . . . . . . Tel: (020) 7238 5435
    GMOs, Seeds Plants and Forestry. . . . . . . . . . . . . . . Mr Brian Dickinson . . . . . . . . . . . . . . . . . . . . . . . Tel: (020) 7238 5719
    International Environmental Law . . . . . . . . . . . . . . . Mr Alistair McGlone . . . . . . . . . . . . . . . . . . . . . . Tel: (020) 7238 3395
    Investigations . . . . . . . . . . . . . . . . . . . . . . . . . . . Ms Jan Panting . . . . . . . . . . . . . . . . . . . . . . . . . . Tel: (020) 7238 1246
    Legal Services to Rural Payments Agency . . . . . . . . . . Mr Ian Corbett. . . . . . . . . . . . . . . . . . . . . . . . . . . Tel: (0118) 953 1904
    Marine and Product Licensing . . . . . . . . . . . . . . . . Mr Peter Davis. . . . . . . . . . . . . . . . . . . . . . . . . . . Tel: (020) 7238 3367
    Prosecutions . . . . . . . . . . . . . . . . . . . . . . . . . . . . Mr Chris Burke . . . . . . . . . . . . . . . . . . . . . . . . . . Tel: (020) 7238 1239
    Veterinary medicine . . . . . . . . . . . . . . . . . . . . . . . Mr Peter Davis. . . . . . . . . . . . . . . . . . . . . . . . . . . Tel: (020) 7238 3367
    Waste and Energy . . . . . . . . . . . . . . . . . . . . . . . . Ms Anne Sachs . . . . . . . . . . . . . . . . . . . . . . . . . . Tel: (020) 7238 1234
    Water . . . . . . . . . . . . . . . . . . . . . . . . . . . . . . . . . Mr Charles Allen. . . . . . . . . . . . . . . . . . . . . . . . . Tel: (020) 7238 3380

# DEPARTMENT FOR ENVIRONMENT, FOOD AND RURAL AFFAIRS

**Library**
Head of Library and Translations Branch . . . . . . . . . . . . Mr Kevin Jackson . . . . . . . . . . . . . . . . . . . . . . . . . Tel: (020) 7238 3327

**Limestone Pavement Orders** . . . . . . . . . . . . . . . . . . . . . Ms Susan Carter . . . . . . . . . . . . . . . . . . . . . . . . . . . Tel: (0117) 372 8178

**Litter** . . . . . . . . . . . . . . . . . . . . . . . . . . . . . . . . . . . . . Ms Sue Ellis . . . . . . . . . . . . . . . . . . . . . . . . . . . . . . Tel: (020) 7944 6410

**Live Animal Exports: Welfare** . . . . . . . . . . . . . . . . . . . Mr John Bourne . . . . . . . . . . . . . . . . . . . . . . . . . . . Tel: (020) 7904 6179

**Livestock**
Director, Sustainable Agriculture and Livestock Products . . Ms Sonia Phippard . . . . . . . . . . . . . . . . . . . . . . . . . Tel: (020) 7238 3062
Auction Markets . . . . . . . . . . . . . . . . . . . . . . . . . . . Dr Nafees Meah . . . . . . . . . . . . . . . . . . . . . . . . . . . Tel: (020) 7238 3139
Beef and Sheep: Supplies and Trade . . . . . . . . . . . . . . Mr Ivor Llewelyn . . . . . . . . . . . . . . . . . . . . . . . . . . Tel: (020) 7270 8565
Beef Labelling: EU Rules . . . . . . . . . . . . . . . . . . . . . Mr Ivor Llewelyn . . . . . . . . . . . . . . . . . . . . . . . . . . Tel: (020) 7270 8060
Identification . . . . . . . . . . . . . . . . . . . . . . . . . . . . . Mr Malcolm Hunt . . . . . . . . . . . . . . . . . . . . . . . . . Tel: (020) 7904 6260
Insurance/ Levy - Livestock Illness . . . . . . . . . . . . . . Mr Mike Segal . . . . . . . . . . . . . . . . . . . . . . . . . . . Tel: (020) 7238 3066
Livestock Strategy . . . . . . . . . . . . . . . . . . . . . . . . . Mr Mike Segal . . . . . . . . . . . . . . . . . . . . . . . . . . . Tel: (020) 7238 3066
Milk and Milk Products . . . . . . . . . . . . . . . . . . . . . Mr Andrew Slade . . . . . . . . . . . . . . . . . . . . . . . . . . Tel: (020) 7270 8207
Pigs, Deer, Small Livestock . . . . . . . . . . . . . . . . . . . Mr Andrew Slade . . . . . . . . . . . . . . . . . . . . . . . . . . Tel: (020) 7270 8462
Poultry and Eggs . . . . . . . . . . . . . . . . . . . . . . . . . . Mr Andrew Slade . . . . . . . . . . . . . . . . . . . . . . . . . . Tel: (020) 7238 3083
Red Meat Industry Forum . . . . . . . . . . . . . . . . . . . . Mr Mike Segal . . . . . . . . . . . . . . . . . . . . . . . . . . . Tel: (020) 7238 3066
Rendering Industry . . . . . . . . . . . . . . . . . . . . . . . . Mr Mike Segal . . . . . . . . . . . . . . . . . . . . . . . . . . . Tel: (020) 7238 3066
Tagging . . . . . . . . . . . . . . . . . . . . . . . . . . . . . . . . Mr Malcolm Hunt . . . . . . . . . . . . . . . . . . . . . . . . . Tel: (020) 7904 6260

**Marketing, Agricultural** . . . . . . . . . . . . . . . . . . . . . . Mr Jeremy Cowper . . . . . . . . . . . . . . . . . . . . . . . . . Tel: (020) 7238 6117

**Marine Environment**
Policy . . . . . . . . . . . . . . . . . . . . . . . . . . . . . . . . . Mr John Roberts . . . . . . . . . . . . . . . . . . . . . . . . . . Tel: (020) 7944 5260
Science . . . . . . . . . . . . . . . . . . . . . . . . . . . . . . . . Dr Nick Coulson . . . . . . . . . . . . . . . . . . . . . . . . . . Tel: (020) 7238 1578

**Milk and Milk Products** . . . . . . . . . . . . . . . . . . . . . . Mr Andrew Slade . . . . . . . . . . . . . . . . . . . . . . . . . . Tel: (020) 7270 8207

**Montreal Protocol** . . . . . . . . . . . . . . . . . . . . . . . . . . Ms Sarah Hendry . . . . . . . . . . . . . . . . . . . . . . . . . . Tel: (020) 7944 5220

**Moorland Access Schemes** . . . . . . . . . . . . . . . . . . . . Mr John Osmond . . . . . . . . . . . . . . . . . . . . . . . . . . Tel: (020) 7238 6907

**Movement Orders, Animal** . . . . . . . . . . . . . . . . . . . . Mr Simon Hewitt . . . . . . . . . . . . . . . . . . . . . . . . . . Tel: (020) 7904 6019

**Mushrooms** . . . . . . . . . . . . . . . . . . . . . . . . . . . . . . Mr David Jones . . . . . . . . . . . . . . . . . . . . . . . . . . . Tel: (020) 7270 1038

**National Parks** . . . . . . . . . . . . . . . . . . . . . . . . . . . . Ms Susan Carter . . . . . . . . . . . . . . . . . . . . . . . . . . . Tel: (0117) 372 8178

**Nature Conservancy Orders** . . . . . . . . . . . . . . . . . . . Mr John Osmond . . . . . . . . . . . . . . . . . . . . . . . . . . Tel: (020) 7238 6907

**Nitrate Vulnerable Zones**
Policy . . . . . . . . . . . . . . . . . . . . . . . . . . . . . . . . . Mr Daniel Instone . . . . . . . . . . . . . . . . . . . . . . . . . Tel: (020) 7082 8290
Science . . . . . . . . . . . . . . . . . . . . . . . . . . . . . . . . Mr Peter Costigan . . . . . . . . . . . . . . . . . . . . . . . . . Tel: (020) 7238 1533

**Noise and Nuisance** . . . . . . . . . . . . . . . . . . . . . . . . . Dr Martin Williams . . . . . . . . . . . . . . . . . . . . . . . . Tel: (020) 7944 6270

**Objective 1 and 5b Programmes** . . . . . . . . . . . . . . . . Mr Graham Cory . . . . . . . . . . . . . . . . . . . . . . . . . . Tel: (020) 7238 6442

**Oilseeds** . . . . . . . . . . . . . . . . . . . . . . . . . . . . . . . . . Mr Andrew Kuyk . . . . . . . . . . . . . . . . . . . . . . . . . . Tel: (020) 7238 6494

**Olive Oil / Olives** . . . . . . . . . . . . . . . . . . . . . . . . . . Mr David Jones . . . . . . . . . . . . . . . . . . . . . . . . . . . Tel: (020) 7270 1038

**Open Government** . . . . . . . . . . . . . . . . . . . . . . . . . . Ms Caroline Smith . . . . . . . . . . . . . . . . . . . . . . . . . Tel: (020) 7238 5786

**Organic Farming** . . . . . . . . . . . . . . . . . . . . . . . . . . Mr Andrew Perrins . . . . . . . . . . . . . . . . . . . . . . . . . Tel: (020) 7238 1113

**Packaging** . . . . . . . . . . . . . . . . . . . . . . . . . . . . . . . . Mr Bob Ryder . . . . . . . . . . . . . . . . . . . . . . . . . . . . Tel: (020) 7944 6582

# DEPARTMENT FOR ENVIRONMENT, FOOD AND RURAL AFFAIRS

**Parliamentary Clerk** .................................. Miss Deirdre Kennedy .................................. Tel: (020) 7238 5455

**Peas** .................................. Mr David Jones .................................. Tel: (020) 7238 1038

**Pesticides** .................................. Dr Sue Popple .................................. Tel: (01904) 455921

**Pests, Control - Wildlife** .................................. Mr Martin Capstick .................................. Tel: (0117) 372 8233

**Pet Passports**
    Policy .................................. Ms Alison Reeves .................................. Tel: (020) 7904 6769
    Veterinary .................................. Dr Fred Landeg .................................. Tel: (020) 7904 6185

**Pigs and Wild Boar** .................................. Mr Andrew Slade .................................. Tel: (020) 7270 8462

**Plant Variety Rights and Seeds Office**
*White House Lane, Huntingdon Road, Cambridge, CB3 0LF*
    Controller .................................. Ms Heather Hamilton .................................. Tel: (01223) 342380

**Plants**
*Foss House, 1-2 Peasholme Green, York, YO1 2PX*
    Plant Health .................................. Mr Stephen Hunter .................................. Tel: (01904) 455188
    Plant Health and Seeds Inspectorate
        Chief Inspector .................................. Mr Don Savage .................................. Tel: (01904) 455161
    Plant Variety Rights and Seeds Office
*White House Lane, Huntingdon Road, Cambridge, CB3 0LF*
    Controller .................................. Ms Heather Hamilton .................................. Tel: (01223) 342380s

**Potatoes** .................................. Mr David Jones .................................. Tel: (020) 7238 1038

**Poultry**
    Diseases .................................. Ms Sue Eades .................................. Tel: (020) 7904 8184
    Policy .................................. Mr Andrew Slade .................................. Tel: (020) 7238 3083

**Press and Communications**
    Director, Communications .................................. Mr Lucian Hudson .................................. Tel: (020) 7238 6140
    Deputy Director, Communications .................................. Ms Kelly Freeman .................................. Tel: (020) 7238 5409
    Head, News .................................. Mr Martyn Smith .................................. Tel: (020) 7238 5498

**Price Fixing, Agricultural: European Union** .................................. Mr Tom Eddy CBE .................................. Tel: (020) 7238 3048

**Procurement and Contracts (Departmental)** .................................. Mr David Rabey .................................. Tel: (020) 7273 8910

**Protein Crops** .................................. Mr Andrew Kuyk .................................. Tel: (020) 7238 6494

**Public Appointments** .................................. Ms Caroline Smith .................................. Tel: (020) 7238 5786

**Quarantine Premises** .................................. Dr Fred Landeg .................................. Tel: (020) 7904 6185

**Rabies**
    Policy .................................. Ms Alison Reeves .................................. Tel: (020) 7904 6769
    Veterinary .................................. Dr Fred Landeg .................................. Tel: (020) 7904 6185

**Radioactive Substances** .................................. Mr Richard Wood .................................. Tel: (020) 7944 6250

**Rats, Control** .................................. Mr Martin Capstick .................................. Tel: (0117) 372 8233

**Recycling** .................................. Ms Sue Ellis .................................. Tel: (020) 7944 6410

**Red Meat Industry Forum** .................................. Mr Mike Segal .................................. Tel: (020) 7238 3066

# DEPARTMENT FOR ENVIRONMENT, FOOD AND RURAL AFFAIRS

**Regions: Liaison with Government Offices** . . . . . . . . . . . . Ms Ann Tarran . . . . . . . . . . . . . . . . . . . . . . . . . . Tel: (020) 7238 5522
*(See also separate section entitled - Government Offices for the Regions)*

**Regulation**
    Better Policy . . . . . . . . . . . . . . . . . . . . . . . . . . . . Ms Lindsay Harris . . . . . . . . . . . . . . . . . . . . . . Tel: (020) 7238 6540
    Taskforce . . . . . . . . . . . . . . . . . . . . . . . . . . . . . . . . Mr Terry Bird . . . . . . . . . . . . . . . . . . . . . . . . . . Tel: (020) 7238 6540

**Rendering Industry** . . . . . . . . . . . . . . . . . . . . . . . . . . . Mr Mike Segal . . . . . . . . . . . . . . . . . . . . . . . . . . Tel: (020) 7238 3066

**Rice** . . . . . . . . . . . . . . . . . . . . . . . . . . . . . . . . . . . . . . . Mr Andrew Kuyk . . . . . . . . . . . . . . . . . . . . . . . . Tel: (020) 7238 6494

**Right to Roam** . . . . . . . . . . . . . . . . . . . . . . . . . . . . . . . Ms Susan Carter. . . . . . . . . . . . . . . . . . . . . . . . . Tel: (0117) 372 8178

**Rights of Way, Public** . . . . . . . . . . . . . . . . . . . . . . . . . Ms Susan Carter. . . . . . . . . . . . . . . . . . . . . . . . . Tel: (0117) 372 8178

**Rural Development**
    Director, Rural Economies and Communities . . . . . . . . . . Mr Paul Elliott. . . . . . . . . . . . . . . . . . . . . . . . . . Tel: (020) 7238 5700
    Director, Wildlife , Countryside, Land Use and
        Better Regulation . . . . . . . . . . . . . . . . . . . . . Mr Brian Harding . . . . . . . . . . . . . . . . . . . . . . Tel: (020) 7238 1175
    Common Agricultural Policy and Expenditure . . . . . . . . . Mr Martin Nesbit . . . . . . . . . . . . . . . . . . . . . . Tel: (020) 7238 6286
    Corporate Strategy, England Rural
        Development Programme . . . . . . . . . . . . . . . . . . . . Ms Ann Tarran . . . . . . . . . . . . . . . . . . . . . . . . . Tel: (020) 7238 5522
    Economies, Rural . . . . . . . . . . . . . . . . . . . . . . . . . . Mr Graham Cory . . . . . . . . . . . . . . . . . . . . . . . Tel: (020) 7238 6442
    England Rural Development Programme . . . . . . . . . . . . . Mr Paul Eggington. . . . . . . . . . . . . . . . . . . . . . Tel: (020) 7238 6636
    European Union Structural Funds . . . . . . . . . . . . . . . . . Mr Graham Cory . . . . . . . . . . . . . . . . . . . . . . . Tel: (020) 7238 6442
    Farm Diversification . . . . . . . . . . . . . . . . . . . . . . . . . Mr Martin Nesbit . . . . . . . . . . . . . . . . . . . . . . Tel: (020) 7238 5672
    Forestry. . . . . . . . . . . . . . . . . . . . . . . . . . . . . . . . . . Mr Ray Anderson. . . . . . . . . . . . . . . . . . . . . . . Tel: (020) 7238 1115
    Hedgerows. . . . . . . . . . . . . . . . . . . . . . . . . . . . . . . . Mr John Osmond . . . . . . . . . . . . . . . . . . . . . . . Tel: (020) 7238 6907
    Land Management . . . . . . . . . . . . . . . . . . . . . . . . . . . Ms Jane Brown . . . . . . . . . . . . . . . . . . . . . . . . Tel: (020) 7238 5699
    Objectives 1 and 5b. . . . . . . . . . . . . . . . . . . . . . . . . . Mr Graham Cory . . . . . . . . . . . . . . . . . . . . . . . Tel: (020) 7238 6442
    Rural Affairs Forum. . . . . . . . . . . . . . . . . . . . . . . . . . Mr Chris Dunabin . . . . . . . . . . . . . . . . . . . . . . Tel: (020) 7238 6141
    Rural Communities . . . . . . . . . . . . . . . . . . . . . . . . . . Mr Chris Dunabin . . . . . . . . . . . . . . . . . . . . . . Tel: (020) 7238 6141
    Rural Delivery Review. . . . . . . . . . . . . . . . . . . . . . . . Mr Martin Nisbet . . . . . . . . . . . . . . . . . . . . . . Tel: (020) 7238 6239
    Rural Development Programme Implementation Scheme . . Mr Martin Nesbit . . . . . . . . . . . . . . . . . . . . . . Tel: (020) 7238 5672
    Rural Development Service *(see separate entry below)*
    Rural Enterprise . . . . . . . . . . . . . . . . . . . . . . . . . . . . Mr Peter Cleasby . . . . . . . . . . . . . . . . . . . . . . . Tel: (020) 7238 5607
    Rural Services. . . . . . . . . . . . . . . . . . . . . . . . . . . . . . Mr David Coleman. . . . . . . . . . . . . . . . . . . . . . Tel: (020) 7238 6914

**Rural Development Service**
    Head, Rural Development Service . . . . . . . . . . . . . . . . . Mr John Adams . . . . . . . . . . . . . . . . . . . . . . . . Tel: (020) 7238 6292
    Business Process Director . . . . . . . . . . . . . . . . . . . . . . Mr Jeff Robinson . . . . . . . . . . . . . . . . . . . . . . . Tel: (020) 7238 6292
    Technical Advice. . . . . . . . . . . . . . . . . . . . . . . . . . . . Mr Alan Hooper. . . . . . . . . . . . . . . . . . . . . . . . Tel: (020) 7238 6292
    Regional Offices
    *East of England*
      *Block B, Government Buildings, Brooklands Avenue, Cambridge, CB2 2DR*
      Regional Manager. . . . . . . . . . . . . . . . . . . . . . . . Mr Martin Edwards . . . . . . . . . . . . . . . . . . . . . Tel: (01223) 462727
    *East Midlands*
      *Block 7, Government Buildings, Chalfont Drive, Nottingham, NG8 3SN*
      Regional Manager. . . . . . . . . . . . . . . . . . . . . . . . Ms Susan Buckenham . . . . . . . . . . . . . . . . . . . Tel: (0115) 929 1191
    *North East*
      *Government Buildings, Kenton Bar, Newcastle-upon-Tyne, NE5 3EW*
      Regional Manager. . . . . . . . . . . . . . . . . . . . . . . . Ms Fiona Gough . . . . . . . . . . . . . . . . . . . . . . . Tel: (0191) 286 3377
    *North West*
      *Electra Way, Crewe Business Park, Crewe, CW1 6GJ*
      Regional Manager . . . . . . . . . . . . . . . . . . . . . . . . Mr Tony Percival . . . . . . . . . . . . . . . . . . . . . . Tel: (01270) 754000
    *South East*
      *Block A, Government Buildings, Coley Park, Reading, Berkshire, RG1 6DT*
      Regional Manager. . . . . . . . . . . . . . . . . . . . . . . . Mr Nick Beard. . . . . . . . . . . . . . . . . . . . . . . . . Tel: (0118) 958 1222
    *South West*
      *Block 3, Government Buildings, Burghill Road, Westbury-on-Trym, BS10 6NJ*
      Regional Manager. . . . . . . . . . . . . . . . . . . . . . . . Mr David Sisson . . . . . . . . . . . . . . . . . . . . . . . Tel: (0117) 959 1000
    *West Midlands*
      *Block C, Government Buildings, Whittingham Road, Worcester, WR5 2LQ*
      Regional Manager. . . . . . . . . . . . . . . . . . . . . . . . Ms Carol Deakins . . . . . . . . . . . . . . . . . . . . . . Tel: (01905) 763355

# DEPARTMENT FOR ENVIRONMENT, FOOD AND RURAL AFFAIRS

*Rural Development Services (Continued)*
 *Yorkshire and the Humber*
  *Government Buildings, Otley Road, Lawnswood, Leeds, LS16 5QT*
   Regional Manager. . . . . . . . . . . . . . . . . . . . . . . . . . Mr Mike Silverwood . . . . . . . . . . . . . . . . . . . . . . . . . Tel: (0113) 261 3333

**Rural Economy / Development** . . . . . . . . . . . . . . . . . . Mr Graham Cory . . . . . . . . . . . . . . . . . . . . . . . . . . . Tel: (020) 7238 6442

**Science**
*1a Page Street, London, SW1P 4PQ*
  Chief Scientist . . . . . . . . . . . . . . . . . . . . . . . . . . . . Professor Howard Dalton . . . . . . . . . . . . . . . . . . . . . Tel: (020) 7238 1502
  Deputy Chief Scientist . . . . . . . . . . . . . . . . . . . . . . . Dr Miles Parker . . . . . . . . . . . . . . . . . . . . . . . . . . . Tel: (020) 7238 1502
  Agriculture, Environment and Food Technology . . . . . . . Dr John Sherlock . . . . . . . . . . . . . . . . . . . . . . . . . . Tel: (020) 7238 1502
  Chemicals and GM Crops. . . . . . . . . . . . . . . . . . . . . . Mr Colin Church . . . . . . . . . . . . . . . . . . . . . . . . . . Tel: (020) 7944 5231
  Research Policy and International Science . . . . . . . . . . . Dr Tony Burne. . . . . . . . . . . . . . . . . . . . . . . . . . . . Tel: (020) 7238 1650
  Veterinary, Fisheries and Aquatic Science . . . . . . . . . . . Dr Nick Coulson . . . . . . . . . . . . . . . . . . . . . . . . . . Tel: (020) 7238 1578

**Sea Defence**
  Head of Flood Management . . . . . . . . . . . . . . . . . . . . Ms Sarah Nason . . . . . . . . . . . . . . . . . . . . . . . . . . . Tel: (020) 7238 6115

**Sea Fisheries Inspectorate**
  Chief Inspector . . . . . . . . . . . . . . . . . . . . . . . . . . . . Mr Nigel Gooding . . . . . . . . . . . . . . . . . . . . . . . . . Tel: (020) 7238 5798

**Sewage/Sewers** . . . . . . . . . . . . . . . . . . . . . . . . . . . . Mr Daniel Instone . . . . . . . . . . . . . . . . . . . . . . . . . . Tel: (020) 7944 5360

**Set-Aside** . . . . . . . . . . . . . . . . . . . . . . . . . . . . . . . . Mr Andrew Kuyk . . . . . . . . . . . . . . . . . . . . . . . . . . Tel: (020) 7238 6494

**Sheep**
  BSE Contingency Planning . . . . . . . . . . . . . . . . . . . . Mr Mike Segal . . . . . . . . . . . . . . . . . . . . . . . . . . . . Tel: (020) 7238 3066
  Regimes . . . . . . . . . . . . . . . . . . . . . . . . . . . . . . . . . Mr Ivor Llewelyn . . . . . . . . . . . . . . . . . . . . . . . . . . Tel: (020) 7270 8565
  Scab . . . . . . . . . . . . . . . . . . . . . . . . . . . . . . . . . . . . Mr Alick Simmons . . . . . . . . . . . . . . . . . . . . . . . . . Tel: (020) 7904 6049
  Scrapie . . . . . . . . . . . . . . . . . . . . . . . . . . . . . . . . . . Mr Francis Marlow . . . . . . . . . . . . . . . . . . . . . . . . . Tel: (020) 7904 6492
  Sheep TSE Division . . . . . . . . . . . . . . . . . . . . . . . . . Mr Francis Marlow. . . . . . . . . . . . . . . . . . . . . . . . . . Tel: (020) 7904 6492
  Wool . . . . . . . . . . . . . . . . . . . . . . . . . . . . . . . . . . . Mr Ivor Llewelyn . . . . . . . . . . . . . . . . . . . . . . . . . . Tel: (020) 7270 8565

**Shellfish** . . . . . . . . . . . . . . . . . . . . . . . . . . . . . . . . . Mr Richard Cowan CBE . . . . . . . . . . . . . . . . . . . . . . Tel: (020) 7270 8188

**Slaughterhouses** . . . . . . . . . . . . . . . . . . . . . . . . . . . Mr Mike Segal . . . . . . . . . . . . . . . . . . . . . . . . . . . . Tel: (020) 7238 3066

**Sludge** . . . . . . . . . . . . . . . . . . . . . . . . . . . . . . . . . . Mr Daniel Instone . . . . . . . . . . . . . . . . . . . . . . . . . . Tel: (020) 7944 5360

**Smallholdings** . . . . . . . . . . . . . . . . . . . . . . . . . . . . . Mr Andrew Perrins . . . . . . . . . . . . . . . . . . . . . . . . . Tel: (020) 7238 1114

**Soil Protection** . . . . . . . . . . . . . . . . . . . . . . . . . . . . Mr Alan Taylor . . . . . . . . . . . . . . . . . . . . . . . . . . . . Tel: (020) 7238 6315

**SSSIs (Sites of Special Scientific Interest)** . . . . . . . . . . Mr Martin Capstick . . . . . . . . . . . . . . . . . . . . . . . . . Tel: (0117) 372 8233

**Statistics**
  Director, Economics and Statistics . . . . . . . . . . . . . . . . Mr David Thompson . . . . . . . . . . . . . . . . . . . . . . . . Tel: (020) 7238 3292
  Chief Statistician: Environment Protection . . . . . . . . . . . Mr John Custance . . . . . . . . . . . . . . . . . . . . . . . . . . Tel: (020) 7944 6440
  Agricultural Market Reports. . . . . . . . . . . . . . . . . . . . . Mr Peter Helm *(York)* . . . . . . . . . . . . . . . . . . . . . . . Tel: (01904) 455250
  Agricultural Price Indices . . . . . . . . . . . . . . . . . . . . . . Mr Peter Helm *(York)* . . . . . . . . . . . . . . . . . . . . . . . Tel: (01904) 455253
  Air Quality, Global Atmosphere . . . . . . . . . . . . . . . . . . Mr John Custance . . . . . . . . . . . . . . . . . . . . . . . . . . Tel: (020) 7944 6440
  BSE . . . . . . . . . . . . . . . . . . . . . . . . . . . . . . . . . . . . Dr Mandy Bailey . . . . . . . . . . . . . . . . . . . . . . . . . . Tel: (020) 7904 8054
  Commodities; Crops: Food and Drink . . . . . . . . . . . . . . Mr Stuart Platt *(York)* . . . . . . . . . . . . . . . . . . . . . . . Tel: (01904) 455557
  Environmental Statistics. . . . . . . . . . . . . . . . . . . . . . . . Mr John Custance . . . . . . . . . . . . . . . . . . . . . . . . . . Tel: (020) 7944 6440
  Farm Censuses and Surveys . . . . . . . . . . . . . . . . . . . . Mr Peter Helm *(York)* . . . . . . . . . . . . . . . . . . . . . . . Tel: (01904) 455332
  Fish . . . . . . . . . . . . . . . . . . . . . . . . . . . . . . . . . . . . Mr Peter Boyling . . . . . . . . . . . . . . . . . . . . . . . . . . Tel: (020) 7270 8018
  Food Survey . . . . . . . . . . . . . . . . . . . . . . . . . . . . . . Mr Stuart Platt *(York)* . . . . . . . . . . . . . . . . . . . . . . . Tel: (01904) 455557
  International . . . . . . . . . . . . . . . . . . . . . . . . . . . . . . . Mr Stuart Platt *(York)* . . . . . . . . . . . . . . . . . . . . . . . Tel: (01904) 455557
  Livestock. . . . . . . . . . . . . . . . . . . . . . . . . . . . . . . . . Mr Stuart Platt *(York)* . . . . . . . . . . . . . . . . . . . . . . . Tel: (01904) 455557
  Marine Environment . . . . . . . . . . . . . . . . . . . . . . . . . Mr Peter Boyling . . . . . . . . . . . . . . . . . . . . . . . . . . Tel: (020) 7270 8018
  Market Reports; Prices . . . . . . . . . . . . . . . . . . . . . . . . Mr Peter Helm *(York)* . . . . . . . . . . . . . . . . . . . . . . . Tel: (01904) 455250
  Noise. . . . . . . . . . . . . . . . . . . . . . . . . . . . . . . . . . . . Mr John Custance . . . . . . . . . . . . . . . . . . . . . . . . . . Tel: (020) 7944 6440
  Organic Farming . . . . . . . . . . . . . . . . . . . . . . . . . . . Mr Stuart Platt *(York)* . . . . . . . . . . . . . . . . . . . . . . . Tel: (01904) 455557
  Recycling . . . . . . . . . . . . . . . . . . . . . . . . . . . . . . . . Mr John Custance . . . . . . . . . . . . . . . . . . . . . . . . . . Tel: (020) 7944 6440
  Sustainable Development Indicators. . . . . . . . . . . . . . . . Mr John Custance . . . . . . . . . . . . . . . . . . . . . . . . . . Tel: (020) 7944 6440
  Wildlife. . . . . . . . . . . . . . . . . . . . . . . . . . . . . . . . . . Mr John Custance . . . . . . . . . . . . . . . . . . . . . . . . . . Tel: (020) 7944 6440

# DEPARTMENT FOR ENVIRONMENT,
## FOOD AND RURAL AFFAIRS

**Sugar** . . . . . . . . . . . . . . . . . . . . . . . . . . . . . . Mr Andrew Kuyk . . . . . . . . . . . . . . . . . . . . Tel: (020) 7238 6494

**Sustainable Development**
    Director, Environment Protection Strategy . . . . . . . . . . . . Mr Robert Lowson . . . . . . . . . . . . . . . . . . . . . Tel: (020) 7944 6450
    Europe Environment . . . . . . . . . . . . . . . . . . . . . . . . . Ms Helen Marquard . . . . . . . . . . . . . . . . . . . . Tel: (020) 7944 6570
    Sustainable Agriculture . . . . . . . . . . . . . . . . . . . . . . . Mr Nigel Atkinson . . . . . . . . . . . . . . . . . . . . . Tel: (020) 7238 3119
    Sustainable Development Commission . . . . . . . . . . . . . Mr Scott Ghagan . . . . . . . . . . . . . . . . . . . . . . Tel: (020) 7944 4965
    Sustainable Development Unit . . . . . . . . . . . . . . . . . . . Ms Bronwen Jones . . . . . . . . . . . . . . . . . . . . . Tel: (020) 7238 5904
                                          Ms Andrea Young . . . . . . . . . . . . . . . . . . . . . . Tel: (020) 7944 6230

**Sustainable Food and Fisheries Division** . . . . . . . . . . . . . Dr Donal Murphy-Bokern . . . . . . . . . . . . . . . . . . Tel: (020) 7238 1506

**Tagging of Farm Animals** . . . . . . . . . . . . . . . . . . . . . Mr Malcolm Hunt . . . . . . . . . . . . . . . . . . . . . . Tel: (020) 7904 6260

**Tea** . . . . . . . . . . . . . . . . . . . . . . . . . . . . . . . . . Mr Callton Young . . . . . . . . . . . . . . . . . . . . . . Tel: (020) 7238 3174

**Tobacco** . . . . . . . . . . . . . . . . . . . . . . . . . . . . . . Mr David Jones . . . . . . . . . . . . . . . . . . . . . . . Tel: (020) 7238 1038

**Toxic Substances** . . . . . . . . . . . . . . . . . . . . . . . . . Dr Martin Williams . . . . . . . . . . . . . . . . . . . . . Tel: (020) 7944 6270

**Training and Education (Land-based Industries)** . . . . . . . Mr Peter Cleasby . . . . . . . . . . . . . . . . . . . . . . . Tel: (020) 7238 5607

**Transmissible Spongiform Encephalopathies**
*1a Page Street, London, SW1P 4PQ*
    BSE and Spongiform Encephalopathies . . . . . . . . . . . . . Dr Mandy Bailey . . . . . . . . . . . . . . . . . . . . . . Tel: (020) 7904 8054
    Encephalopathies (TSE) Directorate . . . . . . . . . . . . . . . Dr Peter Nash . . . . . . . . . . . . . . . . . . . . . . . . Tel: (020) 7904 6089
    Sheep TSE Division . . . . . . . . . . . . . . . . . . . . . . . . Mr Francis Marlow . . . . . . . . . . . . . . . . . . . . . Tel: (020) 7904 6492
    Research and Surveillance Unit . . . . . . . . . . . . . . . . . . Dr Mandy Bailey . . . . . . . . . . . . . . . . . . . . . . Tel: (020) 7904 8054
    Veterinary Notifiable TSE Diseases . . . . . . . . . . . . . . . Dr Peter Soul . . . . . . . . . . . . . . . . . . . . . . . . Tel: (020) 7904 8207

**Tuberculosis in Animals (Control)** . . . . . . . . . . . . . . . Ms Sue Eades . . . . . . . . . . . . . . . . . . . . . . . . . Tel: (020) 7904 8184

**UNCTAD** . . . . . . . . . . . . . . . . . . . . . . . . . . . . . . Mr Andrew Lawrence . . . . . . . . . . . . . . . . . . . . Tel: (020) 7238 3005

**Vegetables** . . . . . . . . . . . . . . . . . . . . . . . . . . . . . Mr David Jones . . . . . . . . . . . . . . . . . . . . . . . Tel: (020) 7238 1038

**Vertebrate Pests (Control)** . . . . . . . . . . . . . . . . . . . . Mr Martin Capstick . . . . . . . . . . . . . . . . . . . . . Tel: (0117) 372 8233

**Veterinary**
*1a Page Street, London, SW1P 4PQ*
    Chief Veterinary Officer . . . . . . . . . . . . . . . . . . . . . . Ms Debby Reynolds . . . . . . . . . . . . . . . . . . . . . Tel: (020) 7082 6139
    Director, State Veterinary Service . . . . . . . . . . . . . . . . . Mr Martin Atkinson . . . . . . . . . . . . . . . . . . . . . Tel: (020) 7904 6209
    Deputy Chief Veterinary Officer (Policy) . . . . . . . . . . . . Mr Richard Cawthorne . . . . . . . . . . . . . . . . . . . Tel: (020) 7904 6119
    Contingency Planning . . . . . . . . . . . . . . . . . . . . . . . Ms Ann Waters . . . . . . . . . . . . . . . . . . . . . . . Tel: (020) 7904 6289
    E-coli . . . . . . . . . . . . . . . . . . . . . . . . . . . . . . . . Mr Alick Simmons . . . . . . . . . . . . . . . . . . . . . Tel: (020) 7904 6049
    Embryo Transfer . . . . . . . . . . . . . . . . . . . . . . . . . . Mr Alick Simmons . . . . . . . . . . . . . . . . . . . . . Tel: (020) 7904 6049
    Endemic Diseases . . . . . . . . . . . . . . . . . . . . . . . . . Mr Alick Simmons . . . . . . . . . . . . . . . . . . . . . Tel: (020) 7904 6049
    Exotic Diseases . . . . . . . . . . . . . . . . . . . . . . . . . . . Dr Fred Landeg . . . . . . . . . . . . . . . . . . . . . . . Tel: (020) 7904 6185
    International Trade . . . . . . . . . . . . . . . . . . . . . . . . . Mr Nigel Gibbens . . . . . . . . . . . . . . . . . . . . . . Tel: (020) 7904 6169
    Salmonellosis . . . . . . . . . . . . . . . . . . . . . . . . . . . . Mr Alick Simmons . . . . . . . . . . . . . . . . . . . . . Tel: (020) 7904 6049
    Service Delivery, Veterinary Service . . . . . . . . . . . . . . . Mr Richard Drummond . . . . . . . . . . . . . . . . . . . Tel: (020) 7904 6301
    Surveillance . . . . . . . . . . . . . . . . . . . . . . . . . . . . . Ms Ruth Lysons . . . . . . . . . . . . . . . . . . . . . . . Tel: (020) 7904 8263
    Tuberculosis . . . . . . . . . . . . . . . . . . . . . . . . . . . . Mr Alick Simmons . . . . . . . . . . . . . . . . . . . . . Tel: (020) 7904 6049
    Veterinary Services: English Regions
      East
      *Block A, Government Buildings, Coley Park, Reading, RG1 6DT*
        Head of Veterinary Services (East) . . . . . . . . . . . . . . Mr Gareth Jones . . . . . . . . . . . . . . . . . . . . . . . Tel: (0118) 958 1222
                                                                      ext 3298
      North
      *Windsor House, Cornwall Road, Harrogate, HG1 2PW*
        Head of Veterinary Services (North) . . . . . . . . . . . . . Mr Rob Paul . . . . . . . . . . . . . . . . . . . . . . . . . Tel: (01423) 530678
                                                                       ext 251

# DEPARTMENT FOR ENVIRONMENT, FOOD AND RURAL AFFAIRS

*Veterinary (Continued)*

West

*Block 3, Government Buildings, Burghill Road, Westbury-on-Trim, BS10 6NJ*

Head of Veterinary Services (West) . . . . . . . . . . . . . Mr John Cross . . . . . . . . . . . . . . . . . . . . . . . . . . . Tel: (0117) 959 1000 ext 3552

Veterinary Services: Scotland

*Scottish Executive, Pentland House, 47 Robb's Loan, Edinburgh, EH14 1TY*

Chief Veterinary Officer (Scotland) . . . . . . . . . . . . . Mr Charles Milne . . . . . . . . . . . . . . . . . . . Tel: (0131) 244 6275
Animal Health (Scotland). . . . . . . . . . . . . . . . . . Mr Derrick McIntosh . . . . . . . . . . . . . . . . . Tel: (0131) 244 8270

Veterinary Services: Wales

*State Veterinary Service, Crown Buildings, Cathays Park, Cardiff, CF10 3NQ*

Chief Veterinary Officer, Wales . . . . . . . . . . . . . . . Mr Tony Edwards. . . . . . . . . . . . . . . . . . . . . . . Tel: (092) 2082 5762
Veterinary Surgeons Act . . . . . . . . . . . . . . . . . . . Mr John Bourne. . . . . . . . . . . . . . . . . . . . . . . . Tel: (020) 7904 6179
Welfare. . . . . . . . . . . . . . . . . . . . . . . . . . . . . . . . . Mr David Pritchard . . . . . . . . . . . . . . . . . . . . . Tel: (020) 7904 6464
Zoonoses . . . . . . . . . . . . . . . . . . . . . . . . . . . . . . . Mr Alick Simmons . . . . . . . . . . . . . . . . . . . . . . Tel: (020) 7904 6049

**Village Greens** . . . . . . . . . . . . . . . . . . . . . . . . . . . Mr Graham Cory . . . . . . . . . . . . . . . . . . . . . . . . Tel: (020) 7238 6442

**Voluntary Bodies** . . . . . . . . . . . . . . . . . . . . . . . . . Ms Lindsay Harris. . . . . . . . . . . . . . . . . . . . . . . . Tel: (020) 7238 6540

**Wages (Agricultural)** . . . . . . . . . . . . . . . . . . . . . . . Ms Lindsay Harris . . . . . . . . . . . . . . . . . . . . . . . Tel: (020) 7238 6540

**Waste**

Director, Environment Quality and Waste. . . . . . . . . . . . . *Vacant*. . . . . . . . . . . . . . . . . . . . . . . . . . . . . . . . . Tel: (020) 7944 6660
Batteries . . . . . . . . . . . . . . . . . . . . . . . . . . . . . . . Mrs Sue Ellis . . . . . . . . . . . . . . . . . . . . . . . . . . Tel: (020) 7944 6410
BSE: Waste Implications/Carcass Handling . . . . . . . . . Dr Mandy Bailey . . . . . . . . . . . . . . . . . . . . . . . Tel: (020) 7904 8054
Clinical. . . . . . . . . . . . . . . . . . . . . . . . . . . . . . . . . Mrs Sue Ellis . . . . . . . . . . . . . . . . . . . . . . . . . . Tel: (020) 7944 6410
Composting . . . . . . . . . . . . . . . . . . . . . . . . . . . . . Ms Lindsay Cornish . . . . . . . . . . . . . . . . . . . . . Tel: (020) 7238 8799
Electrical Waste . . . . . . . . . . . . . . . . . . . . . . . . . . Ms Lindsay Cornish . . . . . . . . . . . . . . . . . . . . . Tel: (020) 7944 8799
Energy from Waste . . . . . . . . . . . . . . . . . . . . . . . . Mr Jeremy Eppel . . . . . . . . . . . . . . . . . . . . . . . Tel: (020) 7944 6688
European Union Waste Strategy . . . . . . . . . . . . . . . . Mrs Sue Ellis . . . . . . . . . . . . . . . . . . . . . . . . . . Tel: (020) 7944 6410
Farm Waste. . . . . . . . . . . . . . . . . . . . . . . . . . . . . . Mr Ray Anderson. . . . . . . . . . . . . . . . . . . . . . . Tel: (020) 7238 1115
Hazardous Waste. . . . . . . . . . . . . . . . . . . . . . . . . . Mrs Sue Ellis . . . . . . . . . . . . . . . . . . . . . . . . . . Tel: (020) 7944 6410
Imports and Exports. . . . . . . . . . . . . . . . . . . . . . . . Mrs Sue Ellis . . . . . . . . . . . . . . . . . . . . . . . . . . Tel: (020) 7944 6410
International . . . . . . . . . . . . . . . . . . . . . . . . . . . . . Mrs Sue Ellis . . . . . . . . . . . . . . . . . . . . . . . . . . Tel: (020) 7944 6410
Landfills . . . . . . . . . . . . . . . . . . . . . . . . . . . . . . . . Ms Lindsay Cornish . . . . . . . . . . . . . . . . . . . . . Tel: (020) 7944  8799
Licensing . . . . . . . . . . . . . . . . . . . . . . . . . . . . . . . Mrs Sue Ellis . . . . . . . . . . . . . . . . . . . . . . . . . . Tel: (020) 7944 6410
Local Authorities. . . . . . . . . . . . . . . . . . . . . . . . . . Mrs Sue Ellis . . . . . . . . . . . . . . . . . . . . . . . . . . Tel: (020) 7944 6410
Policy . . . . . . . . . . . . . . . . . . . . . . . . . . . . . . . . . . Mrs Sue Ellis . . . . . . . . . . . . . . . . . . . . . . . . . . Tel: (020) 7944 6410
Radioactive Waste Disposal. . . . . . . . . . . . . . . . . . . Mr Richard Wood . . . . . . . . . . . . . . . . . . . . . . Tel: (020) 7944 6250
Recycling . . . . . . . . . . . . . . . . . . . . . . . . . . . . . . . Mrs Sue Ellis . . . . . . . . . . . . . . . . . . . . . . . . . . Tel: (020) 7944 6410
Shipment Regulation . . . . . . . . . . . . . . . . . . . . . . . Mrs Sue Ellis . . . . . . . . . . . . . . . . . . . . . . . . . . Tel: (020) 7944 6410
Special Waste Regulation. . . . . . . . . . . . . . . . . . . . . Mrs Sue Ellis . . . . . . . . . . . . . . . . . . . . . . . . . . Tel: (020) 7944 6410
Strategy. . . . . . . . . . . . . . . . . . . . . . . . . . . . . . . . . Ms Lindsay Cornish . . . . . . . . . . . . . . . . . . . . . Tel: (020) 7944  8799
Tidy Britain Group. . . . . . . . . . . . . . . . . . . . . . . . . Mrs Sue Ellis . . . . . . . . . . . . . . . . . . . . . . . . . . Tel: (020) 7944 6410
Vehicles (Abandoned and End of Life) . . . . . . . . . . . . Mrs Sue Ellis . . . . . . . . . . . . . . . . . . . . . . . . . . Tel: (020) 7944 6410
Waste Brokers: Registration. . . . . . . . . . . . . . . . . . . Mrs Sue Ellis . . . . . . . . . . . . . . . . . . . . . . . . . . Tel: (020) 7944 6410
Waste Oils Directive . . . . . . . . . . . . . . . . . . . . . . . Mrs Sue Ellis . . . . . . . . . . . . . . . . . . . . . . . . . . Tel: (020) 7944 6410
Water and Waste. . . . . . . . . . . . . . . . . . . . . . . . . . . Mr Daniel Instone . . . . . . . . . . . . . . . . . . . . . . Tel: (020) 7944 5360

**Water**

Director, Water and Land . . . . . . . . . . . . . . . . . . . . Mr Richard Bird . . . . . . . . . . . . . . . . . . . . . . . . Tel: (020) 7082 8315
Chief Inspector, Drinking Water Inspectorate . . . . . . . . Professor Jeni Colbourne MBE . . . . . . . . . . . . . . . Tel: (020) 7082 8048
Abstraction (Licensing Appeals). . . . . . . . . . . . . . . . . Mr Richard Wood . . . . . . . . . . . . . . . . . . . . . . Tel: (020) 7082 8338
Agricultural Pollution . . . . . . . . . . . . . . . . . . . . . . Mr Daniel Instone . . . . . . . . . . . . . . . . . . . . . . Tel: (020) 7082 8290
Bathing . . . . . . . . . . . . . . . . . . . . . . . . . . . . . . . . Mr Daniel Instone . . . . . . . . . . . . . . . . . . . . . . Tel: (020) 7082 8290
By-laws . . . . . . . . . . . . . . . . . . . . . . . . . . . . . . . . Mr Richard Wood . . . . . . . . . . . . . . . . . . . . . . Tel: (020) 7082 8338
Charging . . . . . . . . . . . . . . . . . . . . . . . . . . . . . . . Mr Richard Wood . . . . . . . . . . . . . . . . . . . . . . Tel: (020) 7082 8338
Chemicals and Drinking Water . . . . . . . . . . . . . . . . Professor Jeni Colbourne MBE . . . . . . . . . . . . . . . Tel: (020) 7082 8048
Classification Schemes. . . . . . . . . . . . . . . . . . . . . . . Mr Daniel Instone . . . . . . . . . . . . . . . . . . . . . . Tel: (020) 7082 8290
Conservation . . . . . . . . . . . . . . . . . . . . . . . . . . . . Mr Richard Wood . . . . . . . . . . . . . . . . . . . . . . Tel: (020) 7082 8338
Customer Installations . . . . . . . . . . . . . . . . . . . . . . Mr Richard Wood . . . . . . . . . . . . . . . . . . . . . . Tel: (020) 7082 8338

# DEPARTMENT FOR ENVIRONMENT, FOOD AND RURAL AFFAIRS

*Water (Continued)*

| | | |
|---|---|---|
| Detergents | Mr Daniel Instone | Tel: (020) 7082 8290 |
| Discharges/Waste | Mr Daniel Instone | Tel: (020) 7082 8290 |
| Disconnections | Mr Richard Wood | Tel: (020) 7082 8338 |
| Drinking Water Directive | Professor Jeni Colbourne MBE | Tel: (020) 7082 8048 |
| Drought Orders | Mr Richard Wood | Tel: (020) 7082 8338 |
| Emergencies | Ms Sarah Nason | Tel: (020) 7238 6115 |
| Eutrophication | Mr Daniel Instone | Tel: (020) 7082 8290 |
| Farm Science | Mr Peter Costigan | Tel: (020) 7238 1533 |
| Framework Directive, European Union | Mr Daniel Instone | Tel: (020) 7082 8290 |
| Groundwater Directives/Pollution | Mr Daniel Instone | Tel: (020) 7082 8290 |
| Industrial Pollution | Mr Bob Ryder | Tel: (020) 7082 8656 |
| Lead and Drinking Water | Professor Jeni Colbourne MBE | Tel: (020) 7082 8048 |
| Leakages | Mr Richard Wood | Tel: (020) 7082 8338 |
| Marine (Pollution Policy) | Mr John Roberts | Tel: (020) 7082 8192 |
| Mines (Abandoned): Pollution | Mr Daniel Instone | Tel: (020) 7082 8290 |
| Nitrates Directives | Mr Daniel Instone | Tel: (020) 7944 8290 |
| OFWAT: Liaison | Mr Richard Wood | Tel: (020) 7082 8338 |
| Pesticides | Mr Daniel Instone | Tel: (020) 7082 8290 |
| Pipework Policy | Mr Richard Wood | Tel: (020) 7082 8338 |
| Private Water Companies | Mr Richard Wood | Tel: (020) 7082 8338 |
| Quality | Mr Daniel Instone | Tel: (020) 7082 8290 |
| Security (Water Industry) | Mr Daniel Instone | Tel: (020) 7082 8290 |
| Supply and Regulation | Mr Richard Wood | Tel: (020) 7082 8338 |
| Waste Implementation Programme | Mr John Burns | Tel: (020) 7082 8817 |

| | | |
|---|---|---|
| **Waterways, British, Sponsorship** | Mr John Roberts | Tel: (020) 7082 8192 |
| **Weeds Act** | Mr Ray Anderson | Tel: (020) 7238 1115 |
| **Wetlands (Conservation)** | Mr Martin Capstick | Tel: (0117) 372 8233 |
| **Whales** | Mr Richard Cowan CBE | Tel: (020) 7270 8188 |

**Wildlife**

| | | |
|---|---|---|
| Director, Wildlife, Countryside, Land Use and Better Regulation | Mr Brian Harding | Tel: (020) 7238 1175 |
| Chief Wildlife Inspector | Mr Nick Williams | Tel: (0117) 372 8997 |
| Birds | Mr John Osmond | Tel: (020) 7238 6024 |
| Conservation Policy | Mr Martin Capstick | Tel: (0117) 372 8233 |
| Dangerous Wild Animals | Mr Martin Brasher | Tel: (0117) 372 8277 |
| Endangered Species; Exotic Species | Mr Martin Brasher | Tel: (0117) 372 8277 |
| European Union and Wildlife | Mr Martin Capstick | Tel: (0117) 372 8233 |
| Exports/Imports | Mr Martin Brasher | Tel: (0117) 372 8277 |
| Global Wildlife | Mr Martin Brasher | Tel: (0117) 372 8277 |
| Habitats: European Union Directive | Mr John Osmond | Tel: (020) 7238 6024 |
| International Conservation Policy | Mr Martin Brasher | Tel: (0117) 372 8277 |
| Nature Conservation | Mr John Osmond | Tel: (020) 7238 6024 |
| Non-Native Species Release | Mr Colin Church | Tel: (020) 7944 5231 |
| UNESCO | Mr Martin Brasher | Tel: (0117) 372 8277 |

| | | |
|---|---|---|
| **Woodlands** | Mr Ray Anderson | Tel: (020) 7238 1115 |
| **Wool** | Mr Ivor Llewelyn | Tel: (020) 7270 8565 |
| **Working Time Directive** | Ms Lindsay Harris | Tel: (020) 7238 6540 |

**World Trade Organisation**

| | | |
|---|---|---|
| Economics | Mr Peter Muriel | Tel: (020) 7238 3237 |
| Policy | Mr Andrew Lawrence | Tel: (020) 7238 3005 |

| | | |
|---|---|---|
| **Zoos** | Mr Martin Brasher | Tel: (0117) 372 8277 |

# DEPARTMENT FOR ENVIRONMENT, FOOD AND RURAL AFFAIRS

## OTHER RELEVANT CONTACTS

### AGRICULTURAL LAND

**Agricultural Land Tribunals** . . . . . . . . . . . . . . . . . . . . . . c/o Agricultural Resources and Better Regulation Division, 2C Ergon House, Horseferry Road, London, SW1P 2AL

   Contact . . . . . . . . . . . . . . . . . . . . . . . . . . . . . . . . . . . . Mr Dermot McInerey . . . . . . . . . . . . . . . . . . . . . . . . Tel: (020) 7238 5677

### AGRICULTURAL PAYMENTS

**Integrated Administration and Control Systems**

   **(IACS) Appeals Panel** . . . . . . . . . . . . . . . . . . . . . . Rural Payments Agency, Room 621, Kings House, 33 Kings Road, Reading, RG1 3BU

   Contact Point . . . . . . . . . . . . . . . . . . . . . . . . . . . . . . Mr Peter Crewe . . . . . . . . . . . . . . . . . . . . . . . . . . . . Tel: (0118) 953 1907

**Rural Payments Agency** *(Executive Agency)* . . . . . . . . . . . . Kings House, 33 Kings Road, Reading, RG1 3BU

   Chief Executive . . . . . . . . . . . . . . . . . . . . . . . . . . . . . Mr Johnston McNeill . . . . . . . . . . . . . . . . . . . . . . . . Tel: (0118) 958 3626

   Web: http://www.rpa.gov.uk

### AGRICULTURAL WAGES

**Agricultural Wages Board for England and Wales** . . . . . . Area 2C, Ergon House, Horseferry Road, London, SW1P 2AL

   Chairman . . . . . . . . . . . . . . . . . . . . . . . . . . . . . . . . . . Mr Derek Evans CBE

   Secretary . . . . . . . . . . . . . . . . . . . . . . . . . . . . . . . . . . Mr Dermot McInerney . . . . . . . . . . . . . . . . . . . . . . . Tel: (020) 7238 5677

### AIR QUALITY

**Air Quality Expert Group** . . . . . . . . . . . . . . . . . . . . . . 4/F15, Ashdown House, 123 Victoria Street, London, SW1E 6PE

   Chairman . . . . . . . . . . . . . . . . . . . . . . . . . . . . . . . . . . Professor Mike Pilling

   Secretary . . . . . . . . . . . . . . . . . . . . . . . . . . . . . . . . . . Ms Janet Dixon . . . . . . . . . . . . . . . . . . . . . . . . . . . . Tel: (020) 7082 8421

   E-mail: air.quality@defra.gsi.gov.uk

   Web: http://www.defra.gov.uk/environment/airquality/aqeg/index.htm

**Expert Panel on Air Quality Standards** . . . . . . . . . . . . . Environment Quality Division, Room 4/E14, Ashdown House, 123 Victoria Street, London, SW1E 6D

   Chairman . . . . . . . . . . . . . . . . . . . . . . . . . . . . . . . . . . Professor Stephen Holgate

   Secretary . . . . . . . . . . . . . . . . . . . . . . . . . . . . . . . . . . Dr Martin Meadows . . . . . . . . . . . . . . . . . . . . . . . . . Tel: (020) 7082 8042

   Web: http://www.defra.gov.uk/environment/airquality/aqs/index.htm

### ANIMALS

**Advisory Committee on Animal Feedstuffs** . . . . . . . . . . . Food Standards Agency, Room 415B. Aviation House, 125 Kingsway, London, WC2B 6NH

   Chairman . . . . . . . . . . . . . . . . . . . . . . . . . . . . . . . . . . Dr Chitra Bharucha

   Secretary . . . . . . . . . . . . . . . . . . . . . . . . . . . . . . . . . . Mr Keith Millar . . . . . . . . . . . . . . . . . . . . . . . . . . . . Tel: (020) 7276 8083

   Web: http://www.food.gov.uk

**Farm Animal Welfare Council** . . . . . . . . . . . . . . . . . . . Area 511, 1A Page Street, London, SW1P 4PQ

   Chairman . . . . . . . . . . . . . . . . . . . . . . . . . . . . . . . . . . Dr Judy MacArthur Clark

   Secretary . . . . . . . . . . . . . . . . . . . . . . . . . . . . . . . . . . Miss Kumu Adhihetty . . . . . . . . . . . . . . . . . . . . . . . . Tel: (020) 7904 6534

   Web: http://www.fawc.org.uk

### BEEF

**Beef Assurance Scheme Membership Panel** . . . . . . . . . . . Food Standards Agency, Room 315B. Aviation House, 125 Kingsway, London, WC2B 6NH

   Chairman . . . . . . . . . . . . . . . . . . . . . . . . . . . . . . . . . . Miss Claire Andrews

   Secretary . . . . . . . . . . . . . . . . . . . . . . . . . . . . . . . . . . Mr Keith Greig . . . . . . . . . . . . . . . . . . . . . . . . . . . . . Tel: (020) 7276 8314

   Web: http://www.food.gov.uk

### BIODIVERSITY

**Darwin Advisory Committee** . . . . . . . . . . . . . . . . . . . . . Zone 4/C1, Ashdown House, 123 Victoria Street, London, SW1E 6DE

   Chairman . . . . . . . . . . . . . . . . . . . . . . . . . . . . . . . . . . Professor David Ingram

   Secretary . . . . . . . . . . . . . . . . . . . . . . . . . . . . . . . . . . Ms Glenys Parry . . . . . . . . . . . . . . . . . . . . . . . . . . . Tel: (020) 7082 8446

   Web: http://www.darwin.gov.uk

# DEPARTMENT FOR ENVIRONMENT, FOOD AND RURAL AFFAIRS

*Other Relevant Contacts (Continued)*

## BOTANIC GARDENS

**Royal Botanic Gardens** . . . . . . . . . . . . . . . . . . . . . . . . . . . . . Kew, Richmond-upon-Thames, Surrey, TW9 3AB

    Chairman of Trustees . . . . . . . . . . . . . . . . . . . . . . . . . . . . Eral of Selbourne FRS

    Director . . . . . . . . . . . . . . . . . . . . . . . . . . . . . . . . . . . Professor Peter Crane FRS . . . . . . . . . . . . . . . . . . . . . Tel: (020) 8332 5000

                      Web: http://www.kew.org

## CATTLE AND TB

**Independent Scientific Group on Cattle TB** . . . . . . . . . . Area 105, 1A Page Street, London, SW1P 4PQ

    Chairman . . . . . . . . . . . . . . . . . . . . . . . . . . . . . . . . . . Professor John Bourne

    Secretary . . . . . . . . . . . . . . . . . . . . . . . . . . . . . . . . . . Ms Alexia Flowerday . . . . . . . . . . . . . . . . . . . . . . Tel: (020) 7904 6832

                      Web: http://www.defra.gov.uk/animal/tb/default.htm

## CEREALS

**Home-Grown Cereals Authority** . . . . . . . . . . . . . . . . . . . Caledonia House, 223 Pentonville Road, London, N1 9HY

    Chairman . . . . . . . . . . . . . . . . . . . . . . . . . . . . . . . . . . Mr Anthony Pike

    Chief Executive . . . . . . . . . . . . . . . . . . . . . . . . . . . . . . Dr Paul Biscoe . . . . . . . . . . . . . . . . . . . . . . . . . . . Tel: (020) 7520 3904

                      Web: http://www.hgca.com

## COUNTRYSIDE AND NATURE

**Commons Commissioners** . . . . . . . . . . . . . . . . . . . . . . . . Zone 1/05, Temple Quay House, 2 The Square, Temple Quay,
Bristol, BS1 6EB

    Chief Commissioner . . . . . . . . . . . . . . . . . . . . . . . . . . . Mr Edward Cousins

    Clerk . . . . . . . . . . . . . . . . . . . . . . . . . . . . . . . . . . . . . Mr Nicholas Wilson . . . . . . . . . . . . . . . . . . . . . . . Tel: (0117) 372 8973

                      Web: http://www.defra.gov.uk/wildlife-countryside/issues/commis/index.htm

**Countryside Agency** . . . . . . . . . . . . . . . . . . . . . . . . . . . . John Dower House, Crescent Place, Cheltenham, Gloucestershire, GL50 3RA

    Chairman . . . . . . . . . . . . . . . . . . . . . . . . . . . . . . . . . . Sir Ewan Cameron

    Chief Executive . . . . . . . . . . . . . . . . . . . . . . . . . . . . . . Mr Richard Wakeford . . . . . . . . . . . . . . . . . . . . . . Tel: (01242) 521381

                      E-mail: info@countryside.gov.uk

                      Web: http://www.countryside.gov.uk

**English Nature** . . . . . . . . . . . . . . . . . . . . . . . . . . . . . . . Northminster House, Peterborough, PE1 1UA

    Chairman . . . . . . . . . . . . . . . . . . . . . . . . . . . . . . . . . . Sir Martin Doughty

    Chief Executive . . . . . . . . . . . . . . . . . . . . . . . . . . . . . . Mr Andy Brown . . . . . . . . . . . . . . . . . . . . . . . . . . Tel: (01733) 455000

                      E-mail: enquiries@english-nature.org.uk

                      Web: http://www.english-nature.org.uk

**Joint Nature Conservation Committee** . . . . . . . . . . . . . . Monkstone House, City Road, Peterborough, PE1 1JY

    Chairman . . . . . . . . . . . . . . . . . . . . . . . . . . . . . . . . . . Ms Katherine Bryan

    Managing Director . . . . . . . . . . . . . . . . . . . . . . . . . . . Mr Deryck Steer . . . . . . . . . . . . . . . . . . . . . . . . . Tel: (01733) 562626

                      Web: http://www.jncc.gov.uk

## COVENT GARDEN

**Covent Garden Market Authority** . . . . . . . . . . . . . . . . . . Covent House, New Covent Garden Market, London, SW8 5NX

    Chairman . . . . . . . . . . . . . . . . . . . . . . . . . . . . . . . . . . Mr Leif Mills CBE

    General Manager . . . . . . . . . . . . . . . . . . . . . . . . . . . . . Dr Mike Liggins . . . . . . . . . . . . . . . . . . . . . . . . . . Tel: (020) 7720 2211

                      E-mail: info@cgma.gov.uk

                      Web: http://www.cgma.gov.uk

## CROPS: NON-FOOD USES

**Government-Industry Forum on
Non-Food Uses of Crops** . . . . . . . . . . . . . . . . . . . . . . . . Area 5A, Ergon House, Horseferry Road, London SW1P 2AL

    Chairman . . . . . . . . . . . . . . . . . . . . . . . . . . . . . . . . . . Mr Robert Margetts CBE

    Secretary . . . . . . . . . . . . . . . . . . . . . . . . . . . . . . . . . . Mr Nick Starkey . . . . . . . . . . . . . . . . . . . . . . . . . Tel: (020) 7238 6103

                      Web: http://www.defra.gov.uk/farm/gifnfc

# DEPARTMENT FOR ENVIRONMENT, FOOD AND RURAL AFFAIRS

*Other Relevant Contacts (Continued)*

## ENVIRONMENT

**Advisory Committee on Business and the**
 **Environment** . . . Zone 6/E8, Ashdown House, 123 Victoria Street, London, SW1E 6DE
 Chairman . . . Dr Chris Fay CBE
 Secretary . . . Ms Jane Dennet-Thorpe . . . Tel: (020) 7082 8683
 Web: http://www.defra.gov.uk/environment

**Advisory Committee on Consumer Products and the**
 **Environment** . . . Zone 6/D12 Ashdown House, 123 Victoria Street, London, SW1E 6DE
 Chairman . . . Dr Alan Knight
 Secretary . . . *Vacant* . . . Tel: (020) 7082 8655

**Advisory Committee on Releases to the Environment** . . . . Zone 3/G9, Ashdown House, 123 Victoria Street, SW1E 6DE
 Chairman . . . Professor Christopher Pollock
 Secretary . . . Dr Steven Hill . . . Tel: (020) 7082 8117
 Web: http//:www.environment.defra.gsi.gov.uk

**Advisory Committee on Toxicology of Chemicals in Food,**
 **Consumer Products and the Environment** . . . Food Standards Agency, Room 511C, Aviation House, 125 Kingsway, London, WC2B 6NH
 Chairman . . . Professor Ieuon Hughes
 Secretary . . . Mr Keith Butler . . . Tel: (020) 7276 8522
 Web: http//:www.food.gov.uk/science/committees

**Environment Agency** . . . Rio House, Waterside Drive, Aztec West, Almondsbury, Bristol, BS32 4UD
 Chairman . . . Sir John Harman
 Chief Executive . . . Baroness Young of Old Scone . . . Tel: (01454) 624400
 E-mail: enquiries@environment-agency.co.uk
 Web: http//:www.environment-agency.gov.uk

**Royal Commission on Environmental Pollution** . . . 3rd Floor, 5-8 The Sanctuary, Westminster, London, SW1P 3JS
 Chairman . . . Sir Tom Blundell FRS
 Secretary . . . Dr Peter Hinchcliffe . . . Tel: (020) 7799 8970
 Web: http//:www.rcep.org.uk

## FISHERIES

**Centre for Environment, Fisheries and**
 **Aquaculture Science** *(Executive Agency)* . . . Lowestoft Laboratory, Pakefield Road, Lowestoft, Suffolk, NR33 0HT
 Chief Executive . . . Dr Peter Greig-Smith . . . Tel: (01502) 562244
 Web: http://www.cefas.co.uk

**Sea Fish Industry Authority** . . . 18 Logie Mill, Logie Green Road, Edinburgh, EH7 4HG
 Chairman . . . Mr Andrew Dewar-Durie
 Chief Executive . . . Mr John Rutherford . . . Tel: (0131) 558 3331
 E-mail: seafish@seafish.co.uk
 Web: http://www.seafish.co.uk

# DEPARTMENT FOR ENVIRONMENT, FOOD AND RURAL AFFAIRS

*Other Relevant Contacts (Continued)*

## FLOOD DEFENCES

**Anglian Regional Flood Defence Committee** . . . . . . . . . Kingfisher House, Goldhay Way, Orton Goldhay, Peterborough, PE2 5ZR
Chairman . . . . . . . . . . . . . . . . . . . . . . . . . . . . . . Mr Robert Burgin
Secretary . . . . . . . . . . . . . . . . . . . . . . . . . . . . . . Ms Angela Loughran . . . . . . . . . . . . . . . . . . . . . Tel: (01733) 371811

**Midlands Regional Flood Defence Committee** . . . . . . . . Sapphire East, 550 Streetsbrook Road, Solihull, B91 1QT
Chairman . . . . . . . . . . . . . . . . . . . . . . . . . . . . . . Mr Peter Watts
Secretary . . . . . . . . . . . . . . . . . . . . . . . . . . . . . . Ms Margaret Salter . . . . . . . . . . . . . . . . . . . . . . . Tel: (0121) 711 2324

**North West Regional Flood Defence Committee** . . . . . . Richard Fairclough House, Knutsford Road, Warrington, WA4 1HG
Chairman . . . . . . . . . . . . . . . . . . . . . . . . . . . . . . Mr Sinclair Mcleod
Secretary . . . . . . . . . . . . . . . . . . . . . . . . . . . . . . Miss Julie Cornthwaite . . . . . . . . . . . . . . . . . . . . Tel: (01925) 653999

**Northumbria Regional Flood Defence Committee** . . . . . 21 Park Square, Leeds, LS1 2QG
Chairman . . . . . . . . . . . . . . . . . . . . . . . . . . . . . . Mr Frank Major
Secretary . . . . . . . . . . . . . . . . . . . . . . . . . . . . . . Mr Brian Marley . . . . . . . . . . . . . . . . . . . . . . . . Tel: (0113) 244 0191

**South West Regional Flood Defence Committee** . . . . . . Manley House, Kestrel Way, Exeter, EX2 7LQ
Chairman . . . . . . . . . . . . . . . . . . . . . . . . . . . . . . Miss Debora Clark
Secretary . . . . . . . . . . . . . . . . . . . . . . . . . . . . . . Ms Sarah Harding . . . . . . . . . . . . . . . . . . . . . . . Tel: (01392) 444000

**Southern Regional Flood Defence Committee** . . . . . . . . Guildbourne House, Chatsworth Road, Worthing, BN11 1LD
Chairman . . . . . . . . . . . . . . . . . . . . . . . . . . . . . . Mr Bill Cutting
Secretary . . . . . . . . . . . . . . . . . . . . . . . . . . . . . . Ms Lisa Guiel . . . . . . . . . . . . . . . . . . . . . . . . . . Tel: (01903) 832000

**Thames Regional Flood Defence Committee** . . . . . . . . . King's Meadow House, King's Meadow Road, Reading, RG1 8DQ
Chairman . . . . . . . . . . . . . . . . . . . . . . . . . . . . . . Dr Peter Ryder
Secretary . . . . . . . . . . . . . . . . . . . . . . . . . . . . . . Mr Chris Galvin . . . . . . . . . . . . . . . . . . . . . . . . Tel: (0118) 953 5000

**Wessex Regional Flood Defence Committee** . . . . . . . . . Manley House, Kestrel Way, Exeter, EX2 7LG
Chairman . . . . . . . . . . . . . . . . . . . . . . . . . . . . . . Mr Humphrey Temperley
Secretary . . . . . . . . . . . . . . . . . . . . . . . . . . . . . . Ms Sarah Harding . . . . . . . . . . . . . . . . . . . . . . . Tel: (01392) 444000

**Yorkshire Regional Flood Defence Committee** . . . . . . . 21 Park Square, Leeds, LS1 2QG
Chairman . . . . . . . . . . . . . . . . . . . . . . . . . . . . . . Professor Roy Ward
Secretary . . . . . . . . . . . . . . . . . . . . . . . . . . . . . . Mr Brian Marley . . . . . . . . . . . . . . . . . . . . . . . . Tel: (0113) 244 0191

## FOOD

**English Farming and Food Partnerships** . . . . . . . . . . . . 4th Floor, 45 Ludgate Hill, London, EC4M 7JU
Chairman . . . . . . . . . . . . . . . . . . . . . . . . . . . . . . Mr Jeremy Pope OBE
Secretary . . . . . . . . . . . . . . . . . . . . . . . . . . . . . . Ms Emily Ogle . . . . . . . . . . . . . . . . . . . . . . . . . Tel: (020) 7213 0430
E-mail: info@effp.com
Web: http://www.effp.com

**Food from Britain** . . . . . . . . . . . . . . . . . . . . . . . . . 4th Floor, Manning House, 22 Carlisle Place, London, SW1P 1JA
Chairman . . . . . . . . . . . . . . . . . . . . . . . . . . . . . . Mr Gordon Summerfield CBE
Chief Executive . . . . . . . . . . . . . . . . . . . . . . . . . . Mr David McNair . . . . . . . . . . . . . . . . . . . . . . . . Tel: (020) 7233 5111
E-mail: info@foodfrombritain.com
Web: http://www.foodfrombritain.com

**Food Standards Agency** . . . . . . . . . . . . . . . . . . . . . . Aviation House, 125 Kingsway, London, WC2B 6NH
Chairman . . . . . . . . . . . . . . . . . . . . . . . . . . . . . . Professor Sir John Krebs
Chief Executive . . . . . . . . . . . . . . . . . . . . . . . . . . Mr Jon Bell . . . . . . . . . . . . . . . . . . . . . . . . . . . Tel: (020) 7276 8000
Web: http://www.foodstandards.gov.uk

**Meat Hygiene Service** *(Executive Agency of the Food*
*Standards Agency)* . . . . . . . . . . . . . . . . . . . . . . . . . Kings Pool, Peasholme Green, York, YO1 7PR
Chief Executive . . . . . . . . . . . . . . . . . . . . . . . . . . Mr Chris Lawson . . . . . . . . . . . . . . . . . . . . . . . . Tel: (01904) 455501
E-mail: enquiry@foodstandards.gsi.gov.uk
Web: http://www.food.gov.uk/enforcement/mhservice

# DEPARTMENT FOR ENVIRONMENT, FOOD AND RURAL AFFAIRS

*Other Relevant Contacts (Continued)*

## FORESTRY

**Forestry Commission** . . . . . . . . . . . . . . . . . . . . . . . . . 231 Corstorphine Road, Edinburgh, EH12 7AT

    Chairman . . . . . . . . . . . . . . . . . . . . . . . . . . . . Rt Hon Lord Clark of Windermere

    Director-General . . . . . . . . . . . . . . . . . . . . . . . . Mr Tim Rollinson . . . . . . . . . . . . . . . . . . . . . . . . Tel: (0131) 334 0303

        E-mail: enquiries@forestry.gsi.gov.uk

        Web: http://www.forestry.gov.uk

**Forestry Commission (England)** . . . . . . . . . . . . . . . . Great Eastern House, Tenison Road, Cambridge, CB1 2DU

    Director . . . . . . . . . . . . . . . . . . . . . . . . . . . . . Mr Paul Hill Tout . . . . . . . . . . . . . . . . . . . . . . . Tel: (01223) 314546

        E-mail: sc.nat.off.eng@forestry.gsi.gov.uk

        Web: http://www.forestry.gov.uk

**Forest Enterprise England** *(Executive Agency)* . . . . . . . . . . 340 Bristol Business Park, Coldharbour Lane, Bristol, BS16 1EJ

    Chief Executive . . . . . . . . . . . . . . . . . . . . . . . . . Mr Geoff Hatfield . . . . . . . . . . . . . . . . . . . . . . . Tel: (0117) 906 6000

        Web: http://www.forestry.gov.uk

**Forest Research**

    *(Executive Agency of Forestry Commission)* . . . . . . . . . . . . Alice Holt Lodge, Wrecclesham, Farnham, Surrey, GU10 4LH

    Chief Executive . . . . . . . . . . . . . . . . . . . . . . . . . Professor Jim Lynch . . . . . . . . . . . . . . . . . . . . . . Tel: (01420) 22255

        Web: http://www.forestry.gov.uk/forest_research

**National Forest Company** . . . . . . . . . . . . . . . . . . . . . Enterprise Glade, Bath Lane, Moira, Swadlincote, Derbyshire, DE12 6BD

    Chairman . . . . . . . . . . . . . . . . . . . . . . . . . . . . Mr Viv Astling

    Chief Executive . . . . . . . . . . . . . . . . . . . . . . . . . Ms Susan Bell OBE . . . . . . . . . . . . . . . . . . . . . . . Tel: (01283) 551211

        Web: http://www.nationalforest.org

## HAZARDOUS SUBSTANCES

**Advisory Committee on Hazardous Substances** . . . . . . . Zone 3/E5, Ashdown House, 123 Victoria Street, London, SW1E 6DE

    Chairman . . . . . . . . . . . . . . . . . . . . . . . . . . . . Professor Jane Plant

    Secretary . . . . . . . . . . . . . . . . . . . . . . . . . . . . . Dr John Garrod . . . . . . . . . . . . . . . . . . . . . . . . Tel: (020) 7082 8107

        Web: http://www.defra.gov.uk/environment/chemicals/achs

## HILL FARMING

**Hill Farming Advisory Committee for**

    **England, Wales and Northern Ireland** . . . . . . . . . . . . Area 4D, Ergon House, Horseferry Road, London SW1P 2AL

    Contact . . . . . . . . . . . . . . . . . . . . . . . . . . . . . Mr Nadeem Raja . . . . . . . . . . . . . . . . . . . . . . . . Tel: (020) 7238 6804

        Web: http://www.defra.gov.uk

## HORTICULTURE

**Horticultural Development Council** . . . . . . . . . . . . . . . . Bradbourne House, The Stable Block, East Malling, Kent, ME19 6DZ

    Chairman . . . . . . . . . . . . . . . . . . . . . . . . . . . . Mr Colin Harvey

    Chief Executive . . . . . . . . . . . . . . . . . . . . . . . . . Mr Martin Beckenham . . . . . . . . . . . . . . . . . . . . . Tel: (01732) 848383

        E-mail: hdc@hdc.org.uk

        Web: http://www.hdc.org.uk

**Horticulture Research International** . . . . . . . . . . . . . . . Warwick HRI, Wellesbourne, Warwick, CV35 9EF

    Chairman . . . . . . . . . . . . . . . . . . . . . . . . . . . . Mr Peter Siddall

    Chief Executive . . . . . . . . . . . . . . . . . . . . . . . . . Professor Simon Bright . . . . . . . . . . . . . . . . . . . . Tel: (01789) 470382

        Web: http://www.hri@warwick.ac.uk

# DEPARTMENT FOR ENVIRONMENT, FOOD AND RURAL AFFAIRS

*Other Relevant Contacts (Continued)*

## MEAT AND LIVESTOCK

**Meat and Livestock Commission** . . . . . . . . . . . . . . . . . . . PO Box 44, Winterhill House, Snowdon Drive, Milton Keynes, MK6 1AX
    Chairman . . . . . . . . . . . . . . . . . . . . . . . . . . . . . . . . Mr Peter Barr CBE
    Director-General . . . . . . . . . . . . . . . . . . . . . . . . . . . Mr Kevin Roberts . . . . . . . . . . . . . . . . . . . . . . . . . . . Tel: (01908) 677577
                             Web: http://www.mlc.org.uk

## MILK

**Milk Development Council** . . . . . . . . . . . . . . . . . . . . . . Stroud Road, Cirencester, GL7 6JN
    Chairman . . . . . . . . . . . . . . . . . . . . . . . . . . . . . . . . Mr Brian Peacock
    Chief Executive . . . . . . . . . . . . . . . . . . . . . . . . . . . . Mr Kevin Bellamy . . . . . . . . . . . . . . . . . . . . . . . . . . . Tel: (01285) 646500
                             Web: http://www.mdc.org.uk

## ORGANIC STANDARDS

**Advisory Committee on Organic Standards** . . . . . . . . . . Area 5F, Ergon House, Horseferry Road, London SW1P 2AL
    Chairman . . . . . . . . . . . . . . . . . . . . . . . . . . . . . . . . Mr Andrew Jedwell
    Secretariat . . . . . . . . . . . . . . . . . . . . . . . . . . . . . . . Mr Alex Dasi-Sutton . . . . . . . . . . . . . . . . . . . . . . . . . Tel: (020) 7238 5605
                             Web: http://www.defra.gov.uk/farm/organic

## PACKAGING

**Advisory Committee on Packaging** . . . . . . . . . . . . . . . . 7th Floor, Zone 7/E5, Ashdown House, 123 Victoria Street, London, SW1E 6DE
    Chairman . . . . . . . . . . . . . . . . . . . . . . . . . . . . . . . . Mr John Turner
    Secretariat . . . . . . . . . . . . . . . . . . . . . . . . . . . . . . . Ms Sheila McKinley . . . . . . . . . . . . . . . . . . . . . . . . . Tel: (020) 7082 8775
                             Web: http://www.defra.gov.uk/environment/waste/topics/materials.htm

## PESTICIDES

**Advisory Committee on Pesticides** . . . . . . . . . . . . . . . . Mallard House, 3 Peasholme Green, York, YO1 7PX
    Chairman . . . . . . . . . . . . . . . . . . . . . . . . . . . . . . . . Professor David Coggan
    Secretary . . . . . . . . . . . . . . . . . . . . . . . . . . . . . . . . Ms Jayne Wilder . . . . . . . . . . . . . . . . . . . . . . . . . . . . Tel: (01904) 455702
                             Web: http://www.pesticides.gov.uk/committees/acp/acp.htm
**Pesticides Forum** . . . . . . . . . . . . . . . . . . . . . . . . . . . . Room 317, Mallard House, 3 Peasholme Green, York, YO1 7PX
    Chairman . . . . . . . . . . . . . . . . . . . . . . . . . . . . . . . . Professor Ed Gallagher
    Secretariat . . . . . . . . . . . . . . . . . . . . . . . . . . . . . . . Ms Sue Rambridge
                             Mr Matthew Wells . . . . . . . . . . . . . . . . . . . . . . . . . . Tel: (01904) 455860
                             Web: http://www.defra.gov.uk/environment/pesticidesforum/index/htm
**Pesticides Residues Committee** . . . . . . . . . . . . . . . . . . c/o Pesticides Safety Directorate, Room 308, Mallard House, 3 Peasholme Green, York, YO1 7PX
    Chairman . . . . . . . . . . . . . . . . . . . . . . . . . . . . . . . . Dr Ian Brown
    Secretary . . . . . . . . . . . . . . . . . . . . . . . . . . . . . . . . Ms Tracy Ware . . . . . . . . . . . . . . . . . . . . . . . . . . . . . Tel: (01904) 455758
                             Web: http://www.pesticides.gov.uk
**Pesticides Safety Directorate** *(Executive Agency)* . . . . . . . . Mallard House, Kingspool, 3 Peasholme Green, York, YO1 7PX
    Chief Executive . . . . . . . . . . . . . . . . . . . . . . . . . . . . Dr Kerr Wilson . . . . . . . . . . . . . . . . . . . . . . . . . . . . . Tel: (01904) 455775
                             E-mail: information@psd.defra.gsi.gov.uk
                             Web: http://www.pesticides.gov.uk

## PLANT AND SEEDS

**Plant Varieties and Seeds Tribunal** . . . . . . . . . . . . . . . Block B, Government Buildings, Brooklands Avenue, Cambridge, CB2 2DR
    Secretary . . . . . . . . . . . . . . . . . . . . . . . . . . . . . . . . Ms Jane Barr . . . . . . . . . . . . . . . . . . . . . . . . . . . . . . Tel: (01223) 533508
                             E-mail: jane.m.barr@defra.gsi.gov.uk

# DEPARTMENT FOR ENVIRONMENT, FOOD AND RURAL AFFAIRS

*Other Relevant Contacts (Continued)*

## POTATOES

**British Potato Council** . . . . . . . . . . . . . . . . . . . . . . . 4300 Nash Court, John Smith Drive, Oxford Business Park South,
Oxford, OX4 2RT
    Chairman . . . . . . . . . . . . . . . . . . . . . . . . . . Mr David Walker
    Chief Executive . . . . . . . . . . . . . . . . . . . . . . . . . . . Mrs Helen Priestley . . . . . . . . . . . . . . . . . . . . . . . . . Tel: (01865) 714455
                         E-mail: info@potato.org.uk
                         Web: http://www.potato.org.uk

## RADIOACTIVE WASTE

**Radioactive Waste Management Advisory Committee** . . . Zone 4/E4, Ashdown House, 123 Victoria Street, London, SW1E 6DE
    Chairman . . . . . . . . . . . . . . . . . . . . . . . . . . . Professor Charles Curtis OBE
    Secretary . . . . . . . . . . . . . . . . . . . . . . . . . . . . . . Dr Robert Jackson . . . . . . . . . . . . . . . . . . . . . . . Tel: (020) 7082 8476
                         Web: http://www.defragov.uk/rwmac

*Other Relevant Contacts (Continued)*

## SCIENCE AND RESEARCH

**Central Science Laboratory** *(Executive Agency)* . . . . . . . . Sand Hutton, York, YO41 1LZ
    Chief Executive . . . . . . . . . . . . . . . . . . . . . . . . . . . Professor Mike Roberts . . . . . . . . . . . . . . . . . . . . . . Tel: (01904) 462000
                         E-mail: science@csl.gov.uk
                         Web: http://www.csl.gov.uk
**Science Advisory Council** . . . . . . . . . . . . . . . . . . . . . . Room 202, Cromwell House, Dean Stanley Street, London, SW1P 3JH
    Chairman . . . . . . . . . . . . . . . . . . . . . . . . . . . Professor Roy Anderson
    Secretary . . . . . . . . . . . . . . . . . . . . . . . . . . . . . . Mr Steve Ansell . . . . . . . . . . . . . . . . . . . . . . . . . Tel: (020) 7238 1641

## SPONGIFORM ENCEPHALOPATHY

**Spongiform Encephalopathy Advisory Committee** . . . . . . Area 3/05, 1A Page Street, London, SW1P 4PQ
    Chairman . . . . . . . . . . . . . . . . . . . . . . . . . . . Professor Peter Smith CBE
    Secretary . . . . . . . . . . . . . . . . . . . . . . . . . . . . . . Dr Catherine Boyle . . . . . . . . . . . . . . . . . . . . . . . Tel: (020) 7904 6267

## SUSTAINABLE DEVELOPMENT

**Sustainable Development Commission** . . . . . . . . . . . . . . . Ergon House, 17 Smith Square, London, SW1P 3JR
    Chairman . . . . . . . . . . . . . . . . . . . . . . . . . . . Mr Jonathan Porritt CBE
    Secretary . . . . . . . . . . . . . . . . . . . . . . . . . . . . . . Mr Scott Ghagan . . . . . . . . . . . . . . . . . . . . . . . . . Tel: (020) 7238 4995
                         Web: http://www.sd-commission.gov.uk

## VETERINARY

**Veterinary Laboratories Agency** *(Executive Agency)* . . . . . . Woodham Lane, New Haw, Addlestone, Surrey, KT15 3NB
    Chief Executive . . . . . . . . . . . . . . . . . . . . . . . . . . . Professor Steven Edwards . . . . . . . . . . . . . . . . . . . . . Tel: (01932) 341111
                         E-mail: enquiries@vla.defra.gsi.gov.uk
                         Web: http://www.defra.gov.uk/corporate/vla
**Veterinary Medicines Directorate** *(Executive Agency)* . . . . . Woodham Lane, New Haw, Addlestone, Surrey, KT15 3LS
    Chief Executive . . . . . . . . . . . . . . . . . . . . . . . . . . . Mr Steve Dean . . . . . . . . . . . . . . . . . . . . . . . . . . Tel: (01932) 336911
                         Web: http://www.vmd.gov.uk
**Veterinary Products Committee** . . . . . . . . . . . . . . . . . . . VMD, Woodham Lane, New Haw, Addlestone, Surrey, KT15 3LS
    Chairman . . . . . . . . . . . . . . . . . . . . . . . . . . . Dr David Skilton
    Scientific Secretary . . . . . . . . . . . . . . . . . . . . . . . . Mr Colin Bennett . . . . . . . . . . . . . . . . . . . . . . . . . Tel: (01932) 336911
                         Web: http://www.vpc.gov.uk
**Veterinary Residues Committee** . . . . . . . . . . . . . . . . . . . VMD, Woodham Lane, New Haw, Addlestone, Surrey, KT15 3LS
    Chairman . . . . . . . . . . . . . . . . . . . . . . . . . . . Professor James Bridges
    Secretaries . . . . . . . . . . . . . . . . . . . . . . . . . . . . . Mr Eric Crutcher . . . . . . . . . . . . . . . . . . . . . . . . . Tel: (01932) 338322
                         Mr David Webb
                         Web: http://www.vet-residues-committee.co.uk

# DEPARTMENT FOR ENVIRONMENT, FOOD AND RURAL AFFAIRS

*Other Relevant Contacts (Continued)*

## WATER

**Committee on Products and Processes for use in**

**Public Water Supplies** . . . . . . . . . . . . . . . . . . . . . . . 2/E4 Ashdown House, 123 Victoria Street, London, SW1E 6DE

Chairman . . . . . . . . . . . . . . . . . . . . . . . . . . . . . . Mr Owen Hydes OBE

Technical Secretary . . . . . . . . . . . . . . . . . . . . . . . . . Mr John Ashworth . . . . . . . . . . . . . . . . . . . . . . . . . Tel: (020) 7082 8015

Web: http://www.dwi.gov.uk/cpp/index.htm

**Expert Group on Cryptosporidium in**

**Water Supplies** . . . . . . . . . . . . . . . . . . . . . . . . . . Zone 2/D2, Ashdown House, 123 Victoria Street, London, SW1E 6DE

Chairman . . . . . . . . . . . . . . . . . . . . . . . . . . . . . . Professor Ian Bouchier

Secretary . . . . . . . . . . . . . . . . . . . . . . . . . . . . . . Mr David Drury . . . . . . . . . . . . . . . . . . . . . . . . . . . Tel: (020) 7944 5976

Web: http://www.dwi.gov.uk

**Office of Water Services (OFWAT)** . . . . . . . . . . . . . . . Centre City Tower, 7 Hill Street, Birmingham, B5 4UA

Director-General . . . . . . . . . . . . . . . . . . . . . . . . . . Mr Philip Fletcher CBE . . . . . . . . . . . . . . . . . . . . . . . Tel: (0121) 625 1300

E-mail: enquiries@ofwat.gsi.gov.uk

Web: http://www.ofwat.gov.uk

**Water Regulations Advisory Committee** . . . . . . . . . . . . . Zone 3/H22, Ashdown House, 123 Victoria Street, London, SW1E 6DE

Chairman . . . . . . . . . . . . . . . . . . . . . . . . . . . . . . Professor John Swaffield

Secretary . . . . . . . . . . . . . . . . . . . . . . . . . . . . . . Mr Peter Jiggins . . . . . . . . . . . . . . . . . . . . . . . . . . . Tel: (020) 7944 5395

**Watervoice (OFWAT National Customer Council)** . . . . . Centre City Tower, 7 Hill Street, Birmingham, B5 4UA

Chairman . . . . . . . . . . . . . . . . . . . . . . . . . . . . . . Mr Maurice Terry

Secretary . . . . . . . . . . . . . . . . . . . . . . . . . . . . . . Mr Roy Wardle . . . . . . . . . . . . . . . . . . . . . . . . . . . Tel: (0121) 625 1367

E-mail: enquiries@watervoice.org.uk

Web: http://www.watervoice.org.uk

## WATERWAYS

**British Waterways Board** . . . . . . . . . . . . . . . . . . . . . Willow Grange, Church Road, Watford, Hertfordshire, WD17 4QA

Chairman . . . . . . . . . . . . . . . . . . . . . . . . . . . . . . Dr George Greener

Chief Executive . . . . . . . . . . . . . . . . . . . . . . . . . . . Mr Robin Evans . . . . . . . . . . . . . . . . . . . . . . . . . . . Tel: (01923) 226422

E-mail: pressoffice@britishwaterways.co.uk

Web: http://www.britishwaterways.co.uk

**Inland Waterways Amenity Advisory Council** . . . . . . . . . City Road Lock, 38 Graham Street, Islington, London, N1 8JX

Chairman . . . . . . . . . . . . . . . . . . . . . . . . . . . . . . Viscountess Knollys

Office Manager . . . . . . . . . . . . . . . . . . . . . . . . . . . Ms Bridget Beney . . . . . . . . . . . . . . . . . . . . . . . . . . Tel: (020) 7253 1745

Web: http://www.iwaac.org.uk

## WINE

**Wine Standards Board of the Vintners' Company** . . . . . . Five Kings House, 1 Queen Street Place, London, EC4R 1QS

Chairman . . . . . . . . . . . . . . . . . . . . . . . . . . . . . . Mr Christopher Roberts CB

Secretary and Chief Executive . . . . . . . . . . . . . . . . . . Mr Alan Curran . . . . . . . . . . . . . . . . . . . . . . . . . . . Tel: (020) 7236 9512

Web: http://www.wsb.org.uk

## ZOOS

**Zoos Forum** . . . . . . . . . . . . . . . . . . . . . . . . . . . . Zone 1/16L, Temple Quay House, 2 The Square, Temple Quay, Bristol, BS1 6EB

Chairman . . . . . . . . . . . . . . . . . . . . . . . . . . . . . . *Vacant*

Secretary . . . . . . . . . . . . . . . . . . . . . . . . . . . . . . Mr Robert Vagg . . . . . . . . . . . . . . . . . . . . . . . . . . . Tel: (0117) 372 8209

Web: http://www.wildlife-countryside/gwd/zoosforum

**BVA ANIMAL WELFARE FOUNDATION**

# British Veterinary Association
# Animal Welfare Foundation

*The veterinary professions own charity*

*Committed to improving the welfare of all animals through veterinary science, education and debate*

Our principal aim is to apply the knowledge, skill and compassion of the veterinary surgeon in an effective way by identifying and funding variety research projects and educational activities targeted at improving animal welfare.

We are committed to finding practical solutions to the welfare problems of all animals and distributing this information amongst veterinary practitioners, nurses and students, farmers, animal care workers and the general public.

The BVA Animal Welfare Foundation (BVA:AWF) was established in 1984 by the British Veterinary Association as the veterinary professions own animal welfare charity.

Projects supported by the BVA:AWF have been identified by the trustees, all of whom are veterinary surgeons, as having a direct and practical application for the practitioner in improving animal health and welfare. Knowledge sharing through seminars, and educational activities throughout the profession are also key aspects of the Foundation's work.

Funded entirely by voluntary contributions, the Foundation relies on the generosity of the public to continue its practical and professional approach to improving animal welfare.

**The British Veterinary Association Animal Welfare Foundation**
7 Mansfield Street, London, W1G 9NQ
Tel: (020) 7636 6541   Fax: (020) 7436 2970   E-mail: awf@bva.co.uk

*Registered Charity No 287118*

**bva-awf.org.uk**

## ANIMAL CRUELTY

## ANIMAL HEALTH

## CANINE WELFARE

## RURAL COMMUNITIES

# ENVIRONMENTAL MANAGEMENT

## Institute of Ecology and Environmental Management

45 Southgate Street, Winchester, Hampshire, SO23 9EH

*Telephone* (01962) 868626

*Facsimile* (01962) 868625

*E-mail:* enquiries@ieem.demon.co.uk

*Web:* http://www.ieem.org.uk

*Contact:* Dr Jim Thompson – *Executive Director*

IEEM Aims to advance the science, practice and professionalism of ecology, environmental management and sustainable development. This is achieved by running workshops, conferences and publishing a quarterly journal, *In Practice*, on topical issues.

Membership is recruited from professionals who meet the rigorous standards of the Institute and are drawn from local authorities, government agencies, industry, environmental consultancy, teaching/research, and voluntary environmental organisations.

IEEM provides, through the expertise of our members, guidance on the opportunities offered by sustainable development, as it becomes a more widely accepted concept.

# GLASS INDUSTRY

9 Churchill Way, Chapeltown, Sheffield, S35 2PY

*Telephone* (0114) 290 1850

*Facsimile* (0114) 290 1851

*E-mail:* info@britglass.co.uk

*Web:* http://www.britglass.org.uk

*Contact:* Ms J Knights – *Public Policy Manager*

British Glass, a trade federation and materials organisation, represents the interests of the UK glass industry, through monitoring, interpreting, lobbying and then helping to implement all stages of legislation, whether UK or European, that directly impacts on the industry. A centre of excellence, British Glass, also helps companies around the globe solve their technical, environmental and production challenges.

## LOCAL ENVIRONMENT

Environmental Campaigns (ENCAMS) is an environmental charity which runs the Keep Britain Tidy campaign and a number of Local Environmental Quality (LEQ) programmes, research projects and surveys. Through high profile campaigns and programmes such as Seaside Awards & Blue Flag, Eco Schools, Thames21 and People & Places, ENCAMS fosters individual, corporate and community responsibility for local environmental quality.

*Telephone* (01942) 612621

*E-mail* enquiries@encams.org

*Web* http://www.encams.org

## WILDLIFE

ENGLISH
NATURE

London Office, Devon House
12-15 Dartmouth Street
Queen Anne's Gate
London, SW1H 9BL
*Telephone* (020) 7340 4870
*Facsimile* (020) 7340 4880
*Enquiry Point* (01733) 455101
*E-mail:* enquiries@english-nature.org.uk
*Web:* www.english-nature.org.uk

*Contact:* Alex Machin – *Parliamentary Officer*

The Government's adviser on nature conservation policies in England. Responsible for over 200 National Nature Reserves and 4,000 Sites of Special Scientific Interest. The head office is in Peterborough. There are 22 local area teams and 9 Regional Co-ordinators to promote directly and through others, the conservation of England's wildlife and natural features.

**Working today for nature tomorrow**

# FOREIGN AND COMMONWEALTH OFFICE

Downing Street, London, SW1A 2AL
Tel: (020) 7270 1500
E-mail: [firstname.surname]@fco.gov.uk
Web: http://www.fco.gov.uk
http://www.i-uk.com

## MINISTERS

**Secretary of State** ...................... Rt Hon Jack Straw MP
   *Principal Private Secretary*............... Mr Geoffrey Adams CMG......................... Tel: (020) 7008 2059
   *Special Advisers* ....................... Mr Ed Owen ................................. Tel: (020) 7008 2112
                                           Mr Michael Williams ....................... Tel: (020) 7008 2117

**Minister of State** *(Minister for Europe)*........ Dr Denis MacShane MP
   *Private Secretary* ...................... Mr Peter Boxer ............................. Tel: (020) 7008 8294

**Minister of State**
   *(Minister for the Middle East)* ............. Rt Hon Baroness Symons of Vernham Dean
   *Private Secretary* ...................... Mr Nick Allan............................... Tel: (020) 7008 2090

**Minister of State**
   *(Minister for Trade, also at the DTI)* ........ Mr Douglas Alexander MP
   *Private Secretary* ...................... Mr Peter Elder ............................. Tel: (020) 7008 2127

**Parliamentary Secretary** .................. Mr Chris Mullin MP
   *Private Secretary* ...................... Ms Bharat Joshi ........................... Tel: (020) 7008 2173

**Parliamentary Secretary** .................. Mr Bill Rammell MP
   *Private Secretary* ...................... Mr David Whineray.......................... Tel: (020) 7008 3367

## CIVIL SERVICE

**Permanent Secretary**.................... Sir Michael Jay KCMG
   *Private Secretary* ...................... Ms Menna Rawlings ........................ Tel: (020) 7008 2150

**Director-Generals**
   Chief Clerk / Corporate Affairs / Public Services
      Services ........................... Mr Richard Stagg CMG ...................... Tel: (020) 7008 6415
   Defence / Intelligence ................... Mr David Richmond ........................ Tel: (020) 7008 2176
   EU/Economic Director.................... Mr Graham Fry............................. Tel: (020) 7008 2732
   European Union and Policy .............. Ms Nicola Brewer .......................... Tel: (020) 7008 2732
   Political Director ....................... Mr John Sawers CMG ....................... Tel: (020) 7008 3916

**Directors**
   Africa ............................... Mr James Bevan ........................... Tel: (020) 7008 2203
   Americas and Overseas Territories ........ Mr Robert N Culshaw MVO.................. Tel: (020) 7008 2216
   Asia and Pacific ...................... Mr Nigel Cox ............................. Tel: (020) 7270 1500
   Consular Services ..................... Mr Paul Sizeland.......................... Tel: (020) 7008 0223
   Finance.............................. Mr Rick Todd ............................. Tel: (020) 7008 0266
   Global Issues......................... Ms Philippa Drew ......................... Tel: (020) 7008 2211
   Human Resources ..................... Mr Darren Warren ......................... Tel: (020) 7008 0580
   International Security.................... Mr Edward Oakden ........................ Tel: (020) 7008 2183
   Iraq................................. Mr John Buck ............................. Tel: (020) 7270 1500
   Legal Adviser ........................ Sir Michael Wood CMG...................... Tel: (020) 7008 3080
   Mediterranean, Europe Bilateral, Resources... Mr Dominic Chilcott ...................... Tel: (020) 7008 2396
   Middle East/ North Africa ............... Mr Edward Chaplin CMG OBE................. Tel: (020) 7008 2198
   South Asia Pacific .................... Mr Tom Phillips CMG ...................... Tel: (020) 7008 2865
   Strategy, Innovation and Information ....... Mr Simon Fraser .......................... Tel: (020) 7008 4149
   Wider Europe ........................ Ms Linda Duffield.......................... Tel: (020) 7008 2193

# FOREIGN AND COMMONWEALTH OFFICE

**Special Representatives**

Afghanistan . . . . . . . . . . . . . . . . . . . . . . . . . . . Mr Tom Phillips CMG . . . . . . . . . . . . . . . . . . . . . . Tel: (020) 7270 1500

Cyprus . . . . . . . . . . . . . . . . . . . . . . . . . . . . . . . . Lord Hannay GCMG CH . . . . . . . . . . . . . . . . . . . . . Tel: (020) 7270 1500

Georgia . . . . . . . . . . . . . . . . . . . . . . . . . . . . . . . Sir Brian Fall KCMG . . . . . . . . . . . . . . . . . . . . . . Tel: (020) 7270 1500

Sudan . . . . . . . . . . . . . . . . . . . . . . . . . . . . . . . . Mr Alan Goulty CMG . . . . . . . . . . . . . . . . . . . . . Tel: (020) 7270 1500


**Chief Executive, FCO Services** . . . . . . . . . . . . Mr Stephen Sage . . . . . . . . . . . . . . . . . . . . . . . . Tel: (020) 7008 0053


**Chief Executive, UK Trade and Investment** . . Sir Stephen Brown KCVO . . . . . . . . . . . . . . . . . . . . Tel: (020) 7215 4643


**Her Majesty's Vice-Marshal of**
   **the Diplomatic Corps** . . . . . . . . . . . . . . . Mr Charles de Chassiron CVO . . . . . . . . . . . . . . . . . Tel: (020) 7008 3000


# SUBJECT RESPONSIBILITIES AND CONTACTS


**Accounts** *(see below under Resource Accounting Department)*


**Adriatic (Eastern) Department**

*FCO, Downing Street West, London, SW1A 2AL*

   *(Albania, Bosnia Herzegovina, Croatia, Kosovo, Macedonian Republic, Montenegro, Serbia, former Yugoslavia)*

   Director . . . . . . . . . . . . . . . . . . . . . . . . . . . . Ms Linda Duffield

   Head of Department . . . . . . . . . . . . . . . . . . . . Ms Karen Pierce CVO

   Deputy Head of Department . . . . . . . . . . . . . . Mr Paul Fox

                                                  *enquiries* . . . . . . . . . . . . . . . . . . . . . . . . . . . . . . . Tel: (020) 7008 2756/3433/2372


**Afghanistan Unit**

*FCO, Whitehall, London, SW1A 2AH*

   UK Special Representative . . . . . . . . . . . . . . Mr Tom Phillips CMG . . . . . . . . . . . . . . . . . . . . . . Tel: (020) 7008 2866

   Head of Unit . . . . . . . . . . . . . . . . . . . . . . . . Ms Jan Thompson . . . . . . . . . . . . . . . . . . . . . . . . Tel: (020) 7008 2995


**Africa (Equatorial) Department**

*FCO, King Charles Street, London, SW1A 2AH*

   *(Benin, Burkina Faso, Burundi, Cameroon, Cape Verdi, Central African Republic, Chad, Congo, Cote d'Ivoire, Democratic Republic of Congo, Djibouti, ECOWAS, Equatorial Guinea, Eritrea, Ethiopia, Gabon, Gambia, Ghana, Guinea, Guinea Bissau, Kenya, Liberia, Mali, Niger, Nigeria, OAU, Rwanda, Sierra Leone, Somalia, Tanzania, Togo, Uganda, Zaire)*

   Director . . . . . . . . . . . . . . . . . . . . . . . . . . . . Mr James Bevan

   Head of Department . . . . . . . . . . . . . . . . . . . . Mr Tim Hitchens OBE

   Deputy Heads of Department . . . . . . . . . . . . . Mr Nigel Bowie

                                                  Mr Patrick Moody

                                                  *enquiries* . . . . . . . . . . . . . . . . . . . . . . . . . . . . . . . Tel: (020) 7008 2903


**Africa, North** *(see below under Near East and North Africa Department)*


**Africa (Southern) Department**

*FCO, King Charles Street, London, SW1A 2AH*

   *(Angola, Botswana, The Comoros, Lesotho, Madagascar, Mauritius, Malawi, Mozambique, Namibia, Sao Tomé and Principe, Seychelles, South Africa, Swaziland, Zambia, Zimbabwe, South African Development Community)*

   Director . . . . . . . . . . . . . . . . . . . . . . . . . . . . Mr James Bevan

   Head of Department . . . . . . . . . . . . . . . . . . . . Mr Andrew Lloyd

   Deputy Head of Department . . . . . . . . . . . . . . Mr Fergus Cochrane-Dyet

                                                  *enquiries* . . . . . . . . . . . . . . . . . . . . . . . . . . . . . . . Tel: (020) 7008 2535


**Americas** *(see below under Latin America, and North America Departments)*

# FOREIGN AND COMMONWEALTH OFFICE

**Arms Control** *(see below under Counter-Proliferation Department)*

**Asia, South** *(see below under South Asian Department)*

**Asia, South Eastern** *(see below under South East Asian Department)*

**Atlantic** *(see below under Overseas Territories Department)*

**Audit** *(see below under Internal Audit Department)*

**Aviation, Maritime and Energy Department**
*FCO, King Charles Street, London, SW1A 2AH*
> Director . . . . . . . . . . . . . . . . . . . . . . . . . . . Ms Philippa Drew
> Head of Department . . . . . . . . . . . . . . . . . . Mr Andrew Levi
> Deputy Head of Department . . . . . . . . . . . . Mr Shaun Cleary
>> *enquiries* . . . . . . . . . . . . . . . . . . . . . . . . . . . . . . . . . . . Tel: (020) 7008 2625

**Caribbean Team**
*FCO, King Charles Street, London, SW1A 2AP*
> Director . . . . . . . . . . . . . . . . . . . . . . . . . . . Mr Robert Culshaw MVO
> Head, Caribbean Team . . . . . . . . . . . . . . . . Mr John Marshall
>> *enquiries* . . . . . . . . . . . . . . . . . . . . . . . . . . . . . . . . . . . Tel: (020) 7008 2481

**China / Hong Kong Department**
*FCO, Whitehall, London, SW1A 2AP*
> Director . . . . . . . . . . . . . . . . . . . . . . . . . . . Mr Nigel Cox
> Head of Department . . . . . . . . . . . . . . . . . . Mr Denis Keefe
> Deputy Head of Department . . . . . . . . . . . . Mr David Ellis
>> *enquiries* . . . . . . . . . . . . . . . . . . . . . . . . . . . . . . . . . . . Tel: (020) 7008 3074

**Commonwealth Co-ordination Department**
*FCO, Whitehall, London, SW1A 2AL*
> Director . . . . . . . . . . . . . . . . . . . . . . . . . . . Ms Philippa Drew
> Head of Department . . . . . . . . . . . . . . . . . . Mr Asif Ahmad
> Deputy Head of Department . . . . . . . . . . . . Mr Tony Humphries OBE
>> *enquiries* . . . . . . . . . . . . . . . . . . . . . . . . . . . . . . . . . . . Tel: (020) 7008 2943

**Conferences and Visits** *(see below under FCO Services Department)*

**Consular Directorate**
*FCO, Room G/49, Old Admiralty Building, London, SW1A 2PA*
> Director Consular Services . . . . . . . . . . . . . . Mr Paul Sizeland
> Consular Assistance . . . . . . . . . . . . . . . . . . . Mr Richard Morris
> Consular Crisis . . . . . . . . . . . . . . . . . . . . . . Mr Ralph Publicover
> Consular Service - Quality . . . . . . . . . . . . . . Mr Tim Flear MVO
> Consular Service - Resources . . . . . . . . . . . . Mr David Popplestone
> Passports and Documentary . . . . . . . . . . . . . Mr David Clegg MVO
>> Births, Marriages, Deaths . . . . . . . . . . . *enquiries* . . . . . . . . . . . . . . . . . . . . . . . . . . . . . . . . . Tel: (020) 7008 0186
>> Claims . . . . . . . . . . . . . . . . . . . . . . . . . *enquiries* . . . . . . . . . . . . . . . . . . . . . . . . . . . . . . . . . Tel: (020) 7008 0179
>> Legal Matters (International) . . . . . . . . . *enquiries* . . . . . . . . . . . . . . . . . . . . . . . . . . . . . . . . . Tel: (020) 7008 0185
>> Legalisation . . . . . . . . . . . . . . . . . . . . . *enquiries* . . . . . . . . . . . . . . . . . . . . . . . . . . . . . . . . . Tel: (020) 7008 1111
>> Nationality and Passports . . . . . . . . . . . *enquiries (9.30am – 12.30pm)* . . . . . . . . . . . . . . . . . . Tel: (020) 7008 0186
>> Travel Advice Unit . . . . . . . . . . . . . . . . *enquiries* . . . . . . . . . . . . . . . . . . . . . . . . . . . . . . . . . Tel: (020) 7008 0232

**Consultancy Group** *(see below under FCO Services Department)*

# FOREIGN AND COMMONWEALTH OFFICE

**Counter-Proliferation Department**
*FCO, Downing Street West, London, SW1A 2AH*

Director............................ Mr Edward Oakden
Head of Department.................... Mr David Landsman
Deputy Heads of Department ............. Mr Patrick Lamb
Mr Andrew Turner
*enquiries* ................................. Tel: (020) 7008 2261/2751

**Counter-Terrorism Policy Department**
*FCO, King Charles Street, London, SW1A 2AH*

Director............................ Mr Edward Oakden
Head of Department.................... Mr Rob Macaire
*enquiries* ................................. Tel: (020) 7008 2583

**Crime, International** *(see below under Drugs and International Crime Department)*

**Defence Policy** *(see above under Counter-Proliferation and Security Policy Departments)*

**Diplomatic Services Families Association**
*FCO, Old Admiralty Building, London, SW1A 2PA*

Chairwoman ........................ Ms Emilie Salvesen
Vice-Chairwoman ..................... Ms Marianne Gass
Executive Secretary ................... Ms Christine Easter
*enquiries* ................................. Tel: (020) 7008 0286

**Diplomatic Services Language Centre**
*FCO, Old Admiralty Building, London, SW1A 2PA*

Head of Centre ....................... Dr Vanessa Davies
*enquiries (switchboard)* ...................... Tel: (020) 7008 1500

**Disarmament** *(see above under Counter-Proliferation Department)*

**Drugs and International Crime Department**
*FCO, King Charles Street, London, SW1A 2AH*

Director............................ Mr Edward Oakden
Head of Department and UK Special Representative
for International Drugs Issues .......... Ms Lesley Pallet
Deputy Head of Department.............. Mr Guy Warrington
*enquiries* ................................. Tel: (020) 7008 1835/1808

**Eastern Adriatic** *(see above under Adriatic (Eastern) Department)*

**Eastern Department**
*FCO, Downing Street West, London, SW1A 2AL*

*(Armenia, Azerbaijan, Belarus, Caspian Energy Issues, Georgia, Kazakhstan, Kyrgyzstan, Moldova, Russia, Tajikstan, Turkmenistan, Ukraine, Uzbekistan)*

Director............................ Ms Linda Duffield
Head of Department.................... Mr Simon Butt
Deputy Head of Department.............. Mr Dominic Schroeder
*enquiries* ................................. Tel: (020) 7008 2427/2423/3831

# FOREIGN AND COMMONWEALTH OFFICE

**Economic Policy Department**

*FCO, Whitehall, London, SW1A 2AH*

Director-General . . . . . . . . . . . . . . . . . . . . . Mr Graham Fry CMG

Head of Department/Chief Economist. . . . . . . Mr Creon Butler

Deputy Heads of Department

Development Issues, Globalisation, International

Financial Institutions, Business, Development Issues

Financial Crime, Summitings . . . . . . . . Mr Hasan Bakhshi

G8, OECD, Economic Crime and Tax,

Investment and Business Relations,

Emerging Markets Programme . . . . . . . Mr Graham Minter

*enquiries* . . . . . . . . . . . . . . . . . . . . . . . . . . . . . . . . Tel: (020) 7008 2732

**Environment Policy Department**

*FCO, King Charles Street, London, SW1A 2AH*

Director. . . . . . . . . . . . . . . . . . . . . . . . . . . Ms Philippa Drew

Head of Department. . . . . . . . . . . . . . . . . . . Ms Valerie Caton

Deputy Head of Department. . . . . . . . . . . . . Mr Dominic Meiklejohn

*enquiries* . . . . . . . . . . . . . . . . . . . . . . . . . . . . . . . . Tel: (020) 7008 4131

**Estate Strategy Unit**

*FCO, Apollo House, 36 Wellesley Road, Croydon, CR0 9YA*

Director. . . . . . . . . . . . . . . . . . . . . . . . . . . Mr Richard Stagg CMG

Head of Unit . . . . . . . . . . . . . . . . . . . . . . . Mr Julian Metcalfe

Deputy Head of Unit . . . . . . . . . . . . . . . . . Mr Jeremy Neate

*enquiries* . . . . . . . . . . . . . . . . . . . . . . . . . . . . . . . . Tel: (020) 8253 6358

**European Union (External) - Directorate**

*FCO, Downing Street East, London, SW1A 2AL*

Director-General . . . . . . . . . . . . . . . . . . . . . Ms Nicola Brewer

Assistant Director . . . . . . . . . . . . . . . . . . . . . Mr Tim Barrow LVO MBE

*enquiries* . . . . . . . . . . . . . . . . . . . . . . . . . . . . . . . . Tel: (020) 7008 3812

Team Leaders . . . . . . . . . . . . . . . . . . . . . . . Mr Charles Garrett *(Enlargement and Wider Europe)*

*enquiries* . . . . . . . . . . . . . . . . . . . . . . . . . . . . . . . . Tel: (020) 7008 3018

Mr Andrew Key *(Accession States, International Development, Trade)*

*enquiries* . . . . . . . . . . . . . . . . . . . . . . . . . . . . . . . . Tel: (020) 7008 3018

Mr James Morrison *(Common Foreign and Security Policy)*

*enquiries* . . . . . . . . . . . . . . . . . . . . . . . . . . . . . . . . Tel: (020) 7008 2807

**European Union (Internal) - Directorate**

*FCO, Downing Street East, London, SW1A 2AL*

Director-General . . . . . . . . . . . . . . . . . . . . . Ms Nicola Brewer

Assistant Director . . . . . . . . . . . . . . . . . . . . . Mr David Frost

Team Leaders . . . . . . . . . . . . . . . . . . . . . . . Mr Tom Drew *(Inter Governmental Conference)*

Ms Mara Goldstein *(Germany)*

Mr Simon Manley *(Economics, Central Europe)*

*enquiries* . . . . . . . . . . . . . . . . . . . . . . . . . . . . . . . . Tel: (020) 7008 3388

**European Union - Mediterranean Department**

*FCO, King Charles Street, London, SW1A 2AH*

*(Andorra, Cyprus, Gibraltar, Greece, Holy See Malta, Spain, Portugal, Turkey)*

Director. . . . . . . . . . . . . . . . . . . . . . . . . . . Mr Dominic Chilcott

Head of Department. . . . . . . . . . . . . . . . . . . Mr Geoff Gillham

Deputy Heads of Department . . . . . . . . . . . . Mr Rob Fenn *(Eastern Mediterranean)*

Ms Wendy Wyver *(Western Mediterranean)*

*enquiries* . . . . . . . . . . . . . . . . . . . . . . . . . . . . . . . . Tel: (020) 7008 2011

# FOREIGN AND COMMONWEALTH OFFICE

**Financial Compliance Unit**
*FCO, Whitehall, SW1A 2AH*
Director.............................Mr Rick Todd
Head of Unit ........................Mr David Major
*enquiries*.................................Tel: (020) 7008 8275

**Financial Planning and Performance Department**
*FCO, Old Admiralty Building, Whitehall, London, SW1A 2AF*
Director.............................Mr Rick Todd
Head of Department....................Mr Tristran Price
Deputy Heads of Department ..............Mr Noel Langley
Mr Matthew Owen
Mr James Tansley
*enquiries*.................................Tel: (020) 7008 1085

**FCO Services Department**
*FCO, King Charles Street, London, SW1A 2AH*
Chief Executive.......................Mr Stephen Sage...........................Tel: (01908) 515165
*Client Services*
Head of Client Services ..............Ms Joy Herring...........................Tel: (01908) 515165
*Conference and Visits (Positive Image UK Service Delivery Group)*
Head of Group.....................Mr John Elgie...........................Tel: (020) 7008 8101
Head of VIP Visits and Sponsored Visits ..Ms Corinne Kitsell
*enquiries*...........................Tel: (020) 7008 8101
Head of Conferences Events and
Government Hospitality and
Lancaster House................Mr Terry McAree ..........................Tel: (020) 7008 8101
*Facilities Services Delivery Group*
*Hanslope Park, Hanslope, Milton Keynes, MK19 7BH*
Head of Group.....................Mr Nigel Morris
*enquiries*...........................Tel: (020) 8253 8007 *(Home)*
Tel: (020) 8253 6247 *(Overseas)*
*Finance Branch*
*Hanslope Park, Hanslope, Milton Keynes, MK19 7BH*
Head of Branch ...................Mr Kerry Simmonds
*enquiries*...........................Tel: (01908) 516876
*Human Resources Group*
*Hanslope Park, Hanslope, Milton Keynes, MK19 7BH*
Head of Group.....................Ms Elaine Kennedy
*enquiries*...........................Tel: (01908) 515007
*Information Communications and Technical (ICT)*
*King Charles Street, London, SW1A 2AH*
*(also at Hanslope Park, Hanslope, Milton Keynes, MK19 7BH)*
Head of Communication Centre ........Mr Bill Dunningham
Deputy Head of Communication Centre ...Mr David Harvey MBE
*enquiries*...........................Tel: (020) 7008 2976
*People and Best Practice Delivery Group*
Head of Group.....................Dr Vanessa Davies
*enquiries*...........................Tel: (020) 7270 1500
*Supply Chain Service Delivery Group*
*Hanslope Park, Hanslope, Milton Keynes, MK19 7BH*
Head of Group.....................Mr Rod Peters
Deputy Head of Group...............Mr Paul Bell
Global Procurement Services ..........Mr Mike Breen
Logistical Services..................Mr Eddie Stephenson
Office Services ....................Mr Paul Bell
Purchasing Services................Mr Maurice Campbell
*enquiries*...........................Tel: (01908) 515788

# FOREIGN AND COMMONWEALTH OFFICE

**Geneva Convention** (*see below under United Nations Department*)

**Human Resources**
*FCO, G/34 Old Admiralty Building, London, SW1A 2PA*

Superintending Director. . . . . . . . . . . . . . . . . Mr David Warren
Assistant Directors,
    Health and Welfare . . . . . . . . . . . . . . . . . Mr Andrew George
    Legal. . . . . . . . . . . . . . . . . . . . . . . . . . . . Ms Diane Cother
                               Ms Carole Sweeney
Pay and Benefits Policy
    Head of Team. . . . . . . . . . . . . . . . . . . . Mr David Powell
Professional Development, Assistant Directors . Mr Howard Drake
                               Mr Richard Tauwhare
                               Mr Gerry Reffo
Workforce Planning. . . . . . . . . . . . . . . . . . . Mr Simon Pease
                               *enquiries* . . . . . . . . . . . . . . . . . . . . . . . . . . . . . . . . . . Tel: (020) 7270 1500

**Human Rights Policy Department**
*FCO, King Charles Street, London, SW1A 2AH*

Director. . . . . . . . . . . . . . . . . . . . . . . . . . . Ms Philippa Drew
Head of Department. . . . . . . . . . . . . . . . . . . Mr Jon Benjamin
Deputy Head of Department. . . . . . . . . . . . . Mr Chris Trott
                               *enquiries* . . . . . . . . . . . . . . . . . . . . . . . . . . . . . . . . . . Tel: (020) 7008 3616

**Immigration** (*see below under United Kingdom Visas*)

**Internal Audit Department** (*Joint FCO and Department for International Development*)
*FCO, King Charles Street, London, SW1E 2AH*

Director. . . . . . . . . . . . . . . . . . . . . . . . . . . Mr Rick Todd
Head of Internal Audit. . . . . . . . . . . . . . . . . Mr Jon Hews
Audit Manager. . . . . . . . . . . . . . . . . . . . . . . Mr Trevor Jarvis
                               *enquiries* . . . . . . . . . . . . . . . . . . . . . . . . . . . . . . . . . . Tel: (020) 7008 8010

**IT Strategy Unit**
*FCO, Old Admiralty Building, London, SW1A 2PA*

Director General . . . . . . . . . . . . . . . . . . . . . Mr Richard Stagg
Head of Unit . . . . . . . . . . . . . . . . . . . . . . . . Mr Nick Westcott
Deputy Head of Unit . . . . . . . . . . . . . . . . . . Mr Nick Clouting
                               *enquiries* . . . . . . . . . . . . . . . . . . . . . . . . . . . . . . . . . . Tel: (020) 7008 0524

**Latin America Department**
*FCO, King Charles Street, London, SW1A 2AP*

    (*All Latin American countries; Latin American and Caribbean regional organisations*)
Director. . . . . . . . . . . . . . . . . . . . . . . . . . . Mr Robert Culshaw MVO
Head of Department. . . . . . . . . . . . . . . . . . . Mr Steve Williams
Deputy Head of Department. . . . . . . . . . . . . Mr Trevor Moore

**Law of the Sea** (*see above under Aviation, Maritime and Energy Department*)

**Legal Advisers**
*FCO, King Charles Street, London, SW1A 2AH*

Legal Adviser . . . . . . . . . . . . . . . . . . . . . . . Sir Michael Wood KCMG
Deputy Legal Advisers. . . . . . . . . . . . . . . . . Mr John Grainger
                               Mr Ian Hendry CMG
                               Mr Christopher Whomersley
                               *enquiries* . . . . . . . . . . . . . . . . . . . . . . . . . . . . . . . . . . Tel: (020) 7008 3080/3081

# FOREIGN AND COMMONWEALTH OFFICE

## Middle East Department

*FCO, Downing Street West, London, SW1A 2AL*

*(Bahrain, Iran, Iraq, Kuwait, Oman, Qatar, Saudi Arabia, UAE, Yemen Republic)*

Director . . . . . . . . . . . . . . . . . . . . . . . . Mr Edward Chaplin CMG OBE
Head of Department . . . . . . . . . . . . . . . . . . Mr Charles Gray CMG
Deputy Head of Department . . . . . . . . . . . . . Mr Jolyon Welsh
*enquiries* . . . . . . . . . . . . . . . . . . . . . . . . . . . . . . . . . Tel: (020) 7008 2997

## Near East and North Africa Department

*FCO, Downing Street West, London, SW1A 2AL*

*(Algeria, Egypt, Israel, Jordan, Lebanon, Libya, Mauritania, Morocco, Sudan, Syria, Tunisia, West Bank and Gaza Strip, Arab/Israeli dialogue)*

Director . . . . . . . . . . . . . . . . . . . . . . . . Mr Edward Chaplin CMG OBE
Head of Department . . . . . . . . . . . . . . . . . . Mr Nicholas Archer
Deputy Head of Department . . . . . . . . . . . . . Ms Rosemary Waugh
*enquiries* . . . . . . . . . . . . . . . . . . . . . . . . . . . . . . . . . Tel: (020) 7008 3751

## News *(see below under Press Office)*

## North America Department

*FCO, Whitehall, London, SW1 2AP*

*(Canada, Puerto Rico, USA, US Virgin Islands)*

Director . . . . . . . . . . . . . . . . . . . . . . . . Mr Robert Culshaw MVO
Head of Department . . . . . . . . . . . . . . . . . . Mr Martin Rickerd OBE
Deputy Head of Department . . . . . . . . . . . . . Mr David Hunt
*enquiries* . . . . . . . . . . . . . . . . . . . . . . . . . . . . . . . . . Tel: (020) 7008 2663

## North East Asia and Pacific Department

*FCO, King Charles Street, London, SW1A 2AP*

*(Australia, Cook Islands, Federated States of Micronesia, Fiji, Japan, Kiribati, Korea (Democratic Peoples Republic) Korea (Republic), Marshall Islands, Micronesia, Mongolia, Nauru, New Zealand, Palau, Papua New Guinea, Solomon Islands, Tonga, Tuvalu, Vanuatu, Western Samoa, French and US Territories in South Pacific, Administration of Pitcairn)*

Director . . . . . . . . . . . . . . . . . . . . . . . . Mr Nigel Cox
Head of Department . . . . . . . . . . . . . . . . . . Mr Simon Smith
Deputy Head of Department . . . . . . . . . . . . . Mr Hugo Shorter
*enquiries* . . . . . . . . . . . . . . . . . . . . . . . . . . . . . . . . . Tel: (020) 7008 2952 / 2960

## Online Communications Department

*FCO, King Charles Street, London, SW1A 2AP*

Director . . . . . . . . . . . . . . . . . . . . . . . . Mr Simon Fraser
Head of Department . . . . . . . . . . . . . . . . . . Mr Richard Codrington
Deputy Head of Department . . . . . . . . . . . . . Mr Moray Angus
*enquiries* . . . . . . . . . . . . . . . . . . . . . . . . . . . . . . . . . Tel: (020) 7008 6106

## Organisation for Security and Co-operation in Europe/Council of Europe Department

*FCO, OSCE Unit, FCO, Whitehall, London, SW1A 2AH*

Director . . . . . . . . . . . . . . . . . . . . . . . . Ms Linda Duffield
Head of Department . . . . . . . . . . . . . . . . . . Mr Peter January
Deputy Head of Department . . . . . . . . . . . . . Ms Anneli Conroy
*enquiries* . . . . . . . . . . . . . . . . . . . . . . . . . . . . . . . . . Tel: (020) 7008 2426

## Overseas Territories Department

*FCO, King Charles Street, London, SW1A 2AH*

*(Anguilla, Ascension Island, Bermuda, British Virgin Islands, Cayman Islands, Falkland Islands, Montserrat, St Helena, South Georgia, South Sandwich Islands, Tristan da Cunha, Turks and Caicos Islands)*

Director . . . . . . . . . . . . . . . . . . . . . . . . Mr Robert Culshaw MVO
Head of Department . . . . . . . . . . . . . . . . . . Mr Tony Crumbie OBE
Deputy Heads of Department . . . . . . . . . . . Ms Sarah Booker
Mr Roy Osborne
*enquiries* . . . . . . . . . . . . . . . . . . . . . . . . . . . . . . . . . Tel: (020) 7008 2643

# FOREIGN AND COMMONWEALTH OFFICE

**Parliamentary Clerk** . . . . . . . . . . . . . . . . . . . . Mr Jeremy Hill . . . . . . . . . . . . . . . . . . . . . . . . . . . . . Tel: (020) 7008 4005

**Parliamentary Relations and Devolution Department**
*FCO, King Charles Street, London, SW1 2AH*

Director . . . . . . . . . . . . . . . . . . . . . . . . . . . . Mr Simon Fraser
Head of Department . . . . . . . . . . . . . . . . . . . Mr Matthew Hamlyn
Deputy Head of Department . . . . . . . . . . . . . Ms Sue Breeze
Parliamentary Clerk . . . . . . . . . . . . . . . . . . . Mr Jeremy Hill
  *enquiries* . . . . . . . . . . . . . . . . . . . . . . . . . . . . . . . . . . . Tel: (020) 7008 2234/2235/2236

**Partnerships and Networks Development Unit**
*FCO, King Charles Street, London, SW1 2AH*

Director . . . . . . . . . . . . . . . . . . . . . . . . . . . . Mr Simon Fraser
Head of Department . . . . . . . . . . . . . . . . . . . Mr Fraser Wheeler
Faith Groups and Ethnic Minorities Adviser . . . Mr Mockbul Alt
  *enquiries* . . . . . . . . . . . . . . . . . . . . . . . . . . . . . . . . . . . Tel: (020) 7008 1500

**Personnel Directorate** *(see above under Human Resources Directorate)*

**Press Office**
*FCO, Downing Street West, London, SW1A 2AL*

Director . . . . . . . . . . . . . . . . . . . . . . . . . . . . Mr Simon Fraser
Press Secretary . . . . . . . . . . . . . . . . . . . . . . . Mr John Williams
Head of News Room . . . . . . . . . . . . . . . . . . . Mr Peter Reid . . . . . . . . . . . . . . . . . . . . . . . . . . . . . Tel: (020) 7008 3100

**Prism Programme**
*FCO, Old Admiralty Building, London, SW1A 2PA*

Director . . . . . . . . . . . . . . . . . . . . . . . . . . . . Mr Rick Todd
Programme Manager . . . . . . . . . . . . . . . . . . . Ms Andy Tucker
Deputy Programme Managers . . . . . . . . . . . . . Mr Roger Seager
  Mr Giles Whitaker
  *enquiries* . . . . . . . . . . . . . . . . . . . . . . . . . . . . . . . . . . . Tel: (020) 7008 0385

**Procurement Policy Department**
*FCO, 1/116 Old Admiralty Building, London, SW1A 2PA*

Director of Finance . . . . . . . . . . . . . . . . . . . . Mr Rick Todd
Head of Procurement Policy . . . . . . . . . . . . . . Mr Michael Gower
Deputy Head of Procurement Policy . . . . . . . . Mr Charles Sime
  *enquiries* . . . . . . . . . . . . . . . . . . . . . . . . . . . . . . . . . . . Tel: (020) 7008 0924

**Protocol Division**
*FCO, 1/55 Old Admiralty Building, W1A 2PA*

Director-General . . . . . . . . . . . . . . . . . . . . . . Mr Richard Stagg
Head of Division and Vice-Marshal of the
  Diplomatic Corps . . . . . . . . . . . . . . . . . . . . Mr Charles de Chassiron cvo
Deputy Head of Division . . . . . . . . . . . . . . . . Mr Chris Osborne

# FOREIGN AND COMMONWEALTH OFFICE

**Public Diplomacy Policy Department**
*FCO, King Charles Street, London, SW1A 2AH*

| | |
|---|---|
| Director......................... | Mr Simon Fraser |
| Head of Department.................. | Mr Paul Madden |
| Deputy Head of Department............. | Mr Charles Winnington-Ingram |
| | *enquiries*.................................. Tel: (020) 7008 1618 |

**Records and Historical Department**
*FCO, Old Admiralty Building, London, SW1A 2PA*

| | |
|---|---|
| Director of Information................. | Mr Simon Fraser |
| Head of Department.................. | Mrs Heather Yasamee |
| Deputy Head of Department............. | Mr Richard Bevins |
| Chief Historian ..................... | Ms Gill Bennett OBE |
| | *enquiries*.................................. Tel: (020) 7008 1129 |

**Red Cross** *(see below under United Nations Department)*

**Refugee Policy** *(see below under United Nations Department)*

**Research Analysis**
*FCO, King Charles Street, London, SW1A 2AH*

| | |
|---|---|
| Director......................... | Mr Simon Fraser |
| Head of Research and Analysis ........... | Mr Simon Buckle |
| Heads of Research Groups | |
|     Africa........................... | Dr Clare Thomas |
|     Americas ........................ | Mr Patrick Holdich |
|     Asia (South and South East) ........... | Ms Kathleen Kazer |
|     Asia (Northern) and Pacific............ | Mr Rod Wye |
|     Central Europe and Eastern Adriatic...... | Dr Joanna Hanson |
|     Eastern ........................ | Mr Duncan Allan |
|     Europe, Western and Southern ......... | Dr Shellagh Ellwood |
|     Global Issues ...................... | Mr Paul Bentall |
|     Middle East and North Africa .......... | Mr Greg Shapland |
| | *enquiries*.................................. Tel: (020) 7008 5942 |

**Resource Accounting Department**
*FCO, Room 1/45, Old Admiralty Building, London, SW1A 2PA*

| | |
|---|---|
| Director......................... | Mr Rick Todd |
| Head of Department and Chief Accountant.... | Mr Iain Morgan |
| | *enquiries*.................................. Tel: (020) 7008 1063 |

**Science and Technology Unit**
*FCO, King Charles Street, London, SW1A 2AH*

| | |
|---|---|
| Director......................... | Ms Philippa Drew |
| Head of Unit ...................... | Ms Fiona Clouder Richards |
| Deputy Head of Unit .................. | Mr Richard Jones |
| | *enquiries*.................................. Tel: (020) 7008 8288 |

**Security Policy Department**
*FCO, Downing Street East, London, SW1A 2AH*

| | |
|---|---|
| Director......................... | Mr Edward Oakden |
| Head of Department.................. | Mr Paul Johnston |
| Deputy Heads of Department ............. | Mr Robert Deane |
| | Ms Jennifer Anderson |
| | *enquiries*.................................. Tel: (020) 7008 3131 |

# FOREIGN AND COMMONWEALTH OFFICE

**Security Strategy Unit** *(Joint with Ministry of Defence)*
*FCO, Old Admiralty Building, London, SW1A 2PA*

| | |
|---|---|
| Director | Mr Richard Stagg |
| Head of Unit | Mr Peter Milletts |
| Deputy Head of Unit | Mr Julian Chandler |
| *enquiries* | Tel: (020) 7008 1153 |

**South Asian Department**
*FCO, Whitehall, London, SW1A 2AP*

*(Bangladesh, Bhutan, India, Maldives, Nepal, Pakistan, Sri Lanka)*

| | |
|---|---|
| Director | Mr Tom Phillips CMG |
| Head of Department | Mr Stephen Smith OBE |
| Deputy Head of Department | Mr James Dauris |
| *enquiries* | Tel: (020) 7008 2388 |

**South East Asian Department**
*FCO, Whitehall, London, SW1A 2AH*

*(Brunei, Burma, Cambodia, East Timor, Indonesia, Laos, Malaysia, Philippines, Singapore, Thailand, Vietnam, Association of South East Asian Nations)*

| | |
|---|---|
| Director | Mr Nigel Cox |
| Head of Department | Mr Michael Reilly |
| Deputy Head of Department | Ms Valerie Brownridge |
| *enquiries* | Tel: (020) 7008 2600 |

**South Pacific** *(see above under North East Asia and Pacific Department)*

**Strategy and Innovation Directorate**
*FCO, King Charles Street, London, SW1A 2AH*

| | |
|---|---|
| Director | Mr Simon Fraser |
| Assistant Director | Ms Vivien Life |
| Team Leaders | Mr Nick Kay *(Strategic Policy Advice)* |
| | Mr Andrew Key *(Delivery Strategy)* |
| | Mr John Krauss *(Internal Communications Strategy)* |
| *enquiries* | Tel: (020) 7008 2911 |

**Sudan Unit**
*FCO, King Charles Street, London, SW1A 2AH*

| | |
|---|---|
| UK Special Representative for Sudan | Mr Alan Goulty CMG |
| Head of Unit | Dr Alastair McPhaill |
| *enquiries* | Tel: (020) 7008 3947 |

**United Kingdom Visas** *(Joint FCO and Home Office)*
*FCO, King Charles Street, London, SW1A 2AH (Correspondence)*
*89 Albert Embankment, London, SW1E 7TP (Office)*

| | |
|---|---|
| Director | Mr Richard Stagg CMG *(Foreign Office)* |
| | Mr Bill Jeffrey *(Home Office)* |
| Head, UK Visas | Mr Robin Barnett |
| Deputy Heads, UK Visas | Mr Tony Mercer *(Operations)* |
| | Mr Paul Sherar *(Modernisation)* |
| | Mr Keith Moss *(Policy)* |
| *enquiries* | Tel: (020) 7008 8438 |
| Web | http://www.ukvisas.gov.uk |

**UK Trade and Investment** *(see under Department of Trade and Industry)*

# FOREIGN AND COMMONWEALTH OFFICE

**United Nations Department**

*FCO, King Charles Street, London, SW1A 2AH*

| | |
|---|---|
| Director. . . . . . . . . . . . . . . . . . . . . . . . . . . . | Ms Philippa Drew |
| Head of Department. . . . . . . . . . . . . . . . . . . | Mr William Harrison cvo |
| Deputy Heads of Department . . . . . . . . . . . . | Ms Sarah MacIntosh *(Peacekeeping, Security Issues, Sanctions)* |
| | Ms Helen Taylor *(War Crimes; UN-Finance, Development and Reform)* |
| Head, Government Diamonds Office. . . . . . . . | Mr Clive Wright |
| | *enquiries* . . . . . . . . . . . . . . . . . . . . . . . . . . . . . . . . Tel: (020) 7008 3583 |

**Whitehall Liaison Department**

*FCO, Downing Street West, London, SW1A 2AL*

| | |
|---|---|
| Director-General . . . . . . . . . . . . . . . . . . . . . . | *Vacant* |
| Head of Department. . . . . . . . . . . . . . . . . . . | Mr Matthew Kidd |
| Deputy Head of Department. . . . . . . . . . . . . | Mr Iain Kelly |
| | *enquiries* . . . . . . . . . . . . . . . . . . . . . . . . . . . . . . . . Tel: (020) 7008 2350 |

# FOREIGN AND COMMONWEALTH OFFICE

## OTHER RELEVANT CONTACTS

**BROADCASTING**

**BBC World Service and BBC Monitoring** .... Bush House, Strand, London, WC2B 4PH

    Director *(Acting)* ...................... Mr Nigel Chapman ............................. Tel: (020) 7240 3456

        E-mail: nigel.chapman@bbc.co.uk

**BRITISH COUNCIL**

**British Council** ......................... 10 Spring Gardens, London, SW1A 2BN

    Chairman .......................... Baroness Kennedy of the Shaws QC *(until November 2004)*

        Rt Hon Neil Kinnock *(from November 2004)*

    Director-General ..................... Mr David Green CMG ......................... Tel: (020) 7930 8466

        E-mail: general.enquiries@britishcouncil.org

        Web: http://www.britishcouncil.org

**CHINA**

**Great Britain-China Centre** ............... 15 Belgrave Square, London, SW1X 8PS

    Chairman .......................... Mr David Brewer

    Director ........................... Mr Calum Macleod ........................... Tel: (020) 7235 6696

        E-mail: contact@gbcc.org.uk  Web: http://www.gbcc.org.uk

**COMMONWEALTH**

**Commonwealth Institute** .................. Kensington High Street, London, W8 6NQ

    Chairman .......................... Ms Judith Hanratty OBE

    Chief Executive ...................... Ms Judy Curry ............................. Tel: (020) 7603 4535

        Web: http://www.commonwealth.org.uk

**Commonwealth Parliamentary Association** ... 7 Millbank, London, SW1P 3JA

    Secretary-General ..................... Hon Denis Marshall QSO ...................... Tel: (020) 7799 1460

        E-mail: hq.sec@cpahq.org

        Web: http://www.cpahq.org

**CONFERENCE CENTRE**

**Wilton Park** *(Executive Agency)* .............. Wiston House, Steyning, West Sussex, BN44 3DZ

    Chairman, Academic Council ............. Dr Farhan Nizami

    Chief Executive ...................... Mr Colin Jennings ........................... Tel: (01903) 817766

        Web: http://www.wiltonpark.org.uk

**DIPLOMATIC SERVICE**

**Diplomatic Service Appeal Board** .......... c/o Human Resources Directorate (Employment Policy), FCO, Room 2/68,

        Old Admiralty Building, Whitehall, London, SW1A 2PA

    Chairman .......................... Sir Franklin Berman

    Secretary .......................... Mr Craig Hannah ........................... Tel: (020) 7008 1455

**EASTERN AND CENTRAL EUROPE**

**British Association for Central and**

    **Eastern Europe** ..................... 10 Westminster Palace Gardens, Artillery Row, London, SW1P 1RL

    Chairman .......................... Rt Hon Lord Radice

    Director ........................... Sir John Birch KCVO CMG ..................... Tel: (020) 7976 0766

        E-mail: bacee@bacee.org.uk  Web: http://www.bacee.org.uk/bacee

**FOREIGN COMPENSATION**

**Foreign Compensation Commission** ........ Room SG111, Old Admiralty Building, Whitehall, London, SW1A 2PA

    Chairman .......................... Dr John Barker

    Secretary .......................... *Vacant* ................................. Tel: (020) 7008 1321

**GCHQ**

**Government Communications Headquarters** . Hubble Road, Cheltenham, Gloucestershire, GL51 DEX

    Director ........................... Mr David Pepper ............................ Tel: (01242) 221491

        Web: http://www.gchq.gov.uk

# FOREIGN AND COMMONWEALTH OFFICE

*Other Relevant Contacts (Continued)*

**INTELLIGENCE**
**Secret Intelligence Service (MI6)**. . . . . . . . . . PO Box 1300 London, SE1 1BD
    Chief Executive. . . . . . . . . . . . . . . . . . . . . . Mr John Scarlett CMG OBE

**MARSHALL AID COMMEMORATION**
**Marshall Aid Commemoration Commission** . . Association of Commonwealth Universities, 36 Gordon Square, London, WC1H 0PF
    Chairman . . . . . . . . . . . . . . . . . . . . . . . . . . . Mr Jonathan Taylor
    Executive Secretary . . . . . . . . . . . . . . . . . . . . Professor Michael Gibbons . . . . . . . . . . . . . . . . . . . . Tel: (020) 7380 6700
                             Web: http://www.marshallscholarship.org

**RUSSIA**
**Britain-Russia Centre** . . . . . . . . . . . . . . . . . . Wilcot House, 42 Southwark Street, London, SE1 1UN
    Chairman . . . . . . . . . . . . . . . . . . . . . . . . . . . *Vacant*
    Director. . . . . . . . . . . . . . . . . . . . . . . . . . . . . Mr Godfrey Cromwell . . . . . . . . . . . . . . . . . . . . . . . . . Tel: (020) 7378 8222
                             Web: http://www.bewc.org

**WESTMINSTER FOUNDATION**
**Westminster Foundation for Democracy** . . . . 2nd Floor, 125 Pall Mall, London, SW1Y 5EA
    Chairman . . . . . . . . . . . . . . . . . . . . . . . . . . . Mr Mike Gapes MP
    Chief Executive. . . . . . . . . . . . . . . . . . . . . . . Mr David French. . . . . . . . . . . . . . . . . . . . . . . . . . . . Tel: (020) 7930 0408
                             Web: http://www.wfd.org

**WINE**
**Government Hospitality Advisory Committee**
    **for the Purchase of Wine** . . . . . . . . . . . . . Lancaster House, Stable Yard, St James's, London, SW1A 1BB
    Chairman . . . . . . . . . . . . . . . . . . . . . . . . . . . Sir David Wright
    Secretary. . . . . . . . . . . . . . . . . . . . . . . . . . . . Mr Robert Alexander . . . . . . . . . . . . . . . . . . . . . . . . . Tel: (020) 7008 8517
                             E-mail: robert.alexander@fco.gov.uk

# UNITED NATIONS

## UNITED NATIONS ASSOCIATION
3 Whitehall Court, London, SW1A 2EL

*Telephone:* (020) 7930 2931
*Facsimile:* (020) 7930 5893
*E-mail:* mharper@una-uk.org
*Web:* http://www.una-uk.org

*Contact:* Mr Malcolm Harper, CMG – *Director*

We are a membership organisation which, independent of all political affiliations, lobbies the British government, diplomats in the UK, religious, trade union, business and other leaders and, through other UNAs, their governments to promote the greater use of the United Nations in world affairs. We also hold parliamentary and other seminars on key UN issues and run educational projects through the UNA Trust.

We are an active member of the World Federation of United Nations Associations, which enjoys Category I Consultative Status with the United Nations Economic and Social Council. We have roster status in many UN Conferences and other activities.

The UNA Trust (Registered Charity number 256236) supports UNA's educational and other charitable works.

The UNA Trust also runs the National UK Adopt-A-Minefield Programme which supports UN Mine Clearing Projects and Survivor Assistance.

# DEPARTMENT OF HEALTH

Richmond House, 79 Whitehall, London, SW1A 2NS
Tel: (020) 7210 3000  Fax: (020) 7210 5523
E-mail: dhmail@doh.gsi.gov.uk  Web: http://www.doh.gov.uk

Quarry House, Quarry Hill, Leeds, LS2 7UE
Tel: (0113) 254 5000

## MINISTERS

**Secretary of State** . . . . . . . . . . . . . . . . . . . . . . . . . . . Rt Hon John Reid MP
*Principal Private Secretary* . . . . . . . . . . . . . . . . . . . . Mr Dominic Hardy . . . . . . . . . . . . . . . . . . . . . . . . Tel: (020) 7210 5158
*Special Advisers* . . . . . . . . . . . . . . . . . . . . . . . . . . . . Mr Stephen Bates . . . . . . . . . . . . . . . . . . . . . . . . . Tel: (020) 7210 5945
Prof Paul Corrigan . . . . . . . . . . . . . . . . . . . . . . . . . Tel: (020) 7210 5945
Mr Richard Olszewski . . . . . . . . . . . . . . . . . . . . . . Tel: (020) 7210 5942

**Minister of State** . . . . . . . . . . . . . . . . . . . . . . . . . . . Rt Hon John Hutton MP
*Private Secretary* . . . . . . . . . . . . . . . . . . . . . . . . . . . Mr Tony Sampson . . . . . . . . . . . . . . . . . . . . . . . . . Tel: (020) 7210 5105

**Minister of State** . . . . . . . . . . . . . . . . . . . . . . . . . . . Ms Rosie Winterton MP
*Private Secretary* . . . . . . . . . . . . . . . . . . . . . . . . . . . Mr Alastair Finney . . . . . . . . . . . . . . . . . . . . . . . . . Tel: (020) 7210 5325

**Parliamentary Secretary** . . . . . . . . . . . . . . . . . . . . . Miss Melanie Johnson MP
*Private Secretary* . . . . . . . . . . . . . . . . . . . . . . . . . . . Ms Emily Stott . . . . . . . . . . . . . . . . . . . . . . . . . . . . Tel: (020) 7210 5114

**Parliamentary Secretary** . . . . . . . . . . . . . . . . . . . . . Dr Stephen Ladyman MP
*Private Secretary* . . . . . . . . . . . . . . . . . . . . . . . . . . . Ms Wendy Brown . . . . . . . . . . . . . . . . . . . . . . . . . Tel: (020) 7210 5564

**Parliamentary Secretary** . . . . . . . . . . . . . . . . . . . . . Lord Warner
*Private Secretary (Acting)* . . . . . . . . . . . . . . . . . . . . Ms Catherine Davies . . . . . . . . . . . . . . . . . . . . . . Tel: (020) 7210 5826

## CIVIL SERVICE

*Note: Staff with (0113) telephone numbers are based in Leeds.*

**Permanent Secretary and NHS Chief Executive** . . . . . . Sir Nigel Crisp KCB
*Private Secretary* . . . . . . . . . . . . . . . . . . . . . . . . . . . Mr David McNeil . . . . . . . . . . . . . . . . . . . . . . . . . . Tel: (020) 7210 5145

**Chief Medical Officer and Group Director, Standards
and Quality** . . . . . . . . . . . . . . . . . . . . . . . . . . . . . . . Professor Sir Liam Donaldson
*Private Secretary* . . . . . . . . . . . . . . . . . . . . . . . . . . . Ms Rachel Dickson . . . . . . . . . . . . . . . . . . . . . . . . Tel: (020) 7210 5150

**Directors / Senior Management**
Communications Director . . . . . . . . . . . . . . . . . . . . . . Ms Sian Jarvis . . . . . . . . . . . . . . . . . . . . . . . . . . . . Tel: (020) 7210 5440
Delivery, Group Director . . . . . . . . . . . . . . . . . . . . . . . Mr John Bacon . . . . . . . . . . . . . . . . . . . . . . . . . . . . Tel: (020) 7210 4991
Head of Delivery . . . . . . . . . . . . . . . . . . . . . . . . . . . . . Mr Ivan Ellul . . . . . . . . . . . . . . . . . . . . . . . . . . . . . Tel: (0113) 254 5574
Finance and Investment Director . . . . . . . . . . . . . . . . . Mr Richard Douglas . . . . . . . . . . . . . . . . . . . . . . . . Tel: (020) 7210 5429
Modernisation Director . . . . . . . . . . . . . . . . . . . . . . . . Mr David Fillingham . . . . . . . . . . . . . . . . . . . . . . . Tel: (020) 7210 5711
NHS Human Resources Director . . . . . . . . . . . . . . . . . Mr Andrew Foster . . . . . . . . . . . . . . . . . . . . . . . . . Tel: (020) 7210 5907
NHS Information Management and Technology, Director . Mr Richard Granger . . . . . . . . . . . . . . . . . . . . . . . . Tel: (020) 7210 5588
Research and Development Director . . . . . . . . . . . . . . . Professor Sir John Pattison . . . . . . . . . . . . . . . . . . Tel: (020) 7210 5556
Specialist Health Services Director . . . . . . . . . . . . . . . Professor Aidan Halligan . . . . . . . . . . . . . . . . . . . . Tel: (020) 7210 5608
Strategy and Business Development, Director . . . . . . . . Mr Hugh Taylor CB . . . . . . . . . . . . . . . . . . . . . . . . Tel: (020) 7210 5449
User Experience and Involvement Director . . . . . . . . . . Mrs Sarah Mullally . . . . . . . . . . . . . . . . . . . . . . . . Tel: (020) 7210 5598

## SUBJECT RESPONSIBILITIES AND CONTACTS

**Abortion: Health Education** . . . . . . . . . . . . . . . . . . . . Ms Cathy Hamlyn . . . . . . . . . . . . . . . . . . . . . . . . . Tel: (020) 7972 5355

**Access to Health Care**
Director, Access and Choice . . . . . . . . . . . . . . . . . . . . Ms Margaret Edwards . . . . . . . . . . . . . . . . . . . . . . Tel: (0113) 254 6177
Access Delivery . . . . . . . . . . . . . . . . . . . . . . . . . . . . . Mr Mark Svenson . . . . . . . . . . . . . . . . . . . . . . . . . Tel: (0113) 254 5214
Redesign Team . . . . . . . . . . . . . . . . . . . . . . . . . . . . . . Dr Helen Bevan . . . . . . . . . . . . . . . . . . . . . . . . . . . Tel: (0116) 222 5150

# DEPARTMENT OF HEALTH

**Accident and Emergency** . . . . . . . . . . . . . . . . . . . . . Mr Mark Davies . . . . . . . . . . . . . . . . . . . . . . . . . Tel: (020) 7210 5930

**Adoption** . . . . . . . . . . . . . . . . . . . . . . . . . . . . . . . . Mr David Holmes . . . . . . . . . . . . . . . . . . . . . . . . Tel: (020) 7972 4629

**AIDS and HIV** . . . . . . . . . . . . . . . . . . . . . . . . . . . . Dr Linda Lazarus . . . . . . . . . . . . . . . . . . . . . . . . Tel: (020) 7972 5751

**Air Pollutants** . . . . . . . . . . . . . . . . . . . . . . . . . . . . Miss Julia Cumberledge . . . . . . . . . . . . . . . . . . . Tel: (020) 7972 5130

**Alcohol Misuse Policy** . . . . . . . . . . . . . . . . . . . . . . Ms Cathy Hamlyn . . . . . . . . . . . . . . . . . . . . . . . . Tel: (020) 7972 5355

**Ambulance Services** . . . . . . . . . . . . . . . . . . . . . . . . Mr Daniel Scheffer . . . . . . . . . . . . . . . . . . . . . . . Tel: (020) 7210 5126

**Anaesthetics** . . . . . . . . . . . . . . . . . . . . . . . . . . . . . Ms Ann Stephenson . . . . . . . . . . . . . . . . . . . . . . Tel: (020) 7972 4173

**Anatomy: HM Inspector** . . . . . . . . . . . . . . . . . . . . . Dr Jeremy Metters . . . . . . . . . . . . . . . . . . . . . . . Tel: (020) 7972 4551

**Anti-Microbial Resistance** . . . . . . . . . . . . . . . . . . . . Dr Jane Leese . . . . . . . . . . . . . . . . . . . . . . . . . . . Tel: (020) 7972 1526

**Bioethics** . . . . . . . . . . . . . . . . . . . . . . . . . . . . . . . . Mr Nick Dean . . . . . . . . . . . . . . . . . . . . . . . . . . . Tel: (020) 7972 5061

**Biotechnology** . . . . . . . . . . . . . . . . . . . . . . . . . . . . Dr Alison Wight . . . . . . . . . . . . . . . . . . . . . . . . . Tel: (020) 7972 5357

**Blood** . . . . . . . . . . . . . . . . . . . . . . . . . . . . . . . . . . Mr Richard Gutowski . . . . . . . . . . . . . . . . . . . . . Tel: (020) 7972 3764

**Bloodborne Viruses** . . . . . . . . . . . . . . . . . . . . . . . . Dr Linda Lazarus . . . . . . . . . . . . . . . . . . . . . . . . Tel: (020) 7972 5751

**Breastfeeding** . . . . . . . . . . . . . . . . . . . . . . . . . . . . Dr Sheela Reddy . . . . . . . . . . . . . . . . . . . . . . . . Tel: (020) 7972 1365

**BSE** . . . . . . . . . . . . . . . . . . . . . . . . . . . . . . . . . . . . Dr Rowena Jecock . . . . . . . . . . . . . . . . . . . . . . . Tel: (020) 7972 5048

**Cancer**
   Director, National Cancer Services . . . . . . . . . . . . . . Professor Michael Richards . . . . . . . . . . . . . . . . . . Tel: (020) 7922 8009
   Cancer and Coronary Heart Disease Task Force Manager . Ms Heather Gwynn . . . . . . . . . . . . . . . . . . . . . . . Tel: (020) 7972 4839
   NHS Cancer Services . . . . . . . . . . . . . . . . . . . . . . . Mr Stephen Waring . . . . . . . . . . . . . . . . . . . . . . . Tel: (020) 7972 4819

**Capacity, Plurality and Choice** . . . . . . . . . . . . . . . . Mr Bob Ricketts . . . . . . . . . . . . . . . . . . . . . . . . . Tel: (020) 7210 5455

**Capital Investment** . . . . . . . . . . . . . . . . . . . . . . . . . Mr John Holden . . . . . . . . . . . . . . . . . . . . . . . . . Tel: (0113) 254 5970

**Cardiac Health Services**
   Branch Head, Health Cardiac Services . . . . . . . . . . . . Mr Gavin Larner . . . . . . . . . . . . . . . . . . . . . . . . . Tel: (020) 7972 4971
   Coronary Heart Disease Task Force Manager . . . . . . . . Ms Heather Gwynn . . . . . . . . . . . . . . . . . . . . . . . Tel: (020) 7972 4839
   Medical Adviser, Health Cardiac Services . . . . . . . . . . Dr Mike McGovern . . . . . . . . . . . . . . . . . . . . . . . Tel: (020) 7972 4837

**Chief Medical Officer** . . . . . . . . . . . . . . . . . . . . . . . Professor Sir Liam Donaldson
   *Private Secretary* . . . . . . . . . . . . . . . . . . . . . . . . . . Ms Rachel Dickson . . . . . . . . . . . . . . . . . . . . . . . Tel: (020) 7210 5150
   Deputy Chief Medical Officer . . . . . . . . . . . . . . . . . . Professor Aidan Halligan . . . . . . . . . . . . . . . . . . . Tel: (020) 7210 5706

**Children**
   Adoption . . . . . . . . . . . . . . . . . . . . . . . . . . . . . . . . Mr David Holmes . . . . . . . . . . . . . . . . . . . . . . . . Tel: (020) 7972 4629
   Child Health . . . . . . . . . . . . . . . . . . . . . . . . . . . . . . Mr Jonathan Stopes-Roe . . . . . . . . . . . . . . . . . . . . Tel: (020) 7972 4336
   Children in Need . . . . . . . . . . . . . . . . . . . . . . . . . . . Ms Janet Grauberg . . . . . . . . . . . . . . . . . . . . . . . . Tel: (020) 7972 4355
   Children's Services . . . . . . . . . . . . . . . . . . . . . . . . . Ms Janet Grauberg . . . . . . . . . . . . . . . . . . . . . . . . Tel: (020) 7972 4355
   Children's Task Force . . . . . . . . . . . . . . . . . . . . . . . . Ms Janice Shersby . . . . . . . . . . . . . . . . . . . . . . . . Tel: (020) 7972 4067
   Clinical Director, Children . . . . . . . . . . . . . . . . . . . . Professor Al Aynsley-Green . . . . . . . . . . . . . . . . . . Tel: (020) 7972 4203
   National Service Framework, Children's . . . . . . . . . . . . Ms Claire Phillips . . . . . . . . . . . . . . . . . . . . . . . . Tel: (020) 7972 4908
   Residential Care . . . . . . . . . . . . . . . . . . . . . . . . . . . Ms Janet Grauberg . . . . . . . . . . . . . . . . . . . . . . . . Tel: (020) 7972 4355

**Childbirth** . . . . . . . . . . . . . . . . . . . . . . . . . . . . . . . Mr Jonathan Stopes-Roe . . . . . . . . . . . . . . . . . . . . Tel: (020) 7972 4336

**Chiropody** . . . . . . . . . . . . . . . . . . . . . . . . . . . . . . . Ms Kay East . . . . . . . . . . . . . . . . . . . . . . . . . . . . Tel: (020) 7972 4497

**CJD** . . . . . . . . . . . . . . . . . . . . . . . . . . . . . . . . . . . . Dr Ailsa Wight . . . . . . . . . . . . . . . . . . . . . . . . . . Tel: (020) 7972 5357

# DEPARTMENT OF HEALTH

**Clinical and Cost Effectiveness**

    Head, Clinical and Cost Effectiveness . . . . . . . . . . . . . . Mr Alan Angilley . . . . . . . . . . . . . . . . . . . . . . . . . . Tel: (0113) 254 5403

    Senior Medical Officer . . . . . . . . . . . . . . . . . . . . . . . Dr Peter Clappison . . . . . . . . . . . . . . . . . . . . . . . . . . Tel: (0113) 254 6280

    Special Projects . . . . . . . . . . . . . . . . . . . . . . . . . . . . Mr Charles Dobson . . . . . . . . . . . . . . . . . . . . . . . . . Tel: (0113) 254 5227

**Clinical Governance** . . . . . . . . . . . . . . . . . . . . . . . . . . . . . Mr Steve O'Neill . . . . . . . . . . . . . . . . . . . . . . . . . . . . Tel: (0116) 295 2019

**Clinical Quality** . . . . . . . . . . . . . . . . . . . . . . . . . . . . . . . . . Mrs Patience Wilson . . . . . . . . . . . . . . . . . . . . . . . . Tel: (020) 7972 5176

**Communicable Diseases** . . . . . . . . . . . . . . . . . . . . . . . . . . Dr Graham Bickler . . . . . . . . . . . . . . . . . . . . . . . . . . Tel: (020) 7972 5116

**Communications** *(see below under Publicity and Communications)*

**Community Care** *(see below under Social Care)*

**Complaints (Hospitals)** . . . . . . . . . . . . . . . . . . . . . . . . . . Mr Adrian Landon . . . . . . . . . . . . . . . . . . . . . . . . . . Tel: (0113) 254 5679

**Complementary Medicine** . . . . . . . . . . . . . . . . . . . . . . . . Dr Martin Sturges . . . . . . . . . . . . . . . . . . . . . . . . . . Tel: (0113) 254 5673

**Conception (Assisted)** . . . . . . . . . . . . . . . . . . . . . . . . . . . Ms Liz Woodeson . . . . . . . . . . . . . . . . . . . . . . . . . . Tel: (020) 7972 5361

**Confidentiality Issues** . . . . . . . . . . . . . . . . . . . . . . . . . . . Mr Phil Walker . . . . . . . . . . . . . . . . . . . . . . . . . . . . . Tel: (0113) 254 6090

**Consent to Treatment** . . . . . . . . . . . . . . . . . . . . . . . . . . . Ms Elaine Cooper . . . . . . . . . . . . . . . . . . . . . . . . . . . Tel: (020) 7972 4499

**Coronary Heart Disease Policy** . . . . . . . . . . . . . . . . . . . Ms Imogen Sharp . . . . . . . . . . . . . . . . . . . . . . . . . . . Tel: (020) 7972 4494

**Corporate Management, Departmental**

    Director, Change Management . . . . . . . . . . . . . . . . . . . Ms Ruth Carnall . . . . . . . . . . . . . . . . . . . . . . . . . . . . Tel: (020) 7210 5757

    Director, Corporate Affairs . . . . . . . . . . . . . . . . . . . . . Mr Hugh Taylor CB . . . . . . . . . . . . . . . . . . . . . . . . . . Tel: (020) 7210 5449

    Career Management . . . . . . . . . . . . . . . . . . . . . . . . . . Mr John Middleton . . . . . . . . . . . . . . . . . . . . . . . . . . Tel: (020) 7972 5657

    Change Management and Development . . . . . . . . . . . . Mr Mark Collyer . . . . . . . . . . . . . . . . . . . . . . . . . . . . Tel: (020) 7972 5812

    Corporate Change . . . . . . . . . . . . . . . . . . . . . . . . . . . Mr David Clark . . . . . . . . . . . . . . . . . . . . . . . . . . . . . Tel: (020) 7972 5841

    Corporate Development . . . . . . . . . . . . . . . . . . . . . . . Ms Olga Senior . . . . . . . . . . . . . . . . . . . . . . . . . . . . . Tel: (020) 7210 5164

    Customer Service Centre . . . . . . . . . . . . . . . . . . . . . . Ms Linda Percival . . . . . . . . . . . . . . . . . . . . . . . . . . . Tel: (020) 7210 5975

    Equality Strategy . . . . . . . . . . . . . . . . . . . . . . . . . . . . Ms Elizabeth Al-Khalifa . . . . . . . . . . . . . . . . . . . . . . Tel: (020) 7972 4488

    Information Management . . . . . . . . . . . . . . . . . . . . . . Ms Linda Wishart . . . . . . . . . . . . . . . . . . . . . . . . . . . Tel: (020) 7972 5925

    Information Services . . . . . . . . . . . . . . . . . . . . . . . . . Dr Andrew Holt . . . . . . . . . . . . . . . . . . . . . . . . . . . . Tel: (020) 7972 6557

    International and Constitutional . . . . . . . . . . . . . . . . . Mr Nick Boyd . . . . . . . . . . . . . . . . . . . . . . . . . . . . . . Tel: (020) 7210 4851

    Medicines, Pharmacy and Industry . . . . . . . . . . . . . . Dr Felicity Harvey . . . . . . . . . . . . . . . . . . . . . . . . . . Tel: (020) 7210 5522

    Policy and Planning . . . . . . . . . . . . . . . . . . . . . . . . . . Mr Iain Ellul . . . . . . . . . . . . . . . . . . . . . . . . . . . . . . . Tel: (0113) 254 5574

**Critical Care** . . . . . . . . . . . . . . . . . . . . . . . . . . . . . . . . . . . Dr Valerie Day . . . . . . . . . . . . . . . . . . . . . . . . . . . . . Tel: (020) 7972 2957

**Dentistry**

    Chief Dental Officer . . . . . . . . . . . . . . . . . . . . . . . . . Professor Raman Bedi . . . . . . . . . . . . . . . . . . . . . . . Tel: (020) 7972 3997

    Senior Dental Officer . . . . . . . . . . . . . . . . . . . . . . . . Dr Chris Audrey . . . . . . . . . . . . . . . . . . . . . . . . . . . . Tel: (020) 7972 3994

    Services . . . . . . . . . . . . . . . . . . . . . . . . . . . . . . . . . . Miss Almas Mithani . . . . . . . . . . . . . . . . . . . . . . . . . Tel: (020) 7972 3978

**Diabetes National Service Framework** . . . . . . . . . . . . . Dr Gillian Chapman . . . . . . . . . . . . . . . . . . . . . . . . . Tel: (020) 7972 4543

**Diagnostic Services** . . . . . . . . . . . . . . . . . . . . . . . . . . . . Mr Keith Smith . . . . . . . . . . . . . . . . . . . . . . . . . . . . Tel: (0113) 254 6508

**Disability, Physical**

    Medical . . . . . . . . . . . . . . . . . . . . . . . . . . . . . . . . . . Dr Jeffrey Graham . . . . . . . . . . . . . . . . . . . . . . . . . . Tel: (020) 7972 4710

    Policy . . . . . . . . . . . . . . . . . . . . . . . . . . . . . . . . . . . Mr Ian Berry . . . . . . . . . . . . . . . . . . . . . . . . . . . . . . Tel: (020) 7972 4249

                                            Ms Sue White . . . . . . . . . . . . . . . . . . . . . . . . . . . . . Tel: (0113) 254 6246

**Distinction Awards** . . . . . . . . . . . . . . . . . . . . . . . . . . . . Ms Janet Walden . . . . . . . . . . . . . . . . . . . . . . . . . . . Tel: (020) 7972 5003

**Doctors' Pay** . . . . . . . . . . . . . . . . . . . . . . . . . . . . . . . . . Mr Andy Sutherland . . . . . . . . . . . . . . . . . . . . . . . . . Tel: (0113) 254 5877

**Domestic Violence** . . . . . . . . . . . . . . . . . . . . . . . . . . . . . Ms Janet Grauberg . . . . . . . . . . . . . . . . . . . . . . . . . . Tel: (020) 7972 4355

# DEPARTMENT OF HEALTH

**Drugs, Misuse**
Nursing Officer . . . . . . . . . . . . . . . . . . . . . . . . . . . . . . . . . Ms Nola Ishmael . . . . . . . . . . . . . . . . . . . . . . . . . . Tel: (020) 7972 3742
Policy . . . . . . . . . . . . . . . . . . . . . . . . . . . . . . . . . . . . . . . Ms Cathy Hamlyn . . . . . . . . . . . . . . . . . . . . . . . . . Tel: (020) 7972 5355

**Economics**
Chief Economic Adviser . . . . . . . . . . . . . . . . . . . . . . . Professor Barry McCormick . . . . . . . . . . . . . . . . . . Tel: (020) 7972 5220
Economics . . . . . . . . . . . . . . . . . . . . . . . . . . . . . . . . . . Mr Richard Murray . . . . . . . . . . . . . . . . . . . . . . . . Tel: (020) 7972 5213
Mr Nick York . . . . . . . . . . . . . . . . . . . . . . . . . . . . Tel: (0113) 254 5577
Operational . . . . . . . . . . . . . . . . . . . . . . . . . . . . . . . . . Mr Andre Hare . . . . . . . . . . . . . . . . . . . . . . . . . . . Tel: (020) 7972 5201
Operational Research . . . . . . . . . . . . . . . . . . . . . . . . . Dr Geoff Royston . . . . . . . . . . . . . . . . . . . . . . . . . . Tel: (0113) 254 5576

**Education (Medical)** . . . . . . . . . . . . . . . . . . . . . . . . . Ms Helen Fields . . . . . . . . . . . . . . . . . . . . . . . . . . . Tel: (0113) 254 5687

**Elderly**
Community Care . . . . . . . . . . . . . . . . . . . . . . . . . . . . . . Mr Richard Campbell . . . . . . . . . . . . . . . . . . . . . . . Tel: (020) 7972 4027
Health and Social Care . . . . . . . . . . . . . . . . . . . . . . . . Ms Anne McDonald . . . . . . . . . . . . . . . . . . . . . . . . Tel: (020) 7972 4098
Medical Care . . . . . . . . . . . . . . . . . . . . . . . . . . . . . . . . Miss Helen Robinson . . . . . . . . . . . . . . . . . . . . . . . Tel: (020) 7972 4020
Older People's Task Force . . . . . . . . . . . . . . . . . . . . . . Mr Craig Muir . . . . . . . . . . . . . . . . . . . . . . . . . . . . Tel: (020) 7972 4089

**Elective Care Policy** . . . . . . . . . . . . . . . . . . . . . . . . . Ms Liz Fleck . . . . . . . . . . . . . . . . . . . . . . . . . . . . . . Tel: (0113) 254 5199

**Embryology and Assisted Conception** . . . . . . . . . . . . Ms Liz Woodeson . . . . . . . . . . . . . . . . . . . . . . . . . . Tel: (020) 7972 5361

**Emergency Care Strategy** . . . . . . . . . . . . . . . . . . . . . Mr Mark Davies . . . . . . . . . . . . . . . . . . . . . . . . . . . Tel: (020) 7210 5930

**End of Life Decisions** . . . . . . . . . . . . . . . . . . . . . . . . Mr Nick Dean . . . . . . . . . . . . . . . . . . . . . . . . . . . . Tel: (020) 7972 5061

**Enquiries (General)** . . . . . . . . . . . . . . . . . . . . . . . . . *enquiries* . . . . . . . . . . . . . . . . . . . . . . . . . . . . . . . . Tel: (020) 7210 4850

**Environment and Health** . . . . . . . . . . . . . . . . . . . . . . Dr David Harper CBE . . . . . . . . . . . . . . . . . . . . . . . Tel: (020) 7972 5353

**Environmental Microbiology** . . . . . . . . . . . . . . . . . . . Dr Meredith Bradbury . . . . . . . . . . . . . . . . . . . . . . Tel: (020) 7972 5347

**Environmental Pollution** . . . . . . . . . . . . . . . . . . . . . . Dr Robert Maynard . . . . . . . . . . . . . . . . . . . . . . . . Tel: (020) 7972 5118

**Equal Opportunities**
Head, Equality Strategy . . . . . . . . . . . . . . . . . . . . . . . Ms Elizabeth Al-Khalifa . . . . . . . . . . . . . . . . . . . . . Tel: (020) 7972 4488
Equality Issues . . . . . . . . . . . . . . . . . . . . . . . . . . . . . . Mr Barry Mussenden . . . . . . . . . . . . . . . . . . . . . . . Tel: (020) 7972 4692
Ms Lydia Yee . . . . . . . . . . . . . . . . . . . . . . . . . . . . . Tel: (020) 7972 4813

**Estates, Departmental** . . . . . . . . . . . . . . . . . . . . . . . Mr Mike Rainsford . . . . . . . . . . . . . . . . . . . . . . . . . Tel: (020) 7972 5719

**European Union Relations** . . . . . . . . . . . . . . . . . . . . Mr Nick Boyd . . . . . . . . . . . . . . . . . . . . . . . . . . . . . Tel: (020) 7210 4851

**Evidence** . . . . . . . . . . . . . . . . . . . . . . . . . . . . . . . . . . Dr Jennie Carpenter . . . . . . . . . . . . . . . . . . . . . . . . Tel: (0113) 254 5934

**Executive Agencies: Sponsorship** . . . . . . . . . . . . . . . Mr Peter Lemmey . . . . . . . . . . . . . . . . . . . . . . . . . . Tel: (020) 7972 3776

**Family Planning** . . . . . . . . . . . . . . . . . . . . . . . . . . . . Ms Cathy Hamlyn . . . . . . . . . . . . . . . . . . . . . . . . . Tel: (020) 7972 5355

**Finance and Investment Directorate**
Director of Finance . . . . . . . . . . . . . . . . . . . . . . . . . . Mr Richard Douglas . . . . . . . . . . . . . . . . . . . . . . . . Tel: (020) 7210 5429
Accounting . . . . . . . . . . . . . . . . . . . . . . . . . . . . . . . . . Mr Jeff Tomlinson . . . . . . . . . . . . . . . . . . . . . . . . . Tel: (0113) 254 5421
Audit, Internal . . . . . . . . . . . . . . . . . . . . . . . . . . . . . . Mr Bill Burleigh . . . . . . . . . . . . . . . . . . . . . . . . . . . Tel: (020) 7972 2732
Cash, Administration and Financial Effectiveness . . . . . Mr Peter Kendall . . . . . . . . . . . . . . . . . . . . . . . . . . Tel: (020) 7972 2763
Corporate and Financial Services . . . . . . . . . . . . . . . . Mr Jeff Tomlinson . . . . . . . . . . . . . . . . . . . . . . . . . Tel: (0113) 254 5421
Financial Management . . . . . . . . . . . . . . . . . . . . . . . . Mr Alastair MacLellan . . . . . . . . . . . . . . . . . . . . . . Tel: (0113) 254 5424
Physical Capacity . . . . . . . . . . . . . . . . . . . . . . . . . . . . Mr Peter Coates . . . . . . . . . . . . . . . . . . . . . . . . . . . Tel: (020) 7972 1141
Private Finance and Investment . . . . . . . . . . . . . . . . . Mr John Holden . . . . . . . . . . . . . . . . . . . . . . . . . . . Tel: (0113) 254 5970
Resource Allocation . . . . . . . . . . . . . . . . . . . . . . . . . . Mr Carl Vincent . . . . . . . . . . . . . . . . . . . . . . . . . . . Tel: (0113) 254 5508
Resource Planning and Acquisition . . . . . . . . . . . . . . . Mr Martin Campbell . . . . . . . . . . . . . . . . . . . . . . . . Tel: (0113) 254 5174

# DEPARTMENT OF HEALTH

**Foetal Tissue (Use of)** .......................... Mr Nick Dean .......................... Tel: (020) 7972 5061

**Folic Acid - Food Nutrition** ..................... Ms Imogen Sharp ...................... Tel: (020) 7972 4494

**Fostering**. ...................................... Mr David Holmes...................... Tel: (020) 7972 4629

**Foundation Trusts, NHS**
   Head, NHS Foundation Trusts.................... Ms Claire Moriarty ................. Tel: (020) 7210 5870
   Policy........................................... Ms Julia Hickling.................. Tel: (0113) 254 5276

**Fraud** *(see below under Other Relevant Contacts – Fraud)*

**Genetics and Genetic Testing**
   Head, Genetics, Embryology and Assisted Conception . . . Ms Liz Woodeson.......................... Tel: (020) 7972 5361

**GPs**
   Policy........................................... Mrs Debbie Mellor OBE ..................... Tel: (0113) 254 6126
   Workforce....................................... Mr Andy Sutherland...................... Tel: (0113) 254 5877

**Health Action Zones**. ............................. Ms Donna Sidonio ..................... Tel: (0113) 254 5246

**Health and Social Care:**
   Head, Health and Social Care Delivery Division ....... Ms Julie Taylor ..................... Tel: (020) 7292 5846
   Head, Health and Social Care Standards
      and Quality Division ......................... Mr Alan Doran....................... Tel: (020) 7210 5302

**Health Authorities**
   Accounts........................................ Mr Jeff Tomlinson ..................... Tel: (0113) 254 5421
   Appointments ................................... Mr Peter Lemmy ...................... Tel: (020) 7972 3776
   Efficiency Monitoring .......................... Mr Alastair MacLellan ................. Tel: (0113) 254 5424
   Funding ........................................ Mr Carl Vincent....................... Tel: (0113) 254 5508

**Health Inequalities Unit** ........................ Dr Deidre Cunningham ................. Tel: (020) 7972 3754

**Health Records: Access** .......................... Mr Malcolm Pearce ..................... Tel: (0113) 254 6004

**Health Service Commissioner (Liaison with)** ........ Mr Malcolm Baguley ..................... Tel: (0113) 254 6108

**Health Visitors** ................................. Mrs Flora Goldhill ..................... Tel: (020) 7210 5749

**Heart Disease**. ................................... Ms Imogen Sharp ...................... Tel: (020) 7972 4494

**Home Helps** ...................................... Mr Richard Campbell. .................. Tel: (020) 7972 4027

**Hospital Acquired Infections** .................... Dr Jane Leese ........................ Tel: (020) 7972 1526

**Imaging**. ......................................... Mr Stephen Trilvas.................... Tel: (020) 7972 8178

**Infertility** ..................................... Ms Liz Woodeson....................... Tel: (020) 7972 5361

**Information** *(see also below under Press and Communications)*
   Director, Communications ....................... Ms Sian Jarvis ....................... Tel: (020) 7210 5440
   Enquiries (General Public) ..................... *enquiries* ........................ Tel: (020) 7210 4850

**Information Policy Unit** *(see below under IT, NHS)*

**Intensive Care, Adult** ........................... Mr Keith Young....................... Tel: (020) 7210 5927

**International Relations** .......................... Mr Nick Boyd ........................ Tel: (020) 7210 4851

**Investment** *(see above under Finance and Investment Directorate)*

# DEPARTMENT OF HEALTH

**IT, Departmental**

| | | |
|---|---|---|
| Head, Information Services Division | Dr Andrew Holt | Tel: (020) 7972 6557 |
| CSC IT Services | Mrs Sue Lake | Tel: (020) 7972 5280 |
| Financial Management | Mrs Judith Dainty | Tel: (020) 7972 5737 |
| Services | Mr Chris Horsey | Tel: (020) 7972 6063 |

**IT, NHS**

| | | |
|---|---|---|
| Director-General, NHS Information Management and Technology | Mr Richard Granger | Tel: (020) 7210 5588 |
| Head, Information Policy Unit | Dr Peter Drury | Tel: (0113) 254 6256 |
| Information Governance | Mr Phil Walker | Tel: (0113) 254 6090 |
| Information Policy | Dr Pam Westley | Tel: (0113) 254 6005 |
| Programme Management | Mr Mike Walker | Tel: (0113) 254 6252 |
| Service Development | Ms Lesley Hannam | Tel: (0113) 254 6264 |
| Social Care | Mr Roger Staton | Tel: (020) 7972 4469 |
| Strategic Planning | Mr Mike Walker | Tel: (0113) 254 6252 |

**Laboratories: Monitoring and Good Practice** ... Dr Roger Alexander ... Tel: (020) 7273 0580

**Leadership**

| | | |
|---|---|---|
| Director, NHS Leadership Centre | Ms Penny Humphris | Tel: (020) 7592 1053 |

**Legal Services**
*48 Carey Street, London, WC2A 2LS*

| | | |
|---|---|---|
| Solicitor | Ms Marilyn Morgan CB | Tel: (020) 7412 1404 |

**Legislation** ... Mr Richard Carter ... Tel: (020) 7210 5845

**Lifestyles, Policy Dissemination** ... Miss Patsy Bailey ... Tel: (020) 7972 5795

**Maternity Care** ... Mr Jonathan Stopes-Roe ... Tel: (020) 7972 4336

**Meals on Wheels** ... Mr Crispin Acton ... Tel: (020) 7972 4036

**Medical Education** ... Ms Helen Fields ... Tel: (0113) 254 5687

**Medical Officer, Chief** *(see above under Chief Medical Officer)*

**Medical Regulation** ... Mr Lee McGill ... Tel: (020) 7210 5150

**Mental Health**

| | | |
|---|---|---|
| Legislation | Mr Andrew Sieff | Tel: (020) 7210 4573 |
| Medical Care | Mr Anthony Sheehan | Tel: (0113) 254 3825 |
| Policy and Performance, Social Care | Ms Anne Richardson | Tel: (020) 7972 4431 |

**Midwifery** ... Professor Anna Maslin ... Tel: (020) 7210 4856

**Modernisation Agency**

| | | |
|---|---|---|
| Director, Modernisation Agency | Mr David Fillingham | Tel: (020) 7210 5711 |
| Corporate Development | Ms Caroline Corrigan | Tel: (020) 7061 6840 |
| New Ways of Working | Ms Judy Hargadon | Tel: (020) 7210 5732 |
| Service Improvement | Mr Michael Scott | Tel: (020) 7210 5986 |

**NHS Direct National Programme** ... Mr Paul Jenkins ... Tel: (0113) 254 5021

**NHS Plus** ... Dr Kit Harling ... Tel: (020) 7972 3831

**Nursing**

| | | |
|---|---|---|
| Chief Nursing Officer/Director of Nursing | Mrs Sarah Mullally | Tel: (020) 7210 5598 |
| Assistant Chief Nursing Officers | Mrs Kate Billingham | Tel: (020) 7210 4946 |
| | Mr David Moore | Tel: (0113) 254 5206 |
| Corporate Development | Mr Peter Allanson | Tel: (020) 7210 5356 |
| Education, Training and Pay | Ms Anna Robinson | Tel: (0113) 254 5783 |

# DEPARTMENT OF HEALTH

**Nutrition** . . . . . . . . . . . . . . . . . . . . . . . . . . . . . . . . Dr Sheela Reddy . . . . . . . . . . . . . . . . . . . . . . . . . Tel: (020) 7972 1365

**Older People** *(see above under Elderly)*

**Open Government** . . . . . . . . . . . . . . . . . . . . . . . . . . Miss Jill Moorcroft . . . . . . . . . . . . . . . . . . . . . . . Tel: (020) 7972 5872

**Ophthalmic Services** . . . . . . . . . . . . . . . . . . . . . . . . Miss Almas Mithani . . . . . . . . . . . . . . . . . . . . . . Tel: (020) 7972 3978

**Organ Donors** . . . . . . . . . . . . . . . . . . . . . . . . . . . . . *enquiries* . . . . . . . . . . . . . . . . . . . . . . . . . . . . . . Tel: (0845) 606 0400

**Osteopaths** . . . . . . . . . . . . . . . . . . . . . . . . . . . . . . . Ms Kay East . . . . . . . . . . . . . . . . . . . . . . . . . . . . Tel: (020) 7972 4497

**Palliative Care Policy** . . . . . . . . . . . . . . . . . . . . . . Mr Stephen Waring . . . . . . . . . . . . . . . . . . . . . . Tel: (020) 7972 4819

**Parliamentary Clerk** . . . . . . . . . . . . . . . . . . . . . . . Mr Neil Townley . . . . . . . . . . . . . . . . . . . . . . . . Tel: (020) 7210 5808

**Pathogens** . . . . . . . . . . . . . . . . . . . . . . . . . . . . . . . . Dr Meredith Bradbury . . . . . . . . . . . . . . . . . . . . Tel: (020) 7972 5347

**Pathology** . . . . . . . . . . . . . . . . . . . . . . . . . . . . . . . . Ms Ann Stephenson . . . . . . . . . . . . . . . . . . . . . . Tel: (020) 7972 4173

**Patient Empowerment / Involvement** . . . . . . . . . . . . Mr David Mowat . . . . . . . . . . . . . . . . . . . . . . . . . Tel: (020) 7210 5995

**Patient's Charter** . . . . . . . . . . . . . . . . . . . . . . . . . . Ms Lesley Hilton . . . . . . . . . . . . . . . . . . . . . . . . Tel: (0113) 254 6134

**Pay (NHS)** . . . . . . . . . . . . . . . . . . . . . . . . . . . . . . . Mr Ben Dyson . . . . . . . . . . . . . . . . . . . . . . . . . . Tel: (0113) 254 5771

**Personnel: NHS Human Resources**
    Director, Human Resources . . . . . . . . . . . . . . . . . . Mr Andrew Foster . . . . . . . . . . . . . . . . . . . . . . . Tel: (020) 7210 5907
    Deputy Director, Development . . . . . . . . . . . . . . . . Mr Martin Staniforth . . . . . . . . . . . . . . . . . . . . . Tel: (0113) 254 6365
    Deputy Director, Learning and
        Personal Development . . . . . . . . . . . . . . . . . . . Professor Maggie Pearson . . . . . . . . . . . . . . . . . Tel: (0113) 254 6722
    Deputy Director, Research . . . . . . . . . . . . . . . . . . . Mr David Amos . . . . . . . . . . . . . . . . . . . . . . . . . Tel: (0113) 254 6169
    Corporate Affairs and Partnership . . . . . . . . . . . . . Mr John Ennis . . . . . . . . . . . . . . . . . . . . . . . . . . Tel: (0113) 254 6633
    Corporate Development (Human Resources) . . . . . . Mr Richard Mundon . . . . . . . . . . . . . . . . . . . . . . Tel: (0113) 254 5730
    Education / Quality Assurance . . . . . . . . . . . . . . . . Ms Sarah Goulding . . . . . . . . . . . . . . . . . . . . . . . Tel: (0113) 254 5835
    Employment Policy . . . . . . . . . . . . . . . . . . . . . . . . Ms Debbie Mellor OBE . . . . . . . . . . . . . . . . . . . . Tel: (0113) 254 6126
    GPs . . . . . . . . . . . . . . . . . . . . . . . . . . . . . . . . . . . . Mr Ian Dodge . . . . . . . . . . . . . . . . . . . . . . . . . . . Tel: (0113) 254 6893
    Health Workplace Team (NHS Plus) . . . . . . . . . . . . Dr Kit Harling . . . . . . . . . . . . . . . . . . . . . . . . . . Tel: (020) 7972 3831
    Initial Qualifications . . . . . . . . . . . . . . . . . . . . . . . Ms Helen Fields . . . . . . . . . . . . . . . . . . . . . . . . . Tel: (0113) 254 5687
    New Ways of Working, NHS Modernisation Agency . . . . . Ms Judy Hargadon . . . . . . . . . . . . . . . . . . . . . . . Tel: (020) 7210 5732
    Pay (NHS) . . . . . . . . . . . . . . . . . . . . . . . . . . . . . . . Mr Ben Dyson . . . . . . . . . . . . . . . . . . . . . . . . . . Tel: (0113) 254 5771
    Post-Qualifications and Professional Development . . . . . Mr Paul Loveland . . . . . . . . . . . . . . . . . . . . . . . . Tel: (0113) 254 5856
    Strategic Medical Workforce . . . . . . . . . . . . . . . . . Dr Julia Moore . . . . . . . . . . . . . . . . . . . . . . . . . . Tel: (020) 7210 5056
    Student Support (NHS) . . . . . . . . . . . . . . . . . . . . . Ms Helen Fields . . . . . . . . . . . . . . . . . . . . . . . . . Tel: (0113) 254 5687
    Workforce Development . . . . . . . . . . . . . . . . . . . . . Mr Tim Sands . . . . . . . . . . . . . . . . . . . . . . . . . . Tel: (0113) 254 5829

**Pharmaceuticals**
    Head, Medicines, Pharmacy and Industry Group . . . . . . Dr Felicity Harvey . . . . . . . . . . . . . . . . . . . . . . . Tel: (020) 7210 5522
    Chief Pharmaceutical Officer . . . . . . . . . . . . . . . . . Dr Jim Smith . . . . . . . . . . . . . . . . . . . . . . . . . . . Tel: (020) 7210 5761
    Deputy Chief Pharmaceutical Officer . . . . . . . . . . . Ms Jeanette Howe . . . . . . . . . . . . . . . . . . . . . . . . Tel: (020) 7210 5048
    Charges . . . . . . . . . . . . . . . . . . . . . . . . . . . . . . . . . Mr Mike Brownlee . . . . . . . . . . . . . . . . . . . . . . . Tel: (020) 7210 5400
    Industry . . . . . . . . . . . . . . . . . . . . . . . . . . . . . . . . Mr Shaun Gallagher . . . . . . . . . . . . . . . . . . . . . . Tel: (020) 7210 5659
    NHS Exports . . . . . . . . . . . . . . . . . . . . . . . . . . . . . Mr Shaun Gallagher . . . . . . . . . . . . . . . . . . . . . . Tel: (020) 7210 5659
    Prescribing . . . . . . . . . . . . . . . . . . . . . . . . . . . . . . Mr Kevin Guinness . . . . . . . . . . . . . . . . . . . . . . Tel: (020) 7210 4944
    Price Regulation Scheme . . . . . . . . . . . . . . . . . . . . Mr Mike Brownlee . . . . . . . . . . . . . . . . . . . . . . . Tel: (020) 7210 5400
    Testing . . . . . . . . . . . . . . . . . . . . . . . . . . . . . . . . . Dr Roger Alexander . . . . . . . . . . . . . . . . . . . . . . Tel: (020) 7273 0580
                   Dr Gerard Lee . . . . . . . . . . . . . . . . . . . . . . . . . . Tel: (020) 7273 0568

**Physiotherapists** . . . . . . . . . . . . . . . . . . . . . . . . . . . Ms Kay East . . . . . . . . . . . . . . . . . . . . . . . . . . . . Tel: (020) 7972 4497

**Poisons: National Information Service** . . . . . . . . . . . Mr Gareth Jones . . . . . . . . . . . . . . . . . . . . . . . . . Tel: (020) 7972 5015

**Port Health** . . . . . . . . . . . . . . . . . . . . . . . . . . . . . . Dr Graham Bickler . . . . . . . . . . . . . . . . . . . . . . . Tel: (020) 7972 5116

# DEPARTMENT OF HEALTH

Prescribing: Primary Care .......................... Dr Felicity Harvey .......................... Tel: (020) 7210 5522

Prescription Charges .......................... Mr Mike Brownlee .......................... Tel: (020) 7210 5400

Press *(see below under Publicity and Communications)*

## Primary Care
| | | |
|---|---|---|
| Chief Dental Officer | Professor Raman Bedi | Tel: (020) 7972 3995 |
| Chief Pharmaceutical Officer | Dr Jim Smith | Tel: (020) 7210 5761 |
| Access to Primary Care | Mr Rob Webster | Tel: (0113) 254 5288 |
| GPs | Mr Rob Webster | Tel: (0113) 254 5288 |
| National Primary Care Development Team | Dr John Oldham | Tel: (0161) 237 2084 |
| National Primary and Care Trust Development Programme | Ms Barbara Hakin | Tel: (01274) 321802 |
| Performance Development Unit | Mr Giles Wilmore | Tel: (0113) 254 6389 |
| Prescribing | Mr Kevin Guinness | Tel: (020) 7210 4944 |
| Systems and Partnerships | Mr Chris Dowse | Tel: (0113) 254 6572 |

## Prison Health
| | | |
|---|---|---|
| Prison Clinical Services | Dr Savas Hadjipavlou | Tel: (020) 7972 4580 |
| Prison Health (General) | Mr John Boynington | Tel: (020) 7972 3925 |
| Prison Mental Health Services | Mr Simon Reeve | Tel: (020) 7972 5604 |
| Prison Nursing Health Strategy | Mr Richard Bradshaw | Tel: (020) 7972 4767 |
| Prison Public Health Services | Dr Mary Piper | Tel: (020) 7972 4952 |

## Public Health and Clinical Quality Directorate
*Skipton House, 80 London Road, London, SE1 6LH*
*Wellington House, 133-35 Waterloo Road, London, SE1 8UG*
| | | |
|---|---|---|
| Chief Medical Officer and Group Director, Standards and Quality | Professor Sir Liam Donaldson | Tel: (020) 7210 5150 |
| Division Head | Professor Don Nutbeam | Tel: (020) 7972 3750 |

## Publicity and Communications
| | | |
|---|---|---|
| Director, Communications | Ms Sian Jarvis | Tel: (020) 7210 5440 |
| Deputy Director, Marketing Communications | Mr Wyn Roberts | Tel: (020) 7210 5635 |
| Deputy Director, Media | Mr Jon Hibbs | Tel: (020) 7210 5478 |
| Deputy Director, Strategic Communications | Mr John Worne | Tel: (020) 7210 5893 |
| Corporate Development, Communications | Mrs Susan Miller | Tel: (020) 7972 5251 |

## Purchasing Policy, (Departmental)
| | | |
|---|---|---|
| General | Mr Gareth Jones | Tel: (020) 7972 6065 |
| IT | Mr Ian Gordon | Tel: (020) 7972 6139 |

Quality Issues (NHS) .......................... Mrs Patience Wilson .......................... Tel: (020) 7972 5176

Radiation (Environmental) .......................... Dr Hilary Walker .......................... Tel: (020) 7972 5122

Regulatory Bodies .......................... Mr Martin Sturges .......................... Tel: (0113) 254 5673

Renal Service Framework .......................... Dr Gillian Chapman .......................... Tel: (020) 7972 4543

## Research and Development
| | | |
|---|---|---|
| Director-General, NHS Information Management and Technology | Mr Richard Granger | Tel: (020) 7210 5588 |
| Director, Research and Development | Professor Sir John Pattison | Tel: (020) 7210 5556 |
| Assistant Director, Research and Development | Dr Peter Greenaway | Tel: (020) 7972 5644 |
| Corporate Affairs | Ms Anne Kauder | Tel: (020) 7210 5828 |
| Policy | Professor Gillian Parker | Tel: (020) 7972 5624 |
| | Mr Marc Taylor | Tel: (0113) 254 6159 |

Science .......................... Dr Peter Greenway .......................... Tel: (020) 7972 5644

Scientists. Health Care .......................... Ms Sue Hill .......................... Tel: (020) 7972 4822

# DEPARTMENT OF HEALTH

**Secure Accommodation** . . . . . . . . . . . . . . . . . . . . . . . . . . . . Mr Martin Harrison . . . . . . . . . . . . . . . . . . . . . . . . . Tel: (020) 7972 4051

**Sexual Health**
    Nursing Officer . . . . . . . . . . . . . . . . . . . . . . . . . . . . . . . Ms Nola Ishmael . . . . . . . . . . . . . . . . . . . . . . . . . . . Tel: (020) 7972 3742
    Policy . . . . . . . . . . . . . . . . . . . . . . . . . . . . . . . . . . . . . . Ms Cathy Hamlyn . . . . . . . . . . . . . . . . . . . . . . . . . Tel: (020) 7972 5355

**Sexually Transmitted Diseases** . . . . . . . . . . . . . . . . . . . Ms Nola Ishmael . . . . . . . . . . . . . . . . . . . . . . . . . . . Tel: (020) 7972 3742

**Skin Cancer Prevention** . . . . . . . . . . . . . . . . . . . . . . . . . Ms Imogen Sharp . . . . . . . . . . . . . . . . . . . . . . . . . . Tel: (020) 7972 4494

**Smoking** . . . . . . . . . . . . . . . . . . . . . . . . . . . . . . . . . . . . . Ms Imogen Sharp . . . . . . . . . . . . . . . . . . . . . . . . . . Tel: (020) 7972 4494

**Social Care**
*Wellington House, 133-155 Waterloo Road, London, SE1 8UG*
    Children's National Service Framework . . . . . . . . . . . . . Ms Claire Phillips . . . . . . . . . . . . . . . . . . . . . . . . . . Tel: (020) 7972 4908
    Corporate Development (Social Care) . . . . . . . . . . . . . . . Mrs Anthea Smith . . . . . . . . . . . . . . . . . . . . . . . . . Tel: (020) 7972 4296
    Community Care . . . . . . . . . . . . . . . . . . . . . . . . . . . . . . Mr Richard Campbell . . . . . . . . . . . . . . . . . . . . . . . Tel: (020) 7972 4027
    Disabilities . . . . . . . . . . . . . . . . . . . . . . . . . . . . . . . . . . Mr Ian Berry . . . . . . . . . . . . . . . . . . . . . . . . . . . . . Tel: (020) 7972 4249
                                      Ms Sue White . . . . . . . . . . . . . . . . . . . . . . . . . . . . Tel: (0113) 254 6246
    Mental Health . . . . . . . . . . . . . . . . . . . . . . . . . . . . . . . . Ms Anthony Sheehan . . . . . . . . . . . . . . . . . . . . . . Tel: (0113) 254 3825
    Modernisation of Social Care . . . . . . . . . . . . . . . . . . . . . Mr Jonathan Stopes-Roe . . . . . . . . . . . . . . . . . . . . Tel: (020) 7972 4336
    Older People's Services . . . . . . . . . . . . . . . . . . . . . . . . . Mr Craig Muir . . . . . . . . . . . . . . . . . . . . . . . . . . . . Tel: (020) 7972 4089
    Policy . . . . . . . . . . . . . . . . . . . . . . . . . . . . . . . . . . . . . . Mr Giles Denham . . . . . . . . . . . . . . . . . . . . . . . . . Tel: (020) 7972 4045
    Training . . . . . . . . . . . . . . . . . . . . . . . . . . . . . . . . . . . . Mr Jonathan Stopes-Roe . . . . . . . . . . . . . . . . . . . . Tel: (020) 7972 4336
    Workforce . . . . . . . . . . . . . . . . . . . . . . . . . . . . . . . . . . . Mr Jonathan Stopes-Roe . . . . . . . . . . . . . . . . . . . . Tel: (020) 7972 4336
    *(see also under Health and Social Care above)*

**Solicitor** . . . . . . . . . . . . . . . . . . . . . . . . . . . . . . . . . . . . . Ms Marilyn Morgan CB . . . . . . . . . . . . . . . . . . . . . . Tel: (020) 7412 1404

**Specialist Health Services**
    Deputy Chief Medical Officer, Specialist Health Services . Professor Aidan Halligan . . . . . . . . . . . . . . . . . . . . Tel: (020) 7210 5464
    Head, Specialist Health Services . . . . . . . . . . . . . . . . . . Ms Ann Stephenson . . . . . . . . . . . . . . . . . . . . . . . Tel: (020) 7972 4173

**Speech Therapists** . . . . . . . . . . . . . . . . . . . . . . . . . . . . . Ms Kay East . . . . . . . . . . . . . . . . . . . . . . . . . . . . . Tel: (020) 7972 4497

**Statistics**
*Skipton House, 80 London Road, London, SE1 6LH*
    Director, Statistics . . . . . . . . . . . . . . . . . . . . . . . . . . . . . Dr John Fox . . . . . . . . . . . . . . . . . . . . . . . . . . . . . Tel: (020) 7972 5362
    Acute Services . . . . . . . . . . . . . . . . . . . . . . . . . . . . . . . Mr Richard Willmer . . . . . . . . . . . . . . . . . . . . . . . . Tel: (0113) 254 5521
    Alcohol/Drugs Misuse . . . . . . . . . . . . . . . . . . . . . . . . . . Miss Patsy Bailey . . . . . . . . . . . . . . . . . . . . . . . . . Tel: (020) 7972 5795
    Ambulance Services . . . . . . . . . . . . . . . . . . . . . . . . . . . Mr Lesz Lancucki . . . . . . . . . . . . . . . . . . . . . . . . . Tel: (020) 7972 5533
    Children . . . . . . . . . . . . . . . . . . . . . . . . . . . . . . . . . . . . Ms Annie Sorbie . . . . . . . . . . . . . . . . . . . . . . . . . . Tel: (020) 7972 5573
    Community Health, Demographic . . . . . . . . . . . . . . . . . Ms Gillian Goddard . . . . . . . . . . . . . . . . . . . . . . . . Tel: (020) 7972 5561
    Dental, Optical . . . . . . . . . . . . . . . . . . . . . . . . . . . . . . . Mr Jim Stokoe . . . . . . . . . . . . . . . . . . . . . . . . . . . Tel: (020) 7972 5377
    Drugs Misuse . . . . . . . . . . . . . . . . . . . . . . . . . . . . . . . . Miss Patsy Bailey . . . . . . . . . . . . . . . . . . . . . . . . . Tel: (020) 7972 5795
    Earnings (NHS) . . . . . . . . . . . . . . . . . . . . . . . . . . . . . . Ms Valerie Gray . . . . . . . . . . . . . . . . . . . . . . . . . . Tel: (0113) 254 5115
    General Medical Practitioners . . . . . . . . . . . . . . . . . . . . Dr Louise Wood . . . . . . . . . . . . . . . . . . . . . . . . . . Tel: (020) 7273 0698
    Hospital Care . . . . . . . . . . . . . . . . . . . . . . . . . . . . . . . . Mr Richard Willmer . . . . . . . . . . . . . . . . . . . . . . . . Tel: (020) 7972 5521
    Medical and Dental Workforce . . . . . . . . . . . . . . . . . . . Mr John Bates . . . . . . . . . . . . . . . . . . . . . . . . . . . Tel: (0113) 254 5878
    Mental Health . . . . . . . . . . . . . . . . . . . . . . . . . . . . . . . . Mr David Daniel . . . . . . . . . . . . . . . . . . . . . . . . . . Tel: (020) 7972 5545
    Nutrition . . . . . . . . . . . . . . . . . . . . . . . . . . . . . . . . . . . . Mr Richard Bond . . . . . . . . . . . . . . . . . . . . . . . . . Tel: (020) 7972 5675
    Ophthalmic Services (General) . . . . . . . . . . . . . . . . . . . Ms Nazeema Momin . . . . . . . . . . . . . . . . . . . . . . . Tel: (020) 7972 5506
    Performance Indicators (NHS) . . . . . . . . . . . . . . . . . . . Mr Simon Peck . . . . . . . . . . . . . . . . . . . . . . . . . . Tel: (0113) 254 5433
    Pharmaceutical Services (Community) . . . . . . . . . . . . . Mr Jim Stokoe . . . . . . . . . . . . . . . . . . . . . . . . . . . Tel: (020) 7972 5377
    Prescription Statistics and Analysis . . . . . . . . . . . . . . . . Mr Jim Stokoe . . . . . . . . . . . . . . . . . . . . . . . . . . . Tel: (020) 7972 5377
    Public Health . . . . . . . . . . . . . . . . . . . . . . . . . . . . . . . . Mr Richard Willmer . . . . . . . . . . . . . . . . . . . . . . . . Tel: (020) 7972 5521
    Smoking . . . . . . . . . . . . . . . . . . . . . . . . . . . . . . . . . . . . Ms Patsy Bailey . . . . . . . . . . . . . . . . . . . . . . . . . . Tel: (020) 7972 5795
    Social Services - Population Groups and Surveys . . . . . . Mrs Ann Custance . . . . . . . . . . . . . . . . . . . . . . . . . Tel: (020) 7972 5571
    Waiting Lists (NHS) . . . . . . . . . . . . . . . . . . . . . . . . . . . Mr Mark Svenson . . . . . . . . . . . . . . . . . . . . . . . . . Tel: (0113) 254 5214
    Waiting Times . . . . . . . . . . . . . . . . . . . . . . . . . . . . . . . . Ms Liz Fleck . . . . . . . . . . . . . . . . . . . . . . . . . . . . . Tel: (0113) 254 5199
    Women's Health . . . . . . . . . . . . . . . . . . . . . . . . . . . . . . Mr Lesz Lancucki . . . . . . . . . . . . . . . . . . . . . . . . . Tel: (020) 7972 5533
    Workforce . . . . . . . . . . . . . . . . . . . . . . . . . . . . . . . . . . . Mr John Bates . . . . . . . . . . . . . . . . . . . . . . . . . . . Tel: (0113) 254 5878

# DEPARTMENT OF HEALTH

**Strategy and Business Development** . . . . . . . . . . . . . . . Mr Peter Allanson . . . . . . . . . . . . . . . . . . . . . . . . . . . Tel: (020) 7210 5356

**Strategy Unit** . . . . . . . . . . . . . . . . . . . . . . . . . . . . . . . . Professor Chris Ham . . . . . . . . . . . . . . . . . . . . . . . . . . Tel: (020) 7210 5305

**Stroke Prevention** . . . . . . . . . . . . . . . . . . . . . . . . . . . . Ms Imogen Sharp . . . . . . . . . . . . . . . . . . . . . . . . . . . . Tel: (020) 7972 4494

**Suicide** . . . . . . . . . . . . . . . . . . . . . . . . . . . . . . . . . . . . . Mr Anthony Sheehan . . . . . . . . . . . . . . . . . . . . . . . . . Tel: (0131) 254 3825

**Surrogacy** . . . . . . . . . . . . . . . . . . . . . . . . . . . . . . . . . . . Ms Liz Woodeson . . . . . . . . . . . . . . . . . . . . . . . . . . . . Tel: (020) 7972 5361

**Teenage Pregnancy** . . . . . . . . . . . . . . . . . . . . . . . . . . . Ms Nola Ishmael . . . . . . . . . . . . . . . . . . . . . . . . . . . . Tel: (020) 7972 3742

**Telemedicine** . . . . . . . . . . . . . . . . . . . . . . . . . . . . . . . . Mrs Sue Sharples . . . . . . . . . . . . . . . . . . . . . . . . . . . . Tel: (0113) 254 7373

**Tobacco Advertising Ban** . . . . . . . . . . . . . . . . . . . . . . Ms Imogen Sharp . . . . . . . . . . . . . . . . . . . . . . . . . . . . Tel: (020) 7972 4494

**Transfusion Medicine** . . . . . . . . . . . . . . . . . . . . . . . . . Dr Vicki King . . . . . . . . . . . . . . . . . . . . . . . . . . . . . . . Tel: (020) 7972 1531

**Transplants** . . . . . . . . . . . . . . . . . . . . . . . . . . . . . . . . . . Dr Gillian Chapman . . . . . . . . . . . . . . . . . . . . . . . . . . Tel: (020) 7972 4543

**Treatment Abroad** . . . . . . . . . . . . . . . . . . . . . . . . . . . . Mr Bob Ricketts . . . . . . . . . . . . . . . . . . . . . . . . . . . . . Tel: (020) 7210 5455

**Trusts, NHS**
    Accounts and Allocations . . . . . . . . . . . . . . . . . . . . Mr Jeff Tomlinson . . . . . . . . . . . . . . . . . . . . . . . . . . . Tel: (0113) 254 5412
    Financial Management . . . . . . . . . . . . . . . . . . . . . . . Mr Alastair MacLellan . . . . . . . . . . . . . . . . . . . . . . . . Tel: (0113) 254 5424
    Resource Allocation . . . . . . . . . . . . . . . . . . . . . . . . . Mr Carl Vincent . . . . . . . . . . . . . . . . . . . . . . . . . . . . . Tel: (0113) 254 5508

**Vaccination and Immunisation** . . . . . . . . . . . . . . . . . . Dr David Salisbury . . . . . . . . . . . . . . . . . . . . . . . . . . . Tel: (020) 7972 1522

**Voluntary Sector** . . . . . . . . . . . . . . . . . . . . . . . . . . . . . Mr David Mowat . . . . . . . . . . . . . . . . . . . . . . . . . . . . . Tel: (020) 7910 5995

**Waiting Times**
    Policy . . . . . . . . . . . . . . . . . . . . . . . . . . . . . . . . . . . . . Ms Liz Fleck . . . . . . . . . . . . . . . . . . . . . . . . . . . . . . . . Tel: (0113) 254 5199
    Statistics . . . . . . . . . . . . . . . . . . . . . . . . . . . . . . . . . . . Mr Simon Peck . . . . . . . . . . . . . . . . . . . . . . . . . . . . . . Tel: (0113) 254 5433

**Web Information Management** . . . . . . . . . . . . . . . . . . . Mrs Linda Wishart . . . . . . . . . . . . . . . . . . . . . . . . . . . Tel: (020) 7972 5925

**Welfare Food Scheme** . . . . . . . . . . . . . . . . . . . . . . . . . . Ms Imogen Sharp . . . . . . . . . . . . . . . . . . . . . . . . . . . . Tel: (020) 7972 4494

**Women's Health Care Policy** . . . . . . . . . . . . . . . . . . . . Mr Jonathan Stopes-Roe . . . . . . . . . . . . . . . . . . . . . . . Tel: (020) 7972 4336

**Workforce, Medical** *(See above under Personnel: NHS Human Resources)*

**World Health Organisation (WHO)** . . . . . . . . . . . . . . . Mr Nick Boyd . . . . . . . . . . . . . . . . . . . . . . . . . . . . . . . Tel: (020) 7210 4851

**Youth Treatment Centres** . . . . . . . . . . . . . . . . . . . . . . . Miss Janet Grauberg . . . . . . . . . . . . . . . . . . . . . . . . . . Tel: (020) 7972 4355

**Zoonoses** . . . . . . . . . . . . . . . . . . . . . . . . . . . . . . . . . . . . Mrs Maggie Tomlinson . . . . . . . . . . . . . . . . . . . . . . . . Tel: (020) 7972 5136

## OTHER RELEVANT CONTACTS

**AIDS**
**Expert Advisory Group on AIDS** . . . . . . . . . . . . . . . . . Room 631B, Skipton House, 80 London Road, London, SE1 6LH
    Chairman *(Acting)* . . . . . . . . . . . . . . . . . . . . . . . . . . . Professor Donald Jeffries
    Scientific Secretary . . . . . . . . . . . . . . . . . . . . . . . . . . . Dr Linda Lazarus . . . . . . . . . . . . . . . . . . . . . . . . . . . . . Tel: (020) 7972 5751
                                                   Web: http://www.doh.gov.uk/eaga/index.htm

**AIR POLLUTANTS**
**Committee on the Medical Effects of Air Pollutants** . . . Room 652C, Skipton House, 80 London Road, London, SE1 6LH
    Chairman . . . . . . . . . . . . . . . . . . . . . . . . . . . . . . . . . . Professor Jon Ayres
    Medical Secretary . . . . . . . . . . . . . . . . . . . . . . . . . . . . Miss Julia Cumberledge . . . . . . . . . . . . . . . . . . . . . . . . Tel: (020) 7972 5130
                                                   Web: http://www.doh.gov.uk/comeap

# DEPARTMENT OF HEALTH

*Other Relevant Contacts (Continued)*

**ANTIMICROBIOLOGICAL RESISTANCE**
**Specialist Advisory Committee on**
    **Antimicrobial Substances** ..................... Room 630B, Skipton House, 80 London Road, London, SE1 6LH
    Chairman .................................. Professor Richard Wise
    Secretary.................................. Ms Sally Wellsteed ..................... Tel: (020) 7972 5041
**Family Health Service Appeal Authority**............ 30 Victoria Avenue, Harrogate, HG1 5PR
    Chairman .................................. Mr Alan Crute
    Chief Executive............................. Mr Paul Burns ...................... Tel: (01423) 530280
                           E-mail: mail@fhsaa.nhs.uk
                           Web: http://www.fhsaa.nhs.uk

**APPOINTMENTS**
**NHS Appointments Commission**................... Blenheim House, West One, Duncombe Street, Leeds, LS1 4PL
    Chairman .................................. Sir William Wells
    Chief Executive............................. Dr Roger Moore ...................... Tel: (0113) 394 2999
                           Web: http://www.apcomm.nhs.uk

**AUDIT**
**Audit Commission for Local Authorities and the**
    **NHS in England and Wales**.................... 1 Vincent Square, London, SW1P 2PN
    Chairman .................................. Mr James Strachan
    Chief Executive............................. Mr Steve Bundred ...................... Tel: (020) 7828 1212
                           Web: http://www.audit-commission.gov.uk

**BIOLOGICAL STANDARDS**
**National Biological Standards Board** .............. Blanche Lane, South Mimms, Potters Bar, Hertfordshire, EN6 3QG
    Chairman .................................. Professor Gordon Duff
    Chief Executive............................. Dr Stephen Inglis ...................... Tel: (01707) 641000
                           E-mail: enquiries@nibsc.ac.uk
                           Web: http://www.nibsc.ac.uk

**BLOOD**
**National Blood Service**.......................... Oak House, Reeds Crescent, Watford, Hertfordshire, WD24 4QN
    Chairman .................................. Mr Michael Fogden CB
    Chief Executive............................. Mr Martin Gorham ...................... Tel: (01923) 486800
                           Web: http://www.blood.co.uk

**BLOODBORNE VIRUSES**
**UK Advisory Panel for Health Care Workers Infected**
    **with Bloodborne Viruses Unit**................. Health Protection Agency, Communicable Disease Surveillance Centre,
                           61 Colindale, London, NW9 5EQ
    Chairman .................................. Lady [Winifred] Tumim
    Medical Secretary ............................ Dr Fortune Ucebe
    Senior Administrator .......................... Ms Helen Janecek ...................... Tel: (020) 8200 6868

**BORDERLINE PRODUCTS / SUBSTANCES**
**Advisory Committee on Borderline Substances**....... NICE, Mid City Place, 71 High Holborn, London, WC1V 6NA
    Chairman .................................. Dr Ian White
    Secretary.................................. Ms Jo Davis ...................... Tel: (020) 7067 5800
                           Web: http://www.nice.nhs.uk
**Independent Review Panel on the Classification of**
    **Borderline Products** ......................... c/o Medicines Control Agency, Market Towers, 1 Nine Elms Lane,
                           London, SW8 5NQ
    Chairman .................................. Sir Robert Downey
    Secretary.................................. Mr Sean Fletcher ...................... Tel: (020) 7084 2878
                           Web: http://www.mhra.gov.uk

**BREAST CANCER**
**Advisory Committee on Breast Cancer Screening**..... Room 411, Wellington House, 133-155 Waterloo Road, London, SE1 8UG
    Chairman .................................. Professor Valerie Beral
    Secretary.................................. Mr Tim Elliot ...................... Tel: (020) 7972 4194

# DEPARTMENT OF HEALTH

*Other Relevant Contacts (Continued)*

**CARE STANDARDS**
**Care Standards Tribunal** . . . . . . . . . . . . . . . . . . . . . . . 18 Pocock Street, London, SE1 0BW
    President . . . . . . . . . . . . . . . . . . . . . . . . . . . . . . . . . Judge David Pearl
    Secretary . . . . . . . . . . . . . . . . . . . . . . . . . . . . . . . . . Ms Barbara Erne . . . . . . . . . . . . . . . . . . . . . . . . . Tel: (020) 7960 0660
                        Web: http://www.doh.gov.uk/cst

**CLINICAL ASSESSMENT**
**National Clinical Assessment Authority** . . . . . . . . . . . . 7th Floor, Market Towers, 1 Nine Elms Lane, London, SW8 5NQ
    Chairman . . . . . . . . . . . . . . . . . . . . . . . . . . . . . . . . . Mr Bob Nicholls OBE
    Chief Executive . . . . . . . . . . . . . . . . . . . . . . . . . . . . . Dr Alistair Scotland . . . . . . . . . . . . . . . . . . . . . . . Tel: (020) 7273 0850
                        E-mail: ncaa@ncaa.nhs.uk
                        Web: http://www.ncaa.nhs.uk

**CLINICAL EXCELLENCE**
**Advisory Committee on Clinical Excellence Awards** . . . Area 531B, Skipton House, 80 London Road, London, SE1 6LH
    Chairman . . . . . . . . . . . . . . . . . . . . . . . . . . . . . . . . . Lady [Elizabeth] Vallance
    Medical Director . . . . . . . . . . . . . . . . . . . . . . . . . . . . Professor Sir Netar Mallick
    Secretary . . . . . . . . . . . . . . . . . . . . . . . . . . . . . . . . . Ms Mary Holt . . . . . . . . . . . . . . . . . . . . . . . . . . . Tel: (020) 7972 5049
                        Web: http://www.doh.gov.uk/accea

**CLINICAL STANDARDS**
**National Institute for Clinical Excellence** . . . . . . . . . . . Mid City Place, 71 High Holborn, London, WC1V 6NA
    Chairman . . . . . . . . . . . . . . . . . . . . . . . . . . . . . . . . . Professor Sir Michael Rawlins
    Chief Executive . . . . . . . . . . . . . . . . . . . . . . . . . . . . . Mr Andrew Dillon . . . . . . . . . . . . . . . . . . . . . . . . Tel: (020) 7067 5800
                        E-mail: nice@nice.nhs.uk
                        Web: http://www.nice.org.uk

**DENTISTRY**
**Dental Practice Board** . . . . . . . . . . . . . . . . . . . . . . . . . Temple Grove, Compton Place Road, Eastbourne, East Sussex, BN20 8AD
    Chairman . . . . . . . . . . . . . . . . . . . . . . . . . . . . . . . . . Mrs Mary Wylie
    Chief Executive . . . . . . . . . . . . . . . . . . . . . . . . . . . . . Mr John Taylor . . . . . . . . . . . . . . . . . . . . . . . . . . Tel: (01323) 433550
                        E-mail: helpdesk@dpb.nhs.uk
                        Web: http://www.dpb.nhs.uk
**Dental Vocational Training Authority** . . . . . . . . . . . . . . Masters House, Temple Grove, Compton Place Road, Eastbourne,
                        East Sussex, BN20 8AD
    Chairman . . . . . . . . . . . . . . . . . . . . . . . . . . . . . . . . . Mr Ralph Davies
    Secretary . . . . . . . . . . . . . . . . . . . . . . . . . . . . . . . . . Mrs Andrea Goring . . . . . . . . . . . . . . . . . . . . . . . Tel: (01323) 431189
                        Web: http://www.dvta.org.uk
**Dental Vocational Training Authority Appeal Board** . . Room G10, Wellington House, 133-155 Waterloo Road, London, SE1 8UG
    Chairman . . . . . . . . . . . . . . . . . . . . . . . . . . . . . . . . . Mrs Margaret Astbury
    Secretary . . . . . . . . . . . . . . . . . . . . . . . . . . . . . . . . . Mrs Gillian Farnfield . . . . . . . . . . . . . . . . . . . . . . Tel: (020) 7972 4586
                        Web: http://www.doh.gov.uk
**Standing Dental Advisory Committee** . . . . . . . . . . . . . . Room G10, Wellington House, 133-155 Waterloo Road, London, SE1 8UG
    Chairman . . . . . . . . . . . . . . . . . . . . . . . . . . . . . . . . . *Vacant*
    Secretary . . . . . . . . . . . . . . . . . . . . . . . . . . . . . . . . . Mrs Gillian Farnfield . . . . . . . . . . . . . . . . . . . . . . Tel: (020) 7972 4586

**DRUG MISUSE**
**National Treatment Agency for Substance Misuse** . . . . . 5th Floor, Hannibal House, Elephant and Castle, London, SE1 6TE
    Chairman . . . . . . . . . . . . . . . . . . . . . . . . . . . . . . . . . Baroness Massey
    Chief Executive . . . . . . . . . . . . . . . . . . . . . . . . . . . . . Mr Paul Hayes . . . . . . . . . . . . . . . . . . . . . . . . . . Tel: (020) 7972 2214
                        E-mail: nta.enquiries@nta-nhs.org.uk
                        Web: http://www.nta.nhs.uk

**EDUCATION**
**Steering Committee on Pharmacy**
      **Postgraduate Education** . . . . . . . . . . . . . . . . . . . School of Pharmacy and Pharmaceutical Sciences, University of Manchester,
                        Oxford Road, Manchester, M13 9PL
    Secretary . . . . . . . . . . . . . . . . . . . . . . . . . . . . . . . . . Ms Clare Hallam . . . . . . . . . . . . . . . . . . . . . . . . . Tel: (0161) 778 4000
                        E-mail: cppe@man.ac.uk

# DEPARTMENT OF HEALTH

*Other Relevant Contacts (Continued)*

## ESTATES

**NHS Estates** *(Executive Agency)* . . . . . . . . . . . . . . . . . . . . Department of Health, 1 Trevelyan Square, Boar Lane, Leeds, LS1 6AE
   Chief Executive . . . . . . . . . . . . . . . . . . . . . . . . . . . . . . Mr Peter Wearmouth . . . . . . . . . . . . . . . . . . . . . . . Tel: (0113) 254 7000
   E-mail: nhs.estates@doh.gov.uk
   Web: http://www.nhs.estates.gov.uk

## FAMILY HEALTH SERVICES

**Family Health Services Appeal Authority** . . . . . . . . . . . 30 Victoria Avenue, Harrogate, HG1 5PR
   Chairman . . . . . . . . . . . . . . . . . . . . . . . . . . . . . . . . . . Mr Alan Crute
   Chief Executive . . . . . . . . . . . . . . . . . . . . . . . . . . . . . Mr Paul Burns . . . . . . . . . . . . . . . . . . . . . . . . . . . . . Tel: (01423) 530280
   Web: http://www.fhsaa.nhs.uk

## FOOD

**Advisory Committee on the Micro-biological
Safety of Food** . . . . . . . . . . . . . . . . . . . . . . . . . . . . . Food Standards Agency, Room 808C, Aviation House, 125 Kingsway,
   London, WC2B 6NH
   Chairman . . . . . . . . . . . . . . . . . . . . . . . . . . . . . . . . . . *Vacant*
   Secretary . . . . . . . . . . . . . . . . . . . . . . . . . . . . . . . . . . . Dr Lucy Foster . . . . . . . . . . . . . . . . . . . . . . . . . . . . . Tel: (020) 7276 8947
   Web: http://www.food.gov.uk/science/ouradvisors/microbiogsafety
**Advisory Committee on Novel Foods and Processes** . . . Food Standards Agency, Room 515B, Aviation House, 125 Kingsway,
   London, WC2B 6NH
   Chairman . . . . . . . . . . . . . . . . . . . . . . . . . . . . . . . . . . Dr Mike Garson
   Secretary . . . . . . . . . . . . . . . . . . . . . . . . . . . . . . . . . . . Dr Sandy Lawrie . . . . . . . . . . . . . . . . . . . . . . . . . . . Tel: (020) 7276 8595
   Web: http://www.food.gov.uk/science/ouradvisors/novelfoods
**Advisory Committee on Research
(Food Standards Agency)** . . . . . . . . . . . . . . . . . . . . . Food Standards Agency, Room 203C, Aviation House, 125 Kingsway,
   London, WC2B 6NH
   Chairman . . . . . . . . . . . . . . . . . . . . . . . . . . . . . . . . . . Professor Michael Lean
   Secretary . . . . . . . . . . . . . . . . . . . . . . . . . . . . . . . . . . . Dr Richard Burt . . . . . . . . . . . . . . . . . . . . . . . . . . . . Tel: (020) 7276 8785
   Web: http://www.food.gov.uk/science/ouradvisors/acr
**Committee on Carcinogenicity of Chemicals in Food,
Consumer Products and the Environment** . . . . . . . Room 692D, Skipton House, 80 London Road, London, SE1 6LH
   Chairman . . . . . . . . . . . . . . . . . . . . . . . . . . . . . . . . . . Professor Peter Blain
   Secretariat . . . . . . . . . . . . . . . . . . . . . . . . . . . . . . . . . . Mr Khandubhai Mistry . . . . . . . . . . . . . . . . . . . . . . . Tel: (020) 7972 5020
   Web: http://www.doh.gov.uk/coc/index.htm
**Committee on Mutagenicity of Chemicals in Food,
Consumer Products and the Environment** . . . . . . . Room 692D, Skipton House, 80 London Road, London, SE1 6LH
   Chairman . . . . . . . . . . . . . . . . . . . . . . . . . . . . . . . . . . Professor Peter Farmer
   Secretariat . . . . . . . . . . . . . . . . . . . . . . . . . . . . . . . . . . Mr Khandubhai Mistry . . . . . . . . . . . . . . . . . . . . . . . Tel: (020) 7972 5020
   Web: http://www.doh.gov.uk/com/index.htm
**Committee on Toxicology of Chemicals in Food,
Consumer Products and the Environment** . . . . . . . Food Standards Agency, Room 615B, Aviation House, 125 Kingsway,
   London, WC2B 6NH
   Chairman . . . . . . . . . . . . . . . . . . . . . . . . . . . . . . . . . . Professor Ieuan Hughes
   Secretary . . . . . . . . . . . . . . . . . . . . . . . . . . . . . . . . . . . Mr Keith Butler . . . . . . . . . . . . . . . . . . . . . . . . . . . . Tel: (020) 7276 8522
   E-mail: keith.butler@foodstandards.gsi.gov.uk
**Consumer Committee** . . . . . . . . . . . . . . . . . . . . . . . . . . Food Standards Agency, Room 615B, Aviation House, 125 Kingsway,
   London, WC2B 6NH
   Chairman . . . . . . . . . . . . . . . . . . . . . . . . . . . . . . . . . . Mrs Nancy Robson
   Secretary . . . . . . . . . . . . . . . . . . . . . . . . . . . . . . . . . . . Ms Jaswinder Bangar . . . . . . . . . . . . . . . . . . . . . . . . Tel: (020) 7276 8641
   Web: http://www.food.gov.uk
**Expert Group on Vitamins and Minerals** . . . . . . . . . . . Food Standards Agency, Room 511C Aviation House, 125 Kingsway,
   London, WC2B 6NH
   Chairman . . . . . . . . . . . . . . . . . . . . . . . . . . . . . . . . . . Professor Michael Langman
   Secretaries . . . . . . . . . . . . . . . . . . . . . . . . . . . . . . . . . . Ms Jillian Pitt . . . . . . . . . . . . . . . . . . . . . . . . . . . . . . Tel: (020) 7276 8000
   Dr Natalie Thatcher
   Web: http://www.food.gov.uk
**Food Standards Agency** . . . . . . . . . . . . . . . . . . . . . . . . Room 511C, Aviation House, 125 Kingsway, London, WC2B 6NH
   Chairman . . . . . . . . . . . . . . . . . . . . . . . . . . . . . . . . . . Professor Sir John Krebs
   Chief Executive . . . . . . . . . . . . . . . . . . . . . . . . . . . . . Dr John Bell . . . . . . . . . . . . . . . . . . . . . . . . . . . . . . . Tel: (020) 7276 8000
   Web: http://www.foodstandards.gov.uk
**Meat Hygiene Appeals Tribunal for England and Wales** Room 315B, Aviation House, 125 Kingsway, London, WC2B 6NH
   Chairman . . . . . . . . . . . . . . . . . . . . . . . . . . . . . . . . . . Mrs Rosy Amin-Mannion
   Secretary . . . . . . . . . . . . . . . . . . . . . . . . . . . . . . . . . . . Ms Vanessa Charles . . . . . . . . . . . . . . . . . . . . . . . . . Tel: (020) 7276 8386

# DEPARTMENT OF HEALTH

*Other Relevant Contacts: Food (Continued)*

**Meat Hygiene Advisory Committee** . . . . . . . . . . . . . . . . Food Standards Agency, Aviation House, 125 Kingsway, London, WC2B 6NH
    Chairman . . . . . . . . . . . . . . . . . . . . . . . . . . . . . . . . . Mr Iain MacDonald
    Secretary. . . . . . . . . . . . . . . . . . . . . . . . . . . . . . . . . . Ms Rosalind Glover . . . . . . . . . . . . . . . . . . . . . . . . . Tel: (020) 7276 8320
**Scientific Advisory Committee on Nutrition** . . . . . . . . . Room 703, Wellington House, 133-157 Waterloo Road, London, SE1 8UG
    Chairman . . . . . . . . . . . . . . . . . . . . . . . . . . . . . . . . . Professor Alan Jackson
    Secretaries . . . . . . . . . . . . . . . . . . . . . . . . . . . . . . . . Dr Sheela Reddy . . . . . . . . . . . . . . . . . . . . . . . . . . . Tel: (020) 7972 1365
        Dr Alison Tedstone
        Web: http://www.sacn.gov.uk

## FOUNDATION TRUSTS
**Independent Regulator of NHS Foundation Trusts** . . . . Regus House, 12 St James' Square, London, SW1Y 4RB
    Chairman . . . . . . . . . . . . . . . . . . . . . . . . . . . . . . . . . Mr William Moyes . . . . . . . . . . . . . . . . . . . . . . . . . . Tel: (0870) 0991668
        Web: http://www.nhsft-regulator.gov.uk

## FRAUD AND SECURITY
**NHS Counter Fraud and Security Management Service** Weston House, 246 High Holborn, London, WC1V 7EX
    Chairman . . . . . . . . . . . . . . . . . . . . . . . . . . . . . . . . . Mr Bill Darling
    Chief Executive. . . . . . . . . . . . . . . . . . . . . . . . . . . . . Mr Jim Gee . . . . . . . . . . . . . . . . . . . . . . . . . . . . . . . Tel: (020) 7895 4500
        Web: http://www.cfsms.nhs.uk

## GENE THERAPY
**Gene Therapy Advisory Committee** . . . . . . . . . . . . . . . . Area 652C, Skipton House, 80 London Road, London, SE1 6LH
    Chairman . . . . . . . . . . . . . . . . . . . . . . . . . . . . . . . . . Professor Norman Nevin
    Secretary. . . . . . . . . . . . . . . . . . . . . . . . . . . . . . . . . . Ms Monica Preuss . . . . . . . . . . . . . . . . . . . . . . . . . . Tel: (020) 7972 1518
        Web: http://www.doh.gov.uk/genetics/gtac.htm

## GENETICS
**Genetics and Insurance Committee** . . . . . . . . . . . . . . . . Room 652C Skipton House, 80 London Road, London, SE1 6LH
    Chairman . . . . . . . . . . . . . . . . . . . . . . . . . . . . . . . . . Professor David Johns
    Secretary. . . . . . . . . . . . . . . . . . . . . . . . . . . . . . . . . . Mr Daniel Gooch . . . . . . . . . . . . . . . . . . . . . . . . . . . Tel: (020) 7972 1518
        Web: http://www.doh.gov.uk/genetics/gaic/index.htm
**Human Genetics Commission** . . . . . . . . . . . . . . . . . . . . Room 652C, Skipton House, 80 London Road, London, SE1 6LH
    Chairman . . . . . . . . . . . . . . . . . . . . . . . . . . . . . . . . . Baroness Kennedy of the Shaws QC
    Secretary. . . . . . . . . . . . . . . . . . . . . . . . . . . . . . . . . . Dr Mark Bale . . . . . . . . . . . . . . . . . . . . . . . . . . . . . . Tel: (020) 7972 1518
        Web: http://www.hgc.gov.uk

## HEALTH BODIES
    *Details of Health Bodies can be obtained from the Department of Health enquiry line* . . . . . . . . . . . . . . . . . . . . Tel: (020) 7210 4850

## HEALTH PROFESSIONS
**Council for the Regulation of Health Professionals** . . . . 1st Floor, Kierran Cross, 11 The Strand, London, WC2N 5HR
    Chairman . . . . . . . . . . . . . . . . . . . . . . . . . . . . . . . . . Ms Jane Wesson
    Chief Executive. . . . . . . . . . . . . . . . . . . . . . . . . . . . . Mrs Isobel Nisbet. . . . . . . . . . . . . . . . . . . . . . . . . . . Tel: (020) 7389 8030
        Web: http://www.crhp.org.uk
**Health Professions Council**. . . . . . . . . . . . . . . . . . . . . . 184 Kennington Park Road, London, SE11 4BU
    President . . . . . . . . . . . . . . . . . . . . . . . . . . . . . . . . . . Professor Norma Brooks
    Chief Executive. . . . . . . . . . . . . . . . . . . . . . . . . . . . . Mr Marc Seal . . . . . . . . . . . . . . . . . . . . . . . . . . . . . . Tel: (020) 7582 0866
        Web: http://www.hpc-uk.org

## HEALTH PROTECTION
**Health Protection Agency**. . . . . . . . . . . . . . . . . . . . . . . Level 11, The Adelphi, 1-11 John Adam Street, London, WC2N 6HT
    Chairman . . . . . . . . . . . . . . . . . . . . . . . . . . . . . . . . . Sir William Stewart FRS
    Chief Executive. . . . . . . . . . . . . . . . . . . . . . . . . . . . . Professor Dr Pat Troop CBE . . . . . . . . . . . . . . . . . . Tel: (020) 7339 1300
        Web: http://www.hpa.org.uk

## HEALTH SERVICE COMMISSIONER *(see below under Ombudsman)*

# DEPARTMENT OF HEALTH

*Other Relevant Contacts (Continued)*

## HEALTHCARE IMPROVEMENT / INSPECTION
**Healthcare Commission** . . . . . . . . . . . . . . . . . . . . . . . Finsbury Tower, 103-105 Burnhill Row, London, EC1M 8TG
    Chairman . . . . . . . . . . . . . . . . . . . . . . . . . . . . . . Professor Sir Ian Kennedy
    Chief Executive. . . . . . . . . . . . . . . . . . . . . . . . . . Ms Anna Walker . . . . . . . . . . . . . . . . . . . . . . . . . Tel: (020) 7448 9401
        Web: http://www.healthcarecommission.org.uk
**Health Development Agency** . . . . . . . . . . . . . . . . . . Holborn Gate, 330 High Holborn, London, WC1V 7BA
    Director for Health Improvement . . . . . . . . . . . . . . . . Ms Yve Buckland
    Chief Executive. . . . . . . . . . . . . . . . . . . . . . . . . . Professor Richard Parish . . . . . . . . . . . . . . . . . . . Tel: (020) 7430 0850
        Web: http://www.hda-online.org.uk

## HEPATITIS
**Advisory Group on Hepatitis** . . . . . . . . . . . . . . . . . . Room 631B, Skipton House, 80 London Road, London, SE1 6LH
    Chairman . . . . . . . . . . . . . . . . . . . . . . . . . . . . . . Professor Howard Thomas
    Secretary. . . . . . . . . . . . . . . . . . . . . . . . . . . . . . . Dr Hugh Nicholas . . . . . . . . . . . . . . . . . . . . . . . . Tel: (020) 7972 6061
        Web: http://www.doh.gov.uk/agh.agh.htm

## HOMEOPATHIC PRODUCTS
**Advisory Board on the Registration of**
**Homeopathic Products** . . . . . . . . . . . . . . . . . . . . . . c/o Market Towers, 1 Nine Elms Lane, London, SW8 5NQ
    Chairman . . . . . . . . . . . . . . . . . . . . . . . . . . . . . . Dr Timothy Chambers
    Secretary. . . . . . . . . . . . . . . . . . . . . . . . . . . . . . . Mr Leslie Whitbread . . . . . . . . . . . . . . . . . . . . . . Tel: (020) 7273 0451
        E-mail: leslie.whitbread@mhra.gsi.gov.uk

## HUMAN FERTILISATION
**Human Fertilisation and Embryology Authority** . . . . . . Paxton House, 30 Artillery Lane, London, E1 7LS
    Chairman . . . . . . . . . . . . . . . . . . . . . . . . . . . . . . Ms Suzi Leather
    Chief Executive. . . . . . . . . . . . . . . . . . . . . . . . . . Mrs Angela McNab . . . . . . . . . . . . . . . . . . . . . . . Tel: (020) 7377 5077
        E-mail: admin@hfea.gtov.uk
        Web: http://www.hfea.gov.uk

## INFORMATION
**NHS Information Authority** . . . . . . . . . . . . . . . . . . . Aston Cross, Rocky Lane, Birmingham, B6 5RQ
    Chairman . . . . . . . . . . . . . . . . . . . . . . . . . . . . . . Professor Alastair Bellingham CBE
    Chief Executive. . . . . . . . . . . . . . . . . . . . . . . . . . Dr Gwyn Thomas . . . . . . . . . . . . . . . . . . . . . . . . Tel: (0121) 333 0333
        Web: http://www.nhsia.nhs.uk

## LITIGATION
**NHS Litigation Authority** . . . . . . . . . . . . . . . . . . . . Napier House, 24 High Holborn, London, WC1V 6AZ
    Chairman . . . . . . . . . . . . . . . . . . . . . . . . . . . . . . Mr Ron Bradshaw
    Chief Executive. . . . . . . . . . . . . . . . . . . . . . . . . . Mr Steve Walker . . . . . . . . . . . . . . . . . . . . . . . . . Tel: (020) 7430 8700
        Web: http://www.nhsla.com

## LOGISTICS
**NHS Logistics Authority** . . . . . . . . . . . . . . . . . . . . . West Way, Cotes Park Industrial Estate, Alfreton, Derbyshire, DE55 4QJ
    Chairman . . . . . . . . . . . . . . . . . . . . . . . . . . . . . . Mr Philip Champ
    Chief Executive. . . . . . . . . . . . . . . . . . . . . . . . . . Mr Barry Mellor. . . . . . . . . . . . . . . . . . . . . . . . . . Tel: (01773) 724000
        Web: http://www.logistics.nhs.uk

## MATERIALS *(see below under Pharmaceuticals, Medicines)*

## MEDICAL ADVISORY COMMITTEE
**Standing Medical Advisory Committee** . . . . . . . . . . . . Area 418, Wellington House, 135-155 Waterloo Road, London, SE1 8UG
    Chairman . . . . . . . . . . . . . . . . . . . . . . . . . . . . . . *Vacant*
    Chief Executive. . . . . . . . . . . . . . . . . . . . . . . . . . Mrs Melissa Naylor . . . . . . . . . . . . . . . . . . . . . . . Tel: (020) 7972 4198
        Web: http://www.doh.gov.uk/smac.htm

## MEDICAL DEVICES / MEDICINES *(see below under Pharmaceuticals, Medicines)*

## MENTAL HEALTH
**Mental Health Review Tribunals** . . . . . . . . . . . . . . . . Wellington House, 135-155 Waterloo Road, London, SE1 8UG
    Head of Secretariat . . . . . . . . . . . . . . . . . . . . . . . . Mrs Margaret Burn. . . . . . . . . . . . . . . . . . . . . . . . Tel: (020) 7972 4577

# DEPARTMENT OF HEALTH

*Other Relevant Contacts (Continued)*

**MICROBIOLOGY**
**Microbiological Research Authority** . . . . . . . . . . . . . . . CAMR, Porton Down, Near Salisbury, Wiltshire, SP4 0JG
    Chairman . . . . . . . . . . . . . . . . . . . . . . . . . . . Sir William Stewart
    Chief Executive . . . . . . . . . . . . . . . . . . . . . . . . Dr Roger Gilmour . . . . . . . . . . . . . . . . . . . . . . . . Tel: (01980) 612100
    Web: http://www.camr.org.uk

**MODERNISATION**
**NHS Modernisation Agency** . . . . . . . . . . . . . . . . . Richmond House, 79 Whitehall, London, SW1A 2NS
    Director . . . . . . . . . . . . . . . . . . . . . . . . . . . . . Mr David Fillingham . . . . . . . . . . . . . . . . . . . . . . . Tel: (0845) 600 0700
    Web: http://www.modern.nhs.uk

**NHS DIRECT**
**NHS Direct** . . . . . . . . . . . . . . . . . . . . . . . . . . . . Richmond House, 79 Whitehall, London, SW1A 2NS
    Chairman . . . . . . . . . . . . . . . . . . . . . . . . . . . Mr David Edmonds CBE
    Chief Executive . . . . . . . . . . . . . . . . . . . . . . . . Mr Ed Lester . . . . . . . . . . . . . . . . . . . . . . . . . Tel: (0845) 4647
    Web: http://www.nhsdirect.nhs.uk

**NURSING AND MIDWIFERY**
**Nursing and Midwifery Council** . . . . . . . . . . . . . . . 23 Portland Place, London, W1B 1PZ
    President . . . . . . . . . . . . . . . . . . . . . . . . . . . Mr Jonathan Asbridge
    Chief Executive and Registrar . . . . . . . . . . . . . . . . . Mrs Sarah Thewlis . . . . . . . . . . . . . . . . . . . . . . Tel: (020) 7637 7181
    Web: http://www.nmc-uk.org
**Standing Nursing and Midwifery Advisory Committee** . Room 1519, Richmond House, 79 Whitehall, London, SW1A 2NS
    Chairman . . . . . . . . . . . . . . . . . . . . . . . . . . . Mrs Vicky Bailey
    Secretary . . . . . . . . . . . . . . . . . . . . . . . . . . . Mrs Grethe Ridgway . . . . . . . . . . . . . . . . . . . . . Tel: (020) 7210 4868
    Web: http://www.doh.gov.uk/snmac.index.htm

**OMBUDSMAN**
**Health Service Commissioner** . . . . . . . . . . . . . . . . Millbank Tower, Millbank, London, SW1P 4QP
    Commissioner . . . . . . . . . . . . . . . . . . . . . . . . . Ms Ann Abraham
    Secretary . . . . . . . . . . . . . . . . . . . . . . . . . . . Mrs Margaret Baker . . . . . . . . . . . . . . . . . . . . . Tel: (0845) 015 4033
    Web: http://www.ombudsman.org.uk

**OSTEOPATHY**
**General Osteopathic Council** . . . . . . . . . . . . . . . . . Osteopathy House, 176 Tower Bridge Road, London, SE1 3LU
    Chairman . . . . . . . . . . . . . . . . . . . . . . . . . . . Mr Nigel Clarke . . . . . . . . . . . . . . . . . . . . . . . Tel: (020) 7357 6655
    Chief Executive . . . . . . . . . . . . . . . . . . . . . . . . Miss Madeline Craggs
    E-mail: info@osteopathy.org.uk
    Web: http://www.osteopathy.org.uk

**PATHOGENS**
**Advisory Committee on Dangerous Pathogens** . . . . . . . 6th Floor, North Wing, Rose Court, 2 Southwark Bridge, London, SE1 9HS
    Chairman . . . . . . . . . . . . . . . . . . . . . . . . . . . Professor Roger Freeman
    Secretaries . . . . . . . . . . . . . . . . . . . . . . . . . . Ms Hanna Lewis *(Department of Health)* . . . . . . . . . Tel: (020) 7717 6230
    Dr Jim Neilson *(Health and Safety Executive)*
    Web: http://www.doh.gov.uk/acdp

**PATIENT INVOLVEMENT**
**Commission for Patient and**
  **Public Involvement in Health** . . . . . . . . . . . . . . . . 7th Floor, 120 Edmund Street, Birmingham, B3 2ES
    Chairman . . . . . . . . . . . . . . . . . . . . . . . . . . . Ms Sharon Grant
    Chief Executive . . . . . . . . . . . . . . . . . . . . . . . . Ms Laura McMurtie . . . . . . . . . . . . . . . . . . . . . Tel: (0121) 222 4500
**Patient Information Advisory Group** . . . . . . . . . . . . . Room 1N35C, Quarry House, Quarry Hill, Leeds, LS2 7UE
    Chairman . . . . . . . . . . . . . . . . . . . . . . . . . . . Professor Joan Higgins
    Secretary . . . . . . . . . . . . . . . . . . . . . . . . . . . Mr Sean Kirwan . . . . . . . . . . . . . . . . . . . . . . . Tel: (0113) 254 6019

**PATIENT SAFETY**
**National Patient Safety Agency** . . . . . . . . . . . . . . . . 4-8 Maple Street, London, W2T 5HD
    Chairman . . . . . . . . . . . . . . . . . . . . . . . . . . . Professor Rory Shore
    Chief Executives *(Joint)* . . . . . . . . . . . . . . . . . . . Ms Sue Osborne
    Ms Susan Williams . . . . . . . . . . . . . . . . . . . . . . Tel: (020) 7927 9500
    E-mail: enquiries@npsa.nhs.uk
    Web: http://www.npsa.nhs.uk

# DEPARTMENT OF HEALTH

*Other Relevant Contacts (Continued)*

## PAY
**Doctors' and Dentists' Review Body**.............. Office of Manpower Economics, Oxford House, 76 Oxford Street, London, W1D 1BS
 Chairman ...................................... Mr Michael Blair QC
 Secretary...................................... Mrs Maureen Foggo ......................... Tel: (020) 7467 7229
  Web: http://www.ome.uk.com
**Pharmacists' Review Panel**..................... Office of Manpower Economics, Oxford House, 76 Oxford Street, London, W1D 1BS
 Chairman ...................................... *Vacant*
 Secretary...................................... Mrs Gwyneth Edwards ..................... Tel: (020) 7467 7227
  Web: http://www.ome.uk.com
**Review Body for Nursing and Other Health Professions Allied to Medicine**................. Office of Manpower Economics, Oxford House, 76 Oxford Street, London, W1D 1BS
 Chairman ...................................... Professor Sir Clive Booth
 Secretary...................................... Mrs Gwyneth Edwards ..................... Tel: (020) 7467 7227
  Web: http://www.ome.uk.com

## PENSIONS
**NHS Pensions Agency** *(Executive Agency)* ........... Hesketh House, 200-220 Broadway, Fleetwood, Lancashire, FY7 8LG
 Chief Executive................................ Mrs Pat Corless ........................... Tel: (01253) 774774
  Web: http://www.nhspa.gov.uk

## PHARMACEUTICALS, MEDICINES
**British Pharmacopoeia Commission** .............. Market Towers, 1 Nine Elms Lane, London, SW8 5NQ
 Chairman ...................................... Professor Derek Calam
 Secretary and Scientific Director ................. Dr Gerard Lee ............................ Tel: (020) 7084 2561
  Web: http://www.pharmacopoeia.org.uk
**Committee on the Safety of Devices** ............. Medicines and Healthcare Products Regulatory Agency, 12th Floor, Hannibal House, London, SE1 6TQ
 Chairman ...................................... Mr John Williams CBE
 Secretary...................................... Dr Susanne Ludgate ....................... Tel: (020) 7972 8123
  Web: http://www.mhra.gov.uk
**Committee on the Safety of Medicines** ............ Market Towers, 1 Nine Elms Lane, London, SW8 5NQ
 Chairman ...................................... Professor Gordon Duff
 Secretary...................................... Mr Leslie Whitbread ...................... Tel: (020) 7084 2451
  Web: http://www.mhra.gsi.gov.uk
**Independent Review Body for the Advertising of Medicines**................. Market Towers, 1 Nine Elms Lane, London, SW8 5NQ
 Chairman ...................................... Mr James Watt
 Secretary...................................... Mr Sean Fletcher ......................... Tel: (020) 7084 2878
  Web: http://www.mhra.gov.uk
**Medicines Commission** ......................... Market Towers, 1 Nine Elms Lane, London, SW8 5NQ
 Chairman ...................................... Professor Parveen Kumar
 Secretariat.................................... Mrs Sue Jones ............................ Tel: (020) 7085 2652
  Web: http://www.mca.gov.uk
**Medicines and Healthcare Products Regulatory Agency** *(Executive Agency)*.............. Market Towers, 1 Nine Elms Lane, London, SW8 5NQ
 Chairman ...................................... Professor Alasdair Breckenridge
 Chief Executive................................ Professor Kent Woods ..................... Tel: (020) 7084 2000
  E-mail: info@mhra.gsi.gov.uk
  Web: http://www.mhra.gov.uk
**Prescription Pricing Authority**.................. Bridge House, 152 Pilgrim Street, Newcastle-upon-Tyne, NE1 6SN
 Chairman ...................................... Mrs Ann Galbraith CBE
 Chief Executive................................ Mr Nick Scholte .......................... Tel: (0191) 232 5371
  Web: http://www.ppa.org.uk
**Standing Pharmaceutical Advisory Committee** ....... Room 160, Richmond House, 79 Whitehall, London, SW1A 2NS
 Chairman ...................................... *Vacant*
 Secretary...................................... Ms Diana Kenworthy ...................... Tel: (020) 7210 5755

## PURCHASING *(see below under Supplies)*

## RADIOLOGY
**Administration of Radioactive Substances Advisory Committee** ............... Area 688, Skipton House, 80 London Road, London, SE1 6LH
 Chairman ...................................... Professor James McKillop
 Administrative Secretary ...................... Ms Patricia Brown ....................... Tel: (020) 7972 4802
  Web: http://www.doh.gov.uk/arsac

# DEPARTMENT OF HEALTH

*Other Relevant Contacts (Continued)*

**Committee on Medical Aspects of Radiation in the
    Environment** . . . . . . . . . . . . . . . . . . . . . . . . . . . . . . . c/o National Radiological Protection Board,
                                          Chilton, Didcot, Oxfordshire, OX11 0RQ
    Chairman . . . . . . . . . . . . . . . . . . . . . . . . . . . . . . . . Professor Bryn Bridges
    Secretariat . . . . . . . . . . . . . . . . . . . . . . . . . . . . . . . Dr Roy Hamlet
                                            Miss Julie Kedward . . . . . . . . . . . . . . . . . . . . . . . Tel: (01235) 822629
                                           Web: http://www.comare.org.uk
**National Radiological Protection Board** . . . . . . . . . . . . Chilton, Didcot, Oxfordshire, OX11 0RQ
    Chairman . . . . . . . . . . . . . . . . . . . . . . . . . . . . . . . . Sir William Stewart
    Director . . . . . . . . . . . . . . . . . . . . . . . . . . . . . . . . . Professor Roger Cox . . . . . . . . . . . . . . . . . . . . . . . Tel: (01235) 831600
                                           Web: http://www.nrpb.org.uk

**SECURITY** *(see under Fraud and Security above)*

**SOCIAL CARE**
**Commission for Social Care Inspection (England)** . . . . . Kierran Cross, 11 Strand, London, WC2N 5HR
    Chairman . . . . . . . . . . . . . . . . . . . . . . . . . . . . . . . . Ms Denise Platt
    Chief Inspector . . . . . . . . . . . . . . . . . . . . . . . . . . . . Mr David Behan . . . . . . . . . . . . . . . . . . . . . . . . . Tel: (020) 7389 8023
                                           Web: http://www.csci.gov.uk
**General Social Care Council** . . . . . . . . . . . . . . . . . . . Golding House, 2 Hay's Galleria, London, SE1 2HB
    Chairman . . . . . . . . . . . . . . . . . . . . . . . . . . . . . . . . Mr Rodney Brooke CBE
    Chief Executive . . . . . . . . . . . . . . . . . . . . . . . . . . . . Ms Lynne Berry . . . . . . . . . . . . . . . . . . . . . . . . . Tel: (020) 7397 5100
                                           E-mail: info@gscc.org.uk
                                           Web: http://www.gscc.org.uk

*(see also under Care Standards above)*

**SUPPLIES**
**NHS Purchasing and Supply Agency** *(Executive Agency)* . Premier House, 60 Caversham Road, Reading, RG1 7EB
    Chief Executive . . . . . . . . . . . . . . . . . . . . . . . . . . . . Mr Duncan Eaton CBE . . . . . . . . . . . . . . . . . . . . . Tel: (0118) 980 8600
                                           E-mail: pasa@pasa.nhs.uk
                                           Web: http://www.pasa.nhs.uk

**TOBACCO**
**Scientific Committee on Tobacco and Health** . . . . . . . Room 708, Wellington House, 133-155 Waterloo Road, London, SE1 8UG
    Chairman . . . . . . . . . . . . . . . . . . . . . . . . . . . . . . . . Professor James Friend
    Secretary . . . . . . . . . . . . . . . . . . . . . . . . . . . . . . . . Mr Anthony Doole . . . . . . . . . . . . . . . . . . . . . . . . Tel: (020) 7972 1336
                                           Web: http://www.doh.gov.uk/scoth

**TRANSPLANTS**
**UK Transplant** . . . . . . . . . . . . . . . . . . . . . . . . . . . . Fox Den Road, Stoke Gifford, Bristol, BS34 8RR
    Chairman . . . . . . . . . . . . . . . . . . . . . . . . . . . . . . . . Dr Gwynneth Flower
    Chief Executive . . . . . . . . . . . . . . . . . . . . . . . . . . . . Ms Sue Sutherland . . . . . . . . . . . . . . . . . . . . . . . . Tel: (0117) 975 7575
                                           E-mail: enquiries@uktransplant.nhs.uk
                                           Web: http://www.uktransplant.org.uk
**Unrelated Live Transplant Authority** . . . . . . . . . . . . . . Room 339, Wellington House, 133-155 Waterloo Road, London, SE1 8UG
    Chairman . . . . . . . . . . . . . . . . . . . . . . . . . . . . . . . . Professor Sir Roddy MacSween
    Secretary . . . . . . . . . . . . . . . . . . . . . . . . . . . . . . . . Mr Eddie Scarlet . . . . . . . . . . . . . . . . . . . . . . . . . Tel: (020) 7972 4812
                                           Web: http://www.doh.gov.uk/ultra.htm
**Xenotransplantation Regulatory Authority** . . . . . . . . . . Room 339, Wellington House, 133-155 Waterloo Road, London, SE1 8UG
    Chairman *(Acting)* . . . . . . . . . . . . . . . . . . . . . . . . . . Dr Janet Dewdney
    Secretary . . . . . . . . . . . . . . . . . . . . . . . . . . . . . . . . Ms Jennie Mullins . . . . . . . . . . . . . . . . . . . . . . . . Tel: (020) 7972 4824
                                           Web: http://www.doh.gov.uk/ukxira.htm

**TRUSTS**
    *Details of NHS Trusts can be obtained from the Department of Health enquiry line* . . . . . . . . . . . . . . . . . . . . Tel: (020) 7210 4850

**VACCINATION**
**Joint Committee on Vaccination and Immunisation** . . . Room 602A, Skipton House, 80 London Road, London, SE1 6LH
    Chairman . . . . . . . . . . . . . . . . . . . . . . . . . . . . . . . . Professor Mike Langman
    Medical Secretary . . . . . . . . . . . . . . . . . . . . . . . . . . . Dr David Salisbury . . . . . . . . . . . . . . . . . . . . . . . . Tel: (020) 7972 1522
                                           Web: http://www.doh.gov.uk/jcvi/index.htm

**WORKFORCE**
**Medical Workforce Standing Advisory Committee** . . . . Room 2W06, Quarry House, Quarry Hill, Leeds, LS2 7UE
    Chairman . . . . . . . . . . . . . . . . . . . . . . . . . . . . . . . . Professor Sir Colin Campbell
    Secretary . . . . . . . . . . . . . . . . . . . . . . . . . . . . . . . . Mr Bill Urry . . . . . . . . . . . . . . . . . . . . . . . . . . . . . Tel: (0113) 254 6911

**NHS Professionals** . . . . . . . . . . . . . . . . . . . . . . . . . 3 Lands, Bradford Road, Berkshire, Bradford, BD11 2AH
    Chief Executive . . . . . . . . . . . . . . . . . . . . . . . . . . . . Ms Diane Whittingham . . . . . . . . . . . . . . . . . . . . . Tel: (0845) 120 3182
                                           Web: http://www.nhsprofessionals.co.uk

## ACADEMIC – RESEARCH AND EDUCATION

# INSTITUTE OF RURAL HEALTH

Gregynog, Newtown, Powys, SY16 3PW

*Telephone* (01686) 650800
*Facsimile* (01686) 650300
*Web* www.rural-health.ac.uk

The Institute of Rural Health is an academic centre of excellence. We work in partnership with other organisations to optimise the health and wellbeing of rural people and their communities.

The Institute works in three areas:

**Research** – Key themes include measurement of rural health issues, rural proofing, health and wellbeing outcomes, health and the environment, supporting the rural workforce.

**Training** – Provide continuing education courses for all rural health professionals and host the Welsh Rural Postgraduate Unit.

**Policy** – Raising awareness, at policy making level, or rural health needs through the Rural Health Forum and the Rural Proofing for Health project.

*Chief Executive:* Jane Randall-Smith.
E-mail: janers@rural-health.ac.uk
*Patron:* His Grace the Duke of Westminster KG OBE TD DL
*Registered Charity No:* 1061438

## ADVOCACY

### *Helping Young People*

**NYAS is a socio-legal children's charity providing independent and confidential information, advice, advocacy and legal services for vulnerable children and young people from 0-25. NYAS offers a national Freephone helpline for young people, their parents and carers which can also be accessed by text, email and direct chat. This, together with our network of advocates, across England and Wales, supported by the legal team, allows young people to be supported and heard whenever decisions are being made about their lives. NYAS knows that early intervention prevents minor issues from becoming major problems.**

National Youth Advocacy Service
99-105 Argyle Street
Birkenhead
Merseyside, CH41 6AD

Tel: 0151 649 8700
Fax: 0151 649 8701
E-mail: main@nyas.net
Website: www.nyas.net

**Freephone for young people 0800 61 61 01**

## ALCOHOL CONCERN

# ALCOHOL CONCERN

Waterbridge House, 32-36 Loman Street
London, SE1 0EE

*Telephone* (020) 7928 7377
*Facsimile* (020) 7928 4644
*E-mail* contact@alcoholconcern.org.uk
*Web* www.alcoholconcern.org.uk

*Contact* Eric Appleby – *Chief Executive*

Alcohol Concern is the national agency on alcohol misuse. We work to reduce the incidence and costs of alcohol-related harm and to increase the range and quality of services available to people with alcohol-related problems.

We provide information on the wide range of public policy issues affected by alcohol; including public health, housing, children and families, crime and licensing and support specialist and non-specialist service providers helping to tackle alcohol problems.

*Registered Charity No: 291705*

## CHILD CARE

# NATIONAL COUNCIL OF VOLUNTARY CHILD CARE ORGANISATIONS

Unit 4, Pride Court, 80-82 White Lion Street,
London, N1 9PF

*Telephone* (020) 7833 3319
*Facsimile* (020) 7833 8637
*Web* http://www.ncvcco.org

*Contact* Erica De'Ath OBE – *Chief Executive*

For over 60 years NCVCCO has brought together voluntary child care organisations providing services and acting as advocates for children, young people, their families and communities. We can provide immediate access to the expertise and experience of over 100 leading service providers in the voluntary sector.

## COUNSELLING, PSYCHOTHERAPY, TRAINING

# wpf COUNSELLING AND PSYCHOTHERAPY

23 Kensington Square
London, W8 5HN

*Telephone* (020) 7361 4800
*Facsimile* (020) 7361 4808
*E-mail* appeals@wpf.org.uk
*Web* http://www.wpf.org.uk

*Contact* Mrs Val Potter – *Director*

**wpf** provides long and short term individual counselling and psychotherapy and group therapy for a wide range of emotional, psychological and relationship problems throughout London and in 35 centres nationwide.

**wpf** offers the only national ladder of counselling and psychotherapy training and a range of training for continuing professional development from introductory to graduate level.

*Registered Charity No: 273434*

## EMERGENCY SERVICES

# BRITISH ASSOCIATION FOR IMMEDIATE CARE (BASICS)

Turret House, Turret Lane
Ipswich, Suffolk, IP4 1DL

*Telephone* (0870) 1654 999
*Facsimile* (0870) 1654 949
*E-mail* admin@basics.org.uk
*Web* http://www.basics.org.uk

*Contact* Mrs Ruth Lloyd – *Chief Executive*

BASICS is a voluntary organisation whose members provide skilled medical help at the scene of an accident, medical emergency or during transport to hospital. Our members are alerted by the Emergency Services and arrive at the incident in specially equipped cars.

*Registered Charity No: 276054*

## THE FOSTERING NETWORK

87 Blackfriars Road, London, SE1 8HA
*Telephone* (020) 7620 6400
*Facsimile* (020) 7620 6401
*E-mail* info@fostering.net
*Web* http://www.fostering.net

*Contact* Ms Gerri McAndrew – *Executive Director*

Nowadays, two thirds of all children in public care are fostered while only one in nine live in children's homes. We are Britain's leading charity for fostered children and those who care for them – spearheading national initiatives to improve standards in foster care and providing practical support to social workers, foster carers and young people.

*Registered Charity No: 280852*

## PROPRIETARY ASSOCIATION OF GREAT BRITAIN

Vernon House, Sicilian Avenue, London, WC1A 2QS

*Telephone:* (020) 7421 9318
*Facsimile:* (020) 7421 9317
*E-mail:* gopa.mitra@pagb.co.uk

*Contact* Ms Gopa Mitra MBE –
*Director of Health Policy & Public Affairs*

PAGB represents manufacturers of branded over-the-counter medicines and food supplements in Great Britain. A condition of membership is adherence to the PAGB code of advertising practice, which is applied through pre-publication approval by the Association. This system of self-regulation has existed since PAGB was formed in 1919.

The Association publishes a directory of members' products and a copy of it is <u>available on request.</u>

## BRITISH HEART FOUNDATION

14 Fitzhardinge Street, London, W1H 6DH

*Telephone:* (020) 7725 0664
*Facsimile:* (020) 7724 5082
*E-mail:* oconnorr@bhf.org.uk
*Web:* http://www.bhf.org.uk

*Contact* Mr Ruairi O'Connor – *Public Affairs Officer*

The British Heart Foundation plays a leading role in the fight against heart and circulatory disease, the UK's biggest killer. The Foundation funds research, education and lifesaving equipment and helps heart patients return to a full and active way of life.

*Registered Charity No: 225971*

## COUNSEL AND CARE
## Advice and help for older people

Twyman House, 16 Bonny Street,
London, NW1 9PG

*Telephone* (020) 7241 8555 *(General)*
0845 300 75 85 *(Advice Line)*
*Facsimile* (020) 7267 6877
*Web* http://www.counselandcare.org.uk

*Contact* Mr Martin Green – *Chief Executive*

Counsel and Care engages in two principal activities: providing advice, information and advocacy for older people and their carers around community care issues; and undertaking research aimed at influencing policy and practice in the care of older people.

We are particularly well known for our work on residential and nursing care homes, having addressed issues as varied as privacy, leisure and recreation, death and dying, abuse, risk taking and restraint.

*Registered Charity No: 203429*

## LUNG DISEASE

## BRITISH LUNG FOUNDATION
73-75 GOSWELL ROAD • LONDON • EC1V 7ER • TEL (020) 7688 5555 • CHARITY NUMBER 326730

*Telephone* (020) 7688 5555
*Facsimile* (020) 7688 5556
*E-mail* enquiries@blf-uk.org
*Web* http://www.lunguk.org

*Contact* Dame Helena Shovelton – *Chief Executive*

Lung disease affects over 8 million people in the UK and accounts for more than 25 million lost working days each year.

The British Lung Foundation is the only UK charity raising funds for first-class research into the prevention, diagnosis and treatment and cure of <u>all</u> lung diseases. It also provides practical support to those who join *Breathe Easy*, a self-help club for people with lung conditions, their families and carers, and produces a range of high-quality public information on lung conditions.

The British Lung Foundation relies entirely on voluntary donations and legacies.

## MULTI-NATIONAL HOMES FOR THE ELDERLY

## GRACE AND COMPASSION BENEDICTINES

St. Benedict's Generalate, 1 Manor Road, Kemp Town, Brighton, East Sussex, BN2 5EA

*Telephone* (01273) 680720
*Facsimile* (01273) 680527
*E-mail* generalate@grace&compassion.co.uk
*Web* http://www.dabnet.org/gcb.htm

The order was founded in 1954. It is monastic, but its work is focussed on the old, sick, poor and disadvantaged in England, Sri Lanka, India and Africa. It runs homes for the elderly, clinics and training centres. It is multi-national, with lay participation.

## MULTIPLE SCLEROSIS

## THE MULTIPLE SCLEROSIS SOCIETY OF GREAT BRITAIN AND NORTHERN IRELAND

372 Edgware Road, London, NW2 6ND

*Telephone* (020) 8438 0700    *Facsimile* (020) 8438 0701
*E-mail* info@mssociety.org.uk
*Web* www.mssociety.org.uk

*Contact* Matthew Sowemimo – *Policy Officer*

"The Multiple Sclerosis Society – providing the strength to fight MS. The national charity for everyone affected by MS – working for better care and the eradication of MS." The MS Society actively campaigns to promote the interests of people affected by MS with local and national decision makers.

*Registered Charity No: 207495*

## MIGRAINES

## MIGRAINE ACTION ASSOCIATION

Unit 6, Oakley Hay, Lodge Business Park, Great Folds Road, Great Oakley, Northants, NW18 9AS

*Telephone* (01536) 461333
*Facsimile* (01932) 351257
*E-mail* info@migraine.org.uk
*Web* http://www.migraine.org.uk

*Contact* Mrs A Turner – *Director*

A registered charity founded in 1958 as the British Migraine Association, it provides information, support and encouragement to migraine sufferers and their families, raises general awareness of this condition and supports and encourages research.

*Registered Charity No: 207783*

## MULTIPLE RETAIL OPTICIANS

## PARTIAL SIGHT

## opticians in business
Federation of Ophthalmic & Dispensing Opticians

REPRESENTING REGISTERED OPTICIANS IN BUSINESS

### THE FEDERATION OF OPHTHALMIC AND DISPENSING OPTICIANS (FODO)

199 Gloucester Terrace, London, W2 6LD

*Telephone:* (020) 7298 5151  *Facsimile:* (020) 7298 5111
*E-mail:* optics@fodo.com  *Web:* http://www.fodo.com

*Contact:* Robert Hughes – *Executive Director*

**FODO** represents the interests of the companies, who now dominate the optical market, and works to ensure that policy makers, government and the regulatory bodies take the views of the membership into account.

**FODO** believes that the eye examination has a central role in primary and preventative health care; that it is in the consumer's interests to have regular eye examinations, and works to promote the need for sight correction with charities, the government and campaigning organisations such as the RNIB and the Eyecare Trust.

### THE PARTIALLY SIGHTED SOCIETY
PO Box 322, Doncaster, DN1 2XA

*Telephone* (01302) 323132
*Facsimile* (01302) 368998
E-mail: info@partsight.org.uk
Web: http://www.partsight.org.uk

*Contact* Norman Stenson

The Partially Sighted Society (PSS) exists to help fill a gap which lies where the established optical, health and social services cannot reach. It does so because it employs low vision therapists (specially trained orthoptists) who bring multi-disciplinary skills into face-to-face contact with patients.

PSS offers a comprehensive advice and information service on all aspects of living with sight loss, and on sources of specialised help. Costs are kept low, aided by the generous enthusiasm of volunteers and members, many of whom are themselves partially sighted. Our ambition is to extend and enlarge the valuable work we are doing to all parts of the country, as quickly as funds allow.

*Registered Charity No: 254052*

## PSORIATIC ARTHRITIS & PSORIASIS SUPPORT

### PSORIATIC ARTHROPATHY ALLIANCE
PO Box 111, St Albans, Hertfordshire, AL2 3JQ

*Telephone* (0870) 7703212
*Facsimile* (0870) 7703213
*E-mail* office@paalliance.org
*Web* http://www.paalliance.org

*Contact* Julie Chandler – *Director*

The Psoriatic Arthropathy Alliance is a UK-based national registered charity dedicated to raising awareness and helping people with psoriatic arthritis and its associated skin disorder, psoriasis.

An annual conference is organised in September, with free admission available for members. Subscribing members also receive a Journal.

*Registered Charity No: 1051169*

## RESIDENTIAL CARE HOMES GRANTS

### METHODIST LOCAL PREACHERS MUTUAL AID ASSOCIATION

89 High Street, Rickmansworth, Herts, WD3 1EF

*Telephone* (01923) 775856
*Facsimile* (01923) 710075
*E-mail* headoffice@lpma.demon.co.uk
*Web* http://www.lpma.co.uk

*Contact* Godfrey C Talford MA CHARTERED FCIPD – *General Secretary*

Grants to necessitous Methodist Local Preachers, and proprietorship of Residential Care Homes for members of the Methodist Church, and Lay Preachers of all Christian churches.

*Registered Charity No:* 213001

## VISION IMPAIRMENT

### MACULAR DISEASE SOCIETY

Darwin House, 13a Bridge Street
Andover, Hampshire, SP10 1BE

*Telephone* (01264) 350551
*Facsimile* (01264) 350558
*E-mail* info@maculardisease.org
*Web* http://www.maculardisease.org

*Contact:* Tom Bremridge – *Chief Executive*

Macular Disease destroys central vision. With 14,000 members the Society seeks to build members' confidence and independence. It runs 130 local groups. issues a quarterly magazine, runs a help line and provides counselling. It also sponsors research and monitors development of low vision aids.

*Registered Charity No:* 1001198

# H O M E   O F F I C E

50 Queen Anne's Gate, London, SW1H 9AT
Tel: (0870) 000 1585  Fax: (020) 7273 2065
E mail: public.enquiries@homeoffice.gsi.gov.uk
Web: http://www.homeoffice.gov.uk

**MINISTERS**

**Secretary of State** .............................. Rt Hon David Blunkett MP
    *Principal Private Secretary* ...................... Mr Jonathan Sedgwick.................. Tel: (020) 7273 4647
    *Special Advisers*.............................. Mr Matt Cavanagh...................... Tel: (020) 7273 2713
         Mr Huw Evans ....................... Tel: (020) 7273 2713
         Ms Katharine Raymond.................. Tel: (020) 7273 2852
         Mr Matthew Seward..................... Tel: (020) 7273 2852
         Ms Sophie Linden ..................... Tel: (020) 7273 2852

**Minister of State** *(Crime Reduction, Policing and
    Community Safety)* ......................... Ms Hazel Blears MP
    *Private Secretary*.............................. Mr Richard Austin ..................... Tel: (020) 7273 4606

**Minister of State** *(Citizenship, Immigration and
    Counter-Terrorism)* ........................... Mr Desmond Browne MP
    *Private Secretary*.............................. Mr Neil Roberts ...................... Tel: (020) 7273 2742

**Minister of State** *(Criminal Justice and Law Reform)*...... Rt Hon Baroness Scotland of Asthal QC
    *Private Secretary*.............................. Ms Joanne Drean ...................... Tel: (020) 7273 2741

**Parliamentary Secretary** *(Race Equality, Community
    Policy and Civil Renewal)* ....................... Ms Caroline Flint MP
    *Private Secretary*.............................. Ms Jill Wanliss...................... Tel: (020) 7273 2750

**Parliamentary Secretary** *(Correctional Services)*......... Mr Paul Goggins MP
    *Private Secretary*.............................. Dr Samantha Milton ................... Tel: (020) 7273 3458

**Parliamentary Secretary** *(European and International
    Issues; Anti-Drugs Co-ordination)* ................. Ms Fiona McTaggart MP
    *Private Secretary*.............................. Mr Graham Johnston................... Tel: (020) 7273 2500

**CIVIL SERVICE**

**Permanent Secretary** ........................... Mr John Gieve CB
    *Private Secretary*.............................. Ms Diana Luchford .................... Tel: (020) 7273 2199

**Permanent Secretary and Chief Executive, National
Offender Management Service** ................ Mr Martin Narey
    *Private Secretary*.............................. Ms Ruth Alvey ...................... Tel: (020) 7273 3902

**Permanent Secretary, Crime Policing, Counter -
Terrorism and Delivery** ..................... Mr Leigh Lewis CB
    *Private Secretary*.............................. Ms Claire Gipson .................... Tel: (020) 7273 4519

**Senior Management**
    Director-General, Communities.................... Ms Helen Edwards .................... Tel: (020) 7035 5445
    Director-General, Crime Reduction and Community
        Safety Group......................... Mr Mark Neale ...................... Tel: (020) 7273 2699
    Director-General, Criminal Justice ................. Ms Moira Wallace OBE................. Tel: (020) 8282 6201
    Director-General, Immigration
        and Nationality....................... Mr Bill Jeffrey...................... Tel: (020) 7273 4000
    Director-General, Resources
        and Performance....................... Ms Margaret Aldred ................... Tel: (020) 7273 3285
    Legal Adviser.............................. Mr David Seymour QC .................. Tel: (020) 7273 2681

# HOME OFFICE

## SUBJECT RESPONSIBILITIES AND CONTACTS

**Alcohol**
Drug and Alcohol Research Unit . . . . . . . . . . . . . . . . . Mr David Pyle . . . . . . . . . . . . . . . . . . . . . . . . Tel: (020) 7273 3946

**Animal Scientific Procedures**
Head, Animal Procedures and Coroners Unit and
    Chief Inspector Animals (Scientific Procedures) . . . . . Dr Jon Richmond . . . . . . . . . . . . . . . . . . . . . . . Tel: (020) 7035 5551
Policy . . . . . . . . . . . . . . . . . . . . . . . . . . . . . . . . . . . . . . Mr Martin Walsh . . . . . . . . . . . . . . . . . . . . . . . Tel: (020) 7035 5540

**Anti-Social Behaviour** . . . . . . . . . . . . . . . . . . . . . . . . . Ms Louise Casey . . . . . . . . . . . . . . . . . . . . . . . Tel: (020) 7273 3601

**Asylum**
Deputy Director-General, Asylum Support and Casework . Mr Ken Sutton . . . . . . . . . . . . . . . . . . . . . . . . . Tel: (020) 8760 8373
Director, Asylum and Appeals Policy Directorate . . . . . . Mr Richard Westlake . . . . . . . . . . . . . . . . . . . . Tel: (020) 8760 3023
Director, Asylum Casework . . . . . . . . . . . . . . . . . . . . . . Mr Chris Hudson . . . . . . . . . . . . . . . . . . . . . . . Tel: (020) 8604 7766
Director, National Asylum Support Service . . . . . . . . . . Ms Freda Chaloner . . . . . . . . . . . . . . . . . . . . . . Tel: (020) 8633 0304

**Children and Young People's Unit**
Director, Children and Young People's Unit . . . . . . . . . Ms Althea Efunshile . . . . . . . . . . . . . . . . . . . . . Tel: (020) 7273 1396
Assistant Director, Children and Young People's Unit . . . Mr Andrew McCully . . . . . . . . . . . . . . . . . . . . . Tel: (020) 7273 5818
Children's Fund . . . . . . . . . . . . . . . . . . . . . . . . . . . . . . Ms Wendy Sleath . . . . . . . . . . . . . . . . . . . . . . . Tel: (020) 7273 5385
Communications . . . . . . . . . . . . . . . . . . . . . . . . . . . . . . Ms Monica Kumah . . . . . . . . . . . . . . . . . . . . . . Tel: (020) 7273 6007
Finance and Planning . . . . . . . . . . . . . . . . . . . . . . . . . . Mr Patrick Ibekwe . . . . . . . . . . . . . . . . . . . . . . Tel: (020) 7273 5161
Ministerial Support . . . . . . . . . . . . . . . . . . . . . . . . . . . Ms Jan Stockwell . . . . . . . . . . . . . . . . . . . . . . . Tel: (020) 7273 5628
                                                    Mr Alisa Swarbrick . . . . . . . . . . . . . . . . . . . . . . Tel: (020) 7273 5628
Strategy . . . . . . . . . . . . . . . . . . . . . . . . . . . . . . . . . . . . Mr Ben Morrin . . . . . . . . . . . . . . . . . . . . . . . . . Tel: (020) 7273 5829

**Communications**
Director of Communications . . . . . . . . . . . . . . . . . . . . . Ms Julia Simpson . . . . . . . . . . . . . . . . . . . . . . . Tel: (020) 7273 3757
Deputy Director and Head of Counter-Terrorism
    Communications . . . . . . . . . . . . . . . . . . . . . . . . . . Mr Terry Norman . . . . . . . . . . . . . . . . . . . . . . . Tel: (020) 7273 4166
Deputy Director and Head of Marketing and
    Strategic Communications . . . . . . . . . . . . . . . . . . Ms Anne Nash . . . . . . . . . . . . . . . . . . . . . . . . . Tel: (020) 7273 3853
Assistant Director and
    Head of Direct Communications Unit . . . . . . . . . . . Mr Geoff Sampher . . . . . . . . . . . . . . . . . . . . . . Tel: (020) 7273 3757
Head of Information Services Unit . . . . . . . . . . . . . . . . . Mr Peter Griffiths . . . . . . . . . . . . . . . . . . . . . . . Tel: (020) 7273 2210
Head of Internal Communications . . . . . . . . . . . . . . . . . Mr Bill Reay . . . . . . . . . . . . . . . . . . . . . . . . . . . Tel: (020) 7273 2725
Press Officer . . . . . . . . . . . . . . . . . . . . . . . . . . . . . . . . Mr John Toker . . . . . . . . . . . . . . . . . . . . . . . . . Tel: (020) 7273 3757

**Communities**
*Allington Towers, 19 Allington Street, London SW1E 5EB*
Director-General Communities Group . . . . . . . . . . . . . . Ms Helen Edwards . . . . . . . . . . . . . . . . . . . . . . Tel: (020) 7035 5446
Director, Children and Coroners . . . . . . . . . . . . . . . . . . Ms Nicky Roche . . . . . . . . . . . . . . . . . . . . . . . . Tel: (020) 7035 5446
Director, Race, Cohesion, Equality and Faith . . . . . . . . Mr Mark Carroll . . . . . . . . . . . . . . . . . . . . . . . . Tel: (020) 7273 2482
Active Community Unit . . . . . . . . . . . . . . . . . . . . . . . . Ms Helen Edwards . . . . . . . . . . . . . . . . . . . . . . Tel: (020) 7035 5446
Community Cohesion Unit . . . . . . . . . . . . . . . . . . . . . . Ms Judith Lempriere . . . . . . . . . . . . . . . . . . . . . Tel: (020) 7273 5464
Community Funding . . . . . . . . . . . . . . . . . . . . . . . . . . Mr Neil Frater . . . . . . . . . . . . . . . . . . . . . . . . . Tel: (020) 7035 5438
Strategic Support Group . . . . . . . . . . . . . . . . . . . . . . . Mr Richard Jenkins . . . . . . . . . . . . . . . . . . . . . Tel: (020) 7035 5455

**Coroners** . . . . . . . . . . . . . . . . . . . . . . . . . . . . . . . . . . . . Mr Robert Clifford . . . . . . . . . . . . . . . . . . . . . . Tel: (020) 7035 5540

**Corporate Development and Services**
Director, Corporate Development and Services . . . . . . . . Mr Charles Everett . . . . . . . . . . . . . . . . . . . . . . Tel: (020) 7271 8577
Agreement and Service Delivery . . . . . . . . . . . . . . . . . . Mr Mike Fitzpatrick . . . . . . . . . . . . . . . . . . . . . Tel: (020) 7217 8728
Building and Estate Management Unit . . . . . . . . . . . . . . Mr Tony Edwards . . . . . . . . . . . . . . . . . . . . . . . Tel: (020) 7217 8291
Commercial and Procurement Unit . . . . . . . . . . . . . . . . Ms Wendy Rowlands . . . . . . . . . . . . . . . . . . . . . Tel: (020) 7273 3065
Corporate Support Services Unit . . . . . . . . . . . . . . . . . . Mr Nigel Benger . . . . . . . . . . . . . . . . . . . . . . . . Tel: (020) 7217 0242
E-Business Strategy . . . . . . . . . . . . . . . . . . . . . . . . . . . Mr Chris Fleming . . . . . . . . . . . . . . . . . . . . . . . Tel: (020) 7217 8589
Home Office Pay and Pensions Service . . . . . . . . . . . . . Mr Tony Fitzpatrick *(Liverpool)* . . . . . . . . . . . . Tel: (0151) 934 7412
Information Management Unit . . . . . . . . . . . . . . . . . . . . Mr Peter Lowe . . . . . . . . . . . . . . . . . . . . . . . . . Tel: (020) 7217 8625
IT. Technical . . . . . . . . . . . . . . . . . . . . . . . . . . . . . . . . Mr Paul Vagg . . . . . . . . . . . . . . . . . . . . . . . . . . Tel: (020) 7273 3468
Performance and Strategic Management . . . . . . . . . . . . . Mr Martin Parker . . . . . . . . . . . . . . . . . . . . . . . Tel: (020) 7273 3256
Records Management . . . . . . . . . . . . . . . . . . . . . . . . . . Mr Richard Thompson . . . . . . . . . . . . . . . . . . . Tel: (020) 7273 2150

# HOME OFFICE

**Correctional Services**

| | | |
|---|---|---|
| Commissioner for Correctional Services | Mr Martin Narey | Tel: (020) 7273 3902 |
| Director, Correctional and Rehabilitation | Ms Christine Stewart | Tel: (020) 7273 3902 |
| Director, Finance and Competitions, NOMS | Mr John Steele | Tel: (020) 7273 3902 |
| Director, Finance and Performance, NOMS | Mr Peter Brooke | Tel: (020) 7273 3902 |
| Director, NOMS | Ms Eithne Wallis | Tel: (020) 7273 3468 |

Inspection

*First Floor, Ashley House, 2 Monck Street, London, SW1P 2BQ*

| | | |
|---|---|---|
| H M Chief Inspector of Prisons | Ms Anne Owers CBE | Tel: (020) 7035 2100 |
| H M Chief Inspector of Probation | Mr Andrew Bridges | Tel: (020) 7035 2202 |
| Deputy Chief Inspector, Probation | Ms Frances Flaxington | Tel: (020) 7273 3113 |
| Juvenile Offenders Unit | Mr Simon Hickson | Tel: (020) 7273 3161 |
| Mental Health Unit | Ms Elizabeth Moody | Tel: (020) 7273 4528 |
| | Ms Fiona Spencer | Tel: (020) 7273 2927 |

**Cremation Law** . . . . . . . . . Mr Robert Clifford . . . . . . . . . Tel: (020) 7035 5540

**Crime Reduction and Community Safety**

| | | |
|---|---|---|
| Permanent Secretary for Crime, Policing, Counter-Terrorism and Delivery | Mr Leigh Lewis CB | Tel: (020) 7273 3601 |
| Director-General, Crime Reduction and Community Safety Group | Mr Mark Neale | Tel: (020) 7273 2699 |
| Director, International Crime | Mr Peter Storr | Tel: (020) 7273 2830 |
| Director, Organised Crime | Ms Margaret O'Mara | Tel: (020) 7273 3601 |
| Acquisitive Crime | Mr Marcial Boo | Tel: (020) 7273 2699 |
| Anti-Social Behaviour | Ms Louise Casey | Tel: (020) 7273 3601 |

Crime Reduction College

*The Hawkhills, Easingwold, York, YO61 3EG*

| | | |
|---|---|---|
| Director, Crime Reduction College | Mr Steve Trimmins | Tel: (01347) 825060 |
| Crime Reduction Delivery | Mr Peter Edwards | Tel: (020) 7035 5266 |
| Crime Reduction Policy | Mr Ellie Roy | Tel: (020) 7035 5266 |
| Crime Strategy | Mr Tyson Hepple | Tel: (020) 7273 3601 |
| Criminal Records and Security Industry | Mr Charles Goldie | Tel: (020) 7411 5515 |
| Domestic Violence | Ms Emma Churchill | Tel: (020) 7273 8124 |
| Drug Trafficking and Operational Policy | Mr Richard Rhodes | Tel: (020) 7273 4114 |
| Drugs Legislation and Enforcement Unit | Mr Vic Hogg | Tel: (020) 7273 2346 |
| Firearms | Mr Graham Widdecombe | Tel: (020) 7273 2623 |
| Financial Crime | Mr Jim Bradley | Tel: (020) 7273 3341 |
| Immigration Crime Strategy, Organised | Mr Giles Herbert | Tel: (020) 7273 3341 |
| Judicial Co-operation Unit | Mr Clive Welsh | Tel: (020) 7273 3923 |
| Partnership, Performance and Support | Mr David Truscott | Tel: (020) 7273 3601 |
| Performance and Strategy Management Unit | Mr Martin Parker | Tel: (020) 7273 3256 |
| Proceeds of Crime, Confiscation | Mr Clive Welsh | Tel: (020) 7273 3923 |
| Public Order and Crime Issues Unit | Mr Michael Gillespie | Tel: (020) 7273 3141 |
| Regions and Renewal | Mr John Curtis | Tel: (020) 7273 3601 |
| Serious Organised Crime | Mr Richard Kornicki | Tel: (020) 7273 3601 |
| Street Crime Action Team | Ms Clare Checksfield | Tel: (020) 7273 2951 |
| Terrorism and Protection Unit | *enquiries* | Tel: (020) 7273 2351 |
| Vehicle Crime | Mr Colin Petter | Tel: (020) 7035 5268 |
| Violent Crime | Ms Liz Wickstead | Tel: (020) 7035 5246 |
| Youth Crime | Mr Bernard Lane | Tel: (020) 7273 3162 |

**Criminal Justice**

| | | |
|---|---|---|
| Director-General, Criminal Justice | Ms Moira Wallace OBE | Tel: (020) 8282 6201 |
| Director, Criminal Justice IT | Ms Jo Wright | Tel: (020) 7271 3401 |
| Director, Criminal Justice Systems Performance | Ms Jane Furniss | Tel: (020) 7273 2993 |
| Director, Criminal Law and Policing | Mr Mark Ormorod | Tel: (020) 7273 2932 |
| Director, Race Unit, Criminal Justice System | Mr David Reardon | Tel: (020) 7273 3829 |
| Adult Offenders and Rehabilitation | Ms Louise Dominian | Tel: (020) 8282 6201 |
| Civil Renewal | Mr Henry Tam | Tel: (020) 8282 6201 |
| Crime, Law and Policy Unit | Ms Deborah Grice | Tel: (020) 8282 6201 |

# HOME OFFICE

*Criminal Justice (Continued)*

| | | |
|---|---|---|
| Criminal Justice System, Confidence in | Mr David Evans | Tel: (020) 8282 6201 |
| Criminal Justice System, Local Performance | Ms Ann-Marie Field | Tel: (020) 8282 6201 |
| Criminal Justice System, Planning and Analysis | Mr James Quinault | Tel: (020) 8282 6201 |
| Criminal Procedures and Evidence Unit | Mr Ian Chisholm | Tel: (020) 7273 3063 |
| Electronic Monitoring | Mr James Troon | Tel: (020) 7273 4099 |
| IT (Criminal Justice System) | Mr Mark Gladwin | Tel: (020) 7271 3401 |
| Resources Planning and Communications | Mr Paul David | Tel: (020) 7273 3376 |
| Victims | Mr Frances Flaxington | Tel: (020) 7273 3113 |
| Witnesses | Ms Catherine Lee | Tel: (020) 8282 6224 |

*Note: (020) 8282 numbers are based at 19th Floor, Portland House, Stag Place, London, SW1E 5RS.*

**DNA Database, National** . . . . . . . . . . . . . . . . Mr Bill Potts . . . . . . . . . . . . . . . . . Tel: (020) 7217 8010

**Drugs**

| | | |
|---|---|---|
| Director, Drugs Legislation and Enforcement | Ms Sue Killen | Tel: (020) 7273 4666 |
| Charities | Mr Richard Ivers | Tel: (020) 7273 2860 |
| Communities | | |
|     Criminal Justice | Mr Shereen Sadiq | Tel: (020) 7273 2277 |
|     Renewal | Mr Robin Burgess | Tel: (020) 7273 2947 |
| Drug and Alcohol Research Unit | Mr David Pyle | Tel: (020) 7273 3946 |
| Drugs Legislation and Enforcement Unit | Mr Vic Hogg | Tel: (020) 7273 2346 |
| Inspection | | |
|     Chief Inspector, Drugs Branch | Mr Alan Mcfarlane | Tel: (020) 7273 3778 |
| International | Mr Gabriel Denvir | Tel: (020) 7273 2324 |
| Legislation | Mr Tony Hall | Tel: (020) 7273 4131 |
| | Mr Chris Saint | Tel: (020) 7273 4096 |
| Trafficking and Operational Policy | Mr Richard Rhodes | Tel: (020) 7273 4114 |
| Young People | | |
|     Head, Treatment and Young People Unit | Mr Alastair Bridges | Tel: (020) 7273 8157 |
|     Diversity and Implementation | Ms Julie Clouder | Tel: (020) 7217 8208 |
|     Positive Futures | Mr Neil Watson | Tel: (020) 7273 2892 |
|     Prevention | Ms Joanne Hodges | Tel: (020) 7273 2803 |
|     Treatment | Mr Steve Tippell | Tel: (020) 7273 2149 |

**Entitlement Cards Unit** . . . . . . . . . . . . . Mr Stephen Harrison . . . . . . . . . . . . Tel: (020) 7035 5492

**Equalities**

| | | |
|---|---|---|
| Director, Race, Cohesion, Equality and Faith | Mr Mark Carroll | Tel: (020) 7273 2482 |
| Director, Race and Diversity Action Team | Ms Jenny Rumble | Tel: (020) 7273 3416 |

**European Union**

| | | |
|---|---|---|
| Head, European and International Unit | Ms Win Harris | Tel: (020) 7273 2906 |
| MEDA Unit (helping Turkey to achieve | | |
|     EU Judicial Co-operation standard) | Mr Paul Plummer | Tel: (020) 7273 3711 |

**Extradition**

| | | |
|---|---|---|
| Legislation | Mr Paul Regan | Tel: (020) 7273 2552 |
| Policy | Mr Bob Wood | Tel: (020) 7273 3030 |

**Finance** *(see below under Performance and Finance)*

**Firearms, Crime Reduction** . . . . . . . . . . Mr Graham Widdecombe . . . . . . . . . Tel: (020) 7273 2623

**Forensic Science Service Liaison** . . . . . . Mr Eric Downham . . . . . . . . . . . . . . Tel: (020) 7217 8091

**Human Resources, Departmental**

| | | |
|---|---|---|
| Director, Human Resources | Mr John Marsh | Tel: (020) 7217 0085 |
| Career Development and Assessment Unit | Ms Felicity Clarkson | Tel: (020) 7217 0418 |
| Central Personnel Management Unit | Mr Tony Williams | Tel: (020) 7217 0101 |
| Corporate Support Services Unit | Mr Nigel Benger | Tel: (020) 7217 0242 |
| Corporate Support Services Unit, Merseyside | Mrs Val Duffy *(Liverpool)* | Tel: (0151) 934 7526 |
| Departmental Security Unit | Mr David McDonough OBE | Tel: (020) 7217 0180 |

# HOME OFFICE

*Human Resources, Departmental (Continued)*

| | | |
|---|---|---|
| Health and Safety Policy | Mr Mike Jennings | Tel: (020) 7217 0420 |
| Health and Welfare Advice | Ms Karen Jones | Tel: (020) 7217 8534 |
| Pay and Pensions Service | Mr Tony Fitzpatrick *(Liverpool)* | Tel: (0151) 934 7414 |
| Policy and Employee Relations Unit | Mr Tom Randle | Tel: (020) 7217 0080 |
| Race and Diversity Action Team | Ms Sally Bruce | Tel: (020) 7273 3416 |

**Identity Cards** .......... Ms Katherine Courtney .......... Tel: (020) 7035 5373

**Immigration and Nationality**

*Immigration and Nationality Directorate, Apollo House, 36 Wellesley Road, Croydon, CR9 3RR*

| | | |
|---|---|---|
| Director-General, Immigration and Nationality | Mr Bill Jeffrey | Tel: (020) 7273 4000 |
| Deputy Director-General, Casework | Mr Ken Sutton | Tel: (020) 8760 8373 |
| Senior Director-General, Finance and Services | Mr David Stephens | Tel: (020) 8603 8080 |
| Senior Director-General, Operations | Mr Brody Clarke | Tel: (020) 8760 8532 |
| Senior Director-General, Policy | Mr Nick Baird | Tel: (020) 8760 8524 |
| Appeals | Ms Joyce Irvine | Tel: (020) 8604 6001 |
| Asylum *(See above under Asylum)* | | |
| Business Information Systems and Technology | Mr Stephen Calvard | Tel: (020) 8760 4421 |
| Business Support | Ms Jane Costello | Tel: (020) 8604 1961 |
| | Ms Jane Kennedy | Tel: (020) 8604 1928 |
| Detention Services | Mr Simon Barrett | Tel: (020) 8760 2535 |
| Enforcement and Removals | Mr Colin Allars | Tel: (020) 8760 2221 |
| Enforcement Policy | Mr Matt Laxton | Tel: (020) 8604 1942 |
| Finance and Services | Mr David Stephen | Tel: (020) 8603 8034 |
| Finance, Immigration and Nationality Directorate | Mr Tony Arber | Tel: (020) 8603 8177 |
| Human Resources, Immigration and Nationality | Mr Steven Barnett | Tel: (020) 8760 8001 |
| Immigration and National Policy | Ms Lorraine Rogerson | Tel: (020) 8760 8780 |
| Immigration Service, Major Policy | Mr Don Ingham | Tel: (020) 8760 2205 |
| International Policy | Ms Jenny Rumble | Tel: (020) 8760 8381 |
| Intelligence | Mr David Wilson | Tel: (020) 8745 2412 |
| Intelligence, London | Mr Tony Smith | Tel: (020) 8604 1942 |
| Operations and Enforcement, London | Mr Tony Smith | Tel: (020) 8760 2205 |
| Operations and Enforcement, National | Mr Colin Alard | Tel: (020) 8760 2205 |
| Managed Migration | Ms Paula Higson | Tel: (0114) 259 3633 |
| Policy | Mr Nick Baird | Tel: (020) 8769 8780 |
| Removals | Mr Tony Erne | Tel: (020) 8604 1966 |
| Work Permits | Mr Mick Seals | Tel: (0114) 259 3633 |

**International**

| | | |
|---|---|---|
| Head, European and International Unit | Ms Win Harris | Tel: (020) 7273 2906 |
| Extradition Legislation | Mr Paul Regan | Tel: (020) 7273 2552 |
| Judicial Co-operation Unit | Mr Clive Welsh | Tel: (020) 7273 3923 |
| Police, International | Mr Geoffrey Sonnenberg | Tel: (020) 7273 3929 |
| Policy | Mr Richard Bradley | Tel: (020) 7273 2413 |
| | Mr Simon Regis | Tel: (020) 7273 4083 |

**IT, Departmental**

| | | |
|---|---|---|
| Manager, Information Management and Technology | Mr Peter Lowe | Tel: (020) 7217 8625 |
| E-Business Strategy | Mr Chris Fleming | Tel: (020) 7217 8589 |
| IT. Technical | Mr Paul Vagg | Tel: (020) 7217 8472 |
| Records Management | Mr Richard Thompson | Tel: (020) 7273 2150 |

**Judicial Co-operation, International** .......... Mr Clive Welsh .......... Tel: (020) 7273 3923

**Juvenile Offenders** .......... Mr Simon Hickson .......... Tel: (020) 7273 3161

**Legal Advice**

| | | |
|---|---|---|
| Senior Legal Adviser | Mr David Seymour QC | Tel: (020) 7273 2681 |
| Deputy Legal Advisers | Mr David Noble | Tel: (020) 7273 2527 |
| | Mr Clive Osborne | Tel: (020) 7273 3098 |

# HOME OFFICE

**Marketing** *(see above under Communications)*

**National Crime Squad / National Criminal
    Intelligence Service, Liaison** . . . . . . . . . . . . . . . . . Ms Sarah Hammond . . . . . . . . . . . . . . . . . . . . . Tel: (020) 7273 4193

**Parliamentary Clerk** . . . . . . . . . . . . . . . . . . . . . . . . . . Mr Tony Strutt . . . . . . . . . . . . . . . . . . . . . . . . . . Tel: (020) 7273 3591

**Parole Board** . . . . . . . . . . . . . . . . . . . . . . . . . . . . . . . Ms Christine Glean . . . . . . . . . . . . . . . . . . . . . Tel: (020) 7217 5310

**Performance and Finance**
    Director-General, Resources
        and Performance . . . . . . . . . . . . . . . . . . . . . . . . Ms Margaret Aldred . . . . . . . . . . . . . . . . . . . . . Tel: (020) 7273 3285
    Director, Performance and Finance . . . . . . . . . . . . . . Mr William Nye . . . . . . . . . . . . . . . . . . . . . . . . Tel: (020) 7273 2566
    Accounting and Finance Unit . . . . . . . . . . . . . . . . . . Mr Carl Moynehan . . . . . . . . . . . . . . . . . . . . . Tel: (020) 7273 3621
    Audit and Assurance Unit . . . . . . . . . . . . . . . . . . . . Mr Tim Hurdle . . . . . . . . . . . . . . . . . . . . . . . . Tel: (020) 7802 1844
    Community Cohesion and Race Equality
        Strategy (Finance) . . . . . . . . . . . . . . . . . . . . . . . Mr Phillip Colligan . . . . . . . . . . . . . . . . . . . . . Tel: (020) 7273 2992
    Financial Management and Common Services . . . . . . . . Mr Tony Seale . . . . . . . . . . . . . . . . . . . . . . . . Tel: (020) 7217 0214
    Performance and Delivery Unit . . . . . . . . . . . . . . . . Ms Fiona Spencer . . . . . . . . . . . . . . . . . . . . . Tel: (020) 7273 2762
    Performance and Finance Support Unit . . . . . . . . . . . Ms Alison Barnett . . . . . . . . . . . . . . . . . . . . . Tel: (020) 7273 2499
    Resources and Planning Unit . . . . . . . . . . . . . . . . . Mr Andrew Wren . . . . . . . . . . . . . . . . . . . . . Tel: (020) 7273 8232
    Special Conference Centre . . . . . . . . . . . . . . . . . . . Ms Betty Sandars . . . . . . . . . . . . . . . . . . . . . Tel: (020) 7273 2266
    Strategic Policy Unit . . . . . . . . . . . . . . . . . . . . . . . Mr Ben Jupp . . . . . . . . . . . . . . . . . . . . . . . . Tel: (020) 7273 4681

**Police**
    Director, Police Standards *(Acting)* . . . . . . . . . . . . . . Mr Paul Pugh . . . . . . . . . . . . . . . . . . . . . . . . Tel: (020) 7035 5010
    Director, Policing Policy . . . . . . . . . . . . . . . . . . . . . Mr Stephen Rimmer . . . . . . . . . . . . . . . . . . . . Tel: (020) 7273 2935
    Director, Police Scientific Development . . . . . . . . . . . . *Vacant* . . . . . . . . . . . . . . . . . . . . . . . . . . . . . Tel: (01727) 816298
    Head, Police Leadership and Powers Unit . . . . . . . . . . Mr Paul Pugh . . . . . . . . . . . . . . . . . . . . . . . . Tel: (020) 7273 5010
    Head, Police Performance and Delivery Unit . . . . . . . . Ms Teresa Burnhams . . . . . . . . . . . . . . . . . . . . Tel: (020) 7273 3209
    Head, Police Resource Unit . . . . . . . . . . . . . . . . . . . Mr Andy Ford . . . . . . . . . . . . . . . . . . . . . . . . Tel: (020) 7273 4105
    Head, Head Policing and Organised Crime Unit . . . . . . Mr Stephen Webb . . . . . . . . . . . . . . . . . . . . . Tel: (020) 7273 2678
    Community Relations . . . . . . . . . . . . . . . . . . . . . . . Mr Andrew Morley . . . . . . . . . . . . . . . . . . . . . Tel: (020) 7035 5060
    Complaints . . . . . . . . . . . . . . . . . . . . . . . . . . . . . . Mr Andrew Morley . . . . . . . . . . . . . . . . . . . . . Tel: (020) 7035 5060
    Corruption . . . . . . . . . . . . . . . . . . . . . . . . . . . . . . Mr Andrew Morley . . . . . . . . . . . . . . . . . . . . . Tel: (020) 7035 5060
    Crime Fighting Fund . . . . . . . . . . . . . . . . . . . . . . . Mr Michael Grimwood . . . . . . . . . . . . . . . . . . . Tel: (020) 7273 2748
    Crime Reduction, Operational Policing . . . . . . . . . . . . Mr Ian Whyte . . . . . . . . . . . . . . . . . . . . . . . . Tel: (020) 7273 2748
    Discipline . . . . . . . . . . . . . . . . . . . . . . . . . . . . . . . Mr Andrew Morley . . . . . . . . . . . . . . . . . . . . . Tel: (020) 7035 5060
    Employment and Conditions of Service . . . . . . . . . . . Mr Gordon Davison . . . . . . . . . . . . . . . . . . . . Tel: (020) 7273 3251
    Equality and Diversity . . . . . . . . . . . . . . . . . . . . . . Mr Mark Stephenson . . . . . . . . . . . . . . . . . . . Tel: (020) 7273 2970
    Europol . . . . . . . . . . . . . . . . . . . . . . . . . . . . . . . . Mr Geoffrey Sonnenberg . . . . . . . . . . . . . . . . . Tel: (020) 7273 3929
    Financial Crime . . . . . . . . . . . . . . . . . . . . . . . . . . . Mr Jim Bradley . . . . . . . . . . . . . . . . . . . . . . . Tel: (020) 7273 3341
    High Tech Crime . . . . . . . . . . . . . . . . . . . . . . . . . . Mr Tim Wright . . . . . . . . . . . . . . . . . . . . . . . Tel: (020) 7273 3341
    Immigration Crime Strategy, Organised . . . . . . . . . . . Mr Giles Herbert . . . . . . . . . . . . . . . . . . . . . . Tel: (020) 7273 3341
    Interpol . . . . . . . . . . . . . . . . . . . . . . . . . . . . . . . . Mr Geoffrey Sonnenberg . . . . . . . . . . . . . . . . . Tel: (020) 7273 3929
    IT, Police . . . . . . . . . . . . . . . . . . . . . . . . . . . . . . . Dr Anthony Kent . . . . . . . . . . . . . . . . . . . . . . Tel: (020) 7217 8737
    Knowledge Management . . . . . . . . . . . . . . . . . . . . . Mr Paul Ibrahim . . . . . . . . . . . . . . . . . . . . . . Tel: (020) 7273 3713
    Leadership . . . . . . . . . . . . . . . . . . . . . . . . . . . . . . Ms Patricia McFarlane . . . . . . . . . . . . . . . . . . . Tel: (020) 7035 5029
    Occupational Health . . . . . . . . . . . . . . . . . . . . . . . . Mr John User . . . . . . . . . . . . . . . . . . . . . . . . Tel: (020) 7273 3201
    Overseas Deployment . . . . . . . . . . . . . . . . . . . . . . . Ms Sue Hay . . . . . . . . . . . . . . . . . . . . . . . . . Tel: (020) 7273 3210
    Pensions . . . . . . . . . . . . . . . . . . . . . . . . . . . . . . . . Mr John Gilbert . . . . . . . . . . . . . . . . . . . . . . . Tel: (020) 7273 2990
    Police Grant . . . . . . . . . . . . . . . . . . . . . . . . . . . . . Mr David Burge . . . . . . . . . . . . . . . . . . . . . . . Tel: (020) 7273 2996
    Powers and Procedures . . . . . . . . . . . . . . . . . . . . . . Mr John Woodcock . . . . . . . . . . . . . . . . . . . . Tel: (020) 7035 5043
    Public Order . . . . . . . . . . . . . . . . . . . . . . . . . . . . . Ms Catherine Webster . . . . . . . . . . . . . . . . . . . Tel: (020) 7273 8166
    Radio, Police . . . . . . . . . . . . . . . . . . . . . . . . . . . . . *Vacant* . . . . . . . . . . . . . . . . . . . . . . . . . . . . . Tel: (020) 7217 8154
    Recruitment Standards . . . . . . . . . . . . . . . . . . . . . . Ms Isobel Rowlands . . . . . . . . . . . . . . . . . . . . Tel: (020) 7273 4396
    Research *(see below under Research, Development and Statistics)*
    Resources . . . . . . . . . . . . . . . . . . . . . . . . . . . . . . . Mr Andy Ford . . . . . . . . . . . . . . . . . . . . . . . . Tel: (020) 7273 3893
    Schengen Information Systems . . . . . . . . . . . . . . . . . Ms Sarah Mann . . . . . . . . . . . . . . . . . . . . . . . Tel: (020) 7273 8254

# HOME OFFICE

*Police (Continued)*

Science

| | | |
|---|---|---|
| Deputy Director, Police Scientific Development | Dr Alan Pratt | Tel: (01727) 816277 |
| Crime Investigation | Mr Terry Kent | Tel: (01727) 816350 |
| Physical Protection | Mr Mark Stroud | Tel: (01727) 816298 |
| Public Protection | Professor Dick Lacey | Tel: (01727) 816330 |
| Support Services | Mr John Scott | Tel: (01727) 816210 |
| Technical Support | Mr Colin Payne | Tel: (01727) 816220 |
| Science and Technology Strategy | Ms Carol Burrows | Tel: (020) 7217 8341 |
| Senior Appointments | Ms Patricia McFarlane | Tel: (020) 7035 5029 |
| Special Constables | Mr Tim Hall | Tel: (020) 7273 3109 |
| Standards | Mr Paul Evans | Tel: (020) 7273 3068 |
| Training | Dr Sue Martin | Tel: (020) 7033 5014 |

## Police Inspectorate

HM Chief Inspector of Police . . . . . Sir Keith Povey QPM . . . . . Tel: (020) 7273 2116

## Press *(see above under Communications)*

## Prisons *(see above under Correctional Services)*

## Prison Inspectorate
*First Floor, Ashley House, 2 Monck Street, London, SW1P 2BQ*

| | | |
|---|---|---|
| H M Chief Inspector of Prisons | Ms Anne Owers CBE | Tel: (020) 7035 2100 |
| H M Deputy Chief Inspector of Prisons | Mr Nigel Newcomen | Tel: (020) 7035 2105 |

## Probation *(see above under Correctional Services)*

## Probation Inspectorate
*First Floor, Ashley House, 2 Monck Street, London, SW1P 2BQ*

H M Chief Inspector of Probation . . . . . Mr Andrew Bridges . . . . . Tel: (020) 7035 2202

## Proceeds of Crime, Confiscation . . . . . Mr Clive Welsh . . . . . Tel: (020) 7273 3923

## Race

| | | |
|---|---|---|
| Director, Race and Diversity Action Team | Ms Jenny Rumble | Tel: (020) 7273 3416 |
| Director, Race, Cohesion, Equality and Faith | Mr Mark Carroll | Tel: (020) 7273 2482 |
| Community Cohesion Unit | Ms Judith Lempriere | Tel: (020) 7035 5464 |
| Community Funding | Mr Rob Murphy | Tel: (020) 7035 5444 |
| Criminal Justice and Race | Mr David Reardon | Tel: (020) 7273 3829 |

## Refugee Integration . . . . . Dr Lesley Duff . . . . . Tel: (020) 8633 0068

## Regions and Renewal Unit . . . . . Mr Betty Moxton . . . . . Tel: (020) 7035 5456

## Research, Development and Statistics

| | | |
|---|---|---|
| Director, Research, Development and Statistics | Professor Paul Wiles | Tel: (020) 7273 2616 |
| Analysing Crime Programme | Ms Jo Simmons | Tel: (020) 7273 3868 |
| Communication and Development Group | Mr Mark Greenhorn | Tel: (020) 7273 3542 |
| Crime and Policing Group (CRSCG) | Mr Jon Simmons | Tel: (020) 7273 3594 |
| | Ms Carole Willis | Tel: (020) 7273 3594 |
| Drugs, Alcohol and Community GRoup | Dr Tony Munton | Tel: (020) 7035 2100 |
| International, Drugs, Economics and Resource Analysis Group | Mr David Pyle | Tel: (020) 7273 2471 |
| Offending and Criminal Justice Group | Dr Carole Hedderman | Tel: (020) 7273 2084 |
| Police and Crime Reduction | | |
| Head, Police and Reducing Crime Unit | Ms Carole Willis | Tel: (020) 7273 2748 |
| Burglary and Crime Reduction | Mr Ian Whyte | Tel: (020) 7273 2748 |
| Early Intervention | Ms Elaine James | Tel: (020) 7273 2748 |
| Evaluation, Overall | Ms Fiona Mclean | Tel: (020) 7273 2748 |
| High Tech Crime | Mr Tim Wright | Tel: (020) 7273 2748 |
| Leadership Management | Ms Patricia McFarlane | Tel: (020) 7035 5029 |
| Strategic Policy | Mr Ben Jupp | Tel: (020) 7273 2616 |

# H O M E   O F F I C E

Schengen Information Systems . . . . . . . . . . . . . . . . . . . Ms Sarah Mann . . . . . . . . . . . . . . . . . . . . . . . . . . Tel: (020) 7273 8254

Science Policy . . . . . . . . . . . . . . . . . . . . . . . . . . . . . Mr Tim Wilson . . . . . . . . . . . . . . . . . . . . . . . . Tel: (020) 7217 8535

Sentencing Policy . . . . . . . . . . . . . . . . . . . . . . . . . . Mr Roderick Macauley . . . . . . . . . . . . . . . . . . Tel: (020) 7273 3790
. . . . . . . . . . . . . . . . . . . . . . . . . . . . . . . . . . . . . . . Ms Beverley Moore . . . . . . . . . . . . . . . . . . . . . Tel: (020) 7273 3790
. . . . . . . . . . . . . . . . . . . . . . . . . . . . . . . . . . . . . . . Ms Diana Symonds . . . . . . . . . . . . . . . . . . . . . Tel: (020) 7273 2636

Sexual Offences Policy . . . . . . . . . . . . . . . . . . . . . . . Ms Ann Collier . . . . . . . . . . . . . . . . . . . . . . . . . Tel: (020) 7273 2267

Statistics *(see above under Research, Development and Statistics)*

Terrorism and Protection Unit . . . . . . . . . . . . . . . . . *enquiries* . . . . . . . . . . . . . . . . . . . . . . . . . . . . . Tel: (020) 7273 2351

Victims . . . . . . . . . . . . . . . . . . . . . . . . . . . . . . . . . . Ms Frances Flaxington . . . . . . . . . . . . . . . . . . . Tel: (020) 7273 4099

Work Permits . . . . . . . . . . . . . . . . . . . . . . . . . . . . . . Mr Mick Seals . . . . . . . . . . . . . . . . . . . . . . . . . Tel: (0114) 259 3633

## OTHER RELEVANT CONTACTS

### ANIMALS
**Animal Procedures Committee** . . . . . . . . . . . . . . . . . 5th Floor, Allington Towers, 19 Allington Street, London, SW1E 5EB
    Chairman . . . . . . . . . . . . . . . . . . . . . . . . . . . . . Rev Professor Michael Banner
    Secretary . . . . . . . . . . . . . . . . . . . . . . . . . . . . . . Mr Richard West . . . . . . . . . . . . . . . . . . . . . . . Tel: (020) 7035 5567
    Web: http://www.apc.gov.uk

### CHARITIES
**Charity Commission** . . . . . . . . . . . . . . . . . . . . . . . . . Harmsworth House, 13-15 Bouverie Street, London, EC4Y 8DP
    Chief Commissioner . . . . . . . . . . . . . . . . . . . . . . Mr John Stoker . . . . . . . . . . . . . . . . . . . . . . . . Tel: (0870) 333 0123
    Web: http://www.charitycommission.gov.uk

### COMMUNITY DEVELOPMENT
**Community Development Foundation** . . . . . . . . . . . . . 60 Highbury Grove, London, N5 2AG
    Chairman of Trustees . . . . . . . . . . . . . . . . . . . . . *Vacant*
    Chief Executive . . . . . . . . . . . . . . . . . . . . . . . . . . Ms Sarah Benioff . . . . . . . . . . . . . . . . . . . . . . . Tel: (020) 7226 5375
    E-mail: admin@cdf.org.uk
    Web: http://www.cdf.org.uk

### CRIME
**Assets Recovery Agency** . . . . . . . . . . . . . . . . . . . . . . PO Box 39992, London, EC4M 7XQ
    Director . . . . . . . . . . . . . . . . . . . . . . . . . . . . . . . Ms Jane Earl . . . . . . . . . . . . . . . . . . . . . . . . . . Tel: (020) 7029 5700
    Web: http://www.assetsrecovery.gov.uk
**Criminal Cases Review Commission** . . . . . . . . . . . . . Alpha Tower, Suffolk Street, Queensway, Birmingham, B1 1TT
    Chairman . . . . . . . . . . . . . . . . . . . . . . . . . . . . . Professor Graham Zellick
    Secretary . . . . . . . . . . . . . . . . . . . . . . . . . . . . . . Ms Fiona Hickman . . . . . . . . . . . . . . . . . . . . . Tel: (0121) 633 1800
    E-mail: ccrc@gtnet.gov.uk
    Web: http://www.ccrc.gov.uk
**Criminal Injuries Compensation Appeals Panel** . . . . . . 11th Floor, Cardinal Tower, 12 Farringdon Road, London, EC1M 3HS
    Chairman . . . . . . . . . . . . . . . . . . . . . . . . . . . . . Mr Roger Goodier
    Secretary . . . . . . . . . . . . . . . . . . . . . . . . . . . . . . Mr Roy Burke . . . . . . . . . . . . . . . . . . . . . . . . . Tel: (020) 7549 4600
    Web: http://www.cicap.gov.uk
**Criminal Injuries Compensation Authority** . . . . . . . . . Morley House, 26-30 Holborn Viaduct, London, EC1A 2JQ
    Chairman / Chief Executive . . . . . . . . . . . . . . . . . Mr Howard Webber . . . . . . . . . . . . . . . . . . . . . Tel: (020) 7842 6800
    Web: http://www.cica.gov.uk
**Criminal Records Bureau** *(Executive Agency)* . . . . . . . Globe House, 89 Ecclestone Square, London, SW1V 1PN
    Chief Executive . . . . . . . . . . . . . . . . . . . . . . . . . . Mr Vince Gaskell . . . . . . . . . . . . . . . . . . . . . . . Tel: (0870) 909 0811
    Web: http://www.crb.gov.uk
**National Crime Squad** . . . . . . . . . . . . . . . . . . . . . . . PO Box 2500, London, SW1V 2WF
    Director-General . . . . . . . . . . . . . . . . . . . . . . . . . Mr William Hughes QPM . . . . . . . . . . . . . . . . . . Tel: (020) 7238 2510
    Web: http://www.nationalcrimesquad.policy.uk
**National Criminal Intelligence Service** . . . . . . . . . . . . PO Box 8000, London, SE11 5EN
    Director-General . . . . . . . . . . . . . . . . . . . . . . . . . Mr Peter Hampson CBE QPM . . . . . . . . . . . . . . . Tel: (020) 7238 8000
    Web: http://www.ncis.gov.uk

### DRUGS
**Advisory Council on the Misuse of Drugs** . . . . . . . . . . Room 243, Home Office, 50 Queen Anne's Gate, London, SW1H 9AT
    Chairman . . . . . . . . . . . . . . . . . . . . . . . . . . . . . Professor Sir Michael Rawlins
    Secretary . . . . . . . . . . . . . . . . . . . . . . . . . . . . . . Mr Stewart Harwood . . . . . . . . . . . . . . . . . . . . Tel: (020) 7273 4096
    E-mail: acmd@homeoffice.gov.uk

# H O M E   O F F I C E

*Other Relevant Contacts (Continued)*

## FORENSIC SCIENCE

**Forensic Science Service** *(Executive Agency)*.......... Trident Court, 2920 Solihull Parkway, Birmingham, B37 7YN
    Director-General................................. Dr Dave Werretts...................... Tel: (0121) 329 8594
                    Web: http://www.forensic.gov.uk

## IMMIGRATION

**Office of the Immigration Service Commissioner** ..... 6th Floor, Fleetbank House, 2-6 Salisbury Square, London, EC4Y 8JX
    Commissioner................................. Mr John Scampion
    Deputy Commissioner........................... Ms Linda Allen........................ Tel: (0845) 000 0046
                    E-mail: info@isc.gov.uk
                    Web: http://www.oisc.gov.uk

## INTELLIGENCE / SECURITY SERVICES

**Investigatory Powers Tribunal**.................... PO Box 33220 London, SW1H 9ZQ
    President ..................................... Rt Hon Lord Justice Mummery
    Secretary ..................................... Mr David Payne ...................... Tel: (020) 7273 4514
**MI5** ........................................... Thames House, 12 Millbank, London, SW1P 1AE
    Director-General............................... Ms Eliza Manningham-Butler ............. Tel: (020) 7930 9000
                    Web: http://www.mi5.gov.uk
**Technical Advisory Board** ....................... PO Box 38542, London, SW1H 9YE
    Chairman ..................................... Mr Liam Strong
                    E-mail: tab@homeoffice.gsi.gov.uk
                    Web: http://www.technicaladvisoryboard.org.uk

## PAROLE

**Parole Board for England and Wales** .............. Abell House, John Islip Street, London, SW1P 4LH
    Chairman ..................................... Sir David Hatch CBE
    Chief Executive .............................. Ms Christine Glenn.................... Tel: (020) 7217 5314
                    E-mail: info@paroleboard.gov.uk
                    Web: http://www.paroleboard.gov.uk

## PASSPORTS

**UK Passport Service** *(Executive Agency)* .............. Globe House, 89 Eccleston Square, London, SW1V 1PN
    Director ...................................... Mr Bernard Herdan.................... Tel: (020) 7901 2000
                    Web: http://www.passport.gov.uk

## POISONS

**Poisons Board** ................................. Room 236, Home Office, 50 Queen Anne's Gate, London, SW1H 9AT
    Chairman ..................................... *Vacant*
    Secretary .................................... Mr Michael Evans..................... Tel: (020) 7273 3126

## POLICE

**Centrex (Central Police Training and Development
    Authority)** .................................. Bramshill, Hook, Hampshire, RG27 0JW
    Chairman ..................................... Sir Clive Booth
    Chief Executive .............................. Mr Paul Pugh ........................ Tel: (01256) 602100
                    Web: http://www.centrex.police.uk
**Independent Police Complaints Commission** ........ 6th Floor, 90 High Holborn, London, WC1V 6BH
    Chairman ..................................... Mr Nick Hardwick
    Chief Executive .............................. Mrs Susan Atkins .................... Tel: (020) 7166 3000
                    E-mail: enquiries@ipcc.gsi.gov.uk
                    Web: http://www.ipcc.gov.uk
**Police Advisory Board for England and Wales** ....... Office of Manpower Economics, Oxford House, 76 Oxford Street,
                    London, W1D 1BS
    Chairman ..................................... Professor Jon Clark
    Secretary .................................... Mr Michael Penny.................... Tel: (020) 7467 7218
                    Web: http://www.ome.uk.com
**Police Arbitration Tribunal** ...................... ACAS, Brandon House, 180 Borough High Street, London, SE1 1LW
    Chairman ..................................... Professor John Goodman CBE
    Secretary .................................... Mr Amit Sen ........................ Tel: (020) 7210 3742
                    E-mail: amit.sen@homeoffice.gsi.gov.uk
                    Web: http://www.homeoffice.gov.uk/pubapps/pdat.htm
**Police Discipline Appeals Tribunals** .............. Police Leadership and Powers Unit, 2nd Floor, Allington Towers,
                    19 Allington Street, London, SW1E 5EB
    *Contact*..................................... Mr Trevor Link ...................... Tel: (020) 7035 5036

# HOME OFFICE

*Other Relevant Contacts: Police (Continued)*

**Police Information Technology Organisation** ........ New King's Beam House, 22 Upper Ground, London, SE1 9QY
    Chairman ............................................ *Vacant*
    Chief Executive ................................. Mr Phillip Webb .................... Tel: (020) 8358 5555
        E-mail: reception@pito.pnn.police.uk
        Web: http://www.pito.org.uk
**Police Negotiating Board** ........................ Office of Manpower Economics, Oxford House, 76 Oxford Street, London, W1D 1BS
    Chairman ............................................ Professor Jon Clark
    Secretary ......................................... Mr Michael Penny .................. Tel: (020) 7467 7218
        Web: http://www.ome.uk.com

## PRISONS / PROBATION
**Correctional Services Accreditation Panel** .......... Room 129, Abel House, John Islip Street, London, SW1P 4LH
    Chairman ............................................ Sir Duncan Nichol
    Secretary ......................................... Mr Mark May ..................... Tel: (020) 7217 5193
**HM Inspectorate of Prisons for England and Wales** ... First Floor, Ashley House, 2 Monck Street, London, SW1P 2BQ
    H M Chief Inspector of Prisons ..................... Ms Anne Owers CBE
    Deputy Chief Inspector ............................ Mr Nigel Newcomen ............... Tel: (0870) 267 4298
        Web: http://www.homeoffice.gov.uk/justice/prisons/inspprisons/index.html
**HM Inspectorate of Probation** ...................... 2nd Floor, Ashley House, 2 Monck Street, London, SW1H 9AT
    H M Chief Inspector of Probation .................. Mr Andrew Bridge. ................ Tel: (020) 7035 2202
    Deputy Chief Inspector ............................ *Vacant*
**HM Prison Service** *(Executive Agency)* .............. Cleland House, Page Street, London, SW1P 4LN
    Director-General ................................. Mr Phil Wheatley ................ Tel: (020) 7217 3000
        E-mail: prisons.dg@homeoffice.gsi.gov.uk
        Web: http://www.hmprisonservice.gov.uk
**Independent Monitoring Boards of Prisons and**
  **Immigration Removal Centres** ................... 2nd Floor, Ashley House, 2 Monck Street, London, SW1P 2BQ
    President of the National Council ................. Sir Peter Lloyd
    Head of Secretariat .............................. Mr Norman McLean ............... Tel: (020) 7035 2254
        Web: http://www.homeoffice.gov.uk/imb
**Prison Service Pay Review Body** ..................... Office of Manpower Economics, 76 Oxford Street, London, W1D 1BS
    Chairman ............................................ Sir Toby Frere KCB
    Secretary ......................................... Mr Mike Cahill ................. Tel: (020) 7467 7226
**Prisons and Probation Ombudsman** .................. Third Floor, Ashley House, 2 Monck Street, London, SW1P 2BQ
    Ombudsman ....................................... Mr Stephen Shaw ................ Tel: (020) 7035 2876
        E-mail: mail@ppo.gsi.gov.uk
        Web: http://www.ppo.gov.uk

## RACE RELATIONS
**Commission for Racial Equality** .................... St Dunstan's House, 201-211 Borough High Street, London, SE1 1GZ
    Chairman ............................................ Mr Trevor Phillips OBE
    Chief Executive ................................. Ms Sheila Rogers ............... Tel: (020) 7939 0000
        Web: http://www.cre.gov.uk
**Race Equality Advisory Panel** ...................... Room 1371, Home Office, 50 Queen Annes Gate London, SW1H 9AT
    Secretary ......................................... Mr James Kingston ............... Tel: (020) 7273 3365
        E-mail: james.kingston@homeoffice.gsi.gov.uk

## SECURITY INDUSTRY
**Security Industry Authority** ....................... 4th Floor, 50 Broadway, London, SW1H 0SA
    Chairman ............................................ Mr Peter Hermitage QPM
    Chief Executive ................................. Mr John Saunders OBE ............ Tel: (020) 7227 3600
        Web: http://www.sia.org.uk

## SENTENCING
**Sentencing Advisory Panel** ......................... Room G11, Allington Towers, 19 Allington Street, London, SW1E 5EB
    Chairman ............................................ Professor Martin Wasik
    Secretary ......................................... Ms Lesley Dix. .................. Tel: (020) 7035 5158
        E-mail: info@sentencing-guidelines.gsi.gov.uk
        Web: http://www.sentencing-advisory-panel.gov.uk

## SURVEILLANCE
**Office of the Surveillance Commissioners** .......... PO Box 29105, London, SW1V 1ZU
    Chief Commissioner ............................... Sir Andrew Leggat
    Secretary ......................................... Ms Jennifer Riach. .............. Tel: (020) 7828 3421
        Web: http://www.surveillancecommissioners.gov.uk

## YOUTH JUSTICE
**Youth Justice Board for England and Wales** ........ 2nd Floor, 11 Carteret Street, London, SW1H 9DL
    Chairman ............................................ Professor Rod Morgan
    Chief Executive ................................. Mr Mark Perfect ................ Tel: (020) 7271 3033
        E-mail: enquiries@yjb.gsi.gov.uk
        Web: http://www.youth-justice-board.gov.uk

## ANTI-VIVISECTION

# BRITISH UNION FOR THE ABOLITION OF VIVISECTION

16a Crane Grove, London, N7 8NN
*Telephone* (020) 7700 4888
*Facsimile* (020) 7700 0252
*E-mail* campaigns@buav.org
*Web* http://www.buav.org

*Contact:* Adolfo Sansolini – *Chief Executive*

Founded in 1898, the British Union for the Abolition of Vivisection (BUAV) is the world's leading anti-vivisection campaigning organisation.

The BUAV is dedicated to using all peaceful means possible to end animal experiments, both nationally and internationally. Through public campaigning, undercover investigations, high profile media activities, political lobbying, legal and scientific expertise, the BUAV spreads its campaign message to as wide and diverse an audience as possible.

Working closely with experts in non-animal (in vitro) technology, the BUAV also promotes the development and use of non-animal tests, research methods that achieve reliable scientific results but without causing animal suffering.

As Chair of the European Coalition to End Animal Experiments and a founding member of the International Council for Animal Protection in OECD Programmes, the BUAV liaises with key animal groups to co-ordinate campaigning initiatives and ensure that laboratory animals are high on the international political agenda.

## ANTI-VIVISECTION

# NATIONAL ANTI-VIVISECTION SOCIETY

261 Goldhawk Road, London, W12 9PE
*Telephone* (020) 8846 9777
*Facsimile* (020) 8846 9712
*E-mail* campaigns@navs.org.uk
*Web* http://www.navs.org.uk

*Contact* Jan Creamer - *Director*

Founded in 1875, the NAVS is the foremost anti-vivisection organisation working to expose the futility and cruelty of animal experiments. The NAVS operates by public education, political lobbying and publicity campaigns to educate and inform both Parliament and the public of the dangers of relying upon animal research.

The NAVS shows animal experiments to be unnecessary, unreliable and unethical. Through its sister organisation, the Lord Dowding Fund for Humane Research (LDF), the group campaigns for better science by funding better science by funding scientists to find and develop alternatives to animal research. Since its inception, the LDF has awarded grants in excess of £1 million to scientific and medical research that does not involve animals.

# ANIMAL DEFENDERS

261 Goldhawk Road, London, W12 9PE
*Telephone:* (020) 8846 9777
*Facsimile:* (020) 8846 9712
*E-mail:* campaigns@animaldefenders.org.uk
*Web:* http://www.animaldefenders.org.uk

*Contact* Jan Creamer – *Director*

Founded in 1990, the Animal Defenders is an international animal welfare and conservation organisation. It aims to educate, create awareness and promote the interest of suppressing all forms of cruelty to animals.

The group lobbies Parliament; produces educational films, reports and literature used by schools, politicians and the media; investigates areas of animal suffering; and conducts international rescues.

Having completed a comprehensive study into the living conditions for circus animals, involving over 7,000 hours of observation and 800 hours of video footage, the Animal Defenders is campaigning to end animal circuses. The study revealed a catalogue of cruelty and confinement for the animals. As a result of the investigation the group secured convictions against three circus animal trainers for cruelty to animals in their care.

# ELECTORAL REFORM SOCIETY

6 Chancel Street, London, SE1 0UU

*Telephone* (020) 7928 1622
*Facsimile* (020) 7401 7789
*E-mail* ers@reform.demon.co.uk
*Web* www.electoral-reform.org.uk

*Contact* Ken Ritchie – *Chief Executive*

The Society campaigns for the modernisation of our democracy through electoral systems which increase voter choice, are more proportional and which ensure the accountability of elected representatives. Its preferred system is the Single Transferable Vote. The Society is also concerned with voter education, voting technologies and candidate selection procedures.

The Society has two subsidiaries: Electoral Reform Services conducts ballots and provides related services to clients including companies, trade unions and professional organisations, while Electoral Reform International Services provides election monitoring and advisory services worldwide.

## SERVICES SUPPORTING FAMILIES WHEN SOMEONE GOES MISSING

# NATIONAL MISSING PERSONS HELPLINE

Roebuck House
284-286 Upper Richmond Road West,
London, SW14 7JE
*Telephone* (020) 8392 4545
*Facsimile* (020) 8878 7752

*Co-Founders* Janet Newman OBE and Mary Asprey OBE

**The National Missing Persons Helpline (NMPH)** is recognised as one of the leading organisations in Europe which supports the families of those left behind when someone goes missing. The Charity, established in 1992, makes contact with vulnerable missing people, and reunites them with their families, if they so wish. NMPH also operates **Message Home Helpline** for those who have left home or are missing and **Runaway Helpline** for anyone 17 or under who has run away or been forced to leave home.

*Registered Charity No:* 1020419

| **NMPH Helpline** | **Runaway Helpline** | **Message Home Helpline** |
|---|---|---|
| **0500 700 700** | **0808 800 70 70** | **0800 700 740** |

# DEPARTMENT FOR INTERNATIONAL DEVELOPMENT

1 Palace Street, London, SW1E 5HE
Tel: (020) 7023 0000  Fax: (020) 7023 0019
Public Enquiry Telephone: (0845) 300 4100
E-mail: enquiry@dfid.gov.uk  Web: http://www.dfid.gov.uk

*Note: (01355) numbers refer to staff based at Abercrombie House, Eaglesham Road, East Kilbride, G75 8EA*

## MINISTERS

**Secretary of State for International Development**. . . . . . Rt Hon Hilary Benn MP
   *Principal Private Secretary*. . . . . . . . . . . . . . . . . . . . . . . . . Mr Moazzam Malik . . . . . . . . . . . . . . . . . . . . . . . . . . . . Tel: (020) 7023 0419
   *Special Advisers*. . . . . . . . . . . . . . . . . . . . . . . . . . . . . . . . Ms Beatrice Stern . . . . . . . . . . . . . . . . . . . . . . . . . . . . . Tel: (020) 7023 0606
                                     Mr Alex Evans. . . . . . . . . . . . . . . . . . . . . . . . . . . . . . . Tel: (020) 7023 0873

**Parliamentary Secretary**. . . . . . . . . . . . . . . . . . . . . . . . . Mr Gareth R Thomas MP
   *Private Secretary* . . . . . . . . . . . . . . . . . . . . . . . . . . . . . . . Ms Elizabeth Peri . . . . . . . . . . . . . . . . . . . . . . . . . . . . . Tel: (020) 7023 0621

## CIVIL SERVICE

**Permanent Secretary**. . . . . . . . . . . . . . . . . . . . . . . . . . . . Mr Suma Chakrabarti
   *Private Secretary* . . . . . . . . . . . . . . . . . . . . . . . . . . . . . . . Mr Charlie Whetham. . . . . . . . . . . . . . . . . . . . . . . . . . Tel: (020) 7023 0514

**Directors-General**

   Corporate Performance and Knowledge Sharing . . . . . . . . Mr Mark Lowcock . . . . . . . . . . . . . . . . . . . . . . . . . . . . Tel: (020) 7023 0439
   Policy and International. . . . . . . . . . . . . . . . . . . . . . . . . . . Mr Masood Ahmed . . . . . . . . . . . . . . . . . . . . . . . . . . . Tel: (020) 7023 0480
   Regional Programmes . . . . . . . . . . . . . . . . . . . . . . . . . . . . Dr Nicola Brewer CMG . . . . . . . . . . . . . . . . . . . . . . . . Tel: (020) 7023 0674

## SUBJECT RESPONSIBILITIES AND CONTACTS

**Accounts Department** *(see below under Finance and Corporate Development)*

**Africa**
   Director, Africa Division . . . . . . . . . . . . . . . . . . . . . . . . . . Mr Dave Fish . . . . . . . . . . . . . . . . . . . . . . . . . . . . . . . Tel: (01355) 843391
   Deputy Director, East and Central Africa . . . . . . . . . . . . . Mr David Batt . . . . . . . . . . . . . . . . . . . . . . . . . . . . . . . Tel: (020) 7023 1025
   Africa Corporate Issues Unit . . . . . . . . . . . . . . . . . . . . . . Mr Richard Dewdney. . . . . . . . . . . . . . . . . . . . . . . . . . Tel: (020) 7023 0077
   Commission for Africa . . . . . . . . . . . . . . . . . . . . . . . . . . . Mr Graham Stegmann . . . . . . . . . . . . . . . . . . . . . . . . . Tel: (020) 7023 0468
   Great Lakes and Horn Department. . . . . . . . . . . . . . . . . . Mr Desmond Curran . . . . . . . . . . . . . . . . . . . . . . . . . . Tel: (020) 7023 0438
   Deputy Director, Southern Africa . . . . . . . . . . . . . . . . . . . Mr Anthony Smith. . . . . . . . . . . . . . . . . . . . . . . . . . . . Tel: (020) 7023 0227
   Deputy Director, West Africa, Sudan, Conflict and
      Humanitarian Policy . . . . . . . . . . . . . . . . . . . . . . . . . . Mr Brian Thomson. . . . . . . . . . . . . . . . . . . . . . . . . . . Tel: (020) 023 0467

**Asia and Pacific**
   Director, Asia and Pacific Division . . . . . . . . . . . . . . . . . . Mr Martin Dinham CBE . . . . . . . . . . . . . . . . . . . . . . . . Tel: (020) 7023 0352
     *Head of Director's Cabinet* . . . . . . . . . . . . . . . . . . . . . Ms Pam Jenkins . . . . . . . . . . . . . . . . . . . . . . . . . . . . . Tel: (020) 7023 0490
   Deputy Director, Asia and Pacific Division. . . . . . . . . . . . Mr Marcus Manuel . . . . . . . . . . . . . . . . . . . . . . . . . . . Tel: (020) 7023 0351
   Asia Policy and Strategy . . . . . . . . . . . . . . . . . . . . . . . . . Mr Jeremy Clarke . . . . . . . . . . . . . . . . . . . . . . . . . . . Tel: (020) 7023 0082
   Country Programmes Unit (Asia) . . . . . . . . . . . . . . . . . . . Mr Stephen McClelland. . . . . . . . . . . . . . . . . . . . . . . . Tel: (020) 7023 1711
   Regional Policy Unit . . . . . . . . . . . . . . . . . . . . . . . . . . . . Mr John Gordon. . . . . . . . . . . . . . . . . . . . . . . . . . . . . Tel: (020) 7023 0881
   Western Asia Department . . . . . . . . . . . . . . . . . . . . . . . . Ms Joy Hutcheon . . . . . . . . . . . . . . . . . . . . . . . . . . . . Tel: (020) 7023 0343

**Central Asia** *(see below under Europe, Middle East and Americas)*

**Civil Society** . . . . . . . . . . . . . . . . . . . . . . . . . . . . . . . . . . . Mr Mike Green . . . . . . . . . . . . . . . . . . . . . . . . . . . . . Tel: (020) 7023 1032

**Commonwealth and United Nations**. . . . . . . . . . . . . . . . . Ms Carol Robson. . . . . . . . . . . . . . . . . . . . . . . . . . . . Tel: (020) 7023 0152

**Conflict and Humanitarian Affairs** . . . . . . . . . . . . . . . . . Mr Michael Mosselmans . . . . . . . . . . . . . . . . . . . . . . . Tel: (020) 7023 0776

**Eastern Europe** *(see below under Europe, Middle East and Americas)*

**Economics / Enterprise**
   Chief Economist . . . . . . . . . . . . . . . . . . . . . . . . . . . . . . . Mr Adrian Wood . . . . . . . . . . . . . . . . . . . . . . . . . . . . Tel: (020) 7023 0522
   Deputy Chief Economist and Head of Economics Profession . Mr John Burton . . . . . . . . . . . . . . . . . . . . . . . . . . . . . Tel: (020) 7023 0000
   Chief Enterprise Development Adviser. . . . . . . . . . . . . . . . Mr David Stanton. . . . . . . . . . . . . . . . . . . . . . . . . . . . Tel: (020) 7023 0263

**Education**
   Head of Education Profession . . . . . . . . . . . . . . . . . . . . . Mr Desmond Bermingham . . . . . . . . . . . . . . . . . . . . . . Tel: (020) 7023 1239

# DEPARTMENT FOR INTERNATIONAL DEVELOPMENT

**Engineering**
Head of Engineering Profession . . . . . . . . . . . . . . . . . . . . . Mr Martin Sergeant . . . . . . . . . . . . . . . . . . . . . . . . . Tel: (020) 7023 0116

**Environment**
Head of Environment Profession . . . . . . . . . . . . . . . . . . . Mr John Warburton . . . . . . . . . . . . . . . . . . . . . . . . . . Tel: (020) 7023 0879
Chief Environment Adviser . . . . . . . . . . . . . . . . . . . . . . . Mr Steve Bass . . . . . . . . . . . . . . . . . . . . . . . . . . . . . . Tel: (020) 7023 0879

**Europe, Middle East and Americas**
Director, Europe, Middle East and Americas Division . . . . . Ms Carolyn Miller . . . . . . . . . . . . . . . . . . . . . . . . . . . . Tel: (020) 7023 0497
Europe, Middle East and Americas Policy
Head of Department . . . . . . . . . . . . . . . . . . . . . . . . . . Ms Brenda Killen . . . . . . . . . . . . . . . . . . . . . . . . . . . Tel: (020) 7023 0893
Europe and Central Asia *(Albania, Armenia, Azerbaijan, Belarus, Bosnia and Herzegovina, Bulgaria, Croatia, Czech Republic, Estonia,*
*Federal Republic of Yugoslavia, Georgia, Hungary, Kazakhstan, Kyrgyz Republic, Latvia, Lithuania, Macedonia, Moldova, Poland,*
*Romania, Slovak Republic, Slovenia, Tajikistan, Turkmenistan, Uzbekistan)*
Head of Department . . . . . . . . . . . . . . . . . . . . . . . . . . Ms Jessica Irvine . . . . . . . . . . . . . . . . . . . . . . . . . . . . Tel: (020) 7023 0463
Iraq Directorate . . . . . . . . . . . . . . . . . . . . . . . . . . . . . . Mr Jim Drummond . . . . . . . . . . . . . . . . . . . . . . . . . . Tel: (020) 7023 0343
Latin America *(Colombia, Costa Rica, Cuba, Ecuador, El Salvador, Guatemala, Honduras, Nicaragua, Venezuela)*
Head of Department . . . . . . . . . . . . . . . . . . . . . . . . . . Mr Richard Teuten . . . . . . . . . . . . . . . . . . . . . . . . . . Tel: (020) 7023 0248
Middle East and North Africa *(Egypt, Jordan, West Bank/Gaza Strip, Yemen)*
Head of Department . . . . . . . . . . . . . . . . . . . . . . . . . . Mr Alistair Fernie . . . . . . . . . . . . . . . . . . . . . . . . . . . Tel: (020) 7023 0860
Overseas Territories *(Anguilla, Montserrat, Pitcairn Islands, St Helena, Tristan da, Cunha, Turks and Caicos Islands)*
Head of Department . . . . . . . . . . . . . . . . . . . . . . . . . . Mr Clive Cramen . . . . . . . . . . . . . . . . . . . . . . . . . . . Tel: (020) 7023 0293

**European Bank for Reconstruction and**
**Development: UK Delegation** . . . . . . . . . . . . . . . . . . . . Mr Mark Downes . . . . . . . . . . . . . . . . . . . . . . . . . . . . Tel: (020) 7023 1672

**European Union**
Head of Department . . . . . . . . . . . . . . . . . . . . . . . . . . . Mr Nick Dyer . . . . . . . . . . . . . . . . . . . . . . . . . . . . . . Tel: (020) 7023 0304

**Evaluation Department** . . . . . . . . . . . . . . . . . . . . . . . . . Mr Mike Hammond . . . . . . . . . . . . . . . . . . . . . . . . . . Tel: (01355) 84 3740

**Finance and Corporate Performance**
Director, Finance and Corporate Performance Division . . . . . Mr Richard Calvert . . . . . . . . . . . . . . . . . . . . . . . . . . . Tel: (020) 7023 1750
Deputy Director, Programme Guidance and Support . . . . . . Mr Stephen Chard . . . . . . . . . . . . . . . . . . . . . . . . . . . Tel: (01355) 843950
Deputy Director, Strategy and Finance . . . . . . . . . . . . . . . Mr Kevin Sparkhall . . . . . . . . . . . . . . . . . . . . . . . . . . Tel: (020) 7023 0510
Internal Audit Department . . . . . . . . . . . . . . . . . . . . . . . Mr Mike Noronha . . . . . . . . . . . . . . . . . . . . . . . . . . . Tel: (020) 7023 0193
Accounts Group . . . . . . . . . . . . . . . . . . . . . . . . . . . . . . Mr Mike Smithson . . . . . . . . . . . . . . . . . . . . . . . . . . . Tel: (01355) 843563
Financial Policy and Practice . . . . . . . . . . . . . . . . . . . . . Mr Ken Grimshaw . . . . . . . . . . . . . . . . . . . . . . . . . . . Tel: (020) 7023 0459
Procurement Group . . . . . . . . . . . . . . . . . . . . . . . . . . . Mr Tony Gardner . . . . . . . . . . . . . . . . . . . . . . . . . . . . Tel: (01355) 843441

**Financial Institutions, International** . . . . . . . . . . . . . . . . Ms Margaret Cund . . . . . . . . . . . . . . . . . . . . . . . . . . . Tel: (020) 7023 0155

**Food and Agriculture, UN Agencies for** . . . . . . . . . . . . . Mr Anthony Beattie . . . . . . . . . . . . . . . . . . . . . . . . . . Tel: (+39) 06 6840 0901

**G8 Presidency**
Director, G8 Presidency and Commission for Africa . . . . . . Mr Graham Stegmann . . . . . . . . . . . . . . . . . . . . . . . . Tel: (020) 7023 0468

**Governance**
Chief Governance Adviser . . . . . . . . . . . . . . . . . . . . . . . Ms Sue Unsworth . . . . . . . . . . . . . . . . . . . . . . . . . . . . Tel: (020) 7023 0000
Deputy Head of Governance Profession . . . . . . . . . . . . . . Mr Max Everest-Phillips . . . . . . . . . . . . . . . . . . . . . . . Tel: (020) 7023 0861

**Health and Human Development**
Chief Human Development Adviser . . . . . . . . . . . . . . . . . Dr Julian Lob-Levyt . . . . . . . . . . . . . . . . . . . . . . . . . . Tel: (020) 7023 0107
Deputy Head of Health Profession . . . . . . . . . . . . . . . . . Mr Stewart Tyson . . . . . . . . . . . . . . . . . . . . . . . . . . . Tel: (020) 7023 0960

**Human Resources**
Director, Human Resources . . . . . . . . . . . . . . . . . . . . . . *Vacant* . . . . . . . . . . . . . . . . . . . . . . . . . . . . . . . . . . . Tel: (01355) 843391
Human Resources Operations . . . . . . . . . . . . . . . . . . . . . Mr John Anning . . . . . . . . . . . . . . . . . . . . . . . . . . . . Tel: (01355) 843137
Human Resources Policy . . . . . . . . . . . . . . . . . . . . . . . . Mr Ian McKendry . . . . . . . . . . . . . . . . . . . . . . . . . . . Tel: (020) 7023 0231
Overseas Pensions . . . . . . . . . . . . . . . . . . . . . . . . . . . . Mr Peter Brough . . . . . . . . . . . . . . . . . . . . . . . . . . . . Tel: (01355) 843444

**Information**
Director, Information, Knowledge . . . . . . . . . . . . . . . . . . *Vacant* . . . . . . . . . . . . . . . . . . . . . . . . . . . . . . . . . . . Tel: (020) 7023 0532
Information and Civil Society . . . . . . . . . . . . . . . . . . . . . Mr Mike Green . . . . . . . . . . . . . . . . . . . . . . . . . . . . . Tel: (020) 7023 1032

**Information Systems and Services** . . . . . . . . . . . . . . . . . Mr Simon Jones . . . . . . . . . . . . . . . . . . . . . . . . . . . . Tel: (01355) 843437

**Infrastructure and Urban Development**
Head of Infrastructure and Urban Development Profession . . Mr Martin Sergeant . . . . . . . . . . . . . . . . . . . . . . . . . . Tel: (020) 7023 0116

**Internal Audit** *(see above under Finance and Corporate Performance)*

# DEPARTMENT FOR INTERNATIONAL DEVELOPMENT

**International Division**

| | | |
|---|---|---|
| Director | Mr Peter Grant | Tel: (020) 7023 0586 |
| Conflict and Humanitarian Affairs | Mr Michael Mosselmans | Tel: (020) 7023 0776 |
| International Division Advisory Team | Ms Rachel Turner | Tel: (020) 7023 0131 |
| International Financial Institutions | Ms Margaret Cund | Tel: (020) 7023 0155 |
| International Trade | Ms Diana Melrose | Tel: (020) 7023 0991 |

**Latin America** .......... Mr Richard Teuten .......... Tel: (020) 7023 0248

**Livelihoods**
Head of Livelihoods Profession .......... Mr Jim Harvey .......... Tel: (020) 7023 0285

**Middle East and North Africa** .......... Mr Alistair Fernie .......... Tel: (020) 7023 0860

**Overseas Territories** .......... Mr Clive Cramen .......... Tel: (020) 7023 0293

**Pensions, Overseas** *(see above under Human Resources)*

**Policy**

| | | |
|---|---|---|
| Director, Policy Division | Ms Sharon White | Tel: (020) 7023 1213 |
| Deputy Directors | Mr Marshall Elliott | Tel: (020) 7023 1263 |
| | Ms Susanna Moorehead | Tel: (020) 7023 0137 |
| | Dr Michael Schultz | Tel: (020) 7023 1264 |

**Private Sector Infrastructure / CDC** .......... Mr Gavin McGillivray .......... Tel: (020) 7023 0224

**Procurement** *(see above under Finance and Corporate Development)*

**Research Department** .......... Mr Paul Spray .......... Tel: (020) 7023 0361

**Rural Livelihoods**
Head, Rural Livelihoods Profession .......... Mr Jim Harvey .......... Tel: (020) 7023 0285

**Social Development**

| | | |
|---|---|---|
| Chief Social Development Adviser | Dr Andrew Norton | Tel: (020) 7023 0566 |
| Deputy Head of Social Development Profession | Ms Pat Holden | Tel: (020) 7023 0441 |

**Statistics**
Chief Statistician and Head of Statistics Profession .......... Mr Roger Edmunds .......... Tel: (020) 7023 0396

**Trade, International** .......... Ms Diane Melrose .......... Tel: (020) 7023 0991

**UNESCO**
UK Permanent Representative .......... Mr Tim Craddock .......... Tel: +33 145 68 27 84

**United Nations** .......... Ms Carol Robson .......... Tel: (020) 7023 0152

## OTHER RELEVANT CONTACTS

**COMMONWEALTH**

**Actis** .......... 2 More London Riverside, London, SE1 2JT
Chairman .......... Rt Hon Earl Cairns CVO CBE .......... Tel: (020) 7234 5000
E-mail: info@act.is  Web: http://www.act.is

**Association of Commonwealth Universities** .......... 36 Gordon Square, London, WC1H 0PF
Secretary-General .......... Dr Michael Gibbons
Executive Secretary .......... Dr John Kirkland .......... Tel: (020) 7380 6700
E-mail: info@acu.ac.uk  Web: http://www.acu.ac.uk

**Commonwealth Scholarship Commission** .......... 36 Gordon Square, London, WC1H 0PF
Chairman .......... Professor Trudy Harpham
Executive Secretary .......... Dr John Kirkland .......... Tel: (020) 7380 6700
E-mail: info@acu.ac.uk  Web: http://www.csfp-online.org

**CROWN AGENTS**

**Crown Agents Holding and Realisation Board** .......... St Nicholas House, St Nicholas Road, Sutton, Surrey, SM1 1EL
Chairman .......... Mr David Probert CBE
Executive Secretariat .......... Ms Lynn Hale .......... Tel: (020) 8643 3311
E-mail: enquiries@crownagency.co.uk  Web: http://www.crownagents.com

**PENSIONS**

**Overseas Service Pensions Scheme Advisory Board** .......... c/o Overseas Pensions Department, Department for International Development, Abercrombie House, Eaglesham Road, East Kilbride, G75 8EA
Chairman .......... Mr Peter Brough
Secretary .......... Mrs Shona Duff .......... Tel: (01355) 843562

## CYPRIOTS IN GREAT
## BRITAIN – FEDERATION

# NATIONAL FEDERATION
# OF CYPRIOTS IN GREAT BRITAIN

Britannia Centre, Britannia Road, London, N12 9RU
*Telephone* (020) 8445 9999 *Facsimile* (020) 8445 9977

*Contact:* Haris Sophoclides – *President*
Andreas Karaolis – *Secretary*

The National Federation is the representative organisation of over 250,000 Greek Cypriots in Britain – the largest and most high profile community outside Cyprus. Established in 1974, the Federation acts as an 'umbrella' organisation to 86 associations and branches of Cypriot political parties based in the UK.

The National Federation represents the UK Cypriot community in the World Federation of Overseas Cypriots, the World Council of Hellenes, the Coordinating Committee Justice for Cyprus and other International fora. In addition to maintaining close links with Cyprus, the aim of the Federation is to promote activities that will help towards achieving the withdrawal of the Turkish occupation forces, the return of the refugees to their homes and the reunification of Cyprus through a just and viable solution, which will bring peace and prosperity to all Cypriots.

## OVERSEAS DEVELOPMENT

# BESO (BRITISH EXECUTIVE SERVICE OVERSEAS)

164 Vauxhall Bridge Road, London, SW1V 2RA

*Telephone* (020) 7630 0644
*Facsimile* (020) 7630 0624
*E-mail* team@beso.org
*Web* http://www.beso.org

*Contact* Elspeth Graham – *Director Corporate Affairs*

BESO is a development agency that provides volunteers to share their experience and expertise with organisations that cannot afford commercial consultants. Advisers respond to requests for assistance from governments and local authorities, media, educational and health institutions, and give technical and managerial advice to small businesses and local industries, in developing economies worldwide.

*Registered Charity No:* 268094

# LAW OFFICERS' DEPARTMENT

Attorney General's Chambers
9 Buckingham Gate, London, SW1E 6JP
Tel: (020) 7271 2400  Fax: (020) 7271 2430
E-mail: lslo@gtnet.gov.uk
Web: http://www.lslo.gov.uk

## MINISTERS

**Attorney General** . . . . . . . . . . . . . . . . . . . . . . . . . . . . . . . Rt Hon Lord Goldsmith QC
**Solicitor General**. . . . . . . . . . . . . . . . . . . . . . . . . . . . . . . . Rt Hon Harriet Harman QC MP
*Private Secretary to the Attorney General and Solicitor General* . . . . . Ms Carolyn Bartlett . . . . . . . . . . . . . . . . . . . . . . Tel: (020) 7271 2405/6

## CIVIL SERVICE

**Head of Legal Secretariat and Head of Department** . . . . . . . Mr David Brummell . . . . . . . . . . . . . . . . . . . . . . Tel: (020) 7271 2401
Deputy Legal Secretary. . . . . . . . . . . . . . . . . . . . . . . . . . . . . Mr Stephen Bramley . . . . . . . . . . . . . . . . . . . . . . Tel: (020) 7271 2403
Establishments Officer . . . . . . . . . . . . . . . . . . . . . . . . . . . . . Ms Jenny Rowe . . . . . . . . . . . . . . . . . . . . . . . . . Tel: (020) 7271 2476
Legal Adviser to Law Officers, Northern Ireland . . . . . . . . . . . . Mr Kevin McGinty . . . . . . . . . . . . . . . . . . . . . . . Tel: (020) 7271 2412
Office Manager. . . . . . . . . . . . . . . . . . . . . . . . . . . . . . . . . . . Ms Robyn Liptrott . . . . . . . . . . . . . . . . . . . . . . . Tel: (020) 7271 2421
Parliamentary Clerk . . . . . . . . . . . . . . . . . . . . . . . . . . . . . . . Mr David Howarth . . . . . . . . . . . . . . . . . . . . . . . Tel: (020) 7271 2406

## OTHER RELEVANT CONTACTS

### PROSECUTION
**Crown Prosecution Service**
*50 Ludgate Hill, London, EC4M 7EX (Non-Ministerial Government Department)*
Director of Public Prosecutions. . . . . . . . . . . . . . . . . . . . . . . Mr Kenneth Macdonald QC
Chief Executive . . . . . . . . . . . . . . . . . . . . . . . . . . . . . . . . . . Mr Richard Foster . . . . . . . . . . . . . . . . . . . . . . . Tel: (020) 7796 8000
Web: http://www.cps.gov.uk

**Crown Prosecution Inspectorate**
*26-28 Old Queen Street London, SW1H 9HP*
HM Chief Inspector . . . . . . . . . . . . . . . . . . . . . . . . . . . . . . . Mr Stephen Wooler . . . . . . . . . . . . . . . . . . . . . . . Tel: (020) 7210 1197
E-mail: office@hmcpsi.gov.uk
Web: http://www.hmcpsi.gov.uk

### FRAUD
**Serious Fraud Office**
*Elm House, 10-16 Elm Street, London, WC1X 0BJ (Non-Ministerial Government Department)*
Director . . . . . . . . . . . . . . . . . . . . . . . . . . . . . . . . . . . . . . . Mr Robert Wardle . . . . . . . . . . . . . . . . . . . . . . . Tel: (020) 7239 7272
E-mail: public.enquiries@sfo.gov.uk
Web: http://www.sfo.gov.uk

### TREASURY SOLICITOR
**Treasury Solicitor's Department**
*Queen Anne's Chambers, 28 Broadway, London SW1H 9JS (Executive Agency)*
HM Procurator General and Treasury Solicitor. . . . . . . . . . . . Dame Juliet Wheldon DCB QC . . . . . . . . . . . . . . . . Tel: (020) 7210 3012
Web: http://www.treasury-solicitor.gsi.gov.uk

# NORTHERN IRELAND OFFICE

### Belfast Office
Stormont Castle, Belfast, BT4 4TT
Tel: (028) 9052 0700

### London Office
11 Millbank, London, SW1P 4PN
Tel: (020) 7210 3000
E-Mail: press.nio@nics.gov.uk
Web: http://www.nio.gov.uk

## MINISTERS

| | | |
|---|---|---|
| **Secretary of State for Northern Ireland** | Rt Hon Paul Murphy MP | |
| *Private Secretary* | Mr David Brooker | Tel: (028) 9052 8107 |
| *Special Advisers* | Mr Adam Higgett | Tel: (020) 7210 6461 |
| | Mr Owen Smith | Tel: (020) 7210 6461 |
| **Minister of State** | Rt Hon John Spellar MP | Tel: (028) 9037 8183 |
| *Private Secretary* | Mrs Fiona Newport | Tel: (020) 7210 6488 |
| **Parliamentary Secretary** | Mr Ian Pearson MP | |
| *Private Secretary* | Ms Cathy Clements | Tel: (028) 9037 8181 |
| | | (020) 7210 6498 |
| **Parliamentary Secretary** | Mr Barry Gardiner MP | |
| *Private Secretary* | Mr Alistair James | Tel: (028) 9052 9184 |
| | | (020) 7210 6500 |
| **Parliamentary Secretary** | Ms Angela Smith MP | |
| *Private Secretary* | Ms Teresa Hewitt | Tel: (028) 9052 2743 |
| | | (020) 7210 0284 |

## CIVIL SERVICE

| | | |
|---|---|---|
| **Permanent Secretary** | Sir Joe Pilling KCB | Tel: (028) 9037 8281 |
| | | (020) 7210 6456 |
| **Head of Civil Service** | Mr Nigel Hamilton | Tel: (028) 9037 8132 |
| **Appointments** | | Tel: (028) 9052 0700 |
| **Devolution and Legal Division** | | Tel: (020) 7210 6576 |
| **Electoral Matters** | | Tel: (020) 7210 6569 |
| **European Union** | | Tel: (020) 7210 6576 |
| **Firearms and Explosives** | | Tel: (028) 9052 0057 |
| **Inward Investment** | | Tel: (020) 7222 0599 |
| **Law Reform** | | |
| *Office of Law Reform, 5 Linenhall Street, Belfast, BT2 8AA* | | Tel: (028) 9054 2900 |
| **Legal Services** | | Tel: (028) 9025 1251 |
| **Legislative Counsel** | | Tel: (028) 7210 6576 |
| **Police Division** | | Tel: (028) 9052 0762 |
| **Political Affairs** | | Tel: (028) 9052 7085 |
| **Press Office** | | Tel: (028) 9037 8268 |
| | | (020) 7210 6518 |
| **Rights and International Relations** | | Tel: (020) 7210 6587 |
| **Security Policy** | | Tel: (020) 9052 7024 |

# NORTHERN IRELAND OFFICE

## NORTHERN IRELAND ADMINISTRATION
Stormont Castle, Stormont Estate
Belfast, BT4 3TT

*Note: At the time of publication the Northern Ireland Assembly and Ministers had been suspended and responsibility for the devolved administration had been assumed by the Northern Ireland Office. The relevant Departments are, therefore, listed here. Should the devolved administration be restored, then responsibility will be returned to the Assembly and the appropriate Assembly Ministers.*

**Head of Northern Ireland Civil Service and**
    **Permanent Secretary**............................... Mr Nigel Hamilton
    *Private Secretary* ...................................... Ms Debbie Sweeney ............... Tel: (028) 9037 8132

**Second Permanent Secretary**.......................... Mr Will Haire
    *Private Secretary* ...................................... Ms Kathryn Menary ............... Tel: (028) 9037 8036

**Civic Forum** ........................................... Ms Rosalie Flanagan .............. Tel: (028) 9037 8123

**Communications**........................................ Mr Stephen Grimason.............. Tel: (028) 9037 8102

**Community Relations** ................................... Ms Mary Bunting .................. Tel: (028) 9052 2857

**Economic Policy** ....................................... Mr Edgar Jardine.................. Tel: (028) 9052 8505

**Emergency Planning** .................................... Ms Dorothy Angus ................ Tel: (028) 9052 8153
    Personnel Division
        Business Development Branch ........................ Mr G Hill........................ Tel; (028) 9052 4722
        Personnel Management Branch....................... Mr R Campton .................... Tel: (028) 9052 4760
        Personnel Services Branch ......................... Mr E Dickson..................... Tel: (028) 9052 4301

**Equality**............................................... Ms Mary Bunting .................. Tel: (028) 9052 2857

**European Affairs** ...................................... Mr Edgar Jardine.................. Tel: (028) 9052 8505

**Freedom of Information**................................. Mr Edgar Jardine.................. Tel: (028) 9052 8505

**Legislation**............................................ Ms Rosalie Flanagan .............. Tel: (028) 9037 8123

**Legislative Council**
*Office of the Legislative Council, Parliament Buildings, Stormont, Belfast, BT4 3SW*.................... Tel: (028) 9052 1307

**Press Office**
    Principal Information Officers ........................ Mr Paddy Cullen .................. Tel: (028) 9037 8116
                                         Mr Don McAleer .................. Tel: (028) 9037 8105

**Public Appointments Body**.............................. Ms Dorothy Angus ................ Tel: (028) 9052 8153

**Public Service Improvement Unit** ...................... Mr Edgar Jardine.................. Tel: (028) 9052 8505

**Victims** ............................................... Ms Mary Bunting .................. Tel: (028) 9052 2857

**Women's Issues** ........................................ Mr Edgar Jardine.................. Tel: (028) 9052 8505

# NORTHERN IRELAND OFFICE

## Department of Agriculture and Rural Development
Dundonald House
Upper Newtownards Road
Belfast, BT4 3SB
Tel: (028) 9052 4999  Fax: (028) 9052 5003
E-mail: library.dardni@nics.gov.uk
Web: http://www.dard.gov.uk

**Responsible Minister** . . . . . . . . . . . . . . . . . . . . . . . . . . . . . . . Mr Ian Pearson MP
*Private Secretary* . . . . . . . . . . . . . . . . . . . . . . . . . . . . . . . . . . . . Mr Philip Gilmore . . . . . . . . . . . . . . Tel: (028) 9052 4159

**Permanent Secretary** . . . . . . . . . . . . . . . . . . . . . . . . . . . . . . . Mr Pat Toal . . . . . . . . . . . . . . . . . . . . Tel: (028) 9052 4608

**Central Policy Group**
    Animal Disease Control . . . . . . . . . . . . . . . . . . . . . . . . . . . . . . . Ms Collette McMaster . . . . . . . . . . . . . Tel: (028) 9052 4660
    Animal Welfare & Trade . . . . . . . . . . . . . . . . . . . . . . . . . . . . . . Ms Colette Connor . . . . . . . . . . . . . . . . Tel: (028) 9052 5362
    Farm Policy. . . . . . . . . . . . . . . . . . . . . . . . . . . . . . . . . . . . . . . . Mr Joe Cassells . . . . . . . . . . . . . . . . . Tel: (028) 9052 4493
    Food Policy . . . . . . . . . . . . . . . . . . . . . . . . . . . . . . . . . . . . . . . Mr Peter Scott . . . . . . . . . . . . . . . . . . Tel: (028) 9052 4496
    Environmental Policy . . . . . . . . . . . . . . . . . . . . . . . . . . . . . . . . Mr Ian McKee . . . . . . . . . . . . . . . . . . . Tel: (028) 9052 4773
    Economic and Statistics Unit . . . . . . . . . . . . . . . . . . . . . . . . . . Mr Tom Stainer . . . . . . . . . . . . . . . . . Tel: (028) 9052 4655
    Fisheries. . . . . . . . . . . . . . . . . . . . . . . . . . . . . . . . . . . . . . . . . Mr Noel Cornick . . . . . . . . . . . . . . . . . Tel: (028) 9052 2438
    Policy Co-ordination including CAP . . . . . . . . . . . . . . . . . . . . . Mr Norman Fulton . . . . . . . . . . . . . . . Tel: (028) 9052 4419
    TSE Branch (Beef, BSE) . . . . . . . . . . . . . . . . . . . . . . . . . . . . . Miss Kate Davey . . . . . . . . . . . . . . . . Tel: (028) 9052 4408

**Central Services Group**
Change Division
    Information Management . . . . . . . . . . . . . . . . . . . . . . . . . . . . . Mr C Bennett . . . . . . . . . . . . . . . . . . . Tel: (028) 9052 4211
    Information Systems and
        Estate Management  . . . . . . . . . . . . . . . . . . . . . . . . . . . . Mr E Long . . . . . . . . . . . . . . . . . . . . . Tel: (028) 9052 4714
    Modernisation Unit . . . . . . . . . . . . . . . . . . . . . . . . . . . . . . . . . Ms B Stuart . . . . . . . . . . . . . . . . . . . . Tel: (028) 9052 4455
                                                         Ms H Hagan . . . . . . . . . . . . . . . . . . . Tel: (028) 9052 5457
Corporate Policy Division
    Central Management Branch . . . . . . . . . . . . . . . . . . . . . . . . . . Mr E Gallagher . . . . . . . . . . . . . . . . . Tel: (028) 9052 4331
    Media Services . . . . . . . . . . . . . . . . . . . . . . . . . . . . . . . . . . . . Mrs B McCusker . . . . . . . . . . . . . . . . Tel: (028) 9052 4619
    Rural Proofing. . . . . . . . . . . . . . . . . . . . . . . . . . . . . . . . . . . . . Ms Lindsay Hodges . . . . . . . . . . . . . . Tel: (028) 9052 4311
Finance Division
    Financial Policy . . . . . . . . . . . . . . . . . . . . . . . . . . . . . . . . . . . . Mr J Ditchfield . . . . . . . . . . . . . . . . . . Tel: (028) 9052 4551
    Internal Audit . . . . . . . . . . . . . . . . . . . . . . . . . . . . . . . . . . . . . Mr S McGuinness . . . . . . . . . . . . . . . . Tel: (028) 9052 3171
Personnel Division
    Business Development Branch . . . . . . . . . . . . . . . . . . . . . . . . . Mr G Hill . . . . . . . . . . . . . . . . . . . . . . Tel; (028) 9052 4722
    Personnel Management Branch . . . . . . . . . . . . . . . . . . . . . . . . Mr R Campton . . . . . . . . . . . . . . . . . . Tel: (028) 9052 4760
    Personnel Services Branch . . . . . . . . . . . . . . . . . . . . . . . . . . . Mr E Dickson . . . . . . . . . . . . . . . . . . . Tel: (028) 9052 4301

**Science Service**
*Dundonald House, Upper Newtownards Road, Belfast BT4 3SB*
    Chief Scientific Officer . . . . . . . . . . . . . . . . . . . . . . . . . . . . . . . . . . . . . . . . . . . . . . . . . . . . . . . . . . . . . . . . . . Tel: (028) 9052 4635
*Newforge Lane, Belfast BT9 5PX*
    Agricultural and Food Economics . . . . . . . . . . . . . . . . . . . . . . . . . . . . . . . . . . . . . . . . . . . . . . . . . . . . . . . . . . Tel: (028) 9025 5204
    Agriculture, Food and Environmental Science . . . . . . . . . . . . . . . . . . . . . . . . . . . . . . . . . . . . . . . . . . . . . . . . . Tel: (028) 9025 5478
    Biometrics . . . . . . . . . . . . . . . . . . . . . . . . . . . . . . . . . . . . . . . . . . . . . . . . . . . . . . . . . . . . . . . . . . . . . . . . . . . . Tel: (028) 9052 5209
    Plant Science . . . . . . . . . . . . . . . . . . . . . . . . . . . . . . . . . . . . . . . . . . . . . . . . . . . . . . . . . . . . . . . . . . . . . . . . . . Tel: (028) 9025 5305
*Stoney Road, Belfast, BT4 3SQ*
    Veterinary Sciences . . . . . . . . . . . . . . . . . . . . . . . . . . . . . . . . . . . . . . . . . . . . . . . . . . . . . . . . . . . . . . . . . . . . Tel: (028) 9052 5600

**Service Delivery Group**
College of Agriculture, Food & Rural Enterprise (CAFRE)
*Greenmount Campus, 22 Greenmount Road, Antrim, BT41 4PU* . . . . Mr Paul McGurnaghan . . . . . . . . . . . . . Tel: (028) 9442 6620
*Loughry Campus, Cookstown, BT80 9AA* . . . . . . . . . . . . . . . . . . . Dr Michael Mullan . . . . . . . . . . . . . . . Tel: (028) 8676 8126
*Enniskillen Campus, Levaghy, Enniskillen, BT74 4GF* . . . . . . . . . . Mr Seamus McAlinney . . . . . . . . . . . . . Tel: (028) 6634 4855

*Department of Agriculture and Rural Development (Continued)*

Environment, Food & Central Services Division
    Countryside Management Branch . . . . . . . . . . . . . . . . . . . . . . . Mr Harry Gracey . . . . . . . . . . . . . . . . . Tel: (028) 9052 4713
    Education and Finance Branch . . . . . . . . . . . . . . . . . . . . . . . . Mrs Pauline Rooney . . . . . . . . . . . . . . Tel: (028) 9052 4413
    Organisational Improvement Branch . . . . . . . . . . . . . . . . . . . . Professor Eric Long . . . . . . . . . . . . . . . Tel: (028) 9052 4718
    Rural Connect Branch . . . . . . . . . . . . . . . . . . . . . . . . . . . . . . Mr Jim Torney . . . . . . . . . . . . . . . . . . . Tel: (028) 9052 4529
    Supply Chain Development Branch . . . . . . . . . . . . . . . . . . . . . Mr John McGaughey . . . . . . . . . . . . . . Tel: (028) 9052 4239
Rural Development Division
    Rural Development Central Branch . . . . . . . . . . . . . . . . . . . . . Mr Michael McLernon . . . . . . . . . . . . . Tel: (028) 9052 4578
    Rural Development Peace Branch . . . . . . . . . . . . . . . . . . . . . . Mr Brian Morrison . . . . . . . . . . . . . . . . Tel: (028) 9054 7188
Rural Payments & Inspection Division
    Payments . . . . . . . . . . . . . . . . . . . . . . . . . . . . . . . . . . . . . . . *enquiries* . . . . . . . . . . . . . . . . . . . . . . Tel: (028) 7131 9900
    Policy . . . . . . . . . . . . . . . . . . . . . . . . . . . . . . . . . . . . . . . . . *enquiries* . . . . . . . . . . . . . . . . . . . . . . Tel: (028) 9052 4595

## Veterinary Service
    Chief Veterinary Officer . . . . . . . . . . . . . . . . . . . . . . . . . . . . . . . . . . . . . . . . . . . . . . . . . . . . . Tel: (028) 9052 4669
    Deputy Chief Veterinary Officer – Implementation . . . . . . . . . . . . . . . . . . . . . . . . . . . . . . . . . . Tel: (028) 9052 4643
    Deputy Chief Veterinary Officer – Policy . . . . . . . . . . . . . . . . . . . . . . . . . . . . . . . . . . . . . . . . . Tel: (028) 9052 4670
    Enzootics . . . . . . . . . . . . . . . . . . . . . . . . . . . . . . . . . . . . . . . . . . . . . . . . . . . . . . . . . . . . . . . . . Tel: (028) 9052 4649
    Epizootics . . . . . . . . . . . . . . . . . . . . . . . . . . . . . . . . . . . . . . . . . . . . . . . . . . . . . . . . . . . . . . . . Tel: (028) 9052 4764
    Field Services – Northern Region . . . . . . . . . . . . . . . . . . . . . . . . . . . . . . . . . . . . . . . . . . . . . . . Tel: (028) 9052 4305
    Field Services – Southern Region . . . . . . . . . . . . . . . . . . . . . . . . . . . . . . . . . . . . . . . . . . . . . . . Tel: (028) 9052 4621
    Meat Hygiene . . . . . . . . . . . . . . . . . . . . . . . . . . . . . . . . . . . . . . . . . . . . . . . . . . . . . . . . . . . . . Tel: (028) 9052 4662
    Slaughterhouses . . . . . . . . . . . . . . . . . . . . . . . . . . . . . . . . . . . . . . . . . . . . . . . . . . . . . . . . . . . Tel: (028) 9052 4662
*Veterinary Service, Stoney Road, Belfast, BT4 3SQ* . . . . . . . . . . . . . . . . . . . . . . . . . . . . . . . . . . . . Tel: (028) 9052 5600

# NORTHERN IRELAND OFFICE

## Department of Culture, Arts and Leisure
Interpoint, 20-24 York Street,
Belfast, BT15 1AQ
Tel: (028) 9025 8825  Fax: (028) 9025 8906
E-mail: dcal@dcalni.gov.uk
Web: http://www.dcalni.gov.uk

**Responsible Minister** . . . . . . . . . . . . . . . . . . . . . . . . . . . . . . . . . . Ms Angela Smith MP
   *Private Secretary* . . . . . . . . . . . . . . . . . . . . . . . . . . . . . . . . . Ms Anne Loughran . . . . . . . . . . . . . . . . Tel: (028) 9025 8807

**Permanent Secretary** . . . . . . . . . . . . . . . . . . . . . . . . . . . . . . . Dr Aideen McGinley . . . . . . . . . . . . . . Tel: (028) 9025 8814

Deputy Secretary . . . . . . . . . . . . . . . . . . . . . . . . . . . . . . . . . . . . . Ms Carol Moore . . . . . . . . . . . . . . . . . . Tel: (028) 9025 8848

Principal Information Officer . . . . . . . . . . . . . . . . . . . . . . . . . . . Mrs Jill Heron . . . . . . . . . . . . . . . . . . . . Tel: (028) 9025 8900

Arts . . . . . . . . . . . . . . . . . . . . . . . . . . . . . . . . . . . . . . . . . . . . . . . . . . . . . . . . . . . . . . . . . . . . . . . . . . . . . . . . . . . . . Tel: (028) 9025 8801

Cultural Diversity . . . . . . . . . . . . . . . . . . . . . . . . . . . . . . . . . . . . . . . . . . . . . . . . . . . . . . . . . . . . . . . . . . . . . . . . Tel: (028) 9025 8821

Inland Fisheries . . . . . . . . . . . . . . . . . . . . . . . . . . . . . . . . . . . . . . . . . . . . . . . . . . . . . . . . . . . . . . . . . . . . . . . . . . Tel: (028) 9025 8801

Inland Waterways . . . . . . . . . . . . . . . . . . . . . . . . . . . . . . . . . . . . . . . . . . . . . . . . . . . . . . . . . . . . . . . . . . . . . . . . Tel: (028) 9025 8801

Libraries . . . . . . . . . . . . . . . . . . . . . . . . . . . . . . . . . . . . . . . . . . . . . . . . . . . . . . . . . . . . . . . . . . . . . . . . . . . . . . . . . Tel: (028) 9025 8801

Linguistic Diversity . . . . . . . . . . . . . . . . . . . . . . . . . . . . . . . . . . . . . . . . . . . . . . . . . . . . . . . . . . . . . . . . . . . . . . . Tel: (028) 9025 8821

Museums . . . . . . . . . . . . . . . . . . . . . . . . . . . . . . . . . . . . . . . . . . . . . . . . . . . . . . . . . . . . . . . . . . . . . . . . . . . . . . . . . Tel: (028) 9025 8801

National Lottery . . . . . . . . . . . . . . . . . . . . . . . . . . . . . . . . . . . . . . . . . . . . . . . . . . . . . . . . . . . . . . . . . . . . . . . . . . Tel: (028) 9025 8801

Policy, Evaluation and Research . . . . . . . . . . . . . . . . . . . . . . . . . . . . . . . . . . . . . . . . . . . . . . . . . . . . . . . . . . . Tel: (028) 9025 8821

Sport . . . . . . . . . . . . . . . . . . . . . . . . . . . . . . . . . . . . . . . . . . . . . . . . . . . . . . . . . . . . . . . . . . . . . . . . . . . . . . . . . . . . Tel: (028) 9025 8801

# NORTHERN IRELAND OFFICE

## Department of Education

Rathgael House, Balloo Road, Bangor
County Down, BT19 7PR
Tel: (028) 9127 9279  Fax: (028) 9127 9100
E-mail: deni@nics.gov.uk
Web: http://www.deni.gov.uk

**Responsible Minister** . . . . . . . . . . . . . . . . . . . . . . . . . . . . . . . . . Mr Barry Gardiner MP
*Private Secretary* . . . . . . . . . . . . . . . . . . . . . . . . . . . . . . . Ms Patricia McBride . . . . . . . . . . . . . . Tel: (028) 9127 9303

**Permanent Secretary** . . . . . . . . . . . . . . . . . . . . . . . . . . . . Mr Gerry McGinn . . . . . . . . . . . . . . . . . Tel: (028) 9127 9309

Deputy Secretary . . . . . . . . . . . . . . . . . . . . . . . . . . . . . . . . . . Dr Eddie Rooney . . . . . . . . . . . . . . . Tel: (028) 9127 9313

Area Boards Resource Allocation and Monitoring (ABRAM) . . . . . . . . . . . . . . . . . . . . . . . . . . . . . . . . . Tel: (028) 9127 9224

Community Relations . . . . . . . . . . . . . . . . . . . . . . . . . . . . . . . . . . . . . . . . . . . . . . . . . . . . . Tel: (028)  9127 9511

Curriculum and Assessment . . . . . . . . . . . . . . . . . . . . . . . . . . . . . . . . . . . . . . . . . . . . . . . . . Tel: (028) 9127 9533

Finance, Departmental . . . . . . . . . . . . . . . . . . . . . . . . . . . . . . . . . . . . . . . . . . . . . . . . . . . . . Tel: (028) 9127 9680

Inspections . . . . . . . . . . . . . . . . . . . . . . . . . . . . . . . . . . . . . . . . . . . . . . . . . . . . . . . . . . . . Tel: (028) 9127 9726

Irish Medium Policy . . . . . . . . . . . . . . . . . . . . . . . . . . . . . . . . . . . . . . . . . . . . . . . . . . . . . . Tel: (028) 9127 9671

Nursery Education . . . . . . . . . . . . . . . . . . . . . . . . . . . . . . . . . . . . . . . . . . . . . . . . . . . . . . . Tel: (028) 9127 9227

Open Enrolment and Transfer Procedure . . . . . . . . . . . . . . . . . . . . . . . . . . . . . . . . . . . . . . . . . . Tel: (028) 9127 9605

Post Primary Review . . . . . . . . . . . . . . . . . . . . . . . . . . . . . . . . . . . . . . . . . . . . . . . . . . . . . . Tel: (028) 9127 9360

Press Office, Principal Information Officer . . . . . . . . . . . . . . . . . . . Mrs Jill Garrett . . . . . . . . . . . . . . . . . Tel: (028) 9127 9356

Pupil Support . . . . . . . . . . . . . . . . . . . . . . . . . . . . . . . . . . . . . . . . . . . . . . . . . . . . . . . . . Tel: (028) 9127 9749

Qualifications and Business Education/Links . . . . . . . . . . . . . . . . . . . . . . . . . . . . . . . . . . . . . . . Tel: (028) 9127 9406

Schools: Maintenance Programme, Major Capital Projects,
Primary and Secondary Development . . . . . . . . . . . . . . . . . . . . . . . . . . . . . . . . . . . . . . . . Tel: (028) 9127 9477

School Meals . . . . . . . . . . . . . . . . . . . . . . . . . . . . . . . . . . . . . . . . . . . . . . . . . . . . . . . . . Tel: (028) 9127 9215

School Transport . . . . . . . . . . . . . . . . . . . . . . . . . . . . . . . . . . . . . . . . . . . . . . . . . . . . . . . Tel: (028) 9127 9585

Special Education . . . . . . . . . . . . . . . . . . . . . . . . . . . . . . . . . . . . . . . . . . . . . . . . . . . . . . . Tel: (028) 9127 9939

Teacher's Salaries
*Waterside House, 75 Duke Street, Londonderry, BT47 1FP* . . . . . . . . . . . . . . . . . . . . . . . . . . . Tel: (028) 7131 9001

Traveller Education . . . . . . . . . . . . . . . . . . . . . . . . . . . . . . . . . . . . . . . . . . . . . . . . . . . . . . Tel: (028) 9127 9589

Youth Service . . . . . . . . . . . . . . . . . . . . . . . . . . . . . . . . . . . . . . . . . . . . . . . . . . . . . . . . . Tel: (028) 9127  9516

# NORTHERN IRELAND OFFICE

## Department for Employment and Learning
Adelaide House
39-49 Adelaide Street
Belfast, BT2 8FD
Tel: (028) 9025 7777  Fax: (028) 9025 7778
E-mail: del@nics.gov.uk
Web: http://www.delni.gov.uk

**Responsible Minister** . . . . . . . . . . . . . . . . . . . . . . . . . . . . . . . . . Mr Barry Gardiner MP
*Private Secretary* . . . . . . . . . . . . . . . . . . . . . . . . . . . . . . . . . . . . . Miss Jill Patton . . . . . . . . . . . . . . . . Tel: (028) 9025 7791

**Permanent Secretary** . . . . . . . . . . . . . . . . . . . . . . . . . . . . . . . . . Mr Will Haire . . . . . . . . . . . . . . . . . Tel: (028) 9025 7834

Deputy Secretaries . . . . . . . . . . . . . . . . . . . . . . . . . . . . . . . . . . . . . Mrs Catherine Bell . . . . . . . . . . . . . . . Tel: (028) 9025 7805
                                                                              Dr Robson Davison . . . . . . . . . . . . . . . Tel: (028) 9025 7876

Adult and Continuing Education . . . . . . . . . . . . . . . . . . . . . . . . . Mr Richard Kenny . . . . . . . . . . . . . . . Tel: (028) 9025 7690

Apprenticeships . . . . . . . . . . . . . . . . . . . . . . . . . . . . . . . . . . . . . . Mr Noel Griffin . . . . . . . . . . . . . . . . . Tel: (028) 9044 1875

Careers Service . . . . . . . . . . . . . . . . . . . . . . . . . . . . . . . . . . . . . . Mr John McKeown . . . . . . . . . . . . . . . Tel: (028) 9025 7869

Employment Legislation (Including European Directives) . . . . . . . . Ms Valerie Reilly . . . . . . . . . . . . . . . . Tel: (028) 9025 7560

European Union . . . . . . . . . . . . . . . . . . . . . . . . . . . . . . . . . . . . . . Mr John Neill . . . . . . . . . . . . . . . . . . Tel: (028) 9025 7874

Finance, Departmental . . . . . . . . . . . . . . . . . . . . . . . . . . . . . . . . . Mr Graeme Wilkinson . . . . . . . . . . . . . Tel: (028) 9025 7620

Further Education . . . . . . . . . . . . . . . . . . . . . . . . . . . . . . . . . . . . . Mr Tony R Edmond . . . . . . . . . . . . . . . Tel: (028) 9025 7476

Higher Education
        Finance . . . . . . . . . . . . . . . . . . . . . . . . . . . . . . . . . . . . . . Mr Geoff Harrison . . . . . . . . . . . . . . . Tel: (028) 9025 7718
        Policy . . . . . . . . . . . . . . . . . . . . . . . . . . . . . . . . . . . . . . . Mr Siobhan Logue . . . . . . . . . . . . . . . Tel: (028) 9025 7573
        Research Policy . . . . . . . . . . . . . . . . . . . . . . . . . . . . . . . . Dr Linda Bradley . . . . . . . . . . . . . . . . Tel: (028) 9025 7607

Investors in People . . . . . . . . . . . . . . . . . . . . . . . . . . . . . . . . . . . Mr Paul Bryans . . . . . . . . . . . . . . . . . Tel: (028) 9044 1773

Management Development . . . . . . . . . . . . . . . . . . . . . . . . . . . . . . Mr Tom Hunter . . . . . . . . . . . . . . . . . Tel: (028) 9044 1770

Postgraduate Awards . . . . . . . . . . . . . . . . . . . . . . . . . . . . . . . . . . Ms Anne Smith . . . . . . . . . . . . . . . . . Tel: (028) 9025 7741

Press
        Principal Information Officer . . . . . . . . . . . . . . . . . . . . . . . Mr Gwyn Treharne . . . . . . . . . . . . . . . Tel: (028) 9025 7790

Redundancy Payments and Related Issues . . . . . . . . . . . . . . . . . . Mr Tim Devine . . . . . . . . . . . . . . . . . Tel: (028) 9025 7520

Skills . . . . . . . . . . . . . . . . . . . . . . . . . . . . . . . . . . . . . . . . . . . . . . Mr Adrian Teer . . . . . . . . . . . . . . . . . Tel: (028) 9044 1831

Student Support . . . . . . . . . . . . . . . . . . . . . . . . . . . . . . . . . . . . . . Ms Rosaleen Duffy . . . . . . . . . . . . . . . Tel: (028) 9025 7699

Teacher Training (Funding and Administration) . . . . . . . . . . . . . . Celia Chambers . . . . . . . . . . . . . . . . . Tel: (028) 9025 7754

Training . . . . . . . . . . . . . . . . . . . . . . . . . . . . . . . . . . . . . . . . . . . . Mr Tommy McVeigh . . . . . . . . . . . . . . Tel: (028) 9044 1841

Universities . . . . . . . . . . . . . . . . . . . . . . . . . . . . . . . . . . . . . . . . . Mr John McGuigan . . . . . . . . . . . . . . . Tel: (028) 9025 7719

# NORTHERN IRELAND OFFICE

## Department of Enterprise, Trade and Investment
Netherleigh House
Massey Avenue
Belfast, BT4 2JP
Tel: (028) 9052 9900  Fax: (028) 9052 9550
E-mail: [firstname.surname]@detini.gov.uk
Web: http://www.nics.gov.uk

**Responsible Minister** . . . . . . . . . . . . . . . . . . . . . . . . . . . . . . . Mr Barry Gardiner MP
    *Private Secretary* . . . . . . . . . . . . . . . . . . . . . . . . . . . . . . . Mr William Donaghy . . . . . . . . . . . . Tel: (028) 9052 9208

**Permanent Secretary**. . . . . . . . . . . . . . . . . . . . . . . . . . . . . . Mr Bruce Robinson . . . . . . . . . . . . . . Tel: (028) 9052 9441

Director, Management Services Group . . . . . . . . . . . . . . . . . . . . . *Vacant*
Director, Policy Group. . . . . . . . . . . . . . . . . . . . . . . . . . . . . . . Mr Wilfie Hamilton . . . . . . . . . . . . . . Tel: (028) 9052 9203

Accounts Branch . . . . . . . . . . . . . . . . . . . . . . . . . . . . . . . . . . . . . . . . . . . . . . . . . . . Tel: (028) 9054 4946

Community Enterprise and Consumer Protection . . . . . . . . . . . . . . . . . . . . . . . . . . . . . . Tel: (028) 9025 3900

Corporate Regulation . . . . . . . . . . . . . . . . . . . . . . . . . . . . . . . . . . . . . . . . . . . . . . . . . Tel: (028) 9023 4488

Credit Unions. . . . . . . . . . . . . . . . . . . . . . . . . . . . . . . . . . . . . . . . . . . . . . . . . . . . . . . . Tel: (028) 9023 4488

Energy . . . . . . . . . . . . . . . . . . . . . . . . . . . . . . . . . . . . . . . . . . . . . . . . . . . . . . . . . . . . . Tel: (028) 9052 9372

Equality and Diversity Unit . . . . . . . . . . . . . . . . . . . . . . . . . . . . . . . . . . . . . . . . . . . . . Tel: (028) 9052 9644

European Programmes . . . . . . . . . . . . . . . . . . . . . . . . . . . . . . . . . . . . . . . . . . . . . . . . . Tel: (028) 9052 9328

General Consumer Council. . . . . . . . . . . . . . . . . . . . . . . . . . . . . . . . . . . . . . . . . . . . . . Tel: (028) 9067 2488

Health and Safety Executive . . . . . . . . . . . . . . . . . . . . . . . . . . . . . . . . . . . . . . . . . . . . . Tel: (028) 9024 3249

Insolvency . . . . . . . . . . . . . . . . . . . . . . . . . . . . . . . . . . . . . . . . . . . . . . . . . . . . . . . . . . Tel: (028) 9025 1441

Invest Northern Ireland. . . . . . . . . . . . . . . . . . . . . . . . . . . . . . . . . . . . . . . . . . . . . . . . . Tel: (028) 9023 9090

Northern Ireland Science Park . . . . . . . . . . . . . . . . . . . . . . . . . . . . . . . . . . . . . . . . . . . Tel: (028) 9053 4560

Personnel, Departmental. . . . . . . . . . . . . . . . . . . . . . . . . . . . . . . . . . . . . . . . . . . . . . . . Tel: (028) 9052 9900

Press Office
    Principal Information Officer . . . . . . . . . . . . . . . . . . . . . . . . Mr Philip Maguire . . . . . . . . . . . . . . . Tel: (028) 9052 9201

Public Appointments Unit. . . . . . . . . . . . . . . . . . . . . . . . . . . . . . . . . . . . . . . . . . . . . . . Tel: (028) 9052 9444

Regulatory Impact, Policy Services . . . . . . . . . . . . . . . . . . . . . . . . . . . . . . . . . . . . . . . . Tel: (028) 9052 9276

Social Economy . . . . . . . . . . . . . . . . . . . . . . . . . . . . . . . . . . . . . . . . . . . . . . . . . . . . . . Tel: (028) 9052 9255

Statistics, Economic . . . . . . . . . . . . . . . . . . . . . . . . . . . . . . . . . . . . . . . . . . . . . . . . . . . Tel: (028) 9052 9344

Strategic Policy Division. . . . . . . . . . . . . . . . . . . . . . . . . . . . . . . . . . . . . . . . . . . . . . . . Tel: (028) 9052 9388

Sustainable Development . . . . . . . . . . . . . . . . . . . . . . . . . . . . . . . . . . . . . . . . . . . . . . . Tel: (028) 9052 9900

Telecommunications Infrastructure . . . . . . . . . . . . . . . . . . . . . . . . . . . . . . . . . . . . . . . . Tel: (028) 9052 9773

Tourism . . . . . . . . . . . . . . . . . . . . . . . . . . . . . . . . . . . . . . . . . . . . . . . . . . . . . . . . . . . . Tel: (028) 9052 9554

Trading Standards Service . . . . . . . . . . . . . . . . . . . . . . . . . . . . . . . . . . . . . . . . . . . . . . . Tel: (028) 9025 3900

# NORTHERN IRELAND OFFICE

## Department of the Environment
Clarence Court
10-18 Adelaide Street
Belfast, BT2 8GB
Tel: (028) 9054 0540  Fax: (028) 9054 0024
E-mail: pressoffice@doeni.gov.uk
Web: http://www.nics.gov.uk/doehome.htm

**Responsible Minister** . . . . . . . . . . . . . . . . . . . . . . . . . . . . . . . . . Ms Angela Smith MP
   *Private Secretary* . . . . . . . . . . . . . . . . . . . . . . . . . . . . . . . . . . . Mr Stuart McDougall . . . . . . . . . . . . . . Tel: (028) 9054 1166
   *Travelling Private Secretary* . . . . . . . . . . . . . . . . . . . . . . . . . . Mrs Teresa Hewitt . . . . . . . . . . . . . . . . Tel: (028) 9052 2514

**Permanent Secretary** . . . . . . . . . . . . . . . . . . . . . . . . . . . . . . . . Mr Stephen Peover . . . . . . . . . . . . . . . . Tel: (028) 9054 0002

Corporate Services . . . . . . . . . . . . . . . . . . . . . . . . . . . . . . . . . . . . Mr Murray Power . . . . . . . . . . . . . . . . . Tel: (028) 9054 0045

DVTA, DVLNI, RSUS (Road
   Safety Vehicle Standards) . . . . . . . . . . . . . . . . . . . . . . . . . . . Mrs Cynthia Smith . . . . . . . . . . . . . . . . Tel: (028) 9054 0001

DVLNI, Chief Executive . . . . . . . . . . . . . . . . . . . . . . . . . . . . . . . Mr Brendan Magee . . . . . . . . . . . . . . . . Tel: (028) 7024 1246

DVTA, Chief Executive . . . . . . . . . . . . . . . . . . . . . . . . . . . . . . . . Mr Stanley Duncan . . . . . . . . . . . . . . . Tel: (028) 9054 7945

Environment and Heritage Service . . . . . . . . . . . . . . . . . . . . . . . Mr Michael Coulter . . . . . . . . . . . . . . . Tel: (028) 9054 3024
   Dr John Faulkner . . . . . . . . . . . . . . . . Tel: (028) 9054 6571
   Mr Richard Rogers . . . . . . . . . . . . . . . Tel: (028) 9054 6570

Environmental Policy Division,
   Environment and Heritage Service . . . . . . . . . . . . . . . . . . . . . Mr Felix Dillon . . . . . . . . . . . . . . . . . . Tel: (028) 9054 1178

Local Government . . . . . . . . . . . . . . . . . . . . . . . . . . . . . . . . . . . . Mr John Ritchie . . . . . . . . . . . . . . . . . . Tel: (028) 9054 0844

Planning Service . . . . . . . . . . . . . . . . . . . . . . . . . . . . . . . . . . . . . Mr David Ferguson . . . . . . . . . . . . . . . Tel: (028) 9054 0648
   Mr Ian Maye . . . . . . . . . . . . . . . . . . . Tel: (028) 9054 0650
   Mr Pat McBride . . . . . . . . . . . . . . . . . Tel: (028) 9054 0649
   Mr Pat Quinn . . . . . . . . . . . . . . . . . . . Tel: (028) 9054 0647

Principal Information Officer . . . . . . . . . . . . . . . . . . . . . . . . . . . . Mr Brian Kirk . . . . . . . . . . . . . . . . . . . Tel: (028) 9054 0013

Road Safety . . . . . . . . . . . . . . . . . . . . . . . . . . . . . . . . . . . . . . . . . Mr Wesley Shannon . . . . . . . . . . . . . . . Tel: (028) 9054 0843

## Department of Finance and Personnel
Rathgael House, Balloo Road, Bangor
County Down, BT19 7NA
Tel: (028) 9127 9279  Fax: (028) 9185 8104
E-mail: [firstname.surname]@dfpni.gov.uk

**Responsible Minister** . . . . . . . . . . . . . . . . . . . . . . . . . . . . . . . . . Mr Ian Pearson MP
*Private Secretary* . . . . . . . . . . . . . . . . . . . . . . . . . . . . . . . . . Mr David McCreedy . . . . . . . . . . . . . . Tel: (028) 9052 9140

**Permanent Secretary** . . . . . . . . . . . . . . . . . . . . . . . . . . . . . . . Mr John Hunter CB . . . . . . . . . . . . . . . Tel: (028) 9185 8174
**Second Permanent Secretary** . . . . . . . . . . . . . . . . . . . . . . . . Dr Andrew McCormick . . . . . . . . . . . Tel: (028) 9052 7437

**Corporate Services Group**
Director . . . . . . . . . . . . . . . . . . . . . . . . . . . . . . . . . . . . Mr David Ferguson . . . . . . . . . . . . . . . Tel: (028) 9185 8045
Departmental Finance . . . . . . . . . . . . . . . . . . . . . . . . . . . . . Mr Jim O'Hagan . . . . . . . . . . . . . . . . . Tel: (028) 9185 8149

**European Union Division**
*Health Estates, Stoney Road,*
*Dundonald, Belfast BT16 1US* . . . . . . . . . . . . . . . . . . . . . . . . Mr Bill Pauley . . . . . . . . . . . . . . . . . . Tel: (028) 9052 3707

**Finance**
Director, Central Finance Group . . . . . . . . . . . . . . . . . . . . . Mr Leo O'Reilly . . . . . . . . . . . . . . . . . Tel: (028) 9127 7601
Director of Supply . . . . . . . . . . . . . . . . . . . . . . . . . . . . . . Mr David Thomson . . . . . . . . . . . . . . . Tel: (028) 9185 8150
Central Expenditure Division . . . . . . . . . . . . . . . . . . . . . . . . . . . . . . . . . . . . . . . . . . . . . . . . . . . . . . . Tel: (028) 9185 8204
Accountability and Accountancy Services Division . . . . . . . . . . . . . . . . . . . . . . . . . . . . . . . . . . . . . . . . Tel: (028) 9185 8203
Rating Policy Division . . . . . . . . . . . . . . . . . . . . . . . . . . . . . . . . . . . . . . . . . . . . . . . . . . . . . . . . . . . . . . Tel: (028) 9127 7668
Strategic Policy Division . . . . . . . . . . . . . . . . . . . . . . . . . . . . . . . . . . . . . . . . . . . . . . . . . . . . . . . . . . . . Tel: (028) 9185 8186

**Internal Audit**
*The Arches Centre, 11-13 Bloomfield Avenue, Belfast, BT5 5AD* . . . . . Mrs Jackie Connolly . . . . . . . . . . . . . . . Tel: (028) 9052 6922

**Law Reform**
*Office of Law Reform, Lancashire House, 5 Linenhall Street, Belfast, BT2 8AA*
Director . . . . . . . . . . . . . . . . . . . . . . . . . . . . . . . . . . . . Ms Ethne Harkness . . . . . . . . . . . . . . . Tel: (028) 9054 2901

**Legal Services**
*Departmental Solicitor's Office, Victoria Hall, 12 May Street, Belfast, BT1 4NL*
Director . . . . . . . . . . . . . . . . . . . . . . . . . . . . . . . . . . . . Mr Robin Cole . . . . . . . . . . . . . . . . . . Tel: (028) 9025 1221

**Personnel (Central)**
*Central Personnel Group, Rosepark House, Upper Newtownards Road, Belfast, BT4 3NR*
Director . . . . . . . . . . . . . . . . . . . . . . . . . . . . . . . . . . . . Ms Linda Brown . . . . . . . . . . . . . . . . . Tel: (028) 9052 6160
Departmental Personnel . . . . . . . . . . . . . . . . . . . . . . . . . . . . . Mr Gerry Cosgrave . . . . . . . . . . . . . . . Tel: (028) 9185 8265

**Press Office**
Principal Information Officer . . . . . . . . . . . . . . . . . . . . . . . . Mr Colin Ross . . . . . . . . . . . . . . . . . . Tel: (028) 9052 7375

**Procurement**
*Central Procurement Directorate, Churchill House, 20-24 Victoria Square, Belfast, BT1 4QW*
Director . . . . . . . . . . . . . . . . . . . . . . . . . . . . . . . . . . . . Mr John McMillen . . . . . . . . . . . . . . . Tel: (028) 9052 0196

# NORTHERN IRELAND OFFICE

## Department of Health, Social Services and Public Safety

Castle Buildings, Stormont Estate
Upper Newtownards Road, Belfast, BT4 3SJ
Tel: (028) 9052 0500  Fax: (028) 9025 0572
E-mail: webmaster@dhsspsni.gov.uk
Web: http://www.dhsspsni.gov.uk

**Responsible Minister** . . . . . . . . . . . . . . . . . . . . . . . . . . . . . . Ms Angela Smith MP
    *Private Secretary* . . . . . . . . . . . . . . . . . . . . . . . . . . . . . . . . Ms Sharon Lindsay . . . . . . . . . . . . . . . Tel: (028) 9052 0642

**Permanent Secretary** . . . . . . . . . . . . . . . . . . . . . . . . . . . . . Mr Clive Gowdy . . . . . . . . . . . . . . . . . . Tel: (028) 9052 0559/0565

**Deputy Secretaries**
    Strategic Planning and Modernisation Group . . . . . . . . . . . . . Mr Paul Simpson . . . . . . . . . . . . . . . . . Tel: (028) 9052 2667
    Resources and Performance Management . . . . . . . . . . . . . . . . . Mr Don Hill . . . . . . . . . . . . . . . . . . . . . Tel: (028) 9052 0560
    Primary, Secondary and Community Care Group . . . . . . . . . . . Mr Andrew Hamilton . . . . . . . . . . . . . . Tel: (028) 9052 3439

**Chief Dental Officer** . . . . . . . . . . . . . . . . . . . . . . . . . . . . . . Mrs Doreen Wilson . . . . . . . . . . . . . . . . Tel: (028) 9052 2940

**Chief Inspector, Social Services Inspectorate** . . . . . . . . . . . . Mr Paul Martin . . . . . . . . . . . . . . . . . . . Tel: (028) 9052 0561

**Chief Medical Officer** . . . . . . . . . . . . . . . . . . . . . . . . . . . . . Dr Henrietta Campbell . . . . . . . . . . . . . . Tel: (028) 9052 0563

**Chief Nursing Officer** . . . . . . . . . . . . . . . . . . . . . . . . . . . . . Miss Judith Hill . . . . . . . . . . . . . . . . . . Tel: (028) 9052 0562

**Chief Pharmaceutical Officer** . . . . . . . . . . . . . . . . . . . . . . . Dr Norman Morrow . . . . . . . . . . . . . . . . Tel: (028) 9052 3219

Accommodation/Management Services . . . . . . . . . . . . . . . . . . . . . . . . . . . . . . . . . . . . . . . . . . . . . . . Tel: (028) 9052 3325

AIDS, HIV . . . . . . . . . . . . . . . . . . . . . . . . . . . . . . . . . . . . . . . . . . . . . . . . . . . . . . . . . . . . . . . . . . Tel: (028) 9052 0716/0772

Audit: Internal . . . . . . . . . . . . . . . . . . . . . . . . . . . . . . . . . . . . . . . . . . . . . . . . . . . . . . . . . . . . . . . Tel: (028) 9025 2652/2642

Cancer Services . . . . . . . . . . . . . . . . . . . . . . . . . . . . . . . . . . . . . . . . . . . . . . . . . . . . . . . . . . . . . . Tel: (028) 9052 2101

Capital Projects . . . . . . . . . . . . . . . . . . . . . . . . . . . . . . . . . . . . . . . . . . . . . . . . . . . . . . . . . . . . . . Tel: (028) 9052 0553

Child Care and Community . . . . . . . . . . . . . . . . . . . . . . . . . . . . . . . . . . . . . . . . . . . . . . . . . . . . . . Tel: (028) 9052 2786

Communicable Diseases . . . . . . . . . . . . . . . . . . . . . . . . . . . . . . . . . . . . . . . . . . . . . . . . . . . . . . . . Tel: (028) 9052 0717

Community Care . . . . . . . . . . . . . . . . . . . . . . . . . . . . . . . . . . . . . . . . . . . . . . . . . . . . . . . . . . . . . . Tel: (028) 9052 2786

Departmental Records Unit . . . . . . . . . . . . . . . . . . . . . . . . . . . . . . . . . . . . . . . . . . . . . . . . . . . . . . Tel: (028) 9052 3349

Departmental Security . . . . . . . . . . . . . . . . . . . . . . . . . . . . . . . . . . . . . . . . . . . . . . . . . . . . . . . . . Tel: (028) 9052 3384

Domestic Violence . . . . . . . . . . . . . . . . . . . . . . . . . . . . . . . . . . . . . . . . . . . . . . . . . . . . . . . . . . . . Tel: (028) 9052 0776

Elderly, Care of . . . . . . . . . . . . . . . . . . . . . . . . . . . . . . . . . . . . . . . . . . . . . . . . . . . . . . . . . . . . . . Tel: (028) 9052 2013

Emergency Planning . . . . . . . . . . . . . . . . . . . . . . . . . . . . . . . . . . . . . . . . . . . . . . . . . . . . . . . . . . . Tel: (028) 9052 2554

Equality Unit . . . . . . . . . . . . . . . . . . . . . . . . . . . . . . . . . . . . . . . . . . . . . . . . . . . . . . . . . . . . . . . . Tel: (028) 9052 2219

Finance . . . . . . . . . . . . . . . . . . . . . . . . . . . . . . . . . . . . . . . . . . . . . . . . . . . . . . . . . . . . . . . . . . . . Tel: (028) 9052 2446

Fire Authority . . . . . . . . . . . . . . . . . . . . . . . . . . . . . . . . . . . . . . . . . . . . . . . . . . . . . . . . . . . . . . . Tel: (028) 9052 2212

*Department of Health, Social Services and Public Safety (Continued)*

Health and Personal Social Services Management Group
*Castle Buildings, Upper Newtownards Road, Belfast, BT4 3JJ* . . . . . . . . . . . Tel: (028) 9052 0500
  Capital Investment Unit . . . . . . . . . . . . . . . . . . . . . . . . . . . . . . . . Tel: (028) 9052 0553
  Dentistry . . . . . . . . . . . . . . . . . . . . . . . . . . . . . . . . . . . . . . . . . Tel: (028) 9052 2940
  Finance . . . . . . . . . . . . . . . . . . . . . . . . . . . . . . . . . . . . . . . . . . Tel: (028) 9052 0775
  GPs; Hospitals Prescribing; Ophthalmic Services;
    Pharmaceuticals . . . . . . . . . . . . . . . . . . . . . . . . . . . . . . . . . . Tel: (028) 9052 2788
  Patients' Charter; Service Delivery; Purchasing . . . . . . . . . . . . . . . . . Tel: (028) 9052 2795
  Pay/Employment Unit . . . . . . . . . . . . . . . . . . . . . . . . . . . . . . . . . Tel: (028) 9052 2431
  Social Services; Trusts . . . . . . . . . . . . . . . . . . . . . . . . . . . . . . . . Tel: (028) 9052 0561
  Hospitals . . . . . . . . . . . . . . . . . . . . . . . . . . . . . . . . . . . . . . . . Tel: (028) 9052 2101

Health Development
  Health Protection Team . . . . . . . . . . . . . . . . . . . . . . . . . . . . . . . . Tel: (028) 9052 2554
  Investing for Health Team . . . . . . . . . . . . . . . . . . . . . . . . . . . . . . . Tel: (028) 9052 0784
  Health Promotion Team . . . . . . . . . . . . . . . . . . . . . . . . . . . . . . . . Tel: (028) 9052 2216
  Drug Strategy Team . . . . . . . . . . . . . . . . . . . . . . . . . . . . . . . . . . Tel: (028) 9052 0780

IT Department . . . . . . . . . . . . . . . . . . . . . . . . . . . . . . . . . . . . . . . Tel: (028) 9054 2201

Laboratory Services . . . . . . . . . . . . . . . . . . . . . . . . . . . . . . . . . . . . Tel: (028) 9052 2101

Manpower: Medical and Paramedical . . . . . . . . . . . . . . . . . . . . . . . . . . Tel: (028) 9052 0781

Maternal Health . . . . . . . . . . . . . . . . . . . . . . . . . . . . . . . . . . . . . . Tel: (028) 9052 2101

Medicines . . . . . . . . . . . . . . . . . . . . . . . . . . . . . . . . . . . . . . . . . . Tel: (028) 9052 3219

Mental Health . . . . . . . . . . . . . . . . . . . . . . . . . . . . . . . . . . . . . . . Tel: (028) 9052 2003

North/South Health Co-operation . . . . . . . . . . . . . . . . . . . . . . . . . . . . Tel: (028) 9052 0565

Occupational Health . . . . . . . . . . . . . . . . . . . . . . . . . . . . . . . . . . . . Tel: (028) 9025 1825

Ophthalmic Services . . . . . . . . . . . . . . . . . . . . . . . . . . . . . . . . . . . . Tel: (028) 9052 2788

Personnel
  Director, Personnel and Corporate Services . . . . . . . . . . . . . . . . . . . . . Tel: (028) 9052 2825

Pharmaceuticals . . . . . . . . . . . . . . . . . . . . . . . . . . . . . . . . . . . . . . Tel: (028) 9052 3219

Planning and Performance Management . . . . . . . . . . . . . . . . . . . . . . . . Tel: (028) 9052 2795

Prescribing . . . . . . . . . . . . . . . . . . . . . . . . . . . . . . . . . . . . . . . . . Tel: (028) 9052 0236

Press Office . . . . . . . . . . . . . . . . . . . . . . . . . . . . . . . . . . . . . . . . . Tel: (028) 9052 0636

Primary Care for Commissioning . . . . . . . . . . . . . . . . . . . . . . . . . . . . Tel: (028) 9052 0237

Public Appointments . . . . . . . . . . . . . . . . . . . . . . . . . . . . . . . . . . . Tel: (028) 9052 0781

Public Health . . . . . . . . . . . . . . . . . . . . . . . . . . . . . . . . . . . . . . . . Tel: (028) 9052 0716

Public Safety . . . . . . . . . . . . . . . . . . . . . . . . . . . . . . . . . . . . . . . . Tel: (028) 9052 0231

Radiology . . . . . . . . . . . . . . . . . . . . . . . . . . . . . . . . . . . . . . . . . . Tel: (028) 9052 0710

Screening Services . . . . . . . . . . . . . . . . . . . . . . . . . . . . . . . . . . . . . Tel: (028) 9052 0713

Smoking and Public Health . . . . . . . . . . . . . . . . . . . . . . . . . . . . . . . Tel: (028) 9052 2216

# NORTHERN IRELAND OFFICE

*Department of Health, Social Services and Public Safety (Continued)*

Social Services . . . . . . . . . . . . . . . . . . . . . . . . . . . . . . . . . . . . . . . . . . . . . . . . . . . . . . . . . . . . . . . . . Tel: (028) 9052 0657

Statistics . . . . . . . . . . . . . . . . . . . . . . . . . . . . . . . . . . . . . . . . . . . . . . . . . . . . . . . . . . . . . . . . . . . . Tel: (028) 9052 2522

Superannuation (HPSS). . . . . . . . . . . . . . . . . . . . . . . . . . . . . . . . . . . . . . . . . . . . . . . . . . . . . . Tel: (028) 7131 9122

Women's Issues . . . . . . . . . . . . . . . . . . . . . . . . . . . . . . . . . . . . . . . . . . . . . . . . . . . . . . . . . . . . . . Tel: (028) 9052 0776

Workforce, Medical . . . . . . . . . . . . . . . . . . . . . . . . . . . . . . . . . . . . . . . . . . . . . . . . . . . . . . . . . . Tel: (028) 9052 0781

# N O R T H E R N   I R E L A N D   O F F I C E

## Department for Regional Development
Clarence Court
10-18 Adelaide Street
Belfast, BT2 8GB
Tel: (028) 9054 0540
Fax: (028) 9054 0024
E-mail: enquiries@drdni.gov.uk
Web: http://www.drdni.gov.uk

**Responsible Minister** . . . . . . . . . . . . . . . . . . . . . . . . . . . . . . . . Mr John Spellar MP
   *Private Secretary (Departmental)* . . . . . . . . . . . . . . . . . . . . . Mr Paul Gill . . . . . . . . . . . . . . . . . . . . . . Tel: (028) 9054 0105

**Permanent Secretary** . . . . . . . . . . . . . . . . . . . . . . . . . . . . . . . Mr Stephen Quinn . . . . . . . . . . . . . . . Tel: (028) 9054 1175

**Deputy Secretaries**
Regional Planning and Transportation . . . . . . . . . . . . . . . . . . . . . Mrs Doreen Brown . . . . . . . . . . . . . . . Tel: (028) 9054 0519
Resources and Management Services . . . . . . . . . . . . . . . . . . . . . . Mr David Sterling . . . . . . . . . . . . . . . . . Tel: (028) 9054 0010

Audit
*Bankmore House, 62-66 Bedford Street, Belfast, BT7 FH*
   Audit Departmental, Internal . . . . . . . . . . . . . . . . . . . . . . . . . . Mr Ronnie Balfour . . . . . . . . . . . . . . . . Tel: (028) 9052 4280

Claims, Public Liability
*Northern House, High Street, Belfast, BT1 2BA*
   Central Claims Unit . . . . . . . . . . . . . . . . . . . . . . . . . . . . . . . . . Mr Stephen Murphy . . . . . . . . . . . . . . . Tel: (028) 9054 4301

*Orchard House, 40 Foyle Street, Londonderry, BT48 6AT* . . . . . . . . . . . . . . . . . . . . . . . . . . . . . . . . . . . . . . . Tel: (028) 7131 9900

Finance (Including Strategic)
   Director . . . . . . . . . . . . . . . . . . . . . . . . . . . . . . . . . . . . . . . . . Mr Jack McGibbon . . . . . . . . . . . . . . . Tel: (028) 9054 0847

Information
   Principal Information Officer / Press Officer . . . . . . . . . . . . . . Mr Paddy Cullen . . . . . . . . . . . . . . . . . Tel: (028) 9054 0817

IT, Departmental . . . . . . . . . . . . . . . . . . . . . . . . . . . . . . . . . . . Ms Caron Alexander . . . . . . . . . . . . . . . Tel: (028) 9054 0323

Personnel (Departmental)
   Director . . . . . . . . . . . . . . . . . . . . . . . . . . . . . . . . . . . . . . . . . Mrs Wendy Johnston . . . . . . . . . . . . . . Tel: (028) 9054 1070

Policy (Including Economics and Statistics)
Central Policy Unit, Director . . . . . . . . . . . . . . . . . . . . . . . . . . . Mr Alan McArthur . . . . . . . . . . . . . . . . Tel: (028) 9054 1195

Ports and Transport Policy
   Director . . . . . . . . . . . . . . . . . . . . . . . . . . . . . . . . . . . . . . . . . Mr Brian White . . . . . . . . . . . . . . . . . . Tel: (028) 9054 7697

Regional Planning and Transportation
   Director . . . . . . . . . . . . . . . . . . . . . . . . . . . . . . . . . . . . . . . . . Mr Mike Thompson . . . . . . . . . . . . . . . Tel: (028) 9054 0794

Roads and Water Policy . . . . . . . . . . . . . . . . . . . . . . . . . . . . . . . Mr Robin Mussen . . . . . . . . . . . . . . . . . Tel: (028) 9054 4711

Roads Service
   Chief Executive . . . . . . . . . . . . . . . . . . . . . . . . . . . . . . . . . . . . Dr Malcolm McKibbin . . . . . . . . . . . . . Tel: (028) 9054 0511

Water Service
   Chief Executive . . . . . . . . . . . . . . . . . . . . . . . . . . . . . . . . . . . . Mrs Katherine Bryan . . . . . . . . . . . . . . Tel: (028) 9035 4749

Water Reform
   Director . . . . . . . . . . . . . . . . . . . . . . . . . . . . . . . . . . . . . . . . . Mrs Jackie Kerr . . . . . . . . . . . . . . . . . . Tel: (028) 9054 1008

# NORTHERN IRELAND OFFICE

## Department for Social Development
Churchill House
Victoria Square
Belfast, BT1 4SD
Tel: (028) 9056 9100 Fax: (028) 9056 9240
E-mail: [firstname.surname]@dsdni.gov.uk
Web: http://www.dsdni.gov.uk

**Minister** ............................................... Rt Hon John Spellar MP
*Private Secretary* ..................................... Mr Allister Macrory ............... Tel: (028) 9056 9216

**Permanent Secretary** ................................ Mr Alan Shannon ................... Tel: (028) 9056 9203

Principal Information Officer ........................... Mr Jim Hamilton ................. Tel: (028) 9056 9211

**Resources, Housing and Social Security Group**
Deputy Secretary,  Principal Establishment and Finance Officer.... Mr Derek Baker ................... Tel: (028) 9056 9205

Central Policy and Co-ordination Unit
*Churchill House, Victoria Square, Belfast, BT1 4SD*
  Director. ....................................... Mr Philip Angus. .................. Tel:  (028) 9056 9775

Housing
*Andras House, Great Victoria Street, Belfast, BT2 7BB*
  Director. ....................................... Mr David Crothers ............... Tel: (028) 9056 1007

Social Security Policy and Legislation
*Castle Buildings, Belfast, BT4 3SG*
  Director. ....................................... Mr John O'Neill .................. Tel: (028) 9056 2434

**Urban Regeneration and Community Development**
Deputy Secretary. ..................................... Mr John McGrath ................. Tel: (028) 9056 9204

Belfast Regeneration Office
*Brookmount Buildings, 42 Fountain Street, Belfast, BT1 5EE*
  Director. ....................................... Mr Frank Duffy ................... Tel: (028) 9025 1973

Regional Development Office
*Brookmount Buildings, 42 Fountain Street, Belfast, BT1 5EE*
  Director *(Acting)* ................................ Mr Liam Quinn ................... Tel: (028) 9025 1901

North West Development Office
*Orchard House, 40 Foyle Street, Londonderry, BT48 6AT*
  Director. ....................................... Mr Declan O'Hare ................ Tel: (028) 7131 9782

Urban Regeneration Strategy Directorate
*Churchill House, Victoria Square, Belfast, BT1 4SD*
  Director. ....................................... Mr Henry Johnston ............... Tel: (028) 9056 9262

Victoria Square Development Team
  Director. ....................................... Mr Jackie Johnston. ............... Tel: (028) 9027 7685

Voluntary & Community Unit
*Churchill House, Victoria Square, Belfast, BT1 4SD*
  Director. ....................................... Mr Dave Wall ................... Tel: (028) 9056 9304

# NORTHERN IRELAND OFFICE

## OTHER RELEVANT CONTACTS

### AGRICULTURE

**Agricultural Research Institute of Northern Ireland** . . . . . . . Large Park, Hillsborough, Co Down, BT26 6DR
Chairman . . . . . . . . . . . . . . . . . . . . . . . . . . . . . . . . . . . . . Mr Walter Smyth OBE
Director *(Acting)* . . . . . . . . . . . . . . . . . . . . . . . . . . . . . . . Dr Sinclair Mayne . . . . . . . . . . . . . . . Tel: (028) 9268 2484
Web: http://www.arini.ac.uk

**Agricultural Wages Board for Northern Ireland** . . . . . . . . . Room 910, Dundonald House, Upper Newtownards Road, Belfast, BT4 3SB
Chairman . . . . . . . . . . . . . . . . . . . . . . . . . . . . . . . . . . . . . Mr William Gillespie OBE
Secretary . . . . . . . . . . . . . . . . . . . . . . . . . . . . . . . . . . . . . Mr Ernie Weatherall . . . . . . . . . . . . . . Tel: (028) 9052 0813
Web: http://www.dardni.ac.uk

**Livestock and Meat Commission for Northern Ireland** . . . . . Lissue House, 31 Ballinderry Road, Lisburn, BT28 2SL
Chairman . . . . . . . . . . . . . . . . . . . . . . . . . . . . . . . . . . . . . Mr Owen Brennan
Chief Executive . . . . . . . . . . . . . . . . . . . . . . . . . . . . . . . . Mr David Rutledge . . . . . . . . . . . . . . . Tel: (028) 9263 3000
Web: http://www.lmcni.com

**Pig Production Development Committee** . . . . . . . . . . . . . . . c/o Northern Ireland, Pig Testing Station, 14 Kirbys Lane, Antrim, BT41 4PP
Chairman . . . . . . . . . . . . . . . . . . . . . . . . . . . . . . . . . . . . . Mr Gary Anderson
Secretary . . . . . . . . . . . . . . . . . . . . . . . . . . . . . . . . . . . . . Mrs Aileen Smith . . . . . . . . . . . . . . . . Tel: (028) 9446 4137

### APPEALS

*(See under Tribunals below)*

### ARTS

**Arts Council of Northern Ireland** . . . . . . . . . . . . . . . . . . . MacNiece House, 77 Malone Road, Belfast, BT9 6AQ
Chairman . . . . . . . . . . . . . . . . . . . . . . . . . . . . . . . . . . . . . Ms Rosemary Kelly
Chief Executive . . . . . . . . . . . . . . . . . . . . . . . . . . . . . . . . Ms Roisín McDonough . . . . . . . . . . . . . Tel: (028) 9038 5200
Web: http://www.artscouncil-ni.org

### ASSEMBLY OMBUDSMAN

**Office of the Assembly Ombudsman for Northern Ireland** . . . 33 Wellington Place, Belfast, BT1 6HN
Ombudsman . . . . . . . . . . . . . . . . . . . . . . . . . . . . . . . . . . . Mr Tom Frawley . . . . . . . . . . . . . . . . . Tel: (028) 9023 3821
E-mail: ombudsman@ni-ombudsman.org.uk
Web: http://www.ni-ombudsman.org.uk

### AUDIT

**Northern Ireland Audit Office** . . . . . . . . . . . . . . . . . . . . . . 106 University Street, Belfast, BT7 1EU
Comptroller and Auditor General . . . . . . . . . . . . . . . . . . . . Mr John Dowdall . . . . . . . . . . . . . . . . Tel: (028) 9025 1000
E-mail: info@niauditoffice.gov.uk
Web: http://www.niauditoffice.gov.uk

### BOUNDARIES

**Boundary Commission for Northern Ireland** . . . . . . . . . . . . Forestview, Purdy's Lane, Belfast, BT8 4AX
Chairman . . . . . . . . . . . . . . . . . . . . . . . . . . . . . . . . . . . . . Rt Hon Michael Martin MP *(Speaker of the House of Commons)*
Secretary . . . . . . . . . . . . . . . . . . . . . . . . . . . . . . . . . . . . . Mr John Fisher . . . . . . . . . . . . . . . . . . Tel: (028) 9069 4800
E-mail: bcni@belfast.org.uk
Web: http://www.boundarycommission.org

### BUILDING AND CONSTRUCTION

**Central Procurement Directorate** . . . . . . . . . . . . . . . . . . . Churchill House, 20-34 Victoria Square, Belfast, BT1 4QW
Director . . . . . . . . . . . . . . . . . . . . . . . . . . . . . . . . . . . . . . Mr John McMillan . . . . . . . . . . . . . . . Tel: (028) 9025 0283
Web: http://www.cpdni.gov.uk

**Construction Industry Training Board** . . . . . . . . . . . . . . . . 17 Dunrod Road, Crumlin, Co Antrim, BT29 4SR
Chairman . . . . . . . . . . . . . . . . . . . . . . . . . . . . . . . . . . . . . Mr Sean Campbell
Chief Executive . . . . . . . . . . . . . . . . . . . . . . . . . . . . . . . . Mr Allan McMullen . . . . . . . . . . . . . . Tel: (028) 9082 5466
Web: http://www.citbni.org.uk

**Northern Ireland Building Regulations**
Advisory Committee . . . . . . . . . . . . . . . . . . . . . . . . . . . . . 9th Floor, River House, 48 High Street, Belfast, BT1 2AW
Chairman . . . . . . . . . . . . . . . . . . . . . . . . . . . . . . . . . . . . . Mr Trevor Martin
Secretary . . . . . . . . . . . . . . . . . . . . . . . . . . . . . . . . . . . . . Mr Hugh Murray . . . . . . . . . . . . . . . . Tel: (028) 9054 2923
E-mail: hugh.murray@dfpni.gov.uk

# NORTHERN IRELAND OFFICE

*Other Relevant Contacts (Continued)*

**BUSINESS DEVELOPMENT** *(See below under Industry)*

**CHARITIES**
Charities Advisory Committee . . . . . . . . . . . . . . . . . . . . . . . . . 4th Floor, Churchill House, Victoria Square, Belfast, BT1 4QW
    Chairman . . . . . . . . . . . . . . . . . . . . . . . . . . . . . . . . . . . . . . Mr Frank Ledwidge OBE
    Secretary. . . . . . . . . . . . . . . . . . . . . . . . . . . . . . . . . . . . . . . Mr Trevor Campbell . . . . . . . . . . . . . . . . Tel: (028) 9056 9650
                                       Web: http://www.dsdni.gov.uk

**CHILDREN**
Children's Commissioner . . . . . . . . . . . . . . . . . . . . . . . . . . . . 17-25 Great Victoria Street, Belfast, BT2 7BN
    Commissioner . . . . . . . . . . . . . . . . . . . . . . . . . . . . . . . . . . . Mr Nigel Williams . . . . . . . . . . . . . . . . Tel: (028) 9031 1616
                                        E-mail: info@niccy.org

**CHILD SUPPORT**
Northern Ireland Child Support Agency *(Executive Agency)* . . . Great Northern Tower, 17 Great Victoria Street, Belfast, BT2 7AD
    Chief Executive. . . . . . . . . . . . . . . . . . . . . . . . . . . . . . . . . . . Mr Gerry Keenan . . . . . . . . . . . . . . . . Tel: (028) 9089 6666
                                        E-mail: belfast-customer-helpline@dup.gsi.gov.uk
                                        Web: http://www.dsdni.gov.uk/csa/introduction.asp

**COMPENSATION**
Compensation Agency *(Executive Agency)* . . . . . . . . . . . . . . . . Royston House, 34 Upper Queen Street, Belfast, BT1 6FD
    Chief Executive. . . . . . . . . . . . . . . . . . . . . . . . . . . . . . . . . . . Miss Anne McCleary . . . . . . . . . . . . . Tel: (028) 9024 5944
                                        Web: http://www.compensationni.gov.uk
Criminal Injuries Compensation Panel . . . . . . . . . . . . . . . . . . 2nd Floor, Corn Exchange Building, Gordon Street, Belfast, BT1 2LG
    Chairman . . . . . . . . . . . . . . . . . . . . . . . . . . . . . . . . . . . . . . Mr Oliver Loughran
    Secretary. . . . . . . . . . . . . . . . . . . . . . . . . . . . . . . . . . . . . . . Mr Bill Gallagher . . . . . . . . . . . . . . . . Tel: (028) 9092 4400
                                        Web: http://www.cicapni.org.uk

**CONSUMERS**
General Consumer Council for Northern Ireland . . . . . . . . . Elizabeth House, 116 Holywood Road, Belfast, BT4 1NY
    Chairman . . . . . . . . . . . . . . . . . . . . . . . . . . . . . . . . . . . . . . Mr Stephen Costello MBE
    Chief Executive. . . . . . . . . . . . . . . . . . . . . . . . . . . . . . . . . . . Ms Eleanor Gill . . . . . . . . . . . . . . . . . Tel: (028) 9067 2488
                                        Web: http://www.gccni.org.uk

**COUNTRYSIDE**
Council for Nature Conservation and the Countryside . . . . . . 5-33 Hill Street, Belfast, BT1 2LA
    Chairman . . . . . . . . . . . . . . . . . . . . . . . . . . . . . . . . . . . . . . Dr Lucinda Blakiston Houston
    Secretariat. . . . . . . . . . . . . . . . . . . . . . . . . . . . . . . . . . . . . . Mr Cyril Francey . . . . . . . . . . . . . . . . Tel: (028) 9054 3076
                                        Web: http://www.ehsni.gov.uk

**COURTS AND LEGAL SERVICES**
Criminal Justice Oversight Commissioner. . . . . . . . . . . . . . . . Floor 2, Forestview, Purdy's Lane, Newtown Breda, Belfast, BT8 7AR
    Commissioner . . . . . . . . . . . . . . . . . . . . . . . . . . . . . . . . . . . Mr Al Hutchinson . . . . . . . . . . . . . . . Tel: (028) 9050 8052
Crown Solicitor's Office . . . . . . . . . . . . . . . . . . . . . . . . . . . . . Royal Courts of Justice, Chichester Street, Belfast, BT1 3JY
    Crown Solicitor . . . . . . . . . . . . . . . . . . . . . . . . . . . . . . . . . . . Mr Oswyn Paulin . . . . . . . . . . . . . . . . Tel: (028) 9054 2555
                                        E-mail: csolibrary@nics.gov.uk
Law Reform Advisory Committee for Northern Ireland . . . . . Lancashire House, 5 Linenhall Street, Belfast BT2 8AA
    Chairman . . . . . . . . . . . . . . . . . . . . . . . . . . . . . . . . . . . . . . Honourable Mr Justice Paul Girvan
    Secretary. . . . . . . . . . . . . . . . . . . . . . . . . . . . . . . . . . . . . . . Miss Clare Irvine . . . . . . . . . . . . . . . . Tel: (028) 9054 2900
                                        Web: http://www.olrni.gov.uk/advisory-site/index.htm
Legal Aid Advisory Committee for Northern Ireland . . . . . . . Northern Ireland Court Service, Windsor House, 9-15 Bedford Street, Belfast, BT2 7LT
    Chairman . . . . . . . . . . . . . . . . . . . . . . . . . . . . . . . . . . . . . . His Honour Judge Smyth QC
    Secretary. . . . . . . . . . . . . . . . . . . . . . . . . . . . . . . . . . . . . . . Mrs Joyce Henderson . . . . . . . . . . . . . Tel: (028) 9041 2261
Legal Secretariat to the Law Officers of Northern Ireland. . . Royal Courts of Justice, Chichester Street, Belfast, BT1 3JY
    Legal Adviser . . . . . . . . . . . . . . . . . . . . . . . . . . . . . . . . . . . . Mr Kevin McGinty . . . . . . . . . . . . . . . Tel: (028) 9054 6082
Life Sentence Review Commissioners . . . . . . . . . . . . . . . . . . 5th Floor, Windsor House, 9-15 Bedford Street, Belfast, BT2 7LT
    Chairman . . . . . . . . . . . . . . . . . . . . . . . . . . . . . . . . . . . . . . Mr Peter Smith QC . . . . . . . . . . . . . . . Tel: (028) 9054 9412
                                        Web: http://www.lsrcni.org.uk

*Other Relevant Contacts: Courts and Legal Services (Continued)*

**Northern Ireland Court Service** . . . . . . . . . . . . . . . . . . . . . . Windsor House, 9-15 Bedford Street, Belfast, BT2 7LT
    Director. . . . . . . . . . . . . . . . . . . . . . . . . . . . . . . . . . . . . . . . Mr David Lavery . . . . . . . . . . . . . . . . Tel: (028) 9032 8594
                                          Web: http://www.courtsni.gov.uk
**Sentence Review Commissioners** . . . . . . . . . . . . . . . . . . . . . . 5th Floor, Windsor House, 9-15 Bedford Street, Belfast, BT2 7SR
    Joint Chairmen . . . . . . . . . . . . . . . . . . . . . . . . . . . . . . . . . . Sir John Blelloch
                                          Mr Brian Curran. . . . . . . . . . . . . . . . . Tel: (028) 9054 9412
                                          Web: http://www.sentencereview.org.uk
**Statute Law Committee for Northern Ireland** . . . . . . . . . . . . 2nd Floor, The Arches Centre, 11-13 Bloomfield Avenue,
                                          Belfast, BT5 5HD
    Chairman . . . . . . . . . . . . . . . . . . . . . . . . . . . . . . . . . . . . . . . Sir Brian Kerr *(Lord Chief Justice of Northern Ireland)*
    Secretary. . . . . . . . . . . . . . . . . . . . . . . . . . . . . . . . . . . . . . . Ms Lyn McCulloch. . . . . . . . . . . . . . . . Tel: (028) 9052 6961

## DISABILITY
**Disability Living Allowance Advisory Board for**
**Northern Ireland** . . . . . . . . . . . . . . . . . . . . . . . . . . . . . . . . . Castle Court, Royal Avenue, Belfast, BT1 1DL
    Chairman . . . . . . . . . . . . . . . . . . . . . . . . . . . . . . . . . . . . . . . Dr Agnes McKnight
    Secretary. . . . . . . . . . . . . . . . . . . . . . . . . . . . . . . . . . . . . . . Dr Martin Donnelly . . . . . . . . . . . . . . . Tel: (028) 9033 6916
*(For Ulster Supported Employment Ltd see below under Training)*

## DRAINAGE
**Drainage Council for Northern Ireland** . . . . . . . . . . . . . . . . . c/o Rivers Agency, Hydebank, 4 Hospital Road, Belfast, BT8 8JP
    Chairman . . . . . . . . . . . . . . . . . . . . . . . . . . . . . . . . . . . . . . . Dr Robert Myers
    Secretary. . . . . . . . . . . . . . . . . . . . . . . . . . . . . . . . . . . . . . . Mr Alan Morton . . . . . . . . . . . . . . . . . . Tel: (028) 9025 3440
                                          Web: http://www.darni.gov.uk/core/dard0350.htm

## ECONOMY
**Northern Ireland Economic Council** . . . . . . . . . . . . . . . . . . . Pearl Assurance House, 1-3 Donegall Square East, Belfast, BT1 5HB
    Chairman . . . . . . . . . . . . . . . . . . . . . . . . . . . . . . . . . . . . . . . Ms Janet Trewsdale OBE
    Director. . . . . . . . . . . . . . . . . . . . . . . . . . . . . . . . . . . . . . . . Mr Victor Hewitt . . . . . . . . . . . . . . . . . Tel: (028) 9023 2125
                                          Web: http://www.niec.org.uk

## EDUCATION
**Council for Catholic Maintained Schools** . . . . . . . . . . . . . . . 160 High Street, Holywood, Co Down, BT18 9HT
    Chairman . . . . . . . . . . . . . . . . . . . . . . . . . . . . . . . . . . . . . . . Rt Rev John McAreavey (Bishop of Dromore)
    Chief Executive. . . . . . . . . . . . . . . . . . . . . . . . . . . . . . . . . . Mr Donald Flanagan. . . . . . . . . . . . . . . Tel: (028) 9042 6972
                                          E-mail: info.ccms@nics.gov.uk
**Education and Library Boards**
    *Belfast*. . . . . . . . . . . . . . . . . . . . . . . . . . . . . . . . . . . . . . . . 40 Academy Street, Belfast, BT1 2NQ
        Chairman. . . . . . . . . . . . . . . . . . . . . . . . . . . . . . . . . . . . Ms Carmel McKinney
        Chief Executive . . . . . . . . . . . . . . . . . . . . . . . . . . . . . . . Mr David Cargo . . . . . . . . . . . . . . . . . Tel: (028) 9056 4000
                                          Web: http://www.belb.org.uk
    *North Eastern* . . . . . . . . . . . . . . . . . . . . . . . . . . . . . . . . . County Hall, 182 Galgorm Road, Ballymena, Co Antrim, BT42 1HN
        Chairman. . . . . . . . . . . . . . . . . . . . . . . . . . . . . . . . . . . . Mrs Joan Christie MBE
        Chief Executive . . . . . . . . . . . . . . . . . . . . . . . . . . . . . . . Mr Gordon Topping OBE . . . . . . . . . . . Tel: (028) 2565 3333
                                          Web: http://www.neelb.org.uk
    *South Eastern* . . . . . . . . . . . . . . . . . . . . . . . . . . . . . . . . . Grahamsbridge Road, Dundonald, BT16 2HS
        Chairman. . . . . . . . . . . . . . . . . . . . . . . . . . . . . . . . . . . . Cllr Robert Gibson
        Chief Executive . . . . . . . . . . . . . . . . . . . . . . . . . . . . . . . Mr Jackie Fitzsimons . . . . . . . . . . . . . Tel: (028) 9056 6200
                                          Web: http://www.seelb.org.uk
    *Southern* . . . . . . . . . . . . . . . . . . . . . . . . . . . . . . . . . . . . . 3 Charlemont Place, The Mall, Armagh, BT61 9AX
        Chairman. . . . . . . . . . . . . . . . . . . . . . . . . . . . . . . . . . . . Mrs Moira Alexander MBE
        Chief Executive . . . . . . . . . . . . . . . . . . . . . . . . . . . . . . . Mrs Helen McClenaghan . . . . . . . . . . Tel: (028) 3751 2200
                                          Web: http://www.selb.org.uk
    *Western* . . . . . . . . . . . . . . . . . . . . . . . . . . . . . . . . . . . . . . 1 Hospital Road, Omagh, Co Tyrone, BT79 0AW
        Chairman. . . . . . . . . . . . . . . . . . . . . . . . . . . . . . . . . . . . Mr Harry Mullan
        Chief Executive . . . . . . . . . . . . . . . . . . . . . . . . . . . . . . . Mr Joseph Martin. . . . . . . . . . . . . . . . Tel: (028) 8241 1411
                                          Web: http://www.welbni.org

*Other Relevant Contacts: Education (Continued)*

**Northern Ireland Council for the Curriculum,**
    **Examinations and Assessment** . . . . . . . . . . . . . . . . . . . . . . Clarendon Dock, 29 Clarendon Road, Belfast, BT1 3BG
    Chairman . . . . . . . . . . . . . . . . . . . . . . . . . . . . . . . . . . . Dr Alan Lennon
    Chief Executive . . . . . . . . . . . . . . . . . . . . . . . . . . . . . . . Mr Gavin Boyd . . . . . . . . . . . . . . . . . . . Tel: (028) 9026 1200
                                      E-mail: info@ccea.org.uk
                                      Web: http://www.ccea.org.uk

**Northern Ireland Higher Education Council** . . . . . . . . . . . . Adelaide House, 39/49 Adelaide Street, Belfast, BT2 8FD
    Chairman . . . . . . . . . . . . . . . . . . . . . . . . . . . . . . . . . . . Mr Tony Hopkins CBE
    Secretary . . . . . . . . . . . . . . . . . . . . . . . . . . . . . . . . . . . Ms Debbie Hayes . . . . . . . . . . . . . . . . Tel: (028) 9025 7081
                                      Web: http://www.delni.gov.uk

**Staff Commission for Education and Library Boards** . . . . . . Forestview, Purdy's Lane, Belfast, BT8 7AR
    Chairman . . . . . . . . . . . . . . . . . . . . . . . . . . . . . . . . . . . Professor Bernard Cullen
    Secretary/Chief Executive . . . . . . . . . . . . . . . . . . . . . . . Mrs Patricia Weir . . . . . . . . . . . . . . . . Tel: (028) 9049 1461
                                      Web: http://www.staffcom.org.uk

**EMPLOYMENT** *(See below under Industrial Relations and under Training)*

**ELECTORAL COMMISSION**
**Electoral Commission** . . . . . . . . . . . . . . . . . . . . . . . . . . Seatem House, 28-32 Alfred Street, Belfast, BT2 8EN
    Head of Northern Ireland Office . . . . . . . . . . . . . . . . . . . . Mr Seamus Magee . . . . . . . . . . . . . . . Tel: (028) 9089 4020
                                      E-mail: infonorthernireland@electoralcommission.org.uk
                                      Web: http://www.electoralcommission.org.uk

**ENERGY**
**Office for the Regulation of Electricity and Gas,**
    **Northern Ireland** . . . . . . . . . . . . . . . . . . . . . . . . . . . . . Brookmount Buildings, 42 Fountain Street, Belfast, BT1 5EE
    Chief Executive . . . . . . . . . . . . . . . . . . . . . . . . . . . . . . . Mr Douglas McIldoon . . . . . . . . . . . . . . Tel: (028) 9031 1575
                                      Web: http://www.nicce.org

**ENTERPRISE** *(see below under Industry)*

**ENVIRONMENT**
**Environment and Heritage Service** *(Executive Agency)* . . . . . . Commonwealth House, 35 Castle Street, Belfast, BT1 1GU
    Chief Executive . . . . . . . . . . . . . . . . . . . . . . . . . . . . . . . Mr Richard Rogers . . . . . . . . . . . . . . . Tel: (028) 9025 1477
                                      Web: http://www.ehsni.gov.uk

**EQUALITY**
**Equality Commission for Northern Ireland** . . . . . . . . . . . . . Equality House, 7-9 Shaftesbury Square, Belfast, BT2 7BP
    Chief Commissioner . . . . . . . . . . . . . . . . . . . . . . . . . . . . Mrs Joan Harbison CBE
    Chief Executive . . . . . . . . . . . . . . . . . . . . . . . . . . . . . . . Ms Evelyn Collins . . . . . . . . . . . . . . . . Tel: (028) 9050 0600
                                      Web: http://www.equalityni.org

**FIRE**
**Fire Authority for Northern Ireland** . . . . . . . . . . . . . . . . . . 1 Seymour Street, Lisburn, BT27 4SX
    Chairman . . . . . . . . . . . . . . . . . . . . . . . . . . . . . . . . . . . Mr William Gillespie OBE
    Chief Fire Officer . . . . . . . . . . . . . . . . . . . . . . . . . . . . . . Mr Colin Lammey . . . . . . . . . . . . . . . . Tel: (028) 9266 4221
                                      Web: http://www.nifb.org.uk

**FISHERIES**
**Fisheries Conservancy Board for**
    **Northern Ireland** . . . . . . . . . . . . . . . . . . . . . . . . . . . . . 1 Mahon Road, Portadown, Craigavon, Co Armagh, BT62 3EE
    Chairman . . . . . . . . . . . . . . . . . . . . . . . . . . . . . . . . . . . Dr Robert Hanna
    Chief Executive . . . . . . . . . . . . . . . . . . . . . . . . . . . . . . . Mrs Karen Simpson . . . . . . . . . . . . . . . Tel: (028) 3833 4666
                                      Web: http://www.fcbni.com

**Foyle, Carlingford and Irish Lights Commission** . . . . . . . . . . 22 Victoria Road, Londonderry, BT47 2AB
    Chairman . . . . . . . . . . . . . . . . . . . . . . . . . . . . . . . . . . . Mr Peter Savage
    Chief Executive . . . . . . . . . . . . . . . . . . . . . . . . . . . . . . . Mr Derick Anderson . . . . . . . . . . . . . . . Tel: (028) 7134 2100
                                      Web: http://www.loughs-agency.org

**Northern Ireland Fishery Harbour Authority** . . . . . . . . . . . . 3 St Patrick's Avenue, Downpatrick, Co Down, BT30 6DW
    Chairman . . . . . . . . . . . . . . . . . . . . . . . . . . . . . . . . . . . Mr Robert Ferris
    Chief Executive . . . . . . . . . . . . . . . . . . . . . . . . . . . . . . . Mr Chris Warnock . . . . . . . . . . . . . . . . Tel: (028) 4461 3844
                                      Web: http://www.nifha.fsnet.co.uk

# NORTHERN IRELAND OFFICE

*Other Relevant Contacts (Continued)*

## FORENSIC SCIENCE

**Forensic Science Agency Northern Ireland** *(Executive Agency)*. 151 Belfast Road, Carrickfergus, Co Antrim, BT38 8PL
Chief Executive . . . . . . . . . . . . . . . . . . . . . . . . . . . . . . . . . . . . . . Mr Brett Hannam . . . . . . . . . . . . . . . . . . . Tel: (028) 9036 1888
Web: http://www.fsni.gov.uk

## FORESTRY

**Forest Service of Northern Ireland** *(Executive Agency)* . . . . . . . Dundonald House, Upper Newtownards Road, Belfast, BT4 3SB
Chief Executive . . . . . . . . . . . . . . . . . . . . . . . . . . . . . . . . . . . . . . Mr Malcolm Beatty . . . . . . . . . . . . . . . Tel: (028) 9052 4480
Web: http://www.forestserviceni.gov.uk

**GAS** *(For Office for the Regulation of Electricity and Gas see above under Energy)*

## HEALTH AND SAFETY

**Health and Safety Executive for Northern Ireland** . . . . . . . . 83 Ladas Drive, Belfast, BT6 9FR
Chairman . . . . . . . . . . . . . . . . . . . . . . . . . . . . . . . . . . . . . . . . Mr Liam McBrinn
Chief Executive . . . . . . . . . . . . . . . . . . . . . . . . . . . . . . . . . . . . . Mr Jim Keyes . . . . . . . . . . . . . . . . . . . Tel: (028) 9024 3249
Web: http://www.hseni.org.uk

## HEALTH AND SOCIAL SERVICES

**Advisory Committee of the Allied Health Professions** . . . . . . Health Promotion Branch, Room C4.22, Castle Buildings,
Belfast, BT4 3PP
Chairman . . . . . . . . . . . . . . . . . . . . . . . . . . . . . . . . . . . . . . . . Mrs Joan Skeffington
Secretary . . . . . . . . . . . . . . . . . . . . . . . . . . . . . . . . . . . . . . . . Miss Elaine Davidson . . . . . . . . . . . . . . Tel: (028) 9052 0526
E-mail: elainedavidson@dhsspsi.gov.uk
**Central Dental Advisory Committee** . . . . . . . . . . . . . . . . . . . Health Promotion Branch, Room C4.22, Castle Buildings,
Belfast, BT4 3PP
Chairman . . . . . . . . . . . . . . . . . . . . . . . . . . . . . . . . . . . . . . . . Professor Gerry Linden
Secretary . . . . . . . . . . . . . . . . . . . . . . . . . . . . . . . . . . . . . . . . Mrs Heather Rainey . . . . . . . . . . . . . . . Tel: (028) 9052 0525
E-mail: heatherrainey@dhsspsi.gov.uk
**Central Medical Advisory Committee** . . . . . . . . . . . . . . . . . . Health Promotion Branch, Room C4.22, Castle Buildings,
Belfast, BT4 3PP
Chairman . . . . . . . . . . . . . . . . . . . . . . . . . . . . . . . . . . . . . . . . Dr John Jenkins
Secretary . . . . . . . . . . . . . . . . . . . . . . . . . . . . . . . . . . . . . . . . Miss Elaine Davidson . . . . . . . . . . . . . . Tel: (028) 9052 0526
E-mail: elainedavidson@dhsspsi.gov.uk
**Central Nursing Advisory Committee** . . . . . . . . . . . . . . . . . . Health Promotion Branch, Room C4.22, Castle Buildings,
Belfast, BT4 3PP
Chairman . . . . . . . . . . . . . . . . . . . . . . . . . . . . . . . . . . . . . . . . Mrs Angela McVeigh
Secretary . . . . . . . . . . . . . . . . . . . . . . . . . . . . . . . . . . . . . . . . Miss Elaine Davidson . . . . . . . . . . . . . . Tel: (028) 9052 0526
E-mail: elainedavidson@dhsspsi.gov.uk
**Central Personal Social Services Advisory Committee** . . . . . . Health Promotion Branch, Room C4.22, Castle Buildings,
Belfast, BT4 3PP
Chairman . . . . . . . . . . . . . . . . . . . . . . . . . . . . . . . . . . . . . . . . Mr Patrick McHugh
Secretary . . . . . . . . . . . . . . . . . . . . . . . . . . . . . . . . . . . . . . . . Mrs Heather Rainey . . . . . . . . . . . . . . . Tel: (028) 9052 0525
E-mail: heatherrainey@dhsspsi.gov.uk
**Central Pharmaceutical Advisory Committee** . . . . . . . . . . . . . Health Promotion Branch, Room C4.22, Castle Buildings,
Belfast, BT4 3PP
Chairman . . . . . . . . . . . . . . . . . . . . . . . . . . . . . . . . . . . . . . . . Ms Sheelagh Hillan
Secretary . . . . . . . . . . . . . . . . . . . . . . . . . . . . . . . . . . . . . . . . Mrs Heather Rainey . . . . . . . . . . . . . . . Tel: (028) 9052 0525
E-mail: heatherrainey@dhsspsi.gov.uk
**Clinical Engineering and Medical Physics**
**Advisory Committee** . . . . . . . . . . . . . . . . . . . . . . . . . . . . . Health Promotion Branch, Room C4.22, Castle Buildings,
Belfast, BT4 3PP
Chairman . . . . . . . . . . . . . . . . . . . . . . . . . . . . . . . . . . . . . . . . Dr Denis Connolly
Secretary . . . . . . . . . . . . . . . . . . . . . . . . . . . . . . . . . . . . . . . . Mr Kieran Blaney . . . . . . . . . . . . . . . . . Tel: (028) 9052 0533
**Clinical Imaging Services Advisory Committee** . . . . . . . . . . . Health Promotion Branch, Room C4.22, Castle Buildings,
Belfast, BT4 3PP
Chairman . . . . . . . . . . . . . . . . . . . . . . . . . . . . . . . . . . . . . . . . *Vacant*
Secretary . . . . . . . . . . . . . . . . . . . . . . . . . . . . . . . . . . . . . . . . Mr Kieran Blaney . . . . . . . . . . . . . . . . . Tel: (028) 9052 0533
**Distinction and Meritorious Service Awards Committee** . . . . . Room D1.3, Castle Buildings, Stormont, Belfast, BT4 3PP
Chairman . . . . . . . . . . . . . . . . . . . . . . . . . . . . . . . . . . . . . . . . Dr Harry McGuigan CBE
Secretary . . . . . . . . . . . . . . . . . . . . . . . . . . . . . . . . . . . . . . . . Mr John Nesbitt . . . . . . . . . . . . . . . . . . Tel: (028) 9052 2817
Web: http://www.dhsspsni.gov.uk/hss/dmsac/dmsac.html

# NORTHERN IRELAND OFFICE

*Other Relevant Contacts: Fisheries (Continued)*

**Health and Personal Social Services Boards Eastern** . . . . . . . Champion House, 12-22 Linenhall Street, Belfast, BT2 8BS
    Chairman . . . . . . . . . . . . . . . . . . . . . . . . . . . . . . . . . . . . . . . Mr David Russell
    Chief Executive . . . . . . . . . . . . . . . . . . . . . . . . . . . . . . . . . Dr Paula Kilbane . . . . . . . . . . . . . . . . . . Tel: (028) 9032 1313
        Web: http://www.ehssb.n-i.nhs.uk
    **Northern** . . . . . . . . . . . . . . . . . . . . . . . . . . . . . . . . . . . . . . . County Hall, 182 Galgorm Road, Ballymena, BT42 1QB
        Chairman . . . . . . . . . . . . . . . . . . . . . . . . . . . . . . . . . . . . Mr Michael Wood MBE
        Chief Executive . . . . . . . . . . . . . . . . . . . . . . . . . . . . . Mr Stuart MacDonnell . . . . . . . . . . . . . Tel: (028) 2565 3333
        Web: http://www.nhssb.n-i.nhs.uk
    **Southern** . . . . . . . . . . . . . . . . . . . . . . . . . . . . . . . . . . . . . . . Tower Hill, Armagh, BT61 9DR
        Chairman . . . . . . . . . . . . . . . . . . . . . . . . . . . . . . . . . . . Mrs Fionnula Cook OBE
        Chief Executive . . . . . . . . . . . . . . . . . . . . . . . . . . . . . Mr Colm Donaghy . . . . . . . . . . . . . . . Tel: (028) 3741 0041
        Web: http://www.shssb.org
    **Western** . . . . . . . . . . . . . . . . . . . . . . . . . . . . . . . . . . . . . . . 15 Gransha Park, Clooney Road, Londonderry, BT47 6FN
        Chairman . . . . . . . . . . . . . . . . . . . . . . . . . . . . . . . . . . . Ms Karen Meehan
        Chief Executive . . . . . . . . . . . . . . . . . . . . . . . . . . . . . Mr Steven Lindsay . . . . . . . . . . . . . . . Tel: (028) 7186 0086
        Web: http://www.whssb.org

**Health and Personal Social Services Executive** . . . . . . . . . . . Dundonald House, Upper Newtownards Road,
        Belfast, BT4 3JJ . . . . . . . . . . . . . . . . . . Tel: (028) 9052 3823
    Chief Executive . . . . . . . . . . . . . . . . . . . . . . . . . . . . . . . . . Mr John Cole

**Health and Social Services Councils**
    *Eastern* . . . . . . . . . . . . . . . . . . . . . . . . . . . . . . . . . . . . . . . . 1st Floor, McKelvey House, 25-27 Wellington Place, Belfast, BT1 6GQ
        Chairman . . . . . . . . . . . . . . . . . . . . . . . . . . . . . . . . . . . Mr Brian Coulter
        Chief Officer . . . . . . . . . . . . . . . . . . . . . . . . . . . . . . . . Mrs Jane Graham . . . . . . . . . . . . . . . Tel: (028) 9032 1230
        Web: http://www.ehssc.org
    *Northern* . . . . . . . . . . . . . . . . . . . . . . . . . . . . . . . . . . . . . . 8 Broadway Avenue, Ballymena, BT43 7AA
        Chairman . . . . . . . . . . . . . . . . . . . . . . . . . . . . . . . . . . . Mr Tom Creaghton
        Chief Officer . . . . . . . . . . . . . . . . . . . . . . . . . . . . . . . . Mr Noel Graham . . . . . . . . . . . . . . . Tel: (028) 2565 5777
        Web: http://www.nhssc.org
    *Southern* . . . . . . . . . . . . . . . . . . . . . . . . . . . . . . . . . . . . . . Quaker Buildings, High Street, Lurgan, BT66 8BB
        Chairman . . . . . . . . . . . . . . . . . . . . . . . . . . . . . . . . . . . Mrs Roisin Foster
        Chief Officer . . . . . . . . . . . . . . . . . . . . . . . . . . . . . . . . Mrs Delia van der Lenden . . . . . . . . . . Tel: (028) 3834 9900
        Web: http://shsscouncil.net
    *Western* . . . . . . . . . . . . . . . . . . . . . . . . . . . . . . . . . . . . . . . Hilltop, Tyrone and Fermanagh Hospital, Omagh, BT79 0NS
        Chairman . . . . . . . . . . . . . . . . . . . . . . . . . . . . . . . . . . . Mr Raymond Rogan
        Chief Officer . . . . . . . . . . . . . . . . . . . . . . . . . . . . . . . . Mrs Maggie Riley . . . . . . . . . . . . . . . Tel: (028) 8225 2555
        E-mail: lpreston@hilltop.n-i.nhs.uk

**Health Estates** *(Executive Agency)* . . . . . . . . . . . . . . . . . . . . Stoney Road, Dundonald, Belfast, BT16 1US
    Chief Executive . . . . . . . . . . . . . . . . . . . . . . . . . . . . . . . . . Mr John Cole . . . . . . . . . . . . . . . . . Tel: (028) 9052 0025
        Web: http://www.dhsspsni.gov.uk/hpss/health-estates

**Health Promotion Agency for Northern Ireland** . . . . . . . . 18 Ormeau Avenue, Belfast, BT2 8HS
    Chairman . . . . . . . . . . . . . . . . . . . . . . . . . . . . . . . . . . . . . . Ms Alice Quinn
    Chief Executive . . . . . . . . . . . . . . . . . . . . . . . . . . . . . . . . . Dr Brian Gaffney . . . . . . . . . . . . . . . . Tel: (028) 9031 1611
        Web: http://www.healthpromotionagency.org.uk

**Laboratory Services Advisory Committee** . . . . . . . . . . . . . . . Health Promotion Branch, Room C4.22, Castle Buildings,
        Belfast, BT4 3PP
    Chairman . . . . . . . . . . . . . . . . . . . . . . . . . . . . . . . . . . . . . . Professor Elizabeth Trimble
    Secretary . . . . . . . . . . . . . . . . . . . . . . . . . . . . . . . . . . . . . . . Mr Kieran Blaney . . . . . . . . . . . . . . . . Tel: (028) 9052 0533

**Mental Health Commission for Northern Ireland** . . . . . . . . . Elizabeth House, 116-118 Holywood Road, Belfast, BT4 1NY
    Chairman . . . . . . . . . . . . . . . . . . . . . . . . . . . . . . . . . . . . . . Mrs Marian O'Neill
    Chief Executive *(Acting)* . . . . . . . . . . . . . . . . . . . . . . . . . Mr Stephen Jackson . . . . . . . . . . . . . . . Tel: (028) 9065 1157
        E-mail: mhc@dhsspsni.gov.uk

**Mental Health Review Tribunal for**
    **Northern Ireland** . . . . . . . . . . . . . . . . . . . . . . . . . . . . . . . . Room 11, Annex 6, Castle Buildings, Belfast, BT4 3PP
    Chairman . . . . . . . . . . . . . . . . . . . . . . . . . . . . . . . . . . . . . . Mr Fraser Elliot QC
    Secretaries . . . . . . . . . . . . . . . . . . . . . . . . . . . . . . . . . . . . . Mrs Esther Clarke
        Ms Alison Bray . . . . . . . . . . . . . . . . . . Tel: (028) 9052 3388
        E-mail: mhrt@dhsspsni.gov.uk

**Northern Ireland Blood Transfusion Service** . . . . . . . . . . . Belfast City Hospital Complex, Lisburn Road, Belfast, BT9 7TS
    Chairman . . . . . . . . . . . . . . . . . . . . . . . . . . . . . . . . . . . . . . Mr Stephen Costello
    Chief Executive . . . . . . . . . . . . . . . . . . . . . . . . . . . . . . . . . Dr Morris McClelland . . . . . . . . . . . . . Tel: (028) 9032 1414
        Web: http://www.nibts.org

*Other Relevant Contacts: Health and Social Services (Continued)*

**Northern Ireland Central Services Agency for Health
and Personal Social Services** . . . . . . . . . . . . . . . . . . . . . . . 25 Adelaide Street, Belfast, BT2 8FH
Chairman . . . . . . . . . . . . . . . . . . . . . . . . . . . . . . . . . . . . . . . Professor Sean Fulton
Chief Executive . . . . . . . . . . . . . . . . . . . . . . . . . . . . . . . . . . Mr Stephen Hodkinson . . . . . . . . . . . . . Tel: (028) 9032 4431
Web: http://www.csa.n-i.nhs.uk

**Northern Ireland Council for Postgraduate
Medical and Dental Education** . . . . . . . . . . . . . . . . . . . . . 5 Annadale Avenue, Belfast, BT7 3JH
Chairman . . . . . . . . . . . . . . . . . . . . . . . . . . . . . . . . . . . . . . . Dr Donald Keegan
Chief Executive . . . . . . . . . . . . . . . . . . . . . . . . . . . . . . . . . . Dr Jack McCluggage . . . . . . . . . . . . . . . Tel: (028) 9049 2731
Web: http://www.nicpmde.com

**Northern Ireland Guardian Ad Litem Authority** . . . . . . . . . . Centre House, 79 Chichester Street, Belfast, BT1 4JE
Chairman . . . . . . . . . . . . . . . . . . . . . . . . . . . . . . . . . . . . . . . Mr James Curran
Executive Director . . . . . . . . . . . . . . . . . . . . . . . . . . . . . . . . Mr Ronnie Williamson . . . . . . . . . . . . . Tel: (028) 9031 6550
Web: http://www.n-i.nhs.uk/Nigalaweb

**Northern Ireland Health Promotion Agency** . . . . . . . . . . . . 18 Ormeau Avenue, Belfast, BT2 8HS
Chairman . . . . . . . . . . . . . . . . . . . . . . . . . . . . . . . . . . . . . . . Ms Alice Quinn
Chief Executive . . . . . . . . . . . . . . . . . . . . . . . . . . . . . . . . . . Dr Brian Gaffney . . . . . . . . . . . . . . . . . Tel: (028) 9031 1611
Web: http://www.healthpromotionagency.org.uk

**Northern Ireland Practice and Education Council
for Nursing and Midwifery** . . . . . . . . . . . . . . . . . . . . . . . Centre House, 79 Chichester Street, Belfast, BT1 4JE
Chairman . . . . . . . . . . . . . . . . . . . . . . . . . . . . . . . . . . . . . . . Mrs Maureen Griffiths
Chief Executive . . . . . . . . . . . . . . . . . . . . . . . . . . . . . . . . . . Miss Paddie Blamey . . . . . . . . . . . . . . . Tel: (028) 9023 8152
Web: http://www.nipec.n-i.nhs.uk

**Northern Ireland Regional Medical Physics Agency** . . . . . . . Musgrove and Clark House, Royal Hospital Site, Grosvenor Road,
Belfast, BT12 6BA
Chairman . . . . . . . . . . . . . . . . . . . . . . . . . . . . . . . . . . . . . . . Professor George Walmsley
Chief Executive . . . . . . . . . . . . . . . . . . . . . . . . . . . . . . . . . . Professor Peter Smith . . . . . . . . . . . . . Tel: (028) 9063 4430
Web: http://www.n-i.nhs.uk/medicalphysics

**Northern Ireland Social Care Council** . . . . . . . . . . . . . . . . . Floor 5, Millennium House, Great Victoria Street, Belfast, BT2 7AQ
Chairman . . . . . . . . . . . . . . . . . . . . . . . . . . . . . . . . . . . . . . . Dr Jeremy Harbison
Chief Executive . . . . . . . . . . . . . . . . . . . . . . . . . . . . . . . . . . Mr Brendan Johnston . . . . . . . . . . . . . Tel: (028) 9041 7600
Web: http://www.niscc.info

**Poisons Board** . . . . . . . . . . . . . . . . . . . . . . . . . . . . . . . . . . . Castle Buildings, Stormont, Belfast, BT4 3SJ
Chairman . . . . . . . . . . . . . . . . . . . . . . . . . . . . . . . . . . . . . . . *Vacant*
Secretary . . . . . . . . . . . . . . . . . . . . . . . . . . . . . . . . . . . . . . . Mrs Lynda Hutcheson . . . . . . . . . . . . . Tel: (028) 9052 2118
**Social Care Tribunal** . . . . . . . . . . . . . . . . . . . . . . . . . . . . . . Room D2.20, Castle Buildings, Stormont, Belfast, BT4 3SQ
Chairmen *(joint)* . . . . . . . . . . . . . . . . . . . . . . . . . . . . . . . . . Mr Harry Black
Mr Kenneth Irvine
Chief Executive . . . . . . . . . . . . . . . . . . . . . . . . . . . . . . . . . . Mr Stuart Baxter . . . . . . . . . . . . . . . . . Tel: (028) 9052 0682
**Tribunal under Section 11 of the Health and
Personal Social Services (NI) Order 1972** . . . . . . . . . . . . General Medical Services Branch, Room D3 Castle Buildings,
Upper Newtownards Road, Belfast, BT4 3SF
Chairman . . . . . . . . . . . . . . . . . . . . . . . . . . . . . . . . . . . . . . . *Vacant* . . . . . . . . . . . . . . . . . . . . . . . . . Tel: (028) 9076 5604

## HISTORIC BUILDINGS/MONUMENTS
**Historic Buildings Council** . . . . . . . . . . . . . . . . . . . . . . . . . Waterman House, 5-33 Hill Street, Belfast, BT1 2LA
Chairman . . . . . . . . . . . . . . . . . . . . . . . . . . . . . . . . . . . . . . . Dr Philip Mowat
Secretariat . . . . . . . . . . . . . . . . . . . . . . . . . . . . . . . . . . . . . . Mr Cyril Francey . . . . . . . . . . . . . . . . . Tel: (028) 9054 3050
Web: http://www.ehsni.gov.uk

**Historic Monuments Council** . . . . . . . . . . . . . . . . . . . . . . . Waterman House, 5-33 Hill Street, Belfast, BT1 2LA
Chairman . . . . . . . . . . . . . . . . . . . . . . . . . . . . . . . . . . . . . . . Mr Richard Black
Secretariat . . . . . . . . . . . . . . . . . . . . . . . . . . . . . . . . . . . . . . Mr Cyril Francey . . . . . . . . . . . . . . . . . Tel: (028) 9054 3076
Web: http://www.ehsni.gov.uk

## HOUSING
**Northern Ireland Housing Executive** . . . . . . . . . . . . . . . . . . The Housing Centre, 2 Adelaide Street, Belfast, BT2 8PB
Chairman . . . . . . . . . . . . . . . . . . . . . . . . . . . . . . . . . . . . . . . Mr Sid McDowell CBE
Chief Executive . . . . . . . . . . . . . . . . . . . . . . . . . . . . . . . . . . Mr Paddy McIntyre . . . . . . . . . . . . . . . Tel: (028) 9024 0588
Web: http://www.nihe.gov.uk

**Rent Assessment Panel** . . . . . . . . . . . . . . . . . . . . . . . . . . . . 2nd Floor, Anders House, 60 Great Victoria Street, Belfast, BT8 7BB
Chairman . . . . . . . . . . . . . . . . . . . . . . . . . . . . . . . . . . . . . . . Mrs Joan McCrum . . . . . . . . . . . . . . . . Tel: (028) 9091 0100
E-mail: rent.officer@dsdni.gov.uk

# NORTHERN IRELAND OFFICE

*Other Relevant Contacts (Continued)*

## HUMAN RIGHTS
**Northern Ireland Human Rights Commission** . . . . . . . . . . . . . Temple Court, 39 North Street, Belfast, BT1 1NA
    Chief Commissioner . . . . . . . . . . . . . . . . . . . . . . . . . . . . . . Professor Brice Dickson
    Chief Executive . . . . . . . . . . . . . . . . . . . . . . . . . . . . . . . . . Ms Paddy Sloan . . . . . . . . . . . . . . . . . . . Tel: (028) 9024 3987
    Web: http://www.nihrc.org

## INDUSTRIAL RELATIONS
**Fair Employment Tribunal** . . . . . . . . . . . . . . . . . . . . . . . . Long Bridge House, 20-24 Waring Street, Belfast, BT1 2EB
    President . . . . . . . . . . . . . . . . . . . . . . . . . . . . . . . . . . . . . . . Mr John McGuire CBE
    Secretary . . . . . . . . . . . . . . . . . . . . . . . . . . . . . . . . . . . . . . . Mr Jim Walker . . . . . . . . . . . . . . . . . . . . . Tel: (028) 9032 7666
    Web: http://www.industrialfairemploymenttribunalsni.gov.uk
**Labour Relations Agency** . . . . . . . . . . . . . . . . . . . . . . . . . . 2-8 Gordon Street, Belfast, BT1 2LG
    Chairman . . . . . . . . . . . . . . . . . . . . . . . . . . . . . . . . . . . . . . . Mr Patrick McCartan
    Chief Executive . . . . . . . . . . . . . . . . . . . . . . . . . . . . . . . . . Mr William Patterson . . . . . . . . . . . . . . . Tel: (028) 9032 1442
    Web: http://www.lra.org.uk
**Northern Ireland Industrial Court** . . . . . . . . . . . . . . . . . . . Room 203, Adelaide House, 39-49 Adelaide Street, Belfast, BT2 8FD
    Chairman . . . . . . . . . . . . . . . . . . . . . . . . . . . . . . . . . . . . . . . Mr Richard Steele
    Secretary . . . . . . . . . . . . . . . . . . . . . . . . . . . . . . . . . . . . . . . Mr Michael McCullough . . . . . . . . . . . . Tel: (028) 9025 7599
    Web: http://www.industrialcourt.gov.uk
**Northern Ireland Industrial Tribunals** . . . . . . . . . . . . . . . . Long Bridge House, 20-24 Waring Street, Belfast, BT1 2EB
    President . . . . . . . . . . . . . . . . . . . . . . . . . . . . . . . . . . . . . . . Mr John McGuire CBE
    Secretary . . . . . . . . . . . . . . . . . . . . . . . . . . . . . . . . . . . . . . . Mr Jim Walker . . . . . . . . . . . . . . . . . . . . . Tel: (028) 9032 7666
    Web: http://www.industrialfairemploymenttribunalsni.gov.uk

## INDUSTRY
**Business Development Service** *(Executive Agency)* . . . . . . . . . . Craigantlet Buildings, Stoney Road, Belfast, BT4 3SX
    Chief Executive *(Acting)* . . . . . . . . . . . . . . . . . . . . . . . . . . . Mr Tom Kennedy . . . . . . . . . . . . . . . . . . Tel: (028) 9052 0444
    Web: http://www.nics.gov.uk/bds
**Enterprise Ulster** . . . . . . . . . . . . . . . . . . . . . . . . . . . . . . . . The Close, Ravenhill Reach, Belfast, BT6 8RB
    Chairman . . . . . . . . . . . . . . . . . . . . . . . . . . . . . . . . . . . . . . . Mr Joe Cowan
    Chief Executive . . . . . . . . . . . . . . . . . . . . . . . . . . . . . . . . . Mr Joe Eagleson . . . . . . . . . . . . . . . . . . . Tel: (028) 9073 6400
    Web: http://www.enterpriseulster.co.uk
**Invest Northern Ireland** . . . . . . . . . . . . . . . . . . . . . . . . . . . 64 Chichester Street, Belfast, BT1 4JX
    Chairman . . . . . . . . . . . . . . . . . . . . . . . . . . . . . . . . . . . . . . . Professor Fabian Monds
    Chief Executive . . . . . . . . . . . . . . . . . . . . . . . . . . . . . . . . . Mr Leslie Morrison . . . . . . . . . . . . . . . . . Tel: (028) 9023 9090
    Web: http://www.investni.com

## INLAND REVENUE
**Inland Revenue Northern Ireland** . . . . . . . . . . . . . . . . . . . Floor 5, Millennium House, 17A-25 Great Victoria Street,
    Belfast, BT2 7BN
    Director . . . . . . . . . . . . . . . . . . . . . . . . . . . . . . . . . . . . . . . . Ms Tina Gallager . . . . . . . . . . . . . . . . . . Tel: (08453) 021469

## INTERNATIONAL FUND
**International Fund for Ireland** . . . . . . . . . . . . . . . . . . . . . . PO Box 2000, Belfast, BT4 2WD
    Joint Directors-General . . . . . . . . . . . . . . . . . . . . . . . . . . . . Ms Orla O'Hanrahan . . . . . . . . . . . . . . . Tel: (028) 9076 8832
    Mr Sandy Smith . . . . . . . . . . . . . . . . . . Tel: (028) 9076 3313
    E-mail: dermot.brangan@ofmdfmni.gov.uk
    Web: http://www.internationalfundforireland.gov.uk

## LAGANSIDE
**Laganside Corporation** . . . . . . . . . . . . . . . . . . . . . . . . . . . . Clarendon Building, 15 Clarendon Road, Belfast, BT1 3BG
    Chairman . . . . . . . . . . . . . . . . . . . . . . . . . . . . . . . . . . . . . . . Mr Tony Hopkins CBE
    Chief Executive . . . . . . . . . . . . . . . . . . . . . . . . . . . . . . . . . Mr Kyle Alexander . . . . . . . . . . . . . . . . . Tel: (028) 9032 8507
    Web: http://www.laganside.com

## LAND
**Land Registers of Northern Ireland** *(Executive Agency)* . . . . . . . Lincoln Building, 27-45 Great Victoria Street, Belfast, BT2 7SL
    Chief Executive . . . . . . . . . . . . . . . . . . . . . . . . . . . . . . . . . Mrs Patricia Montgomery . . . . . . . . . . . . Tel: (028) 9025 1515
    Web: http://www.lrni.gov.uk
**Lands Tribunal for Northern Ireland** . . . . . . . . . . . . . . . . . Royal Courts of Justice, Chichester Street,
    Belfast, BT1 3JJ . . . . . . . . . . . . . . . . . Tel: (028) 9032 7703
    E-mail: lands.tribunal@dfpni.gov.uk
    Web: http://www.landstribunalni.org

*Other Relevant Contacts: Land (Continued)*

**Registry of Deeds** . . . . . . . . . . . . . . . . . . . . . . . . . . . . . . . . Lincoln Building, 27-45 Great Victoria Street,
Belfast, BT2 7SL . . . . . . . . . . . . . . . . . Tel: (028) 9025 1516
**Valuation and Lands Agency** *(Executive Agency)* . . . . . . . . . . . . Queen's Court, 56-66 Upper Queen Street, Belfast, BT1 6FD
Chief Executive . . . . . . . . . . . . . . . . . . . . . . . . . . . . . . . . . . . Mr Nigel Woods . . . . . . . . . . . . . . . . . Tel: (028) 9025 0700
Web: http://www.vla.gov.uk

**LAW** *(see above under Courts and Legal Services)*

**LICENSING (Driver/Vehicle)** *(see below under Transport)*

## LOCAL GOVERNMENT
**Local Government Staff Commission** . . . . . . . . . . . . . . . . . . . . Commission House, 18-22 Gordon Street, Belfast, BT1 2LG
Chairman . . . . . . . . . . . . . . . . . . . . . . . . . . . . . . . . . . . . . . . Mr Sid McDowell CBE
Chief Executive . . . . . . . . . . . . . . . . . . . . . . . . . . . . . . . . . . . Mr Adrian Kerr . . . . . . . . . . . . . . . . . Tel: (028) 9031 3200
Web: http://www.lgsc.org.uk
**Northern Ireland Local Government Officers'
Superannuation Committee** . . . . . . . . . . . . . . . . . . . . . . . . Templeton House, 411 Holywood Road, Belfast, BT4 2LP
Chairman . . . . . . . . . . . . . . . . . . . . . . . . . . . . . . . . . . . . . . . Mr John Galbraith
Secretary . . . . . . . . . . . . . . . . . . . . . . . . . . . . . . . . . . . . . . . Mr Dean Morrice . . . . . . . . . . . . . . . . . Tel: (028) 9076 8025
Web: http://www.nilgosc.org.uk

## LOTTERY
**Northern Ireland Committee of the Big Lottery Fund** . . . . . . 1 Cromac Quay, Cromac Wood, Ormean Road, Belfast, BT7 2JD
Chairman . . . . . . . . . . . . . . . . . . . . . . . . . . . . . . . . . . . . . . . Professor James Kearney
Director . . . . . . . . . . . . . . . . . . . . . . . . . . . . . . . . . . . . . . . . Mr Walter Radar . . . . . . . . . . . . . . . . . Tel: (028) 9055 1455
Web: http://www.community-fund.org.uk

## MILITARY COMPLAINTS
**Independent Assessor of Military Complaints** . . . . . . . . . . . . . Hampton House, 47-53 High Street, Belfast, BT1 2QS
Independent Assessor . . . . . . . . . . . . . . . . . . . . . . . . . . . . . . Mr Jim McDonald LVO MBE . . . . . . . . . . . Tel: (028) 9023 7822

## MUSEUMS AND GALLERIES
**National Museums and Galleries of Northern Ireland** . . . . . . . Botanic Gardens, Belfast, BT9 5AB
Chairman of Trustees . . . . . . . . . . . . . . . . . . . . . . . . . . . . . . . Mrs Margaret Elliott CBE
Chief Executive . . . . . . . . . . . . . . . . . . . . . . . . . . . . . . . . . . . Mr Tim Cooke . . . . . . . . . . . . . . . . . . . Tel: (028) 9038 3000
Web: http://www.magni.org.uk
**Northern Ireland Museums Council** . . . . . . . . . . . . . . . . . . . . 66 Donegall Pass, Belfast, BT7 1BU
Chairman . . . . . . . . . . . . . . . . . . . . . . . . . . . . . . . . . . . . . . . Professor Tom Fraser
Director . . . . . . . . . . . . . . . . . . . . . . . . . . . . . . . . . . . . . . . . Mr Chris Bailey . . . . . . . . . . . . . . . . . . Tel: (028) 9055 0215
Web: http://www.nimc.co.uk

## ORDNANCE SURVEY
**Ordnance Survey of Northern Ireland**
*(Executive Agency)* . . . . . . . . . . . . . . . . . . . . . . . . . . . . . . . Colby House, Stransmillis Court, Belfast, BT9 8BJ
Chief Executive . . . . . . . . . . . . . . . . . . . . . . . . . . . . . . . . . . . Mr Michael Cory . . . . . . . . . . . . . . . . . Tel: (028) 9025 5755
Web: http://www.osni.gov.uk

## PARADES
**Parades Commission** . . . . . . . . . . . . . . . . . . . . . . . . . . . . . . . Windsor House, Belfast, BT12 7EL
Chairman . . . . . . . . . . . . . . . . . . . . . . . . . . . . . . . . . . . . . . . Sir Anthony Holland . . . . . . . . . . . . . . Tel: (028) 9089 5900
Web: http://www.paradescommission.org

## PLANNING
**Planning Appeals Commission** . . . . . . . . . . . . . . . . . . . . . . . . Park House, 87-91, Great Victoria Street, Belfast, BT2 7AG
Chief Commissioner . . . . . . . . . . . . . . . . . . . . . . . . . . . . . . . . Mr John Warke
Chief Administration Officer . . . . . . . . . . . . . . . . . . . . . . . . . . Mr Fergal McCallion . . . . . . . . . . . . . . Tel: (028) 9024 4710
Web: http://www.pacni.gov.uk
**Planning Service** *(Executive Agency)* . . . . . . . . . . . . . . . . . . . Clarence Court, 10-18 Adelaide Street, Belfast, BT2 8GB
Chief Executive *(Acting)* . . . . . . . . . . . . . . . . . . . . . . . . . . . . Mr David Ferguson . . . . . . . . . . . . . . . Tel: (028) 9054 0540
Web: http://www.doeni.gov.uk/planning/index.htm

# NORTHERN IRELAND OFFICE

*Other Relevant Contacts (Continued)*

## POLICE
**Northern Ireland Policing Board** . . . . . . . . . . . . . . . . . . . . . . . . Waterside Tower, 31 Clarendon House, Clarendon Dock, Belfast, BT1 3BG
    Chairman . . . . . . . . . . . . . . . . . . . . . . . . . . . . . . . . . . . . . . . . . Professor Desmond Rea
    Chief Executive . . . . . . . . . . . . . . . . . . . . . . . . . . . . . . . . . . . . . Mr Trevor Reaney . . . . . . . . . . . . . . . . Tel: (028) 9040 8500
        Web: http://www.nipolicingboard.org.uk
**Police Ombudsman for Northern Ireland** . . . . . . . . . . . . . . . . New Cathedral Buildings, St Anne's Square, Belfast, BT1 1PG
    Police Ombudsman . . . . . . . . . . . . . . . . . . . . . . . . . . . . . . . . . . Mrs Nuala O'Loan
    Chief Executive . . . . . . . . . . . . . . . . . . . . . . . . . . . . . . . . . . . . . Mr Samuel Pollock . . . . . . . . . . . . . . . . Tel: (028) 9082 8600
        Web: http://www.policeombudsman.org
**Police Service of Northern Ireland** . . . . . . . . . . . . . . . . . . . . . Brooklyn, 65 Knock Road, Belfast, BT5 6LD
    Chief Constable . . . . . . . . . . . . . . . . . . . . . . . . . . . . . . . . . . . . . Mr Hugh Orde . . . . . . . . . . . . . . . . Tel: (028) 9065 0222
        Web: http://www.psni.police.uk

## POSTAL SERVICE
**Postwatch, Northern Ireland** . . . . . . . . . . . . . . . . . . . . . . . . . . 24-26 Arthur Street, Belfast, BT1 4GA
    Chairman . . . . . . . . . . . . . . . . . . . . . . . . . . . . . . . . . . . . . . . . . Mr John Stringer OBE
    Regional Manager . . . . . . . . . . . . . . . . . . . . . . . . . . . . . . . . . . . Ms Julie Anne McMaster . . . . . . . . . . . Tel: (028) 9027 9300
        E-mail: info@postwatch.co.uk
        Web: http://www.postwatch.co.uk

## PRISONS
**Board of Visitors and Visiting Committees** . . . . . . . . . . . . . . . Boards of Visitors' Secretariat, Room 305, Dundonald House, Upper Newtownards Road, Belfast, BT4 3SU
    Secretariat . . . . . . . . . . . . . . . . . . . . . . . . . . . . . . . . . . . . . . . . . *enquiries* . . . . . . . . . . . . . . . . . . . . . Tel: (028) 9052 5477
**Northern Ireland Prison Service** *(Executive Agency)* . . . . . . . . . Dundonald House, Upper Newtownards Road, Belfast, BT4 3SU
    Director-General . . . . . . . . . . . . . . . . . . . . . . . . . . . . . . . . . . . . Mr Peter Russell . . . . . . . . . . . . . . . . Tel: (028) 9052 2922
        Web: http://www.niprisonservice.gov.uk

## PROBATION
**Probation Board for Northern Ireland** . . . . . . . . . . . . . . . . . . 80-90 North Street, Belfast, BT1 1LD
    Chairman . . . . . . . . . . . . . . . . . . . . . . . . . . . . . . . . . . . . . . . . . Mr Brian Rowntree
    Chief Executive . . . . . . . . . . . . . . . . . . . . . . . . . . . . . . . . . . . . . Mr Noel Rooney . . . . . . . . . . . . . . . . Tel: (028) 9026 2400
        E-mail: info@pbni.org.uk
        Web: http://www.pbni.org.uk

## PROSCRIBED ORGANISATIONS
**Proscribed Organisations Appeal Commission** . . . . . . . . . . . . Field House, 15 Breams Building, London, EC4A 1DZ
    Chairman . . . . . . . . . . . . . . . . . . . . . . . . . . . . . . . . . . . . . . . . . Sir Murray Stuart-Smith . . . . . . . . . . . . Tel: (020) 7070 4200

## PUBLIC RECORDS
**Public Record Office of Northern Ireland**
    *(Executive Agency)* . . . . . . . . . . . . . . . . . . . . . . . . . . . . . . . . . . 66 Balmoral Avenue, Belfast, BT9 6NY
    Chief Executive . . . . . . . . . . . . . . . . . . . . . . . . . . . . . . . . . . . . . Dr Gerald Slater . . . . . . . . . . . . . . . . Tel: (028) 9025 1318
        Web: http://www.proni.nics.gov.uk

## RATES
**Rate Collection Agency** *(Executive Agency)* . . . . . . . . . . . . . . . Oxford House, 49-55 Chichester Street, Belfast, BT1 4HH
    Chief Executive . . . . . . . . . . . . . . . . . . . . . . . . . . . . . . . . . . . . . Mr Arthur Scott . . . . . . . . . . . . . . . . Tel: (028) 9025 2252
        Web: http://www.ratecollectionagencyni.gov.uk

## RIVERS
**Rivers Agency** *(Executive Agency)* . . . . . . . . . . . . . . . . . . . . . . Hydebank, 4 Hospital Road, Belfast, BT8 8JP
    Chief Executive . . . . . . . . . . . . . . . . . . . . . . . . . . . . . . . . . . . . . Mr John Hagan . . . . . . . . . . . . . . . . Tel: (028) 9025 3355
        Web: http://www.riversagencyni.gov.uk

## ROADS *(see below under Transport)*

## RURAL DEVELOPMENT
**Rural Development Council** . . . . . . . . . . . . . . . . . . . . . . . . . . . Loy Street, Cookstown, County Tyrone, BT80 8PZ
    Chairman . . . . . . . . . . . . . . . . . . . . . . . . . . . . . . . . . . . . . . . . . Ms Caroline Breakey
    Chief Executive . . . . . . . . . . . . . . . . . . . . . . . . . . . . . . . . . . . . . Mr Martin McDonald . . . . . . . . . . . . . Tel: (028) 8676 6980

# NORTHERN IRELAND OFFICE

*Other Relevant Contacts (Continued)*

## SOCIAL SECURITY

**Social Security Agency (Northern Ireland)**
*(Executive Agency)* . . . . . . . . . . . . . . . . . . . . . . . . . . . . . . Churchill House, Victoria Square, Belfast, BT1 4SS
Chief Executive . . . . . . . . . . . . . . . . . . . . . . . . . . . . . . . . Mr Gerry Keenan . . . . . . . . . . . . . . . . . Tel: (028) 9025 0250
Web: http://www.ssa.nics.gov.uk
**Social Security Commissioners (Northern Ireland)** . . . . . . . . 1st Floor, Headline Building, 10-14 Victoria Street,
Belfast, BT1 3GG . . . . . . . . . . . . . . . . . Tel: (028) 9033 2344

## SOCIAL SERVICES *(see above under Health and Social Services)*

## SPORT

**Sports Council for Northern Ireland** . . . . . . . . . . . . . . . . . . . House of Sport, Upper Malone Road, Belfast, BT9 5LA
Chairman . . . . . . . . . . . . . . . . . . . . . . . . . . . . . . . . . . . . . Professor Eric Saunders OBE
Chief Executive . . . . . . . . . . . . . . . . . . . . . . . . . . . . . . . . Mr Eamonn McCartan . . . . . . . . . . . . . Tel: (028) 9038 1222
Web: http://www.sportni.org

## STATISTICS

**Northern Ireland Statistics and Research Agency**
*(Executive Agency)* . . . . . . . . . . . . . . . . . . . . . . . . . . . . . . McCauley House, 2-14 Castle Street, Belfast, BT1 1SA
Chief Executive . . . . . . . . . . . . . . . . . . . . . . . . . . . . . . . . Dr Norman Caves . . . . . . . . . . . . . . . . . Tel: (028) 9034 8112
Web: http://www.nisra.gov.uk
**Statistics Advisory Committee for Northern Irealnd** . . . . . . . NISRA, McCauley House, 2-14 Castle Street, Belfast, BT1 1SA
Chairman . . . . . . . . . . . . . . . . . . . . . . . . . . . . . . . . . . . . . Mr Ian Carroll
Secretary . . . . . . . . . . . . . . . . . . . . . . . . . . . . . . . . . . . . . Ms Jacqueline Hyvant . . . . . . . . . . . . . . Tel: (028) 9034 8118
Web: http://www.nisra.gov.uk

## TECHNOLOGY *(see above under Industry)*

## TELECOMMUNICATIONS

**Ofcom** . . . . . . . . . . . . . . . . . . . . . . . . . . . . . . . . . . . . . . . PO Box 2500, Belfast, BT8 8SA
Regional Director . . . . . . . . . . . . . . . . . . . . . . . . . . . . . . Mr Dennis Wolinski . . . . . . . . . . . . . . . Tel: (028) 9081 0200

## TOURISM

**Northern Ireland Tourist Board** . . . . . . . . . . . . . . . . . . . . . St Anne's Court, 59 North Street, Belfast, BT1 1NB
Chairman . . . . . . . . . . . . . . . . . . . . . . . . . . . . . . . . . . . . . Mr Tom McGrath OBE
Chief Executive . . . . . . . . . . . . . . . . . . . . . . . . . . . . . . . . Mr Alan Clarke . . . . . . . . . . . . . . . . . . Tel: (028) 9023 1221
Web: http://www.discovernorthernireland.com

## TRAINING

**Training and Employment Agency Advisory Board** . . . . . . . . 39-49 Adelaide Street, Belfast, BT2 8FD
Chairman . . . . . . . . . . . . . . . . . . . . . . . . . . . . . . . . . . . . . Mr Bill McGinnis OBE
Chief Executive . . . . . . . . . . . . . . . . . . . . . . . . . . . . . . . . Mr Ian Walters . . . . . . . . . . . . . . . . . . . Tel: (028) 9025 7777
Web: http://www.teaonline.gov.uk
**Ulster Supported Employment Ltd** . . . . . . . . . . . . . . . . . . . 182-188 Cambrai Street, Belfast, BT13 3JH
Chairman . . . . . . . . . . . . . . . . . . . . . . . . . . . . . . . . . . . . . Mr David Russell
Chief Executive . . . . . . . . . . . . . . . . . . . . . . . . . . . . . . . . Mr Mitchel Wylie . . . . . . . . . . . . . . . . . Tel: (028) 9035 6600
Web: http://www.usel.co.uk

## TRANSPORT

**Driver and Vehicle Licensing Agency (Northern Ireland)**
*(Executive Agency)* . . . . . . . . . . . . . . . . . . . . . . . . . . . . . . County Hall, Castlerock Road, Coleraine,
County Londonderry, BT51 3TA
Chief Executive . . . . . . . . . . . . . . . . . . . . . . . . . . . . . . . . Mr Brendan Magee . . . . . . . . . . . . . . . Tel: (028) 7034 1249
Web: http://www.doeni.gov.uk/dvlni
**Driver and Vehicle Testing Agency** *(Executive Agency)* . . . . . . Balmoral Road, Belfast, BT12 6QL
Chief Executive . . . . . . . . . . . . . . . . . . . . . . . . . . . . . . . . Mr Stanley Duncan . . . . . . . . . . . . . . . Tel: (028) 9068 1831
Web: http://www.nics.gov.uk/dvta
**Northern Ireland Transport Holding Company** . . . . . . . . . . . Chamber of Commerce House, 22 Great Victoria Street,
Belfast, BT2 7LX
Chairman . . . . . . . . . . . . . . . . . . . . . . . . . . . . . . . . . . . . . Dr Joan Smyth CBE
Director of Corporate Affairs . . . . . . . . . . . . . . . . . . . . . . Mr Jim Aiken . . . . . . . . . . . . . . . . . . . Tel: (028) 9024 3456
E-mail: nithc@dialstart.nat

# N O R T H E R N   I R E L A N D   O F F I C E

*Other Relevant Contacts: Transport (Continued)*

**Roads Service** *(Executive Agency)* . . . . . . . . . . . . . . . . . . . . . . Clarence Court, 10-18 Adelaide Street, Belfast, BT2 8GB
    Chief Executive . . . . . . . . . . . . . . . . . . . . . . . . . . . . . . . . . . . Dr Malcolm McKibbin . . . . . . . . . . . . . Tel: (028) 9054 0540
                                                     Web: http://www.roadsni.gov.uk

## TRIBUNALS
*For information on Child Support, Disability, Medical, Social Security, and Vaccine Damage Tribunals, contact:*
**Appeals Service (Northern Ireland)** . . . . . . . . . . . . . . . . . . . . Cleaver House, 3 Donegall Square North, Belfast, BT1 5GA
    President . . . . . . . . . . . . . . . . . . . . . . . . . . . . . . . . . . . . . . . . . Mr Conil Maclynn
    Manager . . . . . . . . . . . . . . . . . . . . . . . . . . . . . . . . . . . . . . . . . . Ms Lesley Morgan . . . . . . . . . . . . . . . . Tel: (028) 9051 8518
                                                   E-mail: appeals.service.belfast@dsdni.gov.uk

## WASTE MANAGEMENT
**Waste Management Advisory Board** . . . . . . . . . . . . . . . . . . . . 5-33 Hill Street, Belfast, BT1 2LA
    Chairman . . . . . . . . . . . . . . . . . . . . . . . . . . . . . . . . . . . . . . . . . Professor Deborah Boyd
    Secretary . . . . . . . . . . . . . . . . . . . . . . . . . . . . . . . . . . . . . . . . . Mrs Doreen Morrison . . . . . . . . . . . . . . Tel: (028) 9054 3068
                                                   Web: http://www.wmabni.gov.uk

## WATER
**Northern Ireland Water Council** . . . . . . . . . . . . . . . . . . . . . . Room 1-08, 34 College Street, Belfast, BT1 6DR
    Chairman . . . . . . . . . . . . . . . . . . . . . . . . . . . . . . . . . . . . . . . . . Mr David Moore
    Joint Secretaries . . . . . . . . . . . . . . . . . . . . . . . . . . . . . . . . . . . Miss Hazel Campbell . . . . . . . . . . . . . Tel: (028) 9024 4711 Ext: 23392
                                                   Web: http://www.watercouncilni.org
**Water Appeals Commission** . . . . . . . . . . . . . . . . . . . . . . . . . . c/o Planning Appeals, Park House 87-91 Great Victoria Street, Belfast, BT2 7AG
    Chief Commissioner . . . . . . . . . . . . . . . . . . . . . . . . . . . . . . . . . Mr John Warke
    Deputy Chief Commissioner . . . . . . . . . . . . . . . . . . . . . . . . . . Mrs Maire Campbell . . . . . . . . . . . . . . . . Tel: (028) 9024 4710
                                                   Web: http://www.pacni.gov.uk
**Water Service** *(Executive Agency)* . . . . . . . . . . . . . . . . . . . . . Northland House, 3-5 Frederick Street, Belfast, BT1 2NR
    Chief Executive . . . . . . . . . . . . . . . . . . . . . . . . . . . . . . . . . . . Ms Catherine Bryan . . . . . . . . . . . . . . . Tel: (028) 9024 4711
                                                   Web: http://www.waterni.gov.uk

## YOUTH
**Youth Council for Northern Ireland** . . . . . . . . . . . . . . . . . . . Forestview, Purdy's Lane, Belfast, BT8 7AR
    Chairman . . . . . . . . . . . . . . . . . . . . . . . . . . . . . . . . . . . . . . . . . Miss Maire Young
    Director . . . . . . . . . . . . . . . . . . . . . . . . . . . . . . . . . . . . . . . . . . Mr David Guilfoyle . . . . . . . . . . . . . . . . Tel: (028) 9064 3882
                                                   Web: http://www.youthcouncil-ni.org.uk
**Youth Justice Agency for Northern Ireland**
    *(Executive Agency)* . . . . . . . . . . . . . . . . . . . . . . . . . . . . . . . . 41-43 Waring Street, Belfast, BT1 2DY
    Chief Executive . . . . . . . . . . . . . . . . . . . . . . . . . . . . . . . . . . . Mr Martin Mogg CBE . . . . . . . . . . . . . . Tel: (028) 9031 6400
                                                   Web: http://www.youthjusticeagencyni.gov.uk

## GOVERNMENT OFFICES FOR THE REGIONS

# EAST OF ENGLAND
## Government Office for the East of England
Eastbrook, Shaftesbury Road, Cambridge, CB2 2DF
Tel: (01223) 372500
E-mail: [initialsurname].go-east@go-regions.gsi.gov.uk
*or* customerservices.go-east@go-regions.gsi.gov.uk
Web: http://www.go-east.gov.uk

**Regional Director** . . . . . . . . . . . . . . . . . . . . Mrs Caroline Bowdler . . . . . . . . . . . . . . . . . . . . . . . . Tel: (01223) 372502

**Directors**

| | | |
|---|---|---|
| Community Safety and Regeneration . . . . . . . | Ms Sue Howl | Tel: (01223) 372560 |
| Corporate Group . . . . . . . . . . . . . . . . . . | Ms Hilary Cooper | Tel: (01223) 372628 |
| Learning and Local Government . . . . . . . . . | Dr John Street | Tel: (01223) 372536 |
| Planning and Transport . . . . . . . . . . . . . | Mr John Dowie | Tel: (01223) 372723 |
| Relationships and Europe . . . . . . . . . . . . | Mr Martin Oldham | Tel: (01223) 372693 |
| Resilience and Corporate Services . . . . . . . | Mr Clive Whitworth | Tel: (01223) 372998 |
| Sustainable Development and Rural Affairs . . . . . . . . . . . . . . . . . . . . . . | Miss Jane Rabagliati | Tel: (01223) 372759 |

**Corporate Group**

*Planning and Transport*

| | | |
|---|---|---|
| Director . . . . . . . . . . . . . . . . . . . . . | Mr John Dowie | Tel: (01223) 372946 |
| Development Plans Team . . . . . . . . . . . . | Mr Colin Campbell | Tel: (01223) 372946 |
| Planning Casework . . . . . . . . . . . . . . . | Mr Lindsay Speed | Tel: (01223) 372725 |
| Regional and Sub-Regional Planning Team . . . . . . . . . . . . . . . | Mr Michael Hargreaves | Tel: (01223) 372745 |
| Transport . . . . . . . . . . . . . . . . . . . . | Mr John Brown | Tel: (01223) 372752 |

*Regional Strategy and Corporate Development*

| | | |
|---|---|---|
| Director . . . . . . . . . . . . . . . . . . . . . | Ms Hilary Cooper | Tel: (01223) 372628 |
| Knowledge and Information Management . . . . . . . . . . . . . . . . | Ms Jennifer Beaumont | Tel: (01223) 372651 |
| Ministerial and Corporate Development . . . . | Mr Tom McCormick | Tel: (01223) 372650 |
| Regional Strategy . . . . . . . . . . . . . . . | Mr Paul Glossop | Tel: (01223) 372763 |

*Relationships and Europe*

| | | |
|---|---|---|
| Director . . . . . . . . . . . . . . . . . . . . . | Mr Martin Oldham | Tel: (01223) 372693 |
| Business Relations . . . . . . . . . . . . . . . | Mr Nicholas Turner | Tel: (01223) 372612 |
| Central Evaluation and Finance . . . . . . . . | Ms Sue Martin | Tel: (01223) 372681 |
| European . . . . . . . . . . . . . . . . . . . . | Mr David Morrall | Tel: (01223) 372696 |
| Partnerships and Economic Development . . . . . . . . . . . . . . . . | Ms Hilary Bryant | Tel: (01223) 372618 |
| Small Business Service (Deputy Director for the Region) . . . . . . . . . . | Mr Phil Mercer | Tel: (01223) 200810 |
| Trade Partners (UK Central Regional Team) . . . . . . . . . . . . . . . . . . | Mr Robert Driver | Tel: (01223) 200868 |

*Resilience, Corporate Services and Co-location*

| | | |
|---|---|---|
| Director . . . . . . . . . . . . . . . . . . . . . | Mr Clive Whitworth | Tel: (01223) 372998 |
| Corporate Services and Co-location . . . . . . | Mr John McIntosh | Tel: (01223) 372630 |
| Resilience Team . . . . . . . . . . . . . . . . | Mr Jeff Stacy | Tel: (01223) 372994 |

## GOVERNMENT OFFICES FOR THE REGIONS

*Government Office for the East of England (Continued)*

### Social Inclusion Group

*Community Safety and Regeneration*

| | | |
|---|---|---|
| Director | Ms Sue Howl | Tel: (01223) 372760 |
| Rural | Mr Mike Barnes | Tel: (01223) 372777 |
| Sustainable Development Awareness | Mr Jo Hefford | Tel: (01223) 372761 |

*Learning and Local Government*

| | | |
|---|---|---|
| Director | Mr John Street | Tel: (01223) 372536 |
| Housing | Mr Martin Lutman | Tel: (01223) 372550 |
| Learning, Support | Mr Keith Hawkins | Tel: (01223) 372526 |
| | Mr Mervyn Stokes | Tel: (01223) 372527 |
| Local Government | Mr John Coolbear | Tel: (01223) 372541 |
| Sure Start | Ms Anne Houlihan | Tel: (01223) 372514 |

*Sustainable Development and Rural Affairs*

| | | |
|---|---|---|
| Director | Miss Jane Rabagliati | Tel: (01223) 372599 |
| Community Development | Ms Sue Lowe | Tel: (01223) 372599 |
| Crime Reduction | Ms Jan Roberts | Tel: (01223) 372580 |
| Department of Culture, Media and Sport | Ms Nejla Sabberton | Tel: (01223) 372609 |
| Government Office Drugs Team | Mr Matthew Kelly | Tel: (01223) 372577 |
| Neighbourhood Renewal | Mr Keith Harding | Tel: (01223) 372598 |
| | Ms Sue Hay | Tel: (01223) 372596 |

### East of England Development Agency

The Business Centre, Station Road, Histon, Cambridge, CB4 9LQ
Tel: (0845) 456 9200  Fax: (01223) 713940
E-mail: knowledge@eeda.org.uk
Web: http://www.eeda.org.uk

| | |
|---|---|
| **Chairman** | Mr Vincent Watts |
| **Chief Executive** | Mr David Marlow |

## GOVERNMENT OFFICES FOR THE REGIONS

### EAST MIDLANDS
### Government Office for the East Midlands

The Belgrave Centre, Stanley Place, Talbot Street, Nottingham, NG1 5GG
Tel: (0115) 971 2400  Fax: (0115) 971 2404
E-mail: enquiries.goem@go-regions.gsi.gov.uk
Web: http://www.go-em.gov.uk

**Regional Director** . . . . . . . . . . . . . . . . . . . . . . . . . . . . . . . . Ms Melanie Alker . . . . . . . . . . . . . . . . . . . . . Tel: (0115) 971 2672

**Directors**

Deputy Directors . . . . . . . . . . . . . . . . . . . . . . . . . Mr Rowena Limb . . . . . . . . . . . . . . . . . . . . Tel: (0115) 971 2670
Mr Will Wiseman . . . . . . . . . . . . . . . . . . . . Tel: (0115) 971 2551
Head of Enterprise and Education. . . . . . . . . . . . . . . . Mr Barrie Whittamore. . . . . . . . . . . . . . . . Tel: (0115) 971 2694
Head of Local Government Team . . . . . . . . . . . . . . . . Ms Alison Adams . . . . . . . . . . . . . . . . . . Tel: (0115) 971 2681
Head of Neighbourhood Renewal Team . . . . . . . . . . . . . . Mr Geoff Milner . . . . . . . . . . . . . . . . . . Tel: (0115) 971 2654
Head of Planning and Transport . . . . . . . . . . . . . . . . . Ms Karin Staples . . . . . . . . . . . . . . . . . Tel: (0115) 971 2593
Head of Sustainable Communities Team . . . . . . . . . . . . . Mr Giles Hughes . . . . . . . . . . . . . . . . . . Tel: (0115) 971 2674

**European Directorate**

Director . . . . . . . . . . . . . . . . . . . . . . . . . . . . . . . . Mr Robert Smith. . . . . . . . . . . . . . . . . . . . Tel: (0115) 971 2480
Head of European Finance and Policy Team . . . . . . . . . . . Mr Peter Holmes . . . . . . . . . . . . . . . . . . Tel: (0115) 971 2714
Head of European Regional
Development Fund Team. . . . . . . . . . . . . . . . . . . . . . Ms Cecilia Emery. . . . . . . . . . . . . . . . . . . Tel: (0115) 971 2707
Head of European Social Fund Team. . . . . . . . . . . . . . . Ms Jeanette Horton. . . . . . . . . . . . . . . . . Tel: (0115) 971 2608

**Education and Skills**

DfES School Directorate Adviser. . . . . . . . . . . . . . . . . . Ms Pauline Smith . . . . . . . . . . . . . . . . . . Tel: (0771) 1380179
Basic Skills: Regional Director . . . . . . . . . . . . . . . . . . Ms Lisa Capper . . . . . . . . . . . . . . . . . . . Tel: (0115) 971 2702
Special Educational Needs: Regional Co-ordination. . . . . . . Ms Pat Graham. . . . . . . . . . . . . . . . . . . . Tel: (0115) 971 2543
Sure Start/Children's Fund: Regional Manager. . . . . . . . . . Ms Pauline Jones . . . . . . . . . . . . . . . . . Tel: (0115) 971 2651

**Health**

Regional Director of Public Health . . . . . . . . . . . . . . . . Professor Lindsey Davies CBE . . . . . . . . . . . Tel: (0115) 971 4750
Assistant Regional Director of Public Health. . . . . . . . . . . Mr Jonathan Harris. . . . . . . . . . . . . . . . . Tel: (0115) 971 4753
Deputy Regional Director of Public Health . . . . . . . . . . . Dr Nick Salfield . . . . . . . . . . . . . . . . . . Tel: (0115) 971 4752
Consultant in Public Health Medicine. . . . . . . . . . . . . . Dr Judy Jones. . . . . . . . . . . . . . . . . . . . Tel: (0115) 971 4766
Business Manager. . . . . . . . . . . . . . . . . . . . . . . . . Mr Andrew Morris . . . . . . . . . . . . . . . . . Tel: (0115) 971 4759

**Information**

Regional Director, Government News Network. . . . . . . . . . Mr Peter Smith. . . . . . . . . . . . . . . . . . . . Tel: (0115) 971 2781

**Trade Partners UK**

International Trade Director . . . . . . . . . . . . . . . . . . . . Mr Peter Hogarth . . . . . . . . . . . . . . . . . Tel: (0115) 988 8566
Deputy International Trade Director . . . . . . . . . . . . . . . Ms Brian Drescher . . . . . . . . . . . . . . . . . Tel: (0115) 988 8468

### East Midlands Regional Development Agency

Apex Court, City Link, Nottingham, NG2 4LA
Tel: (0115) 988 8300  Fax: (0115) 985 3666
E-mail: info@emda.org.uk  Web: http://www.emda.org.uk

**Chairman** . . . . . . . . . . . . . . . . . . . . . . . . . . . . . . . Mr Derek Mapp
**Chief Executive** . . . . . . . . . . . . . . . . . . . . . . . . . . . Mr Martin Briggs

## GOVERNMENT OFFICES FOR THE REGIONS

### LONDON
### Government Office for London
Riverwalk House, 157-161 Millbank, London, SW1P 4RR
Tel: (020) 7217 3456  Fax: (020) 7217 3450
E-mail: enquiries.gol@go-regions.gov.uk
[initialsurname].gol@go-regions.gov.uk
Web: http://www.go-london.gov.uk

**Regional Director** . . . . . . . . . . . . . . . . . . . . . . . . . . . . . . . Ms Liz Meek . . . . . . . . . . . . . . . . . . . . . . . Tel: (020) 7217 3151
    *Personal Assistant* . . . . . . . . . . . . . . . . . . . . . . . . . . . Ms Loraine Dalligan . . . . . . . . . . . . . . . . Tel: (020) 7217 3387

**Directors**
    Central and South . . . . . . . . . . . . . . . . . . . . . . . . . . . . . Mr Richard Wragg . . . . . . . . . . . . . . . . . . . Tel: (020) 7217 3272
    Corporate and Change Management . . . . . . . . . . . . . . . . . Ms Anne Griffiths . . . . . . . . . . . . . . . . . . Tel: (020) 7217 3242
    Crime Reduction . . . . . . . . . . . . . . . . . . . . . . . . . . . . . . Ms Ellie Roy . . . . . . . . . . . . . . . . . . . . . . . Tel: (020) 7217 3071
    GOL Central Unit . . . . . . . . . . . . . . . . . . . . . . . . . . . . . Ms Marion Kerr . . . . . . . . . . . . . . . . . . . . . Tel: (020) 7217 3354
    Government / GLA Liaison and ERDF . . . . . . . . . . . . . . . Mr Jonathan Tillson . . . . . . . . . . . . . . . . . Tel: (020) 7217 3389
    London Resilience Team . . . . . . . . . . . . . . . . . . . . . . . . . Mr Zyg Kowalczyk . . . . . . . . . . . . . . . . . . Tel: (020) 7217 3014
    North and West Division . . . . . . . . . . . . . . . . . . . . . . . . Ms Liz Walton . . . . . . . . . . . . . . . . . . . . . Tel: (020) 7217 3086
    Planning . . . . . . . . . . . . . . . . . . . . . . . . . . . . . . . . . . . Mr Andrew Melville . . . . . . . . . . . . . . . . . Tel: (020) 7217 3140
    Thames Gateway . . . . . . . . . . . . . . . . . . . . . . . . . . . . . Ms Corinne Lyons . . . . . . . . . . . . . . . . . . Tel: (020) 7217 3362

**Central and South**
    Head of Division . . . . . . . . . . . . . . . . . . . . . . . . . . . . . Mr Richard Wragg . . . . . . . . . . . . . . . . . . . Tel: (020) 7217 3272
    Children's Fund . . . . . . . . . . . . . . . . . . . . . . . . . . . . . . Mr Stephen Harwood . . . . . . . . . . . . . . . . Tel: (020) 7217 3300
    Connexions Unit . . . . . . . . . . . . . . . . . . . . . . . . . . . . . Ms Brenda Pearson . . . . . . . . . . . . . . . . . Tel: (020) 7217 3306
    Education and Skills . . . . . . . . . . . . . . . . . . . . . . . . . . . Mr Jim Burns . . . . . . . . . . . . . . . . . . . . . . Tel: (020) 7217 3294
    Housing and Local Government . . . . . . . . . . . . . . . . . . . Ms Louise Matlock . . . . . . . . . . . . . . . . . . Tel: (020) 7217 3258
    New Opportunities Fund . . . . . . . . . . . . . . . . . . . . . . . . Ms Ceri Jones . . . . . . . . . . . . . . . . . . . . . . Tel: (020) 7217 3268
    Regional Adult Basic Skills . . . . . . . . . . . . . . . . . . . . . . Ms Rozi Premji . . . . . . . . . . . . . . . . . . . . . Tel: (020) 7217 3282
    Special Education Needs . . . . . . . . . . . . . . . . . . . . . . . . Ms Mary Kuhn . . . . . . . . . . . . . . . . . . . . . Tel: (020) 7217 3231
    Sure Start . . . . . . . . . . . . . . . . . . . . . . . . . . . . . . . . . Ms Lonica Vanclay . . . . . . . . . . . . . . . . . Tel: (020) 7217 3160
    Teacher Recruitment and Retention . . . . . . . . . . . . . . . . Ms Roselyn Unegbu . . . . . . . . . . . . . . . . . Tel: (020) 7217 3392

**Corporate and Change Management**
    Head of Division . . . . . . . . . . . . . . . . . . . . . . . . . . . . . Ms Anne Griffiths . . . . . . . . . . . . . . . . . . Tel: (020) 7217 3242
    Accommodation and Finance . . . . . . . . . . . . . . . . . . . . . Mr Paul Tobia . . . . . . . . . . . . . . . . . . . . . Tel: (020) 7217 3358
    Communications and New Media . . . . . . . . . . . . . . . . . . Ms Fay Quayle . . . . . . . . . . . . . . . . . . . . . Tel: (020) 7217 3127
    Financial Appraisal and Monitoring . . . . . . . . . . . . . . . . Mr Andrew Atherton . . . . . . . . . . . . . . . . Tel: (020) 7217 3274
    IT and Telecommunications . . . . . . . . . . . . . . . . . . . . . Mr John Joyce . . . . . . . . . . . . . . . . . . . . . Tel: (020) 7217 3348
    Personnel and Development Unit . . . . . . . . . . . . . . . . . . Mr Graham Roberts . . . . . . . . . . . . . . . . . Tel: (020) 7217 3106

**Crime Reduction**
    Deputy Head, Crime Reduction Division . . . . . . . . . . . . Ms Ellie Roy . . . . . . . . . . . . . . . . . . . . . . . Tel: (020) 7217 3071
        Central and South . . . . . . . . . . . . . . . . . . . . . . . . . . Ms Lucy Dawes . . . . . . . . . . . . . . . . . . . . Tel: (020) 7217 3523
        Health . . . . . . . . . . . . . . . . . . . . . . . . . . . . . . . . . Mr Vincent Tanti . . . . . . . . . . . . . . . . . . . Tel: (020) 7217 3291
        North and West . . . . . . . . . . . . . . . . . . . . . . . . . . . Ms Ann McDaid . . . . . . . . . . . . . . . . . . . . Tel: (020) 7217 3293
        Thames Gateway . . . . . . . . . . . . . . . . . . . . . . . . . . Mr Simon Harding . . . . . . . . . . . . . . . . . . Tel: (020) 7217 3251
        Transport . . . . . . . . . . . . . . . . . . . . . . . . . . . . . . . Mr John Waterman . . . . . . . . . . . . . . . . . Tel: (020) 7217 3087
    Youth Crime Unit . . . . . . . . . . . . . . . . . . . . . . . . . . . . Mr Roger Wilshaw . . . . . . . . . . . . . . . . . . Tel: (020) 7217 3497

**Drugs Prevention Advisory Service** . . . . . . . . . . . . . . . Mr Steve Robinson . . . . . . . . . . . . . . . . . . Tel: (020) 7217 3428

**GOL Central Unit**
    Head of Division . . . . . . . . . . . . . . . . . . . . . . . . . . . . . Ms Marion Kerr . . . . . . . . . . . . . . . . . . . . . Tel: (020) 7217 3354
    Head of Neighbourhood Renewal Unit . . . . . . . . . . . . . . Ms Brenda Pearson . . . . . . . . . . . . . . . . . Tel: (020) 7217 3306
    Co-ordination and Briefing . . . . . . . . . . . . . . . . . . . . . . Mr Ian Bellingham . . . . . . . . . . . . . . . . . . Tel: (020) 7217 3145
    Department of Culture, Media and Sport Interests . . . . . . Mr Andy Ganf . . . . . . . . . . . . . . . . . . . . . Tel: (020) 7217 3514

## GOVERNMENT OFFICES FOR THE REGIONS

*Government Office for London: GOL Central Unit (Continued)*

| | | |
|---|---|---|
| Neighbourhood Renewal Policy | Ms Brenda Pearson | Tel: (020) 7217 3306 |
| | Ms Heather White | Tel: (020) 7217 3049 |
| Neighbourhood Renewal Skills and Knowledge | Ms Sally Randall | Tel: (020) 7217 3064 |
| New Deal for Communities and Neighbourhood Management Co-ordination | Mr Michael Dynan-Oakley | Tel: (020) 7217 3644 |
| Public Order and Community Cohesion | Ms Hyacinth Parsons | Tel: (020) 7217 3059 |
| Research, Analysis and Intelligence | Ms Harvinder Mankoo | Tel: (020) 7217 3133 |
| Stakeholders Voluntary Sector | Mr Mike Desborough | Tel: (020) 7217 3042 |
| Sustainable Development | Ms Penny Bramwell | Tel: (020) 7217 3435 |

### Government / GLA Liaison and ERDF

| | | |
|---|---|---|
| Head of Division | Mr Jonathan Tillson | Tel: (020) 7217 3389 |
| GLA/LDA Policy | Ms Kirstin Green | Tel: (020) 7217 3413 |
| Transport (Roads and General) | Mr Ben Stafford | Tel: (020) 7217 3180 |

### Government News Network (London and South East)

| | | |
|---|---|---|
| Regional Director | Ms Virginia Burdon | Tel: (020) 7261 8762 |

### London Resilience Team

| | | |
|---|---|---|
| Head of Division | Mr Zyg Kowalczyk | Tel: (020) 7217 3014 |
| Deputy Head of Division | Mr Malcolm Sims | Tel: (020) 7217 3028 |

### North and North West

| | | |
|---|---|---|
| Head of Division | Ms L:iz Walton | Tel: (020) 7217 3086 |
| Education and Skills | Mr Andy Mitchell | Tel: (020) 7217 3297 |
| Housing and Local Government | Mr Don Thomas | Tel: (020) 7217 3020 |

### Planning

| | | |
|---|---|---|
| Head of Division | Mr Andrew Melville | Tel: (020) 7217 3140 |
| Planning Casework | Ms Mide Beaumont | Tel: (020) 7217 3143 |
| | Mr Simon Brown | Tel: (020) 7217 3168 |
| Strategic Planning | Mr Tony Thompson | Tel: (020) 7217 3148 |

### Thames Gateway

| | | |
|---|---|---|
| Head of Division | Ms Corinne Lyons | Tel: (020) 7217 3362 |
| Crime Reduction | Mr Simon Harding | Tel: (020) 7217 3251 |
| Education and Skills | Mr Jonathan Fairclough | Tel: (020) 7217 3522 |
| Housing and Local Government | Ms Lucy Hargreaves | Tel: (020) 7217 3010 |
| | Mr Geth Williams | Tel: (020) 7217 3253 |
| Housing Policy | Mr Peter Brittain | Tel: (020) 7217 3680 |
| Local Government and Housing Co-ordination | Mr John Monks | Tel: (020) 7217 3285 |

### Trade, Industry and Europe

| | | |
|---|---|---|
| Business Connect | Mr Ian Williams | Tel: (020) 7217 3216 |
| Enterprise | Ms Jane Lord | Tel: (020) 7217 3538 |
| European Programmes | Ms Lorraine Harris | Tel: (020) 7217 3067 |
| Finance, Buses and Major Projects | Mr Max Peacock | Tel: (020) 7217 3425 |
| GLA/LDA Policy | Ms Kirstin Green | Tel: (020) 7217 3413 |
| Innovation | Mr Peter Whittington | Tel: (020) 7217 3215 |
| Transport (Roads and General) | Mr Ben Stafford | Tel: (020) 7217 3180 |

### The Greater London Authority

City Hall, The Queen's Walk, London, SE1 2AA
Tel: (020) 7983 4000  Fax: (020) 7983 4008
E-mail: mayor@london.gov.uk  Web: http://www.london.gov.uk

| | | |
|---|---|---|
| **Chair, London Assembly** | Mr Brian Coleman GLA | |
| **Mayor of London** | Mr Ken Livingstone | |
| **Deputy Mayor** | Ms Nicky Gavron GLA | |

# GOVERNMENT OFFICES FOR THE REGIONS

## NORTH EAST
### Government Office for the North East
Wellbar House, Gallowgate, Newcastle-upon-Tyne, NE1 4TD
Tel: (0191) 201 3300 Fax: (0191) 202 3988
E-mail: general.enquiries.gone@go-regions.gov.uk
Web: http://www.go-ne.gov.uk

**Regional Director** . . . . . . . . . . . . . . . . . . . . . . . . . . . . . . . . Mr Jonathan Blackie . . . . . . . . . . . . . . . . . . . . . . Tel: (0191) 202 3801
   Support Office . . . . . . . . . . . . . . . . . . . . . . . . . . . . . . . . . *Vacant*. . . . . . . . . . . . . . . . . . . . . . . . . . . . . . Tel: (0191) 202 3564

**Directors**
   Business Group. . . . . . . . . . . . . . . . . . . . . . . . . . . . . . . . Mr Andrew Lewis . . . . . . . . . . . . . . . . . . . . . . Tel: (0191) 202 3803
   Communities Group . . . . . . . . . . . . . . . . . . . . . . . . . . . . Mr Alan Brown . . . . . . . . . . . . . . . . . . . . . . . Tel: (0191) 202 3745
   Environment Group. . . . . . . . . . . . . . . . . . . . . . . . . . . . . Mr John Bainton . . . . . . . . . . . . . . . . . . . . . . Tel: (0191) 202 3521
   Public Health Group. . . . . . . . . . . . . . . . . . . . . . . . . . . . Dr Bill Kirkup. . . . . . . . . . . . . . . . . . . . . . . . Tel: (0191) 202 1345
   Regional Group. . . . . . . . . . . . . . . . . . . . . . . . . . . . . . . Mr Jim Darlington . . . . . . . . . . . . . . . . . . . . . Tel: (0191) 202 3650

**Communities Group**
   Director, Communities Group . . . . . . . . . . . . . . . . . . . . Mr Alan Brown . . . . . . . . . . . . . . . . . . . . . . . Tel: (0191) 202 3745
      Children's Fund . . . . . . . . . . . . . . . . . . . . . . . . . . . . Ms Jackie McHanwell . . . . . . . . . . . . . . . . . . . . Tel: (0191) 202 3742
      Community Cohesion, Education and
        Community Development, New
        Opportunities Fund . . . . . . . . . . . . . . . . . . . . . . *Vacant*. . . . . . . . . . . . . . . . . . . . . . . . . . . . . . Tel: (0191) 202 3834
      Connexions/Careers . . . . . . . . . . . . . . . . . . . . . . Mr Eric Bannister . . . . . . . . . . . . . . . . . . . . . Tel: (0191) 202 3559
      Sure Start . . . . . . . . . . . . . . . . . . . . . . . . . . . . . . Ms Jayne Moules . . . . . . . . . . . . . . . . . . . . . . Tel: (0191) 202 3674
   *Neighbourhood Renewal and Crime Reduction*
      Director, Neighbourhood Renewal and
        Crime Reduction . . . . . . . . . . . . . . . . . . . . . . . . Ms Fiona Young . . . . . . . . . . . . . . . . . . . . . . Tel: (0191) 202 3885
      Crime Reduction. . . . . . . . . . . . . . . . . . . . . . . . . Mr Chris Warden. . . . . . . . . . . . . . . . . . . . . . Tel: (0191) 202 3713
      Drug Prevention Advisory Service . . . . . . . . . . . . . . *Vacant*. . . . . . . . . . . . . . . . . . . . . . . . . . . . . . Tel: (0191) 202 2223
      Local Strategic Partnerships (North) . . . . . . . . . . . . *Vacant*. . . . . . . . . . . . . . . . . . . . . . . . . . . . . . Tel: (0191) 202 3570
      Local Strategic Partnerships (South) . . . . . . . . . . . . Mr Peter Hanley . . . . . . . . . . . . . . . . . . . . . . Tel: (0191) 202 3668
      New Deal for Communities . . . . . . . . . . . . . . . . . . Mr Tom Smyth. . . . . . . . . . . . . . . . . . . . . . . Tel: (0191) 202 3661
      Policy Team . . . . . . . . . . . . . . . . . . . . . . . . . . . . Mr Fintan Hayes . . . . . . . . . . . . . . . . . . . . . . Tel: (0191) 202 3779
      Skills and Knowledge Fund,
        Construction Adviser . . . . . . . . . . . . . . . . . . . . Mr Barry Errington . . . . . . . . . . . . . . . . . . . . Tel: (0191) 202 3667

**Competitiveness and Europe Group**
   Director, Competitiveness and Europe. . . . . . . . . . . . . Mr Andrew Lewis . . . . . . . . . . . . . . . . . . . . . . Tel: (0191) 202 3803
   Business Performance and Skills. . . . . . . . . . . . . . . . . Mr Robin Fallon . . . . . . . . . . . . . . . . . . . . . . Tel: (0191) 202 3808
   Culture and Enterprise . . . . . . . . . . . . . . . . . . . . . . . Mr Jamie McKay . . . . . . . . . . . . . . . . . . . . . . Tel: (0191) 202 3878
   RDA Sponsorship . . . . . . . . . . . . . . . . . . . . . . . . . . Mr Ken Mitchie *(Acting)* . . . . . . . . . . . . . . . . . Tel: (0191) 202 3547
   Residential Training Unit . . . . . . . . . . . . . . . . . . . . . Ms Pam Gray. . . . . . . . . . . . . . . . . . . . . . . . Tel: (0191) 202 3666
   *Europe*
      Director, Europe . . . . . . . . . . . . . . . . . . . . . . . . . Mr John Rundle. . . . . . . . . . . . . . . . . . . . . . . Tel: (0191) 202 3923
        Objective 2. . . . . . . . . . . . . . . . . . . . . . . . . . . Mr Keith Raine . . . . . . . . . . . . . . . . . . . . . . Tel: (0191) 202 3923
        Objective 3. . . . . . . . . . . . . . . . . . . . . . . . . . . Mr John Downs . . . . . . . . . . . . . . . . . . . . . . Tel: (0191) 202 3834

**Environment Group**
   Director, Environment Group . . . . . . . . . . . . . . . . . . . Mr John Bainton . . . . . . . . . . . . . . . . . . . . . . Tel: (0191) 202 3521
   Casework Team. . . . . . . . . . . . . . . . . . . . . . . . . . . . . Ms Julie Hume . . . . . . . . . . . . . . . . . . . . . . . Tel: (0191) 202 3300
   Environment and Rural Affairs . . . . . . . . . . . . . . . . . . Ms Rebecca Cowburn . . . . . . . . . . . . . . . . . . . . Tel: (0191) 202 3595
   Transport Team. . . . . . . . . . . . . . . . . . . . . . . . . . . . . Mr Andrew Johnson. . . . . . . . . . . . . . . . . . . . . Tel: (0191) 202 3716
   *Built Environment*
      Director, Built Environment . . . . . . . . . . . . . . . . . . Ms Diana Pearce . . . . . . . . . . . . . . . . . . . . . . Tel: (0191) 202 3677
        Housing Team . . . . . . . . . . . . . . . . . . . . . . . . . Mr Adrian Hadden . . . . . . . . . . . . . . . . . . . . . Tel: (0191) 202 3658
        Planning Team . . . . . . . . . . . . . . . . . . . . . . . . Ms Caroline Burden. . . . . . . . . . . . . . . . . . . . . Tel: (0191) 202 3625

# GOVERNMENT OFFICES FOR THE REGIONS

*Government Office for the North East (Continued)*

## Public Health Group

| | | |
|---|---|---|
| Director, Public Health Group | Dr Bill Kirkup | Tel: (0191) 301 1345 |
| Deputy Director, Public Health | Mr John Woodhouse | Tel: (0191) 202 3756 |
| Business Management | Mr Jason Smith | Tel: (0191) 202 3913 |
| NHS Support | Ms Tracy Sharp | Tel: (0191) 202 3635 |

## Regional Group

| | | |
|---|---|---|
| Director | Mr Jim Darlington | Tel: (0191) 202 3650 |

*Corporate Services*

| | | |
|---|---|---|
| Director, Corporate Services | Ms Lynda Keith OBE | Tel: (0191) 202 2208 |
| Central Finance | Mr Mike Bradley | Tel: (0191) 202 3930 |
| Facilities Management | Mr Mark Leetion | Tel: (0191) 202 3523 |
| Personnel | Mrs Lynne Dersley | Tel: (0191) 202 3980 |
| Regional Strategy | Mr John Heywood | Tel: (0191) 202 3824 |
| Relocation Project Manager | Mr Terry Cain | Tel: (0191) 202 3594 |

*Regional Intelligence / Emergency Planning*

| | | |
|---|---|---|
| Director, Regional Intelligence and Emergency Planning | Mr Bryan Rees | Tel: (0191) 202 3669 |
| Communications | Ms Helen Steadman | Tel: (0191) 202 3893 |
| Knowledge Management | Mr Eddie Wrigley | Tel: (0191) 202 3721 |
| Regional Intelligence | Mr Philip Edwards | Tel: (0191) 202 3300 |
| Regional Resilience | Mr David Hay | Tel: (0191) 202 3300 |

## One North East
## (North East Regional Development Agency)

Stella House
Goldcrest Way, Newburn Riverside
Newcastle-upon-Tyne, NE15 8NV
Tel: (0191) 229 6200  Fax: (0191) 229 6201
Web: http://www.onenortheast.co.uk

| | |
|---|---|
| **Chairman** | Mrs Margaret Fay |
| **Chief Executive** | Mr Alan Clarke |

# GOVERNMENT OFFICES FOR THE REGIONS

## NORTH WEST
## Government Office for the North West

City Tower, Piccadilly Plaza, Manchester, M1 4BE
Tel: (0161) 952 4000  Fax: (0161) 982 4099

Cunard Building, Pier Head, Water Street, Liverpool, L3 1QB
Tel: (0151) 224 6302  Fax: (0151) 224 6470

E-mail: [initial&surname]gonw@go-regions.gov.uk
Web: http://www.go-nw.gov.uk

**Regional Director** . . . . . . . . . . . . . . . . . . . . . . . . . . . . Mr Keith Barnes . . . . . . . . . . . . . . . . . . . . . Tel: (0161) 952 4018

**Directors**

| | | |
|---|---|---|
| Communities. . . . . . . . . . . . . . . . . . . . . . . . . . . . . . . . | Mr Peter Styche. . . . . . . . . . . . . . . . . . . . . . | Tel: (0161) 952 4211 |
| Competitiveness and Infrastructure . . . . . . . . . . . . . . . . . . | Mr David Higham . . . . . . . . . . . . . . . . . . . . | Tel: (0161) 952 4439 |
| Corporate Services . . . . . . . . . . . . . . . . . . . . . . . . | Mr David Hopewell . . . . . . . . . . . . . . . . . . . | Tel: (0161) 952 4418 |
| Education and Social Inclusion . . . . . . . . . . . . . . . . . . . | Mr Nigel Burke . . . . . . . . . . . . . . . . . . . . . . | Tel: (0161) 952 4470 |
| Environment and Rural. . . . . . . . . . . . . . . . . . . . . . . . | Mr Neil Cumberlidge . . . . . . . . . . . . . . . . . . | Tel: (0161) 952 4083 |
| Europe . . . . . . . . . . . . . . . . . . . . . . . . . . . . . . . . . | Ms Jo Lappin. . . . . . . . . . . . . . . . . . . . . . . . | Tel: (0161) 952 4088 |
| European Programmes . . . . . . . . . . . . . . . . . . . . . . | Mr John Flamson. . . . . . . . . . . . . . . . . . . . . | Tel: (0151) 224 6334 |
| | Mr Chris Musson . . . . . . . . . . . . . . . . . . . . . | Tel: (0151) 224 6442 |
| Home Office. . . . . . . . . . . . . . . . . . . . . . . . . . . . . | Ms Gail Porter. . . . . . . . . . . . . . . . . . . . . . . | Tel: (0161) 952 4220 |
| | Ms David Smith. . . . . . . . . . . . . . . . . . . . . . | Tel: (0161) 952 4073 |
| Local Government Practice . . . . . . . . . . . . . . . . . . . | Mr Mike Greenwood . . . . . . . . . . . . . . . . . . | Tel: (0161) 952 4079 |
| Neighbourhood Renewal . . . . . . . . . . . . . . . . . . . . | Mr Kevin Brady. . . . . . . . . . . . . . . . . . . . . . | Tel: (0161) 952 4274 |
| | Mr Brian Holmes. . . . . . . . . . . . . . . . . . . . . | Tel: (0151) 224 6414 |
| Public Health. . . . . . . . . . . . . . . . . . . . . . . . . . . . | Mr John Ashton. . . . . . . . . . . . . . . . . . . . . . | Tel: (0161) 952 4432 |
| Spatial Development. . . . . . . . . . . . . . . . . . . . . . . . | Ms Jackie Potter . . . . . . . . . . . . . . . . . . . . . | Tel: (0161) 952 4203 |

## North West Development Agency

PO Box 37, Renaissance House
Centre Park, Warrington, WA1 1XB
Tel: (01925) 400100  Fax: (01925) 400400
E-mail: information@nwda.co.uk
Web: http://www.nwda.co.uk

**Chairman** . . . . . . . . . . . . . . . . . . . . . . . . . . . . . . . Mr Bryan Gray MBE
**Chief Executive** . . . . . . . . . . . . . . . . . . . . . . . . . . . . Mr Steven Broomhead

# GOVERNMENT OFFICES FOR THE REGIONS

## SOUTH EAST
## Government Office for the South East

Bridge House, 1 Walnut Tree Close, Guildford, Surrey, GU1 4GA
Tel: (01483) 882255  Fax: (01483) 882269
E-mail: reception.gose@go-regions.gov.uk  Web: http://www.go-se.gov.uk

**Regional Director** . . . . . . . . . . . . . . . . . . . . . . . . . . . . . . Mr Paul Martin . . . . . . . . . . . . . . . . . . . . . . . Tel: (01483) 882260
  *Secretariat* . . . . . . . . . . . . . . . . . . . . . . . . . . . . . Mr Rob Smith . . . . . . . . . . . . . . . . . . . . . . Tel: (01483) 882470

**Directors**
  Environment, Europe and Culture . . . . . . . . . . . . . . . . . Ms Alison Parker . . . . . . . . . . . . . . . . . . . . . Tel: (01483) 882350
  Finance and Corporate Management . . . . . . . . . . . . . . Mr Peter Craggs . . . . . . . . . . . . . . . . . . . . . . Tel: (01483) 882460
  Public Health  . . . . . . . . . . . . . . . . . . . . . . . . . . . . . . Dr Mike Gill . . . . . . . . . . . . . . . . . . . . . . . . . Tel: (01483) 882485
  Trade and Industry . . . . . . . . . . . . . . . . . . . . . . . . . . Mr Julian Lomas . . . . . . . . . . . . . . . . . . . . . . Tel: (01483) 882400
  Transport . . . . . . . . . . . . . . . . . . . . . . . . . . . . . . . . . Mr Andrew Roberts . . . . . . . . . . . . . . . . . . . . Tel: (01483) 882270

**Area Directors**
  Berkshire, Buckinghamshire and Oxfordshire . . . . . . . . . Mr Julian Lomas . . . . . . . . . . . . . . . . . . . . . . Tel: (01483) 882400
  Hampshire and Isle of Wight . . . . . . . . . . . . . . . . . . . . Mr Colin Byrne . . . . . . . . . . . . . . . . . . . . . . . Tel: (01483) 882300
  Kent . . . . . . . . . . . . . . . . . . . . . . . . . . . . . . . . . . . . . Mr Mark Billsborough . . . . . . . . . . . . . . . . . . Tel: (01483) 882500
  Surrey, East and West Sussex . . . . . . . . . . . . . . . . . . . Mr Andrew Roberts . . . . . . . . . . . . . . . . . . . . Tel: (01483) 882270

**Business Competitiveness**
  Berkshire, Buckinghamshire, Oxfordshire . . . . . . . . . . . . Ms Faith Charnock-Wilson . . . . . . . . . . . . . . . Tel: (01483) 882540
  Hampshire and Isle of Wight . . . . . . . . . . . . . . . . . . . . Ms Angela Alderman . . . . . . . . . . . . . . . . . . . Tel: (01483) 882382
  Kent . . . . . . . . . . . . . . . . . . . . . . . . . . . . . . . . . . . . . Mr Fergus Morley . . . . . . . . . . . . . . . . . . . . . Tel: (01483) 882530
  Surrey, East and West Sussex . . . . . . . . . . . . . . . . . . . Mr Roger Lee . . . . . . . . . . . . . . . . . . . . . . . . Tel: (01483) 882541

**Culture, Media and Sport** . . . . . . . . . . . . . . . . . . . . . . Mr Dan Chadwick . . . . . . . . . . . . . . . . . . . . . Tel: (01483) 882281

**Education Strategy** . . . . . . . . . . . . . . . . . . . . . . . . . . . Mrs Cathy Evans . . . . . . . . . . . . . . . . . . . . . . Tel: (01483) 882364

**Energy and Environmental Management** . . . . . . . . . . . . Ms Louise Whall . . . . . . . . . . . . . . . . . . . . . . Tel: (01483) 882896

**Enquiries**
  Berkshire, Buckinghamshire, Oxfordshire . . . . . . . . . . . . Ms Nadia Latif . . . . . . . . . . . . . . . . . . . . . . . Tel: (01483) 882401
  Hampshire and Isle of Wight . . . . . . . . . . . . . . . . . . . . Ms Amanda Bennett . . . . . . . . . . . . . . . . . . . Tel: (01483) 882312
  Kent . . . . . . . . . . . . . . . . . . . . . . . . . . . . . . . . . . . . . Mrs Lesley Woodhams . . . . . . . . . . . . . . . . . . Tel: (01483) 882501
  Surrey, East and West Sussex . . . . . . . . . . . . . . . . . . . Ms Tulin Sagun . . . . . . . . . . . . . . . . . . . . . . . Tel: (01483) 882271

**European Social Fund** . . . . . . . . . . . . . . . . . . . . . . . . Mr David Steed . . . . . . . . . . . . . . . . . . . . . . . Tel: (01483) 882474

**European Union (Inter-Regional)** . . . . . . . . . . . . . . . . Ms Elysia Compton . . . . . . . . . . . . . . . . . . . . Tel: (01483) 882316

**Health and Safety** . . . . . . . . . . . . . . . . . . . . . . . . . . . Mr Will Smythson . . . . . . . . . . . . . . . . . . . . . Tel: (01483) 882464

**Home Office Issues** . . . . . . . . . . . . . . . . . . . . . . . . . . Mr Hugh Marriage OBE . . . . . . . . . . . . . . . . . . Tel: (01483) 884834
  Crime Reduction . . . . . . . . . . . . . . . . . . . . . . . . . . . . Mr Richard Oldfield . . . . . . . . . . . . . . . . . . . . Tel: (01483) 884821
  Drugs . . . . . . . . . . . . . . . . . . . . . . . . . . . . . . . . . . . . Mrs Clare Marett . . . . . . . . . . . . . . . . . . . . . . Tel: (01483) 882432

**Housing and Communities**
  Regional Lead . . . . . . . . . . . . . . . . . . . . . . . . . . . . . . Mr Mark Billsborough . . . . . . . . . . . . . . . . . . Tel: (01483) 822500
  Berkshire, Buckinghamshire, Oxfordshire . . . . . . . . . . . . Mr Mark Norman . . . . . . . . . . . . . . . . . . . . . . Tel: (01483) 882437
  Hampshire and Isle of Wight . . . . . . . . . . . . . . . . . . . . Mr John Dunk . . . . . . . . . . . . . . . . . . . . . . . . Tel: (01483) 882320
  Kent . . . . . . . . . . . . . . . . . . . . . . . . . . . . . . . . . . . . . Ms Bernice O'Reilly . . . . . . . . . . . . . . . . . . . . Tel: (01483) 882524
  Surrey, East and West Sussex . . . . . . . . . . . . . . . . . . . Ms Eileen McDonald . . . . . . . . . . . . . . . . . . . Tel: (01483) 882386

# GOVERNMENT OFFICES FOR THE REGIONS

*Government Office for the South East (Continued)*

**National Lottery** . . . . . . . . . . . . . . . . . . . . . . . . . . Mr Dan Chadwick . . . . . . . . . . . . . . . . . . . . . Tel: (01483) 882281

**Neighbourhood Renewal.** . . . . . . . . . . . . . . . . . . . . . Ms Angela Hammond. . . . . . . . . . . . . . . . . . . Tel: (01483) 882346

**Planning**
    Regional Lead on Planning . . . . . . . . . . . . . . . . Mr Colin Byrne . . . . . . . . . . . . . . . . . . . . . Tel: (01483) 882300
    Berkshire, Buckinghamshire, Oxfordshire . . . . . . . . . . . . Mr Nigel Welbourn . . . . . . . . . . . . . . . . Tel: (01483) 882402
    Hampshire and Isle of Wight. . . . . . . . . . . . . . . . . Mr Mike Ellis . . . . . . . . . . . . . . . . . . . . . Tel: (01483) 882304
    Kent. . . . . . . . . . . . . . . . . . . . . . . . . . . . . . . . . . . . Ms Maureen Pullen . . . . . . . . . . . . . . . . . . Tel: (01483) 882496
    Surrey, East and West Sussex . . . . . . . . . . . . . . . . Mr John Aldworth . . . . . . . . . . . . . . . . . . Tel: (01483) 882372

**Regional Planning Guidance** . . . . . . . . . . . . . . . . . . . Ms Eike Muller . . . . . . . . . . . . . . . . . . . . . Tel: (01483) 882371

**Regional Resilience**. . . . . . . . . . . . . . . . . . . . . . . . . . Mr Ted Vary . . . . . . . . . . . . . . . . . . . . . . . Tel: (01483) 882444

**Regional Strategy** . . . . . . . . . . . . . . . . . . . . . . . . . . . Mr Tony Daniels . . . . . . . . . . . . . . . . . . . . Tel: (01483) 882273

**Rural (Defra)**. . . . . . . . . . . . . . . . . . . . . . . . . . . . . . Mr Douglas Driver . . . . . . . . . . . . . . . . . . . Tel: (01483) 882298

**Small Business Service** . . . . . . . . . . . . . . . . . . . . . . . Mr Kevin Hunt . . . . . . . . . . . . . . . . . . . . . Tel: (01483) 500783

**Sustainable Development** . . . . . . . . . . . . . . . . . . . . . . Ms Louise Whall . . . . . . . . . . . . . . . . . . . . Tel: (01483) 882896

**Training**
    Regional Lead on Skills and New Deal Issues . . . . . . . . . Mr Julian Lomas . . . . . . . . . . . . . . . . . . . Tel: (01483) 882400
    Connexions. . . . . . . . . . . . . . . . . . . . . . . . . . . . . . . Mr Stephen Burt . . . . . . . . . . . . . . . . . . . Tel: (01483) 882277
    Learning and Skills Councils:
        Berkshire, Buckinghamshire, Oxfordshire . . . . . . . . . Ms Lesley Taylor . . . . . . . . . . . . . . . . . . . Tel: (01483) 882330
        Hampshire and Isle of Wight. . . . . . . . . . . . . . . . Ms Cathy Evans. . . . . . . . . . . . . . . . . . . . . Tel: (01483) 882333
        Kent. . . . . . . . . . . . . . . . . . . . . . . . . . . . . . . . . Mr Fergus Morley . . . . . . . . . . . . . . . . . . . Tel: (01483) 882530
        Surrey, East and West Sussex . . . . . . . . . . . . . . . Mr Richard Young. . . . . . . . . . . . . . . . . . . Tel: (01483) 882380

**Transport**
    Hampshire and Isle of Wight. . . . . . . . . . . . . . . . . Mr David Cooper . . . . . . . . . . . . . . . . . . . Tel: (01483) 882410
    Berkshire, Buckinghamshire, Oxfordshire . . . . . . . . . . . . Mr John Rider . . . . . . . . . . . . . . . . . . . . . Tel: (01483) 884831
    Kent, Surrey, East and West Sussex . . . . . . . . . . . . . . Mr Lee Sambrook . . . . . . . . . . . . . . . . . . . Tel: (01483) 882393
    Transport Strategy. . . . . . . . . . . . . . . . . . . . . . . . . Mr David Cooper . . . . . . . . . . . . . . . . . . . Tel: (01483) 882410

**Urban Regeneration** . . . . . . . . . . . . . . . . . . . . . . . . . Mr John Dunk . . . . . . . . . . . . . . . . . . . . . Tel: (01483) 882320

**Voluntary Sector**. . . . . . . . . . . . . . . . . . . . . . . . . . . . Ms Janet Novak . . . . . . . . . . . . . . . . . . . . Tel: (01483) 882322

## South East Regional Development Agency (SEEDA)
Cross Lanes, Guildford, GU1 1YA
Tel: (01483) 484200  Fax: (01483) 484247
Web: http://www.seeda.co.uk

**Chairman** . . . . . . . . . . . . . . . . . . . . . . . . . . . . . . . . . Mr James Braithwaite CBE
**Chief Executive** . . . . . . . . . . . . . . . . . . . . . . . . . . . . Mr Anthony Dunnett

## GOVERNMENT OFFICES FOR THE REGIONS

### SOUTH WEST
### Government Office for the South West

1st and 2nd Floor, 2 Rivergate, Temple Quay, Bristol, BS1 6ED
Tel: (0117) 900 1700  Fax: (0117) 900 1900
E-mail: contactus.gosw@go-regions.gsi.gov.uk
Web: http://www.gosw.gov.uk

Mast House, Shepherds Wharf, 24 Sutton Road, Plymouth, PL4 0HJ
Tel: (01752) 635000  Fax: (01752) 227647
E-mail: goswdc@eurobell.co.uk
Web: http://www.gosw.gov.uk

**Regional Director** . . . . . . . . . . . . . . . . . . . . . . . . . . . . . . Ms Jane Henderson . . . . . . . . . . . . . . . . . . . . . Tel: (0117) 900 1701
   *Personal Assistant* . . . . . . . . . . . . . . . . . . . . . . . . . . Mr Duraid Silarbi . . . . . . . . . . . . . . . . . . . . . Tel: (0117) 900 1713
   *Personal Secretary* . . . . . . . . . . . . . . . . . . . . . . . . . . . Ms Janet Comley . . . . . . . . . . . . . . . . . . . . . . Tel: (0117) 900 1702

**Community Safety Directorate**
   Director . . . . . . . . . . . . . . . . . . . . . . . . . . . . . . . . . Mr Paul Rowlandson . . . . . . . . . . . . . . . . . . . Tel: (0117) 900 1855
   Crime Reduction. . . . . . . . . . . . . . . . . . . . . . . . . . . . Ms Miriam Minty . . . . . . . . . . . . . . . . . . . . . . Tel: (0117) 900 1866
   Bristol Crime and Drugs Partnership . . . . . . . . . . . . . . . Mr Rick Palmer . . . . . . . . . . . . . . . . . . . . . . . Tel: (0117) 900 1938
   Government Office Drugs Team . . . . . . . . . . . . . . . . . . Mrs Damaris Le Grand . . . . . . . . . . . . . . . . . . Tel: (0117) 900 3513
   Resilience Team . . . . . . . . . . . . . . . . . . . . . . . . . . . . . Mr Tony Thompson . . . . . . . . . . . . . . . . . . . . Tel: (0117) 900 3575

**Corporate Services Directorate**
   Director . . . . . . . . . . . . . . . . . . . . . . . . . . . . . . . . . Mr Malcolm Davey. . . . . . . . . . . . . . . . . . . . . Tel: (0117) 900 1707
   Business Support . . . . . . . . . . . . . . . . . . . . . . . . . . . Mr Paul Russell. . . . . . . . . . . . . . . . . . . . . . . . Tel: (0117) 900 3525
   Finance, Audit and Planning. . . . . . . . . . . . . . . . . . . . Mr Neil Hartley . . . . . . . . . . . . . . . . . . . . . . . . Tel: (0117) 900 1748
   Human Resources. . . . . . . . . . . . . . . . . . . . . . . . . . . Ms Susan Robson . . . . . . . . . . . . . . . . . . . . . . Tel: (0117) 900 1722

**Local Government, Housing and Planning Directorate**
   Director . . . . . . . . . . . . . . . . . . . . . . . . . . . . . . . . . Mr Thoss Shearer. . . . . . . . . . . . . . . . . . . . . . Tel: (0117) 900 1709
   Assistant Director (Gloucestershire, Wiltshire,
      Swindon) . . . . . . . . . . . . . . . . . . . . . . . . . . . . . Mr Huw Lloyd-Jones . . . . . . . . . . . . . . . . . . . Tel: (0117) 900 1890
   Head of Planning . . . . . . . . . . . . . . . . . . . . . . . . . . . Mr Tom King. . . . . . . . . . . . . . . . . . . . . . . . . Tel: (0117) 900 1886
   Local Government and Housing. . . . . . . . . . . . . . . . . . Mr Paul Roberts . . . . . . . . . . . . . . . . . . . . . . . Tel: (0117) 900 1821
   Statutory Planning Decisions. . . . . . . . . . . . . . . . . . . Mr Alan Wright . . . . . . . . . . . . . . . . . . . . . . . Tel: (0117) 900 1863

**Regional Policies, Enterprise and Skills Directorate**
   Director . . . . . . . . . . . . . . . . . . . . . . . . . . . . . . . . . Mrs Liz Carter . . . . . . . . . . . . . . . . . . . . . . . . Tel: (0117) 900 1703
   Culture and Tourism. . . . . . . . . . . . . . . . . . . . . . . . . Ms Sally Edgington . . . . . . . . . . . . . . . . . . . . Tel: (0117) 900 3561
   Enterprise (Bristol) . . . . . . . . . . . . . . . . . . . . . . . . . Mr Stuart Tarr . . . . . . . . . . . . . . . . . . . . . . . . Tel: (0117) 900 1768
   Europe (Plymouth) . . . . . . . . . . . . . . . . . . . . . . . . . Mr Bob Punchard . . . . . . . . . . . . . . . . . . . . . Tel: (01752) 635075
   Regional Development and Regional
      Governance . . . . . . . . . . . . . . . . . . . . . . . . . . . . Mr Mike Ashworth. . . . . . . . . . . . . . . . . . . . . Tel: (0117) 900 1706
   Small Business Service . . . . . . . . . . . . . . . . . . . . . . . Mr Brian McCarthy . . . . . . . . . . . . . . . . . . . . Tel: (0117) 933 0281
   UK Trade and Investment . . . . . . . . . . . . . . . . . . . . . Mr Paul Williams . . . . . . . . . . . . . . . . . . . . . . Tel: (0117) 933 0209
*Note: Small Business Service and UK Trade and Investment are located at: 4th Floor, 100 Temple Street, Bristol, BS1 6AE*

# GOVERNMENT OFFICES FOR THE REGIONS

*Government office for the South West (Continued)*

**Regional Public Health**
Director . . . . . . . . . . . . . . . . . . . . . . . . . . . . . . . . Dr Gabriel Scally . . . . . . . . . . . . . . . . . . . . . Tel: (0117) 900 3530

**Sustainability, Intelligence and Rural Affairs Directorate**
Director . . . . . . . . . . . . . . . . . . . . . . . . . . . . . . . Mr Tim Render . . . . . . . . . . . . . . . . . . . . . . . Tel: (0117) 900 1717
Assistant Director (Somerset and Dorset) . . . . . . . . . . . . Mr Steve Bone . . . . . . . . . . . . . . . . . . . . . . . Tel: (0117) 900 1747
Communication and Intelligence . . . . . . . . . . . . . . . . . Mrs Anna Blackmore . . . . . . . . . . . . . . . . . . . Tel: (0117) 900 1817
Food Farming and Rural Development . . . . . . . . . . . . . . Mr David Ball . . . . . . . . . . . . . . . . . . . . . . . . Tel: (0117) 900 1796
Sustainable and Environmental Technologies . . . . . . . . . Mr Mike Twomey . . . . . . . . . . . . . . . . . . . . . . Tel: (0117) 900 1804

**Transport and European Programmes Directorate**
Director . . . . . . . . . . . . . . . . . . . . . . . . . . . . . . . Mr Richard Bayly . . . . . . . . . . . . . . . . . . . . . Tel: (01752) 635050
Deputy Director . . . . . . . . . . . . . . . . . . . . . . . . . . Mr Philip Johnson . . . . . . . . . . . . . . . . . . . . . Tel: (01752) 635060
Assistant Director (Devon and Cornwall) . . . . . . . . . . . . Ms Sally Axworthy . . . . . . . . . . . . . . . . . . . . . Tel: (01752) 635035
Briefing, Intelligence and Ministerial Business . . . . . . . . Mr Tony Steele . . . . . . . . . . . . . . . . . . . . . . . Tel: (01752) 605066
ESF and Learning . . . . . . . . . . . . . . . . . . . . . . . . . . Ms Sarah Beeson . . . . . . . . . . . . . . . . . . . . . . Tel: (01752) 635124
European Accountability . . . . . . . . . . . . . . . . . . . . . Mr Mike Armstrong . . . . . . . . . . . . . . . . . . . . Tel: (01752) 635030
Facilities Management (Plymouth) . . . . . . . . . . . . . . . . Ms Jo Birnie . . . . . . . . . . . . . . . . . . . . . . . . . Tel: (01752) 635066
Objective 1 . . . . . . . . . . . . . . . . . . . . . . . . . . . . . . Mr Gareth Grimshaw . . . . . . . . . . . . . . . . . . . Tel: (01752) 635041
Objective 2 . . . . . . . . . . . . . . . . . . . . . . . . . . . . . . Ms Viv Stevens . . . . . . . . . . . . . . . . . . . . . . . Tel: (01752) 635011
Transport . . . . . . . . . . . . . . . . . . . . . . . . . . . . . . . Mr Peter Dawson . . . . . . . . . . . . . . . . . . . . . . Tel: (0117) 900 1883

**Young People, Regeneration and Communities Directorate**
Director . . . . . . . . . . . . . . . . . . . . . . . . . . . . . . . Mr Peter Cloke OBE . . . . . . . . . . . . . . . . . . . . Tel: (0117) 900 1720
Assistant Director (Avon, Community and Local
    Strategic Partnerships) . . . . . . . . . . . . . . . . . . . . . Mr Barry Cornish . . . . . . . . . . . . . . . . . . . . . . Tel: (0117) 900 1839
*Regeneration and Communities*
Deputy Director . . . . . . . . . . . . . . . . . . . . . . . . . . Mr Colin Passey . . . . . . . . . . . . . . . . . . . . . . . Tel: (0117) 900 1737
Community Cohesion and Equality . . . . . . . . . . . . . . . . Mrs Dawn Woods . . . . . . . . . . . . . . . . . . . . . . Tel: (0117) 900 1871
Neighbourhood Renewal (Bristol) . . . . . . . . . . . . . . . . Mr Dave Duggan . . . . . . . . . . . . . . . . . . . . . . Tel: (0117) 900 1816
Neighbourhood Renewal (Plymouth) . . . . . . . . . . . . . . Ms Pippa Ferguson . . . . . . . . . . . . . . . . . . . . . Tel: (01752) 635145
*Young People, Learning and Skills*
Deputy Director . . . . . . . . . . . . . . . . . . . . . . . . . . Mr Colin Passey . . . . . . . . . . . . . . . . . . . . . . . Tel: (0117) 900 1737
Connexions . . . . . . . . . . . . . . . . . . . . . . . . . . . . . . Mrs Nita Murphy . . . . . . . . . . . . . . . . . . . . . . Tel: (0117) 900 1932
Skills for Life . . . . . . . . . . . . . . . . . . . . . . . . . . . . . Ms Janet Hembry . . . . . . . . . . . . . . . . . . . . . . Tel: (0117) 900 1799
Sure Start, Early Years and Childcare . . . . . . . . . . . . . Mrs Cathy Benjamin . . . . . . . . . . . . . . . . . . . . Tel: (0117) 900 1836

## South West Regional Development Agency
Sterling House, Dix's Field, Exeter, EX1 1QA
Tel: (01392) 214747  Fax: (01392) 214848
E-mail: enquiries@southwestrda.org.uk
Web: http://www.southwestrda.org.uk

**Chairman** . . . . . . . . . . . . . . . . . . . . . . . . . . . . . . . . . Ms Juliet Williams
**Chief Executive** . . . . . . . . . . . . . . . . . . . . . . . . . . . . . Mr Geoffrey Wilkinson

# GOVERNMENT OFFICES FOR THE REGIONS

## WEST MIDLANDS
## Government Office for the West Midlands

77 Paradise Circus, Queensway, Birmingham, B1 2DT
Tel: (0121) 212 5050 Fax: (0121) 212 1010
E-mail: enquiries.gowm@go-regions.gov.uk
Web: http://www.go-wm.gov.uk

Regional Director . . . . . . . . . . . . . . . . . . . . . . . . . . . . . . Mr Graham Garbutt
   *Personal Assistant* . . . . . . . . . . . . . . . . . . . . . . . . . . . . Mr Simon Roose . . . . . . . . . . . . . . . . . . . . . . . Tel: (0121) 212 5055
   *Personal Secretary* . . . . . . . . . . . . . . . . . . . . . . . . . . . Ms Minerva Fletcher . . . . . . . . . . . . . . . . . . . . . Tel: (0121) 212 5258

**Directors**
   Northern Division . . . . . . . . . . . . . . . . . . . . . . . . . . . Ms Philippa Holland . . . . . . . . . . . . . . . . . . . Tel: (0121) 212 5087
   South Eastern Division . . . . . . . . . . . . . . . . . . . . . . . . Mr Chris Beesley . . . . . . . . . . . . . . . . . . . . . . Tel: (0121) 212 5350
   Western Division . . . . . . . . . . . . . . . . . . . . . . . . . . . Mr Brin Davies . . . . . . . . . . . . . . . . . . . . . . . Tel: (0121) 212 5354
   Corporate Services Division. . . . . . . . . . . . . . . . . . . . . Mr Jack Markiewicz. . . . . . . . . . . . . . . . . . . . Tel: (0121) 212 5218
   Crime Reduction, Social Inclusion
      and National Division . . . . . . . . . . . . . . . . . . . . . Ms Margaret Geary . . . . . . . . . . . . . . . . . . . . Tel: (0121) 212 5100
   Public Health Division . . . . . . . . . . . . . . . . . . . . . . . Professor Rod Griffiths. . . . . . . . . . . . . . . . . . Tel: (0121) 212 5347
   Regional Policy and Europe Division. . . . . . . . . . . . . . Mr Chris Marsh . . . . . . . . . . . . . . . . . . . . . . . Tel: (0121) 212 5206

**Corporate Service Division**
   Director . . . . . . . . . . . . . . . . . . . . . . . . . . . . . . . . . Mr Jack Markiewicz. . . . . . . . . . . . . . . . . . . . Tel: (0121) 212 5218
   Corporate Development. . . . . . . . . . . . . . . . . . . . . . . Ms Carole Rogers . . . . . . . . . . . . . . . . . . . . . Tel: (0121) 212 5324
   Corporate Strategy Team . . . . . . . . . . . . . . . . . . . . . . Ms Amanda Kennett . . . . . . . . . . . . . . . . . . . Tel: (0121) 212 5044
   Finance and Procurement Team . . . . . . . . . . . . . . . . . Mr Tony Chapman. . . . . . . . . . . . . . . . . . . . . Tel: (0121) 212 5039
   Ministerial Business and Communications. . . . . . . . . . Mr John Houlihan . . . . . . . . . . . . . . . . . . . . . Tel: (0121) 212 5083
   Personnel . . . . . . . . . . . . . . . . . . . . . . . . . . . . . . . . Mr Nick Whyte . . . . . . . . . . . . . . . . . . . . . . . Tel: (0121) 212 5174

**Crime Reduction, Social Inclusion and National Division**
   Director . . . . . . . . . . . . . . . . . . . . . . . . . . . . . . . . . Ms Margaret Geary . . . . . . . . . . . . . . . . . . . . Tel: (0121) 212 5100
   Community Cohesion Co-ordinator . . . . . . . . . . . . . . Mr Aftab Rahman . . . . . . . . . . . . . . . . . . . . . Tel: (0121) 214 2002
   Crime Reduction Manager. . . . . . . . . . . . . . . . . . . . . Ms Glenda Joseph . . . . . . . . . . . . . . . . . . . . . Tel: (0121) 214 2005
   Drug Strategy Team . . . . . . . . . . . . . . . . . . . . . . . . . Mr Peter Johnson. . . . . . . . . . . . . . . . . . . . . . Tel: (0121) 212 5276
   Partnership Support Manager . . . . . . . . . . . . . . . . . . Ms Bridget Brickley. . . . . . . . . . . . . . . . . . . . Tel: (0121) 214 2001
   Regional Central Unit National Focus Team . . . . . . . . . Mr Alistair Reekie. . . . . . . . . . . . . . . . . . . . . Tel: (0121) 212 5311
   Regional Research Team. . . . . . . . . . . . . . . . . . . . . . . Dr James Hodgkinson . . . . . . . . . . . . . . . . . . Tel: (0121) 212 5118
   Social Inclusion Team. . . . . . . . . . . . . . . . . . . . . . . . Ms Chris Eade. . . . . . . . . . . . . . . . . . . . . . . . Tel: (0121) 212 5138
   Youth Development Manager . . . . . . . . . . . . . . . . . . . Mr Gavin Butler. . . . . . . . . . . . . . . . . . . . . . . Tel: (0121) 212 5230

**Northern Division**
   Director . . . . . . . . . . . . . . . . . . . . . . . . . . . . . . . . . Ms Phillippa Holland. . . . . . . . . . . . . . . . . . . Tel: (0121) 212 5087
   Deputy Director . . . . . . . . . . . . . . . . . . . . . . . . . . . . Mr David Marr. . . . . . . . . . . . . . . . . . . . . . . . Tel: (0121) 212 5209
   Business, Europe and Skills Team. . . . . . . . . . . . . . . . . Mr Bob Fenley. . . . . . . . . . . . . . . . . . . . . . . . Tel: (0121) 214 2014
   Communities Team: Black Country . . . . . . . . . . . . . . . Mr Terry Cotton. . . . . . . . . . . . . . . . . . . . . . . Tel: (0121) 212 5318
   Communities Team: Staffordshire . . . . . . . . . . . . . . . . Mr Kevin Griffiths . . . . . . . . . . . . . . . . . . . . . Tel: (0121) 212 5251
   Local Government Team . . . . . . . . . . . . . . . . . . . . . . . Mrs Leo Castledine . . . . . . . . . . . . . . . . . . . . Tel: (0121) 212 5032
   Planning and Transport Team . . . . . . . . . . . . . . . . . . . Mr Ian Smith. . . . . . . . . . . . . . . . . . . . . . . . . Tel: (0121) 212 5285

# GOVERNMENT OFFICES FOR THE REGIONS

*Government Office for the West Midlands (Continued)*

## Public Health Division

Director . . . . . . . . . . . . . . . . . . . . . . . . . . . . . . . . . . . . . . . Professor Rod Griffiths . . . . . . . . . . . . . . . . . . Tel: (0121) 212 5347

## Regional Policy and Europe Division

Director . . . . . . . . . . . . . . . . . . . . . . . . . . . . . . . . . . . . . . Mr Chris Marsh . . . . . . . . . . . . . . . . . . . . . . . . Tel: (0121) 212 5205
European Structural Funds Team . . . . . . . . . . . . . . . . . . . Mr Keith Brown . . . . . . . . . . . . . . . . . . . . . . . . Tel: (0121) 212 5154
Finance, Accountability and Compliance Team . . . . . . . . Mr Tony Chapman . . . . . . . . . . . . . . . . . . . . . . Tel: (0121) 212 5039
Regional Policy
    (including Culture, Media and Sport) . . . . . . . . . . . . . Ms Liz Charlton . . . . . . . . . . . . . . . . . . . . . . . . Tel: (0121) 212 5229
Regional Sponsorship and Governance Team . . . . . . . . . . Mr Nic Cole . . . . . . . . . . . . . . . . . . . . . . . . . . . Tel: (0121) 212 5203

## South Eastern Division

Director . . . . . . . . . . . . . . . . . . . . . . . . . . . . . . . . . . . . . . Mr Chris Beesley . . . . . . . . . . . . . . . . . . . . . . . Tel: (0121) 212 5350
Deputy Director . . . . . . . . . . . . . . . . . . . . . . . . . . . . . . . . Ms Melanie Alker . . . . . . . . . . . . . . . . . . . . . . . Tel: (0121) 212 5430
Business, Europe and Skills Team . . . . . . . . . . . . . . . . . . . Mr Mark Foley . . . . . . . . . . . . . . . . . . . . . . . . . Tel: (0121) 212 5395
Communities Team . . . . . . . . . . . . . . . . . . . . . . . . . . . . . . Mrs Andrea Whitworth . . . . . . . . . . . . . . . . . . . Tel: (0121) 212 5428
Connexions and Education . . . . . . . . . . . . . . . . . . . . . . . . Mr John Robertson . . . . . . . . . . . . . . . . . . . . . . Tel: (0121) 212 5441
Local Government and Housing . . . . . . . . . . . . . . . . . . . . Mr John Dickinson . . . . . . . . . . . . . . . . . . . . . . Tel: (0121) 212 5430
Planning and Transport Team . . . . . . . . . . . . . . . . . . . . . . Ms Judith Pizzey . . . . . . . . . . . . . . . . . . . . . . . Tel: (0121) 212 5421

## Western Division

Director . . . . . . . . . . . . . . . . . . . . . . . . . . . . . . . . . . . . . . Mr Brin Davies . . . . . . . . . . . . . . . . . . . . . . . . . Tel: (0121) 212 5354
Deputy Director . . . . . . . . . . . . . . . . . . . . . . . . . . . . . . . . Ms Sue Todd . . . . . . . . . . . . . . . . . . . . . . . . . . . Tel: (0121) 212 5353
Business, Europe and Skills Team . . . . . . . . . . . . . . . . . . . Mr Mel Davis . . . . . . . . . . . . . . . . . . . . . . . . . . Tel: (0121) 212 5426
Local Government and Communities Team . . . . . . . . . . . Mr Paul Stratford . . . . . . . . . . . . . . . . . . . . . . . Tel: (0121) 212 5407
Planning and Transport Team . . . . . . . . . . . . . . . . . . . . . . Mr Peter Williams . . . . . . . . . . . . . . . . . . . . . . Tel: (0121) 212 5454
Rural Affairs Team . . . . . . . . . . . . . . . . . . . . . . . . . . . . . . Mr David Howatson . . . . . . . . . . . . . . . . . . . . . Tel: (0121) 212 5400

### Advantage West Midlands
### (West Midlands Development Agency)

3 Priestley Wharf, Holt Street
Birmingham, B7 4BN
Tel: (0121) 380 3500  Fax: (0121) 380 3501
E-mail: info@advantagewm.co.uk
Web: http://www.advantagewm co.uk

**Chairman** . . . . . . . . . . . . . . . . . . . . . . . . . . . . . . . . . . . . . Mr Nick Paul

**Chief Executive** . . . . . . . . . . . . . . . . . . . . . . . . . . . . . . . . Mr John Edwards

# GOVERNMENT OFFICES FOR THE REGIONS

## YORKSHIRE AND THE HUMBER
## Government Office for Yorkshire and the Humber

PO Box 213, City House, New Station Street, Leeds, LS1 4US
Tel: (0113) 280 0600  Fax: (0113) 283 6394
E-mail: [initial.surname]goyh@go-regions.gsi.gov.uk
Web: http://www.goyh.gov.uk

**Regional Director** . . . . . . . . . . . . . . . . . . . . . . . . . . . . . . Ms Felicity Everiss . . . . . . . . . . . . . . . . . . . . Tel: (0113) 283 5200
   *Executive Assistant* . . . . . . . . . . . . . . . . . . . . . . . . . . . Ms Lynne Jamieson . . . . . . . . . . . . . . . . . . . . Tel: (0113) 283 5203

### Directors
Community Safety . . . . . . . . . . . . . . . . . . . . . . . . . . . . . . Ms Jacqui Lewis . . . . . . . . . . . . . . . . . . . . . . . Tel: (0113) 283 5429
Competitiveness and Sustainability . . . . . . . . . . . . . . . . . . Ms Margaret Jackson . . . . . . . . . . . . . . . . . . . Tel: (0113) 233 8200
Corporate Services . . . . . . . . . . . . . . . . . . . . . . . . . . . . Mr Nick Best . . . . . . . . . . . . . . . . . . . . . . . . . . Tel: (0113) 283 5204
Objective 1 Programme, South Yorkshire . . . . . . . . . . . . . Ms Sylvia Yates . . . . . . . . . . . . . . . . . . . . . . . . Tel: (01709) 763670
People and Communities . . . . . . . . . . . . . . . . . . . . . . . . . Ms Isobel Mills . . . . . . . . . . . . . . . . . . . . . . . . Tel: (0113) 283 5386
Regional Affairs . . . . . . . . . . . . . . . . . . . . . . . . . . . . . . Mr John Jarvis . . . . . . . . . . . . . . . . . . . . . . . . . Tel: (0113) 283 6407
Rural Issues . . . . . . . . . . . . . . . . . . . . . . . . . . . . . . . . . Mr Gordon Kingston . . . . . . . . . . . . . . . . . . . Tel: (0113) 283 5860

### Competitiveness and Sustainability Group
Director, Competitiveness and Sustainability . . . . . . . . . . Ms Margaret Jackson . . . . . . . . . . . . . . . . . . . Tel: (0113) 233 8200
Director, European Secretariat . . . . . . . . . . . . . . . . . . . Ms Alison Biddulph . . . . . . . . . . . . . . . . . . . . . Tel: (0113) 233 8340
European Business Support . . . . . . . . . . . . . . . . . . . . . . . *Vacant* . . . . . . . . . . . . . . . . . . . . . . . . . . . . . . . Tel: (0113) 233 8375
European Funds Finance Team Leader . . . . . . . . . . . . . . Mr Adrian Smith . . . . . . . . . . . . . . . . . . . . . . . Tel: (0113) 233 8207
European Structural Funds and Community
   Development . . . . . . . . . . . . . . . . . . . . . . . . . . . . . . Mr John Millar . . . . . . . . . . . . . . . . . . . . . . . . Tel: (0113) 233 8260
Innovation and Best Practice . . . . . . . . . . . . . . . . . . . . . Mr John Baragwanath . . . . . . . . . . . . . . . . . . . Tel: (0113) 233 8217
Integrated Transport . . . . . . . . . . . . . . . . . . . . . . . . . . . Mr Phil Jones . . . . . . . . . . . . . . . . . . . . . . . . . Tel: (0113) 283 6608
Objective 1 Programme, South Yorkshire,
   Director . . . . . . . . . . . . . . . . . . . . . . . . . . . . . . . . . Ms Sylvia Yates . . . . . . . . . . . . . . . . . . . . . . . . Tel: (01709) 763670
Programme Management . . . . . . . . . . . . . . . . . . . . . . . . Mr Kevin Bennett . . . . . . . . . . . . . . . . . . . . . . Tel: (01709) 763601
Small Business Service: Deputy Director . . . . . . . . . . . . . Mr Richard Norbury . . . . . . . . . . . . . . . . . . . . Tel: (0113) 394 9829
Strategy, Communications, Themes and
   Evaluation . . . . . . . . . . . . . . . . . . . . . . . . . . . . . . . Ms Jayne Crosse . . . . . . . . . . . . . . . . . . . . . . . Tel: (01709) 763616
UK Trade and Investment:
   Director . . . . . . . . . . . . . . . . . . . . . . . . . . . . . . . . . Mr Mark Robson . . . . . . . . . . . . . . . . . . . . . . Tel: (0113) 394 9821
   Deputy Director . . . . . . . . . . . . . . . . . . . . . . . . . . . Mr Graham Percival . . . . . . . . . . . . . . . . . . . . Tel: (0113) 394 9822

### Corporate Services
Director, Resilience Planning and Corporate
   Services . . . . . . . . . . . . . . . . . . . . . . . . . . . . . . . . . Mr Nick Best . . . . . . . . . . . . . . . . . . . . . . . . . . Tel: (0113) 283 5204
Deputy Director, Resilience Planning . . . . . . . . . . . . . . . Ms Jo Gillespie . . . . . . . . . . . . . . . . . . . . . . . . Tel: (0113) 283 6362
Finance and Audit . . . . . . . . . . . . . . . . . . . . . . . . . . . . Mr Paul Crossan . . . . . . . . . . . . . . . . . . . . . . . Tel: (0113) 283 6477
Office Solutions . . . . . . . . . . . . . . . . . . . . . . . . . . . . . . Ms Christine Morton . . . . . . . . . . . . . . . . . . . . Tel: (0113) 283 6355
People and Business Development . . . . . . . . . . . . . . . . . Mr David Walmsley . . . . . . . . . . . . . . . . . . . . . Tel: (0113) 283 6355

# GOVERNMENT OFFICES FOR THE REGIONS

*Government Office for Yorkshire and the Humber (Continued)*

## People and Communities Group

| | | |
|---|---|---|
| Director, People and Communities. | Ms Isobel Mills | Tel: (0113) 283 5386 |
| Children's Fund: Regional Manager. | Ms Deidre Quinn | Tel: (0113) 283 5272 |
| Director, Community Safety. | Ms Jacqui Lewis | Tel: (0113) 283 6382 |
| Connexions. | Mr Derek Ireland | Tel: (0113) 283 5259 |
| Local Government and Housing. | Mr Peter Campey | Tel: (0113) 283 6400 |
| | Mr Chris Meyrick | Tel: (0113) 283 6324 |
| | Mr John Taylor | Tel: (0113) 283 6427 |
| Local Strategic Partnerships Co-ordination | Ms Janet Munn | Tel: (0113) 283 6672 |
| Director, Neighbourhood Renewal | Ms Carol Cooper-Smith | Tel: (0113) 283 6414 |
| | Mr Steve Nesbitt | Tel: (0113) 283 6694 |
| Planning: North and West Yorkshire | Mr Geoff Dibb | Tel: (0113) 283 6351 |
| Planning: South Yorkshire and Humber. | Mr Bryan Davies | Tel: (0113) 283 6351 |
| Street Crime, West Yorkshire | Mr Mick Chambers | Tel: (0113) 283 6664 |
| Sure Start: Regional Manager | Ms Anne-Marie Graham. | Tel: (0113) 283 5427 |

## Regional Group

| | | |
|---|---|---|
| Director, Regional Affairs | Mr John Jarvis | Tel: (0113) 283 6407 |
| Director, Rural | Mr Gordon Kingston | Tel: (0113) 283 5860 |
| Intelligence and Evaluation. | Mr Kevin Hopkins | Tel: (0113) 283 5321 |
| Ministerial Business | Mr Bernard McLoughlin. | Tel: (0113) 283 6681 |
| RDA Sponsorship | Mr Martin Seymour | Tel: (0113) 283 4883 |
| Regional Planning, Transport and Evaluation | Mr David Owen | Tel: (0113) 283 6439 |
| Rural Team | Mr Tim Godson | Tel: (0113) 283 4881 |
| Department of Culture Media and Sport Adviser | Ms Amanda Potter | Tel: (0113) 283 5452 |

## Regional Public Health Group

| | | |
|---|---|---|
| Director, Regional Public Health Group | Mr Paul Johnstone | Tel: (0113) 283 6459 |
| Deputy Director, Health Protection and Intelligence | Mr Colin Pollock | Tel: (0113) 283 5270 |
| Deputy Director, Regeneration and Development. | Mr Peter Counsell | Tel: (0113) 283 6602 |

### Yorkshire Forward
### (Yorkshire and the Humber Regional Development Agency)
Victoria House, 2 Victoria Place
Leeds, LS11 5AE
Tel: (0113) 394 9600  Fax: (0113) 243 1088
Web: http://www.yorkshire-forward.com

| | |
|---|---|
| **Chairman** | Mr Terry Hodgkinson |
| **Chief Executive** | Mr Martin Havenhand |

# SCOTLAND OFFICE

*(for Scotland Office see under Department for Constitutional Affairs at p 253)*

# DEPARTMENT OF TRADE AND INDUSTRY

1 Victoria Street, London, SW1H 0ET
Tel: (020) 7215 5000  Fax: (020) 7215 0105
E-mail: [firstname.surname]@dti.gsi.gov.uk
Web: http://www.dti.gov.uk

## MINISTERS

**Secretary of State for Trade and Industry**
*(also Minister for Women)* ...................... Rt Hon Patricia Hewitt MP
*Principal Private Secretary* ...................... Mr Matthew Hilton .................... Tel: (020) 7215 5621
*Special Advisers* ............................. Mr Jim Godfrey. ...................... Tel: (020) 7215 6620
Mr Roger Sharp ...................... Tel: (020) 7215 6480
Ms Deborah Lincoln *(Women's Issues)* ...... Tel: (020) 7215 3971

**Minister of State** *(Minister for E-Commerce and*
*Competiveness)* ............................ Mr Mike O'Brien MP
*Private Secretary*. ............................ Mr Peter Elder ...................... Tel: (020) 7215 2129

**Minister of State** *(Minister for Industry and the Regions;*
*also Deputy Minister for Women)* ................ Rt Hon Jacqui Smith MP
*Private Secretary*. ............................ Mr Spencer Mahony ................... Tel: (020) 7215 6202

**Minister of State** *(Minister for Trade)*. ............... Mr Douglas Alexander MP
*(also at the Foreign and Commonwealth office)*
*Private Secretary*. ............................ Mr Bryan Payne ...................... Tel: (020) 7215 5144

**Parliamentary Secretary** *(Small Business)* ........... Mr Nigel Griffiths MP
*Private Secretary*. ............................ Mrs Claire Ball. .................... Tel: (020) 7215 5503

**Parliamentary Secretary** *(Science and Innovation)* ..... Lord Sainsbury of Turville
*Private Secretary*. ............................ Mr Joe Burns ....................... Tel: (020) 7215 5624

**Parliamentary Secretary** *(Employment Relations,*
*Competition, and Consumers)* .................... Mr Gerry Sutcliffe MP
*Private Secretary*. ............................ Mr Gareth Maybury .................. Tel: (020) 7215 5568

## CIVIL SERVICE

**Permanent Secretary** ........................... Sir Robin Young KCB
*Private Secretary*. ........................... Mr Tom Ridge ...................... Tel: (020) 7215 5536

**Chief Scientific Adviser and Head of Office**
**of Science and Technology** .................. Professor Sir David King FRS ............. Tel: (020) 7215 3821

**Group Chief Executive UK Trade and Investment**. . . Sir Stephen Brown KCVO

**Senior Management**
Director-General, Business Group. ............... Mr Mark Gibson .................... Tel: (020) 7215 4178
Director General, Economics ................... Ms Vicky Pryce .................... Tel: (020) 7215 6059
Director-General, Energy Group ................ Ms Joan MacNaughton ............... Tel: (020) 7215 0301
Director-General, Europe and World Trade Group..... Mr Edmund Hosker ................... Tel: (020) 7215 4445
Director-General, Fair Markets Group. ........... Mr Stephen Haddrill. ............... Tel: (020) 7215 6845
Director-General, Innovation Group .............. Mr David Hughes .................... Tel: (020) 7215 1703
The Solicitor and Director General Legal Services..... Mr Anthony Inglese ................ Tel: (020) 7215 3039
Director-General, Research Councils .............. Sir Keith O'Nions ................. Tel: (020) 7215 3803
Director-General, Services Group ................ Dr Catherine Bell CB ............... Tel: (020) 7215 5589
Director, Strategy Unit ....................... Mr Geoff Dart. .................... Tel: (020) 7215 2590

# DEPARTMENT OF TRADE AND INDUSTRY

## SUBJECT RESPONSIBILITIES AND CONTACTS

*Note: (i) These come under the auspices jointly of the Department of Trade and Industry and the Foreign and Commonwealth Office.*
*(ii) In addition to 1 Victoria Street, the Department of Trade and Industry also has offices in London at the following locations:*

*10 Victoria Street, London, SW1N 0NN*

*Kingsgate House, 66-74 Victoria Street, London, SW1E 6SW*

*4 Abbey Orchard Street, London, SW1P 2HT*

*Elizabeth House, 39 York Road, London, SE1 7LJ*

*151 Buckingham Palace Road, London, SW1W 9SS*

**Director, Financial Reporting Policy**...............Mr John Grewe...................Tel: (020) 7215 0223

**Aerospace Industry**

    Director, Aerospace and Defence....................Ms Penny Ciniewicz..............Tel: (020) 7215 1139

    Director, Aerospace and Defence Industries Technology...Mr David Way..............Tel: (020) 7215 1129

    Aerospace Equipment...........................Mr Bob Insley.................Tel: (020) 7215 0968

    Policy/Aeroengines............................Mr Roger Bourne...............Tel: (020) 7215 5000

    Airframes Policy..............................Ms Patricia Judd..............Tel: (020) 7215 1539

    Aviation Environment..........................Mr Peter Newton...............Tel: (020) 7215 1117

    Aircraft Systems Technologies....................Dr Gill Richards..............Tel: (020) 7215 1175

    Airframes

        Industry Relations...........................Mr Bob Insley.................Tel: (020) 7215 0968

        Policy......................................Ms Patricia Judd..............Tel: (020) 7215 1539

    Policy/Business Support Analyst..................Mr Bob Collier................Tel: (020) 7215 1156

    Defence

        Industrial Policy............................Mr Paul Hawker................Tel: (020) 7215 1125

        Procurement.................................Mr Robert Waters..............Tel: (020) 7215 1173

    Economics and Life Science Sector................Mr Michael Hodson.............Tel: (020) 7215 5000

    Engines

        Industry Relations...........................Mr Bob Insley.................Tel: (020) 7215 0968

        Policy......................................Mr Roger Bourne...............Tel: (020) 7215 1128

    Environmental Issues, Aviation...................Mr Peter Newton...............Tel: (020) 7215 1117

    Equipment....................................Mr Bob Insley.................Tel: (020) 7215 0968

    Market Analyses..............................Mr Robert Morris..............Tel: (020) 7215 1174

    Structures and Materials Technologies.............Dr Sarah Bishop...............Tel: (020) 7215 1157

                                           Dr Gillian Richards...........Tel: (020) 7215 1175

    Naval Equipment..............................Mr Bob Insley.................Tel: (020) 7215 0968

    Propulsion Technologies.........................Mr Ian Wilson.................Tel: (020) 7215 2973

    Technology...................................Dr Ray Kingcombe..............Tel: (020) 7215 1115

    Trade Policy.................................Ms Patricia Judd..............Tel: (020) 7215 1539

**Agri-business**...................................Dr Sue Armfield...............Tel: (020) 7215 5000

**Bioscience / Biotechnology**

    Director, Bioscience..........................Dr Monica Darnbrough..........Tel: (020) 7215 5000

    Deputy Director, Bioscience.....................Dr Martin Anthony.............Tel: (020) 7215 5000

    Section Head, Industry Economics and

        Statistics Directorate........................Mr Alan Bevan.................Tel: (020) 7215 1886

    America Team Leader...........................Mr Paul Mullins...............Tel: (020) 7215 1183

    Asia Team – Automotive.........................Mr Barry Cole.................Tel: (020) 7215 5884

    Assistant Director, Bioenergy and Solar...........Mr Gary Shanahan..............Tel: (020) 7215 6483

    Biopharmaceuticals and Pharmaceuticals...........Mr Nick Cooper................Tel: (020) 7215 5000

    Biotechnology, Small Firms Group.................Mr Bob Wiggins................Tel: (020) 7215 5000

    Bio-Wise Programme...........................Mr David Armitt...............Tel: (020) 7215 5000

    Business Relations, Bioscience..................Mr Graham Branton.............Tel: (020) 7215 5000

    Economics, Life Science Sector..................Mr Michael Hodson.............Tel: (020) 7215 1848

    Environmental Biotechnology.....................Mr David Armitt...............Tel: (020) 7215 5000

    Head of European and International Bio-issues.......Ms Anna Cummins...............Tel: (020) 7215 5000

    Head of Knowledge Transfer Team..................Dr William Leitch.............Tel: (020) 7215 4110

# DEPARTMENT OF TRADE AND INDUSTRY

**Business**

| | | |
|---|---|---|
| Director-General, Business Group | Mr Mark Gibson | Tel: (020) 7215 4178 |
| Business Support | Mr Nick Hallett | Tel: (020) 7215 0856 |
| | Mr David Saunders | Tel: (020) 7215 0913 |
| Business Support Delivery | Mr Adam Dawson | Tel: (020) 7215 0915 |
| Business Support Policy | *Vacant* | Tel: (020) 7215 0917 |
| Change Management Team | Ms Amanda Brooks | Tel: (020) 7215 1142 |
| Economics and Statistics | Mr Christopher Moir | Tel: (020) 7215 1927 |
| ICTs in New Ways of Working | Mr Geoff Ireland | Tel: (020) 7215 1332 |

**Business Relations**

| | | |
|---|---|---|
| Director, Business Relations 1 | Mr John Alty | Tel: (020) 7215 3723 |
| Director, Business Relations 2 - Communication Industries | Mr David Hendon | Tel: (020) 7215 1201 |
| Director, Business Relations Policy Unit | Ms Rosa Wilkinson | Tel: (020) 7215 3752 |
| Director, Postal Services Directorate | Mr Mark Higson | Tel: (020) 7215 4115 |
| Director, Strategic Management | Ms Sheila Morris | Tel: (020) 7215 3749 |
| Business Relations Central Unit | Ms Sheila Morris | Tel: (020) 7215 3749 |
| Construction | Dr Rodger Evans | Tel: (020) 7215 4164 |
| Consumer Goods | Ms Jodi Truss | Tel: (020) 7215 1890 |
| Manufacturing Policy Team Including MAS (Manufacturing Advisory Service) | Mr Martin Berry | Tel: (020) 7215 2927 |
| Materials and Engineering | Mr Simon Edmonds | Tel: (020) 7215 1535 |

**Cars** (*see below under Motor Vehicles*)

**Chemicals**

| | | |
|---|---|---|
| Director, Chemicals Directorate | Dr David Jennings | Tel: (020) 7215 2911 |
| Analysis and Regulatory | Mr Patrick Walsh | Tel: (020) 7215 1146 |
| Business Relations | | |
| Commodity Chemicals | Mr Philip Edwards | Tel: (020) 7215 4163 |
| Consumer Chemicals, Plastic & Rubber | Mr Mike Sellek | Tel: (020) 7215 1893 |
| Speciality Chemicals | Mr David Friday | Tel: (020) 7215 1475 |
| Chemicals Unit, Innovation and Growth | Dr Peter Brooke | Tel: (020) 7215 1107 |
| Economics Advice | Mr Alan Bevan | Tel: (020) 7215 1886 |

**Coal** (*see below under Energy*)

**Communications, Departmental** (*see below under Press and Publicity*)

**Company Law / Investigations**

| | | |
|---|---|---|
| Director, Corporate Law; Governance | Ms Bernadette Kelly | Tel: (020) 7215 0206 |
| Inspector of Companies | Mr Robert Burns | Tel: (020) 7215 3048 |
| Accountancy Adviser | Mr Andrew Watchman | Tel: (020) 7215 0221 |
| Community Enterprise | | |
| Director, Companies and Community Enterprise | Mr Keith Masson | Tel: (020) 7215 0220 |
| Director's Remuneration and Pay | Mr David Styles | Tel: (020) 7215 0211 |
| European Union Directives: Accounting and Financial Reporting Policy | Mr John Grewe | Tel: (020) 7215 0223 |
| Financial Services Authority, Liaison | Mr Cliff Callaghan | Tel: (020) 7215 3051 |
| Insider Dealing | | |
| Complaints | Mr Cliff Callaghan | Tel: (020) 7215 3051 |
| Applications, Consideration | Mr Cliff Callaghan | Tel: (020) 7215 3051 |
| Companies Acts 1985 and 1989 | Mr John Gardner | Tel: (020) 7215 3097 |
| Insurance Companies | Mr John Gardner | Tel: (020) 7215 3097 |
| Investigations | Mr Anthony Robertshaw | Tel: (020) 7215 3095 |
| Overseas Regulatory Authorities | Mrs Bridget Chase | Tel: (020) 7215 3021 |
| Legal Advice | | |
| Investigations | Mr Scott Milligan | Tel: (020) 7215 3144 |
| Prosecutions | Mr Lal Nawbatt | Tel: (020) 7215 3132 |
| Liaison with Serious Fraud Office and Takeover Panel | Mrs Bridget Chase | Tel: (020) 7215 3021 |
| London Stock Exchange, Liaison | Mr Cliff Callaghan | Tel: (020) 7215 3051 |
| Modern Company Law | | |
| Joint Head of Companies Bill Team | Miss Anne Willcocks | Tel: (020) 7215 3838 |
| Joint Head of Companies Bill Team | Mr Richard Carter | Tel: (020) 7215 6552 |

# DEPARTMENT OF TRADE AND INDUSTRY

*Company Law / Investigations (Continued)*

| | | |
|---|---|---|
| Non-Executive Director, Review | Ms Anne Willocks | Tel: (020) 7215 5000 |
| Office of Fair Trading, Liaison | Mr Roger Watson | Tel: (020) 7215 3017 |
| Partnership Law | Mr John Grewe | Tel: (020) 7215 0223 |

**Competition**

| | | |
|---|---|---|
| Director, Consumer and Competition Policy | Mr Jonathan Rees | Tel: (020) 7215 0310 |
| Cross Market Interventions | Miss Fiona Price | Tel: (020) 7215 0338 |
| Economic Regulation and Reform | Mr Thoss Shearer | Tel: (020) 7215 3975 |
| Director, Europe and International | Mr Tony Sims | Tel: (020) 7215 6472 |
| Specific Market Inventions | Ms Pat Sellers | Tel: (020) 7215 0027 |
| Director, Strategy and Delivery | Ms Katherine Wright | Tel: (020) 7215 5420 |

**Construction Industry**

| | | |
|---|---|---|
| Director, Construction | Ms Elizabeth Whatmore | Tel: (020) 7215 3718 |
| Construction Business Improvement | Dr Rodger Evans | Tel: (020) 7215 4164 |
| Construction Line and CENELEC | Ms Margaret Lovett | Tel: (020) 7215 3712 |
| Construction Products | Mr David Payne | Tel: (020) 7215 1522 |
| Construction Market Intelligence | Mr Keith Folwell | Tel: (020) 7215 1248 |

**Consumers / Consumer Goods**

| | | |
|---|---|---|
| Director, Consumer Goods and Services | Ms Jane Swift | Tel: (020) 7215 1905 |
| Deputy Director, Consumer | Mr Sandy Grom | Tel: (020) 7215 2963 |
| Advertising Standards | Mr Martyn Rapley | Tel: (020) 7215 0342 |
| Advice and Information, Consumer Direct | Mr Mitchell Leimon | Tel: (020) 7215 6413 |
| Business Services | Ms Lesley Forsdike | Tel: (020) 7215 4153 |
| Ceramics | Ms Jodi Truss | Tel: (020) 7215 1890 |
| Citizen's Advice Bureau | Mr Mitchell Leimon | Tel: (020) 7215 6413 |
| Consumer Credit | Mr Adrian Walker-Smith | Tel: (020) 7215 5000 |
| Consumer Goods | Ms Jodi Truss | Tel: (020) 7215 1890 |
| Consumer Safety | Mrs Pat Sellers | Tel: (020) 7215 0028 |
| Doorstep Selling | Mr Peter Evans | Tel: (020) 7215 5000 |
| Estate Agents | Mr Brian Swift | Tel: (020) 7215 3089 |
| Joint Environmental Markets Unit - Goods and Services | Mr Stephen De Souza | Tel: (020) 7215 3757 |
| Marketing | Mr Henry Marsden | Tel: (020) 7215 1989 |
| Mergers | Mr Tony Metcalfe | Tel: (020) 7215 0326 |
| National Consumer Council | Mr Francis Rogers | Tel: (020) 7215 0317 |
| Retail | Mr Andrew Bacchus | Tel: (020) 7215 1541 |
| Sale of Goods and Services, Legal | Mr Malcolm Smith | Tel: (020) 7215 3593 |

**Defence Industries and Procurement** *(see above under Aerospace Industry)*

**Departmental Services**

| | | |
|---|---|---|
| Director-General, Services Group | Dr Catherine Bell CB | Tel: (020) 7215 5572 |
| E-Strategy and Major Projects | Mr Andrew Matthew | Tel: (020) 7215 3678 |
| Estates and Facilities Management | Mr Mike Rainsford | Tel: (020) 7855 3688 |
| Finance | Mr Peter Mason | Tel: (020) 7215 6848 |
| Finance and Resource Management | Mr David Evans | Tel: (020) 7215 6851 |
| Human Resources and Change Management | Mrs Shirley Pointer | Tel: (020) 7215 8994 |
| Information and Communications Technology Services | *Vacant* | Tel: (020) 7215 3651 |
| Information and Workplace Services | Ms Yvonne Gallagher | Tel: (020) 7215 3630 |
| Information Policy and Services | Mrs Eileen Maclachlan | Tel: (020) 7215 1701 |
| Internal Audit | Mr Jon Whitfield | Tel: (020) 7215 2873 |

*(see also under Finance, Departmental and Human Resources Departmental)*

**Detergents** . . . . . . . . . . . . . . . . Mr Mike Sellek . . . . . . . . . . . . . Tel: (020) 7215 1211

**Dumping**

| | | |
|---|---|---|
| Anti-Dumping Unit | Mrs Cynthia Reid | Tel: (020) 7215 4580 |

# DEPARTMENT OF TRADE AND INDUSTRY

## Economics

| | | |
|---|---|---|
| Director-General, Economics and Chief Economic Adviser . | Ms Vicky Pryce | Tel: (020) 7215 6615 |
| Deputy Chief Economic Adviser | Mr Ken Warwick | Tel: (020) 7215 6338 |
| Director, Economic Analysis | Mr Mark Conaty | Tel: (020) 7215 6338 |
| Director, Energy Markets Unit | Mr Neil Hirst | Tel: (020) 7215 2761 |
| Director, Industry Economics and Statistics | Mr Christopher Moir | Tel: (020) 7215 1927 |
| Director, International Economics | Mr Peter Dodd | Tel: (020) 7215 4586 |
| Director, Strategy Development (Research and Analysis) | Mr Adrian Gault | Tel: (020) 7215 2679 |
| Aerospace and Defence | Mr Michael Hodson | Tel: (020) 7215 5000 |
| Automotive Industries | Mr Paul Crawford | Tel: (020) 7215 1864 |
| Broadcasting Technologies | Mr Ivan Bishop | Tel: (020) 7215 1831 |
| Climate Change | Ms Lorraine Hamid | Tel: (020) 7215 6246 |
| | Mr Peter Roscoe | Tel: (020) 7215 5837 |
| Competitiveness Studies, Sector | Mr Robert Kuenzel | Tel: (020) 7215 2982 |
| Construction | Mr Bernard Vogl | Tel: (020) 7215 0966 |
| Digital Industries | Mr Michael Crosse | Tel: (020) 7215 1861 |
| Doha Development Agenda | Mr Ramil Burden | Tel: (020) 7215 4467 |
| E-Commerce | Mr Michael Crosse | Tel: (020) 7215 1861 |
| Energy | | |
| Director, Energy Economics | Mr Adrian Gault | Tel: (020) 7215 2679 |
| Demand Projections | Mr Roger Lampert | Tel: (020) 7215 2689 |
| | Ms Margaret Maier | Tel: (020) 7215 2702 |
| Electricity Markets | Mr David McAlonan | Tel: (020) 7215 2694 |
| | Mr Richard Penn | Tel: (020) 7215 2683 |
| Environment | Ms Emma Camp | Tel: (020) 7215 1627 |
| | Mr Trevor Reid | Tel: (020) 7215 5843 |
| Gas, Downstream | Ms Sally Williams | Tel: (020) 7215 2700 |
| Modelling | Mr David Wilson | Tel: (020) 7215 2687 |
| Power Stations Emissions Projections | Mr David Wilson | Tel: (020) 7215 2687 |
| Recycling Policy | Mr Trevor Reid | Tel: (020) 7215 5843 |
| Engineering | Mr Paul Crawford | Tel: (020) 7215 1864 |
| European Economic Reform Agenda | Ms Helen Grimshaw | Tel: (020) 7215 4585 |
| External Trade Policies | Mr John Marshall | Tel: (020) 7215 4590 |
| Inward Investment | Ms Helen Grimshaw | Tel: (020) 7215 4585 |
| Joint Environmental Markets | Mr Alan Bevan | Tel: (020) 7215 1886 |
| Life Science | Mr Michael Hodson | Tel: (020) 7215 5000 |
| Oil Markets | Mr Paul Bailey | Tel: (020) 7215 5287 |
| Publishing | Mr Michael Crosse | Tel: (020) 7215 1861 |
| Regional Economics | Ms Margaret McEvoy | Tel: (020) 7215 5685 |
| Trade Partners UK Evaluation | Mr Christopher Alexander | Tel: (020) 7215 4225 |
| Trade Performance | Mr Christopher Alexander | Tel: (020) 7215 4225 |

## Electricity *(see below under Energy: Electricity)*

## Employment Agency Licensing Office

| | | |
|---|---|---|
| *Helpline* | *enquiries* | Tel: (0845) 955 5105 |
| European Strategy and Labour Market Flexibility | Ms Jane Whewell | Tel: (020) 7215 5731 |
| Employment Agency Standards Policy and Regulations | | |
| Chief Inspector | Mr Vic Patterson | Tel: (020) 7215 5708 |

## Employment Relations / Practices

| | | |
|---|---|---|
| Director, Employment Relations | Ms Janice Munday | Tel: (020) 7215 3815 |
| Agency Workers | Ms Jane Whewell | Tel: (020) 7215 5731 |
| Dispute Resolution | Ms Sarah Rhodes | Tel: (020) 7215 0146 |
| Diversity and Equality | Ms Rosalind McCarthy-Ward | Tel: (020) 7215 0149 |
| Employee Involvement | Ms Jane Whewell | Tel: (020) 7215 5731 |
| Employment Rights, Selected | Ms Rosalind McCarthy-Ward | Tel: (020) 7215 5549 |
| Employment Market Analysis and Research | Mr Grant Fitzner | Tel: (020) 7215 5753 |
| Equal Treatment Directive, European Union | Ms Rosalind McCarthy-Ward | Tel: (020) 7215 0149 |
| European Strategy and Labour Market Flexibility | Ms Jane Wheswell | Tel: (020) 7215 5731 |
| Fixed Term Contracts | Ms Jane Whewell | Tel: (020) 7215 5731 |
| Homeworkers | Ms Jane Whewell | Tel: (020) 7215 5731 |
| Maternity Leave | *Vacant* | Tel: (020) 7215 5000 |
| Minimum Wage | *Vacant* | Tel: (020) 7215 5000 |
| Part-time Work | *Vacant* | Tel: (020) 7215 5000 |

# DEPARTMENT OF TRADE AND INDUSTRY

*Employment Relations / Practices (Continued)*

| | | |
|---|---|---|
| Participation and Skills | Ms Julie Carney | Tel: (020) 7215 5549 |
| Paternity Leave | *Vacant* | Tel: (020) 7215 5000 |
| Public Holidays | *Vacant* | Tel: (020) 7215 5000 |
| Public Interest Disclosure Act | Mr Jim Mitchell | Tel: (020) 7215 5752 |
| Trade Unions | Ms Sarah Rhodes | Tel: (020) 7215 0146 |
| TUPE | Ms Sarah Rhodes | Tel: (020) 7215 0146 |
| Working Parents | Ms Julie Carney | Tel: (020) 7215 5549 |
| Work Life Balance | Ms Julie Carney | Tel: (020) 7215 5549 |
| Works Councils | Mr Iain Adlington | Tel: (020) 7215 3806 |

## Energy: Coal

| | | |
|---|---|---|
| Director, Coal Industry | Ms Bronwen Northmore | Tel: (020) 7215 5004 |
| Director, Coal Policy | Ms Anne Taylor | Tel: (020) 7215 5344 |
| Clean Coal Technology | Mr Charles Pearce | Tel: (020) 7215 2669 |
| Coal Technology | Mr David Crockford | Tel: (020) 7215 2667 |
| Concessionary Coal | Mr Adrian Hyde | Tel: (020) 7215 2656 |
| Health Claims | | |
|     Director, Coal Health Claims Unit | Mrs Ann Taylor CBE | Tel: (020) 7215 5344 |
|     Policy | Mr Nick French | Tel: (020) 7215 5631 |
|     Surface Dust | Mr Nick French | Tel: (020) 7215 5631 |
|     Vibration Related Diseases | Ms Christine Chamberlain | Tel: (020) 7215 5521 |
| Industry Sponsorship | Mr Peter Mason | Tel: (020) 7215 5003 |
| Liabilities Management | Mr Alan Edwards | Tel: (020) 7215 5524 |
| Liabilities Unit, Nuclear and Coal | Mr Peter Waller | Tel: (020) 7215 2182 |
| Pensions, British Coal | Mr Adrian Hyde | Tel: (020) 7215 2656 |
| Privatisation, Residual Issues | Mr David Leitch | Tel: (020) 7215 5252 |
| Regulation and Sponsorship | Mr David Leitch | Tel: (020) 7215 5252 |
| Respiratory Disease | Mr Nigel Smith | Tel: (020) 7215 2626 |
| Statistics | Mr Mike Janes | Tel: (020) 7215 5186 |
| Vibration Related Disease | Ms Christine Chamberlain | Tel: (020) 7215 5521 |

## Energy: Electricity

| | | |
|---|---|---|
| Director, Licensing and Consents Unit | Mr Richard Mellish | Tel: (020) 7215 6001 |
|     Consents Offshore | Ms Cathy Allen | Tel: (020) 7215 0479 |
| | Dr Caroline Roberts | Tel: (020) 7215 2381 |
|     Onshore | Mr Laurence Cadman | Tel: (020) 7215 2889 |
| Embedded Generation | Mr Philip Baker | Tel: (020) 7215 2675 |
| Emergency Planning | Mr Vernon Brown | Tel: (020) 7215 5246 |
| Energy Markets | Mrs Sue Harrison | Tel: (020) 7215 2778 |
| European Policy | Mrs Sue Harrison | Tel: (020) 7215 2778 |
| Market Regulation | Mr Anthony Segal | Tel: (020) 7215 5352 |
| Regulatory Policy | Mr Edward Blades | Tel: (020) 7215 2121 |
| Statistics | Mr Mike Janes | Tel: (020) 7215 5186 |
| Supply Security | Ms Anne Locke | Tel: (020) 7215 5293 |
| Technology | Mr Philip Baker | Tel: (020) 7215 2675 |
| Trading Reform | Mr Giles Sibun | Tel: (020) 7215 0237 |
| Transmission | Ms Maria Bazell | Tel: (020) 7215 6159 |
| Wayleaves | Mr Lawrence Cadman | Tel: (020) 7215 2889 |
| Wind | | |
|     Offshore Windfarm Consents | Ms Caroline Roberts | Tel: (020) 7215 2831 |

## Energy: General

| | | |
|---|---|---|
| Director-General, Energy | Ms Joan MacNaughton | Tel: (020) 7215 0301 |
| Deputy Director-General, Energy Markets Unit | Mr Neil Hirst | Tel: (020) 7215 2761 |
| Director, Domestic and European Energy | Dr Elizabeth Baker | Tel: (020) 7215 2729 |
| Director, Engineering Inspectorate | Dr Peter Fenwick | Tel: (020) 7215 2856 |
| Director, Innovation and Business | Ms Clair Durkin | Tel: (020) 7215 0248 |
| Director, International and Infrastructure | Ms Ann Eggington | Tel: (020) 7215 5249 |
| Director, Social Issues and Information | Mr Graham White | Tel: (020) 7215 2696 |
|     Bio-energy | Mr Gary Shanahan | Tel: (020) 7215 6483 |
| Climate Change, Economics | Ms Lorraine Hamid | Tel: (020) 7215 6246 |
| | Mr Peter Roscoe | Tel: (020) 7215 6166 |

# DEPARTMENT OF TRADE AND INDUSTRY

*Energy: General (Continued)*

Coal *(see above under Energy: Coal)*
Communications, Energy Group . . . . . . . . . . . . . . . . . . . . Ms Liz Santry . . . . . . . . . . . . . . . . . . . . . . . . . . . . Tel: (020) 7215 5278
Competition . . . . . . . . . . . . . . . . . . . . . . . . . . . . . . . . . Mr John Havard . . . . . . . . . . . . . . . . . . . . . . . . . . Tel: (020) 7215 5546
Demand Projections . . . . . . . . . . . . . . . . . . . . . . . . . . . Mr Roger Lampert . . . . . . . . . . . . . . . . . . . . . . . . . Tel: (020) 7215 2689
. . . . . . . . . . . . . . . . . . . . . . . . . . . . . . . . . . . . . . . . . . Ms Margaret Maier . . . . . . . . . . . . . . . . . . . . . . . . Tel: (020) 7215 2702
Economics
    Environment and Energy . . . . . . . . . . . . . . . . . . . Ms Emma Campbell . . . . . . . . . . . . . . . . . . . Tel: (020) 7215 1627
    Markets Analysis . . . . . . . . . . . . . . . . . . . . . . . . . . Mr David McAlonan . . . . . . . . . . . . . . . . . . . . Tel: (020) 7215 2694
    . . . . . . . . . . . . . . . . . . . . . . . . . . . . . . . . . . . . . . Mr Richard Penn . . . . . . . . . . . . . . . . . . . . . . . Tel: (020) 7215 2683
    Modelling and Projections . . . . . . . . . . . . . . . . . . Mr David Wilson . . . . . . . . . . . . . . . . . . . . . . . Tel: (020) 7215 2687
    Recycling, Packaging and Waste Management . . . . . . Mr Trevor Reid . . . . . . . . . . . . . . . . . . . . . . . . Tel: (020) 7215 5843
Electricity *(see above under Energy: Electricity)*
Emergency Planning . . . . . . . . . . . . . . . . . . . . . . . . . . Mr Vernon Brown . . . . . . . . . . . . . . . . . . . . . . . . . Tel: (020) 7215 5246
Emissions Projections . . . . . . . . . . . . . . . . . . . . . . . . . Mr David Wilson . . . . . . . . . . . . . . . . . . . . . . . . . . Tel: (020) 7215 2687
Energy Demands, Projections . . . . . . . . . . . . . . . . . . . Ms Margaret Maier . . . . . . . . . . . . . . . . . . . . . . . . Tel: (020) 7215 2702
Energy Markets Unit . . . . . . . . . . . . . . . . . . . . . . . . . . Mr Neil Hirst . . . . . . . . . . . . . . . . . . . . . . . . . . . . . Tel: (020) 7215 2761
Energy White Paper . . . . . . . . . . . . . . . . . . . . . . . . . . Mr Jonathan Booth . . . . . . . . . . . . . . . . . . . . . . . . Tel: (020) 7215 2672
European Markets . . . . . . . . . . . . . . . . . . . . . . . . . . . . Mrs Sue Harrison . . . . . . . . . . . . . . . . . . . . . . . . . Tel: (020) 7215 2778
Gas *(see below under Energy - Oil and Gas)*
Hydrogen and Fuel Cells . . . . . . . . . . . . . . . . . . . . . . . Mr Ray Eaton . . . . . . . . . . . . . . . . . . . . . . . . . . . . Tel: (020) 7215 2650
Innovation and Business . . . . . . . . . . . . . . . . . . . . . . . Ms Clair Durkin . . . . . . . . . . . . . . . . . . . . . . . . . . Tel: (020) 7215 0242
International Energy . . . . . . . . . . . . . . . . . . . . . . . . . . . Mrs Loraine Dawson . . . . . . . . . . . . . . . . . . . . . . . Tel: (020) 7215 3990
International Unit . . . . . . . . . . . . . . . . . . . . . . . . . . . . Mr David Irving . . . . . . . . . . . . . . . . . . . . . . . . . . Tel: (020) 7215 2812
Licensing Consents . . . . . . . . . . . . . . . . . . . . . . . . . . . Mr Jim Campbell . . . . . . . . . . . . . . . . . . . . . . . . . Tel: (01224) 254011
Nuclear Liabilities Management . . . . . . . . . . . . . . . . . . Mr Terry Selby . . . . . . . . . . . . . . . . . . . . . . . . . . . Tel: (020) 7215 3841
Nuclear *(see below under Energy: Nuclear)*
Renewable Energy Development . . . . . . . . . . . . . . . . . . Mr Roy Collins . . . . . . . . . . . . . . . . . . . . . . . . . . . Tel: (020) 7215 2645
Oil *(See below under Energy: Oil and Gas)*
Renewables UK . . . . . . . . . . . . . . . . . . . . . . . . . . . . . . Mrs Sarah Kydd *(Aberdeen)* . . . . . . . . . . . . . . . Tel: (01224) 254001
Safety
    Director, Nuclear Safety and Security . . . . . . . . . . . . . Mr Charles Bridge . . . . . . . . . . . . . . . . . . . . . Tel: (020) 7215 2879
Solar Programmes . . . . . . . . . . . . . . . . . . . . . . . . . . . . Mr Gary Shanahan . . . . . . . . . . . . . . . . . . . . . . . . Tel: (020) 7215 6483
Statistics
    Director, Energy, Social Issues, Information
      and Statistics . . . . . . . . . . . . . . . . . . . . . . . . . . Mr Graham White . . . . . . . . . . . . . . . . . . . . . Tel: (020) 7215 2696
    Energy Balance Statistics . . . . . . . . . . . . . . . . . . . . Mr Chris Bryant . . . . . . . . . . . . . . . . . . . . . . Tel: (020) 7215 0124
Strategy, Energy
    Development . . . . . . . . . . . . . . . . . . . . . . . . . . . . Mr Adrian Gault . . . . . . . . . . . . . . . . . . . . . . Tel: (020) 7215 2679
    Strategic Issues . . . . . . . . . . . . . . . . . . . . . . . . . . . Mr David Hayes . . . . . . . . . . . . . . . . . . . . . . Tel: (020) 7215 3988
Sustainable Energy *(see below under Energy: Renewable / Sustainable)*
Wind and Water Programmes . . . . . . . . . . . . . . . . . . . Mr John Overton . . . . . . . . . . . . . . . . . . . . . . . . . Tel: (020) 7215 6481

## Energy: Nuclear

Director, International Policy and Programmes . . . . . . . . . Mr Ian Downing . . . . . . . . . . . . . . . . . . . . . . . Tel: (020) 7215 2883
Office for Civil Nuclear Security
*Harwell, Didcot, Oxfordshire, OX11 0RA*
    Director, Civil Nuclear Security . . . . . . . . . . . . . . . . . Mr Michael Buckland-Smith . . . . . . . . . . . . Tel: (01235) 432924
BNFL, Corporate Governance . . . . . . . . . . . . . . . . . . . . Mr Steve Wheeler . . . . . . . . . . . . . . . . . . . . . . . . . Tel: (020) 7215 5524
Central and Eastern Europe Safety Issues . . . . . . . . . . . . Mr Stephen Truswell . . . . . . . . . . . . . . . . . . . . . . . Tel: (020) 7215 6522
Civil Nuclear Emergency Planning . . . . . . . . . . . . . . . . Mr Peter Edwards . . . . . . . . . . . . . . . . . . . . . . . . . Tel: (020) 7215 2746
Closed Cities . . . . . . . . . . . . . . . . . . . . . . . . . . . . . . . . Mr David Vincent . . . . . . . . . . . . . . . . . . . . . . . . . Tel: (020) 7215 2878
Corporate Governance . . . . . . . . . . . . . . . . . . . . . . . . . Mr Stephen Spivey . . . . . . . . . . . . . . . . . . . . . . . . . Tel: (020) 7215 0430
Decommissioning . . . . . . . . . . . . . . . . . . . . . . . . . . . . Mr Peter Waller . . . . . . . . . . . . . . . . . . . . . . . . . . . Tel: (020) 7215 2182
Euratom . . . . . . . . . . . . . . . . . . . . . . . . . . . . . . . . . . . Mr Gerard Franks . . . . . . . . . . . . . . . . . . . . . . . . . Tel: (020) 7215 2550
International Atomic Energy Authority . . . . . . . . . . . . . . Mr Maurice Strike . . . . . . . . . . . . . . . . . . . . . . . . . Tel: (020) 7215 2757
International Liability and Safety Issues . . . . . . . . . . . . . Mr Ian Downing . . . . . . . . . . . . . . . . . . . . . . . . . . Tel: (020) 7215 2883
Insurance and Liability . . . . . . . . . . . . . . . . . . . . . . . . . Mr Ian Downing . . . . . . . . . . . . . . . . . . . . . . . . . . Tel: (020) 7215 2883
Liabilities Unit, Nuclear and Coal . . . . . . . . . . . . . . . . . Mr Peter Waller . . . . . . . . . . . . . . . . . . . . . . . . . . . Tel: (020) 7215 2182
OECD . . . . . . . . . . . . . . . . . . . . . . . . . . . . . . . . . . . . Mr Maurice Strike . . . . . . . . . . . . . . . . . . . . . . . . . Tel: (020) 7215 2757

# DEPARTMENT OF TRADE AND INDUSTRY

*Energy: Nuclear (Continued)*

Office for Civil Nuclear Security

| | | |
|---|---|---|
| Finance and Management Services | Mr Martin Lambert | Tel: (01235) 432939 |
| Intelligence Assessment | Dr John Reynolds | Tel: (01235) 432929 |
| Standards and Operation | Mr Chris Price | Tel: (01235) 432944 |
| Plutonium Disposition | Mr David Vincent | Tel: (020) 7215 2878 |
| Regulatory Reform | Mr David Rutland | Tel: (020) 7215 2893 |
| Safety and Fission Research Policy | Mr Steven Walsgrove | Tel: (020) 7215 5395 |
| Safety and Security | Mr Patrick Robinson | Tel: (020) 7215 1632 |
| Security Policy, Nuclear | Mr John Foggo | Tel: (020) 7215 6540 |
| Social Issues | Mr David Bramble | Tel: (020) 7215 0282 |

UKAEA

| | | |
|---|---|---|
| Constabulary - Legislation | Ms Kate Allan | Tel: (020) 7215 2893 |
| Corporate Governance | Mr David Rutland | Tel: (020) 7215 0262 |
| Policy | Mr Ian Gregory | Tel: (020) 7215 0261 |
| Waste Management | Mr Geoff Dessent | Tel: (020) 7215 2785 |

**Energy: Oil and Gas**

| | | |
|---|---|---|
| Director, Domestic and European Energy Markets | Dr Elizabeth Baker | Tel: (020) 7215 2769 |
| Director, Oil and Gas Industry Development | Mr Iain Todd *(Aberdeen)* | Tel: (01224) 254032 |
| Director, International and Infrastructure | Dr Ann Eggington | Tel: (020) 7215 5248 |
| Business to Business | Mrs Ann Rosbrook *(Aberdeen)* | Tel: (01224) 254003 |
| Competition and Gas | Mr John Havard | Tel: (020) 7215 5546 |
| Continental Shelf Delimitations | Mr Jim Campbell *(Aberdeen)* | Tel: (01224) 254093 |
| Delimitation, Transboundary Issues | Mrs Gill Campbell | Tel: (020) 7215 5093 |
| Development of Industry | Mrs Celia Mackie *(Aberdeen)* | Tel: (01224) 254099 |
| Economics | | |
| Oil Markets | Mr Paul Bailey | Tel: (020) 7215 5287 |
| Emergency Planning, Downstream | Mr Jim Law | Tel: (020) 7215 5535 |
| Emergencies - Operations | Mr Jim Campbell *(Aberdeen)* | Tel: (01224) 254093 |
| Emergency Planning, Gas Industry | Mr Vernon Brown | Tel: (020) 7215 5246 |
| Environmental Issues, Offshore | Mr Jim Campbell *(Aberdeen)* | Tel: (01224) 254093 |
| Exports (British Trade International) | Mr Brian Gallagher *(Glasgow)* | Tel: (0141) 228 3633 |
| External Relationships | Mr Owen Jenkins | Tel: (020) 7215 5223 |
| Fabrication, Oil and Gas Industry | Dr Peter Christie | Tel: (020) 7215 6200 |
| Hydrocarbons | Mr Simon Toole | Tel: (020) 7215 5046 |
| International | Ms Lorraine Dawson | Tel: (020) 7215 3990 |
| Iraq Reconstruction | Mr Alan Briggs | Tel: (020) 7215 5276 |
| Levy Collection | Ms Jackie Scott *(Aberdeen)* | Tel: (01224) 254016 |
| Licensing | Mr Simon Toole | Tel: (020) 7215 5046 |
| Licensing Consents Unit | Mr Jim Campbell *(Aberdeen)* | Tel: (01224) 254093 |
| Market, Oil and Gas | Mr Ian Knox | Tel: (01224) 254096 |
| Market Regulation (Gas) | Mr Steve Whittington | Tel: (020) 7215 6035 |
| Networks, Gas | Mr John Havard | Tel: (020) 7215 5546 |
| Oil Refining, Downstream and Distribution | Mr Robert Saunders | Tel: (020) 7215 5119 |
| Oil Retailing | Mr Brian Allison | Tel: (020) 7215 6527 |
| Oil Taxation, North Sea | Mr Mike Earp | Tel: (020) 7215 5271 |
| PILOT Secretariat | Ms Angela Latta *(Aberdeen)* | Tel: (01224) 254090 |
| Regulatory Policy | Mr Edward Blades | Tel: (020) 7215 2731 |
| Sponsorship, Oil and Gas Industry | Dr Peter Christie | Tel: (020) 7215 6200 |
| Statistics, North Sea | Mr Philip Beckett | Tel: (020) 7215 5260 |
| Statistics, Oil and Gas | Mr Martin Young | Tel: (020) 7215 5184 |
| Supplies, Oil and Gas Industry | Mr Jonathan Elliott-Jones *(Aberdeen)* | Tel: (01224) 254094 |
| Supply Chain Competitiveness | Mr Bill Nicholson *(Aberdeen)* | Tel: (01224) 254090 |
| Taxation Policy, North Sea | Mr Mike Earp | Tel: (020) 7215 5271 |
| Technical Matters | Mr Simon Toole | Tel: (020) 7215 5046 |
| Technology and Innovation | Mr Stewart Camerons *(Aberdeen)* | Tel: (01224) 254077 |
| Trading Arrangements, Gas Industry | Mr John Havard | Tel: (020) 7215 5546 |
| Training, Oil and Gas Industry | Mr Bill Cattanach *(Aberdeen)* | Tel: (01224) 254097 |
| Transboundary Issues | Mrs Gill Campbell | Tel: (020) 7215 5093 |
| Upstream Infrastructure Policy, Gas | Ms Celia Frank | Tel: (020) 7215 5039 |
| Well Records | Mr Simon Toole | Tel: (020) 7215 5046 |

*Offices also at: Atholl House, 86-88 Guild Street, Aberdeen, AB11 6AR and 151 Buckingham Palace Road, London, SW1W 9SS*

# DEPARTMENT OF TRADE AND INDUSTRY

## Energy: Renewable / Sustainable

Director, Energy Innovation and Business Unit . . . . . . . . . Ms Claire Durkin . . . . . . . . . . . . . . . . . . . . . Tel: (020) 7215 0242
Director, Renewables and Energy Industry Development . . . Mr Iain Todd *(Aberdeen)* . . . . . . . . . . . . . . . Tel: (01224) 254032
Bio-energy: Technical. . . . . . . . . . . . . . . . . . . . . . . . . . . . Mr Gary Shanahan . . . . . . . . . . . . . . . . . . . Tel: (020) 7215 6483
Renewable Energy Briefing Unit, Sustainable Energy . . . . . Mr John Thorpe . . . . . . . . . . . . . . . . . . . . . . Tel: (020) 7215 6153
Climate Change, Economics . . . . . . . . . . . . . . . . . . . . . . . Ms Lorraine Hamid. . . . . . . . . . . . . . . . . . . Tel: (020) 7215 3785
                                                                 Mr Peter Roscoe . . . . . . . . . . . . . . . . . . . . . Tel: (020) 7215 5837
Communications. . . . . . . . . . . . . . . . . . . . . . . . . . . . . . . . Ms Liz Santry . . . . . . . . . . . . . . . . . . . . . . . Tel: (020) 7215 5278
Consents
   Offshore. . . . . . . . . . . . . . . . . . . . . . . . . . . . . . . . . . . . Ms Cathy Allen. . . . . . . . . . . . . . . . . . . . . . Tel: (020) 7215 0479
                                                                 Ms Caroline Roberts . . . . . . . . . . . . . . . . . . Tel: (020) 7215 2381
   Onshore . . . . . . . . . . . . . . . . . . . . . . . . . . . . . . . . . . . Mr Laurence Cadman . . . . . . . . . . . . . . . . . Tel: (020) 7215 2889
Electrical Technology. . . . . . . . . . . . . . . . . . . . . . . . . . . . Mr Philip Baker . . . . . . . . . . . . . . . . . . . . . Tel: (020) 7215 2675
Fuel Cells . . . . . . . . . . . . . . . . . . . . . . . . . . . . . . . . . . . . Mr Ray Eaton . . . . . . . . . . . . . . . . . . . . . . . Tel: (020) 7215 2650
Policy . . . . . . . . . . . . . . . . . . . . . . . . . . . . . . . . . . . . . . . Mr David Irving . . . . . . . . . . . . . . . . . . . . . Tel: (020) 7215 2812
                                                                 Ms Catherine Murray . . . . . . . . . . . . . . . . . Tel: (020) 7215 2184
Procurement, Renewables. . . . . . . . . . . . . . . . . . . . . . . . Ms Eileen Keeble . . . . . . . . . . . . . . . . . . . . Tel: (020) 7215 5320
Solar Energy: Technical . . . . . . . . . . . . . . . . . . . . . . . . . . Mr Gary Shanahan . . . . . . . . . . . . . . . . . . . Tel: (020) 7215 6483
Solar Programmes. . . . . . . . . . . . . . . . . . . . . . . . . . . . . . Mr Ray Eaton . . . . . . . . . . . . . . . . . . . . . . . Tel: (020) 7215 2650
Sustainable Energy
   Policy . . . . . . . . . . . . . . . . . . . . . . . . . . . . . . . . . . . . . Ms Catherine Murray . . . . . . . . . . . . . . . . . Tel: (020) 7215 2184
   Programmes. . . . . . . . . . . . . . . . . . . . . . . . . . . . . . . . Mrs Barbara Hammond . . . . . . . . . . . . . . . . Tel: (020) 7215 2666
Water, Wind . . . . . . . . . . . . . . . . . . . . . . . . . . . . . . . . . . Mr John Overton. . . . . . . . . . . . . . . . . . . . . Tel: (020) 7215 6481

## Engineering: Automotive *(see below under Motor Vehicles)*

## Engineering Base

Science and Engineering Base Group, Director . . . . . . . . . Dr Chris Henshall. . . . . . . . . . . . . . . . . . . . . Tel: (020) 7215 0183

## Engineering: Electrical and Mechanical

Director, Materials and Engineering Unit . . . . . . . . . . . . . Mr Simon Edmonds. . . . . . . . . . . . . . . . . . . . Tel: (020) 7215 1535
Air Conditioning Equipment. . . . . . . . . . . . . . . . . . . . . . . Ms Jan Weston . . . . . . . . . . . . . . . . . . . . . . . Tel: (020) 7215 1052
European Programmes (Industrial) . . . . . . . . . . . . . . . . . . Mr Trevor Fraser. . . . . . . . . . . . . . . . . . . . . . Tel: (020) 7215 1454
European Union Directives. . . . . . . . . . . . . . . . . . . . . . . . Mr Mike Dodds. . . . . . . . . . . . . . . . . . . . . . . Tel: (020) 7215 1339
Heating Equipment . . . . . . . . . . . . . . . . . . . . . . . . . . . . . Ms Jan Weston . . . . . . . . . . . . . . . . . . . . . . . Tel: (020) 7215 1052
Industry Sponsorship . . . . . . . . . . . . . . . . . . . . . . . . . . . Mr Trevor Fraser. . . . . . . . . . . . . . . . . . . . . . Tel: (020) 7215 1454
IT Related Technologies (Manufacturing) . . . . . . . . . . . . . Mr John Gillis. . . . . . . . . . . . . . . . . . . . . . . . Tel: (020) 7215 1537
Knowledge Management. . . . . . . . . . . . . . . . . . . . . . . . . Dr Ray Kingcombe . . . . . . . . . . . . . . . . . . . . Tel: (020) 7215 1115
Lighting, Power Generation and Distribution Products. . . . Ms Jan Weston . . . . . . . . . . . . . . . . . . . . . . . Tel: (020) 7215 1052
Machine Tools . . . . . . . . . . . . . . . . . . . . . . . . . . . . . . . . Ms Jan Weston . . . . . . . . . . . . . . . . . . . . . . . Tel: (020) 7215 1052
Manufacturing Advisory Service . . . . . . . . . . . . . . . . . . . Mr Martin Berry . . . . . . . . . . . . . . . . . . . . . . Tel: (020) 7215 2927
   Manufacturing Advisory Service (Policy). . . . . . . . . . . Mr Terry Martin . . . . . . . . . . . . . . . . . . . . . . Tel: (020) 7215 1102
Metal Forming and Finishing . . . . . . . . . . . . . . . . . . . . . . Mr Nick Morgan . . . . . . . . . . . . . . . . . . . . . . Tel: (020) 7215 1081
Microtechnologies . . . . . . . . . . . . . . . . . . . . . . . . . . . . . Mr Trevor Fraser. . . . . . . . . . . . . . . . . . . . . . Tel: (020) 7215 1454
Nanotechnologies . . . . . . . . . . . . . . . . . . . . . . . . . . . . . Mr Trevor Fraser. . . . . . . . . . . . . . . . . . . . . . Tel: (020) 7215 1454
Railway Equipment . . . . . . . . . . . . . . . . . . . . . . . . . . . . . Ms Jan Weston . . . . . . . . . . . . . . . . . . . . . . . Tel: (020) 7215 1052
Refrigeration Equipment (Commercial) . . . . . . . . . . . . . . . Ms Jan Weston . . . . . . . . . . . . . . . . . . . . . . . Tel: (020) 7215 1052
Robotics. . . . . . . . . . . . . . . . . . . . . . . . . . . . . . . . . . . . . Mr Trevor Fraser. . . . . . . . . . . . . . . . . . . . . . Tel: (020) 7215 1454
Statistics . . . . . . . . . . . . . . . . . . . . . . . . . . . . . . . . . . . . *Vacant* . . . . . . . . . . . . . . . . . . . . . . . . . . . . . Tel: (020) 7215 1907
Technology/Competitiveness
   Aerospace and Defence Industries . . . . . . . . . . . . . . . Dr Ray Kingcombe. . . . . . . . . . . . . . . . . . . . . Tel: (020) 7215 1115
   Manufacturing Processes . . . . . . . . . . . . . . . . . . . . . . Mr John Gillis. . . . . . . . . . . . . . . . . . . . . . . . Tel: (020) 7215 1537
   Mechanical Engineering. . . . . . . . . . . . . . . . . . . . . . . Mr Trevor Fraser. . . . . . . . . . . . . . . . . . . . . . Tel: (020) 7215 1454
Ventilation Equipment . . . . . . . . . . . . . . . . . . . . . . . . . . . Ms Jan Weston . . . . . . . . . . . . . . . . . . . . . . . Tel: (020) 7215 1052
White Goods . . . . . . . . . . . . . . . . . . . . . . . . . . . . . . . . . . Ms Jan Weston . . . . . . . . . . . . . . . . . . . . . . . Tel: (020) 7215 1052

## Engineering Industry, Sponsorship

Director, Materials and Engineering Unit . . . . . . . . . . . . . Mr Simon Edmonds . . . . . . . . . . . . . . . . . . . . Tel: (020) 7215 1535
Deputy Director, Materials and Engineering Unit . . . . . . . Mr Keith Hodkinson . . . . . . . . . . . . . . . . . . . Tel: (020) 7215 1094

## Engineering Inspectorate

Director, Engineering Inspectorate . . . . . . . . . . . . . . . . . . Dr Peter Fenwick . . . . . . . . . . . . . . . . . . . . . Tel: (020) 7215 2856

# DEPARTMENT OF TRADE AND INDUSTRY

**Environment**

| | | |
|---|---|---|
| Environment and Energy Hotline | *enquiries* | Tel: (0800) 585794 |
| Environmental Regulation | Mr James Marsh | Tel: (020) 7215 1666 |
| Joint DTI / DEFRA Environmental Markets Unit | | |
|     Director | Mr Duncan Prior | Tel: (020) 7215 1624 |
|     Goods and Services | Mr Stephen De Souza | Tel: (020) 7215 3757 |
| Producer Responsibility | Mr Steve Andrews | Tel: (020) 7215 1670 |
| Recycling Policy | Mr Steve Andrews | Tel: (020) 7215 1670 |
| Sustainable Development | Mr Michael Massey | Tel: (020) 7215 1873 |
| Sustainable Technologies | Ms April Vesey | Tel: (020) 7215 1708 |
| Vehicle Recycling | Mr Steve Norgrove | Tel: (020) 7215 2981 |
| Waste | Mr Steve Andrews | Tel: (020) 7215 1670 |

**Equal Opportunities**

| | | |
|---|---|---|
| Director, Women and Equality Unit | Ms Angela Mason | Tel: (020) 7215 5000 |

**Estate Agents (Appeals)** — Mr Brian Swift — Tel: (020) 7215 3089

**Estates and Facilities Management** — Mr Mike Rainsford — Tel: (020) 7855 3688

**E-Strategy, Government's Cross-Departmental**

| | | |
|---|---|---|
| Director, E-Strategy and Major Projects | Mr Andrew Matthew | Tel: (020) 7215 3678 |

**EUREKA Unit** — Mr Philip O'Neil — Tel: (020) 7215 1681

**European Investment Bank** — Ms Julie Farrow — Tel: (020) 7215 6241

**European Union**

| | | |
|---|---|---|
| Director-General, Europe and World Trade | Mr Edmund Hosker | Tel: (020) 7215 4445 |
| Director, Europe and World Trade | Ms Jo Durning | Tel: (020) 7215 5000 |
| Director, Future of Europe | Mr Anthony Murphy | Tel: (020) 7215 8584 |
| Director, European Union Economic Reform | Mr Julian Farrel | Tel: (020) 7215 4393 |
| Agriculture and Trade Policy | Mr Oliver Griffiths | Tel: (020) 7215 4547 |
| Animal Welfare and Trade Policy | Mr Oliver Griffiths | Tel: (020) 7215 4547 |
| Bilaterals | Mr Clive Fleming | Tel: (020) 7215 4460 |
| Cohesion Fund | | |
|     Administration | Mr Andrew Bayer | Tel: (020) 7215 2605 |
|     Policy | Ms Julie Farrow | Tel: (020) 7215 6241 |
| Competitiveness Council | Mr Clive Fleming | Tel: (020) 7215 4460 |
| Corporate Governance Takeovers Directive | Mr Tony Sims | Tel: (020) 7215 6472 |
| Developing Countries and | Mr Oliver Griffiths | Tel: (020) 7215 4547 |
| Economic Reform | Mr David Wilson | Tel: (020) 7215 4384 |
| Energy Market Liberalisation | Mrs Sue Harrison | Tel: (020) 7215 2778 |
| Energy Policy | Mrs Lorraine Dawson | Tel: (020) 7215 3990 |
| Engineering Directives | Mr Mike Dodds | Tel: (020) 7215 1339 |
| Enlargement | Mr Colin Wilson | Tel: (020) 7215 4815 |
| Equal Treatment Directive | Ms Rosalind McCarthy-Ward | Tel: (020) 7215 0149 |
| Euro Preparations | Mr Stephen Webster | Tel: (020) 7215 4495 |
| Future of Europe | Mr Stephen Webster | Tel: (020) 7215 4495 |
| Institutions, European Union | Mr Stephen Webster | Tel: (020) 7215 4495 |
| Internal Market and Industrial Policy | Mr Clive Fleming | Tel: (020) 7215 4460 |
| Labour Market Flexibility | Ms Jane Whewell | Tel: (020) 7215 5731 |
| Legal Advice | Mr Roland Green | Tel: (020) 7215 3425 |
| Market Access | Mr Matthew Conway | Tel: (020) 7215 4565 |
| Parliamentary Scrutiny | Mr Stephen Webster | Tel: (020) 7215 4495 |
| Professional Qualifications | Mr Glyn Williams | Tel: (020) 7215 5731 |
| Single Market | Mr Clive Fleming | Tel: (020) 7215 4460 |
| State Aids | Mr Alec Berry | Tel: (020) 7215 4443 |
| Trade Policy | Dr Elaine Drage | Tel: (020) 7215 4503 |
| Trade with Developing Countries, European Union | Mr Ron Archibald | Tel: (020) 7215 4448 |
| Technical Directives | Mr Iain Nicol | Tel: (020) 7215 1408 |

# DEPARTMENT OF TRADE AND INDUSTRY

**Exports: Control and Licenses**
*4 Abbey Orchard Street, London, SW1P 2HT*

| | | |
|---|---|---|
| Director, Export Control and Non-Proliferation | Mr Mike O'Shea | Tel: (020) 7215 0720 |
| Director, Non-Proliferation | Mr Mel Draper | Tel: (020) 7215 0716 |
| Chemical Weapons Convention | Mr Martin Rudduck | Tel: (020) 7215 0718 |
| Communications | Ms Bernadette Peers | Tel: (020) 7215 8070 |
| Enforcement | Ms Cathy Gilhespy | Tel: (020) 7215 0733 |
| Enquiry Unit | *enquiries* | Tel: (020) 7215 8070 |
| Export Control Act Implementation | Mr Andrew Burke | Tel: (020) 7215 6537 |
| Export Control Organisation | Mr Glyn Williams | Tel: (020) 7215 0521 |
| JEWEL Unit | Mr Roh Hathlia | Tel: (020) 7215 0674 |
| Licensing | | |
|     Head, Licensing Group | Mr Andy Layton | Tel: (020) 7215 0588 |
|     Casework | Mr David Whitehouse | Tel: (020) 7215 0590 |
|     Compliance | Ms Susan Marks | Tel: (020) 7215 0504 |
|     Individual Export Licensing | Mr Gordon Williams | Tel: (020) 7215 0615 |
|     Sanctions | Mr David Whitehouse | Tel: (020) 7215 0590 |
|     Standard Individual Export Licensing Unit | Mr Melvyn Tompkins | Tel: (020) 7215 0585 |
| Management Issues, Export Control Organisation | Mr Brian Johnson | Tel: (020) 7215 0590 |
| Non-Proliferation Policy | Mr Nick Mitchell | Tel: (020) 7215 0714 |
| Head of PolicyBusiness Relations | Ms Jayne Carpenter | Tel: (020) 7215 0516 |
| Policy Unit | Mr Spencer Chilvers | Tel: (020) 7215 0510 |
| Safeguards Office | Mr Glenn Hawkins | Tel: (020) 7215 0739 |
| Technologies Unit | Mr Christopher Parish | Tel: (020) 7215 0650 |

**Explosives** ........... Mr Philip Edwards ........... Tel: (020) 7215 4163

**Export Promotion** (*see below under Trade*)

**Fair Markets Group**

| | | |
|---|---|---|
| Director-General, Fair Markets Group | Mr Stephen Haddrill | Tel: (020) 7215 6845 |

**Finance, Departmental**

| | | |
|---|---|---|
| Director, Finance and Resource Management | Mr David Evans | Tel: (020) 7215 6869 |
| Director, Internal Audit | Ms Helen Taylor | Tel: (020) 7215 4784 |
| Finance | Mr Peter Mason | Tel: (020) 7215 6859 |
| Financial and Accountancy Services Unit | Mr Terry Le Maistre | Tel: (020) 7215 5719 |
| Resource Accounting and Budgeting | Mr Curtis Juman | Tel: (020) 7215 6959 |
| Resource Management | Mr Adam Jackson | Tel: (020) 7215 6847 |

**Footwear Industry** ........... Mr Brian Greenwood ........... Tel: (020) 7215 1640

**Gas** (*see above under Energy - Oil and Gas*)

**Hearing Aid Council** ........... Mr Barry Stephenson ........... Tel: (020) 7215 0319

**Heating, Commercial** ........... Mr David Payne ........... Tel: (020) 7215 1522

**Homeworkers** ........... Ms Jane Whewell ........... Tel: (020) 7215 5731

**Honours** ........... Mr John Arnott ........... Tel: (020) 7215 5000

**Human Resources, Departmental**

| | | |
|---|---|---|
| Director, Human Resources and Change Management | Ms Susan Haird | Tel: (020) 7315 5000 |
| Change and Knowledge Management | Mr Tim Soane | Tel: (020) 7215 5000 |
| Operations | Ms Rosemary Heyhoe | Tel: (020) 7215 5000 |
| People Deployment and Development | Mr Howard Ewing | Tel: (020) 7215 5000 |
| Strategy and Terms of Employment | Ms Jan Dixon | Tel: (020) 7215 5000 |
| | Ms Christine Hewitt | Tel: (020) 7215 5000 |

**Imports** (*see below under Trade Policy*)

# DEPARTMENT OF TRADE AND INDUSTRY

**Innovation**
*151 Buckingham Palace Road, London, SW1W 9SS*

| | | |
|---|---|---|
| Director-General, Innovation Group | Mr David Hughes | Tel: (020) 7215 1703 |
| Director, Facilitating Innovation | Mr John Rhodes | Tel: (020) 7215 4191 |
| Director, Innovation and Sustainable Development | *Vacant* | Tel: (020) 7215 1795 |
| Director, Key Business Technologies | Mr Patrick Mcdonald | Tel: (020) 7215 1795 |
| Director, Standards and Technical Regulations | Mr Rob Brightwell | Tel: (020) 7215 1459 |
| Director, Technological Innovation and Sustainable Development | *Vacant* | Tel: (020) 7215 3734 |
| Accredition Policy | Mr Malcolm Hynd | Tel: (020) 7215 1976 |
| Advanced Computing Technologies | Mr Ray Browne | Tel: (020) 7215 1287 |
| Business and Finance Unit | Dr Nicholas Munn | Tel: (020) 7215 0996 |
| Business Applications and New Technologies | Mr Ray Browne | Tel: (020) 7215 1472 |
| Business Excellence Knowledge Management | Ms Maria Cody | Tel: (020) 7215 6617 |
| Business Finance and Investment | Mr Tony Pedrotti | Tel: (020) 7215 0954 |
| Business Planning and Strategy | Mr Tony Keegan | Tel: (020) 7215 6633 |
| Business Support, DTI Investment in | | |
| Head, Business Support | Mr David Saunders | Tel: (020) 7215 0913 |
| Assessment of DTI Business Support | Mr Derek Albone | Tel: (020) 7215 1672 |
| Economics, Business Support | Mr Nick Hallett | Tel: (020) 7215 0856 |
| IT Programme, Business Support | Mr Adam Dawson | Tel: (020) 7215 0915 |
| Design Policy | Mr Leslie Finch | Tel: (020) 7215 0856 |
| Emerging Technologies and Strategy | Mr Allan Mayo | Tel: (020) 7215 1110 |
| Environmental Regulation | Mr James Marsh | Tel: (020) 7215 1666 |
| EUREKA Unit | Mr Philip O'Neil | Tel: (020) 7215 1681 |
| Facilitating Innovation | Mr Leslie Finch | Tel: (020) 7215 0856 |
| Faraday Partnerships | Mr Kevin Knettett | Tel: (020) 7215 1075 |
| Finance and Business / Investment | Mr Tony Pedrotti | Tel: (020) 7215 0954 |
| Innovation and Business Development | Dr Ian Harrison | Tel: (020) 7215 1075 |
| International Technology Service | Mr Alun German | Tel: (020) 7215 1226 |
| Knowledge Transfer Unit, UK | Mr Kevin Knettett | Tel: (020) 7215 1075 |
| Management Best Practice | Mr Richard Arnott | Tel: (020) 7215 1551 |
| Manufacturing Technologies | Mr John Gillis | Tel: (020) 7215 1537 |
| Nanotechnologies | Mr Trevor Fraser | Tel: (020) 7215 1454 |
| Non-Sectoral Knowledge Transfer | Dr Ian Harrison | Tel: (020) 7215 1075 |
| Postgraduate Training Partnerships | Mr Kevin Knettett | Tel: (020) 7215 1657 |
| Research Base Links | | |
| (LINK Colaborative Research (Scheme)) | Mr Alan Wootton | Tel: (020) 7215 0036 |
| Scientific Research Associations | Ms Roberta Neale | Tel: (020) 7215 3674 |
| Sensors | Dr Ray Kingcombe | Tel: (020) 7215 1115 |
| Standards Policy | | |
| Co-ordination | Ms Michelle Barker | Tel: (020) 7215 1575 |
| Technical Regulations | Mr Rob Brightwell | Tel: (020) 7215 1459 |

**Internal Communications** — Mr John Doherty — Tel: (020) 7215 5459

**Investigations – Companies** *(see above under Company Law and Investigations)*

**Leather Industry** — Mr Russell Kerr — Tel: (020) 7215 1296

# DEPARTMENT OF TRADE AND INDUSTRY

## Legal Services and Advice

| | | |
|---|---|---|
| Solicitor and Director-General, Legal Services | Mr Anthony Inglese | Tel: (020) 7215 3039 |
| Director, Legal Resource Management and Business Law | Mr Carl Warren | Tel: (020) 7215 3170 |
| Director, Legal Services: Business and Consumers | Mrs Tessa Dunstan | Tel: (020) 7215 3426 |
| Director, Legal Services: Employment Discrimination | Ms Rachel Sandby-Thomas | Tel: (020) 7215 3250 |
| Director, Legal Services: Energy, Communications | Ms Deborah Collins | Tel: (020) 7215 3596 |
| Director, Legal Services: Enforcements | Mr Scott Milligan | Tel: (020) 7215 3136 |
| Business Law (Legislation and International Policy Unit) | Ms Sally Moss | Tel: (020) 7215 3275 |
| Coal | Mr Alan Woods | Tel: (020) 7215 3421 |
| Communication Systems | Mr Rowland Green | Tel: (020) 7215 3460 |
| Company Investigations | | |
|     Investigations and Enforcement | Mr Tony Susman | Tel: (020) 7215 3400 |
|     Prosecutions | Mr Lal Nawbatt | Tel: (020) 7215 3132 |
| Company Law and Investigations | Mr Tony Susman | Tel: (020) 7215 3400 |
| Competition Law | Mr Roland Green | Tel: (020) 7215 3425 |
| Computer Misuse | Mr Stephen Hyett | Tel: (020) 7215 3408 |
| Consumer Protection | Mr Bryan Welch | Tel: (020) 7215 3188 |
| Consumer Safety | Ms Eve Race | Tel: (020) 7215 3392 |
| Discrimination | Mr Nigel Lambert | Tel: (020) 7215 3037 |
| Electricity | Mr Richard Swede | Tel: (020) 7215 3478 |
| Electronic Communications | Mr Tony Susman | Tel: (020) 7215 3400 |
| Employees' Rights | Mr Richard Perkins | Tel: (020) 7215 3258 |
| Employment Discrimination | Mr Nick Magyar | Tel: (020) 7215 3569 |
| Employment Relations | Mr Richard Baker | Tel: (020) 7215 3330 |
| Employment Tribunals | Mr Alastair Pitblado | Tel: (020) 7215 3513 |
| European Union Law | Mr Roland Green | Tel: (020) 7215 3425 |
| Extraterritoriality | Mr Hugh Giles | Tel: (020) 7215 3381 |
| Fair Trading | Mr Bryan Welch | Tel: (020) 7215 3188 |
| Human Rights | Mr Nigel Lambert | Tel: (020) 7215 3037 |
| Industrial Relations | Mr Richard Baker | Tel: (020) 7215 3330 |
| Industry | Mr Stephen Hyett | Tel: (020) 7215 3408 |
| Insolvency | Mr Charles Norris | Tel: (020) 7215 3374 |
| Insurance | Mr Alastair Pitblado | Tel: (020) 7215 3513 |
| Intellectual Property | Mr Mark Bucknill | Tel: (020) 7215 3266 |
| Investigations Officer, Chief | Mr Christopher Duggan | Tel: (020) 7215 3147 |
| Law Clerks | Mr Patrick Organ | Tel: (020) 7215 3180 |
| Mergers | Mr Roland Green | Tel: (020) 7215 3425 |
| Mines | Mr Stephen Hyett | Tel: (020) 7215 3408 |
| Nuclear Industry | Miss Serena Hardy | Tel: (020) 7215 3365 |
| Oil and Gas | Mr Alan Woods | Tel: (020) 7215 3421 |
| Postal Services and Electronic Communications | Mr Tony Susman | Tel: (020) 7215 3400 |
| Prosecutions | Mr Lal Nawbatt | Tel: (020) 7215 3132 |
| Public Procurement | Mr Phillip Sorensen | Tel: (020) 7215 3239 |
| Regional Development | Mr Stephen Hyett | Tel: (020) 7215 3408 |
| Redundancy Payments | Mr Alastair Pitblado | Tel: (020) 7215 3513 |
| Sex Discrimination | Mr Nigel Lambert | Tel: (020) 7215 3037 |
| Small Business Service | Mr Stephen Hyett | Tel: (020) 7215 3408 |
| Standards, Technology & Environment (Head) | Mr Keith Broad | Tel: (020) 7215 3540 |
| State Aids | Mr Stephen Hyett | Tel: (020) 7215 3408 |
| Telecommunications | Mr Tony Susman | Tel: (020) 7215 3400 |
| Trade | Mr Hugh Giles | Tel: (020) 7215 3381 |
| Weapons Proliferation | Mr Hugh Giles | Tel: (020) 7215 3381 |
| Weights and Measures | Mr Keith Broad | Tel: (020) 7215 3540 |

## Machine Tools

| | | |
|---|---|---|
| Machine Tools | Mr Nick Morgan | Tel: (020) 7215 1105 |

## Management, Leadership and Skills, Industry

| | | |
|---|---|---|
| Director, Management, Leadership and Skills Team | Ms Pat Jackson | Tel: (020) 7215 1612 |
| Skills and Education | Mr John Baker | Tel: (020) 7215 1684 |
| Team Leaders | Mr Richard Arnott | Tel: (020) 7215 1551 |
| | Mr Jim Mitchell | Tel: (020) 7215 6467 |

# DEPARTMENT OF TRADE AND INDUSTRY

**Marine**

| | | |
|---|---|---|
| Director, Marine | Mr Chris North | Tel: (020) 7215 1601 |
| Economics | Mr Paul Crawford | Tel: (020) 7215 1864 |
| Finance | Mr Geoff Moore | Tel: (020) 7215 0959 |
| International Policy | Mr Geoff Moore | Tel: (020) 7215 0959 |
| Inward Investment | Mr Norman Brice | Tel: (020) 7215 1122 |
| Marine Equipment | Mr Geoff Moore | Tel: (020) 7215 0959 |
| Shipbuilding (General), Ship-repair | Mr Norman Brice | Tel: (020) 7215 1122 |
| Statistics | Mr Michael Clary | Tel: (020) 7215 1887 |
| Warships | Mr Norman Brice | Tel: (020) 7215 1122 |

**Maternity Leave** . . . . . . . . . . . . . . . . . . . . . . . . . . . . . . . Ms Julie Carney . . . . . . . . . . . . . . . . . . . . . Tel: (020) 7215 5549

**Measurements** *(see below under Weights and Measures)*

**Mergers** *(see above under Consumer Affairs and Competition)*

**Metals and Minerals**

| | | |
|---|---|---|
| Director, Materials and Engineering Unit | Mr Simon Edmonds | Tel: (020) 7215 1535 |
| Business Relations | Mr Nick Morgan | Tel: (020) 7215 1081 |
| Engineering and Industrial | Mr Keith Hodgkinson | Tel: (020) 7215 1049 |
| Materials | Mr Gerry Miles | Tel: (020) 7215 1474 |
| Metal Processing | Mr Nick Morgan | Tel: (020) 7215 1081 |
| Minerals | Ms Zoe Dayan | Tel: (020) 7215 1049 |
| Recycling | Mr Nick Morgan | Tel: (020) 7215 1081 |
| Statistics | Mr Michael Clary | Tel: (020) 7215 1887 |
| Steel | Ms Zoe Dayan | Tel: (020) 7215 1049 |

**Monopolies** *(see above under Consumer Affairs and Competition)*

**Motor Vehicles**

| | | |
|---|---|---|
| Director, Automotive Unit | Ms Sarah Chambers | Tel: (020) 7215 1169 |
| Deputy Director, Automotive Unit | Mr Ashley Roberts | Tel: (020) 7215 1311 |
| America Team | Mr Paul Mullins | Tel: (020) 7215 1183 |
| Asia Team | Mr Barry Cole | Tel: (020) 7215 5884 |
| Europe Team | Ms Sue Sadler | Tel: (020) 7215 1965 |
| Components | Mr Ashley Roberts | Tel: (020) 7215 1311 |
| Economics, Automotive Industries | Mr Paul Crawford | Tel: (020) 7215 1864 |
| EUREKA Unit | Mr Philip O'Niel | Tel: (020) 7215 1681 |
| Innovation and Growth | Mr Ashley Roberts | Tel: (020) 7215 1311 |
| Regional Sponsorship Office | | |
| *77 Paradise Circus, Birmingham, B1 2DT* | | |
| Head of Office | Mr Francis Evans | Tel: (0121) 212 5158 |
| Regulatory Issues | Dr Chris Bowden | Tel: (020) 7215 1177 |
| Statistics | Mr Michael Clary | Tel: (020) 7215 1887 |
| Technology and Innovation | Mr Ashley Roberts | Tel: (020) 7215 1311 |

**Nuclear Industries** *(see above under Energy: Nuclear)*

**OFCOM, Liaison** . . . . . . . . . . . . . . . . . . . . . . . . . . . . . Mr John Kemp . . . . . . . . . . . . . . . . . . . . . . . Tel: (020) 7215 1480

**Oil** *(see above under Energy: Oil and Gas)*

**Parliamentary Clerk** . . . . . . . . . . . . . . . . . . . . . . . . . . Mr Tim Williams . . . . . . . . . . . . . . . . . . . . . Tel: (020) 7215 6630

**Paternity Leave** . . . . . . . . . . . . . . . . . . . . . . . . . . . . . . Ms Julie Carney . . . . . . . . . . . . . . . . . . . . . Tel: (020) 7215 5549

**Personnel** *(see above under Human Resources, Departmental)*

# DEPARTMENT OF TRADE AND INDUSTRY

**Pesticides** (Comodity Chemicals, Fertilisers,
Explosives and Industrial Gasses)................... Mr Philip Edwards .................... Tel: (020) 7215 4163

**Petrochemicals** .................................. Mr Mike Sellek........................ Tel: (020) 7215 1211

**Plastics**........................................ Mr Mike Sellek........................ Tel: (020) 7215 1211

**Postal Services**

| | | |
|---|---|---|
| Director, Postal Services......................... | Mr Mark Higson.................... | Tel: (020) 7215 4115 |
| Economic Advice................................. | Mr Martin Simmons ................ | Tel: (020) 7215 1884 |
| European Union Liaison........................... | Ms Jan Wright ..................... | Tel: (020) 7215 1793 |
| International Regulation........................... | Mr Robert Higginson ............... | Tel: (020) 7215 1435 |
| Postal Services.................................. | Mr Rupert Huxter .................. | Tel: (020) 7215 4184 |
| Post Office Network ............................. | Mr Nigel Leese .................... | Tel: (020) 7215 1613 |
| Regulation ..................................... | Mr Robert Higginson ............... | Tel: (020) 7215 1435 |
| Postal Services Act 2000, Implementation........... | Mr Robert Faull ................... | Tel: (020) 7215 1421 |
| Postwatch Liaison................................ | Ms Jan Wright ..................... | Tel: (020) 7215 1793 |
| Royal Mail ..................................... | Mr David Sellman.................. | Tel: (020) 7215 1646 |
| Rural Support................................... | Mr Jonathan Cowdock .............. | Tel: (020) 7215 1466 |
| Shareholder Issues .............................. | Mr Rupert Huxter.................. | Tel: (020) 7215 4184 |
| Universal Banking Service ........................ | Mr Nigel Leese .................... | Tel: (020) 7215 1613 |
| Urban Regeneration and Post Office ............... | Mr Mike Whitehead ................ | Tel: (020) 7215 1775 |

**Power Generation Equipment**...................... Ms Jan Weston ...................... Tel: (020) 7215 1052

**Press and Publicity**

| | | |
|---|---|---|
| Director, Communications ........................ | Ms Sheree Dodd ................... | Tel: (020) 7215 5972 |
| Deputy Director, Communications.................. | Mr Colin Seabrook ................ | Tel: (020) 7215 5970 |
| Internal Communications ......................... | Mr John Doherty.................. | Tel: (020) 7215 5459 |
| Internet and New Media Publicity.................. | Mr Rupert Marsh .................. | Tel: (020) 7215 6190 |
| Marketing Managers.............................. | Mr Roy Harris .................... | Tel: (020) 7215 5152 |
| | Mr Guy Nissen .................... | Tel: (020) 7215 5256 |
| News | | |
| Head of News............................... | Mr Mike Snowdon................. | Tel: (020) 7215 5954 |
| Deputy Directors ........................... | Mr Marcus De Ville ............... | Tel: (020) 7215 5951 |
| | Ms Vickie Sheriff ................. | Tel: (020) 7215 5981 |
| Secretary of State's Chief Press Officer ............ | Ms Caroline Faley................. | Tel: (020) 7215 5377 |
| Speechwriting Unit............................... | Mr Simon Lancaster .............. | Tel: (020) 7215 5590 |
| Strategic Communications......................... | Ms Natalie Craig.................. | Tel: (020) 7215 5716 |
| Press Enquiries (General)......................... | *enquiries*......................... | Tel: (020) 7215 5347 |

**Procurement, (Departmental)**
Director, Resource Management .................... Mr Adam Jackson................... Tel: (020) 7215 6847

**Product Liability**............................... Mr Steve Halls ..................... Tel: (020) 7215 2963

**Public Appointments** ............................ Ms Maureen Verrall ................ Tel: (020) 7215 0816

**Publishing** *(see above under Press and Publicity)*

**Railway Equipment**.............................. Ms Jan Weston...................... Tel: (020) 7215 1052

**Recycling Policy**................................ Mr Steve Andrews.................. Tel: (020) 7215 1670

**Redundancy Payments**
Helpline........................................ *enquiries* ......................... Tel: (0500) 848489
Policy ......................................... Mr Glyn Williams.................. Tel: (020) 7215 5731

**Regions**

| | | |
|---|---|---|
| Deputy Director-General, Regions ................. | Ms Katharine Elliott .............. | Tel: (020) 7215 5606 |
| Director, Industrial Development Unit .............. | Ms Briony Jones ................... | Tel: (020) 7215 5653 |
| Director, Regional Assistance...................... | Mr Andrew Steele................. | Tel: (020) 7215 5574 |
| Director, Regional Development Agencies Sponsorship and Finance................................... | Mr Tony Medawar................. | Tel: (020) 7215 6514 |
| Director, Regional European Funds and Devolution ...... | Mr John Neve .................... | Tel: (020) 7215 2553 |
| Director, Regional Policy ......................... | Mr Peter Bunn ................... | Tel: (020) 7215 6835 |

# DEPARTMENT OF TRADE AND INDUSTRY

*Regions (Continued)*

| | | |
|---|---|---|
| Director, Social Enterprise Unit | Ms Barbara Phillips | Tel: (020) 7215 0293 |
| Aerospace and Defence Industries Liaison | Mr Peter Dallaway | Tel: (020) 7215 5345 |
| Appointments, Regional Boards | Ms Gail Davis | Tel: (020) 7215 3859 |
| Cohesion Fund, European Union | | |
|    Administration | Mr Andrew Bayer | Tel: (020) 7215 2605 |
|    Policy | Ms Julie Farrow | Tel: (020) 7215 6241 |
| Devolution Policy | Mr Bob George | Tel: (020) 7215 3898 |
| Economics | Ms Margaret McEvoy | Tel: (020) 7215 5685 |
| European Union | | |
|    Regulations, Structural and Cohesion Fund | Ms Julie Farrow | Tel: (020) 7215 6241 |
|    Single Programming Document | Mr Graham Thorpe | Tel: (020) 7215 2588 |
| Finance and Administration, Regional Policy | Mr Andrew Bayer | Tel: (020) 7215 2605 |
| Government Regional Offices: Development and Support | Ms Sue Houston | Tel: (020) 7215 5540 |
| Greater London Authority | Mr Paul Steeples | Tel: (020) 7215 2578 |
| Industrial Development | | |
|    Director, Industrial Development Unit | Ms Briony Jones | Tel: (020) 7215 5653 |
|    Assistant Directors | Mr Christian Mole | Tel: (020) 7215 5511 |
| | Mr Andrew Nelson | Tel: (020) 7215 6503 |
| | Mr Adrian Nicholls | Tel: (020) 7215 5425 |
| | Ms Rachel O'Hara | Tel: (020) 7215 2629 |
|    Investment Appraisal | Mr Robert Middleton | Tel: (020) 7215 2547 |
|    Legislation | Ms Jane Hartshorne | Tel: (020) 7215 5641 |
| Phoenix Fund | Mr John Humphreys | Tel: (020) 7215 2505 |
| Policy and Competitiveness | Ms Julie Farrow | Tel: (020) 7215 6241 |
| Regional Assistance | Mr Andrew Steele | Tel: (020) 7215 5574 |
| Regional Democracy | Mr Paul Steeples | Tel: (020) 7215 2578 |
| Regional Development Agencies | | |
|    Finance Co-ordination | Mr Mohan Luthra | Tel: (020) 7215 3884 |
|    Personnel Policies | Ms Susanna Wiltshire | Tel: (020) 7215 3859 |
|    Policy Issues, General | Mr Paul Steeples | Tel: (020) 7215 2578 |
|    Steering Group on RDAs, Departmental | Mr Andrew Dobbie | Tel: (020) 7215 3885 |
| Regional Development Grants | Mr Graham Thorpe | Tel: (020) 7215 2588 |
| Regional Innovation and Clusters | Ms Beccy Eggleton | Tel: (0207) 215 6581 |
| Regional Policy Team | Mr Paul Steeples | Tel: (0207) 215 2578 |
| Regional Selective Assistance | | |
|    Large Projects | Mr Robin Lavery OBE | Tel: (020) 7215 5580 |
|    Policy and Scheme Administration | Mr Graham Thorpe | Tel: (020) 7215 2588 |
|    Regional Development Grants | Mr Graham Thorpe | Tel: (020) 7215 2588 |
| Rural Issues | Mr Paul Steeples | Tel: (020) 7215 2578 |
| Social Enterprise | Ms Barbara Phillips | Tel: (020) 7215 0293 |
| Social Inclusion Issues | Mr John Humphreys | Tel: (020) 7215 2505 |
| Structural Funds Publicity | Ms Zhada Bibi | Tel: (020) 7215 3970 |
| Trans-European Networks | Ms Julie Farrow | Tel: (020) 7215 6241 |
| Urban Issues | Mr Paul Steeples | Tel: (020) 7215 2578 |

**Research Councils**

| | | |
|---|---|---|
| Director-General, Research Councils | Dr John Taylor OBE FRS | Tel: (020) 7215 3804 |

**Retailing**     Mr Andrew Bacchus     Tel: (020) 7215 1541

**Rubber**     Mr Mike Sellek     Tel: (020) 7215 1211

**Science and Technology**

Office of Science and Technology

*Albany House, 94-98 Petty France, London, SW1H 0ST*

| | | |
|---|---|---|
| Chief Scientific Adviser and Head of Office of Science and Technology | Professor Sir David King FRS | Tel: (020) 7215 2011 |
| Director-General, Research Councils | Dr John Taylor OBE FRS | Tel: (020) 7215 3804 |
| Director, Science and Engineering Base | Dr Chris Henshall | Tel: (020) 7215 0183 |
| Exploitation of Science | Mr Stephen de Souza | Tel: (020) 7215 3844 |
| Finance and Funding | Mr Stephen Speed | Tel: (020) 7215 5691 |
| Foresight | Dr Claire Craig | Tel: (020) 7215 6763 |
| Government, Science in | Mrs Judy Britton | Tel: (020) 7215 2780 |
| | Mr Edmund Quilty | Tel: (020) 7215 5669 |

# DEPARTMENT OF TRADE AND INDUSTRY

*Science and Technology (Continued)*

International Science and Technology . . . . . . . . . . . . . . Ms Rachel Jenkinson . . . . . . . . . . . . . . . . . . Tel: (020) 7215 6416
LINK . . . . . . . . . . . . . . . . . . . . . . . . . . . . . . . . . . . . . . . Mr Alan Wootton . . . . . . . . . . . . . . . . . . . . . . Tel: (020) 7215 0036
Research Councils . . . . . . . . . . . . . . . . . . . . . . . . . . . . Dr Frances Saunders . . . . . . . . . . . . . . . . . . Tel: (020) 7215 3943
Science Review . . . . . . . . . . . . . . . . . . . . . . . . . . . . . . . Ms Angela Wilson . . . . . . . . . . . . . . . . . . . . Tel: (020) 7215 3828
Tax Exemption . . . . . . . . . . . . . . . . . . . . . . . . . . . . . . . Ms Roberta Neale . . . . . . . . . . . . . . . . . . . . . Tel: (020) 7215 3674
Transdepartmental Science and Technology . . . . . . . . *Vacant* . . . . . . . . . . . . . . . . . . . . . . . . . . . . . . . . Tel: (020) 7215 3826

## Shipbuilding *(see above under Marine)*

## Single Market Policy . . . . . . . . . . . . . . . . . . . . . . . . . . . . Mr Clive Fleming . . . . . . . . . . . . . . . . . . . . . Tel: (020) 7215 4460

## Social Enterprise

Director, Social Enterprise Unit . . . . . . . . . . . . . . . . . . . Ms Barbara Phillips . . . . . . . . . . . . . . . . . . . Tel: (020) 7215 0293
Assistants Directors, Social Enterprise Unit . . . . . . . . . . Ms Catherine McLeod . . . . . . . . . . . . . . . . . Tel: (020) 7215 5224
Ms Jessica Rafinski . . . . . . . . . . . . . . . . . . . . Tel: (020) 7215 3937
Mr Steven Wallace . . . . . . . . . . . . . . . . . . . . Tel: (020) 7215 3864

## Software and Computer Services

Director, Software and Computer Service . . . . . . . . . . . . Dr Richard Hopkins . . . . . . . . . . . . . . . . . . Tel: (020) 7215 1219

## Space

British National Space Centre
*151 Buckingham Palace Road, London, SW1W 9SS*

Director-General . . . . . . . . . . . . . . . . . . . . . . . . . . . . Dr Colin Hicks . . . . . . . . . . . . . . . . . . . . . . . Tel: (020) 7215 0877
Deputy Director-General, Technology/
Industrial Policy . . . . . . . . . . . . . . . . . . . . . . . . . Dr David Leadbetter . . . . . . . . . . . . . . . . . . Tel: (020) 7215 0705
Director, Space Science Technology,
Rutherford Appleton Laboratory . . . . . . . . . . . . . Professor Richard Holdaway . . . . . . . . . . . . Tel: (01235) 445527
Applications and Programmes . . . . . . . . . . . . . . . . . . Ms Paula Freedman . . . . . . . . . . . . . . . . . . . Tel: (020) 7215 0881
Earth Observation . . . . . . . . . . . . . . . . . . . . . . . . . . . Dr Steve Wilson . . . . . . . . . . . . . . . . . . . . . . Tel: (020) 7215 1422
European Space Agency . . . . . . . . . . . . . . . . . . . . . . . Mr Jim Thomas . . . . . . . . . . . . . . . . . . . . . . Tel: (020) 7215 0867
Meteorology . . . . . . . . . . . . . . . . . . . . . . . . . . . . . . . . Mr Martin Jones . . . . . . . . . . . . . . . . . . . . . Tel: (01344) 854260
Policy and Finance . . . . . . . . . . . . . . . . . . . . . . . . . . . Mr Alan Cooper . . . . . . . . . . . . . . . . . . . . . . Tel: (020) 7215 0894
Space Science . . . . . . . . . . . . . . . . . . . . . . . . . . . . . . . Mr Dave Hall . . . . . . . . . . . . . . . . . . . . . . . . Tel: (020) 7215 0787
Telecommunications and Navigation . . . . . . . . . . . . . . Mr Ian Munro . . . . . . . . . . . . . . . . . . . . . . . Tel: (020) 7215 0934

## Standards and Technical Regulations

Director, Standards and Technical Regulations . . . . . . . . Mr Rob Brightwell . . . . . . . . . . . . . . . . . . . Tel: (020) 7215 1459
Deputy Director, Standards and Technical Regulations . . . . Mr Richard Lawson . . . . . . . . . . . . . . . . . . . Tel: (020) 7215 1469
Accreditation . . . . . . . . . . . . . . . . . . . . . . . . . . . . . . . . . Mr Malcolm Hynd . . . . . . . . . . . . . . . . . . . . Tel: (020) 7215 1976
Co-ordination of Standards Policy . . . . . . . . . . . . . . . . . Ms Michelle Barker . . . . . . . . . . . . . . . . . . . Tel: (020) 7215 1575
Electricity and Gas Safety . . . . . . . . . . . . . . . . . . . . . . . . Mr Richard Harris . . . . . . . . . . . . . . . . . . . . Tel: (020) 7215 1325
European Engineering Directives . . . . . . . . . . . . . . . . . . Mr Mike Dodds . . . . . . . . . . . . . . . . . . . . . . Tel: (020) 7215 1339
European Technical Directives . . . . . . . . . . . . . . . . . . . . Mr Iain Nicol . . . . . . . . . . . . . . . . . . . . . . . . Tel: (020) 7215 1408
International Standards Policy . . . . . . . . . . . . . . . . . . . . . Mr David Willmets . . . . . . . . . . . . . . . . . . . Tel: (020) 7215 1571
Radio and Telecommunications Equipment . . . . . . . . . . . Ms Diana Maxwell . . . . . . . . . . . . . . . . . . . . Tel: (020) 7215 4176
Technical Regulations and Standards Policy . . . . . . . . . . Mr David Willmets . . . . . . . . . . . . . . . . . . . Tel: (020) 7215 1571

## State Aids to Industry

Legal Advice . . . . . . . . . . . . . . . . . . . . . . . . . . . . . . . . . Mr Stephen Hyett . . . . . . . . . . . . . . . . . . . . Tel: (020) 7215 3408

## Statistics

Director, Statistics and Analysis . . . . . . . . . . . . . . . . . . . Mr Glenn Everett . . . . . . . . . . . . . . . . . . . . . Tel: (020) 7215 3276
Director, Industry Economics and Statistics . . . . . . . . . . . Mr Christopher Moir . . . . . . . . . . . . . . . . . . Tel: (020) 7215 1927
Automotive . . . . . . . . . . . . . . . . . . . . . . . . . . . . . . . . . . . Mr Michael Clary . . . . . . . . . . . . . . . . . . . . . Tel: (020) 7215 1887
Bioscience . . . . . . . . . . . . . . . . . . . . . . . . . . . . . . . . . . . . Mr Bill Nutall . . . . . . . . . . . . . . . . . . . . . . . . Tel: (020) 7215 1883
Building Materials . . . . . . . . . . . . . . . . . . . . . . . . . . . . . . Mr Keith Folwell . . . . . . . . . . . . . . . . . . . . . Tel: (020) 7215 1248
Chemicals . . . . . . . . . . . . . . . . . . . . . . . . . . . . . . . . . . . . Mr Bill Nutall . . . . . . . . . . . . . . . . . . . . . . . . Tel: (020) 7215 1883
Coal . . . . . . . . . . . . . . . . . . . . . . . . . . . . . . . . . . . . . . . . . Mr Mike Janes . . . . . . . . . . . . . . . . . . . . . . . Tel: (020) 7215 5186
Construction
General . . . . . . . . . . . . . . . . . . . . . . . . . . . . . . . . . . . . Ms Jackie Sanders . . . . . . . . . . . . . . . . . . . . Tel: (020) 7215 6046
Tender Prices . . . . . . . . . . . . . . . . . . . . . . . . . . . . . . . Mr Robert Packham . . . . . . . . . . . . . . . . . . . Tel: (020) 7215 1699
Consumer Goods . . . . . . . . . . . . . . . . . . . . . . . . . . . . . . . Mr Bill Nutall . . . . . . . . . . . . . . . . . . . . . . . . Tel: (020) 7215 1883
Cross-Sectoral Analysis . . . . . . . . . . . . . . . . . . . . . . . . . . Mr Bill Nutall . . . . . . . . . . . . . . . . . . . . . . . . Tel: (020) 7215 1883

# DEPARTMENT OF TRADE AND INDUSTRY

*Statistics (Continued)*

| | | |
|---|---|---|
| Digital Content | *Vacant* | Tel: (020) 7215 1907 |
| Electrical Engineering | *Vacant* | Tel: (020) 7215 1907 |
| Electricity | Mr Mike Janes | Tel: (020) 7215 5186 |

Energy

| | | |
|---|---|---|
| Director, Energy Efficiency, Information and Statistics | Mr Graham White | Tel: (020) 7215 2695 |
| Data Collection and IT | Mr Steve Roberts | Tel: (020) 7215 2684 |
| Fuel Poverty Analysis | Ms Lesley Petrie | Tel: (020) 7215 2720 |
| Publication and Dissemination | Ms Mari Scullion | Tel: (020) 7215 5183 |
| Engineering | *Vacant* | Tel: (020) 7215 1907 |
| Gas | Mr Mike Janes | Tel: (020) 7215 5186 |
| Labour Input | Mr Michael Clary | Tel: (020) 7215 1887 |
| Marine | Mr Michael Clary | Tel: (020) 7215 1887 |
| Mechanical Engineering | *Vacant* | Tel: (020) 7215 1907 |
| Metals and Minerals | Mr Michael Clary | Tel: (020) 7215 1887 |
| North Sea | Mr Philip Beckett | Tel: (020) 7215 5260 |
| Oil and Gas | Mr Martin Young | Tel: (020) 7215 5184 |
| Operational Research Unit | Mr Chris Young | Tel: (020) 7215 3314 |
| Output and New Orders | Mr Frances Pottier | Tel: (020) 7215 1953 |
| Publishing | *Vacant* | Tel: (020) 7215 1907 |
| Retail | Mr Bill Nutall | Tel: (020) 7215 1883 |
| Shipbuilding | Mr Michael Clary | Tel: (020) 7215 1887 |
| Software | *Vacant* | Tel: (020) 7215 1907 |
| Telecommunications | *Vacant* | Tel: (020) 7215 1907 |
| Vehicles | Mr Michael Clary | Tel: (020) 7215 1887 |

**Steel**     Ms Zoe Dayan     Tel: (020) 7215 1049

**Strategy, Departmental**

| | | |
|---|---|---|
| Director, Strategy Unit | Mr Geoff Dart | Tel: (020) 7215 2599 |
| Director, Performance and Evaluation | Mr Andrew Rees | Tel: (020) 7215 6111 |
| Director, Strategic Planning | Ms Caroline Normand | Tel: (020) 7215 5718 |

**Sustainable Development**

| | | |
|---|---|---|
| Director, Sustainable Development | *Vacant* | Tel: (020) 7215 3734 |
| Environmental Regulation | Mr James Marsh | Tel: (020) 7215 1666 |
| Sustainable Development Policy | Mr Michael Massey | Tel: (020) 7215 1873 |
| Sustainable Technologies | Ms April Vesey | Tel: (020) 7215 1708 |

**Teleworking**     Ms Jane Whewell     Tel: (020) 7215 5731

**Textiles**

| | | |
|---|---|---|
| Director, Textile and Clothing Unit | Mr Brian Greenwood | Tel: (020) 7215 1640 |
| Deputy Director, Textile and Clothing Unit | Mr Graham Wilmington | Tel: (020) 7215 1298 |
| Market Analysis | Ms Anjie Amin | Tel: (020) 7215 5818 |
| Textile and Clothing Design and Fashion | Mr Russell Kerr | Tel: (020) 7215 1296 |

**Trade: British Trade International**

*Kingsgate House, 66-74 Victoria Street, London, SW1E 6SW*

*(Note: British Trade International is jointly responsible to the Department of Trade and Industry and the Foreign and Commonwealth Office.*
*It is chaired by Rt Hon Baroness Symons of Vernham Dean. For Investment UK see UK Trade and Investment below).*

| | | |
|---|---|---|
| Chief Executive | Sir Stephen Brown KCVO | Tel: (020) 7215 5000 |
| Deputy Chief Executive | Mr Ian Jones | Tel: (020) 7215 4933 |
| Deputy Chief Executive (Investment UK) | Mr William Pedder | Tel: (020) 7215 5684 |

Trade Partners UK

Group Directors

| | | |
|---|---|---|
| Business | Mr Peter Tibber | Tel: (020) 7215 4258 |
| International | Mr David Warren | Tel: (020) 7215 8148 |
| Regional | Mr David Warren | Tel: (020) 7215 4933 |
| Strategy and Communications | Mr John Reynolds | Tel: (020) 7215 4866 |

Business Sectors

| | | |
|---|---|---|
| Group Director | Mr Peter Tibber | Tel: (020) 7215 4258 |
| Aerospace and Automotives | Mr John Foote | Tel: (020) 7215 3643 |
| Airports and Other Infrastructure | Mr Geoff Nuttall | Tel: (020) 7215 4296 |

## DEPARTMENT OF TRADE AND INDUSTRY

*British Trade International (Continued)*

| | | |
|---|---|---|
| Biotechnology | Mr Tom Salusbury | Tel: (020) 7215 4631 |
| Chemicals | Ms Lynda O'Brien | Tel: (020) 7215 4623 |
| Communications | Ms Lynda O'Brien | Tel: (020) 7215 4623 |
| Computers and Software | Ms Jane Eardley | Tel: (020) 7215 4993 |
| Construction | Mr Keith Lievesley | Tel: (020) 7215 4296 |
| Consumer Goods | Mr David Shearman | Tel: (020) 7215 4470 |
| Creative Industries | Ms Anna van den Burgh | Tel: (020) 7215 4678 |
| Education and Training | Mr Robert McKim | Tel: (020) 7215 4626 |
| Electronics | Ms Lynda O'Brien | Tel: (020) 7215 4623 |
| Enterprise Scholarship Scheme | Mr Mike Cairns | Tel: (020) 7215 4725 |
| Exhibitions and Seminars Abroad | | |
|    Accreditation and Best Practice | Ms Eileen Barnett | Tel: (0141) 228 3665 |
|    Administration | Mr Jim Drummond | Tel: (0141) 228 3664 |
|    Operations | Ms Jacqueline Rossi | Tel: (0141) 228 3650 |
|    Policy | Mr Ron Archibald | Tel: (0141) 228 3604 |
| Export Finance and Aid Policy | Mr Graham Rowcroft | Tel: (020) 7215 4260 |
| Healthcare | Ms Lynda O'Brien | Tel: (020) 7215 4623 |
| Infrastructure Projects | | |
|    Director | Mr Mel Draper | Tel: (020) 7215 0716 |
| International Business Schemes and Engineering | | |
|    Director | Mr Ken White | Tel: (0141) 228 3772 |
| International Oil and Gas Business | | |
|    Director | Mr Brian Gallagher | Tel: (0141) 228 3633 |
|    Deputy Director | Mr Bob Atkinson | Tel: (0141) 228 3606 |
|    Americas | Mr Keith Melville | Tel: (0141) 228 3607 |
|    Central Asia, Caucasus Iran, Turkey | Mr Craig Jones | Tel: (0141) 228 3645 |
|    China, Pacific Asia, Australia | Mr John Crawford | Tel: (0141) 228 3674 |
|    Europe, Norway, Russia, Sakhalin Island | Mr Bernard O'Hear | Tel: (0141) 228 3677 |
|    Middle East (not Iran), Africa, South Asia | Mr Ian Lockhart | Tel: (0141) 228 3626 |
|    Oil and Gas Policy | Mr Brian Darbyshire | Tel: (0141) 228 3606 |
| IT | Ms Lynda O'Brien | Tel: (020) 7215 4623 |
| Leisure and Tourism | Mr Richard Parry | Tel: (020) 7215 4956 |
| Marine, Metals, Minerals Mechanical | Ms Janet Tingle | Tel: (0141) 228 3617 |
| Mining | Mr Jim Kennedy | Tel: (0141) 228 3643 |
| Overseas Aid (Development Business Team) | Mr Nigel Dickerson | Tel: (020) 7215 8329 |
| Pharmaceutical | Mr Tom Salusbury | Tel: (020) 7215 4631 |
| Railways and Transport Infrastructure | Ms Denise Harris | Tel: (020) 7215 4650 |
| Power | Mr Ray Burleigh | Tel: (020) 7215 4639 |
| Science | Mr Mike Cairns | Tel: (020) 7215 4725 |
| Sectoral Partnerships | | |
|    Director | Mr Tim Torlot | Tel: (020) 7215 4631 |
|    Advisory Groups | Ms Kate Jelley | Tel: (020) 7215 8369 |
| Security Products | Mr Keith Lievesley | Tel: (020) 7215 4296 |
| Service Industries | Ms Anna van den Burgh | Tel: (020) 7215 4678 |
| Services, Sectors, Overseas Aid, Finance and Investment | | |
|    Director | Mr Martin Raven | Tel: (020) 7215 4890 |
| Sport and Leisure | Ms Carolyne Akers | Tel: (020) 7215 4681 |
| Technology | Mr Mike Cairns | Tel: (020) 7215 4725 |
| Visits, Business | Mr Graham Hawes | Tel: (020) 7215 4420 |
| Water, Ports Logistics | Mr Richard Hardiman | Tel: (020) 7215 4592 |

*(Note: International Business and Engineering and International Oil and Gas Business are based at:*
*Tay House, 300 Bath Street, Glasgow, G7 4DX).*

Corporate Resources Group

| | | |
|---|---|---|
| Group Director | Mr Ian Jones | Tel: (020) 7215 4933 |
| Director, Personnel and Finance | Mr Edmund Quilty | Tel: (020) 7215 4600 |
| Finance | Ms Louise Mathias | Tel: (020) 7215 8480 |
| | Mr Nigel Taylor | Tel: (020) 7215 4730 |
| Huma Resources and Training | Ms Anne Morrison | Tel: (020) 7215 8350 |

International Group

| | | |
|---|---|---|
| Group Director | Mr David Warren | Tel: (020) 7215 8148 |
| Directors | | |
|    America | Mr Ken Timmins | Tel: (020) 7215 4320 |

# DEPARTMENT OF °TRADE AND INDUSTRY

*British Trade International (Continued)*

| | | |
|---|---|---|
| Asia and Pacific | Mr Tim Holmes | Tel: (020) 7215 4975 |
| Europe | Mr Malcolm Scott | Tel: (020) 7215 4733 |
| Middle East and Africa | Mr Bill Henderson | Tel: (020) 7215 4952 |

Countries - Sectors and Units

Africa

| | | |
|---|---|---|
| South and Southern Africa | Ms Sandra Martin | Tel: (020) 7215 4967 |
| West, Central and East Africa | Mr Gregor Lusty | Tel: (020) 7215 4832 |

Asia

| | | |
|---|---|---|
| Central Asia, Turkey and South Caucasus | Mr Wayne Lewis | Tel: (020) 7215 4864 |
| South Asia | Mr Mike Connor | Tel: (020) 7215 4880 |
| South East Asia | Ms Debbie Clarke | Tel: (020) 7215 8892 |
| Australasia / Korea | Ms Debbie Clark | Tel: (020) 7215 8892 |
| Central Europe, Russia, Ukraine, Belarus | Mr Wayne Lewis | Tel: (020) 7215 4864 |
| China Markets | Mr Mike Mielniczek | Tel: (020) 7215 4893 |

Europe

| | | |
|---|---|---|
| Southern and Western Europe | Ms Anne Woodward | Tel: (020) 7215 4898 |
| Gulf States | Mr Fergus Harradance | Tel: (020) 7215 8214 |
| Japan | Ms Gillian Baker | Tel: (020) 7215 4806 |
| Latin America | Mr Eric Magson | Tel: (020) 7215 4368 |
| Mexico | Ms Anne Pearcey | Tel: (020) 7215 4601 |
| Near East and North Africa | Ms Sharon Wardle | Tel: (020) 7215 1294 |
| Nordics, Baltics, Ireland | Mr Adrian Hockney | Tel: (020) 7215 4614 |
| USA, Canada | Ms Anne Pearcey | Tel: (020) 7215 4601 |
| Trade Development Co-ordination - Countries | Mr John Alexander | Tel: (020) 7215 8243 |

Regional Group

| | | |
|---|---|---|
| Group Director | Mr Ian Jones | Tel: (020) 7215 4933 |
| Director, Regions | Ms Elizabeth Duthie | Tel: (020) 7215 4012 |
| Deputy Director, Regions | Ms Andrea Owen | Tel: (020) 7215 2422 |
| Policy, Regional | Mr Tony Dewick | Tel: (020) 7215 8421 |

Strategy and Communications Group

| | | |
|---|---|---|
| Group Director | Mr John Reynolds | Tel: (020) 7215 4866 |
| Communications and Marketing | Mr Peter McDermott | Tel: (020) 7215 4043 |
| Change Management | Mr John Doddrell | Tel: (020) 7215 2459 |
| E-Business Programme Director | Mr Ian McKenzie | Tel: (020) 7215 2442 |
| E-Services to Business | Mr Clive Stitt | Tel: (020) 7215 8463 |

## Trade Policy

| | | |
|---|---|---|
| Director-General, Europe and World Trade | Mr Edmund Hosker | Tel: (020) 7215 4445 |
| Director, International Trade Policy | Mr Tim Abraham | Tel: (020) 7215 4576 |
| Director, Market Access | Mr David Andrew | Tel: (020) 7215 4560 |
| Director, State Aids | Mr Alec Berry | Tel: (020) 7215 4443 |
| Director, Trade Policy | Dr Elaine Drage | Tel: (020) 7215 4503 |
| Director, International Economists) | Mr Peter Dodd | Tel: (020) 7215 4521 |
| Anti-Dumping | Mr Ray Symons | Tel: (020) 7215 4551 |
| Bribery, Combating | Mr Tim Abraham | Tel: (020) 7215 4576 |
| Developing Countries and European Union | Mr Ron Archibald | Tel: (020) 7215 4448 |
| Economic Adviser, Inward Investment and Trade Performance | Ms Helen Grimshaw | Tel: (020) 7215 4585 |
| Electronic Commerce | Mr Robert Crowhurst | Tel: (020) 7215 4565 |
| Import Licensing | Mr Brian Howe *(Billingham)* | Tel: (01642) 364306 |
| Import Policy | Mr Colin Bailey | Tel: (020) 7215 4527 |
| International Investment and Competition Policy | Mr David Harvey | Tel: (020) 7215 4504 |
| Market Access | Mr Matthew Conway | Tel: (020) 7215 4565 |
| Services, Trade in | Mr Malcolm McKinnon | Tel: (020) 7215 4555 |
| Single Market Policy, EU | Mr Clive Fleming | Tel: (020) 7215 4460 |
| SITPRO Sponsorship | Mr Robert Crowhurst | Tel: (020) 7215 4565 |
| State Aid Policy | Mr Alec Berry | Tel: (020) 7215 4443 |
| Trade Defence Unit | Mr Ray Symons | Tel: (020) 7215 4551 |

*(Note: Import Licensing Branch is located at Queensway House, West Precinct, Billingham, TS23 2NF).*

| | | |
|---|---|---|
| **Trading Associations** | Mr Patrick Mulligan | Tel: (020) 7215 5000 |
| **Trading Standards** | Ms Jane Swift | Tel: (020) 7215 1905 |

# DEPARTMENT OF TRADE AND INDUSTRY

**UK Online for Business** . . . . . . . . . . . . . . . . . . . . . . . . . . Dr Elizabeth Grant . . . . . . . . . . . . . . . . . . . Tel: (020) 7215 1553

**UK Trade and Investment**
Chief Executive . . . . . . . . . . . . . . . . . . . . . . . . . . . . . . . . Sir Steven Brown KCVO. . . . . . . . . . . . . . . . Tel: (020) 7215 2501
Deputy Chief Executive (Investment UK) . . . . . . . . . . . Mr William Pedder . . . . . . . . . . . . . . . . . . . Tel: (020) 7215 5684
Directors
   International . . . . . . . . . . . . . . . . . . . . . . . . . . . . . . Mr David Cockerham . . . . . . . . . . . . . . . . . . Tel: (020) 7215 2560
   Marketing . . . . . . . . . . . . . . . . . . . . . . . . . . . . . . . . Mr Peter McDermott . . . . . . . . . . . . . . . . . . Tel: (020) 7215 2544
   Operations . . . . . . . . . . . . . . . . . . . . . . . . . . . . . . . Mr Steve O'Leary . . . . . . . . . . . . . . . . . . . . . Tel: (020) 7215 2509
Sections
   Americas . . . . . . . . . . . . . . . . . . . . . . . . . . . . . . . . . Mr John Cohen . . . . . . . . . . . . . . . . . . . . . . . Tel: (020) 7215 2541
   Asia, Pacific, Africa . . . . . . . . . . . . . . . . . . . . . . . . Mr Tony Collingridge . . . . . . . . . . . . . . . . . . Tel: (020) 7215 2523
   Europe . . . . . . . . . . . . . . . . . . . . . . . . . . . . . . . . . . Ms Jeanette Rosenberg . . . . . . . . . . . . . . . . Tel: (020) 7215 2535
   International Investor Development . . . . . . . . . . . . Mr Alister Jones . . . . . . . . . . . . . . . . . . . . . . . Tel: (020) 7215 2569
   Marketing Services . . . . . . . . . . . . . . . . . . . . . . . . Ms Alison Turner . . . . . . . . . . . . . . . . . . . . . Tel: (020) 7215 2544
   Policy, Administration and Finance . . . . . . . . . . . . Ms Janis Cammell. . . . . . . . . . . . . . . . . . . . . Tel: (020) 7215 2503

**Vehicle Industry** (*see above under Motor Industry*)

**Waste**
Policy . . . . . . . . . . . . . . . . . . . . . . . . . . . . . . . . . . . . . . . Mr Steve Andrews. . . . . . . . . . . . . . . . . . . . . Tel: (020) 7215 1670
Vehicle Recycling . . . . . . . . . . . . . . . . . . . . . . . . . . . . . Mr Steve Norgrove . . . . . . . . . . . . . . . . . . . Tel: (020) 7215 2981

**Weights and Measures**
Director, National Measurement System . . . . . . . . . . . . . Mr Denis Walker . . . . . . . . . . . . . . . . . . . . . Tel: (020) 7215 1649
Deputy Director, National Measurement System . . . . . . . Mr Peter Dawes . . . . . . . . . . . . . . . . . . . . . . Tel: (020) 7215 1996
Deputy Director, National Measurement System Policy Unit Mr Robert Gunn . . . . . . . . . . . . . . . . . . . . . . Tel: (020) 7215 1404
Director, Standards and Technical Regulations . . . . . . . . Mr Rob Brightwell . . . . . . . . . . . . . . . . . . . . Tel: (020) 7215 1459
Materials Metrology . . . . . . . . . . . . . . . . . . . . . . . . . . . Ms Joan Cocksedge. . . . . . . . . . . . . . . . . . . . Tel: (020) 7215 1718
Policy . . . . . . . . . . . . . . . . . . . . . . . . . . . . . . . . . . . . . . Mr David Legg . . . . . . . . . . . . . . . . . . . . . . . Tel: (020) 7215 1195
Site Operations. . . . . . . . . . . . . . . . . . . . . . . . . . . . . . . Mr Mike Nally . . . . . . . . . . . . . . . . . . . . . . . Tel: (020) 7215 7151

**Windfarms**. . . . . . . . . . . . . . . . . . . . . . . . . . . . . . . . . . . Ms Caroline Roberts . . . . . . . . . . . . . . . . . . . Tel: (020) 7215 2831

**Women and Equality Unit**
Director, Women and Equality Unit . . . . . . . . . . . . . . . . Ms Angela Mason . . . . . . . . . . . . . . . . . . . . . Tel: (020) 7215 5000
Childcare. . . . . . . . . . . . . . . . . . . . . . . . . . . . . . . . . . . . Ms Kate Allan . . . . . . . . . . . . . . . . . . . . . . . . Tel: (020) 7215 5000
Domestic Violence. . . . . . . . . . . . . . . . . . . . . . . . . . . . . Ms Liz Chennells . . . . . . . . . . . . . . . . . . . . . Tel: (020) 7215 5000
Equal Pay . . . . . . . . . . . . . . . . . . . . . . . . . . . . . . . . . . . Ms Hilary Samson-Barry . . . . . . . . . . . . . . . Tel: (020) 7215 5000
Equality Co-ordination . . . . . . . . . . . . . . . . . . . . . . . . Ms Kate Allan . . . . . . . . . . . . . . . . . . . . . . . . Tel: (020) 7215 5000
Gender Equality and Social Justice. . . . . . . . . . . . . . . . . Ms Liz Chennells . . . . . . . . . . . . . . . . . . . . . Tel: (020) 7215 5000
Productivity and Diversity . . . . . . . . . . . . . . . . . . . . . . Ms Hilary Samson-Barry . . . . . . . . . . . . . . . Tel: (020) 7215 5000
Sexual Orientation . . . . . . . . . . . . . . . . . . . . . . . . . . . . Ms Liz Chennells . . . . . . . . . . . . . . . . . . . . . Tel: (020) 7215 5000

**Working Time (European Union)** . . . . . . . . . . . . . . . . . Ms Julie Carney . . . . . . . . . . . . . . . . . . . . . . Tel: (020) 7215 5549

**World Trade**
Director-General, World Trade . . . . . . . . . . . . . . . . . . . . Mr Edmund Hosker . . . . . . . . . . . . . . . . . . . Tel: (020) 7215 4445
Director, International Trade Policy . . . . . . . . . . . . . . . . Mr Tim Abraham . . . . . . . . . . . . . . . . . . . . . Tel: (020) 7215 4576
Communications, Publicity. . . . . . . . . . . . . . . . . . . . . . . Ms Nicola Cullen . . . . . . . . . . . . . . . . . . . . . Tel: (020) 7215 4410
Developing Countries . . . . . . . . . . . . . . . . . . . . . . . . . . Mr Tim Abraham . . . . . . . . . . . . . . . . . . . . . Tel: (020) 7215 4576
Disputes. . . . . . . . . . . . . . . . . . . . . . . . . . . . . . . . . . . . . Mr John Overton. . . . . . . . . . . . . . . . . . . . . . Tel: (020) 7215 4522
Economics . . . . . . . . . . . . . . . . . . . . . . . . . . . . . . . . . . . Mr Stephen Johnston. . . . . . . . . . . . . . . . . . . Tel: (020) 7215 4536
International Economics. . . . . . . . . . . . . . . . . . . . . . . . . Mr Peter Dodd . . . . . . . . . . . . . . . . . . . . . . . Tel: (020) 7215 4521
International Investment and Competition Policy. . . . . . . Mr David Harvey . . . . . . . . . . . . . . . . . . . . . Tel: (020) 7215 4504
Negotiations. . . . . . . . . . . . . . . . . . . . . . . . . . . . . . . . . . Dr Susan Baxter . . . . . . . . . . . . . . . . . . . . . . Tel: (020) 7215 4485
Public Procurement and EU also and WTO. . . . . . . . . . . Ms Anne Turner . . . . . . . . . . . . . . . . . . . . . . Tel: (020) 7215 5000
Services, Trade in. . . . . . . . . . . . . . . . . . . . . . . . . . . . . . Mr Malcolm McKinnon . . . . . . . . . . . . . . . . Tel: (020) 7215 4555
World Trade Organisation Unit. . . . . . . . . . . . . . . . . . . . Mr John Overton. . . . . . . . . . . . . . . . . . . . . . Tel: (020) 7215 4522

**Works Councils**. . . . . . . . . . . . . . . . . . . . . . . . . . . . . . . . Mr Iain Adlington. . . . . . . . . . . . . . . . . . . . . Tel: (020) 7215 3806

# DEPARTMENT OF TRADE AND INDUSTRY

## OTHER RELEVANT CONTACTS

### ARBITRATION

**Advisory Conciliation and Arbitration Service** . . . . . . . . Brandon House, 180 Borough High Street, London, SE1 1OW
    Chairman . . . . . . . . . . . . . . . . . . . . . . . . . . . . . . Ms Rita Donaghy OBE
    Chief Executive . . . . . . . . . . . . . . . . . . . . . . . . . . . Mr John Taylor . . . . . . . . . . . . . . . . . . . . . Tel: (0845) 747 4747
    Web: http://www.acas.org.uk

**Central Arbitration Committee** . . . . . . . . . . . . . . . . . . . . Discovery House, 28-42 Banner Street, London, EC1Y 8QE
    Chairman . . . . . . . . . . . . . . . . . . . . . . . . . . . . . . Sir Michael Burton QC
    Chief Executive . . . . . . . . . . . . . . . . . . . . . . . . . . . Mr Graeme Charles . . . . . . . . . . . . . . . . . . . . Tel: (020) 7251 9747
    E-mail: enquiries@cac.gov.uk
    Web: http://www.cac.gov.uk

### AEROSPACE

**Aerospace Committee** . . . . . . . . . . . . . . . . . . . . . . . . . Bay 472, 151 Buckingham Palace Road, London, SW1W 9SS
    Chairman . . . . . . . . . . . . . . . . . . . . . . . . . . . . . . Mr Colin Green
    Secretary . . . . . . . . . . . . . . . . . . . . . . . . . . . . . . . Mr Bob Insley . . . . . . . . . . . . . . . . . . . . . . . Tel: (020) 7215 1958

### ATOMIC ENERGY

**UK National Authority Advisory Committee** . . . . . . . . . . DTI, 4 Abbey Orchard Street, London, SW1P 2HT
    Chairman . . . . . . . . . . . . . . . . . . . . . . . . . . . . . . Dr Thomas Inch
    Secretary . . . . . . . . . . . . . . . . . . . . . . . . . . . . . . . Mr Alistair East . . . . . . . . . . . . . . . . . . . . . . Tel: (020) 7215 0691
    Web: http://www.dti.gov.uk/non-proliferation/naac

### BIOTECHNOLOGY

**Agriculture and Environment Biotechnology**
**Commission** . . . . . . . . . . . . . . . . . . . . . . . . . . . . . . . Area 479, 1 Victoria Street, London, SW1H 0ET
    Chairman . . . . . . . . . . . . . . . . . . . . . . . . . . . . . . Professor Malcolm Grant
    Secretary . . . . . . . . . . . . . . . . . . . . . . . . . . . . . . . Mr Paul van Heyninger . . . . . . . . . . . . . . . . . Tel: (020) 7215 6508
    Web: http://www.aebc.gov.uk

### BUSINESS INCUBATION FUND

**Business Incubation Fund Investment Panel** . . . . . . . . . . Bay 603, Kingsgate House, 66-74 Victoria Street, London SW1E 6SW
    Chairman . . . . . . . . . . . . . . . . . . . . . . . . . . . . . . Mr John Bridge
    Secretary *(Acting)* . . . . . . . . . . . . . . . . . . . . . . . . . Mr Anthony Walters . . . . . . . . . . . . . . . . . . Tel: (020) 7215 8218

### COAL *(see below under Energy)*

### COMMUNICATIONS INDUSTRY

**OFCOM** . . . . . . . . . . . . . . . . . . . . . . . . . . . . . . . . . . . Riverside House, 2A Southwark Bridge Road, London, SE1 9HA
    Chairman . . . . . . . . . . . . . . . . . . . . . . . . . . . . . . Lord Currie
    Chief Executive . . . . . . . . . . . . . . . . . . . . . . . . . . . Mr Stephen Carter . . . . . . . . . . . . . . . . . . . Tel: (020) 7981 3000
    E-mail: contact@ofcom.org.uk
    Web: http://www.ofcom.org.uk

### COMPANIES

**Companies House** *(Executive Agency)* . . . . . . . . . . . . . . . . Crown Way, Cardiff, CF14 3UZ
    Chief Executive . . . . . . . . . . . . . . . . . . . . . . . . . . . Ms Claire Clancy . . . . . . . . . . . . . . . . . . . . . Tel: (0870) 333 3636
    Web: http://www.companieshouse.gov.uk

### COMPETITION *(see below under Trading Practices)*

### CONSUMERS

**Consumers Credit Appeals Secretariat** . . . . . . . . . . . . . . Room 131, Department of Trade and Industry, 10 Victoria Street,
    London SW1H 0NN
    *Contact* . . . . . . . . . . . . . . . . . . . . . . . . . . . . . . . . Mr Brian Swift . . . . . . . . . . . . . . . . . . . . . . . Tel: (020) 7215 3089
    E-mail: consumercredit.appeals@dti.gov.uk

**National Consumer Council** . . . . . . . . . . . . . . . . . . . . . 20 Grosvenor Gardens, London, SW1W 0DH
    Chairman . . . . . . . . . . . . . . . . . . . . . . . . . . . . . . Ms Deidre Hutton CBE
    Chief Executive . . . . . . . . . . . . . . . . . . . . . . . . . . . Mr Ed Mayo . . . . . . . . . . . . . . . . . . . . . . . . Tel: (020) 7730 3469
    E-mail: info@ncc.org.uk
    Web: http://www.ncc.org.uk

*(See also above under Communications Industry and below under Energy, Postal Services and Trading Practices)*

# DEPARTMENT OF TRADE AND INDUSTRY

*Other Relevant Contacts (Continued)*

## COPYRIGHT

**Copyright Tribunal** . . . . . . . . . . . . . . . . . . . . . . . . . . . Room 1/8, Patent Office, Harmsworth House, 13-15 Bouverie Street, London, EC4Y 8DP

Chairman . . . . . . . . . . . . . . . . . . . . . . . . . . . . . . . . . . Mr Christopher Tootal

Deputy Chairmen . . . . . . . . . . . . . . . . . . . . . . . . . . . . Mr Christopher Floyd

Mr Simon Thorley . . . . . . . . . . . . . . . . . . . Tel: (020) 7596 6510

Web: http://www.patent.gov.uk/copy/tribunal/index.htm

## DESIGN

**Design Council** . . . . . . . . . . . . . . . . . . . . . . . . . . . . . 34 Bow Street, London, WC2E 7DL

Chairman . . . . . . . . . . . . . . . . . . . . . . . . . . . . . . . . . . Sir Christopher Frayling

Chief Executive . . . . . . . . . . . . . . . . . . . . . . . . . . . . . Mr David Kester . . . . . . . . . . . . . . . . . . . Tel: (020) 7420 5200

Web: http://www.designcouncil.org.uk

## EMPLOYMENT APPEALS *(see below under Industrial Tribunals)*

## ENERGY

**Advisory Committee on Carbon**

**Abatement Technologies** . . . . . . . . . . . . . . . . . . . . . 1 Victoria Street, London, SW1H 0ET

Chairman . . . . . . . . . . . . . . . . . . . . . . . . . . . . . . . . . . Mrs Bronwen Northmoore

Secretary . . . . . . . . . . . . . . . . . . . . . . . . . . . . . . . . . . Mr Charles Pearce . . . . . . . . . . . . . . . . . . . Tel: (020) 7215 2669

Web: http://www.dti.gov.uk/cct/accat

**British Nuclear Fuels plc** . . . . . . . . . . . . . . . . . . . . . 110 Daresbury Park, Warrington, Cheshire, WA4 4GB

Chairman . . . . . . . . . . . . . . . . . . . . . . . . . . . . . . . . . . Mr Hugh Collum

Chief Executive . . . . . . . . . . . . . . . . . . . . . . . . . . . . . Mr Michael Parker . . . . . . . . . . . . . . . . . . . Tel: (01925) 832000

Web: http://www.bnfl.com

**Coal Authority** . . . . . . . . . . . . . . . . . . . . . . . . . . . . . 200 Lichfield Lane, Mansfield, NG18 4RG

Chairman . . . . . . . . . . . . . . . . . . . . . . . . . . . . . . . . . . Mr John Harris

Chief Executive . . . . . . . . . . . . . . . . . . . . . . . . . . . . . Dr Ian Roxburgh . . . . . . . . . . . . . . . . . . . Tel: (01623) 427162

Web: http://www.coal.gov.uk

**Energywatch** . . . . . . . . . . . . . . . . . . . . . . . . . . . . . . . 4th Floor, Artillery House, Artillery Row, London, SW1P 1RT

Chairman . . . . . . . . . . . . . . . . . . . . . . . . . . . . . . . . . . Mr Andrew Horsler

Chief Executive . . . . . . . . . . . . . . . . . . . . . . . . . . . . . Mr Alan Asher . . . . . . . . . . . . . . . . . . . Tel: (020) 7799 8340

Web: http://www.energywatch.org.uk

**Fuel Poverty Advisory Group** . . . . . . . . . . . . . . . . . 1 Victoria Street, London, SW1H 0ET

Chairman . . . . . . . . . . . . . . . . . . . . . . . . . . . . . . . . . . Mr Peter Lehmann

Joint Secretary . . . . . . . . . . . . . . . . . . . . . . . . . . . . . . Mr John Mason (Defra) . . . . . . . . . . . . . . . Tel: (020) 7215 6531

Web: http://www.dti.gov.uk/energy/consumers/fuel_poverty/index.html

**HM Inspectorate of Mines** . . . . . . . . . . . . . . . . . . . . 6th Floor, St Anne's House, University Road, Bootle, L20 3RA

Chief Inspector . . . . . . . . . . . . . . . . . . . . . . . . . . . . . . Mr Dan Mitchell . . . . . . . . . . . . . . . . . . . Tel: (0151) 951 4059

E-mail: dan.mitchell@hse.gsi.gov.uk

Web: http://www.hse.co.uk

**Office of Gas and Electricity Markets (OFGEM)** . . . . . . . 9 Millbank, London, SW1P 3GE

Chairman . . . . . . . . . . . . . . . . . . . . . . . . . . . . . . . . . . Sir John Mogg . . . . . . . . . . . . . . . . . . . Tel: (020) 7901 7000

Chief Executive . . . . . . . . . . . . . . . . . . . . . . . . . . . . . Mr Alaistair Buchanan

Web: http://www.ofgem.gov.uk

**Renewables Advisory Board** . . . . . . . . . . . . . . . . . . . 3rd Floor, Atholl House, 86-88 Guild Street, Aberdeen, AB11 6AR

Chairman . . . . . . . . . . . . . . . . . . . . . . . . . . . . . . . . . . Mr Stephen Timms MP *(Minister of State, DTI)*

Secretary . . . . . . . . . . . . . . . . . . . . . . . . . . . . . . . . . . Mr Shantha Shan . . . . . . . . . . . . . . . . . . . Tel: (01224) 254087

**Sustainable Energy Policy Advisory Panel** . . . . . . . . . Bay 490, 1 Victoria Street, London, SW1H 0ET

Secretary . . . . . . . . . . . . . . . . . . . . . . . . . . . . . . . . . . Mr David Tree . . . . . . . . . . . . . . . . . . . Tel: (020) 7215 2237

**United Kingdom Atomic Energy Authority** . . . . . . . . . Marshall Building, 521 Downs Way, Harwell, Didcot, Oxfordshire, OX11 0RA

Chairman . . . . . . . . . . . . . . . . . . . . . . . . . . . . . . . . . . Mr Denis Tunicliffe CBE

Chief Executive . . . . . . . . . . . . . . . . . . . . . . . . . . . . . Mr Dipesh Shah . . . . . . . . . . . . . . . . . . . Tel: (01235) 436900

Web: http://www.ukaea.org.uk

## ESTATE AGENTS

**Estate Agents Appeals Secretariat** . . . . . . . . . . . . . . . Room 231, 10 Victoria Street, London, SW1H 0NN

Contact . . . . . . . . . . . . . . . . . . . . . . . . . . . . . . . . . . . Mr Brian Swift . . . . . . . . . . . . . . . . . . . Tel: (020) 7215 3089

E-mail: estateagency.appeals@dti.gsi.gov.uk

# DEPARTMENT OF TRADE AND INDUSTRY

*Other Relevant Contacts (Continued)*

**ENTERPRISE**

**Distributed Generation Co-ordination Group** . . . . . . . . . 1 Victoria Street, London, SW1H 0ET
    Joint Chairmen . . . . . . . . . . . . . . . . . . . . . . . . . . . . . . . Mr Neil Hurst *(DTI)*
        Mr John Neilson *(OFGEM)*
    Joint Secretaries . . . . . . . . . . . . . . . . . . . . . . . . . . . . . Mr Philip Baker
        Mr Arthur Cook . . . . . . . . . . . . . . . . . . . . . . . Tel: (020) 7215 2675

**EQUAL OPPORTUNITIES**

**Equal Opportunities Commission** . . . . . . . . . . . . . . . . . . . Arndale House, Arndale Centre, Manchester, M4 3EQ
    Chairman . . . . . . . . . . . . . . . . . . . . . . . . . . . . . . . . . . . Ms Julie Mellor
    Chief Executive . . . . . . . . . . . . . . . . . . . . . . . . . . . . . . Ms Caroline Slocock . . . . . . . . . . . . . . . . . . Tel: (0845) 6015901
        E-mail: info@eoc.org.uk
        Web: http://www.eoc.org.uk

**ETHNIC MINORITY BUSINESS**

**Ethnic Minority Business Forum** . . . . . . . . . . . . . . . . . . . Bay 663, Small Business Service, Kingsgate House, 66-74 Victoria Street, London, SW1E 6SW
    Chairman . . . . . . . . . . . . . . . . . . . . . . . . . . . . . . . . . . . Ms Yvonne Thompson
    Secretary . . . . . . . . . . . . . . . . . . . . . . . . . . . . . . . . . . . Ms Sharon Batson . . . . . . . . . . . . . . . . . . . . Tel: (020) 7215 8355
        Web: http://www.ethnicbusiness.org

**EXPORTS**

**Export Credits Guarantee Advisory Council** . . . . . . . . . . PO Box 2200, 2 Exchange Tower, Harbour Exchange Square, London, E14 9GS
    Chairman . . . . . . . . . . . . . . . . . . . . . . . . . . . . . . . . . . . Ms Liz Airey
    Chief Executive . . . . . . . . . . . . . . . . . . . . . . . . . . . . . . Mr John Weiss . . . . . . . . . . . . . . . . . . . . . . Tel: (020) 7512 7208

**Export Credits Guarantee Department** . . . . . . . . . . . . . . PO Box 2200, 2 Exchange Tower, Harbour Exchange Square, London, E14 9GS
    Chief Executive . . . . . . . . . . . . . . . . . . . . . . . . . . . . . . Mr Patrick Crawford . . . . . . . . . . . . . . . . . Tel: (020) 7512 7000
        Web: http://www.ecgd.gov.uk

**SITPRO Ltd (Simple Trade Procedures)** . . . . . . . . . . . . . 8th Floor, Oxford House, 76 Oxford Street, London, W1D 1BS
    Chairman . . . . . . . . . . . . . . . . . . . . . . . . . . . . . . . . . . . Lord Bhatia OBE
    Chief Executive . . . . . . . . . . . . . . . . . . . . . . . . . . . . . . Mr David Wakeford MBE . . . . . . . . . . . . . . . Tel: (020) 7467 7280
        E-mail: info@sitpro.co.uk
        Web: http://www.sitpro.org.uk

**FAIR TRADING** *(see below under Trading Practices)*

**FINANCIAL SERVICES**

**Financial Services Compensation Scheme** . . . . . . . . . . . . 7th Floor, Lloyds Chambers, 1 Portsoken Street, London, E1 8BN
    Chairman . . . . . . . . . . . . . . . . . . . . . . . . . . . . . . . . . . . Mr Nigel Hamilton
    Chief Executive *(Acting)* . . . . . . . . . . . . . . . . . . . . . . . . Mr Ron Devlin . . . . . . . . . . . . . . . . . . . . . . Tel: (020) 7892 7300
        Web: http://www.fscs.org.uk

**HALLMARKS**

**British Hallmarking Council** . . . . . . . . . . . . . . . . . . . . . . St Philip's House, St Philip's Place, Birmingham, B3 2PP
    Chairman . . . . . . . . . . . . . . . . . . . . . . . . . . . . . . . . . . . Rt Hon Sir Adam Butler
    Secretary . . . . . . . . . . . . . . . . . . . . . . . . . . . . . . . . . . . Mr David Gwyther . . . . . . . . . . . . . . . . . . Tel: (0121) 200 3300
        Web: http://www.britishhallmarkingcouncil.gov.uk

**HEARING AIDS**

**Hearing Aid Council** . . . . . . . . . . . . . . . . . . . . . . . . . . . Witan Court, Upper Fourth Street, Milton Keynes, MK9 1EH
    Chairman . . . . . . . . . . . . . . . . . . . . . . . . . . . . . . . . . . . Mr Christopher Hughes
    Registrar . . . . . . . . . . . . . . . . . . . . . . . . . . . . . . . . . . . Mr Christopher Reid . . . . . . . . . . . . . . . . . Tel: (01908) 235700
        E-mail: hac@thehearingaidcouncil.org.uk
        Web: http://www.thehearingaidcouncil.org.uk

# DEPARTMENT OF TRADE AND INDUSTRY

*Other Relevant Contacts (Continued)*

## INDUSTRIAL DEVELOPMENT
**Distributed Generation Co-ordination Group** . . . . . . . . . 1 Victoria Street, London, SW1H 0ET
    Chairmen . . . . . . . . . . . . . . . . . . . . . . . . . . . . . . . . . . . . . . Mr Neil Hirst *(OFGEM)*
                          Mr John Neilson *(Head of Markets, DTI)*
    Secretaries . . . . . . . . . . . . . . . . . . . . . . . . . . . . . . . . . . . . . Mr Arthur Cook *(OFGEM)*
                          Mr Philip Baker *(DTI)* . . . . . . . . . . . . . . . . . Tel: (020) 7215 2675
                          Web: http://www.distributed-generation.org.uk
**Industrial Development Advisory Board** . . . . . . . . . . . . . . Room 3103, 1 Victoria Street, London, SW1H 0ET
    Chairman . . . . . . . . . . . . . . . . . . . . . . . . . . . . . . . . . . . . . . Sir Victor Blank
    Secretariat . . . . . . . . . . . . . . . . . . . . . . . . . . . . . . . . . . . . . Mr Andrew Steel . . . . . . . . . . . . . . . . . . . Tel: (020) 7215 2597
                          E-mail: andrew.steel@rsme.dti.gov.uk

## INDUSTRIAL TRIBUNALS
**Employment Appeal Tribunal** . . . . . . . . . . . . . . . . . . . . . . Audit House, 58 Victoria Embankment, London, EC4Y 0DS
    President . . . . . . . . . . . . . . . . . . . . . . . . . . . . . . . . . . . . . . Sir Michael Burton QC
    Registrar . . . . . . . . . . . . . . . . . . . . . . . . . . . . . . . . . . . . . . Miss Pauline Donleavy . . . . . . . . . . . . . . . . Tel: (020) 7273 1041
                          Web: http://www.employmentappeals.gov.uk
**Employment Tribunals Service** *(Executive Agency)* . . . . . . Central Office, 7th Floor, 19-29 Woburn Place, London, WC1H 0LU
    Chief Executive . . . . . . . . . . . . . . . . . . . . . . . . . . . . . . . . Dr Roger Heathcote . . . . . . . . . . . . . . . . . . Tel: (020) 7273 8666
    President *(England and Wales)* . . . . . . . . . . . . . . . . . . . . His Honour Judge Goolam Meeran
    President *(Scotland)* . . . . . . . . . . . . . . . . . . . . . . . . . . . . Mr Colin Milne
    Secretary *(England and Wales)* . . . . . . . . . . . . . . . . . . . . Mrs Lynn Adams . . . . . . . . . . . . . . . . . . . . Tel: (020) 7273 8666
    Secretary *(Scotland)* . . . . . . . . . . . . . . . . . . . . . . . . . . . Mr Douglas Easton . . . . . . . . . . . . . . . . . . Tel: (0141) 204 0730
                          Web: http://www.ets.gov.uk

## INSOLVENCY
**Insolvency Practitioners Tribunal** . . . . . . . . . . . . . . . . . . c/o The Insolvency Service. Area 5.1, PO Box 203, 21 Bloomsbury Street, London, WC1B 3QW
    Secretary . . . . . . . . . . . . . . . . . . . . . . . . . . . . . . . . . . . . . Ms Penny Lloyd . . . . . . . . . . . . . . . . . . . . Tel: (020) 7291 6896
                          E-mail: penny.lloyd@insolvency.gsi.gov.uk
**Insolvency Service** *(Executive Agency)* . . . . . . . . . . . . . . PO Box 203, 21 Bloomsbury Street, London, WC1B 3QW
    Chief Executive . . . . . . . . . . . . . . . . . . . . . . . . . . . . . . . . Mr Desmond Flynn . . . . . . . . . . . . . . . . . . Tel: (020) 7637 1110
                          E-mail: central.enquiryline@insolvency.gsi.gov.uk
                          Web: http://www.insolvency.gov.uk

## LOW PAY
**Low Pay Commission** . . . . . . . . . . . . . . . . . . . . . . . . . . . . 2nd Floor, Elizabeth House, 39 York Road, London, SE1 7NQ
    Chairman . . . . . . . . . . . . . . . . . . . . . . . . . . . . . . . . . . . . . . Mr Adair Turner
    Secretary . . . . . . . . . . . . . . . . . . . . . . . . . . . . . . . . . . . . . Ms Kate Harre . . . . . . . . . . . . . . . . . . . . . Tel: (020) 7855 4543
                          E-mail: lpc@lowpay.gov.uk
                          Web: http://www.lowpay.gov.uk

## MEASUREMENT
**Measurement Advisory Committee** . . . . . . . . . . . . . . . . . . Innovation Group, 151 Buckingham Palace Road, London, SW1W 9SS
    Chairman . . . . . . . . . . . . . . . . . . . . . . . . . . . . . . . . . . . . . . Dr Colin Gaskell CBE
    Secretary . . . . . . . . . . . . . . . . . . . . . . . . . . . . . . . . . . . . . Mr Alastair Hooley . . . . . . . . . . . . . . . . . . Tel: (020) 7215 1405
                          Web: http://www.dti.gov.uk/nms

## PARTNERSHIP FUND
**Partnership Fund Assessment Panel** . . . . . . . . . . . . . . . . . Employment Relations Directorate, Upper Ground Floor, 1 Victoria Street, London, SW1H 0ET
    Chairman . . . . . . . . . . . . . . . . . . . . . . . . . . . . . . . . . . . . . . Mr William Coupar
                          E-mail: partnership@dti.gsi.gov.uk

## PATENTS
**Intellectual Property Advisory Committee** . . . . . . . . . . . The Patent Office, Room 3B40, Concept House, Cardiff Road, Newport, South Wales, NP10 8QQ
    Chairman . . . . . . . . . . . . . . . . . . . . . . . . . . . . . . . . . . . . . . Mr Ian Harvey
    Secretary . . . . . . . . . . . . . . . . . . . . . . . . . . . . . . . . . . . . . Mr Richard Malcahy . . . . . . . . . . . . . . . . . Tel: (01633) 814553
                          Web: http://www.intellectual-property.gov.uk/ipac
**Patent Office** *(Executive Agency)* . . . . . . . . . . . . . . . . . . Concept House, Cardiff Road, Newport, South Wales, NP10 8QQ
    Chief Executive . . . . . . . . . . . . . . . . . . . . . . . . . . . . . . . . Mr Ron Marchant . . . . . . . . . . . . . . . . . . . Tel: (01633) 814000
                          Web: http://www.patent.gov.uk

# DEPARTMENT OF TRADE AND INDUSTRY

*Other Relevant Contacts (Continued)*

## POSTAL SERVICES

**Post Office**........................................ 80-86 Old Street, London, EC1 9NN
    Chairman............................................ Mr Alan Leighton
    Chief Executive .................................... Mr David Mills ........................ Tel: (020) 7250 2888
                                  Web: http://www.postofficelimited.com

**Postal Services Commission** ...................... 5th Floor, Hercules House, Hercules Road, London SE1 7DB
    Chairman............................................ Mr Nigel Stapleton
    Chief Executive .................................... Mr Martin Stanley ..................... Tel: (020) 7593 2100
                                   Web: http://www.psc.gov.uk

**Postwatch (Consumer's Council for Postal Services)** .... 28-30 Grosvenor Gardens, London, SW1W 0TT
    Chairman............................................ Mr Peter Carr
    Chief Executive .................................... Mr Gregor McGregor ................... Tel: (020) 7259 1200
                                   E-mail: info@postwatch.co.uk
                                   Web: http://www.postwatch.co.uk

**Royal Mail Group plc**.............................. 148 Old Street, London, EC1V 9HQ
    Chairman............................................ Mr Alan Leighton
    Chief Executive .................................... Mr Adam Crozier ..................... Tel: (020) 7250 2888
                                   Web: http://www.royalmail.com

## QUEEN'S AWARDS

**The Queen's Awards Office**........................ 151 Buckingham Palace Road, London, SW1W 9SS
    Secretary *(Acting)*................................ Mr Stephen Brice .......... Tel: (020) 7222 2277
                                     E-mail: info@queensawards.org.uk
                                     Web: http://www.queensawards.org.uk

## REGIONAL DEVELOPMENT AGENCIES

**East of England**.................................. The Business Centre, Station Road, Histon, Cambridge, CB4 9LQ
    Chairman............................................ Mr Richard Ellis
    Chief Executive .................................... Mr David Marlow ..................... Tel: (1223) 713900
                                   Web: http//:www.eeda.org.uk

**East Midlands** ................................... Apex Court, City Link, Nottingham, NG2 4LA
    Chairman............................................ Mr Derek Mapp
    Chief Executive .................................... Mr Martin Briggs ..................... Tel: (0115) 988 8300
                                   Web: http//:www.emda.org.uk

**London** .......................................... Devon House, 58-60 St Katherine's Way, London, E1W 1JX
    Chairman............................................ Ms Honor Chapman
    Chief Executive .................................... Mr Michael Ward ..................... Tel: (020) 7680 2000
                                   Web: http//:www.lda.gov.uk

**North East** *(One NorthEast)* ..................... Stella House, Newburn, Riverside, Newcastle-upon-Tyne, NE1 8NV
    Chairman............................................ Ms Margaret Fry
    Chief Executive .................................... Mr Alan Clarke...................... Tel: (0191) 229 6200
                                   Web: http//:www.onenortheast.co.uk

**North West** ...................................... Renaissance House, PO Box 37, Renaissance House, Centre Park, Warrington, WA1 1XB
    Chairman............................................ Mr Bryan Gray
    Chief Executive .................................... Mr Steven Broomhead.................. Tel: (01925) 400400
                                   Web: http//:www.nwda.co.uk

**South East** *(SEEDA)* ............................. SEEDA Headquarters, Cross Lanes, Guildford, GU1 1YA
    Chairman............................................ Mr James Braithwaite CBE
    Chief Executive .................................... Ms Pam Alexander ..................... Tel: (01483) 484200
                                   Web: http//:www.seeda.co.uk

**South West** ...................................... Sterling House, Dix's Field, Exeter, EX1 1QA
    Chairman............................................ Ms Juliet Williams
    Chief Executive .................................... Mr Geoffrey Wilkinson ................ Tel: (01392) 214747
                                   Web: http//:www.southwestengland.co.uk

**West Midlands** *(Advantage West Midlands)*........ 3 Priestley Wharf, Holt Street, Birmingham, B7 4BN
    Chairman............................................ Mr Nick Paul
    Chief Executive .................................... Mr John Edwards ..................... Tel: (0121) 380 3500
                                   Web: http//:www.advantagewm.co.uk

**Yorkshire and Humber** *(Yorkshire Forward)*....... Victoria House, 2 Victoria Place, Leeds, LS11 5AE
    Chairman............................................ Mr Terry Hidgkinson
    Chief Executive .................................... Mr Martin Havenhand................. Tel: (0113) 394 9600
                                   Web: http//:www.yorkshire-forward.com

# DEPARTMENT OF TRADE AND INDUSTRY

*Other Relevant Contacts (Continued)*

## RENEWABLES
**Renewable Advisory Board**......................3rd Floor, Atholl House, 86-88 Guild Street, Aberdeen, AB11 6AR
    Chairman..................................Mr Stephen Timms MP *(Minister of State, DTI)*
    Secretary.................................Mrs Chris Kelly......................Tel: (01224) 254087

## RESEARCH COUNCILS
**Biotechnology and Biological Sciences Research Council** . Polaris House, North Star Avenue, Swindon, SN2 1UH
    Chairman..................................Dr Peter Ringrose CBE
    Chief Executive............................Professor Julia Goodfellow CBE............Tel: (01793) 413200
    Web: http://www.bbsrc.ac.uk
**Council for the Central Laboratory of the**
  **Research Councils**......................Rutherford Appleton Laboratory, Chilton, Didcott, Oxfordshire, OX11 0QX
    Chairman..................................Professor Sir Graeme Davies
    Chief Executive............................Professor Sir John Wood................Tel: (01235) 821900
    Web: http://www.cclrc.ac.uk
**Economic and Social Research Council**..............Polaris House, North Star Avenue, Swindon, SN2 1UJ
    Chairman..................................Ms Frances Cairncross
    Chief Executive............................Professor Ian Diamond.................Tel: (01793) 413000
    Web: http://www.esrc.ac.uk
**Engineering and Physical Sciences Research Council** ...Polaris House, North Star Avenue, Swindon, SN2 1ET
    Chairman..................................Professor Dame Julia Higgins DBE FRS
    Chief Executive............................Professor John O'Reilly................Tel: (01793) 444000
    Web: http://www.epsrc.ac.uk
**Medical Research Council**......................20 Park Crescent, London, W1B 1AL
    Chairman..................................Sir Anthony Cleaver
    Chief Executive............................Professor Colin Blakemore FRS...........Tel: (020) 7636 5422
    Web: http://www.mrc.ac.uk
**Natural Environment Research Council**..............Polaris House, North Star Avenue, Swindon, SN2 1EU
    Chairman..................................Mr Rob Margetts CBE
    Chief Executive............................Professor John Lawton CBE FRS...........Tel: (01793) 411500
    Web: http://www.nerc.ac.uk
**Particle Physics and Astronomy Research Council**.....Polaris House, North Star Avenue, Swindon, SN2 1SZ
    Chairman..................................Dr Peter Warry
    Chief Executive............................Professor Ian Halliday FRSE.............Tel: (01793) 442000
    Web: http://www.pparc.ac.uk

## SCIENCE AND TECHNOLOGY
**Council for Science and Technology**................1 Victoria Street, London, SW1H 0ET
    Chairman..................................Sir David King *(Chief Scientific Adviser to Government)*
    Secretary.................................Mr Lynn Edwards.....................Tel: (020) 7215 5671
    Web: http://www.cst.gov.uk
**National Environmental Technology Centre**..........AEA Technology, Culham, Abingdon, Oxfordshire, OX14 3ED
    Technical Director..........................Mr Jeff Dolland......................Tel: (0870) 190 6456
    Web: http://www.aeat-env.com

## SMALL BUSINESSES
**Small Business Council**..........................Bay 642, Kingsgate House, 66-74 Victoria Street, London, SW1E 6SW
    Chairman..................................Mr William Sargent
    Secretary.................................Ms Catherine Capon...................Tel: (020) 7215 8519
    Web: http://www.sbs.gov.uk
**Small Business Investment Task Force**..............Level 2, St Mary's House, c/o Moorfoot, Sheffield, S1 4PQ
    Chairman..................................Sir David Cooksey
    Secretary.................................Ms Jane Fairclough...................Tel: (0114) 279 4378
    Web: http://www.sbs.gov.uk
**Small Business Services** *(Executive Agency)*............66-74 Victoria Street, London, SW1H 6SW
    Chief Executive............................Mr Martin Wyn Griffiths...............Tel: (020) 7215 4014
    Web: http://www.sbs.gov.uk

# DEPARTMENT OF TRADE AND INDUSTRY

*Other Relevant Contacts (Continued)*

## TRADE AND INVESTMENT
**UK Trade and Investment** . . . . . . . . . . . . . . . . . . . . . . . . Tay House, 300 Bath Street, Glasgow, G2 4DX
    Chairman . . . . . . . . . . . . . . . . . . . . . . . . . . . . . . . . . . . . . Mr Ian Bill
    Secretary . . . . . . . . . . . . . . . . . . . . . . . . . . . . . . . . . . . . . Mrs Beryl Reid . . . . . . . . . . . . . . . . . . . . . . . Tel: (0141) 228 3695
                             Web: http://www.uktradeinvest.gov.uk

## TRADE UNIONS AND EMPLOYER ORGANISATIONS
**Certification Office for Trade Unions**
    **and Employers' Organisations** . . . . . . . . . . . . . . . . . . Brandon House, 180 Borough High Street, London, SE1 1LW
    Certification Officer . . . . . . . . . . . . . . . . . . . . . . . . . . . . . Mr David Cockburn . . . . . . . . . . . . . . . . . . Tel: (020) 7210 3734
                             E-mail: cert@acas.org.uk
                             Web: http://www.certoffice.org

## TRADING PRACTICES
**Competition Appeal Tribunal** . . . . . . . . . . . . . . . . . . . . Victoria House, Bloomsbury Place, London, WC1A 2EA
    President . . . . . . . . . . . . . . . . . . . . . . . . . . . . . . . . . . . . . Sir Christopher Bellamy
    Registrar . . . . . . . . . . . . . . . . . . . . . . . . . . . . . . . . . . . . . Mr Charles Dhanowa . . . . . . . . . . . . . . . . . . Tel: (020) 7271 0395
                             Web: http://www.catribunal.org
**Competition Commission** . . . . . . . . . . . . . . . . . . . . . . . . New Court, 48 Carey Street, London, WC2A 2JT
    Chairman . . . . . . . . . . . . . . . . . . . . . . . . . . . . . . . . . . . . . Sir Derek Morris
    Chief Executive and Secretary . . . . . . . . . . . . . . . . . . . . Mr Robert Foster . . . . . . . . . . . . . . . . . . . . . Tel: (020) 7271 0100
                             Web: http://www.competition-commission.org.uk
**Competition Service** . . . . . . . . . . . . . . . . . . . . . . . . . . . . Victoria House, Bloomsbury Place, London, WC1A 2EA
    Director . . . . . . . . . . . . . . . . . . . . . . . . . . . . . . . . . . . . . . Mr Jeremy Straker . . . . . . . . . . . . . . . . . . . . Tel: (020) 7979 7979
**Office of Fair Trading** . . . . . . . . . . . . . . . . . . . . . . . . . . . Fleetbank House, 2-6 Salisbury Square, London, EC4Y 8JX
    Chairman . . . . . . . . . . . . . . . . . . . . . . . . . . . . . . . . . . . . . Mr John Vickers
    Executive Director . . . . . . . . . . . . . . . . . . . . . . . . . . . . . Ms Penny Boys . . . . . . . . . . . . . . . . . . . . . . Tel: (020) 7211 8000
                             Web: http://www.oft.gov.uk

## WEIGHTS AND MEASURES
**National Weights and Measures**
    **Laboratory** *(Executive Agency)* . . . . . . . . . . . . . . . . . . Stanton Avenue, Teddington, Middlesex, TW11 0JZ
    Chief Executive . . . . . . . . . . . . . . . . . . . . . . . . . . . . . . . Dr Jeff Llewellyn . . . . . . . . . . . . . . . . . . . . . Tel: (020) 8943 7272
                             E-mail: info@nwml.gov.uk
                             Web: http://www.nwml.gov.uk
**National Physical Laboratory** . . . . . . . . . . . . . . . . . . . . Queen's Road, Teddington, Middlesex, TW11 0LW
    Managing Director . . . . . . . . . . . . . . . . . . . . . . . . . . . . . Dr Bob McGuinness . . . . . . . . . . . . . . . . . . Tel: (020) 8977 3222
                             Web: http://www.npl.co.uk

## WOMEN
**Women's National Commission** . . . . . . . . . . . . . . . . . . . 1st Floor, 35 Great Smith Street, London, SW1P 3BQ
    Chair . . . . . . . . . . . . . . . . . . . . . . . . . . . . . . . . . . . . . . . . Ms Margaret Prosser
    Director . . . . . . . . . . . . . . . . . . . . . . . . . . . . . . . . . . . . . . Ms Janet Veitch . . . . . . . . . . . . . . . . . . . . . . Tel: (020) 7276 2555
                             Web: http://www.thewnc.org.uk

## WORK - LIFE BALANCE
**Advisory Committee on Work – Life Balance** . . . . . . . . . 1 Victoria Street, London, SW1H 0ET
    Chairman . . . . . . . . . . . . . . . . . . . . . . . . . . . . . . . . . . . . . Mr Alan Johnson MP *(Minister of State, DTI)*
    Secretary . . . . . . . . . . . . . . . . . . . . . . . . . . . . . . . . . . . . . Ms Anna De Pascali . . . . . . . . . . . . . . . . . . Tel: (020) 7215 6249
                             Web: http://www.dti.gov.uk/work-lifebalance

# Association of Convenience Stores

## Representing 30,000 stores at the heart of neighbourhoods

### Key Issues:
Employment

Urban & Rural Development

Regulation

Licensing and Age-Restricted Sales

Tax and Bootlegging

Crime and Security

### Contact:
### Shane Brennan, Public Affairs Executive
### shane.brennan@acs.org.uk

Federation House,

17 Farnborough Street,

Farnborough, GU14 8AG

Tel: 01252 515001  Fax: 01252 515002

Web: http://www.thelocalshop.com

# S I G O M A

*The Special Interest Group of Municipal Authorities (Outside London)*
*Within the LGA*

SIGOMA represents 48 local authorities, including most of England's urban areas outside the capital. Our members call for adequate resources and local discretion to provide us with a fair chance to tackle poverty, deprivation and educational failure blighting the chances of the people we represent.

The work of SIGOMA is actively supported by our Parliamentary Group of some 150 MPs which provide a vital channel for us getting our message across to those we need to influence.

SIGOMA has been successful in delivering the message to Government and played a major role in securing changes to the system for funding local authorities. The revised system saw our authorities receive an overall increase in grant for 2003/04 of 7.1% compared to the national average of 5.9% - a total of £755m or £120m more than the average.

However there is still work to be done if we are to be able to continue to deliver both the national agenda and local priority issues. Over the coming year SIGOMA will be involved in research and lobbying on a number of key financial and urban issues to ensure that the needs of our communities are met. These will include:

- The New Prudential Framework for Investment
- Further improvements in formulae for distributing resources
- Council tax revaluation and reform
- The Government's 'Balance of Funding' review
- Housing – liveability and quality of life issues
- Health - current issues / resource distribution

SIGOMA can be contacted on 01226 773101
Or c/o Barnsley MBC, P O Box 14, Town Hall Barnsley S70 2AQ

The chairman of the MPs group, Bill O'Brien MP, can also be contacted through the above office

www.sigoma.gov.uk

## *A Voice for Urban Areas*

## COAL PRODUCERS CONFEDERATION

## ENGINEERING

### CONFEDERATION OF UK COAL PRODUCERS
Confederation House, Thornes Office Park,
Denby Dale Road, Wakefield,
West Yorkshire,
WF2 7AN

*Telephone* (01924) 200802
*Facsimile* (01924) 200796
*E-mail* dg@coalpro.demon.co.uk
*Web* http://wwwcoalpro.co.uk

*Contact* Brian J Rostron – *Director General*

Principal UK coal producers' trade association representing UK companies engaged in coal production, processing, marketing and post-mining land reclamation and regeneration. Represents UK coal producers on the European Coal and Steel Communities Consultative Committee. Members of Euriscoal – European importers and suppliers of coal.

Glass and Glazing Federation

### GLASS AND GLAZING FEDERATION
44-48 Borough High Street. London, SE1 1XB

*Telephone* (0870) 042 4255  *Facsimile* (0870) 042 4266
*Web* http://www.ggf.org.uk

*Contact:* Catherine Hogan - *Director of Public Relations*

The Glass and Glazing Federation (GGF) is the recognised leading authority for employers and companies within the flat glass, glazing, home improvement, plastics and window film industries.

The GGF oversees the training requirements of the industry and has a Training Provider Network which administers the NVQ/SVQs on all aspects of glazing from fitting windows to producing sealed glazing units.

## ENERGY

## ENERGY

65 Buckingham Gate, London, SW1E 6AP

*Telephone* (020) 7222 9717
*Facsimile* (020) 7202 0943
*Web* www.bnfl.com

*Contact* Rory O'Neill – *Manager, Parliamentary Affairs*

BNFL is an international knowledge based business focused on serving two main customer groups, global nuclear utilities and Governments, by providing a broad portfolio of unique skills and expertise.

Our activities include fuel manufacture, reactor services, electricity generation and spent fuel management services, through to decommissioning and clean-up services.

### BRITISH WIND ENERGY ASSOCIATION
Renewable Energy House, 1 Aztec Row
Berners Road, London, N1 0PW

*Telephone* (020) 7689 1960
*Facsimile* (020) 7689 1969
*E-mail* info@bwea.com
*Web* http://www.bwea.com
http://www.deepgreenpower.org
http://www.offshorewindfarms.co.uk

*Contact:* Marcus Rand – *Chief Executive*

Trade association representing companies and individuals with an interest in the UK wind resource.

## HOME IMPROVEMENTS

### NATIONAL HOME IMPROVEMENT COUNCIL

Carlyle House, 235 Vauxhall Bridge Road,
London, SW1V 1EJ
*Telephone: (020) 7828 8230*
*Facsimile: (020) 7828 0667*
*E-mail: info@nhic.org.uk*
*Web: http://www.nhic.org.uk*

*Contact:* Graham S Ponting - *Executive Director*

The NHIC represents the most important body of companies and organisations that work in the home improvement sector and they earnestly believe in higher standards of materials and workmanship, backing this with codes of practice, guarantees and warranties. It's objectives are to encourage a vibrant modernisation and renovation market in the private and public housing sectors both to improve the housing stock and the business opportunities for members.

## HOUSE BUILDING – INSURANCE

### NATIONAL HOUSE-BUILDING COUNCIL

Buildmark House, Chiltern Avenue, Amersham,
Buckinghamshire, HP6 5AP

*Telephone* (01494) 735262  *Facsimile* (01494) 735365
*E-mail* ahoward@nhbc.co.uk  *Web* http://www.nhbc.co.uk

*Contact* Andrew Howard – *Head of Corporate Communications*

NHBC is the UK authority on new home construction.

NHBC's expertise informs the industry through our Standards, inspection service, technical advice and guidance to house builders. NHBC has approximately 18,000 registered builders who agree to comply with our Rules and Standards, and registers 85% of all new homes in the UK.

Around 1.6 million homes are currently benefiting form our 10 year warranty and insurance cover, called 'Buildmark'.

*Raising house-building standards for homebuyers*

## LOCAL GOVERNMENT

### ASSOCIATION OF LARGER LOCAL COUNCILS

PO Box 191, Macclesfield, Cheshire, SK11 0FG

*Telephone* (01260) 226323
*Facsimile* (01260) 226329
*E-mail* john.dixon-dawson@sunderland.ac.uk

*Contact* John Dixon-Dawson – *Executive Director*

The aim of the Association is to enhance the role and quality of services provided by Local Councils. By taking appropriate action on Central Government policy issues and with the provision of an efficient advisory service, members benefit from a regular exchange of information and best practice.

## MACHINE TOOL TECHNOLOGY

**The Manufacturing Technologies Association**
62 Bayswater Road, London, W2 3PS
Tel: (020) 7298 6400  Fax (020) 7298 6430
Email: info@mta.org.uk  Web: www.mta.org.uk
**Contact:  Public Affairs Manager**

MTA represents the UK machine tool and manufacturing technology sector. It provides a range of services to help its member companies to sell their products in the UK and overseas, which contributes to the competitiveness of the UK manufacturing industry and, therefore, the UK economy as a whole.

**Membership Services include:**
- Overseas Representation
- UK & overseas Market Intelligence
- Education & Training, Competitions
- Technical advice on UK & International Standards & Safety Codes of Practice
- Statistical Information & Industry Forecasts
- Import/Export Advice
- Assistance at UK and Overseas Exhibitions
- Promotion of skills training & Training Grants
- Parliamentary Representation & Lobbying
- Business Support Helpline
- Group Insurance Scheme

*"Promoting Competitiveness"*

# R E S E A R C H   C O U N C I L

## ESRC

Polaris House, North Star Avenue
Swindon, SN2 1UJ

*Telephone* (01793) 413122   *Fax* (01793) 413130
*Email* exrel@esrc.ac.uk   *Web* http://www.esrc.ac.uk

*Contact* External Relations Division

**Let's Think . . .** The best public policy is grounded in an understanding of people and their social and economic behaviour. As the UK's premier funder of leading edge, independent research, we aim to make a strong contribution to economic competitiveness, the effectiveness of public services and policy, and quality of life.

Our extensive research portfolio ranges from the impacts of devolution and the challenges presented by the productivity gap, to street crime, teaching and learning, the future of work and the impact of information technology on people's lives. We fund a first class programme of research training for new academics more than 2,000 in any one year. And we support world-leading resources, such as the British Household Panel Study (BHPS), the National Child Development Study (NCDS) and the British Cohort Study.

More information about ESRC, are funded research and its relevance to you can be found on our website, www.esrc.ac.uk.

# R E G U L A T O R Y   B O D Y

## icstis

### THE INDEPENDENT COMMITTEE FOR THE SUPERVISION OF STANDARDS OF TELEPHONE INFORMATION SERVICES

Clove Building, 4 Maguire Street,
London, SE1 2NQ

*Telephone* (020) 7940 7474  *Facsimile* (020) 7940 7456
**Free helpline 0800 500 212**
*Press Office* (020) 7940 7408
*E-mail* secretariat@icstis.org.uk
*Web* http://www.icstis.org.uk

*Contacts* Rob Dwight – *Media & Public Relations Officer*
Sarah James – *External Relations Officer*

ICSTIS regulates the content and advertising of all premium rate charged telecommunications services. These offer information and entertainment via fixed telephony, mobile telephony (SMS, WAP), fax, the Internet or interactive TV. Services must be advertised on 090 dialling codes (certain mobile services may also use short access codes – typically four or five digits). ICSTIS investigates complaints and has the power to fine companies and bar access to services if they breach its Code of Practice. ICSTIS is chaired by Sir Peter North CBE QC.

# S O A P   &   D E T E R G E N T S

The UKCPI (UK Cleaning Products Industry Association) is the professional body representing the hygiene, surface care and cleaning product industry in the UK. From soap to washing powders, disinfectants to polishes, all these products fundamentally support the everyday lives of millions of consumers. The UKCPI deals with government and the public alike, providing representation, information and advice in all aspects of the cleaning, surface care and hygiene products industry.

The UKCPI aims and objectives are:

• To provide member companies with representation, information and clear advice on legislative and industry wide issues

• To speak on behalf of the Industry by providing Government and the European Commission with information and technical advice to ensure that effects on UKCPI members are taken into account in legislation

• To provide the public and opinion farmers with factual information regarding cleaning, hygiene and surface care products.

The Association continues to be proactive in its representation of the industry and has also taken initiatives such as increasing the understanding of the industry in schools and in furthering the awareness of the importance of cleanliness and hygiene.

For more information on the wide range of activities in which the UKCPI is involved, and a full range of factsheets on topics of interest to the industry, visit our website at www.ukcpi.org or contact us at:

1st Floor, Century House, Old Mill Place, High Street, Tattenhall, Cheshire, CH3 9RJ

*Telephone:* (01829) 770055   *Facsimile:* (01829) 770101
*E-mail:* ukcpi@ukcpi.org   *Web:* http://www.ukcpi.org

## SHIPBUILDING & ENGINEERING

# CONFEDERATION OF SHIPBUILDING AND ENGINEERING UNIONS

140-142 Walworth Road, London, SE17 1JW

Telephone (020) 7703 2215  Facsimile (020) 7252 7397

The Confederation of Shipbuilding & Engineering Unions (C.S.E.U.) is the monitoring and bargaining unit for pay and working conditions throughout many of Great Britain's vital industries. It seeks to promote and maintain the interests of more than one million skilled and unskilled men and women, with particular attention to their health, safety and living standards. By promoting constructive negotiation at an early stage wherever its members' pay and conditions are likely to be affected, C.S.E.U. is an important contributor to productivity, and hence to the nation's overall prosperity and well-being.

C.S.E.U. members are particularly active in the following industries:

• COMMERCIAL SHIPBUILDING • NAVAL CONSTRUCTION • SHIP REPAIR • ORDNANCE SUPPLIES •

• WEAPONS TECHNOLOGY • POWER GENERATION • MILITARY & COMMERCIAL AIRCRAFT •

• PETROCHEMICALS • IRON & STEEL PRODUCTION • VEHICLE BUILDING • TRANSPORT •

*– Incorporating our foremost trade unions in manufacturing, design and development –*

## STEEL AND METAL INDUSTRIES

# ISTC THE COMMUNITY UNION

Swinton House, 324 Gray's Inn Road
London, WC1X 8DD

*Telephone* (020) 7239 1200
*Facsimile* (020) 7278 8378
*E-mail* istc@istc-tu.org
*Web* http://www.istc-tu.org

*Contacts* Michael Leahy OBE – *General Secretary*
Joe Mann – *Political Officer*

## WOOD OCCUPATIONS/ TRADES

# THE INSTITUTE OF CARPENTERS

35 Hayworth Road, Sandiacre, Nottingham, NG10 5LL

*Telephone* (0115) 949 0641
*Facsimile* (0115) 949 1664
*E-mail* centroff@innotts.co.uk
*Web* http://www.central-office.co.uk

*Contact* David R Winson ACIOB, FIOS, FFB, FIOC - *Secretary*

The Institute of Carpenters, founded in 1890, has the prime objective of advancing the science and practice of Carpentry and Joinery in the public interest. With a membership expanding across the UK and overseas, the experience and knowledge accumulated makes this organisation a valuable source of information.

# DEPARTMENT FOR TRANSPORT

Great Minster House, 76 Marsham Street
London, SW1P 4DR
Tel: (020) 7944 8300
Web: http://www.dft.gov.uk

## MINISTERS

**Secretary of State for Transport** . . . . . . . . . . . . . . . . . Rt Hon Alistair Darling MP
   *Private Secretary* . . . . . . . . . . . . . . . . . . . . . . . . . . . . . . Mr Andrew Campbell . . . . . . . . . . . . . . . . . . . . . . . Tel: (020) 7944 3011
   *Special Advisers* . . . . . . . . . . . . . . . . . . . . . . . . . . . . Mr Andrew Maugham . . . . . . . . . . . . . . . . . . . . . Tel: (020) 7944 4505
                                                           Mr Sam White . . . . . . . . . . . . . . . . . . . . . . . . . . . . . Tel: (020) 7944 4377

**Minister of State** . . . . . . . . . . . . . . . . . . . . . . . . . . . . . Mr Tony McNulty MP
   *Private Secretary* . . . . . . . . . . . . . . . . . . . . . . . . . . . . Ms Emma Cliffe . . . . . . . . . . . . . . . . . . . . . . . . . . . Tel: (020) 7944 6932

**Parliamentary Secretary** . . . . . . . . . . . . . . . . . . . . . Charlotte Atkins MP
   *Private Secretary* . . . . . . . . . . . . . . . . . . . . . . . . . . . . Miss Deborah Heenan . . . . . . . . . . . . . . . . . . . . . Tel: (020) 7944 3082

**Parliamentary Secretary** . . . . . . . . . . . . . . . . . . . . . Mr David Jamieson MP
   *Private Secretary* . . . . . . . . . . . . . . . . . . . . . . . . . . . . Ms Naomi Hunt . . . . . . . . . . . . . . . . . . . . . . . . . . Tel: (020) 7944 3084

## CIVIL SERVICE

**Permanent Secretary** . . . . . . . . . . . . . . . . . . . . . . . . . Mr David Rowlands
   *Private Secretary* . . . . . . . . . . . . . . . . . . . . . . . . . . . . Mr Ben Still . . . . . . . . . . . . . . . . . . . . . . . . . . . . . . Tel: (020) 7944 3017

**Directors-General**

Director-General, Driver, Vehicle and Operator . . . . . . Mr Stephen Hickey . . . . . . . . . . . . . . . . . . . . . . . Tel: (020) 7944 5463
Director-General, Railways, Aviation, Logistics,
   Maritime and Security . . . . . . . . . . . . . . . . . . . . . Ms Sue Killen . . . . . . . . . . . . . . . . . . . . . . . . . . . . Tel: (020) 7944 6830
Director-General, Roads, Regional and Local Transport Mr Robert Devereux . . . . . . . . . . . . . . . . . . . . . . . Tel: (020) 7944 2667
Director-General, Strategy, Finance and Delivery . . . . . Mr Willy Rickett . . . . . . . . . . . . . . . . . . . . . . . . . . Tel: (020) 7944 3240

## SUBJECT RESPONSIBILITIES AND CONTACTS

### Accidents
Air
*Berkshire Copse Road, Aldershot, GU11 2HH*
   Chief Inspector, Air Accidents . . . . . . . . . . . . . . . Mr Ken Smart . . . . . . . . . . . . . . . . . . . . . . . . . . . . Tel: (01252) 510300
   Deputy Chief Inspector, Air Accidents . . . . . . . . . Mr David King . . . . . . . . . . . . . . . . . . . . . . . . . . . Tel: (01252) 510300
Marine
   Chief Inspector, Marine Accidents Investigation . . . Mr Stephen Meyer . . . . . . . . . . . . . . . . . . . . . . . . Tel: (023) 8039 5528
   Deputy Chief Inspector . . . . . . . . . . . . . . . . . . . . . Mr Stephen Clinch . . . . . . . . . . . . . . . . . . . . . . . . Tel: (023) 8039 5529
Rail
   Chief Inspector, Rail Accidents Investigation . . . . . Ms Carolyn Griffiths . . . . . . . . . . . . . . . . . . . . . . Tel: (023) 7849 5522

### Aviation
Director, Aviation . . . . . . . . . . . . . . . . . . . . . . . . . . . . Mr David McMillan . . . . . . . . . . . . . . . . . . . . . . . Tel: (020) 7944 4740
Airports
   Manager, Airports Policy Division . . . . . . . . . . . . . Mr Jonathan Sharrock . . . . . . . . . . . . . . . . . . . . . Tel: (020) 7944 3920
   Air Transport White Paper . . . . . . . . . . . . . . . . . . Mr David Gray . . . . . . . . . . . . . . . . . . . . . . . . . . . Tel: (020) 7944 3287
   Capacity, Future . . . . . . . . . . . . . . . . . . . . . . . . . . Mr Chris Cain . . . . . . . . . . . . . . . . . . . . . . . . . . . . Tel: (020) 7944 3223
   Capacity Usage . . . . . . . . . . . . . . . . . . . . . . . . . . . Mr Jonathan Sharrock . . . . . . . . . . . . . . . . . . . . . Tel: (020) 7944 3920
   Cargo . . . . . . . . . . . . . . . . . . . . . . . . . . . . . . . . . . . Mr Chris Cain . . . . . . . . . . . . . . . . . . . . . . . . . . . . Tel: (020) 7944 3223
   Civil and Operational Matters . . . . . . . . . . . . . . . . Mr Alan Nafzger . . . . . . . . . . . . . . . . . . . . . . . . . Tel: (020) 7944 3398
   Local Authority Airports . . . . . . . . . . . . . . . . . . . . Mr Alan Nafzger . . . . . . . . . . . . . . . . . . . . . . . . . Tel: (020) 7944 3398
   Regional . . . . . . . . . . . . . . . . . . . . . . . . . . . . . . . . Mr Chris Cain . . . . . . . . . . . . . . . . . . . . . . . . . . . . Tel: (020) 7944 3223
   Public Safety Zone Boundaries . . . . . . . . . . . . . . . Mr Alan Nafzger . . . . . . . . . . . . . . . . . . . . . . . . . Tel: (020) 7944 3398
   Slot Allocations . . . . . . . . . . . . . . . . . . . . . . . . . . . Mr Nigel Milton . . . . . . . . . . . . . . . . . . . . . . . . . . Tel: (020) 7944 5816
   South East and East England . . . . . . . . . . . . . . . . Mr Anthony Ferguson . . . . . . . . . . . . . . . . . . . . . Tel: (020) 7944 3227
Civil Aviation
   Manager, Civil Aviation . . . . . . . . . . . . . . . . . . . . . Ms Ann Godfrey . . . . . . . . . . . . . . . . . . . . . . . . . . Tel: (020) 7944 5843
   Air Rage . . . . . . . . . . . . . . . . . . . . . . . . . . . . . . . . Mr Peter Smith . . . . . . . . . . . . . . . . . . . . . . . . . . . Tel: (020) 7944 5893
   Air Transport White Paper . . . . . . . . . . . . . . . . . . Mr David Gray . . . . . . . . . . . . . . . . . . . . . . . . . . . Tel: (020) 7944 3287
   Civil Aviation Authority Sponsorship . . . . . . . . . . . Ms Dorothy Parkin . . . . . . . . . . . . . . . . . . . . . . . Tel: (020) 7944 6378

# DEPARTMENT FOR TRANSPORT

*Aviation (Continued)*

Competition: Domestic and European

Aviation Matters . . . . . . . . . . . . . . . . . . . . . . . . Mr Glen Cronin . . . . . . . . . . . . . . . . . . . . . . . . . . Tel: (020) 7944 5882

Consumer Protection . . . . . . . . . . . . . . . . . . . . . . Mr Peter Smith . . . . . . . . . . . . . . . . . . . . . . . . . . Tel: (020) 7944 5893

Detention of Aircraft. . . . . . . . . . . . . . . . . . . . . . . Mr Alan Nafzger . . . . . . . . . . . . . . . . . . . . . . . . Tel: (020) 7944 3398

Disruptive Passengers . . . . . . . . . . . . . . . . . . . . . Mr Glenn Cronin . . . . . . . . . . . . . . . . . . . . . . . . Tel: (020) 7944 5882

Domestic and European Union Air Traffic. . . . . . . Mr Bruce Coombs . . . . . . . . . . . . . . . . . . . . . . . Tel: (020) 7944 6369

Economics

Manager, Economics, Aviation, Maritime and

International . . . . . . . . . . . . . . . . . . . . . . . . . . . Mr Michael Mann . . . . . . . . . . . . . . . . . . . . . . . Tel: (020) 7944 3950

Advice, Economic . . . . . . . . . . . . . . . . . . . . . . . Mr Eric Weinstein . . . . . . . . . . . . . . . . . . . . . . . Tel: (020) 7944 3171

Airports . . . . . . . . . . . . . . . . . . . . . . . . . . . . . . Mr Jeff Thompson . . . . . . . . . . . . . . . . . . . . . . . Tel: (020) 7944 3063

Emissions *(see below under Noise and Emissions)*

Environment

Manager, Environment Aviation Division . . . . . . . Mr Graham Pendlebury . . . . . . . . . . . . . . . . . . . Tel: (020) 7944 3930

Eurocontrol

Policy . . . . . . . . . . . . . . . . . . . . . . . . . . . . . . . Mr Bruce Coombs . . . . . . . . . . . . . . . . . . . . . . . Tel: (020) 7944 6369

Route Charging . . . . . . . . . . . . . . . . . . . . . . . . Ms Dorothy Parkin. . . . . . . . . . . . . . . . . . . . . . . Tel: (020) 7944 6378

European Civil Aviation Conference . . . . . . . . . . . . . Mr Michael Smethers . . . . . . . . . . . . . . . . . . . . . Tel: (020) 7944 4710

European Union Co-ordination . . . . . . . . . . . . . . . . Mr Glenn Cronin . . . . . . . . . . . . . . . . . . . . . . . . Tel: (020) 7944 5882

Future of Aviation White Paper . . . . . . . . . . . . . . . Mr David Gray. . . . . . . . . . . . . . . . . . . . . . . . . . Tel: (020) 7944 3287

International

Manager, International Aviation and Safety . . . . . . Mr Michael Smethers . . . . . . . . . . . . . . . . . . . . . Tel: (020) 7944 4710

Africa, Middle East and Europe . . . . . . . . . . . . . *Vacant*. . . . . . . . . . . . . . . . . . . . . . . . . . . . . . . . Tel: (020) 7944 5802

America. . . . . . . . . . . . . . . . . . . . . . . . . . . . . . Mr Huw Hopkins . . . . . . . . . . . . . . . . . . . . . . . . Tel: (020) 7944 5803

North and Central America, Caribbean and

South America . . . . . . . . . . . . . . . . . . . . . . . Mr Nigel Milton. . . . . . . . . . . . . . . . . . . . . . . . . Tel: (020) 7944 5816

International Civil Aviation Conference Policy . . . . Mr Michael Smethers . . . . . . . . . . . . . . . . . . . . . Tel: (020) 7944 4710

Management Support Unit, RALMS . . . . . . . . . . . . . Mr Frank Evans. . . . . . . . . . . . . . . . . . . . . . . . . Tel: (020) 7944 5659

National Air Traffic Service, Sponsorship . . . . . . . . . Ms Dorothy Parkin. . . . . . . . . . . . . . . . . . . . . . . Tel: (020) 7944 6378

Noise and Emissions, Aircraft

Gatwick . . . . . . . . . . . . . . . . . . . . . . . . . . . . . Mr Philip Grindrod . . . . . . . . . . . . . . . . . . . . . . Tel: (020) 7944 4079

Heathrow. . . . . . . . . . . . . . . . . . . . . . . . . . . . . Mr Paul Reardon . . . . . . . . . . . . . . . . . . . . . . . . Tel: (020) 7944 4857

Helicopters . . . . . . . . . . . . . . . . . . . . . . . . . . . Mr Philip Grindrod . . . . . . . . . . . . . . . . . . . . . . Tel: (020) 7944 4079

International . . . . . . . . . . . . . . . . . . . . . . . . . . . Mr Roger Gardner . . . . . . . . . . . . . . . . . . . . . . . Tel: (020) 7944 8387

Legislation. . . . . . . . . . . . . . . . . . . . . . . . . . . . Mr Philip Grindrod . . . . . . . . . . . . . . . . . . . . . . Tel: (020) 7944 4079

Standards. . . . . . . . . . . . . . . . . . . . . . . . . . . . . Ms Jill Adam . . . . . . . . . . . . . . . . . . . . . . . . . . . Tel: (020) 7944 4858

Stansted, Manchester, and Coventry . . . . . . . . . . Ms Roberta McWatt. . . . . . . . . . . . . . . . . . . . . . Tel: (020) 7944 4855

Public Safety Zone Boundaries . . . . . . . . . . . . . . . . Mr Alan Nafzger . . . . . . . . . . . . . . . . . . . . . . . . Tel: (020) 7944 3398

Safety, Aviation . . . . . . . . . . . . . . . . . . . . . . . . . . Ms Pat Ricketts. . . . . . . . . . . . . . . . . . . . . . . . . Tel: (020) 7944 6241

Security

Aviation Inspectorate . . . . . . . . . . . . . . . . . . . . Mr Sean Bodkin. . . . . . . . . . . . . . . . . . . . . . . . . Tel: (020) 7944 2592

Domestic . . . . . . . . . . . . . . . . . . . . . . . . . . . . . Ms Petra Wilkinson . . . . . . . . . . . . . . . . . . . . . . Tel: (020) 7944 2784

International . . . . . . . . . . . . . . . . . . . . . . . . . . . Mr Richard Orrin. . . . . . . . . . . . . . . . . . . . . . . . Tel: (020) 7944 2888

Security Policy and Implementation . . . . . . . . . . . Mr Peter Kirk . . . . . . . . . . . . . . . . . . . . . . . . . . Tel: (020) 7944 2851

Statistics . . . . . . . . . . . . . . . . . . . . . . . . . . . . . . . *Vacant*. . . . . . . . . . . . . . . . . . . . . . . . . . . . . . . . Tel: (020) 7944 4276

Traffic Management Policy, Air. . . . . . . . . . . . . . . . Mr Bruce Coombs . . . . . . . . . . . . . . . . . . . . . . . Tel: (020) 7944 6369

*(see also below under Security, Transport)*

## Buses

Manager, Buses and Taxis Division. . . . . . . . . . . . . . Ms Sandra Webber . . . . . . . . . . . . . . . . . . . . . . . Tel: (020) 7944 3706

Bus Lanes . . . . . . . . . . . . . . . . . . . . . . . . . . . . . . Mr John Gant. . . . . . . . . . . . . . . . . . . . . . . . . . . Tel: (020) 7944 2468

Bus Priority in Traffic. . . . . . . . . . . . . . . . . . . . . . Mr David Williams . . . . . . . . . . . . . . . . . . . . . . . Tel: (020) 7944 2595

Buses Policy . . . . . . . . . . . . . . . . . . . . . . . . . . . . Mr David Farmer . . . . . . . . . . . . . . . . . . . . . . . . Tel: (020) 7944 2283

Community Transport. . . . . . . . . . . . . . . . . . . . . . . Mr Peter Openshaw . . . . . . . . . . . . . . . . . . . . . . Tel: (020) 7944 2284

Concessionary Fares. . . . . . . . . . . . . . . . . . . . . . . Mr Andrew Colski . . . . . . . . . . . . . . . . . . . . . . . Tel: (020) 7944 2157

Fuel Duty Rebate, Bus Operators . . . . . . . . . . . . . . Mr David Farmer. . . . . . . . . . . . . . . . . . . . . . . . Tel: (020) 7944 2283

Local Authority Owned Companies . . . . . . . . . . . . . Mr Andrew Colski . . . . . . . . . . . . . . . . . . . . . . . Tel: (020) 7944 2157

Rural Bus Grants . . . . . . . . . . . . . . . . . . . . . . . . . Mr David Farmer. . . . . . . . . . . . . . . . . . . . . . . . Tel: (020) 7944 2283

Social Exclusion. . . . . . . . . . . . . . . . . . . . . . . . . . Mr Peter Openshaw . . . . . . . . . . . . . . . . . . . . . . Tel: (020) 7944 2284

Urban Bus Challenge Scheme. . . . . . . . . . . . . . . . . Mr David Farmer. . . . . . . . . . . . . . . . . . . . . . . . Tel: (020) 7944 2283

# DEPARTMENT FOR TRANSPORT

**Business Delivery, Departmental**

| | | |
|---|---|---|
| Director, Business Delivery | Mr Michael Herron | Tel: (020) 7944 6050 |
| Manager, Corporate Secretariat | Mr Peter Sanders | Tel: (020) 7944 8823 |
| Manager, IT Services, | Mr Eamonn McDonough | Tel: (020) 7944 5050 |
| Freedom of Information | Mr Mike Carty | Tel: (020) 7944 5825 |
| Regulation | Ms Lynn Stevens | Tel: (020) 7944 4307 |

**Charging, Road Users** .......... Mr Mike Goodwin .......... Tel: (020) 7944 6106

**Communications**

| | | |
|---|---|---|
| Director, Communications | Mr Charles Skinner | Tel: (020) 7944 4650 |
| Marketing and Corporate Communications | | |
|   Head, Marketing and Corporate Communications | Mr David Murphy | Tel: (020) 7944 4623 |
|   Editorial and Internal Communications | Ms Alison Hadley | Tel: (020) 7944 3396 |
|   Resource Management | Mr John Bull | Tel: (020) 7944 4636 |
| Media Centre | | |
|   Head of News | Mr Simon Wren | Tel: (020) 7944 4671 |
|   Communication, Planning and Briefing | Mr Thomas Elliott | Tel: (020) 7944 4634 |
|   Publicity | Ms Joanne Rushton | Tel: (020) 7944 4369 |
|   Transport Media Desk | Mr George O'Neill | Tel: (020) 7944 3395 |
| New Media, Print and Publishing | Mr Andy Seal | Tel: (020) 7944 4665 |
| Strategic Communications | | |
|   Manager, Strategic Communications | Mr Nick Court | Tel: (020) 7944 6992 |
|   Strategic Planning Bureau | Mr Tom Elliott | Tel: (020) 7944 4634 |
| Web | Ms Sioned Richards | Tel: (020) 7944 4678 |

**Congestion Charging, London** .......... Ms Claire Spink .......... Tel: (020) 7944 8820

**Cycling** .......... Mr Chris Watts .......... Tel: (020) 7944 2146

**Disabled Drivers**

Mobility Advice and Vehicle Information Service ..... Mr Rolf Lamsdale .......... Tel: (01344) 661001
*(see also below under Mobility)*

**Driver, Vehicle and Operator Group**

| | | |
|---|---|---|
| Director-General, Driver, Vehicle and Operator | Mr Stephen Hickey | Tel: (020) 7944 5463 |
| Director, Group Modernisation | Mr Andrew Stott | Tel: (020) 7944 2050 |
| Agency Business and Finance Sponsorship | Mr Jim Milner | Tel: (020) 7944 4508 |
| Planning | Ms Marian Duncan | Tel: (020) 7944 3983 |
| Press and Communications | Mr Andrew Wiles | Tel: (020) 7944 8131 |
| Resources | Mr Jonathan Moor | Tel: (020) 7944 4597 |
| Secretariat | Mr Richard Verge | Tel: (0117) 372 8477 |

Traffic Area Offices *(see below under Other Contacts - Vehicle and Operator Services Agency)*

**Economics**

| | | |
|---|---|---|
| Director, Transport Analysis and Economics | Mr Chris Riley | Tel: (020) 7944 3640 |
|   Manager, Economics, Aviation, Maritime and International | Mr Michael Mann | Tel: (020) 7944 3950 |
| Manager, Integrated Transport Economics and Appraisal | Mr Tom Worsley | Tel: (020) 7944 4880 |
| Manager, Operational Research Unit | Mr Richard Taylor | Tel: (020) 7944 8227 |
| Manager, Railways Economics and Modelling | Ms Tracey Waltho | Tel: (020) 7944 6139 |
| Manager, Transport Analysis and Review | Mr Nigel Campbell | Tel: (020) 7944 3610 |
| Aggregated Transport Model, Development | Mr Mark Weiner | Tel: (020) 7944 4379 |
| Air Transport Economics Methodology | Mr Eric Weinstein | Tel: (020) 7944 3171 |
|   Airports | Mr Jeff Thompson | Tel: (020) 7944 3063 |
| Environment and Investment | Mr Lars Rognelien | Tel: (020) 7944 5230 |
| In-House Policy Consultancy | Ms Priscilla Russell | Tel: (020) 7944 4507 |
| | Ms Alison Rutherford | Tel: (020) 7944 4507 |
| Land Values | Ms Jennie Rayson | Tel: (020) 7944 3679 |
| Maritime and Shipping | Mr Geoff Dawe | Tel: (020) 7944 3119 |
| Modelling and Methodology | Mr Chris Smith | Tel: (020) 7944 4910 |

# DEPARTMENT FOR TRANSPORT

*Economics (Continued)*

| | | |
|---|---|---|
| National Transport Model | Ms Liz Cox | Tel: (020) 7944 2924 |
| Operational Research Unit | Mr Richard Taylor | Tel: (020) 7944 8227 |
| Rail Network | Mr Brendan Meghen | Tel: (020) 7944 6184 |
| Regeneration and Transport | Mr Paul Chapman | Tel: (020) 7944 6177 |
| Road Schemes | Mr Paul Chapman | Tel: (020) 7944 6177 |
| Road Transport Industries | Mr Steve Grayson | Tel: (020) 7944 2285 |
| Targets | Ms Jennie Rayson | Tel: (020) 7944 3679 |
| Ten Year Plan Investment and Productivity | Mr Lars Rognelien | Tel: (020) 7944 5230 |
| Valuation of Travel Time | Mr Paul Chapman | Tel: (020) 7944 6177 |

**Emergencies, Civil**

| | | |
|---|---|---|
| Manager, Defence and Civil Contingency Planning | Mr John Fuller | Tel: (020) 7944 3135 |
| Duty Office | Mr Martin Leppert | Tel: (020) 7944 3135 |
| Policy | Mr Jim Burchell | Tel: (020) 7944 5122 |

**Estates**

| | | |
|---|---|---|
| Manager, Procurement and Estates Division | Mr Mike Acheson | Tel: (020) 7944 3067 |
| Contract Letting Service | Mr Keith Harwood | Tel: (020) 7944 8491 |
| Estates and Property Team | Mr Mark Matthews | Tel: (020) 7944 4709 |
| HQ Services | Mr Alan Barnes | Tel: (020) 7944 4459 |
| New Facilities, London HQ | Mr John Temple | Tel: (020) 7944 8456 |
| Procurement, Estates | Mr Roger Reed | Tel: (020) 7944 8431 |
| Security | Mr Jeremy Blyth | Tel: (020) 7944 8041 |

**European Union**

| | | |
|---|---|---|
| Manager, Europe Division | Mr John Stevens | Tel: (020) 7944 3760 |
| Major European Union Developments | Mr Paul Hayes | Tel: (020) 7944 5341 |
| Transport Council | Mr Roger Smith | Tel: (020) 7944 5315 |
| Transport Policy Branch | Mr John Carr | Tel: (020) 7944 5308 |

**Finance, Departmental**

| | | |
|---|---|---|
| Director, Corporate Finance | Ms Kate Mingay | Tel: (020) 7944 8160 |
| Director, Transport Finance | Mr Ken Beeton | Tel: (020) 7944 6960 |
| Corporate Adviser | Mr Nick Joyce | Tel: (020) 7944 8160 |
| Manager, Audit and Risk Assessment | Mr Amarjit Atkar | Tel: (020) 7944 5189 |
| Manager, Finance Accounting Services Division | Ms Caroline Rolfe | Tel: (020) 7944 4937 |
| Manager, Financial Management Division | Mr Stephen Reeves | Tel: (020) 7944 8896 |
| Manager, Transport Finance Strategy Division | Mr Tim Wellburn | Tel: (020) 7944 2760 |
| Accounting | Mr Basil Tsiakkiros | Tel: (020) 7944 6797 |
| Agencies and "Quangos" | Mr David Partridge | Tel: (020) 7944 2903 |
| Audit | Mr Peter Carroll | Tel: (020) 7944 6917 |
| Audit and Risk Management | Mr Stuart Dalglish | Tel: (020) 7944 6773 |
| | Mr Nigel Wootton | Tel: (020) 7944 6783 |
| Capital Planning | Mr Malcolm Lowe | Tel: (020) 7944 6952 |
| Estimates Co-ordination | Mr Graham Shaul | Tel: (020) 7944 2634 |
| Euro Preparations | Mr Philip Broad | Tel: (020) 7944 3535 |
| Finance Desk | Mr Alan Aitchison | Tel: (020) 7944 6967 |
| Internal Audit | Mr David Rix | Tel: (020) 7944 6500 |
| Monitoring and Reporting | Mr James McKendrick | Tel: (020) 7944 2659 |
| Risk Management | Mr Stuart Dalglish | Tel: (020) 7944 6773 |
| | Mr Nigel Wootton | Tel: (020) 7944 6783 |
| Training, Finance | Mr Tim Nolan | Tel: (020) 7944 1710 |

**Freight and Logistics**

| | | |
|---|---|---|
| Director, Logistics and Maritime Transport | Mr Brian Wadsworth | Tel: (020) 7944 2750 |
| Director, Major Projects Directorate | Mr Mike Fuhr | Tel: (020) 7944 2918 |
| Manager, Freight Logistics | Mr Martin Jones | Tel: (020) 7944 2761 |
| Manager, Radioactive Material Transport | Mr Clive Young | Tel: (020) 7944 5795 |
| Manager, Road Freight Operations Policy | Ms Helen Morris | Tel: (020) 7944 8810 |
| Dangerous Goods | Mr Jeff Hart | Tel: (020) 7944 2758 |
| Drivers' Hours | Mr Peter Dean | Tel: (020) 7944 2757 |
| Enforcement, Road Freight Operations | Mr Malcolm Blake-Lawson | Tel: (020) 7944 2254 |
| Freight Facilities Grant | Mr John Lilley | Tel: (020) 7944 6846 |

# DEPARTMENT FOR TRANSPORT

*Freight and Logistics (Continued)*

| | | |
|---|---|---|
| Goods Vehicles Operator Licences Policy | Mr Richard Verge | Tel: (020) 7944 8477 |
| Inland Waterways | Mr John Lilley | Tel: (020) 7944 6846 |
| International Policies | Mr Gerry Sreenan | Tel: (020) 7944 2773 |
| International Road Freight Office | Ms Fiona Forster | Tel: (0191) 201 4038 |
| Logistics | Mr Andrew Ashbourne | Tel: (020) 7944 2767 |
| Lorry Road User Charging | Mr David Lamberti | Tel: (020) 7944 3970 |
| | Mr Peter Thomas | Tel: (020) 7944 2429 |
| Nuclear and Radioactive Safety | | |
| Assessment | Mr Jim Stewart | Tel: (020) 7944 5777 |
| International Regulations | Mr Edmund Morgan-Warren | Tel: (020) 7944 5769 |
| Package Design | Mr Edmund Morgan-Warren | Tel: (020) 7944 5769 |
| Regulation Compliance | Mr Chris Pecover | Tel: (020) 7944 5775 |
| Perishable Food, Transportation | Mr Gerry Sreenan | Tel: (020) 7944 2773 |
| Policy | Ms Marie Carleton | Tel: (020) 7944 2123 |
| Radioactive Material Transport | Mr Clive Young | Tel: (020) 7944 5795 |
| Radioactive Packages: | | |
| Design, Handling and Storage: Engineering | Mr Edmund Morgan-Warren | Tel: (020) 7944 5769 |
| Design, Handling and Storage: Regulation | Mr Chris Pecover | Tel: (020) 7944 5775 |
| Regulation, Road Freight Operations | Mr Peter Dean | Tel: (020) 7944 2757 |
| Regulatory Enforcements | Mr Malcolm Blake-Lawson | Tel: (020) 7944 2254 |
| Road Haulage Forum | Mr Andrew Ashbourne | Tel: (020) 7944 2767 |
| Statistics: | | |
| Manager, Transport Statistics, Freight Division | Ms Antonia Roberts | Tel: (020) 7944 4280 |
| European and International | Ms Lucy De Jong | Tel: (020) 7944 4129 |
| Freight Statistics Dissemination | Mr Colin Brailsford | Tel: (020) 7944 4748 |
| Road Freight | Mr Chris Overson | Tel: (020) 7944 3093 |
| Sustainable Distribution Research | Mr Roger Worth | Tel: (020) 7944 4512 |
| Sustainable Distribution Strategy | Ms Judith Ritchie | Tel: (020) 7944 2765 |
| Tachographs | Mr Peter Dean | Tel: (020) 7944 2757 |
| Working Time Directive | Mr Ian Timpson | Tel: (020) 7944 4446 |

| | | |
|---|---|---|
| **Highway Code** | Mr David Padfield | Tel: (020) 7944 2057 |

## Human Resources, Departmental

| | | |
|---|---|---|
| Director, Human Resources | Mr Julian Duxfield | Tel: (020) 7944 6200 |
| Manager, Customer Services | Ms Judith Marshall-Camm | Tel: (020) 7944 8126 |
| Manager, Flexible Deployment Project | Ms Penny Brooke | Tel: (020) 7944 3378 |
| Manager, Strategy, Talent and Reward | Ms Christine Bennett | Tel: (020) 7944 5443 |
| Appointments and Human Resource Strategy | Mr Chris Byrne | Tel: (020) 7944 3348 |
| Casework | Ms Carolyn Coote | Tel: (020) 7944 3202 |
| Employee Relations | Mr Neil Stoker | Tel: (020) 7944 4879 |
| Equality and Diversity Unit | Ms Vicky Stewart | Tel: (020) 7944 6151 |
| Fast Stream | Ms Liz Godfrey | Tel: (020) 7944 5324 |
| Investors in People | Ms Liz Godfrey | Tel: (020) 7944 5324 |
| Occupational Health and Safety | Ms Chris Batten | Tel: (020) 7944 2955 |
| Pay and Pensions Services | Mr Andy Lee | Tel: (020) 7944 3204 |
| Payroll Administration | Mr Graham Cox | Tel: (020) 7944 3204 |
| Quality Management Unit | Mr Trevor Smith | Tel: (020) 7944 3591 |
| Vetting | Mr John Underwood | Tel: (020) 7944 3374 |

## Humps, Road

| | | |
|---|---|---|
| Regulations | Mr Adrian Waddams | Tel: (020) 7944 2056 |
| Technical | Mr Ray Gercans | Tel: (020) 7944 2978 |

## Integrated and Local Transport

| | | |
|---|---|---|
| Director, Integrated and Local Transport | Mr Bob Linnard | Tel: (020) 7944 2970 |
| Manager, Buses and Taxis Division | Ms Sandra Webber | Tel: (020) 7944 3706 |
| Manager, Charging and Local Transport Division | Ms Patricia Hayes | Tel: (020) 7944 2470 |
| Manager, Economics, Local Transport and General | Mr Mike Walsh | Tel: (020) 7944 2280 |
| Manager, Local Transport Policy Division | Ms Alison Munro | Tel: (020) 7944 6942 |
| Manager, Traffic Management Division | Mr Mike Talbot | Tel: (020) 7944 2980 |
| Manager, Transport Statistics: Personal Travel Division | Ms Barbara Noble | Tel: (020) 7944 3079 |

# DEPARTMENT FOR TRANSPORT

*Integrated and Local Transport (Continued)*

| | | |
|---|---|---|
| Accessibility Planning | Ms Caroline Fish | Tel: (020) 7944 2235 |
| Beacon Councils and Local Transport | Ms Caroline Fish | Tel: (020) 7944 2235 |
| Best Value and Local Transport | Ms Caroline Fish | Tel: (020) 7944 2235 |
| Bus Lanes | Mr John Gant | Tel: (020) 7944 2468 |
| Buses Policy | Mr David Farmer | Tel: (020) 7944 2283 |
| Charging Development Partnership | Mr Mike Goodwin | Tel: (020) 7944 6106 |
| Community Transport | Mr Peter Openshaw | Tel: (020) 7944 2284 |
| Concessionary Fares | Mr Andrew Colski | Tel: (020) 7944 2157 |
| Congestion Charging (London) | Ms Claire Spink | Tel: (020) 7944 8820 |
| Congestion Charging (Policy) | Mr Mike Goodwin | Tel: (020) 7944 6106 |
| Cycling | Mr Chris Watts | Tel: (020) 7944 2146 |
| Environmental Traffic Management Issues | Mr Ray Gercans | Tel: (020) 7944 2978 |
| Economics, Road Transport Industries | Mr Steve Grayson | Tel: (020) 7944 2285 |
| Highways Funding, Local | Mr Eric Burley | Tel: (020) 7944 2248 |
| Local Authorities | | |
| Congestion | Mr Chris Widgery | Tel: (020) 7944 2945 |
| Liaison | Mr Duncan Price | Tel: (020) 7944 2241 |
| Local Transport Outside London | Mr Matthew Coleman | Tel: (020) 7944 2238 |
| Local Transport Plans and Delivery | Mr Richard Buckley | Tel: (020) 7944 2242 |
| London and South East | Mr Nick Bisson | Tel: (020) 7944 4530 |
| Lorry Road User Charging | Mr David Lamberti | Tel: (020) 7944 3970 |
| | Mr Peter Thomas | Tel: (020) 7944 2429 |
| Multi-Modal Corridor Studies | Mr Philip Mills | Tel: (020) 7944 6084 |
| Parking Enforcement | Mr John Gant | Tel: (020) 7944 2468 |
| Parking Levy Schemes | Mr Mike Goodwin | Tel: (020) 7944 6106 |
| Private Hire Vehicles | Mr Rupert Cope | Tel: (020) 7944 2291 |
| | Ms Helen Smith | Tel: (020) 7944 2270 |
| Public Expenditure and Local Transport | Ms Rosalind Saper | Tel: (020) 7944 6729 |
| Regional Transport Strategies | Mr Nigel Vaughan | Tel: (020) 7944 2228 |
| Road User Charging | Mr Mike Goodwin | Tel: (020) 7944 6106 |
| Rural Transport Policy | Mr Nigel Vaughan | Tel: (020) 7944 2228 |
| School Travel | Ms Jacqui Wilkinson | Tel: (020) 7944 4898 |
| South East Issues | Ms Natasha Robinson | Tel: (020) 7944 8016 |
| Statistics | | |
| Bus, Coach and Taxi | Mr Kerrick Macafee | Tel: (020) 7944 4589 |
| National Travel Survey | Ms Dorothy Salathiel | Tel: (020) 7944 6594 |
| Local Authority | Mr Stephen Reynolds | Tel: (020) 7944 4746 |
| Neighbourhood | Mr Michael Baxter | Tel: (020) 7944 8849 |
| Rail Passengers | Mr Kerrick Macafee | Tel: (020) 7944 4589 |
| Travel Plans and Awareness | Mr Drew Hird | Tel: (020) 7944 4892 |
| Underground Passengers | Mr Kerrick Macafee | Tel: (020) 7944 4589 |
| Street Works | Mr Tim Barrow | Tel: (020) 7944 8046 |
| Sustainable Travel | Ms Jacqui Wilkinson | Tel: (020) 7944 4898 |
| Taxis | Mr Rupert Cope | Tel: (020) 7944 2291 |
| | Ms Helen Smith | Tel: (020) 7944 2270 |
| Thames Gateway | Ms Natasha Robinson | Tel: (020) 7944 8016 |
| Traffic | | |
| General | Ms Kitty Vernon | Tel: (020) 7944 2598 |
| Management and Parking | Mr John Gant | Tel: (020) 7944 2468 |
| Management and Traffic Control | Mr David Williams | Tel: (020) 7944 2595 |
| Signs, Technical Advice Branch | Mr Brian Lyus | Tel: (020) 7944 2987 |
| Travel Awareness Campaigns | Ms Jacqui Wilkinson | Tel: (020) 7944 4898 |
| Travel Plans and School Travel | Ms Jacqui Wilkinson | Tel: (020) 7944 4898 |
| Unadopted Roads | Mr Tim Barrow | Tel: (020) 7944 8046 |
| Walking | Mr Chris Watts | Tel: (020) 7944 2146 |
| Walkway Byelaws | Mr John Gant | Tel: (020) 7944 2468 |
| Workplace Parking, Charging | Mr Mike Goodwin | Tel: (020) 7944 6106 |

**International Issues, Departmental Focal Point** ..... Mr Paul Hayes ..... Tel: (020) 7944 5341

# DEPARTMENT FOR TRANSPORT

**IT Services, Departmental**

Manager, IT Services . . . . . . . . . . . . . . . . . . . . . . . . Mr Eamonn McDonough . . . . . . . . . . . . . . . . . Tel: (020) 7944 5050
Customer Relations . . . . . . . . . . . . . . . . . . . . . . . . Mr Ian Leat . . . . . . . . . . . . . . . . . . . . . . . . . . . Tel: (020) 7944 5080
Infrastructure Management (including IT Helpdesk) . . . Mr Eamonn McDonough . . . . . . . . . . . . . . . . . Tel: (020) 7944 5070
IT Programme Management . . . . . . . . . . . . . . . . . . . Mr Steven Jordan . . . . . . . . . . . . . . . . . . . . . . . Tel: (020) 7944 5060
Quality and Business Management . . . . . . . . . . . . . . Mr John Murray . . . . . . . . . . . . . . . . . . . . . . . . Tel: (020) 7944 3315

**Legal**

Director, Legal Services . . . . . . . . . . . . . . . . . . . . . Mr Christopher Muttukumaru . . . . . . . . . . . . . . Tel: (020) 7944 4770
Aviation . . . . . . . . . . . . . . . . . . . . . . . . . . . . . . . . . Mr Alan Jones . . . . . . . . . . . . . . . . . . . . . . . . . Tel: (020) 7944 6180
Driving . . . . . . . . . . . . . . . . . . . . . . . . . . . . . . . . . Mr Stephen Rock . . . . . . . . . . . . . . . . . . . . . . . Tel: (020) 7944 6631
Employment . . . . . . . . . . . . . . . . . . . . . . . . . . . . . . Mr Martin Bedford . . . . . . . . . . . . . . . . . . . . . . Tel: (020) 7944 4732
European Union Law . . . . . . . . . . . . . . . . . . . . . . . Ms Ginny Harrison . . . . . . . . . . . . . . . . . . . . . . Tel: (020) 7944 3434
Highways . . . . . . . . . . . . . . . . . . . . . . . . . . . . . . . . Mr Hussein Kaya . . . . . . . . . . . . . . . . . . . . . . . Tel: (020) 7944 8882
Human Rights . . . . . . . . . . . . . . . . . . . . . . . . . . . . Mr Stephen Rock . . . . . . . . . . . . . . . . . . . . . . . Tel: (020) 7944 6631
Management Support, Legal Services Directorate . . . . . Mr Geoffrey Willars . . . . . . . . . . . . . . . . . . . . . Tel: (020) 7944 5087
Marine . . . . . . . . . . . . . . . . . . . . . . . . . . . . . . . . . . Ms Ginny Harrison . . . . . . . . . . . . . . . . . . . . . . Tel: (020) 7944 3434
Procurement . . . . . . . . . . . . . . . . . . . . . . . . . . . . . . Ms Karen Booth . . . . . . . . . . . . . . . . . . . . . . . . Tel: (020) 7944 4732
Railways
  Construction and Operation . . . . . . . . . . . . . . . . Ms Elizabeth Walsh . . . . . . . . . . . . . . . . . . . . . Tel: (020) 7944 6130
  Track and Safety . . . . . . . . . . . . . . . . . . . . . . . Mr Robert Caune . . . . . . . . . . . . . . . . . . . . . . . Tel: (020) 7944 8097
Road Safety . . . . . . . . . . . . . . . . . . . . . . . . . . . . . . Mr Stephen Rock . . . . . . . . . . . . . . . . . . . . . . . Tel: (020) 7944 6631
Secondary Legislation . . . . . . . . . . . . . . . . . . . . . . . Mr David Ingham . . . . . . . . . . . . . . . . . . . . . . . Tel: (020) 7944 4753
Shipping . . . . . . . . . . . . . . . . . . . . . . . . . . . . . . . . Ms Ginny Harrison . . . . . . . . . . . . . . . . . . . . . . Tel: (020) 7944 3434
Vehicles . . . . . . . . . . . . . . . . . . . . . . . . . . . . . . . . . Ms Julie Murnane . . . . . . . . . . . . . . . . . . . . . . . Tel: (020) 7944 6463

**Lighthouses** . . . . . . . . . . . . . . . . . . . . . . . . . . . . . Mr Phil Hart . . . . . . . . . . . . . . . . . . . . . . . . . . . Tel: (020) 7944 5195

**Logistics** *(see above under Freight and Logistics)*

**London Underground**

Policy . . . . . . . . . . . . . . . . . . . . . . . . . . . . . . . . . . . Ms Ellen Duffy . . . . . . . . . . . . . . . . . . . . . . . . . Tel: (020) 7944 8713
Security . . . . . . . . . . . . . . . . . . . . . . . . . . . . . . . . . Mr David Elbourne . . . . . . . . . . . . . . . . . . . . . . Tel: (020) 7944 6712

**Maritime Transport**

Director, Logistics and Maritime . . . . . . . . . . . . . . . Mr Brian Wadsworth . . . . . . . . . . . . . . . . . . . . . Tel: (020) 7944 2750
Manager, Ports Division . . . . . . . . . . . . . . . . . . . . . Mr Phil Carey . . . . . . . . . . . . . . . . . . . . . . . . . . Tel: (020) 7944 5001
Manager, Shipping Policy Division 1 . . . . . . . . . . . . . Mr Davie Rowe . . . . . . . . . . . . . . . . . . . . . . . . . Tel: (020) 7944 3710
Manager, Shipping Policy Division 2 . . . . . . . . . . . . . Ms Theresa Crossley . . . . . . . . . . . . . . . . . . . . . Tel: (020) 7944 3650
Economics, Maritime and Shipping . . . . . . . . . . . . . . Mr Geoff Dawe . . . . . . . . . . . . . . . . . . . . . . . . . Tel: (020) 7944 3119
Emergencies, Defence Planning . . . . . . . . . . . . . . . . Mr Jim Burchell . . . . . . . . . . . . . . . . . . . . . . . . Tel: (020) 7944 5122
Freight Facilities Grant . . . . . . . . . . . . . . . . . . . . . . Mr John Lilley . . . . . . . . . . . . . . . . . . . . . . . . . Tel: (020) 7944 6846
International
  Commercial Relations . . . . . . . . . . . . . . . . . . . . Mr David Milroy . . . . . . . . . . . . . . . . . . . . . . . . Tel: (020) 7944 5423
  Legal Negotiations . . . . . . . . . . . . . . . . . . . . . . Mr John Wren . . . . . . . . . . . . . . . . . . . . . . . . . Tel: (020) 7944 5452
  Permanent Representative, International
    Maritime Organisation . . . . . . . . . . . . . . . . . . Mr Thomas Allan . . . . . . . . . . . . . . . . . . . . . . . Tel: (020) 7944 5270
Management Support, Logistics and Maritime Division . Mr Jim Richardson . . . . . . . . . . . . . . . . . . . . . . Tel: (020) 7944 2133
Marine Accidents Investigation
  Chief Inspector, Marine Accidents Investigation . . . Mr Stephen Meyer . . . . . . . . . . . . . . . . . . . . . . Tel: (023) 8039 5528
  Deputy Chief Inspector . . . . . . . . . . . . . . . . . . . Mr Stephen Clinch . . . . . . . . . . . . . . . . . . . . . . Tel: (023) 8039 5529
Marine Environment, Protection of . . . . . . . . . . . . . . Mr John Mairs . . . . . . . . . . . . . . . . . . . . . . . . . Tel: (020) 7944 5417
Maritime and Coastguard Agency, Sponsorship . . . . . . Mr Kevin Deadman . . . . . . . . . . . . . . . . . . . . . . Tel: (020) 7944 5425
Pollution Response . . . . . . . . . . . . . . . . . . . . . . . . . Mr John Mairs . . . . . . . . . . . . . . . . . . . . . . . . . Tel: (020) 7944 5417
Ports
  Ports and Harbours, General . . . . . . . . . . . . . . . Mr Mike Davies . . . . . . . . . . . . . . . . . . . . . . . . Tel: (020) 7944 5086
  Ports Casework . . . . . . . . . . . . . . . . . . . . . . . . . Mr Colin Morris . . . . . . . . . . . . . . . . . . . . . . . . Tel: (020) 7944 5077
  Port Lights and Navigation . . . . . . . . . . . . . . . . . Mr Phil Hart . . . . . . . . . . . . . . . . . . . . . . . . . . . Tel: (020) 7944 5195
Quality Shipping Campaign . . . . . . . . . . . . . . . . . . . Mr Kevin Deadman . . . . . . . . . . . . . . . . . . . . . . Tel: (020) 7944 5425
Safety, Maritime . . . . . . . . . . . . . . . . . . . . . . . . . . . Mr Kevin Deadman . . . . . . . . . . . . . . . . . . . . . . Tel: (020) 7944 5425
Security, Maritime
  EU Port Security Directive . . . . . . . . . . . . . . . . . Ms Jessica Bowles . . . . . . . . . . . . . . . . . . . . . . Tel: (020) 7944 5902
  UK Ports and UK Registered Vessels . . . . . . . . . . Mr Ashley Reeve . . . . . . . . . . . . . . . . . . . . . . . Tel: (020) 7944 2865

# DEPARTMENT FOR TRANSPORT

*Maritime Transport (Continued)*

Ship Recycling............................... Mr Kevin Deadman ..................... Tel: (020) 7944 5425
Statistics ..................................... Mr Alan Brown ........................ Tel: (020) 7944 4441
UK Shipping Industry, General................. Ms Anne Broome ...................... Tel: (020) 7944 5438
Working Hours................................ Mr Kevin Deadman ..................... Tel: (020) 7944 5425

**Ministerial Support Unit**........................ Mr Stephen Batchelor ................. Tel: (020) 7944 4473

**Mobility**

Manager, Mobility and Inclusion Unit.............. Ms Ann Frye .......................... Tel: (020) 7944 4460
Disability Policy............................... Ms Sue Sharp ........................ Tel: (020) 7944 4917
Engineering and Research Branch ............... Mr Donald Macdonald ................. Tel: (020) 7944 4923
Social Inclusion and Personal Security Branch ...... Ms Miranda Carter..................... Tel: (020) 7944 4913
Mobility Advice and Vehicle Information Service ..... Mr Rolf Lamsdale .................... Tel: (01344) 661001
Mobility Research Projects...................... Mr Brian Ellison ...................... Tel: (01344) 661004

**Olympic Bid Issues**............................ Mr David Morris ....................... Tel: (020) 7944 2394

**Parking** ...................................... Mr John Gant......................... Tel: (020) 7944 2468

**Parliamentary Clerk**........................... Mr Paul Davies ....................... Tel: (020) 7944 4472

**Ports** *(see above under Maritime Transport)*

**Press** *(see above under Communications)*

**Private Hire Cars** ............................ Mr Rupert Cope....................... Tel: (020) 7944 2291
Ms Helen Smith....................... Tel: (020) 7944 2270

**Procurement**

Manager, Procurement and Estates Division ........ Mr Mike Acheson ..................... Tel: (020) 7944 3067
Advice...................................... Mr Keith Harwood .................... Tel: (020) 7944 8491
Contracts ................................... Mr Keith Harwood .................... Tel: (020) 7944 8491
Estates Procurement ......................... Mr Roger Reed ....................... Tel: (0200 7944 8431
Flexible Business Projects ..................... Ms Sue McGlashan .................... Tel: (020) 7944 8248
Procurement Policy and Strategy................. Mr Mike Matthews.................... Tel: (020) 7944 8480
Quality Management Unit...................... Mr Trevor Smith ...................... Tel: (020) 7944 3591
Special Projects ............................. Mr John Temple....................... Tel: (020) 7944 8456

**Radioactive Materials, Transportation**

Head, Radioactive Materials Transport Division ...... Mr Clive Young........................ Tel: (020) 7944 5795
Nuclear Critical Safety Assessment............... Mr Jim Stewart........................ Tel: (020) 7944 5777
Radioactive Packages:
  Design, Handling and Storage: Engineering....... Mr Edmund Morgan-Warren ........... Tel: (020) 7944 5769
  Design, Handling and Storage: Regulation ....... Mr Chris Pecover...................... Tel: (020) 7944 5775

**Railways**

Director, Rail Performance...................... Ms Vivien Bodnar ..................... Tel: (020) 7944 4250
Director, Rail Strategy and Resources............. Mr Mark Lambirth ..................... Tel: (020) 7944 4250
Director, Major Projects ....................... Mr Mike Fuhr ........................ Tel: (020) 7944 4250
Manager, Rail International ..................... Ms Liz Duthie ........................ Tel: (020) 7944 3920
Manager, Railways Economics and Modelling........ Ms Tracey Waltho ..................... Tel: (020) 7944 6139
Managers, Railway Finance and Strategy .......... Mr Sandy Bishop ..................... Tel: (020) 7944 3920
Mr Michael Fawcett.................... Tel: (020) 7944 3920
Manager, Railways Major Projects ............... Mr Andrew Murray .................... Tel: (020) 7944 3251
Manager, Railways Reliability
  and Communications ....................... Mr Phil West......................... Tel: (020) 7944 3190
Manager, Railway Safety........................ Mr John Aspinall...................... Tel: (020) 7944 2647
Manager, Railways Sponsorship ................. Mr Ian McBrayne..................... Tel: (020) 7944 3280
Briefing .................................... Ms Rachel Evans...................... Tel: (020) 7944 8828
British Transport Police, Byelaws and British Rail
  Consequentials............................ Mr Charles Godfrey ................... Tel: (020) 7944 6930
Mr David Meredith.................... Tel: (020) 7944 6763

# DEPARTMENT FOR TRANSPORT

*Railways (Continued)*

Channel Tunnel

 Concession............................... Mr Colin Poole ........................... Tel: (020) 7944 6829

 Finance ..................................... Mr Peter Allen.......................... Tel: (020) 7944 6869

 Land and Planning...................... Mr Richard West....................... Tel: (020) 7944 6618

 Policy, Future ........................... Ms Tamsin Alker....................... Tel: (020) 7944 5728

 Security ................................... Mr David Elbourne .................... Tel: (020) 7944 6712

Contingency PLanning ...................... Mr Mike Ainsworth ................... Tel: (020) 7944 6843

Crossrail .......................................... Mr Ewan West........................... Tel: (020) 7944 6754

Database, Rail Information.................. Mr Tim Lawson ........................ Tel: (020) 7944 3562

East London Line Extension ............... Mr Ewan West........................... Tel: (020) 7944 6754

Economic Advice

 Fares ...................................... Mr Andrew Price ...................... Tel: (020) 7944 6789

 Franchising .............................. Mr Andrew Price ...................... Tel: (020) 7944 6789

 Passenger Operation.................... Mr Chris Simpson ..................... Tel: (020) 7944 6754

 Modelling................................. Mr Brian Turner ....................... Tel: (020) 7944 6759

 Network Rail ............................ Mr Brendan Meghen ................. Tel: (020) 7944 6184

 Rail Industry ............................ Mr Chris Simpson ..................... Tel: (020) 7944 6754

Employment Issues............................ Ms Nanette Chisholm................ Tel: (020) 7944 6949

Environment Issues ........................... Mr Joseph Odiari ...................... Tel: (020) 7944 6986

European Union Legislation ................ Mr Colin Poole ........................ Tel: (020) 7944 6829

Eurotunnel....................................... Mr Ewan West........................... Tel: (020) 7944 6754

Fares .............................................. Mr Andrew Price ...................... Tel: (020) 7944 6789

Franchises, London and South East....... Mr Malcolm Macdonald ............. Tel: (020) 7944 6842

Freight............................................ Mr Ian Corfield ........................ Tel: (020) 7944 6167

Grants ............................................ Mr Malcolm Macdonald ............. Tel: (020) 7944 6842

Heritage.......................................... Mr Charles Godfrey ................... Tel: (020) 7944 6930

               Mr David Meredith.................... Tel: (020) 7944 6763

Industrial Relation ........................... Mr Mike Ainsworth ................... Tel: (020) 7944 6843

International .................................... Mr Colin Poole ........................ Tel: (020) 7944 6829

Interoperatability ............................. Mr Mark Bosly......................... Tel: (020) 7944 3148

Major Projects, Land and Planning ....... Mr Richard West....................... Tel: (020) 7944 6618

Manufacturing Industry ..................... Mr Mike Ainsworth ................... Tel: (020) 7944 6843

Network Rail

 Economics................................ Mr Brendan Meghen ................. Tel: (020) 7944 6184

 Policy ..................................... Mr Tom Oscroft ........................ Tel: (020) 7944 6870

Passenger Issues ............................... Mr Joseph Odiari ...................... Tel: (020) 7944 6986

Pensions, Railway Industry.................. Ms Nanette Chisholm................ Tel: (020) 7944 6949

Planning Casework............................ Mr Ian Corfield ........................ Tel: (020) 7944 6167

Policing........................................... Mr Charles Godfrey ................... Tel: (020) 7944 6930

               Mr David Meredith.................... Tel: (020) 7944 6763

Publicity, Stakeholder Communications ............ Ms Sue Daniels ........... Tel: (020) 7944 4615

Rail Passenger Partnership.................. Mr Joseph Odiari ...................... Tel: (020) 7944 6986

Rail Regulator, Sponsorship ............... Mr Paul Lancaster ..................... Tel: (020) 7944 3740

Resources ....................................... Ms Heather Whicker ................. Tel: (020) 7944 6752

Safety............................................. Mr Alan Deighton ..................... Tel: (020) 7944 6616

Statistical Advice.............................. Ms Jenny King.......................... Tel: (020) 7944 6701

Strategic Rail Authority Sponsorship..... Mr Ian Corfield ........................ Tel: (020) 7944 6167

Ten Year Plan Review ....................... *Vacant*................................... Tel: (020) 7944 8874

Thameslink 2000, West Coast Main Line,

 Crossrail and East London Line Extension ....... Mr John Nevitt............. Tel: (020) 7944 6985

Trans-European Rail Network.............. Mr Colin Poole ........................ Tel: (020) 7944 6829

West Coast Main Line ....................... Mr John Nevitt.......................... Tel: (020) 7944 6985

## Regional Transport

Director, Regional Transport............... Ms Brownyn Hill ...................... Tel: (020) 7944 6948

Manager, Regional Transport Policy...... Mr Ian Jordan .......................... Tel: (020) 7944 2384

London and South East....................... Mr Nick Bisson ........................ Tel: (020) 7944 4530

London, Congestion Charging .............. Ms Claire Spink........................ Tel: (020) 7944 8820

London, Olympic Bid Issues................. Mr David Morris ....................... Tel: (020) 7944 2394

North, Midlands and East.................... Ms Alice Baker ......................... Tel: (0170) 568 8829

               Mr Charlie Sunderland............... Tel: (020) 7944 2503

Regional Institutions, Liaison .............. Mr Nigel Vaughan ..................... Tel: (020) 7944 2228

Thames Gateway .............................. Ms Natasha Robinson ................ Tel: (020) 7944 8016

# DEPARTMENT FOR TRANSPORT

**Road Safety** *(see below under Road Transport / Roads)*

**Road Transport / Roads**

| | | |
|---|---|---|
| Director-General, Roads, Regional and Local Transport | Mr Robert Devereux | Tel: (020) 7944 2667 |
| Director, Roads | Mr Stephen Gooding | Tel: (020) 7944 4080 |
| Manager, Licensing, Roadworthiness and Insurance Division | Mr Richard Jones | Tel: (020) 7944 6379 |
| Manager, Roads Policy Division | Ms Sarah Thomson | Tel: (020) 7944 3801 |
| Manager, Road Safety Division | Mr Leslie Packer | Tel: (020) 7944 2060 |
| Manager, Transport, Environment and Taxation | Mr Malcolm Fendick | Tel: (020) 7944 2450 |
| Manager, Transport Statistics: Roads Division | Mr Alan Oliver | Tel: (020) 7944 4270 |
| Bridges | Mr Brian Lyus | Tel: (020) 7944 2987 |
| Bus Priority | Mr John Gant | Tel: (020) 7944 2468 |
| Clear Zones | Mr David Williams | Tel: (020) 7944 2595 |
| Drink / Drugs and Driving, Policy | Mr Robert Davies | Tel: (020) 7944 2045 |
| Driving Impairment | Mr Robert Davies | Tel: (020) 7944 2045 |
| Driver Training and Testing | Ms Sue Faulkner | Tel: (020) 7944 2465 |
| Driving Licenses, EC and International | Mr Fred Hackman | Tel: (020) 7944 2461 |
| Environmental Issues, Roads Policy | Ms Marilyn Waldron | Tel: (020) 7944 5792 |
| Finance, Roads | Mr Paul Foskett | Tel: (020) 7944 3829 |
| Highways Agency Sponsorship | Mr Guy Denman | Tel: (020) 7944 5545 |
| Highways Funding, Local | Mr Eric Burley | Tel: (020) 7944 2248 |
| Inquiries and Human Rights Issues | Mr Tony Sherwood | Tel: (020) 7944 6086 |
| Insurance | Mr Richard Jones | Tel: (020) 7944 6379 |
| Level Crossings | Mr David Williams | Tel: (020) 7944 2595 |
| Lighting | Mr Brian Lyus | Tel: (020) 7944 2987 |
| Local Authority Road Funding | Mr Martin Wells | Tel: (020) 7944 2913 |
| Major Road Schemes | Mr Philip Mills | Tel: (020) 7944 6065 |
| MOT Issues | Mr David Briggs | Tel: (020) 7944 2453 |
| Motor Insurance Issues | Mr Richard Jones | Tel: (020) 7944 6379 |
| Motoring Issues (General) | Ms Julie Osborne | Tel: (020) 7944 6085 |
| Novice Drivers | Ms Sue Faulkner | Tel: (020) 7944 2465 |
| Park and Ride | Mr David Williams | Tel: (020) 7944 2595 |
| Pedestrian Crossings | Mr David Williams | Tel: (020) 7944 2595 |
| Resource Management, Road Transport Directorate | Mr Les Wood | Tel: (020) 7944 2142 |
| Road Humps | Mr Adrian Waddams | Tel: (020) 7944 2056 |
| Road Marking, Technical Advice | Mr Brian Lyus | Tel: (020) 7944 2987 |
| Road Rage | Ms Sue Faulkner | Tel: (020) 7944 2465 |
| Roads Network Usage - Improvement | Ms Marilyn Waldron | Tel: (020) 7944 5792 |
| Roads Policy, Manager | Ms Sarah Thomson | Tel: (020) 7944 3801 |
| Road Safety | | |
|     Manager, Road Safety Division | Mr Leslie Packer | Tel: (020) 7944 2060 |
|     Chief Medical Officer, Road Safety | Mr Tim Carter | Tel: (020) 7944 2030 |
|     Cycle Helmets | Mr David Padfield | Tel: (020) 7944 2057 |
|     Grants | Mr David Padfield | Tel: (020) 7944 2057 |
|     Highway Code | Mr David Padfield | Tel: (020) 7944 2057 |
|     Publicity | Mr Bill Hills | Tel: (020) 7944 3481 |
|     Research | Ms Kate McMahon | Tel: (020) 7944 2040 |
|     Statistics | Ms Valerie Davies | Tel: (020) 7944 6387 |
|     Strategy | Mr Bill Hills | Tel: (020) 7944 3481 |
|     Vulnerable Road Users | Mr David Padfield | Tel: (020) 7944 2057 |
| Road Signs | Ms Kitty Vernon | Tel: (020) 7944 2598 |
| Speed Management | Mr Adrian Waddams | Tel: (020) 7944 2056 |
| Statistics | | |
|     Manager, Transport Statistics: Roads | Mr Alan Oliver | Tel: (020) 7944 4270 |
|     Car Safety Ratings | Ms Valerie Davies | Tel: (020) 7944 6387 |
|     Congestion Monitoring | Ms Mouna Kehil | Tel: (020) 7944 3046 |
|     Drink / Drive | Ms Valerie Davies | Tel: (020) 7944 6387 |
|     Road Maintenance Statistics | Mr Guy Ellis | Tel: (020) 7944 6398 |
|     Road Safety | Ms Valerie Davies | Tel: (020) 7944 6387 |
|     Traffic Census Development Statistics | Mr Phil Hathaway | Tel: (020) 7944 6573 |
|     Vehicle Speeds | Ms Valerie Davies | Tel: (020) 7944 6387 |
|     Vehicles and Taxation | Ms Mouna Kehil | Tel: (020) 7944 3046 |
| Tolled Crossings | Mr Paul Foskett | Tel: (020) 7944 3829 |

# DEPARTMENT FOR TRANSPORT

*Road Transport / Roads (Continued)*

| | | |
|---|---|---|
| Trade Plates | Mr Richard Jones | Tel: (020) 7944 6379 |
| Traffic Management Policy | Mr David Williams | Tel: (020) 7944 2595 |
| Traffic Signs | Ms Kitty Vernon | Tel: (020) 7944 2598 |
| Vehicle Crime | Mr Andrew Park | Tel: (020) 7944 2456 |
| Vehicle Insurance | Mr Richard Jones | Tel: (020) 7944 6379 |
| Vehicles, Technology and Standards | | |
|     Manager, Vehicle Standards and Engineering | Mr Eric Sampson | Tel: (020) 7944 4870 |
|     Bull Bars | Mr Peter O'Reilly | Tel: (020) 7944 2107 |
|     Caravans | Mr Geoff Harvey | Tel: (020) 7944 2075 |
|     Components | Mr Geoff Harvey | Tel: (020) 7944 2075 |
|     Cycles | Mr Geoff Harvey | Tel: (020) 7944 2075 |
|     Electric Vehicles | Mr Geoff Harvey | Tel: (020) 7944 2075 |
|     Excise Duty Issues | *Vacant* | Tel: (020) 7944 2464 |
|     Fuels and Emissions | Mr Richard Jones | Tel: (020) 7944 6379 |
|     Legislation | Mr Ian Yarnold | Tel: (020) 7944 2086 |
|     Pedestrian Protection | Mr Peter O'Reilly | Tel: (020) 7944 2107 |
|     Research Management | Mr Ian Yarnold | Tel: (020) 7944 2086 |
|     Roadworthiness | Mr David Briggs | Tel: (020) 7944 2453 |
|     Safety Devices | Mr Peter O'Reilly | Tel: (020) 7944 2107 |
|     Seat Belts Design | Mr Peter O'Reilly | Tel: (020) 7944 2107 |
|     Side Impact Protection | Mr Peter O'Reilly | Tel: (020) 7944 2107 |
|     Safety Standards | Mr Geoff Harvey | Tel: (020) 7944 2075 |
|     Speed Limiters | Mr Geoff Harvey | Tel: (020) 7944 2086 |
|     Type Approval and Single Vehicle Approval | Mr Richard Jones | Tel: (020) 7944 6379 |
| Vulnerable Road Users | Mr Ray Gercans | Tel: (020) 7944 2978 |

## School Travel

| | | |
|---|---|---|
| Policies | Ms Jacqui Wilkinson | Tel: (020) 7944 4898 |
| Research | Mr Drew Hird | Tel: (020) 7944 4892 |

## Science

| | | |
|---|---|---|
| Chief Scientific Adviser | Professor Frank Kelly | Tel: (020) 7944 8176 |
| Management Policy and Process | Mr Alan Paterson | Tel: (020) 7944 5037 |
| Policy and Research Co-ordination | Mr Walt O'Dowd | Tel: (020) 7944 8176 |
| Science and Evidence Policy Research | Mr Matt White | Tel: (020) 7944 5038 |

## Security, Transport

| | | |
|---|---|---|
| Director, Transport Security | Ms Niki Tompkinson | Tel: (020) 7944 2850 |
| Deputy Director, Transport Security | Mr John Grubb | Tel: (020) 7944 2840 |
| Aviation | | |
|     Inspectorate | Mr Sean Bodkin | Tel: (020) 7944 2592 |
|     Security Domestic | Ms Petra Wilkinson | Tel: (020) 7944 2784 |
|     Security International | Mr Richard Orrin | Tel: (020) 7944 2888 |
|     Security Policy and Implementation | Mr Peter Kirk | Tel: (020) 7944 2851 |
| Maritime Security | | |
|     EU Port Security Directive | Ms Jessica Bowles | Tel: (020) 7944 5902 |
|     UK Ports and UK Registered Vessels | Mr Ashley Reeve | Tel: (020) 7944 2865 |
| Operations Support | Mr Richard Doney | Tel: (020) 7944 2826 |
| Security Regulation of Channel Tunnel, London | | |
|     Underground and Railway Industries | Mr David Elbourne | Tel: (020) 7944 6712 |

## Shipping *(see above under Maritime Transport)*

## Statistics

| | | |
|---|---|---|
| Manager, Transport Statistics Freight | Ms Antonia Roberts | Tel: (020) 7944 4280 |
| Manager, Transport Statistics: Personal Travel Division | Ms Barbara Noble | Tel: (020) 7944 3079 |
| Manager, Transport Statistics: Roads | Mr Alan Oliver | Tel: (020) 7944 4270 |
| Aviation and Airport | *Vacant* | Tel: (020) 7944 4276 |
| Car Safety Ratings | Ms Valerie Davies | Tel: (020) 7944 6387 |
| Congestion Monitoring | Ms Mouna Kehil | Tel: (020) 7944 3046 |
| Drink / Drive | Ms Valerie Davies | Tel: (020) 7944 6387 |
| European and International, Freight | Ms Lucy De Jong | Tel: (020) 7944 4129 |
| Freight Statistics Dissemination | Mr Colin Brailsford | Tel: (020) 7944 4748 |
| International Traffic | Mr Chris Overson | Tel: (020) 7944 3093 |

# DEPARTMENT FOR TRANSPORT

*Statistics (Continued)*

| | | |
|---|---|---|
| Maritime and Ports | Mr Alan Brown | Tel: (020) 7944 4441 |
| Road Traffic | Mr John Garnsworthy | Tel: (020) 7944 3093 |
| Road Maintenance Statistics | Mr Guy Ellis | Tel: (020) 7944 6398 |
| Road Safety | Ms Valerie Davies | Tel: (020) 7944 6387 |
| Speeds | Ms Valerie Davies | Tel: (020) 7944 6387 |
| Traffic Census Development Statistics | Mr Phil Hathaway | Tel: (020) 7944 6573 |
| Vehicles and Taxation | Ms Mouna Kehil | Tel: (020) 7944 3046 |

**Strategy**

| | | |
|---|---|---|
| Director, Transport Strategy and Delivery Directorate | Mr David McMillan | Tel: (020) 7944 5740 |
| Manager, Europe and International Division | Mr John Stevens | Tel: (020) 7944 3760 |
| Manager, Planning and Performance | Mr Peter McCarthy | Tel: (020) 7944 5750 |
| Manager, Strategy and Review | Mr Paul Collins | Tel: (020) 7944 2110 |
| Manager, Transport Research Unit | Ms Gillian Smith | Tel: (020) 7944 3480 |
| Attitudes Research/ Polling | Mr Nick Court | Tel: (020) 7944 6992 |
| Board Secretariat, Department for Transport | Mr Edward Neve | Tel: (020) 7944 8120 |
| Crime and Transport Safety | Ms Lesley Stark | Tel: (020) 7944 5189 |
| Economics *(see above under Economics)* | | |
| Environment and Taxation, Transport | | |
|     Manager, Transport, Environment and Taxation | Mr Malcolm Fendick | Tel: (020) 7944 2450 |
|     Branch 1 | Mr Rupert Furness | Tel: (020) 7944 4899 |
|     Branch 2 | Mr Alan Irving | Tel: (020) 7944 4885 |
|     Branch 3 | Ms Laura Fellowes | Tel: (020) 7944 4901 |
| European Union *(see above under European Union)* | | |
| International | Mr Paul Hayes | Tel: (020) 7944 5341 |
| National Transport Model | Ms Liz Cox | Tel: (020) 7944 2924 |
| Operational Research Unit | Mr Richard Taylor | Tel: (020) 7944 8227 |
| Policy Consultancy, In-House | Ms Priscilla Russell | Tel: (020) 7944 4507 |
| | Ms Alison Rutherford | Tel: (020) 7944 4507 |
| Policy, Transport | | |
|     Cross-Departmental Co-ordination | Ms Caroline Wood | Tel: (020) 7944 2557 |
|     Sponsorship and Co-ordination | Ms Catherine Cornwell | Tel: (020) 7944 5152 |
|     Transport Policy Co-ordination | Mr Nigel Dotchin | Tel: (020) 7944 8082 |
|     Transport Strategy | Mr Phil Dykins | Tel: (020) 7944 2909 |
| Polling and Research, Consumers | Mr Nick Court | Tel: (020) 7944 6992 |
| Project and Programme Management | Mr Mark Bailey | Tel: (020) 7944 2436 |
| Regeneration and Transport | Mr Paul Chapman | Tel: (020) 7944 6177 |
| Research | | |
|     Manager, Transport Research Unit | Ms Gillian Smith | Tel: (020) 7944 3480 |
|     Co-ordination | Mr Chris Fox | Tel: (020) 7944 2481 |
|     Cross Cutting Issues | Ms Helen Bullock | Tel: (020) 7944 4887 |
|     Monitoring Policy | Mr Adrian Leigh | Tel: (020) 7944 5244 |
|     Social Research | Ms Rebecca Stanley | Tel: (020) 7944 66342 |
| Risk Management | Mr Jeremy Hotchkiss | Tel: (020) 7944 3507 |
| | Mr Tim May | Tel: (020) 7944 2197 |
| Science *(see above under Science)* | | |
| Social Inclusion | Ms Miranda Carter | Tel: (020) 7944 4913 |
| Stakeholder Relations | Mr Nick Court | Tel: (020) 7944 6992 |
| Transport Council, European Union | Mr Roger Smith§ | Tel: (020) 7944 5315 |

| | | |
|---|---|---|
| **Taxis** | Mr Rupert Cope | Tel: (020) 7944 2291 |
| | Ms Helen Smith | Tel: (020) 7944 2270 |

**Technology, Transport**

| | | |
|---|---|---|
| Manager, Vehicle Technology and Standards | Mr Eric Sampson | Tel: (020) 7944 4870 |
| Lorry Road User Charging | Mr David Lamberti | Tel: (020) 7944 3970 |
| | Mr Peter Thomas | Tel: (020) 7944 2429 |
| Transport Technology and Telematics | | |
|     Branch 1 | Mr Don Mackinnon | Tel: (020) 7944 6132 |
|     Branch 2 | Ms Cathy Jenkins | Tel: (020) 7944 4851 |

| | | |
|---|---|---|
| **Thameslink** | Mr Peter Sanders | Tel: (020) 7944 8823 |
| **Transport and Works Act Orders** | Mr Ellis Harvey | Tel: (020) 7944 2483 |
| **Transport Direct** | Mr Nick Illsley | Tel: (020) 7944 7392 |

**Vehicles** *(see above under  under Road Transport / Roads)*

# DEPARTMENT FOR TRANSPORT

## OTHER RELEVANT CONTACTS

**AVIATION**
**Civil Aviation Authority** . . . . . . . . . . . . . . . . . . . . . . CAA House, 45-59 Kingsway, London, WC2B 6TE
    Chairman . . . . . . . . . . . . . . . . . . . . . . . . . . . . . . . . . . Sir Roy McNulty . . . . . . . . . . . . . . . . . . . . . . . . Tel: (020) 7379 7311
    Web: http://www.caa.co.uk

**COASTGUARD** *(see below under Marine Safety)*

**DISABILITY**
**Disabled Persons Transport Advisory Committee** . . . . Zone 1/14, Great Minster House, 76 Marsham Street,
    London, SW1P 4DR
    Chairman . . . . . . . . . . . . . . . . . . . . . . . . . . . . . . . . . Mr Neil Betteridge
    Secretariat . . . . . . . . . . . . . . . . . . . . . . . . . . . . . . . . . Mr Andy Kirby . . . . . . . . . . . . . . . . . . . . . . . . . . . Tel: (020) 7944 8012
    E-mail: dptac@dft.gsi.gov.uk
    Web: http://www.dptac.gov.uk

**DRIVERS / VEHICLES**
**Driving Standards Agency** *(Executive Agency)* . . . . . . . Stanley House, 56 Talbot Street, Nottingham, NG1 5GU
    Chief Executive . . . . . . . . . . . . . . . . . . . . . . . . . . . . Mr Gary Austin . . . . . . . . . . . . . . . . . . . . . . . . . . Tel: (0115) 901 2500
    E-mail: customer.services@dsa.gsi.gov.uk
    Web: http://www.dsa.gov.uk
**Vehicle and Operator Services**
  **Agency** *(Executive Agency)* . . . . . . . . . . . . . . . . . . Berkeley House, Croydon Street, Bristol, BS5 0DA
    Chief Executive . . . . . . . . . . . . . . . . . . . . . . . . . . . Mr Maurice Newey . . . . . . . . . . . . . . . . . . . . . . . Tel: (0117) 954 3200
    E-mail: enquiries@vosa.gov.uk
    Web: http://www.vosa.gov.uk
**Vehicle Certification Agency** *(Executive Agency)* . . . . . . Eastgate Office Centre, Eastgate Road, Bristol, BS5 6XX
    Chief Executive . . . . . . . . . . . . . . . . . . . . . . . . . . . Mr Derek Harvey . . . . . . . . . . . . . . . . . . . . . . . . Tel: (0117) 951 5151
    E-mail: enquiries@vca.gov.uk
    Web: http://www.vca.gov.uk

**INTEGRATED TRANSPORT**
**Commission for Integrated Transport** . . . . . . . . . . . . 2nd Floor, 12 St James's Square, London, SW1Y 4RB
    Chairman . . . . . . . . . . . . . . . . . . . . . . . . . . . . . . . . . Professor David Begg . . . . . . . . . . . . . . . . . . . . . Tel: (0870) 735 3916
    Web: http://www.cfit.gov.uk

**LIGHTHOUSES**
**Corporation of Trinity House Lighthouse Service** . . . Trinity House, Trinity Square, Tower Hill, London, EC3N 4DH
    Chairman/Chief Executive/Deputy Master . . . . . . . . . . Rear-Admiral Jeremy DeHalpert CB . . . . . . . . . . . Tel: (020) 7481 6900
    Web: http://www.trinityhouse.co.uk
**Northern Lighthouse Board** . . . . . . . . . . . . . . . . . . . 84 George Street, Edinburgh, EH2 3DA
    Chairman . . . . . . . . . . . . . . . . . . . . . . . . . . . . . . . . . Sheriff Principal Edward Bowen QC
    Chief Executive . . . . . . . . . . . . . . . . . . . . . . . . . . . Mr James Taylor . . . . . . . . . . . . . . . . . . . . . . . . . Tel: (0131) 473 3100
    Web: http://www.nlb.org.uk

**LONDON UNDERGROUND**
**Office of the PPP Arbiter** . . . . . . . . . . . . . . . . . . . . . 12 St James's Square, London, SW1Y 4RB
    Arbiter . . . . . . . . . . . . . . . . . . . . . . . . . . . . . . . . . . . Mr Chris Bolt . . . . . . . . . . . . . . . . . . . . . . . . . . . Tel: (020) 7849 5629
    Web: http://www.ppparbiter.org.uk

**MARINE SAFETY**
**Maritime and Coastguard Agency** *(Executive Agency)* . . Spring Place, 105 Commercial Road, Southampton, SO15 1EG
    Chief Executive . . . . . . . . . . . . . . . . . . . . . . . . . . . Captain Stephen Bligh . . . . . . . . . . . . . . . . . . . . . Tel: (023) 8032 9100
    Web: http://www.mcga.gov.uk

# DEPARTMENT FOR TRANSPORT

*Other Relevant Contacts (Continued)*

**RAIL PASSENGERS**

**London Transport Users Committee** . . . . . . . . . . . . . 6 Middle Street, London, EC1A 7JA
    Chairman . . . . . . . . . . . . . . . . . . . . . . . . . . . . . . . . Ms Suzanne May
    Director . . . . . . . . . . . . . . . . . . . . . . . . . . . . . . . . . . Mr Rufus Barnes . . . . . . . . . . . . . . . . . . . . . . . . . Tel: (020) 7505 9000
                   E-mail: enquiries@ltuc.org.uk
                   Web: http://www.ltuc.org.uk

**Rail Passengers Council** . . . . . . . . . . . . . . . . . . . . . . Whittles House, Pentonville Road, London, N1 9HF
    Chairman . . . . . . . . . . . . . . . . . . . . . . . . . . . . . . . . Mr Stewart Francis
    National Director . . . . . . . . . . . . . . . . . . . . . . . . . . Mr Anthony Smith . . . . . . . . . . . . . . . . . . . . . . . . Tel: (020) 7713 2700
                   E-mail: info@railpassengers.org.uk
                   Web: http://www.railpassengers.org.uk

**Rail Passengers Committee, Eastern England** . . . . . . . 3rd Floor, Zone 4, Stuart House, City Road, Peterborough, PE1 1QF
    Chairman . . . . . . . . . . . . . . . . . . . . . . . . . . . . . . . . Dr Derek Langslow
    Regional Director . . . . . . . . . . . . . . . . . . . . . . . . . . Mr Guy Dangerfield . . . . . . . . . . . . . . . . . . . . . . Tel: (01733) 312188

**Rail Passengers Committee, Midlands** . . . . . . . . . . . . 6th Floor, The McLaren Building, 35 Dale End, Birmingham, B4 7LN
    Chairman . . . . . . . . . . . . . . . . . . . . . . . . . . . . . . . . Mr Phil Davies
    Regional Director . . . . . . . . . . . . . . . . . . . . . . . . . . Mr Paul Fullwood . . . . . . . . . . . . . . . . . . . . . . . . Tel: (0121) 212 2133

**Rail Passengers Committee, North East England** . . . . Ground Floor, Unit 2, Holgate Court, Holgate Park, Poppleton Road,
                   York, YO26 4GB
    Chairman . . . . . . . . . . . . . . . . . . . . . . . . . . . . . . . . Ms Christine Knights
    Regional Director . . . . . . . . . . . . . . . . . . . . . . . . . . Mr Clive Gossop . . . . . . . . . . . . . . . . . . . . . . . . . Tel: (01904) 787711

**Rail Passengers Committee, North West England** . . . 9th Floor, Rail House, Store Street, Manchester, M1 2RP
    Chairman . . . . . . . . . . . . . . . . . . . . . . . . . . . . . . . . Mr Brendan O'Friel
    Regional Director . . . . . . . . . . . . . . . . . . . . . . . . . . Mr John Mooney . . . . . . . . . . . . . . . . . . . . . . . . . Tel: (0161) 244 5982

**Rail Passengers Committee, Scotland** . . . . . . . . . . . . 5th Floor, Corunna House, 29 Cadogan Street, Glasgow, G2 7AB
    Convenor . . . . . . . . . . . . . . . . . . . . . . . . . . . . . . . . Mr Mike Lunan
    Regional Director . . . . . . . . . . . . . . . . . . . . . . . . . . Mr Robert Samson . . . . . . . . . . . . . . . . . . . . . . . Tel: (0141) 221 7760

**Rail Passengers Committee, Southern England** . . . . . . 3rd Floor, Centric House, 390-391 Strand, London, WC2R 0LT
    Chairman . . . . . . . . . . . . . . . . . . . . . . . . . . . . . . . . Mr Tim Nicholson
    Regional Director . . . . . . . . . . . . . . . . . . . . . . . . . . Mr Mark Woodbridge . . . . . . . . . . . . . . . . . . . . . Tel: (020) 7240 5308

**Rail Passengers Committee, Wales** . . . . . . . . . . . . . . St David's House, Wood Street, Cardiff, CF10 1ES
    Chairman . . . . . . . . . . . . . . . . . . . . . . . . . . . . . . . . Mr Colin Foxall
    Regional Director . . . . . . . . . . . . . . . . . . . . . . . . . . Mr Clive Williams . . . . . . . . . . . . . . . . . . . . . . . . Tel: (029) 2022 7247
                   E-mail: info.wales@railpassengers.org.uk

**Rail Passengers Committee, Western England** . . . . . . 10th Floor, Tower House, Fairfax Street, Bristol, BS1 3BN
    Chairman . . . . . . . . . . . . . . . . . . . . . . . . . . . . . . . . Mr Christopher Irwin
    Regional Director . . . . . . . . . . . . . . . . . . . . . . . . . . Mr Sean O'Neill . . . . . . . . . . . . . . . . . . . . . . . . . . Tel: (0117) 926 5703

**RAILWAYS**

**HM Railway Inspectorate** . . . . . . . . . . . . . . . . . . . . . Rose Court, 2 Southwark Bridge, London, SE1 9HS
    Chief Inspector and Director of Rail Safety . . . . . . . . . Mr Alan Sefton . . . . . . . . . . . . . . . . . . . . . . . . . . . Tel: (020) 7717 6502
                   E-mail: alan.sefton@hse.gsi.gov.uk
                   Web: http://www.hse.gov.uk

**Office of the Rail Regulator** . . . . . . . . . . . . . . . . . . . 1 Waterhouse Square, 138-142 Holborn, London, EC1N 2TQ
    Rail Regulator . . . . . . . . . . . . . . . . . . . . . . . . . . . . . Mr Tom Winsor . . . . . . . . . . . . . . . . . . . . . . . . . . Tel: (020) 7282 2000
                   E-mail: rail.library@orr.gsi.gov.uk
                   Web: http://www.rail-reg.gov.uk

**Strategic Rail Authority** . . . . . . . . . . . . . . . . . . . . . . 55 Victoria Street, London, SW1H 0EU
    Chairman and Chief Executive . . . . . . . . . . . . . . . . . Mr Richard Bowker . . . . . . . . . . . . . . . . . . . . . . . Tel: (020) 7654 6000
                   Web: http://www.sra.gov.uk

**ROADS**

**Highways Agency** *(Executive Agency)* . . . . . . . . . . . . . Corporate Centre, 123 Buckingham Palace Road, London, SW1W 3HA
    Chief Executive . . . . . . . . . . . . . . . . . . . . . . . . . . . Mr Archie Robertson . . . . . . . . . . . . . . . . . . . . . . Tel: (08459) 556575
                   Web: http://www.highways.gov.uk

**Standing Committee on Trunk Road Assessment** . . . . Zone 3/04, Great Minster House, Marsham Street, London, SW1P 4DR
    Chairman . . . . . . . . . . . . . . . . . . . . . . . . . . . . . . . . Ms Eileen Mackay
    Secretary . . . . . . . . . . . . . . . . . . . . . . . . . . . . . . . . Dr Paul Chapman . . . . . . . . . . . . . . . . . . . . . . . . Tel: (020) 7944 6177

# DEPARTMENT FOR TRANSPORT

*Other Relevant Contacts (Continued)*

**TRAFFIC COMMISSIONERS/LICENSING AUTHORITIES**

**Eastern Traffic Area Office** . . . . . . . . . . . . . . . . . . . . City House, 126-130 Hills Road, Cambridge, CB2 1NP
    Commissioner. . . . . . . . . . . . . . . . . . . . . . . . . . . . . . Mr Geoffrey Simms . . . . . . . . . . . . . . . . . . . . . . . Tel: (01792) 454390

**North Eastern and North Western**
    **Traffic Area Office** . . . . . . . . . . . . . . . . . . . . . . . . . Hillcrest House, 386 Harehills Lane, Leeds, LS9 6NF
    Commissioner (North East) . . . . . . . . . . . . . . . . . . . Mr Tom McCartney
    Commissioner (North West) . . . . . . . . . . . . . . . . . . Ms Beverley Bell . . . . . . . . . . . . . . . . . . . . . . . . Tel: (0113) 254 3290

**Scottish Traffic Area Office** . . . . . . . . . . . . . . . . . . . Argyle House, 3 Lady Lawson Street, Edinburgh, EH3 9SE
    Commissioner. . . . . . . . . . . . . . . . . . . . . . . . . . . . . . Ms Joan Aitken . . . . . . . . . . . . . . . . . . . . . . . . . . Tel: (0131) 200 4905

**South Eastern and Metropolitan Traffic Area Office** . Ivy House, 3 Ivy Terrace, Eastbourne, East Sussex, BN21 4QT
    Commissioner. . . . . . . . . . . . . . . . . . . . . . . . . . . . . . Mr Christopher Heaps . . . . . . . . . . . . . . . . . . . . . Tel: (01323) 452400

**West Midlands and Wales Traffic Area Office** . . . . . . Cumberland House, 200 Broad Street, Birmingham, B15 1TD
    Commissioner. . . . . . . . . . . . . . . . . . . . . . . . . . . . . . Mr David Dixon. . . . . . . . . . . . . . . . . . . . . . . . . . . Tel: (0121) 609 6823

**Western Traffic Area Office** . . . . . . . . . . . . . . . . . . . 2 Rivergate, Temple Quay, Bristol, BS1 6EH
    Commissioner. . . . . . . . . . . . . . . . . . . . . . . . . . . . . . Mr Philip Brown . . . . . . . . . . . . . . . . . . . . . . . . . Tel: (0117) 900 8577

**VEHICLES** *(See above under Drivers / Vehicles)*

# PASSENGER TRANSPORT CONFEDERATION

# RAIL

## THE CONFEDERATION OF PASSENGER TRANSPORT UK

Imperial House, 15-19 Kingsway, London, WC2B 6UN
*Telephone*: (020) 7240 3131
*Facsimile*: (020) 7240 6565
*E-mail*: simonp@cpt-uk.org
*Web*: http://www.cpt-uk.org/cpt
*24hr Media & Crisis Control Line*: 01893 380709

*Contact*: Simon Posner – *Director of Communications*

The Confederation of Passenger Transport UK (CPT) is the national trade association that represents the UK's bus, coach and light rail operators. CPT provides members with legislative, technical and operational advice, nationally recognised training programmes, mutual aid, crisis control, trade shows, seminars and codes of practice.

    CPT is consulted by, and has close working links with, UK and EU legislators, media, associated organisations, specialist bodies and opinion formers.

ASSOCIATION *of* TRAIN OPERATING COMPANIES

## ASSOCIATION OF TRAIN OPERATING COMPANIES (ATOC)

40 Bernard Street, London, WC1N 1BY

*Telephone:* (020) 7904 3010
*Facsimile:* (020) 7904 3081
*Web:* www.atoc.org

Contact: John Dennis – Communications Manager

ATOC is the official voice for the passenger rail industry – representing train companies to the Government and other opinion formers on transport policy issues. ATOC also manages many joint activities for train operators, including revenue allocation and settlement, impartial retailing, National Rail Enquiries, Railcard marketing, staff travel arrangements, international products, travel agent licensing, and relationships with Transport for London.

speaking for airports

The **Airport Operators Association** (AOA) is the trade association that represents UK airports and is the principal body with whom the Government and regulatory authorities consult on airport matters.

The AOA brings member airports together to share expertise and develop common approaches across the full spectrum of airport issues.

The AOA promotes the continued successful development of UK airports and aviation in partnership with its members and other stakeholders. Aviation is a substantial industry in the UK, contributing:

- *Employment* – 500,000 direct and indirect jobs

- *Output* – £10 billion a year to UK GDP and £2.5 billion to the Chancellor

- *Exports* – £41 billion of goods and services

Our membership comprises 72 airports representing all of the nation's international hub and major regional airports in addition to many serving community, business and leisure aviation. A further 150 plus companies are Associate Members of the AOA.

Contact for further information:

Michelle Di Leo – Head of Media and Public Affairs,
AOA, 3 Birdcage Walk, London SW1H 9JJ
Tel: 020 7222 2249  Fax: 020 7976 7405
E-mail: michelledileo@aoa.org.uk
Web: http://www.aoa.org.uk

# H  M  T R E A S U R Y

1 Horse Guards Road, London, SW1A 2HQ
*Switchboard:* Tel: (020) 7270 5000  *Enquiries* Tel: (020) 7270 4558  Fax: (020) 7270 5653
E-mail: public.enquiries@hm-treasury.gsi.gov.uk
Web: http://www.hm-treasury.gov.uk

## MINISTERS

**Chancellor of the Exchequer** . . . . . . . . . . . . . . . . . . . Rt Hon Gordon Brown MP
   *Principal Private Secretary* . . . . . . . . . . . . . . . . . . . . . . Mr Mark Bowman . . . . . . . . . . . . . . . . . . . . . . . . . . . . . . Tel: (020) 7270 4330
   *Political Secretary* . . . . . . . . . . . . . . . . . . . . . . . . . . . Ms Sue Nye . . . . . . . . . . . . . . . . . . . . . . . . . . . . . . . . . . Tel: (020) 7270 5012
   *Special Advisers* . . . . . . . . . . . . . . . . . . . . . . . . . . . . . Mr Ian Austin. . . . . . . . . . . . . . . . . . . . . . . . . . . . . . . . . Tel: (020) 7270 1823
                                                   Mr Spencer Livermore . . . . . . . . . . . . . . . . . . . . . . . . Tel: (020) 7270 5027

**Chief Secretary** . . . . . . . . . . . . . . . . . . . . . . . . . . . . . . Rt Hon Paul Boateng MP
   *Private Secretary*. . . . . . . . . . . . . . . . . . . . . . . . . . . . . Mr Dan Rosenfield . . . . . . . . . . . . . . . . . . . . . . . . . . . . Tel: (020) 7270 4339
   *Special Advisers* . . . . . . . . . . . . . . . . . . . . . . . . . . . . . Mr Jonathan Ashworth . . . . . . . . . . . . . . . . . . . . . . . . Tel: (020) 7270 1817
                                                   Ms Nicola Murphy . . . . . . . . . . . . . . . . . . . . . . . . . . . Tel: (020) 7270 1823

**Paymaster General** . . . . . . . . . . . . . . . . . . . . . . . . . . . Rt Hon Dawn Primarolo MP
   *Private Secretary*. . . . . . . . . . . . . . . . . . . . . . . . . . . . . Mr Andy Gordon. . . . . . . . . . . . . . . . . . . . . . . . . . . . . . Tel: (020) 7270 4349

**Financial Secretary**. . . . . . . . . . . . . . . . . . . . . . . . . . . Mr Stephen Timms MP
   *Private Secretary*. . . . . . . . . . . . . . . . . . . . . . . . . . . . . Mr Guy Davison . . . . . . . . . . . . . . . . . . . . . . . . . . . . . . Tel: (020) 7270 4340

**Economic Secretary** . . . . . . . . . . . . . . . . . . . . . . . . . . Mr John Healey MP
   *Private Secretary*. . . . . . . . . . . . . . . . . . . . . . . . . . . . . Mr Sam Woods . . . . . . . . . . . . . . . . . . . . . . . . . . . . . . . Tel: (020) 7270 4350

## CIVIL SERVICE

**Permanent Secretary** . . . . . . . . . . . . . . . . . . . . . . . . . Mr Gus O'Donnell CB
   *Private Secretary*. . . . . . . . . . . . . . . . . . . . . . . . . . . . . Mr Ciaran Martin . . . . . . . . . . . . . . . . . . . . . . . . . . . . . Tel: (020) 7270 4360

### Managing Directors

Budget and Public Finances . . . . . . . . . . . . . . . . . . . . . . Sir Nick Stern. . . . . . . . . . . . . . . . . . . . . . . . . . . . . . . . Tel: (020) 7270 5650
Corporate Services . . . . . . . . . . . . . . . . . . . . . . . . . . . . . Ms Hilary Douglas CB . . . . . . . . . . . . . . . . . . . . . . . . . Tel: (020) 7270 1364
Financial Management, Reporting and Audit. . . . . . . . . . Sir Andrew Likierman. . . . . . . . . . . . . . . . . . . . . . . . . . Tel: (020) 7270 5175
Financial Regulation and Industry . . . . . . . . . . . . . . . . . Mr James Sassoon. . . . . . . . . . . . . . . . . . . . . . . . . . . . . Tel: (020) 7270 5113
Macroeconomic Policy and International Finance . . . . . . . Mr Jon Cunliffe CB . . . . . . . . . . . . . . . . . . . . . . . . . . . Tel: (020) 7270 5201
Public Services . . . . . . . . . . . . . . . . . . . . . . . . . . . . . . . . Mr Nicholas Macpherson . . . . . . . . . . . . . . . . . . . . . . . Tel: (020) 7270 4563

## SUBJECT RESPONSIBILITIES AND CONTACTS

### Accounts

   Treasury Officer of Accounts . . . . . . . . . . . . . . . . . . . Mr Brian Glickman. . . . . . . . . . . . . . . . . . . . . . . . . . . . Tel: (020) 7270 4886
   Second Treasury Officer of Accounts. . . . . . . . . . . . . . Mr Rob Molan . . . . . . . . . . . . . . . . . . . . . . . . . . . . . . . Tel: (020) 7270 4886
   Accountancy, Central . . . . . . . . . . . . . . . . . . . . . . . . . Mr David Loweth . . . . . . . . . . . . . . . . . . . . . . . . . . . . . Tel: (020) 7270 4554
   Accounting Resources: Development . . . . . . . . . . . . . . Mr Mal Singh . . . . . . . . . . . . . . . . . . . . . . . . . . . . . . . . Tel: (020) 7270 4364
   Accounts, Finance and Purchasing Strategy . . . . . . . . Ms Louise Tulett. . . . . . . . . . . . . . . . . . . . . . . . . . . . . . Tel: (020) 7270 1555
   Exchequer Funds and Accounts . . . . . . . . . . . . . . . . . . Mr Ian Taylor . . . . . . . . . . . . . . . . . . . . . . . . . . . . . . . . Tel: (020) 7270 4714
   Single Data System Development . . . . . . . . . . . . . . . . . Mr Ian Carruthers. . . . . . . . . . . . . . . . . . . . . . . . . . . . . Tel: (020) 7270 4554
   Whole of Government Accounts . . . . . . . . . . . . . . . . . . Mr Ian Carruthers. . . . . . . . . . . . . . . . . . . . . . . . . . . . . Tel: (020) 7270 4554

### Audit

   Internal . . . . . . . . . . . . . . . . . . . . . . . . . . . . . . . . . . . . *Vacant* . . . . . . . . . . . . . . . . . . . . . . . . . . . . . . . . . . . . . Tel: (020) 7270 1570
   Assurance Control and Risk Team . . . . . . . . . . . . . . . . Mr Chris Butler . . . . . . . . . . . . . . . . . . . . . . . . . . . . . . . Tel: (020) 7270 1681

### Banking and General Insurance . . . . . . . . . . . . . . . . . Ms Susan Catchpole . . . . . . . . . . . . . . . . . . . . . . . . . . . Tel: (020) 7270 5294

### Better Public Service s . . . . . . . . . . . . . . . . . . . . . . . . Mr Stephen Mitchell. . . . . . . . . . . . . . . . . . . . . . . . . . . Tel: (020) 7270 5516

### Budget and Public Finances

   Director . . . . . . . . . . . . . . . . . . . . . . . . . . . . . . . . . . . . Sir Nick Stern. . . . . . . . . . . . . . . . . . . . . . . . . . . . . . . . Tel: (020) 7270 4370
   Managing Directors . . . . . . . . . . . . . . . . . . . . . . . . . . Mr Nicholas Holgate. . . . . . . . . . . . . . . . . . . . . . . . . . . Tel: (020) 7270 5496

# H M  T R E A S U R Y

Mr Dave Ramsden . . . . . . . . . . . . . . . . . . . . . . . . . . . . . Tel: (020) 7270 4419

**Budget Co-ordination**. . . . . . . . . . . . . . . . . . . Mr Tom Josephs . . . . . . . . . . . . . . . . . . . . . . . . . Tel: (020) 7270 4776

**Business, Technology and Innovation** . . . . . . . . . . Mr Mike Crabtree . . . . . . . . . . . . . . . . . . . . . . . . Tel: (020) 7270 4667

**Capital Markets and Governance** . . . . . . . . . . . . . . Mr David Lawton . . . . . . . . . . . . . . . . . . . . . . . . . Tel: (020) 7270 4381

**Civil List**. . . . . . . . . . . . . . . . . . . . . . . . . . . . . . . Mr Ian Taylor . . . . . . . . . . . . . . . . . . . . . . . . . . . . Tel: (020) 7270 4714

**Commerce, Government**
Office of Government Commerce
*Trevelyan House, Great Peter Street, London, SW1P 2BY*
Web: http://www.ogc.gov.uk
Chief Executive . . . . . . . . . . . . . . . . . . . . . . . Mr John Oughton . . . . . . . . . . . . . . . . . . . . . Tel: (020) 7271 1351
Executive Directors
    Corporate Services . . . . . . . . . . . . . . . . . . . Mr Bryan Avery . . . . . . . . . . . . . . . . . . . . . . Tel: (020) 7271 1353
    Gateways Programme . . . . . . . . . . . . . . . . . . Mr Ian Glenday . . . . . . . . . . . . . . . . . . . . . . Tel: (020) 7271 1328
    Supplier and Government
      Marketplace Development . . . . . . . . . . . . . . . . Mr Martin Sykes . . . . . . . . . . . . . . . . . . . . . Tel: (020) 7271 1451
Audit, Internal . . . . . . . . . . . . . . . . . . . . . . . . Mr John Comley . . . . . . . . . . . . . . . . . . . . . Tel: (020) 7271 1401
Best Practice . . . . . . . . . . . . . . . . . . . . . . . . . Mr Bob Assirati . . . . . . . . . . . . . . . . . . . . . . Tel: (020) 7271 1306
Business Change and IT Development . . . . . . . . . . . Mr Tony Betts. . . . . . . . . . . . . . . . . . . . . . . . Tel: (01603) 704754
Collaboration and Property Co-ordination . . . . . . . . Mr Mike Burt . . . . . . . . . . . . . . . . . . . . . . . Tel: (020) 7271 2661
Communications. . . . . . . . . . . . . . . . . . . . . . . . Mr Marcus Bennett . . . . . . . . . . . . . . . . . . . Tel: (01603) 704890
Consultancy . . . . . . . . . . . . . . . . . . . . . . . . . . Mr Stephen Mitchell . . . . . . . . . . . . . . . . . . Tel: (01603) 704620
Corporate Planning and Strategic Communications . . . . Ms Sue Broyd . . . . . . . . . . . . . . . . . . . . . . . Tel: (020) 7271 1313
Corporate Services . . . . . . . . . . . . . . . . . . . . . Mr Bryan Avery . . . . . . . . . . . . . . . . . . . . . . Tel: (020) 7271 1353
Customer Events . . . . . . . . . . . . . . . . . . . . . . Ms Sue Broyd . . . . . . . . . . . . . . . . . . . . . . . Tel: (020) 7271 1313
Customer Relationships, Key . . . . . . . . . . . . . . . Mr Jon Perigo . . . . . . . . . . . . . . . . . . . . . . . Tel: (01603) 704595
Customer Systems Services . . . . . . . . . . . . . . . . Mr Nic Hopkins . . . . . . . . . . . . . . . . . . . . . Tel: (01603) 704536
Delivery Skills Development Centre . . . . . . . . . . . . Ms Jane Grant . . . . . . . . . . . . . . . . . . . . . . Tel: (020) 7271 1477
Development . . . . . . . . . . . . . . . . . . . . . . . . . Mr David Gigg . . . . . . . . . . . . . . . . . . . . . . Tel: (0797) 328 5203
E-Commerce . . . . . . . . . . . . . . . . . . . . . . . . . Dr John Stewart . . . . . . . . . . . . . . . . . . . . . Tel: (01603) 704712
Finance and Procurement . . . . . . . . . . . . . . . . . Mr Bob Ellis . . . . . . . . . . . . . . . . . . . . . . . . Tel: (020) 7271 1314
Gateways Programme . . . . . . . . . . . . . . . . . . . Mr Ian Glenday . . . . . . . . . . . . . . . . . . . . . . Tel: (020) 7271 1328
Human Resources . . . . . . . . . . . . . . . . . . . . . Mr Paul Jones . . . . . . . . . . . . . . . . . . . . . . . Tel: (020) 7271 1316
Information Technology Modernisation . . . . . . . . . . Mr Tony Betts . . . . . . . . . . . . . . . . . . . . . . . Tel: (01603) 704754
Legal Adviser . . . . . . . . . . . . . . . . . . . . . . . . . Ms Phinella Henderson . . . . . . . . . . . . . . . . Tel: (020) 7271 1378
Parliamentary Business . . . . . . . . . . . . . . . . . . Mr Graham Turvey . . . . . . . . . . . . . . . . . . . Tel: (020) 7271 1369
Policy Managers
    Corporate Services . . . . . . . . . . . . . . . . . . . Mr Duncan Slaughter . . . . . . . . . . . . . . . . . Tel: (020) 7271 1433
    Suppliers . . . . . . . . . . . . . . . . . . . . . . . . . Mr Stephen Tokley . . . . . . . . . . . . . . . . . . . Tel: (020) 7271 1463
Press . . . . . . . . . . . . . . . . . . . . . . . . . . . . . . Mr David Prior . . . . . . . . . . . . . . . . . . . . . . Tel: (020) 7271 1381
Procurement Policy . . . . . . . . . . . . . . . . . . . . . Ms Anne Turner . . . . . . . . . . . . . . . . . . . . . Tel: (020) 7211 1330
Property and Construction Development . . . . . . . . . Mr Arnold Butler . . . . . . . . . . . . . . . . . . . . Tel: (020) 7271 2705
Property and Construction Disposals. . . . . . . . . . . . Mr Michael Burt . . . . . . . . . . . . . . . . . . . . . Tel: (020) 7271 2661
Research and Guidance . . . . . . . . . . . . . . . . . . Dr John Stewart . . . . . . . . . . . . . . . . . . . . . Tel: (01603) 704712
Successful Delivery . . . . . . . . . . . . . . . . . . . . . Ms Vanessa Carpenter . . . . . . . . . . . . . . . . . Tel: (020) 7271 1343
Supplier and Government Marketplace Development . . . Mr Martin Sykes . . . . . . . . . . . . . . . . . . . . . Tel: (020) 7271 1451
Supplier Relations . . . . . . . . . . . . . . . . . . . . . Mr Ian Tough . . . . . . . . . . . . . . . . . . . . . . . Tel: (020) 7271 2639

**Communications**
Head of Communications and Strategy . . . . . . . . . . Mr Damian McBride . . . . . . . . . . . . . . . . . . Tel: (020) 7270 5252
Press Office . . . . . . . . . . . . . . . . . . . . . . . . . . Mr Paul Kissack . . . . . . . . . . . . . . . . . . . . . Tel: (020) 7270 5245

**Competition, Regulation and Energy Markets**. . . . . . Ms Helen Fleming . . . . . . . . . . . . . . . . . . . . . Tel: (020) 7270 4774

**Corporate and Private Finance**. . . . . . . . . . . . . . . Mr Oliver Robbins . . . . . . . . . . . . . . . . . . . . . Tel: (020) 7270 4905

# H M   T R E A S U R Y

**Corporate Services and Development**
    Managing Director . . . . . . . . . . . . . . . . . . . Ms Hilary Douglas CB . . . . . . . . . . . . . . . . . . . . . . . . . Tel: (020) 7270 1691

**Country: Economics and Policy** . . . . . . . . . . . . . . . Mr Andrew Kilpatrick . . . . . . . . . . . . . . . . . . . . . . . . Tel: (020) 7270 5395

**Credit Unions** . . . . . . . . . . . . . . . . . . . . . . . . . . . . . . Ms Susan Catchpole . . . . . . . . . . . . . . . . . . . . . . . . . Tel: (020) 7270 5294

**Culture** . . . . . . . . . . . . . . . . . . . . . . . . . . . . . . . . . . . . . Mr Steven Meek . . . . . . . . . . . . . . . . . . . . . . . . . . . . Tel: (020) 7270 1770

**Debt and Reserves Management** . . . . . . . . . . . . . . . Ms Alison Holland . . . . . . . . . . . . . . . . . . . . . . . . . . Tel: (020) 7270 4337

**Defence, Diplomacy and Intelligence** . . . . . . . . . . . Mr John Dodds . . . . . . . . . . . . . . . . . . . . . . . . . . . . . Tel: (020) 7270 4829

**Devolved Countries and Regions** . . . . . . . . . . . . . . . Mrs Ros Dunn . . . . . . . . . . . . . . . . . . . . . . . . . . . . . . Tel: (020) 7270 4652

**Economic Assessment** . . . . . . . . . . . . . . . . . . . . . . . . Mr Chris Kelly . . . . . . . . . . . . . . . . . . . . . . . . . . . . . . Tel: (020) 7270 5514

**Economist Group Management Unit** . . . . . . . . . . . . *Vacant* . . . . . . . . . . . . . . . . . . . . . . . . . . . . . . . . . . . . Tel: (020) 7270 4571

**Education, Training and Culture** . . . . . . . . . . . . . . . Mr Steven Meek . . . . . . . . . . . . . . . . . . . . . . . . . . . . Tel: (020) 7270 1770

**Enterprise Issues** . . . . . . . . . . . . . . . . . . . . . . . . . . . . Ms Fiona Henderson . . . . . . . . . . . . . . . . . . . . . . . . . Tel: (020) 7270 4667

**Environment, Food and Rural Policy** . . . . . . . . . . . Ms Mridul Brivati . . . . . . . . . . . . . . . . . . . . . . . . . . . Tel: (020) 7270 4650
                                                       Ms Sarah Mullen . . . . . . . . . . . . . . . . . . . . . . . . . . . . Tel: (020) 7270 4650

**Environment, Transport Taxes**
    **and Saving Incentives** . . . . . . . . . . . . . . . . . . . . . Mr Paul O'Sullivan . . . . . . . . . . . . . . . . . . . . . . . . . . Tel: (020) 7270 5549

**Euro Preparations Unit** . . . . . . . . . . . . . . . . . . . . . . Ms Hilary Thompson . . . . . . . . . . . . . . . . . . . . . . . . . Tel: (020) 7270 4845

**European Financial Services** . . . . . . . . . . . . . . . . . . Mr Clive Maxwell . . . . . . . . . . . . . . . . . . . . . . . . . . . Tel: (020) 7270 4486

**European Union**
    Co-ordination and Strategy . . . . . . . . . . . . . . . . . Mr Stewart James . . . . . . . . . . . . . . . . . . . . . . . . . . . Tel: (020) 7270 4432
    Economic and Monetary Union . . . . . . . . . . . . . . . Mr Ian Walker . . . . . . . . . . . . . . . . . . . . . . . . . . . . . Tel: (020) 7270 4302
    Euro Preparations . . . . . . . . . . . . . . . . . . . . . . . . . Ms Hillary Thompson . . . . . . . . . . . . . . . . . . . . . . . . Tel: (020) 7270 4845
    European Economic Reform . . . . . . . . . . . . . . . . . Mr Paul Rankin . . . . . . . . . . . . . . . . . . . . . . . . . . . . . Tel: (020) 7270 4362
    Finance . . . . . . . . . . . . . . . . . . . . . . . . . . . . . . . . . . Mr Geoffrey Lloyd . . . . . . . . . . . . . . . . . . . . . . . . . . Tel: (020) 7270 5584
    Financial Services, European . . . . . . . . . . . . . . . . Mr Clive Maxwell . . . . . . . . . . . . . . . . . . . . . . . . . . . Tel: (020) 7270 4486
    International Taxation and . . . . . . . . . . . . . . . . . . . Mr David Richardson . . . . . . . . . . . . . . . . . . . . . . . . Tel: (020) 7270 4629

**Exchequer Funds and Accounts** . . . . . . . . . . . . . . . . Mr Ian Taylor . . . . . . . . . . . . . . . . . . . . . . . . . . . . . . Tel: (020) 7270 4714

**Expenditure Policy, General** . . . . . . . . . . . . . . . . . . . Mr Jonathan Stephens . . . . . . . . . . . . . . . . . . . . . . . Tel: (020) 7270 5516

**Expenditure Statistics, General** . . . . . . . . . . . . . . . . Mr Allen Ritchie . . . . . . . . . . . . . . . . . . . . . . . . . . . . Tel: (020) 7270 5343

**Facilities and Contracts Management** . . . . . . . . . . . Mr Paul Pegler . . . . . . . . . . . . . . . . . . . . . . . . . . . . . Tel: (020) 7270 4830

**Finance and Purchasing Strategy** . . . . . . . . . . . . . . Ms Louise Tulett . . . . . . . . . . . . . . . . . . . . . . . . . . . . Tel: (020) 7270 1555

**Financial Crime** . . . . . . . . . . . . . . . . . . . . . . . . . . . . . Ms Heather Kempton . . . . . . . . . . . . . . . . . . . . . . . . Tel: (020) 7270 4622

**Financial Management: Reporting and Audit**
    Director and Principal Finance Officer . . . . . . . . . . Professor Sir Andrew Likierman . . . . . . . . . . . . . . . . Tel: (020) 7270 5175
    Treasury Officer of Accounts . . . . . . . . . . . . . . . . Mr Brian Glicksman . . . . . . . . . . . . . . . . . . . . . . . . . Tel: (020) 7270 4886

# H M  T R E A S U R Y

**Financial Regulation and Industry**
    Managing Director . . . . . . . . . . . . . . . . . . . . . . . . . . Mr James Sassoon. . . . . . . . . . . . . . . . . . . . . . . . . . . Tel: (020) 7270 5113
    Deputy Directors . . . . . . . . . . . . . . . . . . . . . . . . . . . Mr John Kingman. . . . . . . . . . . . . . . . . . . . . . . . Tel: (020) 7270 6325
                                   Mr Phil Wynn Owen. . . . . . . . . . . . . . . . . . . . . . . . Tel: (020) 7270 4448

**Financial Regulation and Sanctions, International** . . . Mr David Faulkner . . . . . . . . . . . . . . . . . . . . . . . . . . . Tel: (020) 7270 5550

**Financial Services, Access to Markets** . . . . . . . . . . . Mr Peter Maydon . . . . . . . . . . . . . . . . . . . . . . . . . . . Tel: (020) 7270 5298

**Financial Stability and Regulatory Policy** . . . . . . . . . Mr Paul Sanderson . . . . . . . . . . . . . . . . . . . . . . . . . . Tel: (020) 7270 4381

**Financial Systems and International Standards** . . . . . Ms Lucy Makinson . . . . . . . . . . . . . . . . . . . . . . . . . . Tel: (020) 7270 4750

**Global Policy and Institutions** . . . . . . . . . . . . . . . . . Mr Jonathan Ockenden. . . . . . . . . . . . . . . . . . . . . . . Tel: (020) 7270 1357

**Fiscal and Macroeconomic Policy** . . . . . . . . . . . . . . . Mr Robert Woods . . . . . . . . . . . . . . . . . . . . . . . . . . . Tel: (020) 7270 5514

**Health** . . . . . . . . . . . . . . . . . . . . . . . . . . . . . . . . . . Mr John Hall . . . . . . . . . . . . . . . . . . . . . . . . . . . . . . Tel: (020) 7270 5033

**Home Office, Legal and Communities** . . . . . . . . . . . . Mr Julian Kelly. . . . . . . . . . . . . . . . . . . . . . . . . . . . . Tel: (020) 7270 4999

**Housing and Urban**. . . . . . . . . . . . . . . . . . . . . . . . . Mr James Bowler . . . . . . . . . . . . . . . . . . . . . . . . . . . Tel: (020) 7270 4771

**Human Resources**. . . . . . . . . . . . . . . . . . . . . . . . . . Mr Chris Pearson . . . . . . . . . . . . . . . . . . . . . . . . . . . Tel: (020) 7270 5159

**Insurance and Banking** . . . . . . . . . . . . . . . . . . . . . . Ms Susan Catchpole . . . . . . . . . . . . . . . . . . . . . . . . . Tel: (020) 7270 5294

**International Financial Services** . . . . . . . . . . . . . . . . Ms Lucy Makinson . . . . . . . . . . . . . . . . . . . . . . . . . . Tel: (020) 7270 4750

**International Debt and Capital Markets**. . . . . . . . . . . Mr Harold Freeman . . . . . . . . . . . . . . . . . . . . . . . . . Tel: (020) 7270 4797

**International Monetary Fund** . . . . . . . . . . . . . . . . . . Mr Stephen Pickford. . . . . . . . . . . . . . . . . . . . . . . . . Tel: (020) 7270 4682

**International Poverty Reduction** . . . . . . . . . . . . . . . . Ms Beverly Warmington . . . . . . . . . . . . . . . . . . . . . . Tel: (020) 7270 5263

**IT, Departmental** . . . . . . . . . . . . . . . . . . . . . . . . . . Mrs Bernadette Cass. . . . . . . . . . . . . . . . . . . . . . . . . Tel: (020) 7270 5400

**Labour Market Policy** . . . . . . . . . . . . . . . . . . . . . . . Ms Alison Cottrell . . . . . . . . . . . . . . . . . . . . . . . . . . Tel: (020) 7270 4724

**Learning Skills and Development, Departmental** . . . . Ms Sally Sheen. . . . . . . . . . . . . . . . . . . . . . . . . . . . . Tel: (020) 7270 1515

**Librarian, Departmental** . . . . . . . . . . . . . . . . . . . . . Ms Jean Clayton . . . . . . . . . . . . . . . . . . . . . . . . . . . . Tel: (020) 7270 5259

**Local Government** . . . . . . . . . . . . . . . . . . . . . . . . . . Mr Paul Johnston . . . . . . . . . . . . . . . . . . . . . . . . . . . Tel: (020) 7270 4767

**Macroeconomic Policy and Prospects**
    Managing Director . . . . . . . . . . . . . . . . . . . . . . . . . . Mr Jon Cunliffe CB . . . . . . . . . . . . . . . . . . . . . . . . . . Tel: (020) 7270 5209
    Directors . . . . . . . . . . . . . . . . . . . . . . . . . . . . . . . . . Mr Simon Brooks . . . . . . . . . . . . . . . . . . . . . . . . . . . Tel: (020) 7270 5454
                                     Ms Melanie Dawes . . . . . . . . . . . . . . . . . . . . . . . . . . Tel: (020) 7270 4470
                                     Ms Sue Owen . . . . . . . . . . . . . . . . . . . . . . . . . . . . . Tel: (020) 7270 4460
                                     Mr Stephen Pickford CB. . . . . . . . . . . . . . . . . . . . . . Tel: (020) 7270 4682

**Parliamentary Clerk**. . . . . . . . . . . . . . . . . . . . . . . . . Mr David Martin. . . . . . . . . . . . . . . . . . . . . . . . . . . . Tel: (020) 7270 4520

**Personnel Management and Training**. . . . . . . . . . . . . Ms Sally Sheen. . . . . . . . . . . . . . . . . . . . . . . . . . . . . Tel: (020) 7270 1515

**Press** *(see above under Communications)*

**Productivity and Structural Reform**. . . . . . . . . . . . . . Mr Jitinder Kolhi . . . . . . . . . . . . . . . . . . . . . . . . . . . Tel: (020) 7270 4774

# H  M   T R E A S U R Y

**Public Sector Finance - Advice and Developments** . . Mr Graham Parker . . . . . . . . . . . . . . . . . . . . . . . . . . . . Tel: (020) 7270 5130

**Public Service Pensions** . . . . . . . . . . . . . . . . . . . . . . . Mr David Deaton . . . . . . . . . . . . . . . . . . . . . . . . . . . Tel: (020) 7270 5590

**Public Services**

Managing Director, Public Services . . . . . . . . . . . . . . Mr Nicholas Macpherson . . . . . . . . . . . . . . . . . . . . Tel: (020) 7270 5939

Directors . . . . . . . . . . . . . . . . . . . . . . . . . . . . . . . . . . . Ms Anita Charlsworth . . . . . . . . . . . . . . . . . . . . . . . . Tel: (020) 7270 4430

Mr Joe Grice . . . . . . . . . . . . . . . . . . . . . . . . . . . . . Tel: (020) 7270 4481

Mr Jonathan Stephens . . . . . . . . . . . . . . . . . . . . . . Tel: (020) 7270 4660

Delivery Analysis . . . . . . . . . . . . . . . . . . . . . . . . . . . . Mr Joe Grice . . . . . . . . . . . . . . . . . . . . . . . . . . . . . Tel: (020) 7270 4481

Better Public Services . . . . . . . . . . . . . . . . . . . . . . . . Mr Stephen Mitchell . . . . . . . . . . . . . . . . . . . . . . . Tel: (020) 7270 5516

Public Services Productivity Panel . . . . . . . . . . . . . . Mr Dean Stokes . . . . . . . . . . . . . . . . . . . . . . . . . . Tel: (020) 7270 4849

Workforce, Innovation and Reward . . . . . . . . . . . . . . Mr Andy Graham . . . . . . . . . . . . . . . . . . . . . . . . . . Tel: (020) 7270 5596

**Regions and Devolved Countries** . . . . . . . . . . . . . . . Mrs Ros Dunn . . . . . . . . . . . . . . . . . . . . . . . . . . . . . Tel: (020) 7270 4652

**Saving and Investment Products** . . . . . . . . . . . . . . . . Mr Paul Kirkham . . . . . . . . . . . . . . . . . . . . . . . . . . . Tel: (020) 7270 5474

**Statistics, General Expenditure** . . . . . . . . . . . . . . . . . Mr Allen Ritchie . . . . . . . . . . . . . . . . . . . . . . . . . . . Tel: (020) 7270 5343

**Tax Administration and Revenues** . . . . . . . . . . . . . . . Mr Peter Short . . . . . . . . . . . . . . . . . . . . . . . . . . . . Tel: (020) 7270 5308

**Tax Policy** . . . . . . . . . . . . . . . . . . . . . . . . . . . . . . . . . . Mr Andrew Lewis . . . . . . . . . . . . . . . . . . . . . . . . . . Tel: (020) 7270 4914

**Taxation (International) and European Union** . . . . . . Mr David Richardson . . . . . . . . . . . . . . . . . . . . . . . Tel: (020) 7270 4629

**Technology, Innovation and Business** . . . . . . . . . . . . Mr Mike Crabtree . . . . . . . . . . . . . . . . . . . . . . . . . . Tel: (020) 7270 4667

**Transport** . . . . . . . . . . . . . . . . . . . . . . . . . . . . . . . . . . . Mr Lewis Atter . . . . . . . . . . . . . . . . . . . . . . . . . . . . . Tel: (020) 7270 4071

**Transport Taxes and Saving Incentives** . . . . . . . . . . . Mr Paul O'Sullivan . . . . . . . . . . . . . . . . . . . . . . . . . Tel: (020) 7270 5549

**Work and Pensions** . . . . . . . . . . . . . . . . . . . . . . . . . . . Mr Peter Betts . . . . . . . . . . . . . . . . . . . . . . . . . . . . Tel: (020) 7270 4799

**Work Incentives and Poverty Analysis** . . . . . . . . . . . Ms Helen John . . . . . . . . . . . . . . . . . . . . . . . . . . . . Tel: (020) 7270 4792

**Workforce, Innovation and Reward** . . . . . . . . . . . . . . Mr Andy Graham . . . . . . . . . . . . . . . . . . . . . . . . . . Tel: (020) 7270 5596

**World Bank** . . . . . . . . . . . . . . . . . . . . . . . . . . . . . . . . . Mr Tom Scholar . . . . . . . . . . . . . . . . . . . . . . . . . . . Tel: (020) 7270 4682

## OTHER RELEVANT CONTACTS

**ACTUARY**

**Government Actuary Department** . . . . . . . . . . . . . . . . 15-17 Furnival Street, London, EC4A 1AB

Government Actuary . . . . . . . . . . . . . . . . . . . . . . . . . Mr Chris Daykin CB . . . . . . . . . . . . . . . . . . . . . . . . . Tel: (020) 7211 2600

E-mail: enquiries@gad.gov.uk

Web: http://www.gad.gov.uk

**BANK OF ENGLAND**

**Bank of England** . . . . . . . . . . . . . . . . . . . . . . . . . . . . . Threadneedle Street, London, EC2R 8AH

Governor . . . . . . . . . . . . . . . . . . . . . . . . . . . . . . . . . Rt Hon Mervyn King . . . . . . . . . . . . . . . . . . . . . . . . Tel: (020) 7601 4444

Web: http://www.bankofengland.co.uk

**CUSTOMS AND EXCISE**

**H M Customs and Excise**

*(Non-Ministerial Government Department)* . . . . . . . . . . New King's Beam House, 22 Upper Ground, London, SE1 9PJ

Chairman . . . . . . . . . . . . . . . . . . . . . . . . . . . . . . . . . Mr Mike Eland . . . . . . . . . . . . . . . . . . . . . . . . . . . . . Tel: (020) 7620 1313

Web: http://www.hmce.gov.uk

# H M  T R E A S U R Y

## DEBT MANAGEMENT

**UK Debt Management Office** *(Executive Agency)* . . . . . . Eastcheap Court, 11 Philpot Lane, London, EC3M 8UD

    Chief Executive . . . . . . . . . . . . . . . . . . . . . . Mr Robert Stheeman . . . . . . . . . . . . . . . . . . . . . . . . Tel: (020) 7862 6500

    Deputy Chief Executive . . . . . . . . . . . . . . . . . . . Ms Jo Wheelan . . . . . . . . . . . . . . . . . . . . . . . . . . Tel: (020) 7862 6531

    Chief Operating Officer. . . . . . . . . . . . . . . . . . . . Mr Jim Juffs. . . . . . . . . . . . . . . . . . . . . . . . . . . . . Tel: (020) 7862 6520

    Secretary to Public Works Loan Commissioners. . . . . . Mr Hamish Watson . . . . . . . . . . . . . . . . . . . . . . . . . Tel: (020) 7862 6617

                Web: http://www.dmo.gov.uk

## FINANCIAL SERVICES

**Financial Services and Markets Tribunal** . . . . . . . . . . 15-19 Bedford Avenue London, WC1B 3AS

    President . . . . . . . . . . . . . . . . . . . . . . . . . . . . . His Honour Stephen Oliver QC

    Secretary . . . . . . . . . . . . . . . . . . . . . . . . . . . . . Mr Richard Lester . . . . . . . . . . . . . . . . . . . . . . . . . Tel: (020) 7612 9649

                Web: http://www.financialtaxtribunals.gov.uk

**Financial Services Authority** . . . . . . . . . . . . . . . . . . 25 The North Colonnade, Canary Wharf, London, E14 5HS

    Chairman . . . . . . . . . . . . . . . . . . . . . . . . . . . . . Mr Callum McCarthy

    Chief Executive . . . . . . . . . . . . . . . . . . . . . . . . . Mr John Tiner . . . . . . . . . . . . . . . . . . . . . . . . . . . Tel: (020) 7066 1000

                Web: http://www.fsa.gov.uk

**Financial Services Compensation Scheme** . . . . . . . . . 7th Floor, Lloyds Chambers, 1 Portsoken Street, London, E1 8BN

    Chairman. . . . . . . . . . . . . . . . . . . . . . . . . . . . . Mr Nigel Hamilton

    Chief Executive . . . . . . . . . . . . . . . . . . . . . . . . . *Vacant* . . . . . . . . . . . . . . . . . . . . . . . . . . . . . . Tel: (020) 7892 7300

                Web: http://www.fscs.org.uk

## INLAND REVENUE *(see below under Tax)*

## MINT

**Royal Mint** *(Executive Agency)* . . . . . . . . . . . . . . . . Llantrisant, Pontyclun, CF72 8YT

    Deputy Master of the Mint . . . . . . . . . . . . . . . . . . Mr Gerald Sheehan. . . . . . . . . . . . . . . . . . . . . . . . . Tel: (01443) 222111

                Web: http://www.royalmint.com

**Royal Mint Advisory Committee on the Design of**
   **Coins, Medals, Seals and Decorations** . . . . . . . . . Llantrisant, Pontyclun, CF72 8YT

    Chairman. . . . . . . . . . . . . . . . . . . . . . . . . . . . . Professor Sir Christopher Frayling

    Secretary . . . . . . . . . . . . . . . . . . . . . . . . . . . . . Dr Kevin Clancy. . . . . . . . . . . . . . . . . . . . . . . . . . Tel: (01443) 623004

                Web: http://www.royalmint.com

## PUBLIC SERVICE PRODUCTIVITY

**Public Services Productivity Panel** . . . . . . . . . . . . . . 1 Horseguards Road, London, SW1A 2HQ

    Secretary. . . . . . . . . . . . . . . . . . . . . . . . . . . . . Mr Dean Stokes . . . . . . . . . . . . . . . . . . . . . . . . . . Tel: (020) 7270 4849

                Web: http://www.hm-treasury.gov.uk/pspp

## PURCHASING

**OCG Buying Solutions** *(Executive Agency of the*
   *Office of Government Commerce)*. . . . . . . . . . . . . . 5th Floor, Royal Liver Building, Pier Head, Liverpool, L3 1PE

    Chief Executive. . . . . . . . . . . . . . . . . . . . . . . . . Mr Hugh Barrett . . . . . . . . . . . . . . . . . . . . . . . . . Tel: (0870) 268 2222

                Web: http://www.ogcbuyingsolutions.gov.uk

## SAVINGS

**National Savings and Investments** *(Executive Agency)* . . . Charles House, 375 Kensington High Street, London, W14 8SD

    Director . . . . . . . . . . . . . . . . . . . . . . . . . . . . . . Mr Alan Cook . . . . . . . . . . . . . . . . . . . . . . . . . . . Tel: (020) 7348 9200

                Web: http://www.nsandi.co.uk

## STATISTICS

**Office for National Statistics** *(Executive Agency)*. . . . . . 1 Drummond Gate, London, SW1V 2QQ

    Director of National Statistics and Registrar General . . . . Mr Len Cook. . . . . . . . . . . . . . . . . . . . . . . . . . . . Tel: (020) 7533 5888

                Web: http://www.statistics.gov.uk

**Statistics Commission** . . . . . . . . . . . . . . . . . . . . . . 10 Great George Street, London, SW1P 3AE

    Chairman . . . . . . . . . . . . . . . . . . . . . . . . . . . . . Professor David Rhind CBE FRS FBA

    Chief Executive . . . . . . . . . . . . . . . . . . . . . . . . . Mr Richard Alldritt. . . . . . . . . . . . . . . . . . . . . . . . Tel: (020) 7273 8008

                Web: http://www.statscom.org.uk

# H M   T R E A S U R Y

*Other Relevant Contacts (Continued)*

## TAX
### Inland Revenue
(*Non-Ministerial Government Department*) . . . . . . . . . . . Somerset House, London, WC2R 1LB
Chairman . . . . . . . . . . . . . . . . . . . . . . . . . . . . . . . . . . Sir Nick Montagu ᴋᴄʙ . . . . . . . . . . . . . . . . . . . . . . . . . Tel: (020) 7438 6420
Web: http://www.inlandrevenue.gov.uk
### National Insurance Contributions Office . . . . . . . . . . . Inland Revenue, Room BP1202, Benton Park View, Longbenton,
Newcastle-upon-Tyne, NE98 1ZZ
Director . . . . . . . . . . . . . . . . . . . . . . . . . . . . . . . . . Mr Steve McGrath . . . . . . . . . . . . . . . . . . . . . . . . . . Tel: (0191) 225 5778
### Revenue Adjudicator's Office . . . . . . . . . . . . . . . . . . . 3rd Floor, Haymarket House, 28 Haymarket, London, SW1Y 4SP
Revenue Adjudicator . . . . . . . . . . . . . . . . . . . . . . . Dame Barbara Mills ǫᴄ . . . . . . . . . . . . . . . . . . . . . . Tel: (020) 7930 2292
Web: http://www.adjudicatorsoffice.gov.uk
### Special Commissioners of Income Tax . . . . . . . . . . . . 15-19 Bedford Avenue, London, WC1B 3AS
Clerk to the Special Commissioner . . . . . . . . . . . . . . Mr Richard Lester . . . . . . . . . . . . . . . . . . . . . . . . . . Tel: (020) 7612 9650
Web: http://www.financeandtaxtribunal.gov.uk
### Valuation Office
(*Executive Agency, within the Inland Revenue*). . . . . . . . New Court, Carey Street, London, WC2A 2JE
Chief Executive . . . . . . . . . . . . . . . . . . . . . . . . . . . . Mr Andrew Hudson . . . . . . . . . . . . . . . . . . . . . . . . . Tel: (020) 7506 1700
Web: http://www.voa.gov.uk

### VAT Tribunal (*see under Department for Constitutional Affairs*)

# W A L E S   O F F I C E

(*for Wales Office see Wales Office under Department for Constitutional Affairs at p254*)

## ACCOUNTING

Figuring in the Capital's future

# LONDON SOCIETY OF CHARTERED ACCOUNTANTS

75 Cannon Street, London, EC4N 5BN

| | |
|---|---|
| **Telephone:** | (020) 7556 7053 |
| **Facsimile:** | (020) 7556 7520 |
| **Email:** | lsca@icaew.co.uk |
| **Website:** | http://www.lsca.co.uk |

### Contact: Ian Strange – Regional Manager

The LSCA represents over 37,000 members of the Institute of Chartered Accountants in England and Wales living and working in the London area. We run seminars, conferences, meetings, and comment on legislation and tax and accounting issues. Full details are on our website.

## INVESTMENT BANKING

# LIBA
### LONDON INVESTMENT BANKING ASSOCIATION

6 Frederick's Place, London, EC2R 8BT

*Telephone* (020) 7796 3606
*Facsimile* (020) 7796 4345
*Web* http://www.liba.org.uk

*Contact* Sir Adam Ridley – *Director-General*

The UK is the centre for investment banking in Europe. Assisting customers – international and domestic, public and private sector – to raise capital and to manage their finances is the heart of investment banking business.

The London Investment Banking Association is the UK's principle trade association for firms from all over the world active in the investment banking and securities industry. The Association represents the interests of its members on all aspects of their business and promotes their views to the authorities in the United Kingdom, the European Union and elsewhere. Its objective is to ensure that London continues to be an attractive financial centre in which investment banks will wish to base their activities.

# DEPARTMENT FOR WORK AND PENSIONS

Richmond House, 79 Whitehall, London, SW1A 2NS
Tel: (020) 7238 3000
Enquiries: Tel: (020) 7712 2171
Web: http://www.dwp.gov.uk

## MINISTERS

**Secretary of State for Work and Pensions** . . . . . . . . . . . . Rt Hon Alan Johnson MP
*Principal Private Secretary* . . . . . . . . . . . . . . . . . . . . . . . . Ms Susan Park . . . . . . . . . . . . . . . . . . . . . . . . Tel: (020) 7238 0654
*Special Advisers* . . . . . . . . . . . . . . . . . . . . . . . . . . . . . . . . Mr Tom Clark . . . . . . . . . . . . . . . . . . . . . . . . Tel: (020) 7238 0664
Mr Chris Norton . . . . . . . . . . . . . . . . . . . . . . . Tel: (020) 7238 0664

**Minister of State** *(Minister for Pensions)* . . . . . . . . . . . . . . . Mr Malcolm Wicks MP
*Private Secretary* . . . . . . . . . . . . . . . . . . . . . . . . . . . . . . . . Ms Sara Denton . . . . . . . . . . . . . . . . . . . . . . . Tel: (020) 7238 0671

**Minister of State** *(Minister for Work)* . . . . . . . . . . . . . . . . . Rt Hon Jane Kennedy MP
*Private Secretary* . . . . . . . . . . . . . . . . . . . . . . . . . . . . . . . . Ms Caroline Crowther . . . . . . . . . . . . . . . . . . Tel: (020) 7238 0738

**Parliamentary Secretary** *(Disabled People)* . . . . . . . . . . . . . Ms Maria Eagle MP
*Private Secretary* . . . . . . . . . . . . . . . . . . . . . . . . . . . . . . . . Ms Emma Davis . . . . . . . . . . . . . . . . . . . . . . . Tel: (020) 7238 0684

**Parliamentary Secretary** . . . . . . . . . . . . . . . . . . . . . . . . . . . Mr Chris Pond MP
*Private Secretary* . . . . . . . . . . . . . . . . . . . . . . . . . . . . . . . . Ms Helen Daniels . . . . . . . . . . . . . . . . . . . . . Tel: (020) 7238 0690

**Parliamentary Secretary** . . . . . . . . . . . . . . . . . . . . . . . . . . . Rt Hon Baroness Hollis of Heigham
*Private Secretary* . . . . . . . . . . . . . . . . . . . . . . . . . . . . . . . . Ms Lucy Vause . . . . . . . . . . . . . . . . . . . . . . . Tel: (020) 7238 0678

## CIVIL SERVICE

**Permanent Secretary** . . . . . . . . . . . . . . . . . . . . . . . . . . . . . Sir Richard Mottram KCB
*Private Secretary* . . . . . . . . . . . . . . . . . . . . . . . . . . . . . . . . Ms Judith Tunstall . . . . . . . . . . . . . . . . . . . . . Tel: (020) 7238 0702

**Senior Directors**
Director, Communications . . . . . . . . . . . . . . . . . . . . . . . . . . . Mr Simon MacDowall . . . . . . . . . . . . . . . . . . . Tel: (020) 7238 0744
Director, Finance . . . . . . . . . . . . . . . . . . . . . . . . . . . . . . . . . Mr John Codling . . . . . . . . . . . . . . . . . . . . . . Tel: (0113) 232 4229
Director, Human Resources . . . . . . . . . . . . . . . . . . . . . . . . . . Mr Kevin White CB . . . . . . . . . . . . . . . . . . . . . Tel: (020) 7712 2566
Director, Pensions and Disability . . . . . . . . . . . . . . . . . . . . . . Mr Paul Gray CB . . . . . . . . . . . . . . . . . . . . . . . Tel: (020) 7712 2509
Director, Programme and Systems Delivery . . . . . . . . . . . . . . . Mr Joe Harley . . . . . . . . . . . . . . . . . . . . . . . . Tel: (020) 7712 2373
Director, Work and Welfare Strategy . . . . . . . . . . . . . . . . . . . . Mr Michael Richardson . . . . . . . . . . . . . . . . . . Tel: (020) 7962 8361
Director, Working Age and Children Group . . . . . . . . . . . . . . . Mr Michael Richardson *(acting)* . . . . . . . . . . . . Tel: (020) 7962 8361
Solicitor . . . . . . . . . . . . . . . . . . . . . . . . . . . . . . . . . . . . . . . Ms Marilynne Morgan CB . . . . . . . . . . . . . . . . . Tel: (020) 7412 1528

# DEPARTMENT FOR WORK AND PENSIONS

## SUBJECT RESPONSIBILITIES AND CONTACTS

**Adjudication and Constitutional Issues Division** . . . . . . . . Mr John Griffiths . . . . . . . . . . . . . . . . . . . . . . Tel: (020) 7962 8810

**Analytical Services**

| | | |
|---|---|---|
| Director, Information and Analysis . . . . . . . . . . . . . . . . . . . | Mr Nick Dyson . . . . . . . . . . . . . . . . . . . . . . | Tel: (020) 7962 8611 |
| Chief Research Officer . . . . . . . . . . . . . . . . . . . . . . . . . . . . | Mr George Clark . . . . . . . . . . . . . . . . . . . . . . . | Tel: (020) 7962 8138 |
| Chief Statistician . . . . . . . . . . . . . . . . . . . . . . . . . . . . . . . | Mr Fred Johnson . . . . . . . . . . . . . . . . . . . . . . | Tel: (0191) 225 5438 |
| Information Centre . . . . . . . . . . . . . . . . . . . . . . . . . . . . . . . | Mr David Frazer . . . . . . . . . . . . . . . . . . . . . . . | Tel: (0191) 225 5037 |
| Operational Research Service . . . . . . . . . . . . . . . . . . . . . . | Mr David Barnbrook . . . . . . . . . . . . . . . . . . . | Tel: (020) 7962 8197 |

Senior Economic Advisers

| | | |
|---|---|---|
| Forecasting . . . . . . . . . . . . . . . . . . . . . . . . . . . . . . . . . . | Mr Trevor Huddleston . . . . . . . . . . . . . . . . . | Tel: (020) 7962 8242 |
| Income Analysis . . . . . . . . . . . . . . . . . . . . . . . . . . . . . . . | Mr Gordon Harris . . . . . . . . . . . . . . . . . . . . . . | Tel: (020) 7962 8899 |

**Benefit Fraud**

| | | |
|---|---|---|
| Director, Strategy, Planning and Performance . . . . . . . . . . | Mr Rod Clark . . . . . . . . . . . . . . . . . . . . . . . . . | Tel: (020) 7238 0837 |
| Housing Benefit and Security Division . . . . . . . . . . . . . . . . | Mr Tom Taylor . . . . . . . . . . . . . . . . . . . . . . . . | Tel: (020) 7962 8018 |

Investigations
*Ladywood, 65-77 Summer Row, Birmingham, B3 1LB*

| | | |
|---|---|---|
| Chief Investigation Officer . . . . . . . . . . . . . . . . . . . . . . | Mr Richard Kitchen . . . . . . . . . . . . . . . . . . . . | Tel: (0121) 237 8440 |
| Strategy Unit . . . . . . . . . . . . . . . . . . . . . . . . . . . . . . . . . . | Mr John Alpass . . . . . . . . . . . . . . . . . . . . . . . | Tel: (020) 7712 2361 |

**Benefit Fraud Inspectorate**
*Berkeley House, 12A North Park Road, Harrogate, HG1 5QA*

Director, Benefit Fraud Inspectorate . . . . . . . . . . . . . . . . . Mr Chris Bull . . . . . . . . . . . . . . . . . . . . . . . Tel: (01423) 832945

**Business Design, Departmental**

| | | |
|---|---|---|
| Director, Business Design . . . . . . . . . . . . . . . . . . . . . . . . | Mr Stephen Hewitt . . . . . . . . . . . . . . . . . . . . | Tel: (020) 7273 4001 |
| Central Design Division . . . . . . . . . . . . . . . . . . . . . . . . . . | Mr Jim Lewis . . . . . . . . . . . . . . . . . . . . . . . . . | Tel: (0113) 232 4863 |
| Financial Support Design . . . . . . . . . . . . . . . . . . . . . . . . . | Mr Chris Hayes . . . . . . . . . . . . . . . . . . . . . . . | Tel: (020) 7340 4004 |
| Jobcentre Plus Implementation Project . . . . . . . . . . . . . . . | Mr Jeremy Groombridge . . . . . . . . . . . . . . . . | Tel: (020) 7273 6139 |
| Programme Strategy . . . . . . . . . . . . . . . . . . . . . . . . . . . . . | Mr Tim Read . . . . . . . . . . . . . . . . . . . . . . . . . | Tel: (0113) 232 4216 |
| Provision and Adviser Divisional Head . . . . . . . . . . . . . . . | Ms Florence Lea . . . . . . . . . . . . . . . . . . . . . . . | Tel: (0113) 232 4374 |

**Carers** *(See below under Disabled Clients)*

**Children, Welfare Strategy and Performance**

| | | |
|---|---|---|
| Director, Children Welfare Strategy and Performance . . . . . | Ms Shirley Trundle . . . . . . . . . . . . . . . . . . . . . | Tel: (020) 7962 8498 |
| Child Support . . . . . . . . . . . . . . . . . . . . . . . . . . . . . . . . . | Ms Ruth Siemaszko . . . . . . . . . . . . . . . . . . . . | Tel: (020) 7962 8789 |

**Communications**

| | | |
|---|---|---|
| Director, Communications . . . . . . . . . . . . . . . . . . . . . . . . | Mr Simon MacDowall . . . . . . . . . . . . . . . . . . . | Tel: (020) 7238 0744 |
| Head of Corporate Communications . . . . . . . . . . . . . . . . . | Mr Ken Young . . . . . . . . . . . . . . . . . . . . . . . . | Tel: (020) 7238 0819 |
| Head of Media Relations . . . . . . . . . . . . . . . . . . . . . . . . . | Ms Lindsey French . . . . . . . . . . . . . . . . . . . . . | Tel: (020) 7238 0748 |

Marketing
*Quarry House, Quarry Hill, Leeds, LS2 7UB*

Head, Marketing Communications . . . . . . . . . . . . . . . . . Mr Steve O'Neill . . . . . . . . . . . . . . . . . . . . . . Tel: (0113) 232 4433

**Corporate Services**

| | | |
|---|---|---|
| Director, Commercial and Estates . . . . . . . . . . . . . . . . . . . | Mr David Smith . . . . . . . . . . . . . . . . . . . . . . . | Tel: (020) 7712 2731 |
| Director, Finance . . . . . . . . . . . . . . . . . . . . . . . . . . . . . . . | Mr John Codling . . . . . . . . . . . . . . . . . . . . . . | Tel: (0113) 232 4229 |
| Director, Human Resources . . . . . . . . . . . . . . . . . . . . . . . . | Mr Kevin White CB . . . . . . . . . . . . . . . . . . . . | Tel: (020) 7712 2566 |
| Director, Planning and Performance . . . . . . . . . . . . . . . . . | Mr Jeremy Moore . . . . . . . . . . . . . . . . . . . . . . | Tel: (020) 7238 0811 |
| Director, Project Management . . . . . . . . . . . . . . . . . . . . . . | Mr Peter Crahan . . . . . . . . . . . . . . . . . . . . . . | Tel: (01253) 688915 |
| Assurance Services, Internal . . . . . . . . . . . . . . . . . . . . . . . | Mr Chris Turner . . . . . . . . . . . . . . . . . . . . . . . | Tel: (01756) 799069 |
| Business Management and Performance . . . . . . . . . . . . . . . | Mr Mike Driver . . . . . . . . . . . . . . . . . . . . . . . | Tel: (020) 7238 0625 |
| Commercial Policy and Procurement . . . . . . . . . . . . . . . . . | Mr Rob Wormald . . . . . . . . . . . . . . . . . . . . . . | Tel: (0114) 259 5801 |
| Consultancy and Professional Services . . . . . . . . . . . . . . . | Ms Jane Mortimer . . . . . . . . . . . . . . . . . . . . . | Tel: (020) 7391 3620 |

# DEPARTMENT FOR WORK AND PENSIONS

*Corporate Services (Continued)*

Customer Relations . . . . . . . . . . . . . . . . . . . . . . . . . . . . . . Mr David Pearson . . . . . . . . . . . . . . . . . . . . . Tel: (0114) 209 8006

Estates, Departmental . . . . . . . . . . . . . . . . . . . . . . . . . . Mr Peter Besley . . . . . . . . . . . . . . . . . . . . . . . . Tel: (020) 7200 6406

Procurement Services . . . . . . . . . . . . . . . . . . . . . . . . . . Mr Alan Dowlman . . . . . . . . . . . . . . . . . . . . . . Tel: (0113) 232 7198

Regional Governance. . . . . . . . . . . . . . . . . . . . . . . . . . . Ms Sandra Newton. . . . . . . . . . . . . . . . . . . . . . Tel: (020) 7238 8063

**Data Protection and Freedom of Information Issues**. . . Mr Phillip Morgan . . . . . . . . . . . . . . . . . . . . . Tel: (020) 7962 8690

**Disabled Clients**

Group Director, Disability and Carers Directorate . . . . . . . Mr Bruce Calderwood . . . . . . . . . . . . . . . . . . . Tel: (020) 7962 8339

Director, Disability and Carers . . . . . . . . . . . . . . . . . . . . Mr Terry Moran . . . . . . . . . . . . . . . . . . . . . . . . . Tel: (020) 7962 8339

Benefits, Disability and Carers . . . . . . . . . . . . . . . . . . . . Mr John Hughes . . . . . . . . . . . . . . . . . . . . . . . . . Tel: (020) 7712 2100

Disability Unit . . . . . . . . . . . . . . . . . . . . . . . . . . . . . . . . Ms Liz Tillett. . . . . . . . . . . . . . . . . . . . . . . . . . . . Tel: (020) 7962 8390

**Economics**

Director, Information and Analysis. . . . . . . . . . . . . . . . . . Mr Nick Dyson . . . . . . . . . . . . . . . . . . . . . . . . . . Tel: (020) 7962 8611

Economy and Labour Market. . . . . . . . . . . . . . . . . . . . . Mr Bill Wells. . . . . . . . . . . . . . . . . . . . . . . . . . . . Tel: (020) 7340 3010

Forecasting. . . . . . . . . . . . . . . . . . . . . . . . . . . . . . . . . . . Mr Trevor Huddleston . . . . . . . . . . . . . . . . . . . Tel: (020) 7962 8242

Income Analysis . . . . . . . . . . . . . . . . . . . . . . . . . . . . . . . Mr Gordon Harris . . . . . . . . . . . . . . . . . . . . . . . Tel: (020) 7962 8899

Jobseekers - Analysis . . . . . . . . . . . . . . . . . . . . . . . . . . . Ms Clare Elliott . . . . . . . . . . . . . . . . . . . . . . . . . Tel: (0114) 209 8023

Lone Parents, Older Workers and Disability Analysis. . . . . Ms Rebecca Endean . . . . . . . . . . . . . . . . . . . . . Tel: (020) 7962 8899

Operational Research . . . . . . . . . . . . . . . . . . . . . . . . . . . Mr David Barnbrook . . . . . . . . . . . . . . . . . . . . . Tel: (020) 7962 8197

Pensions - Economic Analysis . . . . . . . . . . . . . . . . . . . . . Mr John Ball . . . . . . . . . . . . . . . . . . . . . . . . . . . . Tel: (020) 7962 8224

**Employer Services (Jobcentre Plus)**

Director, Employer Services . . . . . . . . . . . . . . . . . . . . . . Mr Mark Grimshaw . . . . . . . . . . . . . . . . . . . . . . Tel: (020) 7273 6341

Employer Engagement. . . . . . . . . . . . . . . . . . . . . . . . . . Mr Sandy Davidson . . . . . . . . . . . . . . . . . . . . . . Tel: (0114) 267 7822

**European Union**

European Social Fund. . . . . . . . . . . . . . . . . . . . . . . . . . . Mr Gordon Pursglove . . . . . . . . . . . . . . . . . . . . Tel: (0114 267 7282

Social Policy . . . . . . . . . . . . . . . . . . . . . . . . . . . . . . . . . . Ms Hanna Nicholas . . . . . . . . . . . . . . . . . . . . . . Tel: (020) 7273 3000

**Extending Working Life Division**. . . . . . . . . . . . . . . . . . Ms Mary Pattison. . . . . . . . . . . . . . . . . . . . . . . . . Tel: (020) 7962 8038

**Finance**

Director, Finance . . . . . . . . . . . . . . . . . . . . . . . . . . . . . . Mr John Codling . . . . . . . . . . . . . . . . . . . . . . . . Tel: (0113) 232 4229

Director, Planning and Finance . . . . . . . . . . . . . . . . . . . Mr Keith Palmer . . . . . . . . . . . . . . . . . . . . . . . . . Tel: (020) 7962 8063

Chief Accountant . . . . . . . . . . . . . . . . . . . . . . . . . . . . . . Mr Paul Helmsley . . . . . . . . . . . . . . . . . . . . . . . . Tel: (01253) 332298

Debt Management . . . . . . . . . . . . . . . . . . . . . . . . . . . . . Mr Jeff Taylor . . . . . . . . . . . . . . . . . . . . . . . . . . . Tel: (0191) 225 5648

Director, Finance IS . . . . . . . . . . . . . . . . . . . . . . . . . . . . Mr Alan Wong. . . . . . . . . . . . . . . . . . . . . . . . . . . Tel: (020) 7238 0707

Financial Control and Reporting (Departmental). . . . . . . . Mr Stuart McKinnon-Evans . . . . . . . . . . . . . . . Tel: (0113) 232 4904

Financial Services. . . . . . . . . . . . . . . . . . . . . . . . . . . . . . Mr Phil Robinson . . . . . . . . . . . . . . . . . . . . . . . . Tel: (01253) 332890

Management and Performance. . . . . . . . . . . . . . . . . . . . . Mr Mike Driver . . . . . . . . . . . . . . . . . . . . . . . . . Tel: (020) 7238 0625

Resource Management. . . . . . . . . . . . . . . . . . . . . . . . . . . Mr Dave Thomas . . . . . . . . . . . . . . . . . . . . . . . . Tel: (01253) 332994

**Fraud** *(see above under Benefit Fraud)*

**Health, Disability and Work Division** . . . . . . . . . . . . . . Mr Gareth Williams. . . . . . . . . . . . . . . . . . . . . . . Tel: (020) 7962 8800

**Helplines**

Benefit Enquiry Line *(Disability)*. . . . . . . . . . . . . . . . . . . *enquiries* . . . . . . . . . . . . . . . . . . . . . . . . . . . . . . . Tel: (0800) 882200

Child Benefit Enquiry Line . . . . . . . . . . . . . . . . . . . . . . . *enquiries* . . . . . . . . . . . . . . . . . . . . . . . . . . . . . . . Tel: (0845) 302 1444

Child Support Agency: National Enquiry Line . . . . . . . . . . *enquiries* . . . . . . . . . . . . . . . . . . . . . . . . . . . . . . . Tel: (0845) 713 3133

Winter Fuel Helpline . . . . . . . . . . . . . . . . . . . . . . . . . . . *enquiries* . . . . . . . . . . . . . . . . . . . . . . . . . . . . . . . Tel: (0845) 915 1515

**Housing Benefit** . . . . . . . . . . . . . . . . . . . . . . . . . . . . . . . Mr Paul Howarth . . . . . . . . . . . . . . . . . . . . . . . . Tel: (020) 7962 8029

# DEPARTMENT FOR WORK AND PENSIONS

**Honours** .......................................... Ms Kim Archer ........................ Tel: (020) 7962 8297

**Human Resources**
    Director, Human Resources......................... Mr Kevin White CB. ................. Tel: (020) 7712 2566
    Corporate Human Resources ....................... Ms Gill Adey......................... Tel: (0114) 259 7672
    Diversity and Equality.......................... Dr Barbara Burford .................... Tel: (020) 7962 8646
                                                                          Tel: (0113) 232 7139
    Learning and Development ......................... Mr Mick Holbrook.................... Tel: (020) 7712 8127
    Management ....................................... Ms Kim Archer ...................... Tel: (020) 7962 8297
    Occupational Psychologist......................... Ms Mary Dalgleish.................... Tel: (0114) 259 7757
    People Development ............................... Mr Bill Gormley..................... Tel: (01253) 688992
    Personnel Services, Senior Civil Servants.......... Ms Kim Archer ...................... Tel: (020) 7962 8297
    Recruitment, Selection Policy .................... Ms Helen Bennett .................... Tel: (0114) 259 7844
    Senior Analytical Support ........................ Ms Sue Rice ......................... Tel: (020) 7238 0820

**Independent Living Funds** ....................... Mr John Hughes ...................... Tel: (020) 7712 2100

**Information and Library Services** ................ Mr Graham Monk ...................... Tel: (020) 7962 8322

**International Directorate** *(Joint Group with Department for Education and Skills)*
*Caxton House, Tothill Street, London, SW1H 9NA*
    Director, International............................ Mr Clive Tucker ..................... Tel: (020) 7340 3346
    European Social Fund.............................. Mr Gordon Pursglove ................. Tel: (0114) 267 7282
    International Relations ........................... Ms Marie Niven...................... Tel: (020) 7340 4023

**Information Systems / Information Technology,**
    **Operating Officer**
    Chief Operating Officer .......................... Ms Lesley Strathie.................. Tel: (020) 7273 3000
    Director, Disability and Carers Service IS/IT ...... Ms Sandra Robinson .................. Tel: (01253) 334528
    Director, Finance IS/IT ........................... Mr Alan Wong........................ Tel: (020) 7238 0707
    Director, Jobcentre Plus IS/IT .................... Mr Kevin Bone ...................... Tel: (020) 7273 5136
    Director, Pensions Service IS/IT .................. Mr Martin Bellamy................... Tel: (01253) 334528

**IT (Departmental)**
    Chief Information Officer and Group Director Programme
      Systems and Delivery............................ Mr John Cross ...................... Tel: (020) 7712 2373
    Director, Digital Infrastructure.................. Ms Debbie Heigh..................... Tel: (0113) 232 4823
    External Supply.................................. Mr John Priest ..................... Tel: (01253) 688905
    Information Strategy and Information System Definition .... Mr George Brown..................... Tel: (01253) 664754
    Infrastructure Management ........................ Mr Dennis Coombs ................... Tel: (020) 7238 0632
    Office Infrastructure ............................ Mr John Delamore ................... Tel: (01253) 335842
    Procurement Services ............................. Mr Alan Dowlman .................... Tel: (0113) 232 7198
    Technology Office................................ Mr Kenny Robertson ................. Tel: (01253) 334676
    *(see also above under Business Design and under Corporate Services and below under Modernisation)*

**Jobcentre Plus: Planning and Performance**........... Ms Alison Scott ..................... Tel: (020) 7962 8621
    *(see also above under Employer Services)*

**Labour Market**..................................... Mr Simon Judge...................... Tel: (020) 7712 2832

# DEPARTMENT FOR WORK AND PENSIONS

## Legal Services

| | | |
|---|---|---|
| Solicitor, Head of Law | Ms Marilynne Morgan CB | Tel: (020) 7412 1528 |
| Director , Legal Services (Social Security) | Mr John Catlin | Tel: (020) 7412 1466 |
| Adjudication and Constitutional Issues | Mr Stephen Cooper | Tel: (020) 7412 1372 |
| Bereavement Benefits | Mr Paul Bridges | Tel: (020) 7412 1242 |
| Carer Benefits | Mr Peter Milledge | Tel: (020) 7412 1242 |
| Child Support | Mr Peter Milledge | Tel: (020) 7412 1242 |
| Civil Proceedings | Ms Anita James | Tel: (020) 7412 1402 |
| Commercial Branch | Mr Ronald Powell | Tel: (020) 7412 1400 |
| Contribution Credits | Mr Paul Bridges | Tel: (020) 7412 1242 |
| Disability Rights | Mr John Crane | Tel: (020) 7412 1325 |
| Drafting | Ms Cathy Cooper | Tel: (020) 7412 1339 |
| Earnings Top-Up | Ms Anne McGaughrin | Tel: (020) 7412 1517 |
| Employment Law | Ms Caroline Harold | Tel: (020) 7412 1397 |
| European Union Issues | Mr Frances Logan | Tel: (020) 7412 1483 |
| Housing and Council Tax Benefit | Ms Anne McGaughrin | Tel: (020) 7412 1517 |
| Incapacity Benefit | Mr Peter Milledge | Tel: (020) 7412 1242 |
| Jobseeker's Allowance | Ms Anne McGaughrin | Tel: (020) 7412 1517 |
| Maternity Allowance | Mr Paul Bridges | Tel: (020) 7412 1242 |
| NHS Remission Changes | Ms Anne McGaughrin | Tel: (020) 7412 1517 |
| Pensions | | |
|     Occupational and Personal | Ms Naomi Mallick | Tel: (020) 7412 1596 |
|     State | Mr Paul Bridges | Tel: (020) 7412 1242 |
|     War | Mr Peter Milledge | Tel: (020) 7412 1242 |
| Prosecutions | Ms Sue Edwards | Tel: (020) 7412 1310 |
| Statutory Sick Pay | Mr Paul Bridges | Tel: (020) 7412 1242 |
| Vaccine Damage Payments | Mr Peter Milledge | Tel: (020) 7412 1242 |

## Medical Policy

| | | |
|---|---|---|
| Chief Medical Adviser and Medical Director | Dr Mansel Aylward CB | Tel: (020) 7962 8702 |
| Incapacity Benefits, Sickness Certification, Vocational Rehabilitation | Dr Philip Sawney | Tel: (020) 7962 8838 |
| Industrial Injuries Issues | Dr Susan Reed | Tel: (0113) 232 4266 |
| Industrial Injuries Scheme, Respiratory Diseases and Rehabilitation | Dr Peter Wright | Tel: (020) 7712 2323 |
| Medical Policy Manager | Dr Roger Thomas | Tel: (020) 7712 8450 |
| Quality Issues | Dr Moira Henderson | Tel: (020) 7962 8882 |
| Scientific and Medical Secretary/IIAC Secretariat | Dr Paul Stidolph | Tel: (020) 7962 8412 |
| War Pensions Policy | Dr Anne Braidwood | Tel: (01253) 332582 |

## Modernisation

| | | |
|---|---|---|
| Director, Modernisation and Strategy | Mr Stephen Holt | Tel: (020) 7273 6231 |
| Director, Planning and Finance | Mr Keith Palmer | Tel: (020) 7962 8063 |
| Business Change and Payment | Mr Peter Hull | Tel: (0113) 232 4151 |
| Customer Management System Project | Mr Robert Millin | Tel: (01253) 714647 |
| Digital Office Infrastructure | Ms Debbie Heigh | Tel: (0113) 232 4823 |
| IT Development | Mr Bob Harris | Tel: (0114) 291 1657 |
| IT Modernisation | Mr Kevin Bone | Tel: (020) 7273 6163 |
| Project Manager, Lytham St Annes | Mr Steve O'Keefe | Tel: (01253) 714214 |

*(see also above under Business Design and under Corporate Services and below under Operating Officer and under Payments)*

| | | |
|---|---|---|
| **Motability** | Mr John Hughes | Tel: (020) 7712 2100 |
| **National Employment Panel** | Ms Cay Stratton | Tel: (020) 7340 3005 |
| **Parliamentary Clerk** | Mr Tim Elms | Tel: (020) 7238 0715 |

# DEPARTMENT FOR WORK AND PENSIONS

**Payments**

| | | |
|---|---|---|
| Director, Universal Banking Programme | Ms Shirley Trundle | Tel: (020) 7962 8870 |
| Payment Modernisation Project | Ms Christine Goodfellow | Tel: (0191) 225 9957 |
| Policy and Presentation | Mr Tony Kuczys | Tel: (020) 7962 8036 |

**Pensions**
*The Adelphi, 1-11 John Adam Street, London, WC2N 6HT*

| | | |
|---|---|---|
| Director, Pensions and Disability Directorate | Mr Paul Gray CB | Tel: (020) 7712 2509 |
| Director, Pensions Change Programme | Mr George McCorkell | Tel: (01253) 689711 |
| Director, Pensions Strategy and Client Programme | Ms Hilary Reynolds | Tel: (020) 7962 8300 |
| Business Performance and Change | Mr Phil Bartlett | Tel: (0113) 232 4718 |
| Civil Partnerships and Pensions | Mr Norman Cockett | Tel: (020) 7712 2236 |
| Economic Analysis | Mr John Ball | Tel: (020) 7962 8224 |
| Euro Preparations | Mr Garvin Bowen | Tel: (020) 7962 8365 |
| Finance | Mr Simon Furse | Tel: (020) 7712 2148 |
| Future Pensions Strategy | Mr Jason Feeney | Tel: (0113) 390 6289 |
| Legislation, State Pensions | Mr Norman Cockett | Tel: (020) 7712 2236 |
| Member Protection | Mr Pete Searle | Tel: (020) 7712 2106 |
| Pension Credit | | |
|    Legislation | Mr Stan Godfrey | Tel: (0191) 225 6506 |
|    Programme Manager | Mr Tony Cooper | Tel: (01253) 689995 |
| Pensions Transformation Programme | Ms Sheila Stephen | Tel: (0191) 225 3859 |
| Poverty and Social Exclusion | Mr Tom Taylor | Tel: (020) 7712 2514 |
| Private Pensions | | |
|    Employer Strategy | Ms Mary Helson | Tel: (020) 7962 8449 |
|    Policy Design | Ms Tracy Gale | Tel: (020) 7962 8301 |
|    Policy Implementation | Mr Charles Ramsden | Tel: (020) 7962 8454 |
|    Strategy | Ms Janet Hill | Tel: (020) 7962 8876 |
| State Pensions Centre | Mr Stan Godfrey | Tel: (0191) 225 6506 |
| Stewardship | Mr Richard d'Souza | Tel: (020) 7962 8466 |
| Strategy and Planning | Mr Chris Capella | Tel: (020) 7712 2422 |
| War Pensions | Mr Paul Gray | Tel: (020) 7162 8060 |

**Poverty and Social Exclusion Issues** ... Mr Tom Taylor ... Tel: (020) 7712 2514

**Press Office**

| | | |
|---|---|---|
| Head of Media Relations | Ms Lindsay French | Tel: (020) 7238 0748 |
| Press Office | *enquiries* | Tel: (020) 7238 0866 |

**Research**

| | | |
|---|---|---|
| Operational | Mr David Barnbrook | Tel: (020) 7962 8197 |
| Poverty and Social Exclusion | Mr Tom Taylor | Tel: (020) 7712 2514 |
| Social | Mr George Clark | Tel: (020) 7962 8138 |

**Standards and Service Quality**
*Cavendish House, Newmarket Street, Skipton, Yorkshire, BD23 2PA*

| | | |
|---|---|---|
| Head, Internal Assurance | Mr Christopher Turner | Tel: (01756) 799069 |

**Statistics**

| | | |
|---|---|---|
| Director, Information and Analysis | Mr Nick Dyson | Tel: (020) 7962 8611 |
| Chief Statistician | Mr Fred Johnson | Tel: (0191) 225 5438 |
| Benefit Forecasting | Mr Trevor Huddleston | Tel: (020) 7962 8242 |
| Benefit Take-up | Mr Gordon Harris | Tel: (020) 7962 8899 |
| Collation and Analysis | Mr David Frazer | Tel: (0191) 225 5037 |
| Family Resources Survey | Mr Gordon Harris | Tel: (020) 7962 8899 |
| Labour Market Issues | Mr Bill Wells | Tel: (020) 7712 2278 |
| Operational Research | Mr David Barnbrook | Tel: (020) 7962 8197 |

# DEPARTMENT FOR WORK AND PENSIONS

**Universal Banking Programme**
    Director . . . . . . . . . . . . . . . . . . . . . . . . . . . . . . . . Ms Shirley Trundle . . . . . . . . . . . . . . . . . . . . . Tel: (020) 7962 8870
    Policy and Presentation . . . . . . . . . . . . . . . . . . . . . . . . Mr Tony Kuczys. . . . . . . . . . . . . . . . . . . . . . . . Tel: (020) 7962 8036
    Programme Manager; Payment
        Modernisation Programme . . . . . . . . . . . . . . . . . . . . . Ms Christine Goodfellow . . . . . . . . . . . . . . . Tel: (0191) 225 9957

**Vaccine Damage Payments Scheme** . . . . . . . . . . . . . . . . Mr John Hughes . . . . . . . . . . . . . . . . . . . . . . . Tel: (020) 7712 2100

**Welfare to Work** . . . . . . . . . . . . . . . . . . . . . . . . . . . . . . . . Mr James Richardson. . . . . . . . . . . . . . . . . . . Tel: (020) 7962 8673

**Work and Welfare**
    Director, Work and Welfare Strategy . . . . . . . . . . . . . . . Mr Michael Richardson . . . . . . . . . . . . . . . . . Tel: (020) 7962 8361
    Deputy Director, Work and Welfare Strategy . . . . . . . . . . Mr Jonathan Portes . . . . . . . . . . . . . . . . . . . . Tel: (020) 7962 8456
    Disadvantaged Groups. . . . . . . . . . . . . . . . . . . . . . . . . . Mr John Fuller. . . . . . . . . . . . . . . . . . . . . . . . . Tel: (0114) 267 7200
    Initiatives . . . . . . . . . . . . . . . . . . . . . . . . . . . . . . . . . . . Ms Florence Lea . . . . . . . . . . . . . . . . . . . . . . . Tel: (0113) 232 4374

**Working Age Presentation** . . . . . . . . . . . . . . . . . . . . . . . . Ms Clare Potts. . . . . . . . . . . . . . . . . . . . . . . . . Tel: (020) 7712 2840

**Worktrain**. . . . . . . . . . . . . . . . . . . . . . . . . . . . . . . . . . . . . Mr Neil Atkinson. . . . . . . . . . . . . . . . . . . . . . . Tel: (0114) 267 7341

## OTHER RELEVANT CONTACTS

### APPEALS

**Appeals Service** *(Executive Agency)* . . . . . . . . . . . . . . . . 5th Floor, Fox Court, 14 Gray's Inn Road, London, WC1X 8HN
    President . . . . . . . . . . . . . . . . . . . . . . . . . . . . . . . . . . . . His Honour Judge Michael Harris
    Chief Executive. . . . . . . . . . . . . . . . . . . . . . . . . . . . . . . Ms Christina Townsend . . . . . . . . . . . . . . . . . Tel: (020) 7712 2600
        Web: http://www.appeals-service.gov.uk

### CHILD SUPPORT

**Child Support Agency** *(Executive Agency)* . . . . . . . . . . . . . DWP Longbenton, Benton Park Road, Newcastle-upon-Tyne, NE98 1YX
    Chief Executive. . . . . . . . . . . . . . . . . . . . . . . . . . . . . . . Mr Doug Smith . . . . . . . . . . . . . . . . . . . . . . . Tel: (0845) 713 3133
        E-mail: csa-nel@dwp.gsi.gov.uk
        Web: http://www.dwp.gov.uk/csa
**Social Security and Child Support Commissioners** . . . . . . Procession House, 55 Ludgate Hill, London, EC4M 7JW
    Chief Commissioner . . . . . . . . . . . . . . . . . . . . . . . . . . . His Honour Judge Gary Hickinbottom
    Secretary. . . . . . . . . . . . . . . . . . . . . . . . . . . . . . . . . . . . Mrs Lesley Armes . . . . . . . . . . . . . . . . . . . . . Tel: (020) 7029 9850

### CONTRIBUTIONS

**National Insurance Contributions Office** . . . . . . . . . . . . Inland Revenue, Room BP1202, Benton Park View, Longbenton,
        Newcastle-upon-Tyne, NE98 1ZZ
    Director . . . . . . . . . . . . . . . . . . . . . . . . . . . . . . . . . . . . Mr Steve McGrath . . . . . . . . . . . . . . . . . . . . . Tel: (0191) 225 5778

### DISABILITY

**Disability Employment Advisory Committee** . . . . . . . . . . Room N809, Department for Work and Pensions, Moorfoot,
        Sheffield, S1 4TQ
    Chairman . . . . . . . . . . . . . . . . . . . . . . . . . . . . . . . . . . . Ms Sally Witcher
    Committee Secretary . . . . . . . . . . . . . . . . . . . . . . . . . . . Mr Arthur Blacklock . . . . . . . . . . . . . . . . . . . Tel: (0114) 267 7234
        Web: http://www.deac.org.uk
**Disability Living Allowance Advisory Board**. . . . . . . . . . . The Adelphi, 1-11 John Adam Street, London, WC2N 6HT
    Chairman . . . . . . . . . . . . . . . . . . . . . . . . . . . . . . . . . . . Ms Anne Spaight
    Administrative Manager. . . . . . . . . . . . . . . . . . . . . . . . . Mr Ian Garland . . . . . . . . . . . . . . . . . . . . . . . Tel: (020) 7962 8053
        Web: http://www.dlaab.org.uk
**Disability Rights Commission** . . . . . . . . . . . . . . . . . . . . . 7th Floor, 222 Gray's Inn Road, London, WC1X 8HL
    Chairman . . . . . . . . . . . . . . . . . . . . . . . . . . . . . . . . . . . Mr Bert Massie CBE
    Chief Executive. . . . . . . . . . . . . . . . . . . . . . . . . . . . . . . Mr Bob Niven . . . . . . . . . . . . . . . . . . . . . . . . Tel: (0845) 762 2633
        Web: http://www.drc-gb.org

# DEPARTMENT FOR WORK AND PENSIONS

*Other Relevant Contacts: Disability (Continued)*

**Remploy Ltd.** . . . . . . . . . . . . . . . . . . . . . . . . . . . . . Stone Court, Siskin Drive, Coventry, CV3 4FJ
Chairman . . . . . . . . . . . . . . . . . . . . . . . . . . . . . . . . . Mr Alan Pedder
Chief Executive. . . . . . . . . . . . . . . . . . . . . . . . . . . . . Mr Bob Warner . . . . . . . . . . . . . . . . . . . . . . . Tel: (024) 7651 5804
E-mail: info@remploy.co.uk
Web: http://www.remploy.co.uk

## EMPLOYMENT

**Jobcentre Plus** *(Executive Agency)* . . . . . . . . . . . . . . . . . . . . Caxton House, Tothill Street, London, SW1H 9NA
Chief Executive. . . . . . . . . . . . . . . . . . . . . . . . . . . . Mr David Anderson . . . . . . . . . . . . . . . . . . . . . . Tel: (020) 7273 3000
Web: http://www.jobcentreplus.gov.uk

*Regional Offices*
*East of England* . . . . . . . . . . . . . . . . . . . . . . . . . . . . Beaufort House, Crown Gate, Harlow, CM20 1NA
  Regional Director. . . . . . . . . . . . . . . . . . . . . . . . . . Ms Nicola Bastin . . . . . . . . . . . . . . . . . . . . . . . Tel: (01279) 693803
*East Midlands* . . . . . . . . . . . . . . . . . . . . . . . . . . . . Newtown House, 46 Maid Marian Way, Nottingham, NG1 6GG
  Regional Director. . . . . . . . . . . . . . . . . . . . . . . . . . Mr Mel Groves. . . . . . . . . . . . . . . . . . . . . . . . . Tel: (0115) 989 5960
*London* . . . . . . . . . . . . . . . . . . . . . . . . . . . . . . . . . 236 Gray's Inn Road, London, WC1X 8HL
  Regional Director. . . . . . . . . . . . . . . . . . . . . . . . . . Ms Sheelagh Keyse . . . . . . . . . . . . . . . . . . . . . Tel: (020) 7211 4192
*North East* . . . . . . . . . . . . . . . . . . . . . . . . . . . . . . Broadacre House, Market Street (East), Newcastle-upon-Tyne, NE1 6HQ
  Regional Director . . . . . . . . . . . . . . . . . . . . . . . . . Mr Vince Robinson . . . . . . . . . . . . . . . . . . . . . Tel: (0191) 211 4389
*North West* . . . . . . . . . . . . . . . . . . . . . . . . . . . . . . Ontario House, 2 Furness Quay, Salford, M5 2XZ
  Regional Director. . . . . . . . . . . . . . . . . . . . . . . . . . Mr Terry Moran . . . . . . . . . . . . . . . . . . . . . . . Tel: (0161) 873 128
*South East*. . . . . . . . . . . . . . . . . . . . . . . . . . . . . . . Berkley House, London Square, Guildford, CU1 1YA
  Regional Director. . . . . . . . . . . . . . . . . . . . . . . . . . Mr Neil Couling. . . . . . . . . . . . . . . . . . . . . . . . Tel: (01483) 470135
*South West* . . . . . . . . . . . . . . . . . . . . . . . . . . . . . . The Pithay, Bristol, BS1 2NQ
  Regional Director. . . . . . . . . . . . . . . . . . . . . . . . . . Ms Diana Ross . . . . . . . . . . . . . . . . . . . . . . . . Tel: (0117) 945 6701
*West Midlands*. . . . . . . . . . . . . . . . . . . . . . . . . . . . 2 Duchess Place, Hagley Road, Birmingham, B16 8NS
  Regional Director . . . . . . . . . . . . . . . . . . . . . . . . . Ms Rosemary Thew . . . . . . . . . . . . . . . . . . . . . Tel: (0121) 452 5349
*Yorkshire and the Humber* . . . . . . . . . . . . . . . . . . . . Jubilee House, 33-41 Park Place, Leeds, LS1 2RE
  Regional Director *(Acting)* . . . . . . . . . . . . . . . . . . . Mr Dave White . . . . . . . . . . . . . . . . . . . . . . . . Tel: (0113) 285 8626
*Scotland* . . . . . . . . . . . . . . . . . . . . . . . . . . . . . . . . Argyle House, 3 Lady Lawson Street, Edinburgh, EH3 9SD
  Regional Director *(Acting)* . . . . . . . . . . . . . . . . . . . Ms Grace Kennedy . . . . . . . . . . . . . . . . . . . . . Tel: (0131) 221 4000
*Wales* . . . . . . . . . . . . . . . . . . . . . . . . . . . . . . . . . . Companies House, Crown Way, Maindy, Cardiff, CF14 3UW
  Regional Director *(Acting)* . . . . . . . . . . . . . . . . . . . Mr Dilwyn Clements . . . . . . . . . . . . . . . . . . . . Tel: (029) 2038 2705
**National Employment Panel**. . . . . . . . . . . . . . . . . . . . Level 5A, Caxton House, 6-12 Tothill Street, London, SW1H 9NA
Chairman . . . . . . . . . . . . . . . . . . . . . . . . . . . . . . . . . Mr Sandy Leitch
Director . . . . . . . . . . . . . . . . . . . . . . . . . . . . . . . . . . Ms Kay Stratton
Secretariat. . . . . . . . . . . . . . . . . . . . . . . . . . . . . . . . Ms Jill Hogger. . . . . . . . . . . . . . . . . . . . . . . . . Tel: (020) 7340 4232
Web: http://www.nationalemploymentpanel.org.uk

## HEALTH AND SAFETY

**Health and Safety Executive and Commission** . . . . . . . . . Rose Court, 2 Southwark Bridge, London SE1 9HS
Commission Chairman. . . . . . . . . . . . . . . . . . . . . . . . Mr Bill Callaghan
Director General H & S Executive . . . . . . . . . . . . . . . . . Dr Timothy Walker . . . . . . . . . . . . . . . . . . . . . Tel: (020) 7717 6000
*Public Infoline* . . . . . . . . . . . . . . . . . . . . . . . . Tel: (08701) 545500
Web: http://www.hse.gov.uk

## INDUSTRIAL INJURIES

**Industrial Injuries Advisory Council** . . . . . . . . . . . . . . . . 6th Floor, The Adelphi, 1-11 John Adam Street, London, WC2N 6HT
Chairman . . . . . . . . . . . . . . . . . . . . . . . . . . . . . . . . . Professor Anthony Newman Taylor OBE
Secretary. . . . . . . . . . . . . . . . . . . . . . . . . . . . . . . . . Dr Paul Stidolph . . . . . . . . . . . . . . . . . . . . . . . Tel: (020) 7962 8066
E-mail: iiac@dial.pipex.com
Web: http://www.iiac.org.uk

## PENSIONS

**Occupational Pensions Regulatory Authority** . . . . . . . . . . Invicta House, Trafalgar Place, Brighton, BN1 4DW
Chairman . . . . . . . . . . . . . . . . . . . . . . . . . . . . . . . . . Ms Harriet Maunsell OBE
Chief Executive. . . . . . . . . . . . . . . . . . . . . . . . . . . . . Mr Tony Hobman. . . . . . . . . . . . . . . . . . . . . . . Tel: (01273) 627600
E-mail: helpdesk@opra.gov.uk
Web: http://www.opra.gov.uk

# DEPARTMENT FOR WORK AND PENSIONS

*Other Relevant Contacts: Pensions (Continued)*

**Pensions Appeal Tribunal** . . . . . . . . . . . . . . . . . . . . . . . 48/49 Chancery Lane, London, WC2A 1JF
   President . . . . . . . . . . . . . . . . . . . . . . . . . . . . . Dr Harcourt Concannon
   Secretary. . . . . . . . . . . . . . . . . . . . . . . . . . . . . . Ms Lesley Nay . . . . . . . . . . . . . . . . . . . . . . . Tel: (020) 7947 7033
**Pensions Compensation Board** . . . . . . . . . . . . . . . . . . . . 11 Belgrave Road, London, SW1V 1RB
   Chairman . . . . . . . . . . . . . . . . . . . . . . . . . . . . . Sir Bryan Carsberg
   Secretary. . . . . . . . . . . . . . . . . . . . . . . . . . . . . . Mr Mike Lydon . . . . . . . . . . . . . . . . . . . . . . . Tel: (020) 7828 9794
**Pensions Ombudsman** . . . . . . . . . . . . . . . . . . . . . . . . . . . 11 Belgrave Road, London, SW1V 1RB
   Pensions Ombudsman . . . . . . . . . . . . . . . . . . . . . . Mr David Laverick
   Business Manager . . . . . . . . . . . . . . . . . . . . . . . . Mr Mike Lydon . . . . . . . . . . . . . . . . . . . . . . . Tel: (020) 7834 9144
                                        E-mail: enquiries@pensions-ombudsman.org.uk
                                        Web: http://www.pensions-ombudsman.org.uk
**Pensions Service** *(Executive Agency)* . . . . . . . . . . . . . . . Trevelyan House, 30 Great Peter Street, London, SW1P 2BY
   Chief Executive. . . . . . . . . . . . . . . . . . . . . . . . . . Ms Alexis Cleveland . . . . . . . . . . . . . . . . . . Tel: (020) 7227 1157
                                        Web: http://www.thepensionservice.gov.uk
**Veterans Agency** *(Executive Agency)* . . . . . . . . . . . . . . . Tomlinson House, Norcross, Blackpool, FY5 3WP
   Chief Executive. . . . . . . . . . . . . . . . . . . . . . . . . . Mr Alan Burnham . . . . . . . . . . . . . . . . . . . . Tel: (0800) 1692277
                                        Web: http://www.veteransagency.mod.uk
**War Pensions Committees** . . . . . . . . . . . . . . . . . . . . . . . Tomlinson House, Norcross,
                                        Blackpool, FY5 3WP . . . . . . . . . . . . . . . . . Tel: (01253) 333076
                                        E-mail: help@veteransagency.mod.uk
                                        Web: http://www.veteransagency.mod.uk
   Chairman, Eastern England . . . . . . . . . . . . . . . . . . Mr Ray Holland BEM OBE
   Chairman, East Midlands . . . . . . . . . . . . . . . . . . . Lt Col Peter Poole
   Chairman, London. . . . . . . . . . . . . . . . . . . . . . . . Mr Jack Hargreaves
   Chairman, North East England . . . . . . . . . . . . . . . Mr Paul Kingdom
   Chairman, Northern Ireland. . . . . . . . . . . . . . . . . . Mr John Davies *(Acting)*
   Chairman, North West England . . . . . . . . . . . . . . . Mr Stephen Overton
   Chairman, South East England . . . . . . . . . . . . . . . Mr David Wright
   Chairman, South West England . . . . . . . . . . . . . . . Mr Andrew Adks
   Chairman, Wales. . . . . . . . . . . . . . . . . . . . . . . . . . Mr Tom Frizell
   Chairman, West Midlands . . . . . . . . . . . . . . . . . . . Mr Michael Burrows
   Chairman, West of Scotland. . . . . . . . . . . . . . . . . . Mr Derek Evans
   Chairman, Yorkshire and Humberside . . . . . . . . . . . Mrs Jane Gummer MBE

## RACE

**Race Education and Employment Forum** . . . . . . . . . . . . Adelphi Buildings, 1-11 John Adam Street, London, WC2N 6HT
   Secretariat. . . . . . . . . . . . . . . . . . . . . . . . . . . . . . Mr Ian Roberts . . . . . . . . . . . . . . . . . . . . . . . Tel: (020) 7962 8000

## SOCIAL FUND

**Independent Review Service for the Social Fund** . . . . . . Centre City Podium, 4th Floor, 5 Hill Street, Birmingham, B5 4UB
   Social Fund Commissioner . . . . . . . . . . . . . . . . . . . Sir Richard Tilt
   Office Manager . . . . . . . . . . . . . . . . . . . . . . . . . . . Ms Pauline Adey . . . . . . . . . . . . . . . . . . . . . . Tel: (0121) 606 2100
                                        E-mail: fsc@irs-review.org
                                        Web: http://www.irs-review.gov.uk

## SOCIAL SECURITY

**Office of the Social Security and**
   **Child Support Commissioners** . . . . . . . . . . . . . . . Procession House, 55 Ludgate Hill, London, EC4M 7JW
   Chief Commissioner . . . . . . . . . . . . . . . . . . . . . . . His Honour Judge Gary Hickinbottom
   Secretary. . . . . . . . . . . . . . . . . . . . . . . . . . . . . . . Mrs Lesley Armes . . . . . . . . . . . . . . . . . . . . Tel: (020) 7029 9850
**Social Security Advisory Committee** . . . . . . . . . . . . . . . New Court, Carey Street, London, WC2A 2LS
   Chairman . . . . . . . . . . . . . . . . . . . . . . . . . . . . . . Sir Thomas Boyd-Carpenter KBE
   Secretary. . . . . . . . . . . . . . . . . . . . . . . . . . . . . . . Miss Gill Saunders. . . . . . . . . . . . . . . . . . . . Tel: (020) 7412 1509
                                        E-mail: ssac@dwp.gsi.gov.uk
                                        Web: http://www.ssac.org.uk

## EXECUTIVE RECRUITMENT
## FROM THE ARMED SERVICES

# THE OFFICERS' ASSOCIATION
48 Pall Mall,
London, SW1Y 5JY

*Telephone* (020) 7930 0125   *Facsimile* (020) 7930 9053
E-mail: postmaster@oaed.oeg.uk
Web: http://www.officersassociation.com

*Edinburgh Office*
*Telephone* (0131) 550 1581   *Facsimile* (0131) 557 5819

*Contact* Director, Employment Department

Founded in 1919 by the Earl Haig, and awarded the Royal Charter in 1921, the Association has three departments, Benevolence, Homes and Employment. The Employment Department provides no cost sourcing of managers, professionals and senior technical people who have been commissioned in the Armed Services for the public, private and not-for-profit sectors.

*Registered Charity No:* 201321

## WELFARE AND SOCIAL ORGANISATION

# THE CIVIL SERVICE RETIREMENT FELLOWSHIP
Suite 2, 80A Blackheath Road
London, SE10 8DL

*Telephone* (020) 8691 7411
*Facsimile* (020) 8692 2386
*E-mail* info@csrf.org.uk
Web: http://www.csrf.org.uk

*Contact:* Mrs Jean Cooper – *General Secretary*

The Fellowship (a registered charity) has 500 groups throughout the UK. It organises a welfare visiting service for the ill or housebound. It keeps in touch with retired Civil Servants and their dependents through the group network and provides a wide variety of social activities.

*Registered Charity No:* 255465

# OMBUDSMEN

*Notes:* *(i) The following list comprises various institutions – including public bodies and, in some cases, bodies established by the industries concerned – which handle complaints in their particular areas.*

*(ii) The Parliamentary Commissioner for Administration handles complaints in respect of alleged maladministration by government departments and certain other public bodies. Individuals should channel such complaints through their MP.*

## BROADCASTING
**Ofcom** . . . . . . . . . . . . . . . . . . . . . . . . . . . . . . . . . . Riverside House, 2A Southwark Bridge Road, London, SE1 9HA
    Chairman . . . . . . . . . . . . . . . . . . . . . . . . . . . . . Lord Currie of Marylebones
    Chief Executive . . . . . . . . . . . . . . . . . . . . . . . . . . . . . Mr Stephen Carter . . . . . . . . . . . . . . . . . . . . . . . . . . . Tel: (020) 7981 3000
            Web: http://www.ofcom.co.uk

## CHILD SUPPORT
**The Independent Case Examiner** . . . . . . . . . . . . . . . . PO Box 155, Chester, CH99 9SA
    Examiner . . . . . . . . . . . . . . . . . . . . . . . . . . . . . . . Mrs Jodi Berg . . . . . . . . . . . . . . . . . . . . . . . . . . . . . . . Tel: (0151) 801 8800
            Web: http://www.ind-case-exam.org.uk

## CUSTOMS AND EXCISE
**The Adjudicator's Office** . . . . . . . . . . . . . . . . . . . . . Haymarket House, 28 Haymarket, London, SW1Y 4SP
    Adjudicator . . . . . . . . . . . . . . . . . . . . . . . . . . . . . . . . Dame Barbara Mills . . . . . . . . . . . . . . . . . . . . . . . . . . Tel: (020) 7930 2292
            Web: http://www.adjudicatorsoffice.gov.uk

## ESTATE AGENTS
**Corporate Estate Agents Ombudsman** . . . . . . . . . . . . Beckett House, 4 Bridge Street, Salisbury, SP1 2LX
    Ombudsman . . . . . . . . . . . . . . . . . . . . . . . . . . . . . . . Mr Stephen Carr-Smith . . . . . . . . . . . . . . . . . . . . . . . . Tel: (01722) 333306
            Web: http://www.oea.co.uk

## EUROPEAN UNION
**European Ombudsman** . . . . . . . . . . . . . . . . . . . . . . . 1 Avenue du Président Robert Schuman, BP 403,
            F-67001 Strasbourg, Cedex, France
    European Ombudsman . . . . . . . . . . . . . . . . . . . . . . . Mr Nikifororos Diamandouros . . . . . . . . . . . . . . . . . . . Tel: +33 388 17 2313
            Web: http://www.euro-ombudsman.eu.int

## FINANCIAL SERVICES
**Financial Ombudsman Service** . . . . . . . . . . . . . . . . . South Quay Plaza, 183 Marsh Wall, London, E14 9SR
    Chairman . . . . . . . . . . . . . . . . . . . . . . . . . . . . . . . . Ms Sue Slipman OBE
    Chief Ombudsman . . . . . . . . . . . . . . . . . . . . . . . . . Mr Walter Merricks . . . . . . . . . . . . . . . . . . . . . . . . . . . Tel: (020) 7964 1000
            Web: http://www.financial-ombudsman.org.uk

## GAS AND ELECTRICITY
**Energywatch** . . . . . . . . . . . . . . . . . . . . . . . . . . . . . . 4th Floor, Artillery House, Artillery Row, London, SW1P 1RT
    Chairman . . . . . . . . . . . . . . . . . . . . . . . . . . . . . . . . Mr Ed Gallagher
    Chief Executive . . . . . . . . . . . . . . . . . . . . . . . . . . . . Mr Alan Asher . . . . . . . . . . . . . . . . . . . . . . . . . . . . . . . Tel: (020) 7799 8340
            E-mail: enquiries@energywatch.org.uk
            Web: http://www.energywatch.org.uk

**Office of Gas and Electricity Markets (OFGEM)**
*(Non-Ministerial Government Department)* . . . . . . . . . . . 9 Millbank, London, SW1P 3GE
    Chairman . . . . . . . . . . . . . . . . . . . . . . . . . . . . . . . . Sir John Mogg . . . . . . . . . . . . . . . . . . . . . . . . . . . . . . Tel: (020) 7901 7000
            Mr Alaistair Buchanan
            Web: http://www.ofgem.gov.uk

## HEALTH
**Health Service Ombudsman for England** . . . . . . . . . Millbank Tower, Millbank, London, SW1P 4QP
    Ombudsman . . . . . . . . . . . . . . . . . . . . . . . . . . . . . . Ms Ann Abraham . . . . . . . . . . . . . . . . . . . . . . . . . . . . . Tel: (0845) 015 4033
            Web: http://www.ombudsman.org.uk
**Health Service Ombudsman for Wales** . . . . . . . . . . . 5th Floor, Capital Tower, Greyfriars Road, Cardiff, CF10 3AG
    Ombudsman . . . . . . . . . . . . . . . . . . . . . . . . . . . . . . Mr Adam Peat . . . . . . . . . . . . . . . . . . . . . . . . . . . . . . . Tel: (029) 2039 4621
            Web: http://www.ombudsman.org.uk

*(see also Scottish Public Services Ombudsman, under Scotland below)*

# OMBUDSMEN

**HOUSING**

**Independent Housing Ombudsman** . . . . . . . . . . . . . . Norman House, 105-109 Strand, London, WC2R 0AA
    Ombudsman . . . . . . . . . . . . . . . . . . . . . . . . . . . . . Dr Michael Biles . . . . . . . . . . . . . . . . . . . . . . . . . . . . . . . . . . . Tel: (020) 7836 3630
                        E-mail: ombudsman @ ihos.org.uk
                        Web: http://www.ihos.org.uk

**INLAND REVENUE**

**The Adjudicator's Office** . . . . . . . . . . . . . . . . . . . . . Haymarket House, 28 Haymarket, London, SW1Y 4SP
    Adjudicator. . . . . . . . . . . . . . . . . . . . . . . . . . . . . . . Dame Barbara Mills. . . . . . . . . . . . . . . . . . . . . . . . . . . . Tel: (020) 7930 2292
                        Web: http://www.adjudicatorsoffice.gov.uk

**LEGAL SERVICES**

**Legal Services Ombudsman** . . . . . . . . . . . . . . . . . . . 3rd Floor Sunlight House, Quay Street, Manchester, M3 3JZ
    Ombudsman . . . . . . . . . . . . . . . . . . . . . . . . . . . . . Ms Zahida Manzoor . . . . . . . . . . . . . . . . . . . . . . . . . . Tel: (0161) 839 7262
                        E-mail: lso@olso.gsi.gov.uk
                        Web: http://www.olso.org

**Scottish Legal Services Ombudsman** . . . . . . . . . . . . . 17 Waterloo Place, Edinburgh, EH1 3DL
    Ombudsman . . . . . . . . . . . . . . . . . . . . . . . . . . . . . Mrs Linda Costelloe Baker . . . . . . . . . . . . . . . . . . . . . . Tel: (0131) 556 9123
                        E-mail: slso@slso.gsi.gov.uk
                        Web: http://www.slso.org.uk

**LOCAL GOVERNMENT (ENGLAND)**

**Local Government Ombudsmen for England**
    Ombudsman . . . . . . . . . . . . . . . . . . . . . . . . . . . . . 10th Floor, Millbank Tower, Millbank, London, SW1P 4QP
                        Mr Tony Redmond . . . . . . . . . . . . . . . . . . . . . . . . . . Tel: (020) 7217 4620
                        The Oaks, 2 Westwood Way, Westwood Business Park, Coventry, CV4 8JB
                        Mr Jerry White . . . . . . . . . . . . . . . . . . . . . . . . . . . . . Tel: (024) 7682 0000
                        Beverley House, 17 Shipton Road, York, YO30 5F2
                        Ms Patricia Thomas . . . . . . . . . . . . . . . . . . . . . . . . . . Tel: (01904) 380200
                        Web: http://www.olso.org

**NORTHERN IRELAND**

**Office of the Assembly Ombudsman for**
**Northern Ireland and Northern Ireland**
    **Commissioner for Complaints** . . . . . . . . . . . . . 33 Wellington Place, Belfast, BT1 6HN
    Ombudsman . . . . . . . . . . . . . . . . . . . . . . . . . . . . . Mr Tom Frawley. . . . . . . . . . . . . . . . . . . . . . . . . . . . . Tel: (028) 9023 3821
                        E-mail: ombudsman@ni-ombudsman.org.uk
                        Web: http://www.ni-ombudsman.org.uk

**PARLIAMENT / CENTRAL GOVERNMENT**

**Parliamentary Commissioner for Administration**. . . . Millbank Tower, Millbank, London, SW1P 4QP
    Ombudsman . . . . . . . . . . . . . . . . . . . . . . . . . . . . . Ms Ann Abraham. . . . . . . . . . . . . . . . . . . . . . . . . . . . Tel: (0845) 015 4033
                        E-mail: opca.enquiries@ombudsman.org.uk
                        Web: http://www.ombudsman.org.uk

**PENSIONS**

**Pensions Ombudsman** . . . . . . . . . . . . . . . . . . . . . . . 11 Belgrave Road, London, SW1V 1RB
    Ombudsman . . . . . . . . . . . . . . . . . . . . . . . . . . . . . Mr David Laverick. . . . . . . . . . . . . . . . . . . . . . . . . . . . Tel: (020) 7834 9144
                        E-mail: enquiries@pensions-ombudsman.org.uk
                        Web: http://www.pensions-ombudsman.org.uk

**PERSONAL INFORMATION**

**Office of the Information Commissioner** . . . . . . . . . Wycliffe House, Water Lane, Wilmslow, Cheshire, SK9 5AF
    Commissioner . . . . . . . . . . . . . . . . . . . . . . . . . . . . Mr Richard Thomas . . . . . . . . . . . . . . . . . . . . . . . . . . Tel: (01625) 545700
                        Web: http://www.informationcommissioner.gov.uk

# OMBUDSMEN

## POLICE

**Independent Police Complaints Commission** . . . . . . . 9 High Holborn, London, WC1V 6BH
    Chairman . . . . . . . . . . . . . . . . . . . . . . . . . . . . . . . . . Mr Nick Hardwick . . . . . . . . . . . . . . . . . . . . . . . . . . . . . Tel: (0845) 300 2002
    Chief Executive . . . . . . . . . . . . . . . . . . . . . . . . . . . . Ms Sue Atkains
        E-mail: enquiries@ipcc.gsi.gov.uk
        Web: http://www.ipcc.gov.uk

**Police Ombudsman (Northern Ireland)** . . . . . . . . . . New Cathedral Buildings, St Anne's Square, 17 Church Street, Belfast, BT1 1PG
    Police Ombudsman . . . . . . . . . . . . . . . . . . . . . . . . . Mrs Nuala O'Loan . . . . . . . . . . . . . . . . . . . . . . . . . . . . . Tel: (028) 9082 8600
        Web: http://www.policeombudsman.org

## POSTAL SERVICES

**Postwatch** . . . . . . . . . . . . . . . . . . . . . . . . . . . . . . . . . 28-30 Grosvenor Gardens, London, SW1W 0TT
    Chairman . . . . . . . . . . . . . . . . . . . . . . . . . . . . . . . . . Mr Peter Carr
    Chief Executive . . . . . . . . . . . . . . . . . . . . . . . . . . . . Mr Gregor McGregor . . . . . . . . . . . . . . . . . . . . . . . . . . Tel: (0845) 601 3265
        E-mail: info@postwatch.co.uk
        Web: http://www.postwatch.co.uk

## PRESS

**Press Complaints Commission** . . . . . . . . . . . . . . . . . 1 Salisbury Square, London, EC4Y 8JB
    Chairman . . . . . . . . . . . . . . . . . . . . . . . . . . . . . . . . . Sir Christopher Meyer
    Director . . . . . . . . . . . . . . . . . . . . . . . . . . . . . . . . . . Mr Tim Toumin . . . . . . . . . . . . . . . . . . . . . . . . . . . . . . Tel: (020) 7353 1248
        E-mail: pcc@pcc.org.uk
        Web: http://www.pcc.org.uk

## PRISONS

**Prisons Ombudsman** . . . . . . . . . . . . . . . . . . . . . . . . Ashley House, 2 Monck Street, London, SW1P 2BQ
    Ombudsman *(Acting)* . . . . . . . . . . . . . . . . . . . . . . . Mr David Barnes . . . . . . . . . . . . . . . . . . . . . . . . . . . . . Tel: (020) 7035 2876
        E-mail: mail@ppo.gsi.gov.uk
        Web: http://www.ppo.gov.uk

**Scottish Prisons Complaints Commission** . . . . . . . . . Saughton House, Broomhouse Drive, Edinburgh, EH11 3XD
    Complaints Commissioner . . . . . . . . . . . . . . . . . . . . Mr Vaughan Barrett . . . . . . . . . . . . . . . . . . . . . . . . . . . Tel: (0131) 244 8423
        E-mail: v.barrett@scotland.gov.uk
        Web: http://www.scotland.gov.uk/spcc

## SCOTLAND

**Scottish Public Services Ombudsman** . . . . . . . . . . . . 4-6 Melville Street, Edinburgh, EH3 7HS
    Ombudsman . . . . . . . . . . . . . . . . . . . . . . . . . . . . . . Professor Alice Brown . . . . . . . . . . . . . . . . . . . . . . . . . Tel: (0870) 011 5378
        E-mail: enquiries@scottishombudsman.org.uk
        Web: http://www.scottishombudsman.org.uk

## SECURITY SERVICES

**Investigatory Powers Tribunal** . . . . . . . . . . . . . . . . . PO Box 33220, London, SW1H 9ZQ
    President . . . . . . . . . . . . . . . . . . . . . . . . . . . . . . . . . Rt Hon Lord Justice Mummery
    Secretary . . . . . . . . . . . . . . . . . . . . . . . . . . . . . . . . Mr David Payne . . . . . . . . . . . . . . . . . . . . . . . . . . . . . . Tel: (020) 7273 4514

## TELECOMMUNICATIONS

**Committee for the Supervision of Standards of**
  **Telephone Information Services** . . . . . . . . . . . . . 1st Floor, Clove Building, 4 Maguire Street, London, SE1 2NQ
    Chairman . . . . . . . . . . . . . . . . . . . . . . . . . . . . . . . . . Mr Peter North . . . . . . . . . . . . . . . . . . . . . . . . . . . . . . Tel: (020) 7940 7474
        E-mail: secretariat@icstis.org.uk
        Web: http://www.icstis.org.uk

**OFCOM** . . . . . . . . . . . . . . . . . . . . . . . . . . . . . . . . . . Riverside House, 2A Southwark Bridge Road, London, SE1 9HA
    Chairman . . . . . . . . . . . . . . . . . . . . . . . . . . . . . . . . . Lord Currie
    Chief Executive . . . . . . . . . . . . . . . . . . . . . . . . . . . . Mr Stephen Carter . . . . . . . . . . . . . . . . . . . . . . . . . . . . Tel: (020) 7981 3000
        E-mail: contact@ofcom.org.uk
        Web: http://www.ofcom.org.uk

# OMBUDSMEN

**TRANSPORT**

**London Transport Users Committee** . . . . . . . . . . . . . 6 Middle Street, London, EC1A 7JA

    Chairman . . . . . . . . . . . . . . . . . . . . . . . . . . . . . . Ms Suzanne May

    Director . . . . . . . . . . . . . . . . . . . . . . . . . . . . . . . Mr Rufus Barnes . . . . . . . . . . . . . . . . . . . . . . . . . . . . Tel: (020) 7505 9000

        Web: http://www.ltuc.org.uk

**Rail Passengers Council** . . . . . . . . . . . . . . . . . . . . . Whittles House, 14 Pentonville Road, London, N1 9HF

    Chairman . . . . . . . . . . . . . . . . . . . . . . . . . . . . . . Mr Stewart Francis

    National Director . . . . . . . . . . . . . . . . . . . . . . . . . Mr Anthony Smith . . . . . . . . . . . . . . . . . . . . . . . . . Tel: (020) 7713 2700

        E-mail: info@railpassengers.org.uk

        Web: http://www.railpassengers.org.uk

*(see also Regional Rail Passengers Committees, listed under Department of Transport: Other Contacts)*

**WALES**

**Commission for Local Administration in Wales** . . . . . Derwen House, Court Road, Bridgend, CF31 1BN

    Commissioner . . . . . . . . . . . . . . . . . . . . . . . . . . . Mr Elwyn Moseley . . . . . . . . . . . . . . . . . . . . . . . . . Tel: (01656) 661325

        Web: http://www.ombudsman-wales.org

**Welsh Administration Ombudsman** . . . . . . . . . . . . . . Fifth Floor, Capital Tower, Greyfriars Road, Cardiff, CF10 3AG

    Ombudsman . . . . . . . . . . . . . . . . . . . . . . . . . . . . . Ms Ann Abraham . . . . . . . . . . . . . . . . . . . . . . . . . . Tel: (0845) 015 4033

        E-mail: wao.enquiries@ombudsman.gsi.gov.uk

        Web: http://www.ombudsman.org.uk

**WATER**

**Water Industry Commissioner for Scotland** . . . . . . . Ochil House, Springkerse Business Park, Sterling, FK7 7XE

    Chairman . . . . . . . . . . . . . . . . . . . . . . . . . . . . . . Mr Alan Sutherland . . . . . . . . . . . . . . . . . . . . . . . . . Tel: (01786) 430200

        E-mail: enquiries@watercommission.co.uk

        Web: http://www.watercommissioner.co.uk

**WaterVoice** . . . . . . . . . . . . . . . . . . . . . . . . . . . . . First Floor, Chanelle House, 86 New Street, Birmingham, B2 4BA

    Chairman . . . . . . . . . . . . . . . . . . . . . . . . . . . . . . Sir James Perowne . . . . . . . . . . . . . . . . . . . . . . . . . Tel: (0121) 644 5252

        E-mail: central@watervoice.org.uk

        Web: http://www.watervoice.org.uk

**WaterVoiceWales** . . . . . . . . . . . . . . . . . . . . . . . . . Room 140, Caradog House, 1-6 St Andrew's Place. Cardiff, CF10 3BE

    Chairman . . . . . . . . . . . . . . . . . . . . . . . . . . . . . . Dr John Ford CBE . . . . . . . . . . . . . . . . . . . . . . . . . Tel: (0845) 707 8267

        E-mail: wales@watervoice.org.uk

        Web: http://www.watervoice.org.uk

# Contacts Index

# D

# I

# J

# L

## M

## N

# O

# P

# Q

# R

# Advertisers' Index by Type of Business

# E

# F

# G

# H

# I

# L

# Advertisers' Index by Company Name